GEOMETRY
TEACHER'S EDITION

Kenneth J. Travers
Professor of
Mathematics Education
University of Illinois
Urbana, Illinois

LeRoy C. Dalton
Mathematics Area
Chairperson
Wauwatosa School District
Wauwatosa, Wisconsin

Katherine P. Layton
Mathematics Teacher
Beverly Hills High School
Beverly Hills, California

Laidlaw Brothers • Publishers
A Division of Doubleday & Company, Inc.
River Forest, Illinois

Sacramento, California • Chamblee, Georgia
Dallas, Texas • Toronto, Canada

CONTENTS OF THE TEACHER'S EDITION

ISBN 0-8445-1843-3

Printed in the United States of America
123456789 10 11 12 13 14 15 5432109876

A challenging textbook that considers the individual needs of students and teachers

LAIDLAW GEOMETRY

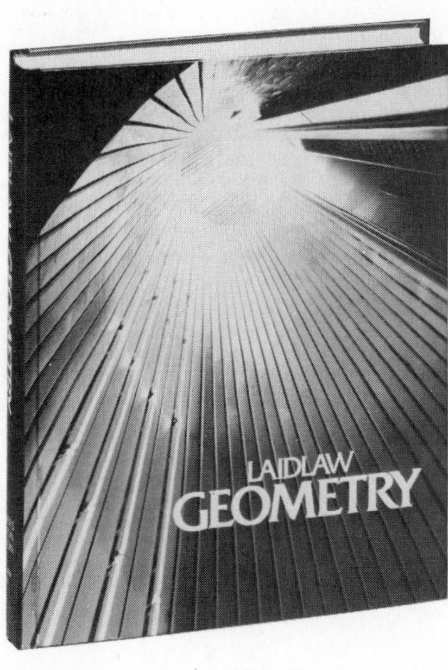

This comprehensive course in geometry gives students a thorough foundation in proof and deductive reasoning. LAIDLAW GEOMETRY effectively presents the fundamentals of geometry along with practical applications, providing students with the tools they need to become successful users of mathematics.

- The content includes traditional Euclidean geometry topics, as well as transformations, locus concepts, three-dimensional extensions of two-dimensional concepts, trigonometry and vectors, coordinate geometry, and additional advanced topics. A chapter on constructions is included. Algebra is integrated throughout the book.
- Proof, deductive reasoning, and logic are introduced in the first chapter and developed formally throughout the text.
- Opportunities for problem solving and applications, including non-routine problems, occur frequently.
- Computer-related activities and materials are included, to help familiarize students with the growing uses of computer technology.
- LAIDLAW GEOMETRY offers many provisions for adapting the course to students' needs and interests.

Comprehensive Content Development Through a Practical Lesson Organization

LAIDLAW GEOMETRY leads students through a clear, consistent learning sequence.

Lesson title states the topic to be covered.

Important properties, postulates, theorems, corollaries, and definitions are prominently highlighted to draw attention, and for quick reference.

Clear, carefully developed explanations with examples and teaching illustrations ensure understanding.

8.4 Parallels and Triangles

In previous mathematics courses, you may have learned that the angles of a triangle have a combined measure of 180. This is a concept you have probably accepted on the basis of intuition or experimentation, because its proof requires knowledge of the Parallel Postulate. Now you are ready to prove this fundamental concept as a theorem.

THEOREM 8.13
The sum of the measures of the angles of a triangle is 180.

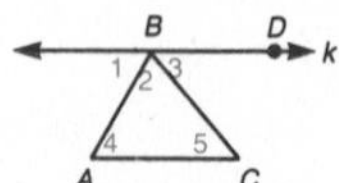

Given: $\triangle ABC$, with $\angle 2$, $\angle 4$, and $\angle 5$ as shown
Prove: $m\angle 4 + m\angle 2 + m\angle 5 = 180$

Proof: Using Postulate 16, let k be the line through B parallel to $\overline{AC}$, forming $\angle 1$ and $\angle 2$ as shown. Let D be a point of k on the same side of $\overleftrightarrow{AB}$ as C. Since $\overline{AC} \parallel \overleftrightarrow{BD}$, A is on the same side of $\overleftrightarrow{BD}$ as C. Therefore, by definition, C is in the interior of $\angle ABD$. By the Angle Addition Postulate, $m\angle ABD = m\angle 2 + m\angle 3$. By the Supplement Postulate, $m\angle 1 + m\angle ABD = 180$. Therefore $m\angle 1 + m\angle 2 + m\angle 3 = 180$. By Theorem 8.8, $m\angle 1 = m\angle 4$ and $m\angle 3 = m\angle 5$, because they are alternate interior angles. By substitution, $m\angle 4 + m\angle 2 + m\angle 5 = 180$.

Theorem 8.13 has three corollaries, whose proofs are left as exercises.

COROLLARY 8.13.1
Given a correspondence between two triangles, if two pairs of corresponding angles are congruent, then the third pair of corresponding angles are congruent.

Thus, in the figure below, if $\angle A \cong \angle A'$ and $\angle B \cong \angle B'$, then $\angle C \cong \angle C'$. As the figure suggests, the corollary applies to noncongruent as well as congruent triangles.

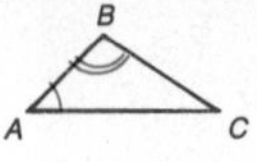

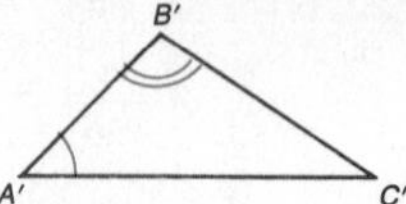

COROLLARY 8.13.2
The acute angles of a right triangle are complementary.

COROLLARY 8.13.3
For any triangle, the measures of an exterior angle is the sum of the measures of the two remote interior angles.

In the figure at the right, $m\angle 1 = m\angle 3 + m\angle 4$, and $m\angle 5 = m\angle 2 + m\angle 3$. If an exterior angle of a triangle is acute, what do you know about the remote interior angles?

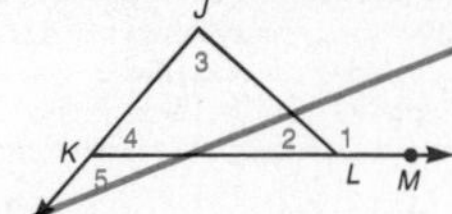

ORAL EXERCISES

Complete the following statements.

1. In $\triangle ABC$, $m\angle A + m\angle B + m\angle C =$ ____.
2. In $\triangle DEF$, if $\angle D$ is a right angle, then ...
3. In $\triangle KLM$ and $\triangle PQR$, if $m\angle K = m$... $m\angle R =$ ____.
4. In $\triangle WXY$, the measure of the exte...

Answer true or false, referring to the...

5. $\angle 5$ is an exterior angle.
6. $\angle 7$ is an exterior angle.
7. $\angle 6 \cong \angle 9$ **8.** $m\angle 2 + m\angle 6 = 9$...
9. $m\angle 2 + m\angle 6 + m\angle 5 = 180$
10. $m\angle 8 = m\angle 2 + m\angle 3$
11. $m\angle 4 = m\angle 2 + m\angle 9$
12. $m\angle 1 = m\angle 2 + m\angle 3$

Complete the following statemen... referring to the figure.

13. If $m\angle T' = 60$, then $m\angle T =$ ____
14. If $m\angle U = 40$, then $m\angle T + m\angle V =$ ____.

WRITTEN EXERCISES

A. If the measures of two angles of a triangle are as follows, what is the measure of the third angle?

1. 27 and 56
2. 149 and 29
3. x and $2x$
4. a and b
5. $45 + y$ and $45 - y$
6. 90 and $\frac{1}{2}d$

B. Find the values for x and y.

7.
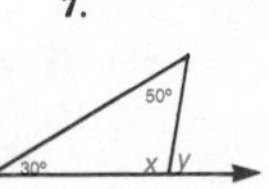

8.
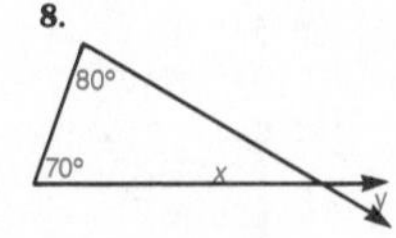

9.
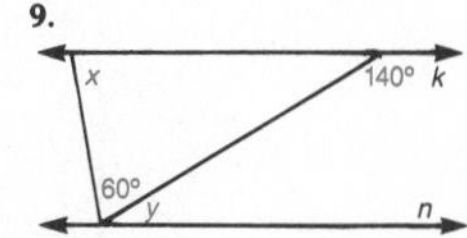

10.
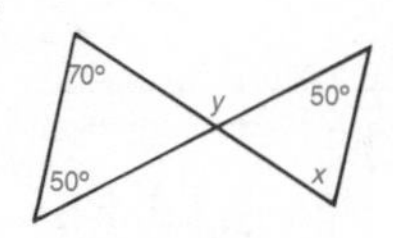

11.
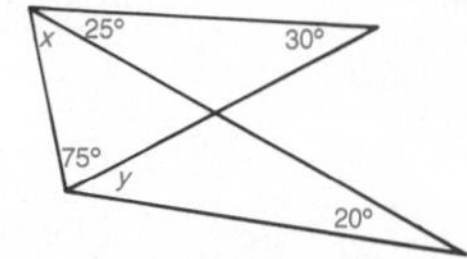

12. In a right triangle, one acute angle is 5 times as large as the other one. Find the measure of each acute angle.
13. The angles of a triangle are in the ratio of 2:3:4. Find the measure of the largest angle.
14. **Given:** $\overrightarrow{CE}$ bisects $\angle DCB$
$\overrightarrow{CE} \parallel \overline{AB}$
Prove: $\overline{AC} \cong \overline{BC}$
State your conclusion in if-then form.

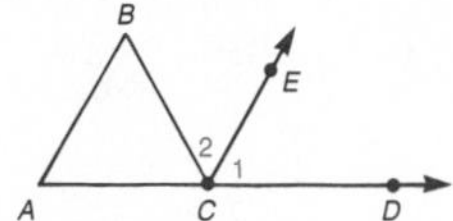

15. State and prove the converse of your conclusion in Exercise 14.
16. Prove Corollary 8.13.1.

C. 17. State Corollary 8.13.2 as a biconditional and prove both cases.
18. Prove Corollary 8.13.3.

238 *Chapter 8 • Parallels*

Abundant exercises, all covering the lesson topic, assure great flexibility in assigning practice. **Every lesson** has:

Oral Exercises for use in class to review or clarify concepts, or as part of the assignment.

Written Exercises to promote mastery of the lesson topic. Always divided into three groups of increasing difficulty, labeled A, B, and C.

Algebra is used in many lessons and exercises, helping the student maintain algebraic concepts and skills. See pages 5-9, 165-168, 364-366, etc.

Plus:

Cumulative Mixed Review is available in the Teacher's Edition margins of every lesson.

Selected Solutions in the back of the book provide the answers to most even-numbered lesson exercises and Chapter Review exercises, to aid study.

Geometry students need a thorough foundation in proof and deductive reasoning. LAIDLAW GEOMETRY enables them to acquire that foundation through an emphasis on proof that begins in the first chapter and builds throughout the book.

Two-column proofs

Chapter 1 introduces students to the concepts of proof and deductive reasoning, using algebraic equations in two-column proofs.

Students get extensive work on formal two-column proofs throughout the book. See pages 5-9, 95-99, 176-178, etc.

4.2 The ASA Congruence Theorem

In the previous section you learned that every SAS correspondence between two triangles is a congruence. You used the SAS postulate to prove that every LL correspondence between two right triangles is also a congruence. In this lesson you will again employ the SAS postulate, this time to prove that every Angle-Side-Angle (ASA) correspondence is a congruence.

THEOREM 4.2 [The Angle-Side-Angle (ASA) Theorem]
Given a correspondence between two triangles (or between a triangle and itself), if two angles and the included side of the first triangle are congruent to the corresponding parts of the second triangle, then the correspondence is a congruence.

Given: $\triangle ABC$ and $\triangle DEF$
$\angle A \cong \angle D$
$\angle B \cong \angle E$
$\overline{AB} \cong \overline{DE}$

Prove: $\triangle ABC \cong \triangle DEF$

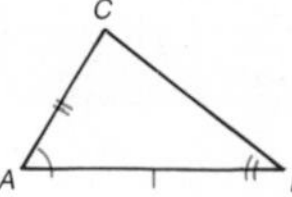

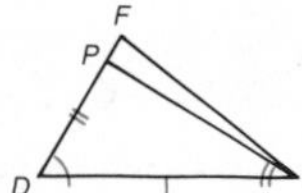

Proof:

STATEMENTS	REASONS
1. $\overrightarrow{DF}$ contains a point P such that $DP = AC$	1. The Point Plotting Theorem
2. $\overline{DP} \cong \overline{AC}$	2. Definition of $\cong$ segments
3. $\overline{AB} \cong \overline{DE}$, $\angle A \cong \angle D$	3. Given
4. $\triangle ABC \cong \triangle DEP$	4. Steps 2, 3, and SAS
5. $\angle ABC \cong \angle DEP$	5. Corres. parts of $\cong$ $\triangle$s are $\cong$.
6. $\angle ABC \cong \angle DEF$	6. Given
7. $\angle DEF \cong \angle DEP$	7. Steps 5, 6, and congruence of $\angle$s is transitive
8. $\overrightarrow{EF} = \overrightarrow{EP}$	8. Step 7 and the Angle Construction Postulate
9. P is on $\overleftrightarrow{DF}$ and $\overleftrightarrow{EF}$	9. Steps 1 and 8
10. F is on $\overleftrightarrow{DF}$ and $\overleftrightarrow{EF}$	10. Definition of vertex
11. $F = P$	11. Two different lines intersect in at most one point.
12. $\triangle ABC \cong \triangle DEF$	12. Steps 4 and 11

100 *Chapter 4 • Congruent Triangles*

Logic

Logic is introduced in the first chapter and is followed by lessons on deductive proof. Logic is used throughout the text. Special features include additional, optional logic topics. See pages 13-15, 87, 129-134, 145, etc.

A lesson on logic in Chapter 5 leads into the topic of indirect proof.

EXPLORATION/Conjunctions

Another term used in logic is the conjunction "and," denoted by "$\wedge$." The sentence $p \wedge q$ is true only when p and q are both true. Knowing this, complete the truth table below to determine whether the relationship "if—then" (denoted by "$\rightarrow$") is transitive. In other words, show "If $p \rightarrow q$ and $q \rightarrow r$, then $p \rightarrow r$" or $[(p \rightarrow q) \wedge (q \rightarrow r)] \rightarrow (p \rightarrow r)$. Note that the table has eight possible outcomes. Why?

p	q	r		$p \rightarrow q$	$q \rightarrow r$	$(p \rightarrow q) \wedge (q \rightarrow r)$	$p \rightarrow r$	$[(p \rightarrow q) \wedge (q \rightarrow r)] \rightarrow (p \rightarrow r)$
T	T	T		T	T	T	T	T
T	T	F		T	F	F	F	T
T	F	T	**1.**	___	___	___	___	___
T	F	F	**2.**	___	___	___	___	___
F	T	T	**3.**	___	___	___	___	___
F	T	F	**4.**	___	___	___	___	___
F	F	T	**5.**	___	___	___	___	___
F	F	F	**6.**	___	___	___	___	___

Exploration **145**

5.2 Indirect Proof

Indirect proofs are a powerful deductive tool. Certain theorems that seem obviously true are difficult to establish in a direct proof. Using the *contrapositive* in an indirect proof often overcomes this difficulty.

In Chapter 3, the definitions of *right angle* and *perpendicular lines* were introduced. If you choose a point on a line in a plane, you can draw a second line perpendicular to the first at that point.

> **THEOREM 5.1** In a given plane, through a given point of a given line, there is one and only one line perpendicular to the given line.

Given: Line l in plane E, with P a point on l

Prove: There exists a unique line $\overleftrightarrow{PY} \perp$ to l at P.

Existence: Prove there *is* one line perpendicular to the given line at the given point.

Uniqueness: Prove there is *only* one line perpendicular to the given line at the given point.

Existence proof:

STATEMEN

1. P on line l in plane E
2. H is one of the half-pl determined by l.
3. X is another point of
4. $\overrightarrow{PY}$ lies in H so that
5. P and Y determine $\overleftrightarrow{P}$

6. $\overleftrightarrow{PY} \perp l$

Given: Line l is the $\perp$ bisector of AB at point C in plane E.

Prove: (1) If P is any point on l, then $PA = PB$, and (2) if $QA = QB$ then Q is a point on l.

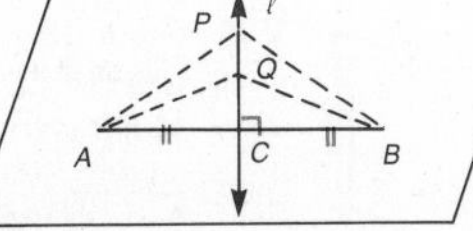

Proof:

Part 1 (Every point on l is equidistant from the endpoints of $\overline{AB}$.):

Let P be any point on l. Either P is the same point as C, or it is a different point on l. (a) If P is the same point as C, then $P = C$, and $PA = PB$ because C or P is the midpoint of $\overline{AB}$. (b) If P is not the same point as C, then $P \neq C$, and $\overline{PC} \cong \overline{PC}$ by the reflexive property, and $\overline{CA} \cong \overline{CB}$ from the definitions of midpoint and congruent segments. $\angle PCA$ and $\angle PCB$ are right angles from the perpendicular bisector. So, $\Delta PCA \cong \Delta PCB$ by SAS. Hence, $PA = PB$.

Part 2 (Any point equidistant from A and B lies on l.):

Let Q be any point in plane E such that $QA = QB$. Either Q is on $\overline{AB}$, or it is not. (a) If Q is on $\overline{AB}$, then Q and C are the same point and $Q = C$ because a line segment has exactly one midpoint. Since C is on l (definition of perpendicular bisector), Q must be on l. (b) If Q is not on $\overline{AB}$, draw the line determined by Q and C. Then, $\overline{QC} \cong \overline{QC}$, $\overline{CA} \cong \overline{CB}$, and $\overline{QA} \cong \overline{QB}$. By SSS, $\Delta QCA \cong \Delta QCB$. Thus, $\angle QCA$ and $\angle QCB$ form a linear pair of congruent angles. Hence, they are right angles. $QC \perp \overline{AB}$. But, by Theorem 5.1, perpendiculars in a plane at a point are unique. So, $\overleftrightarrow{QC}$ and l must be the same line. Therefore, Q is a point of l.

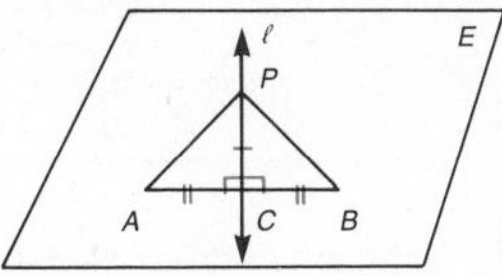

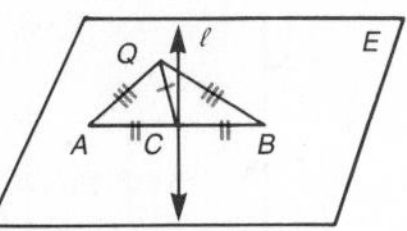

> **COROLLARY 5.2.1**
> Given a segment $\overline{AB}$ and a line l in a plane, if two points of l are equidistant from A and B, then l is the perpendicular bisector $\overline{AB}$.

The proof of this theorem is left as an exercise.

The next logical step in the deductive process is to establish theorems about a perpendicular to a line through a point *off* the line.

Section 5.2 • Indirect Proof **137**

Indirect proof

Students learn to employ indirect proof as an additional deductive tool in Chapter 5. See pages 131-134, 135-140, 141-144, etc.

Both direct and indirect proofs are used to prove the same statements on pages 141-142 and 144.

Paragraph proofs

The text frequently exposes students to the paragraph form of writing proofs, beginning in Chapter 1. See pages 23, 137, 152, etc.

Coordinate geometry proofs

Students learn to write proofs using the theorems and methods of coordinate geometry in Chapter 11, further expanding students' skill in deductive reasoning. See pages 358-362.

Up-to-Date Computer/Technology Strand

Computer, a full-page optional feature in every chapter, involves students in applying computer skills to topics from the chapter. See pages 55, 121, 303, etc.

More Computer Activities are available as blackline masters in the Teacher's Resources or as spirit duplicating masters.

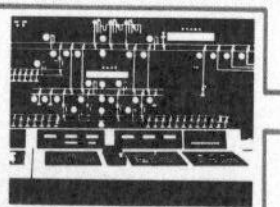

COMPUTER

The creation of coordinate geometry by René Descartes (1596–1650) made it possible to translate geometric relations into algebraic formulas. These formulas can be used with a computer. Consider the two lines at the right, represented by the system of linear equations $Ax + By = C$ and $Mx + Ny = P$. Using the multiplication-addition method to solve the system yields

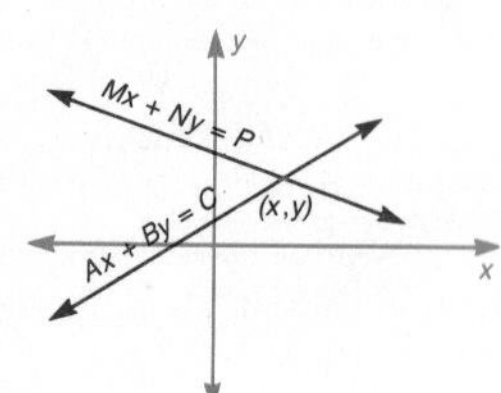

$$x = \frac{CN - BP}{AN - BM} \text{ and } y = \frac{AP - CM}{AN - BM}.$$

The following program will find the point of intersection for two different lines that do not have the same slope.

```
10 PRINT"INPUT THE COEFFICIENTS OF THE TWO LINES"
20 INPUT A,B,C,M,N,P
30 LET D = A*N - B*M
40 LET X = (C*N - B*P)/D
50 LET Y = (A*P - C*M)/D
60 PRINT"THE INTERSECTION IS X =;X" Y=;Y
70 GOTO 10
80 END
```

This program will work only for lines that have unequal slopes.

1. For coefficients, input 1, 2, 3, 4, 5, 6. Compare the results with an input of 3, 4, 5, 6, 7, 8 and with 5, 6, 7, 8, 9, 10.
2. Create a line after line 20 to allow the user to exit the program.
3. Create a line after line 30 to identify and eliminate lines that have the same slope.

In science and mathematics, you must often solve formulas for a single variable before you can use a computer. Solve the formulas below for the variable shown.

4. If $A = \frac{1}{2}bh$, then $b =$ ____.
5. If $E = mc^2$, then $m =$ ____.

Factor b[illegible]ping.

21. $x^3 + 3x^2 - x - 3$ **22.** $t^3 + t^2 - t - 1$

Determine b so that the expression is a trinomial square.

23. $x^2 + 16x + b$ **24.** $x^2 + bx + 81$

Calculator is a frequent textbook feature that promotes students' calculator skills, frequently in problem solving. See pages 38, 301, 324, etc.

CALCULATOR

In the figure below, all surfaces are rectangular. The projections at either end are identical, and the dimensions are as shown. If one quart of paint will cover 130 square feet, how many quarts should you buy to paint the entire surface?

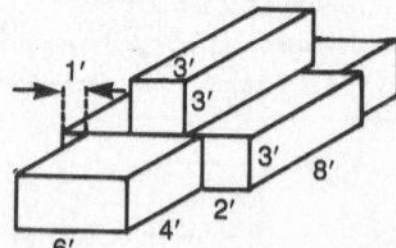

For correlated computer courseware see page T13.

Special Features for Enrichment, Interest, Problem Solving, More Rigor

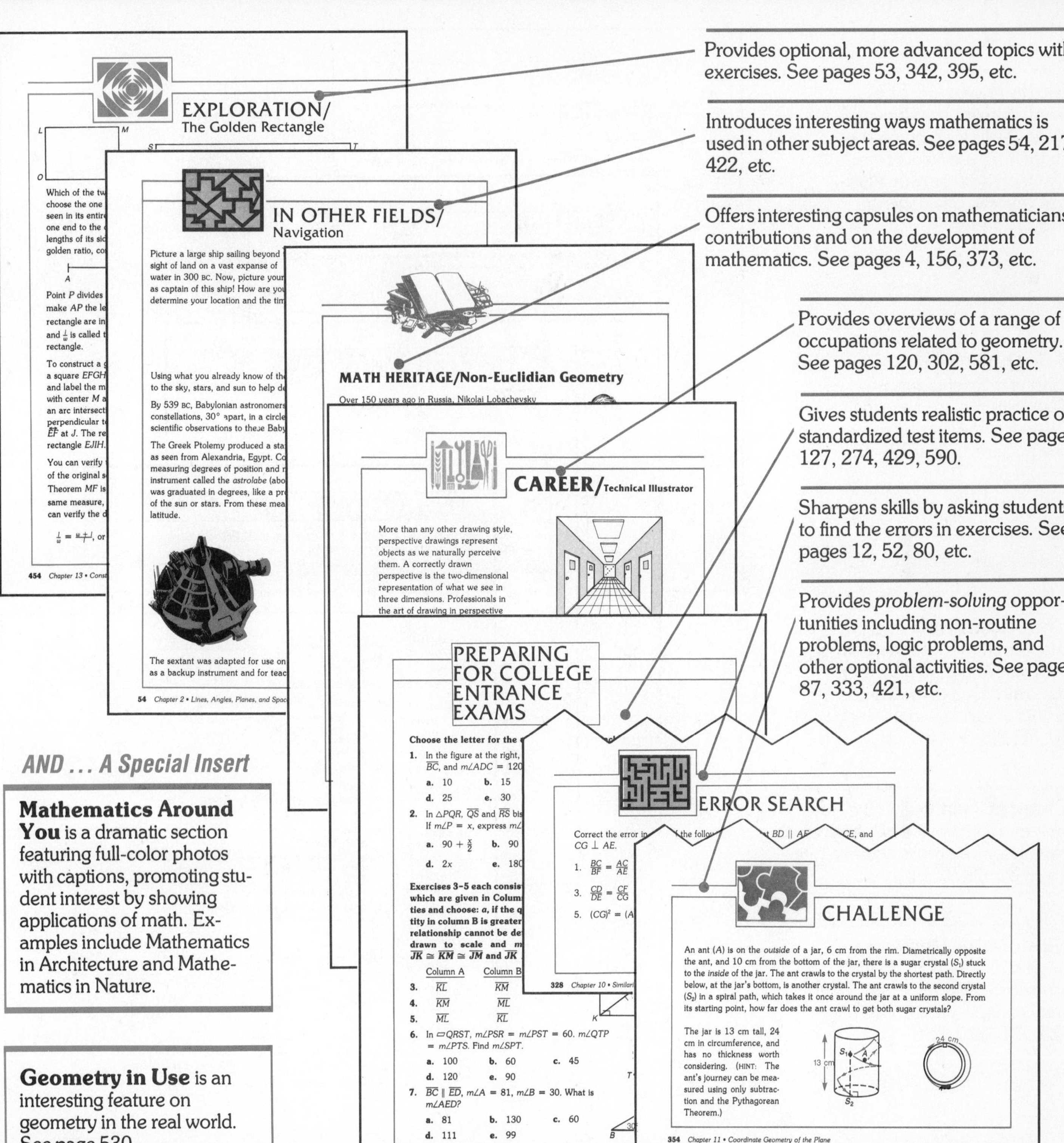

Provides optional, more advanced topics with exercises. See pages 53, 342, 395, etc.

Introduces interesting ways mathematics is used in other subject areas. See pages 54, 217, 422, etc.

Offers interesting capsules on mathematicians' contributions and on the development of mathematics. See pages 4, 156, 373, etc.

Provides overviews of a range of occupations related to geometry. See pages 120, 302, 581, etc.

Gives students realistic practice on standardized test items. See pages 127, 274, 429, 590.

Sharpens skills by asking students to find the errors in exercises. See pages 12, 52, 80, etc.

Provides *problem-solving* opportunities including non-routine problems, logic problems, and other optional activities. See pages 87, 333, 421, etc.

AND ... A Special Insert

Mathematics Around You is a dramatic section featuring full-color photos with captions, promoting student interest by showing applications of math. Examples include Mathematics in Architecture and Mathematics in Nature.

Geometry in Use is an interesting feature on geometry in the real world. See page 530.

Continuous Maintenance, Review, and Testing

Skills Maintenance, in every chapter, lets students review skills from preceding chapters or previous courses. Many of these provide **algebra review.** See pages 53, 119, 372, etc.

Self-Quiz during each chapter gives students a diagnostic tool to check their mastery of the chapter so far. See pages 43, 73, 109, etc.

Chapter Review — 2 pages at chapter-end — includes both a *vocabulary list* and *review exercises, all keyed* to the lessons for further study if needed. See pages 30, 56, 90, etc.

Chapter Test follows the Review and can provide helpful preparation for formal assessment. See pages 32, 58, 92, etc.

Cumulative Reviews on chapters 1-4, 1-8, 9-12, and 9-16 provide maintenance and are entirely multiple-choice. See pages 125, 270, 427, 586.

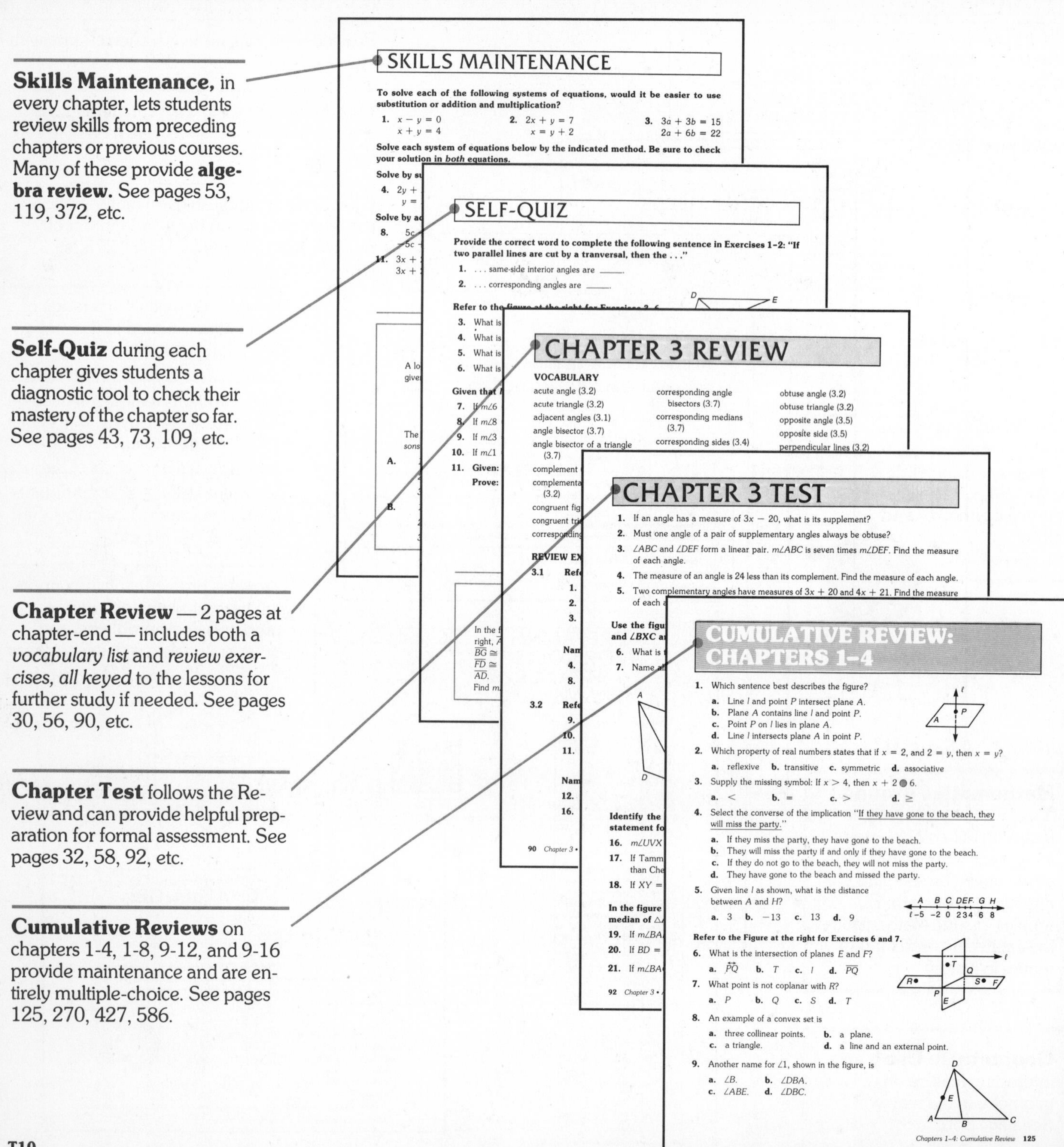

SKILLS MAINTENANCE

To solve each of the following systems of equations, would it be easier to use substitution or addition and multiplication?

1. $x - y = 0$, $x + y = 4$
2. $2x + y = 7$, $x = y + 2$
3. $3a + 3b = 15$, $2a + 6b = 22$

Solve each system of equations below by the indicated method. Be sure to check your solution in *both* equations.

SELF-QUIZ

Provide the correct word to complete the following sentence in Exercises 1–2: "If two parallel lines are cut by a tranversal, then the . . ."

1. . . . same-side interior angles are ____.
2. . . . corresponding angles are ____.

CHAPTER 3 REVIEW

VOCABULARY

acute angle (3.2), acute triangle (3.2), adjacent angles (3.1), angle bisector (3.7), angle bisector of a triangle (3.7), corresponding angle bisectors (3.7), corresponding medians (3.7), corresponding sides (3.4), obtuse angle (3.2), obtuse triangle (3.2), opposite angle (3.5), opposite side (3.5), perpendicular lines (3.2)

CHAPTER 3 TEST

1. If an angle has a measure of $3x - 20$, what is its supplement?
2. Must one angle of a pair of supplementary angles always be obtuse?
3. $\angle ABC$ and $\angle DEF$ form a linear pair. $m\angle ABC$ is seven times $m\angle DEF$. Find the measure of each angle.
4. The measure of an angle is 24 less than its complement. Find the measure of each angle.
5. Two complementary angles have measures of $3x + 20$ and $4x + 21$. Find the measure of each angle.

CUMULATIVE REVIEW: CHAPTERS 1–4

1. Which sentence best describes the figure?
   a. Line l and point P intersect plane A.
   b. Plane A contains line l and point P.
   c. Point P on l lies in plane A.
   d. Line l intersects plane A in point P.
2. Which property of real numbers states that if $x = 2$, and $2 = y$, then $x = y$?
   a. reflexive b. transitive c. symmetric d. associative
3. Supply the missing symbol: If $x > 4$, then $x + 2$ ● 6.
   a. $<$ b. $=$ c. $>$ d. $\geq$
4. Select the converse of the implication "If they have gone to the beach, they will miss the party."
   a. If they miss the party, they have gone to the beach.
   b. They will miss the party if and only if they have gone to the beach.
   c. If they do not go to the beach, they will not miss the party.
   d. They have gone to the beach and missed the party.
5. Given line l as shown, what is the distance between A and H?
   a. 3 b. −13 c. 13 d. 9

Refer to the Figure at the right for Exercises 6 and 7.

6. What is the intersection of planes E and F?
   a. $\overleftrightarrow{PQ}$ b. T c. l d. $\overline{PQ}$
7. What point is not coplanar with R?
   a. P b. Q c. S d. T
8. An example of a convex set is
   a. three collinear points. b. a plane.
   c. a triangle. d. a line and an external point.
9. Another name for $\angle 1$, shown in the figure, is
   a. $\angle B$. b. $\angle DBA$.
   c. $\angle ABE$. d. $\angle DBC$.

Chapters 1–4: Cumulative Review 125

Teacher's Edition: Daily Help in the Page Margins

The extended margins provide daily teaching help adjacent to the full-size student pages (most answers are overprinted on the pages):

Objective(s) of each lesson.

Teacher's Notes: page references to the Teaching Suggestions in the Manual.

Mixed Review to continuously maintain concepts and skills previously introduced, especially **algebra concepts and skills.**

OBJECTIVE

Distinguish between reason, conjecture, chance discovery, and intuition.

TEACHER'S NOTES

See p. T29

MIXED REVIEW

1. What is the contrapositive of "If two sides of a triangle are congruent then the angles opposite these sides are congruent?" If two angles of a triangle are not congruent, then the sides opposite these angles are not congruent.
2. Solve $2x - 3 < 7$. $x < 5$
3. Solve $x + 7 < 2x - 5$. $x > 12$
4. Multiply $4x^2(3x^2 + 2x - 4)$. $12x^4 + 8x^3 - 16x^2$
5. Solve $14 - 3x = 2(x + 31)$. $x = -9\frac{3}{5}$

TEACHER'S RESOURCE MASTERS

Practice Master 16, Part 1

6.1 Conjectures from Experimentation

In previous chapters, your study of geometry has emphasized the idea of equality. Congruent segments and angles have *equal* measure. An isosceles triangle has two sides of *equal* measure. Real situations, however, often involve comparisons of measures that are not *equal*. For example, the flying distance from Houston to New York is *longer* if your plane makes a stop at Chicago. The angle of the sun is *smaller* in the early morning than at high noon.

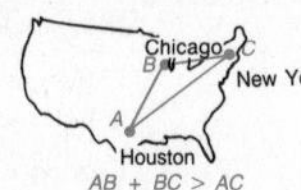

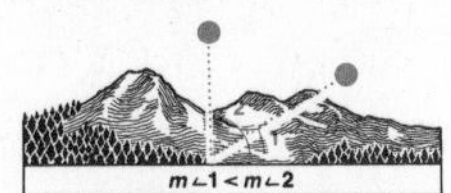

As with congruence, you can deduce general conclusions about figures having unequal measure, and in this chapter you will prove some important theorems about inequalities. You can deduce a great deal about inequalities, though, just by conjecture, a reasonable guess. Once a conjecture has withstood a few tests, it can be added to your body of knowledge.

Before deciding whether to accept or reject this conjecture, you would want to sketch several cases that fulfill the conditions. If the conclusion follows in every test, then you might be inclined to accept the proposed postulate. If, on the other hand, you can sketch just one exception, then you would have to reject the proposed rule. In logic, such an exception is called a **counterexample.**

Try to sketch a counterexample to the "SSA Postulate." In other words, try to draw two triangles with two pairs of sides and a pair of nonincluded angles congruent so that the triangles are not congruent. Only after you have decided whether or not to accept the proposed postulate should you proceed to the next paragraph.

Hopefully, you have decided to reject the "SSA Postulate." Observe that in ΔDAB and ΔDBC, $\overline{DB} \cong \overline{DB}$, $\angle D \cong \angle D$, and $\overline{BA} \cong \overline{BC}$. The condition SSA is satisfied, but the triangles are not congruent. This conjecture was not correct.

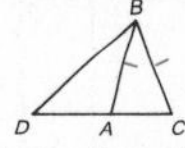

Reason and conjecture are not the only sources of knowledge. From the days of your infancy, you have learned much from **chance discovery.** A child on the playground, for example, may discover by chance that a ball strikes a wall and bounces off at the same angle.

You also gain knowledge from **intuition.** Using your intuition since an early age, you have acquired direct knowledge without conscious reasoning. Watch a child in a sandbox filling a bucket with sand. When the bucket is full, the child stops shoveling and dumps the sand, rather than attempting to force more into a bucket already full. The child intuitively understands a basic principle of physics: *Two things cannot occupy the same space at the same time.*

Intuition will often guide you correctly, but it can also be deceiving. Mathematicians therefore strive to support intuition by the use of inductive and deductive reasoning.

ORAL EXERCISES

1. Name three things you know as a result of intuition.
2. Name three things you know as a result of chance discovery.
3. Name three things you know as a result of conjecture.
4. Name three things you know as a result of proof.
5. Other than chance discovery, proof, conjecture, and intuition, what are some other sources of knowledge?

WRITTEN EXERCISES

A. 1. A black bag contains 50 marbles. One by one, 49 are removed, and each is red in color. From this would you make the conjecture that the 50th marble is also red? Explain.

Section 6.1 • Conjecture from Experimentation 163

ASSIGNMENT GUIDE

Minimum 1-10
Regular 1-11
Maximum 1-11

Oral Exercises

1-4. Answers will vary.

5. Experience, hearsay, and revelation are three possible answers.

Written Exercises

1. A safe conjecture; the probability is high that the 50th marble is also red.

Page references to all masters in Teacher's Resources.

Assignment Guide of exercises for 3 course levels.

Page references to suggested Enrichment Activities in the Manual.

Additional Answers to lesson exercises.

References to the correlated computer courseware.

Teacher's Edition: A Manual that Helps You Plan

The Teacher's Manual beginning on page T14 includes all these resources:

- **A Daily Lesson Assignment Guide** for 3 suggested course levels.
- **A guide to the Supplementary Materials.**
- **Performance Objectives** for every lesson.
- **Enrichment Activities** for every chapter, for use as the teacher decides.

ENRICHMENT ACTIVITIES

Enrichment Activity 1

Have students supply the reasons for each statement below and find the fault in the reasoning.

1. $a = b$ Given
2. $a^2 = ab$ Multiplication Property of Equality
3. $a^2 - b^2 = ab - b^2$ Subtraction Property of Equality
4. $(a + b)(a - b) = b(a - b)$ Factoring and Distributive Property
5. $a + b = b$ Division Property of Equality
6. $2b = b$ Substitution Property of Equality
7. $2 = 1$ Division Property of Equality

Solution: The 'fault' is division by zero in step 5.

Oblong numbers 2, 6, 12, 20 etc. are the product of two successive whole numbers.

Oblong

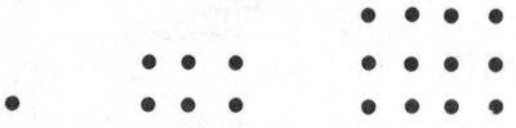

The prime numbers were called linear numbers since they could best be shown in a one line array.

Other number form classifications included pentagonal, hexagonal and heptagonal numbers.

Certain numbers were thought to represent specific

Enrich

The Pyth
tionships
whole nu
6, 10, 15,
25, etc.

7.4 This is a straightforward presentation of the remaining concepts of perpendiculars in space. Students should appreciate and be able to prove Theorem 7.11 without difficulty. More explicit attention is given to existence and uniqueness.

In Other Fields: Joinery Note that *area* is requested as a known idea from previous work in other mathematical classes.

8 • Parallels

Overview The chapter includes parallel conditions in the plane and in space. The 33 theorems and 10 corollaries include many important concepts used in standardized tests and relationships that are used in similar triangles and coordinate geometry. After establishing the necessary conditions for parallelism by definition, the first seven theorems are an excellent way to show the nature of proof in geometry. New ground is broken with an indirect proof and direct deductive proof is used to prove several theorems easily. Attention is given to the importance of the Parallel Postulate and the need for its postulation. The wealth of material requires your judicious choice as to the time and the problems that will be selected for use.

Teaching Suggestions

8.1 Before the students read this section, it is useful to have them describe their concept or definition of parallel. The existence of a plane containing parallel lines is in the definition, and the uniqueness of this plane is established in the first theorem. Other possible definitions are weaker in that they would not be acceptable in non-Euclidean geometries. Theorem 8.5 establishes by indirect proof the foundation to prove 8.6 and 8.7 by direct deduction. A possible abbreviation for Theorem 8.5 is AI→P. Have students identify the contradiction of the exterior angle theorem in the proof of Theorem 8.5. The problem set is given without mention of corresponding angles so that students may use the first five theorems without confusion. Oral Exercise 13 and Written Exercises 8 and 11 are numerical examples of the next two theorems and can be used to prepare for their proof. **Warning:** Oral Exercises 15 and 16 are TRAPS since they cannot be justified without the Parallel Postulate. Convince the students that the converse of AI→P has not been proved.

Written Exercise 12 is the Saccheri Quadrilateral that the Italian monk used to try to prove that a parallel to a given line from an external point was unique. Although we can prove that the upper angles are congruent, without the Parallel Postulate we cannot prove that they are right angles. In a hyperbolic geometry they are acute.

8.2 The corresponding angles definition and theorems are easily developed if the students have mastery of Lesson 8.1. In Oral Exercises 9 and 10, note the converses have not yet been proved. After proving Theorem 8.7 you may wish to have students prove that congruent alternate exterior angles (AE→P) and supplementary interior angles on the same side of a transversal (IASSTS→P) are sufficient to prove parallelism.

8.3 Euclid's fifth axiom is given as the Parallel Postulate. The converses of the theorems in Lessons 8.1 and 8.2 are now easily proved. Again, the first proof is indirect to provide a foundation. Theorem 8.8 can be represented by P→AI. The figure for Written Exercise 14 implies an indirect proof, but a transversal, alternate interior angles, and transitivity can be used for a direct proof.

8.4 In proving Theorem 8.13 discuss why it was necessary to wait until this section to prove the theorem. Written Exercise 17 allows reinforcement of the biconditional theorems. Saccheri's Quadrilateral can now be used to prove the upper base angles are right angles.

Self-Quiz Exercise 14 anticipates later work with parallelograms and Exercise 15 relates to the bimedian theorem.

T31

- **Chapter Overviews.**
- **Teaching Suggestions** for every lesson.
- **Additional Answers** to text exercises.

Full Range of Supplementary Materials for Teaching Support

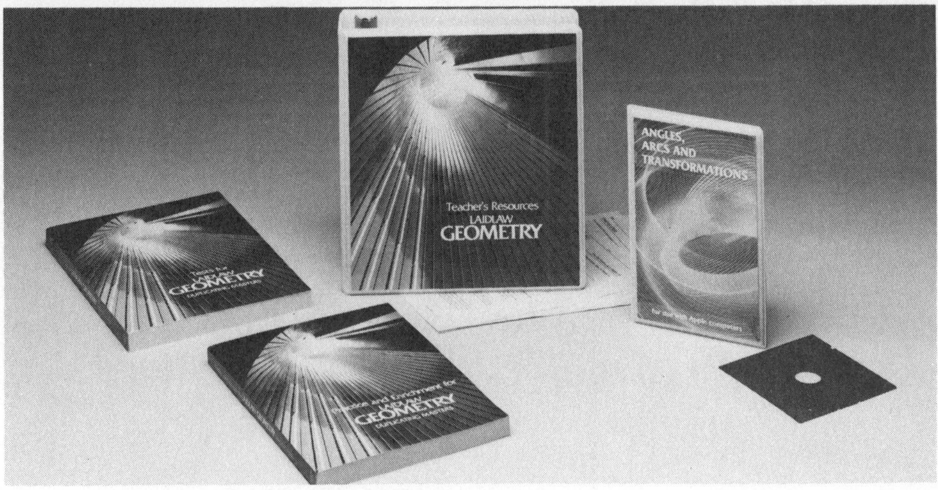

Teacher's Resources. A 3-ring binder that gives you all these blackline masters plus dividers to organize them:

Practice for every lesson

Enrichment activities to assign when appropriate

Computer activities

Tests
- Chapter Tests (free-response and multiple-choice versions)
- Quizzes (two on each chapter)
- Cumulative Tests (quarterly and semester tests, two versions of each, all multiple-choice)

Teaching Aids including reproducible tables, grid paper, etc.

Classroom Management tools including Homework Record, Practice Master Record, Quiz and Test Record, Correlation Chart of Teacher's Resources to textbook, and more.

Spirit Duplicating Masters of the Practice, Enrichment, and Computer activities.

Spirit Duplicating Masters of the Tests and Quizzes.

Solutions Manual giving the teacher detailed solutions to all textbook exercises.

Correlated Software for computer-assisted instruction. Entitled *Angles, Arcs, and Transformations,* includes disk with Teacher's Manual. Students carry out exercises involving angle measure; find measures of arcs and angles using knowledge of circle theorems; and use transformations to map figures onto similar figures.

OTHER COMPREHENSIVE TEXTBOOKS AVAILABLE

LAIDLAW ALGEBRA 1

LAIDLAW ALGEBRA 2 WITH TRIGONOMETRY

DAILY LESSON GUIDE

Assignment Guide

Day	Minimum Course	Regular Course	Maximum Course
1	1.1 1-14	1.1 1-18	1.1 1-18
2	1.2 1-27 odd	1.2 1-27 odd, 29-38	1.2 1-27 odd, 29-40
3	1.3 1-23	1.3 1-33 odd	1.3 1-25 odd, 26-33
4	1.4 1-27 odd	1.4 1-31 odd	1.4 1-25 odd, 26-31
5	1.5 1-16	1.5 1-19 odd	1.5 1-23 odd
6	1.6 1-19	1.6 1-23 odd	1.6 1-19 odd, 20-23
7	Chapter Review	Chapter Review	Chapter Review
8	Chapter Test	Chapter Test	Chapter Test
9	2.1 1-17, 23	2.1 1-23	2.1 1-24
10	2.2 1-15	2.2 1-16	2.2 1-18
11	2.3 1-10, 14-18	2.3 1-12, 14-20	2.3 1-22
12	2.4 1-17	2.4 1-21	2.4 1-24 odd
13	Chapter Review	Chapter Review	Chapter Review
14	Chapter Test	Chapter Test	Chapter Test
15	3.1 1-23 odd	3.1 1-23 odd	3.1 1-27 odd
16	3.1 2-24 even	3.1 6-32 even	3.1 12-28 even, 31-35
17	3.2 1-22	3.2 1-22, 23-27 odd	3.2 15-32

Assignment Guide

Day	Minimum Course	Regular Course	Maximum Course
18	3.3 1-25 odd	3.3 1-29 odd	3.3 1-35 odd
19	3.4 1-16	3.4 1-18	3.4 1-15, 21-22
20	3.5 1-15 odd	3.5 1-19 odd	3.5 1-23 odd
21	3.5 2-24 even	3.5 8-26 even	3.5 16-24 even, 25-30
22	3.6 1-25	3.6 1-35	3.6 1-15 odd, 16-37
23	3.7 1-16	3.7 1-23 odd	3.7 1-15 odd, 19-26
24	Chapter Review	Chapter Review	Chapter Review
25	Chapter Test	Chapter Test	Chapter Test
26	4.1 1-25	4.1 1-26	4.1 1-25 odd, 27-29
27	4.2 1-15	4.2 1-16	4.2 1-15, 17-20
28	4.3 1-15 odd	4.3 1-17 odd	4.3 1-21 odd
29	4.3 2-14 even	4.3 2-16 even	4.3 2-20 even
30	4.4 1-12	4.4 1-18	4.4 1-19
31	4.4 13-20	4.4 19-21	4.4 20-24
32	4.5 1-7	4.5 1-8, 9-13 odd	4.5 5-9 odd, 10-16
33	Chapter Review	Chapter Review	Chapter Review
34	Chapter Test	Chapter Test	Chapter Test
35	Cumulative Review 1-4	Cumulative Review 1-4	Cumulative Review 1-4
36	5.1 1-10	5.1 1-17	5.1 1-18
37	5.1 11-18	5.1 18-19	5.1 19-20
38	5.2 1-13	5.2 1-17 odd	5.2 1-17

Assignment Guide

Day	Minimum Course	Regular Course	Maximum Course
39	5.3 1-18	5.3 1-19	5.3 1-22
40	5.4 1-17	5.4 1-27	5.4 14-26, 27-37 odd
41	5.5 1-10	5.5 1-10	5.5 1-21, 24
42	Chapter Review	Chapter Review	Chapter Review
43	Chapter Test	Chapter Test	Chapter Test
44	6.1 1-10	6.1 1-11	6.1 1-11
45	6.2 1-9	6.2 1-10	6.2 1-12
46	6.3 1-12	6.3 1-15 odd	6.3 1-15 odd, 16-18
47	6.4 1-12	6.4 1-13	6.4 1-15 odd, 16
48	6.5 1-14	6.5 1-16	6.5 1-16
49	6.5 15-25	6.5 17-26	6.5 17-27
50	6.6 1-6	6.6 1-9	6.6 1-7 odd, 8-12
51	6.7 1-11	6.7 1-12	6.7 1-11 odd, 12-14
52	Chapter Review	Chapter Review	Chapter Review
53	Chapter Test	Chapter Test	Chapter Test
54	7.1 1-10	7.1 1-16	7.1 1-18
55	7.2 1-16	7.2 1-17	7.2 1-18
56	7.3 1-10	7.3 1-10	7.3 1-13 odd, 14
57	7.4 1-10	7.4 1-12	7.4 1-13 odd, 14-17
58	Chapter Review	Chapter Review	Chapter Review
59	Chapter Test	Chapter Test	Chapter Test

Assignment Guide

Day	Minimum Course	Regular Course	Maximum Course
60	8.1 1-11 odd	8.1 1-13 odd	8.1 1-15 odd
61	8.1 2-12 even	8.1 2-14 even	8.1 2-16 even
62	8.2 1-9	8.2 1-15 odd	8.2 1-15 odd, 14, 16
63	8.3 1-9	8.3 1-11 odd	8.3 1-15 odd
64	8.4 1-12	8.4 1-17 odd	8.4 1-13 odd, 14-18
65	8.5 1-7	8.5 1-7	8.5 1-7
66	8.5 8-11	8.5 8-14	8.5 8-16
67	8.6 1-9	8.6 1-10	8.6 1-10
68	8.6 11-15	8.6 11-16	8.6 11-19
69	8.7 1-8	8.7 1-10	8.7 1-10
70	8.7 9-11	8.7 11-17 odd	8.7 11-17 odd, 18-19
71	8.8 1-13	8.8 1-22	8.8 1-13 odd, 14-24
72	8.9 1-12	8.9 1-15	8.9 1-16, 18-20
73	Chapter Review	Chapter Review	Chapter Review
74	Chapter Test	Chapter Test	Chapter Test
75	Cumulative Review 1-8	Cumulative Review 1-8	Cumulative Review 1-8
76	Cumulative Review 1-8	Cumulative Review 1-8	Cumulative Review 1-8
77	9.1 1-12	9.1 1-13 odd	9.1 1-13 odd, 14-16
78	9.2 1-13	9.2 1-15	9.2 1-15 odd, 18-19
79	9.3 1-15	9.3 1-19	9.3 1-19 odd, 21-23
80	9.4 1-15	9.4 1-16	9.4 1-15 odd, 16-22

Assignment Guide

Day	Minimum Course	Regular Course	Maximum Course
81	9.5 1-18 odd	9.5 1-21 odd	9.5 1-21 odd, 22-24
82	9.6 1-15	9.6 1-24	9.6 1-30
83	9.6 19-31 odd	9.6 25-35 odd	9.6 31-41 odd
84	Chapter Review	Chapter Review	Chapter Review
85	Chapter Test	Chapter Test	Chapter Test
86	10.1 1-5	10.1 1-35 odd	10.1 1-41 odd
87	10.1 19-33 odd	10.1 10-36 even	10.1 10-40 even
88	10.2 1-15 odd	10.2 1-21 odd	10.2 1-17 odd, 18-22
89	10.3 1-11	10.3 1-17 odd	10.3 1-17 odd, 18-21
90	10.4 1-7 odd, 9-22	10.4 1-7 odd, 9-23	10.4 1-7 odd, 9-26
91	10.5 1-20	10.5 1-27 odd	10.5 1-33 odd
92	10.6 1-20	10.6 1-33 odd	10.6 1-33 odd, 35-40
93	Chapter Review	Chapter Review	Chapter Review
94	Chapter Test	Chapter Test	Chapter Test
95	11.1 1-22	11.1 1-29 odd	11.1 1-29 odd, 30-33
96	11.2 1-14	11.2 1-23 odd	11.2 1-23 odd, 25-29
97	11.3 1-16	11.3 1-18	11.3 1-18, 22-24
98	11.4 1-8	11.4 1-17 odd	11.4 1-25 odd, 26
99	11.5 1-10	11.5 1-15	11.5 1-18
100	11.5 20-24	11.5 20-26	11.5 25-30
101	11.6 1-2	11.6 1-3	11.6 1-4

Assignment Guide

Day	Minimum Course	Regular Course	Maximum Course
102	11.6 3, 6, 9	11.6 6-9	11.6 5-9 odd, 10-11
103	11.7 1-6	11.7 1-13 odd	11.7 1-9 odd, 13-19
104	11.8 1-19 odd	11.8 1-23 odd	11.8 1-23 odd, 25-26
105	Chapter Review	Chapter Review	Chapter Review
106	Chapter Test	Chapter Test	Chapter Test
107	12.1 1-18	12.1 1-27 odd	12.1 1-31 odd, 32
108	12.2 1-13	12.2 1-18	12.2 1-19
109	12.2 20-24	12.2 20-26	12.2 20-27
110	12.3 1-18	12.3 1-22	12.3 1-24
111	12.4 1-19 odd	12.4 1-25 odd	12.4 1-19 odd, 21-26
112	12.5 1-15	12.5 1-23 odd	12.5 1-27 odd
113	12.5 21-26	12.5 2-26 even	12.5 2-32 even
114	12.6 1-15	12.6 1-25 odd	12.6 1-25 odd, 26-27
115	12.7 1-5	12.7 1-5, 11-15	12.7 1-5, 11-15, 23-25
116	12.7 6-15	12.7 16-22, 26-29	12.7 16-22, 26-29, 36-43
117	12.8 1-19 odd	12.8 1-23 odd	12.8 1-35 odd
118	Chapter Review	Chapter Review	Chapter Review
119	Chapter Test	Chapter Test	Chapter Test
120	Cumulative Review 9-12	Cumulative Review 9-12	Cumulative Review 9-12
121	13.1 1-6	13.1 1-9 odd	13.1 1-7 odd, 8-11
122	13.2 1-4	13.2 1-5	13.2 1-7 odd, 9-10

Assignment Guide

Day	Minimum Course	Regular Course	Maximum Course
123	13.3 1-6	13.3 1-10	13.3 6-12
124	13.4 1-11 odd	13.4 1-7 odd, 10-12	13.4 1-7 odd, 12-17
125	Chapter Review	Chapter Review	Chapter Review
126	Chapter Test	Chapter Test	Chapter Test
127	14.1 1-19	14.1 1-25 odd	14.1 1-19 odd, 21-30
128	14.2 1-13	14.2 1-23 odd	14.2 1-15 odd, 20-25
129	14.3 1-8	14.3 1-8	14.3 1-8
130	14.3 9-15	14.3 9-16	14.3 9-18
131	14.4 1-17 odd	14.4 1-21 odd	14.4 1-13 odd, 14-16, 21-22
132	14.5 1-7	14.5 1-11 odd	14.5 1-5 odd, 8-12
133	14.6 1-11	14.6 1-15 odd	14.6 1-11 odd, 12-16
134	14.7 1-8	14.7 1-13 odd	14.7 1-7 odd, 8-14
135	14.8 1-11	14.8 1-21 odd	14.8 1-19 odd, 23-26
136	14.8 20-26	14.8 23-31 odd	14.8 27-32
137	14.9 1-10	14.9 1-15 odd	14.9 1-11 odd, 13-17
138	Chapter Review	Chapter Review	Chapter Review
139	Chapter Test	Chapter Test	Chapter Test
140	15.1 1-9	15.1 1-17 odd	15.1 1-15 odd, 17-22
141	15.1 10-24	15.1 19-35 odd	15.1 23-33 odd, 35-37
142	15.2 1-20	15.2 1-31 odd	15.2 1-29 odd, 36-39
143	15.3 1-19 odd	15.3 1-27 odd, 28-33	15.3 1-27 odd, 28-33, 36-41

Assignment Guide

Day	Minimum Course	Regular Course	Maximum Course
144	15.4 1-14	15.4 1-19 odd, 20-25	15.4 1-19 odd, 20-28
145	15.5 1-12	15.5 1-19	15.5 1-11 odd, 13-19, 21-23
146	15.6 1-11 odd	15.6 1-10	15.6 1-10
147	15.6 2-12 even	15.6 11-15	15.6 11-17, 18
148	15.7 1-15 odd	15.7 1-19 odd	15.7 1-13 odd, 15-21
149	15.8 1-8	15.8 1-11 odd, 12-16, 17-23 odd	15.8 1-9 odd, 11-16, 23-24
150	Chapter Review	Chapter Review	Chapter Review
151	Chapter Test	Chapter Test	Chapter Test
152	16.1 1-15	16.1 1-21 odd	16.1 1-15 odd, 19-21
153	16.1 16-25	16.1 22-28	16.1 23-29 odd, 30-31, 34-35
154	16.2 1-21 odd	16.2 1-29 odd	16.2 1-21 odd, 25-27, 30-33
155	16.3 1-7	16.3 1-13 odd	16.3 1-7 odd, 9-15
156	16.4 1-7	16.4 1-13 odd	16.4 1-9 odd, 11-14
157	16.5 1-6	16.5 1-11 odd	16.5 1-7 odd, 8-11
158	16.6 1-13	16.6 1-19 odd	16.6 1-17 odd, 18-20
159	Chapter Review	Chapter Review	Chapter Review
160	Chapter Test	Chapter Test	Chapter Test
161	Cumulative Review 9-16	Cumulative Review 9-16	Cumulative Review 9-16
162	Cumulative Review 9-16	Cumulative Review 9-16	Cumulative Review 9-16

GUIDE TO TEACHER'S RESOURCES

Use after Section	Practice Master	Quiz or Test	Enrichment Master	Computer Master
1.1	P1, Part 1			
1.2.	P1, Part 2			
1.3	P2, Part 1			
1.4	P2, Part 2	Quiz 1		
1.5	P3, Part 1			
1.6	P3, Part 2	Quiz 2		
Ch. 1		T1-T2		
Test		T33-T34	E1-E2	C1
2.1	P4, Part 1			
2.2	P4, Part 2	Quiz 3		
2.3	P5, Part 1			
2.4	P5, Part 2	Quiz 4		
Ch. 2		T3-T4		
Test		T35-T36	E3	C2
3.1	P6			
3.2	P7, Part 1			
3.3	P7, Part 2	Quiz 5		
3.4	P8, Part 1			
3.5	P8, Part 2			
3.6	P9, Part 1			
3.7	P9, Part 2	Quiz 6		
Ch. 3		T5-T6		
Test		T37-T38	E4	C3
4.1	P10,			
4.2	P11, Part 1			
4.3	P11, Part 2	Quiz 7		
4.4	P12, Part 1			
4.5	P12, Part 2	Quiz 8		
Ch. 4		T7-T8		
Test		T39-T40		C4
Cum. Rev.:		T81-T82		
Ch. 1-4		T83-T84		
5.1	P13			
5.2	P14, Part 1			
5.3	P14, Part 2	Quiz 9		
5.4	P15, Part 1			
5.5	P15, Part 2	Quiz 10		
Ch. 5		T9-T10		
Test		T41-T42	E5	C5

Use after Section	Practice Master	Quiz or Test	Enrichment Master	Computer Master
6.1	P16, Part 1			
6.2	P16, Part 2			
6.3	P17, Part 1	Quiz 11		
6.4	P17, Part 2			
6.5	P17, Part 3			
6.6	P18, Part 1			
6.7	P18, Part 2	Quiz 12		
Ch. 6		T11-T12		
Test		T43-T44		C6
7.1	P19, Part 1			
7.2	P19, Part 2	Quiz 13		
7.3	P20, Part 1			
7.4	P20, Part 2	Quiz 14		
Ch. 7		T13-T14		
Test		T45-T46		C7
8.1	P21			
8.2	P22, Part 1			
8.3	P22, Part 2			
8.4	P23, Part 1	Quiz 15		
8.5	P23, Part 2			
8.6	P24, Part 1			
8.7	P24, Part 2			
8.8	P25, Part 1			
8.9	P25, Part 2	Quiz 16		
Ch. 8		T15-T16		
Test		T47-T48	E6	C8
Cum. Rev:		T85-T88		
Ch. 1-8		T89-T92		
9.1	P26, Part 1			
9.2	P26, Part 2			
9.3	P27, Part 1			
9.4	P27, Part 2	Quiz 17		
9.5	P28, Part 1			
9.6	P28, Part 2	Quiz 18		
Ch. 9		T17-T18		
Test		T49-T50	E7-E8	C9
10.1	P29, Part 1			
10.2	P29, Part 2			
10.3	P30, Part 1			

Use after Section	Practice Master	Quiz or Test	Enrichment Master	Computer Master
10.4	P30, Part 2	Quiz 19		
10.5	P31, Part 1			
10.6	P31, Part 2	Quiz 20		
Ch. 10		T19-T20		
Test		T51-T52	E9	C10
11.1	P32, Part 1			
11.2	P32, Part 2			
11.3	P33, Part 1			
11.4	P33, Part 2	Quiz 21		
11.5	P34, Part 1			
11.6	P34, Part 2			
11.7	P35, Part 1			
11.8	P35, Part 2	Quiz 22		
Ch. 11		T21-T22		
Test		T53-T54	E10	C11
12.1	P36, Part 1			
12.2	P36, Part 2			
12.3	P37, Part 1	Quiz 23		
12.4	P37, Part 2			
12.5	P38, Part 1			
12.6	P38, Part 2			
12.7	P39, Part 1			
12.8	P39, Part 2	Quiz 24		
Ch. 12		T23-T24		
Test		T55-T56	E11-E12	C12
Cu. Rev:		T93-T94		
Ch. 9-12		T95-T96		
13.1	P40, Part 1			
13.2	P40, Part 2			
13.3	P41, Part 1	Quiz 25		
13.4	P41, Part 2	Quiz 26		
Ch. 13		T25-T26		
Test		T57-T58	E13	C13

Use after Section	Practice Master	Quiz or Test	Enrichment Master	Computer Master
14.1	P42, Part 1			
14.2	P42, Part 2			
14.3	P43, Part 1			
14.4	P43, Part 2	Quiz 27		
14.5	P43, Part 3			
14.6	P44, Part 1			
14.7	P44, Part 2			
14.8	P45, Part 1			
14.9	P45, Part 2	Quiz 28		
Ch. 14		T27-T28		
Test		T59-T60	E14-E15	C14
15.1	P46, Part 1			
15.2	P46, Part 2			
15.3	P47, Part 1			
15.4	P47, Part 2	Quiz 29		
15.5	P48, Part 1			
15.6	P48, Part 2			
15.7	P49, Part 1			
15.8	P49, Part 2	Quiz 30		
Ch. 15		T29-T30		
Test		T61-T62		C15
16.1	P50, Part 1			
16.2	P50, Part 2			
16.3	P51, Part 1	Quiz 31		
16.4	P51, Part 2			
16.5	P52, Part 1			
16.6	P52, Part 2	Quiz 32		
Ch. 16		T31-T32		
Test		T63-T64	E16	C16
Cum. Rev:		T97- T100		
Ch. 9-16		T101- T104		

TEACHER'S NOTES

1 • Introduction to Geometry

Overview This chapter introduces the fundamental concept of geometry as a logical mathematical system. Emphasis is placed on the role of undefined terms, postulates, and the development of theorems. Proof of elementary theorems of the real numbers is used as a foundation. The basic concepts of equality, inequality, and equivalence relations are reviewed as part of the algebra. The metric postulates developed by the School Mathematics Study Group are used and should be introduced and developed at the intuitive level without undue emphasis on their technical correctness. Many of this chapter's concepts will be more easily understood during later chapters. Stress the proper use of the notation that is introduced in this chapter.

Teaching Suggestions

1.1 Have the students develop an intuitive set of models for the undefined terms—point, line, and plane. Introduce the double-headed arrow as notation for a line.

Math Heritage: Euclid The notes on Euclid and *Elements* offer students a chance to research and report on a major topic in mathematics.

1.2 The real number properties are reviewed from Algebra 1 and are used as reasons to solve an algebraic equation in a two-column proof format. The ideas of absolute value and principle square root are troublesome to many students and attention to their responses to the Oral Exercises of this section is important.

1.3 The properties of inequalities and equivalence relations will be used throughout the text and need to be stressed both in this section and in future lessons.

1.4 Mastery of the ideas of an implication, its converse, and the biconditional will contribute to the critical thinking skills of the students. The use of the biconditional "iff" will be used for most of the definitions in the text. Stress that a statement can be proven false by a single counterexample or contradiction. Warn students against assuming that the converse is always true.

Self-Quiz Every student should master each item of this quiz as a foundation for future work. This will be an excellent section to use for oral review later in the course.

1.5 The term postulate is introduced, and many students may not grasp the significance of it. The concept that postulates are rules of the game will be reinforced in later lessons. Postulate 1 agrees with most secondary students' idea of the real world. Many students have a poor grasp of the completeness of the real numbers and can benefit from a discussion of the points assigned to

$$\tfrac{1}{8}, \tfrac{1}{4}, \tfrac{1}{2} \ldots$$

on the number line segment between 0 and 1. Also consider irrational numbers and their assigned points to give a better feeling for density and completeness. Postulate 1 can be identified as one of Euclid's axioms. Due to a limited numeration system, early mathematicians did not use metric postulates. (Metric as used here does not refer to the metric system of measurement.)

Math Heritage: Hypatia Students interested in history could report on the library at Alexandria and the importance of mathematicians, such as Pappas, who worked there.

1.6 Although the Ruler Placement Postulate can be proved by algebraic manipulation of coordinate systems, it is postulated to allow the students to orient a point to zero and locate the positive numbers in any convenient direction. The definition of betweenness is based on Postulates 3 and 4. The idea is intuitively acceptable to students and should be developed by the use of drawings. Betweenness can be a difficult concept on a closed curve, so in this text it is considered only on a line. Theorems 1.1 and 1.2 are so obvious that students may wonder why they need to be proved. It is important to know that the "obvious" *can* be proved and that mathematicians consider it important to do so. Numerical examples of the theorems should be used. Equivalence relations such as Theorem 1.3 will be further developed in later chapters. Stress the difference between numerical equalities and set congruences and the notation that is used for segments and their measures. Treat the proof of the Point Plotting Theorem casually, but indicate that it will have many applications in future theorems. Care must be taken with the word *bisect* so that students do not interpret it to mean merely intersect.

Computer The emphasis on flowcharting is less than in previous years, but it uses the style of thinking that is helpful in planning proofs. The BASIC expression ABS(X) for $|x|$ will be useful later when using the distance postulate.

2 • Lines, Angles, Planes, and Space

Overview Chapter 2 establishes space as the set of all points. Convex and nonconvex sets are created and defined to distinguish between the interior and exterior of angles, triangles, and polygons. The definitions for angles and triangles are presented. The seven postulates developed are easily accepted by the students. Avoid overelaborating or putting too much stress on details. Advise the students that the large number of postulates is necessary at this time in order to provide a foundation for proving theorems. There is a total of 22 postulates in this course.

Teaching Suggestions

2.1 Establish the postulates and definitions without undue formality. Since the student has little experience with proof (particularly indirect proof), theorems should not be belabored. Formal proofs can be performed after the presentation of indirect proof and the contrapositive in Chapter 5. Be certain that students understand the meanings of "at least one," "at most one," and "exactly one" as used in this section. The use of "two," as in Written Exercise 5, will mean two *distinctly different* sets throughout the text. Generate a class discussion by using Postulates 1, 3, 5, and 6 to make a plane dense. A similar discussion can be extended to space.

2.2 Stress that the definition of half-plane and edge establishes three sets (the line and two half-planes). Half-line is used but is not formally defined. Students could create a line separation postulate. The words region and opposite sides are both accepted without formal definition. Written Exercises 5–9 provide a chance to discuss the use of analogies on the SAT examinations.

2.3 The definition of angle excludes zero, straight, and reflex angles in order to avoid difficulties in later theorems. In future courses, directed angles can be defined to include them along with negative angles. In the discussion of the interior of angles, stress that "same side" implies that the points are in the same half-plane. Advise students that the phrase "angle of a triangle" will be shortened to just "angle" for convention's sake, but there is a distinction between the two words.

2.4 To avoid confusion, angle measure by radians, mils, etc., will not be used. Angles are only measured in degrees in this text. This section provides a chance to demonstrate that $\angle ABC \cong \angle DEF$ is equivalent to $m\angle ABC = m\angle DEF$ by definition. The majority of the later proofs in the text will interchange congruence and equality expressions without using steps in the proofs. This avoidance of symbol manipulation is better for student comprehension. A similar treatment will be given to $\overline{AB} \cong \overline{CD}$ and AB = CD. In the discussion of the use of the protractor, remind the students that all measuring instruments are subject to some degree of error of precision.

Error Search This proof is true only for convex sets. Have the students consider some nonconvex models.

Chapter 2 Review Exercise 5 previews the concept of skew lines. Discussion of Exercise 7 could include the Ruler Placement Postulate.

3 • Angles, Triangles, and Congruence

Overview With the introduction of Postulates 12, 13, and 14 the foundation is laid for proving several fundamental theorems used in congruent triangle problems. The definitions of angle classifications and relations are presented in a direct manner since students have used these terms and ideas in previous courses. The definitions and theorems relating to supplementary angles may blend together in the students mind. If abbreviations are used, they must contain enough content to make sense to the student. For example, the abbreviation "VAT" for the vertical angle theorem seldom causes confusion. Students will handle this chapter with ease while working with numerical values, but it will take several weeks before they are comfortable with the distinction between many of the theorems and definitions when they are used in proofs. Only experience and practice will solve this problem.

Teaching Suggestions

3.1 Postulates 12 and 13 could be combined into a single postulate similar to the Ruler Postulate. Since they are used only one at a time, they are presented separately for easier use and comprehension. Students may have difficulty identifying linear pairs when several rays with a common endpoint are on the same side of a line. Notice that in the exercises "give the measures of the supplements of the angles" is stated as "name the supplement."

3.2 The definitions are familiar to the students from their past work. This is a good time to stress the biconditional form of definitions. In the discussion of Theorem 2.1, remind the students that there are no zero or negative angles. Theorems 3.2, 3.3, 3.5, and 3.6 are not in the "if-then" form; have students express them in the implication form and advise them that the text form will be easier to use in proving future theorems. A two-column proof of Theorem 3.3 can be used to show the differences in types of proof. Only after several weeks of using these theorems will students be able to recall them accurately. Written Exercises 26 and 27 have solution sets that are inequalities. Exercise 32 offers a chance to review the expression "at most one."

3.3 This section contains two easy but powerful theorems. Before proving the Vertical Angle Theorem, explore several numerical examples in an inductive manner. The proof used in the text relies on Theorem 3.5. A less elegant proof using the Angle Addition Postulate and elementary algebra may be more acceptable to the students. Use several whole number examples to prepare students.

Given: l_1 and l_2 intersect to form angles whose measures are a, b, x and y; a and b are vertical angles, x and y are vertical angles; a and x form a linear pair, b and x form a linear pair.

Prove: a = b

1. $a + x = 180$ (Linear pairs are supp.);
2. $b + x = 180$ (Linear pairs are supp.);
3. $a + x = b + x$ (transitivity);
4. $a = b$ (subtraction).

Since this unit is so short, it provides a chance to review past concepts.

3.4 This section uses a nontechnical approach to the idea of congruent figures. You might wish to demonstrate congruent and noncongruent figures on a geoboard.

3.5 To establish the concept of correspondence between the parts of congruent triangles, list the six possible correct combinations. When making congruence statements, you and your students should always name corresponding vertices in the same order.

3.6 Review the properties of an equivalence relation and theorem 1.3, which states that congruence of segments is an equivalence relation. Also point out to students that congruence of angles is an equivalence relation.

3.7 Some students may confuse medians and altitudes of triangles. You can point out that the *median* goes to the *middle* of the opposite side. The two theorems in this section are readily accepted by the students but will not be proved until the end of the next chapter.

Computer The generation of random numbers will vary from computer to computer. Check your manual to see if the program needs to be modified for your computer.

4 • Congruent Triangles

Overview Triangle congruence is established by postulating SAS and by proving three other theorems. SAS, ASA, and SSS can all be postulated, and this is sometimes done to save time with classes that have difficulty with proof. In *Elements,* Euclid proved all of these by moving one triangle on top of another. This form of "motion geometry" is suspect under modern mathematical logic. Throughout the chapter be certain to stress that congruence statements give a definite correspondence of sides and angles. To identify congruent parts in figures, hash marks are used on the sides and angles are marked with one to three arcs. You may wish to mark angles with a single arc and one to three hash marks.

Teaching Suggestions

4.1 Theorem 4.1 (The LL Theorem) is an example of quickly using a postulate to prove a theorem. Most texts do not include this theorem.

4.2 Note that ASA could have been the postulate and SAS a theorem. The proof of ASA is long but it gives the student a good model of a two-column proof. Overlapping figures are introduced immediately. Advise students to use two different colors to outline the triangles or to draw separate figures for problems. The second sample proof on page 101 shows the proper way to change from congruence statements to equalities. When students have mastered this concept, you may wish to let them restate the "Givens" and save one step.

4.3 The proof used for The Isosceles Triangle Theorem is attributed to Pappus, a mathematician at the library in Alexandria, Egypt. The conventional Euclidean proof involves constructions and overlapping triangles. The proof used here is simpler and more elegant. Reputedly, this argument was also presented in the 1950's by a computer programmed with postulates and definitions from plane geometry. The Converse of The Isosceles Triangle Theorem is kept as a separate theorem (4.4) for ease of identification in future proofs. The abbreviations ITT and CITT can be used to identify these theorems in proofs. In discussing the two corollaries to ITT and CITT, devote some time to the consideration of the biconditional "iff" form of stating theorems. Written Exercise 18 offers a chance to use an indirect proof. The topic will be formally introduced in the next chapter, but this is a good place to give the student an introductory look at the idea.

Self-Quiz Be sure to use more than one example in Exercise 2 as preparation for work on similar triangles.

4.4 Point out that each constructed segment in the proof of the SSS Theorem is justified by logical reasons. Auxiliary sets and their justification will be formally established in the next chapter. The comment at the end of the proof of SSS points out that proofs do not depend on the figure. Written Exercise 24 addresses the other cases of SSS.

4.5 Quadrilaterals are defined to provide a variety of figures to use for congruent triangles. They will be redefined in Chapter 9 on area and polygons. This spiraling on topics is sound educational practice. The second example in this section uses one set of congruent triangles to find corresponding parts to be used in a second set of triangles. Have students be aware of the complexity of planning a proof when this process is needed. Written Exercises 13-16 are difficult proofs for most students. You may want to assist students by providing a plan for the proofs or by listing some of the statements and reasons used in the proofs. Problems omitted while studying this section could be assigned one at a time while working on Chapters 5 and 6.

Calculator A greater use of scientific calculators is becoming more acceptable in secondary mathematics, and students will be guided to use several function keys in these features.

Career: Technical Illustrator Students who have been exposed to mechanical drawing are aware of this technique. The ability to make good models is a real aid to mastering geometry.

Skills Maintenance These formulas are a good review of an Algebra I topic. Exercise 11 is demanding for the average student and deserves special attention.

Exploration Discuss the fact that this section relies on the student's past knowledge of area and volume. Formal definitions have not been established in the text at this point. However, this is not a problem since much of what the student does in this course is formal proof of knowledge that they already have.

Computer The increased use of PASCAL in high schools and colleges has led to more emphasis on topdown programming. Remind students that it is foolish to start on a trip if you don't know where you are going.

Cumulative Review The problems are multiple choice. References can be made to the fact that many standardized tests use this format. The mathematics section of the College Board Examinations is heavily weighted with geometry problems.

5 • Thinking and Proving

Overview The chapter extends the discussion of symbolic logic from Chapter 1 to include the negation, inverse, and contrapositive. This is a valuable way to approach indirect proof. If time and student ability permit, truth tables can be extended to discussion of binary counting and combinations of subsets. With the contrapositive and indirect proof several theorems from earlier chapters can be proved. Existence and uniqueness are discussed to provide a foundation for the introduction of auxiliary sets. The rigor and time spent in this chapter should be determined by the students' ability level and the courses that they plan to take.

Teaching Suggestions

5.1 The logical statements are extended to include negation, inverse, and contrapositive. The most important concept is the contrapositive as a basis for indirect proof.

5.2 The reason used for assumption or "suppose" statements is indirect assumption. Many students for the next several lessons will try to do too many proofs by the indirect method. Make them aware that indirect proofs are used to "break new ground" so that direct proofs can be used. Proof that the square root of two is irrational can be done at this time, which may be found on page E5 of the Teacher's Resource Masters.

5.3 Students often have difficulty with indirect proof. Not only are indirect proofs useful in geometry, but they are used extensively in branches of higher mathematics. It is therefore important for students who plan to take more mathematics to experience success with this technique. Be certain that students identify the contradiction in an indirect proof.

5.4 Be sure that students are aware that auxiliary sets must both exist and be unique.

5.5 This is a technical section that should be treated lightly by all but the most capable students.

Challenge An excellent problem to demonstrate inductive reasoning, working for the first five cases but failing in the sixth.

Computer Discuss other algorithms that students know such as "borrowing" in subtraction.

6 • Inequalities in Geometry

Overview This chapter allows the student to explore noncongruent parts of a triangle and corresponding triangles that are not congruent. A certain ingenuity is required to develop the various proofs. The review of the algebra of inequalities will strengthen the students' ability in this area. Students may experience some difficulty in distinguishing the difference between the theorems for one triangle and those for two different triangles. Medians and altitudes of triangles are defined and theorems relating to them are developed.

Teaching Suggestions

6.1 Students already have an intuitive grasp of the ideas presented in this section. If the students understood the use of the contrapositive in the last chapter it could be applied to the ITT and CITT, as it related to the theorems in this chapter. This will not prove that a side is greater or lesser but will show the existence of inequalities.

6.2 The many proofs involve algebraic inequalities, so this section must be mastered. After the example proof "If $a > b$ then $-a < -b$," the more able students may benefit from proving the quadratic formula with a two-column proof.

Math Heritage: Systems of Measurement Here is an opportunity to discuss the metric system of measurement. Also, remind students that this geometry will apply to any system of measurement which is used consistently throughout a problem.

6.3 Draw examples of triangles where the exterior angle appears in a number of different positions. The proof of the Exterior Angle Theorem is easy for the students to understand once the midpoint is introduced in step 1.

6.4 The two triangle congruence theorems in this section could have been developed at a later point in the course. Establishing them now strengthens any weaknesses that the students may have with inequalities and convinces the students of the importance of congruent triangles. Point out that students must use *corresponding* parts for the SAA Theorem, since it is possible to have two triangles in which two angles and a side of one triangle may equal two angles and a side of the other, but the two triangles are not congruent. An example appears below:

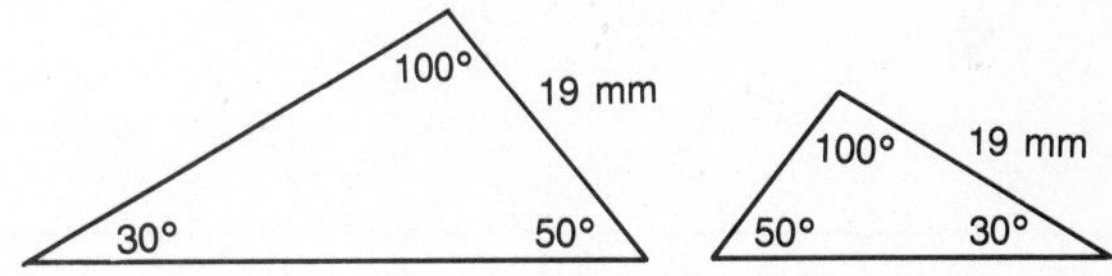

6.5 Theorem 6.4 (Angle Greater-side Greater) and its converse are interesting proofs. Once 6.4 is proved then the converse can be proved by elimination or exhaustion. The contrapositives of ITT and CITT can be discussed at this point. The theorems and definitions in this section are easily accepted by the students, but they still may not question a triangle with sides of 6, 8, and 15. An intuitive look at the distance from a point to a plane could be developed in class discussions as preparation for work in the next chapter.

6.6 Theorem 6.8 is often referred to as the scissors or hinge theorem. The proof of 6.8 is complex, and it and its converse are only used in this section of the text to solve problems. The proof of the converse is not assigned in the written exercises. It is another example of proof by elimination. Written Exercise 12 can be solved directly, or it can also be solved easily by indirect proof if you wish to have the students review this concept. The definition of kite in Written Exercise 11 should include that the quadrilateral is also convex.

6.7 The multiple use of the word altitude for a segment, a line, and a numerical measure should not cause any problem. Be sure that students do the drawings for Written Exercises 1-6.

Exploration This topic lends itself to computer analysis. Students could also consider the ratio of each term to the next term in the sequence. The ratio will approach $\frac{1+\sqrt{5}}{2}$, equation, or approximately 1.618, as a limit. This is the "Golden Ratio" that is so well developed in the film "Donald in Mathemagic Land."

7 • Perpendicular Relationships

Overview During the past 30 years secondary geometry has expanded to include solid geometry transformations and an introduction to analytic geometry and trigonometry. The selection of postulates and rigor has improved. Three-dimensional geometry models have been included throughout the text, and in this chapter perpendicular relations in space are developed. Since two years of work are compressed into one, many of the theorems in the 13 volumes of Euclid's *Elements* are not presented. However this chapter will develop the majority of the concepts of perpendicular relations in space. With so much content, you should be selective in the choice of items that will be covered during the year. Volume problems are essential, and at least some portions of this chapter should be presented. Time may be saved by accepting the theorems without proof and concentrating on the problem sets.

Teaching Suggestions

7.1 Use sufficient discussion and models to be sure that the students are aware that a line must be perpendicular to every line in the plane through the point of intersection in order to be perpendicular to the plane. Reinforce the meaning of the word equidistant by the use of several models. Theorem 7.1 is hard to visualize without a model. The students can gain a better appreciation of space geometry if they use toothpicks, d-sticks, etc., to build their own models.

7.2 The classical proof of Theorem 7.3 is long and involved. For this reason, Theorems 7.1 and 7.2 are lemmas used to break the proof into three sections. The Oral Exercises and Section A of the Written Exercises reinforce the concept of perpendiculars in the plane.

Self-Quiz These true/false questions review important concepts. Have the students give a counterexample for the false statements.

7.3 Attention to uniqueness and existence is necessary in this section. Theorem 7.7 (The Perpendicular Bisecting Plane Theorem) will be the easiest for the students to understand and apply. Written Exercises 9 and 10 should be attempted by all students.

7.4 This is a straightforward presentation of the remaining concepts of perpendiculars in space. Students should appreciate and be able to prove Theorem 7.11 without difficulty. More explicit attention is given to existence and uniqueness.

In Other Fields: Joinery Note that *area* is requested as a known idea from previous work in other mathematical classes.

8 • Parallels

Overview The chapter includes parallel conditions in the plane and in space. The 33 theorems and 10 corollaries include many important concepts used in standardized tests and relationships that are used in similar triangles and coordinate geometry. After establishing the necessary conditions for parallelism by definition, the first seven theorems are an excellent way to show the nature of proof in geometry. New ground is broken with an indirect proof and direct deductive proof is used to prove several theorems easily. Attention is given to the importance of the Parallel Postulate and the need for its postulation. The wealth of material requires your judicious choice as to the time and the problems that will be selected for use.

Teaching Suggestions

8.1 Before the students read this section, it is useful to have them describe their concept or definition of parallel. The existence of a plane containing parallel lines is in the definition, and the uniqueness of this plane is established in the first theorem. Other possible definitions are weaker in that they would not be acceptable in non-Euclidean geometries. Theorem 8.5 establishes by indirect proof the foundation to prove 8.6 and 8.7 by direct deduction. A possible abbreviation for Theorem 8.5 is AI→P. Have students identify the contradiction of the exterior angle theorem in the proof of Theorem 8.5. The problem set is given without mention of corresponding angles so that students may use the first five theorems without confusion. Oral Exercise 13 and Written Exercises 8 and 11 are numerical examples of the next two theorems and can be used to prepare for their proof. **Warning:** Oral Exercises 15 and 16 are TRAPS since they cannot be justified without the Parallel Postulate. Convince the students that the converse of AI→P has not been proved.

Written Exercise 12 is the Saccheri Quadrilateral that the Italian monk used to try to prove that a parallel to a given line from an external point was unique. Although we can prove that the upper angles are congruent, without the Parallel Postulate we cannot prove that they are right angles. In a hyperbolic geometry they are acute.

8.2 The corresponding angles definition and theorems are easily developed if the students have mastery of Lesson 8.1. In Oral Exercises 9 and 10, note the converses have not yet been proved. After proving Theorem 8.7 you may wish to have students prove that congruent alternate exterior angles (AE→P) and supplementary interior angles on the same side of a transversal (IASSTS→P) are sufficient to prove parallelism.

8.3 Euclid's fifth axiom is given as the Parallel Postulate. The converses of the theorems in Lessons 8.1 and 8.2 are now easily proved. Again, the first proof is indirect to provide a foundation. Theorem 8.8 can be represented by P→AI. The figure for Written Exercise 14 implies an indirect proof, but a transversal, alternate interior angles, and transitivity can be used for a direct proof.

8.4 In proving Theorem 8.13 discuss why it was necessary to wait until this section to prove the theorem. Written Exercise 17 allows reinforcement of the biconditional theorems. Saccheri's Quadrilateral can now be used to prove the upper base angles are right angles.

Self-Quiz Exercise 14 anticipates later work with parallelograms and Exercise 15 relates to the bimedian theorem.

8.5 Keep in mind the difference between a convex and a nonconvex quadrilateral. The definition of trapezoids excludes them from the set of parallelograms. This section includes ten theorems and corollaries and moves very quickly. Before considering the converses of Theorems 8.19 to 8.21, it is advisable to have a homework session using only the earlier theorems of this section. Theorem 8.22 is usually called the *bimedian* theorem. It will also be proved in the coordinate geometry chapter.

8.6 It is difficult for students to distinguish between theorems and converses. A worthwhile exercise in this section would be to list the quadrilaterals and their properties and to list the properties that determine the quadrilaterals. Written Exercise 19 is a theorem frequently used in contests. It will also be considered in the coordinate geometry chapter.

8.7 This section can be developed intuitively for the slower classes and may be treated with discussion only. The floor, walls, ceiling, and corners of a rectangular room may be used for a model. In Written Exercise 8 it is possible in some geometries to consider a line as being parallel to itself.

8.8 The treatment of this three-dimensional section will depend upon the students' ability level, the course requirements, and your judgment.

8.9 Projection is an interesting topic that can benefit from the use of an overhead projector to cast shadows of geometric objects. An acute triangle can be tilted to give shadow images that include an obtuse triangle, a right triangle and segments of various lengths.

Skills Maintenance This review should help students to overcome one of the weak areas of their background in algebra. Exercises 26–29 can be incorporated with the notation used in computer languages.

Exploration Build a box using two-way mirrors with the reflective face on the inside. If you shine a light into the interior and then close the lid, trapping the light, will the light keep reflecting from wall to wall and provide a glow that can be observed from the outer or non-reflecting side? Would this cause problems with the local power companies?

Math Heritage: Non-Euclidean Geometry Gauss is often considered the greatest mathematician of history. It is reported that as an elementary student his class was disciplined by having to add the whole numbers from 1 to 100, and he got the answer by recognizing that $1 + 100$, $2 + 99$, $3 + 98$, etc. were 101 and times 50 would give the correct result.

Computer If it is available, the film 'FLATLAND' could be used in this discussion.

9 • Area and Pythagorean Theorem

Overview This chapter introduces the concept of polygonal regions, building upon Postulates 17–20 to determine the areas of those regions. Special attention is paid to finding the altitudes and the areas of rectangles, triangles, parallelograms, and trapezoids. The chapter concludes with the special case of right triangles, introducing the Pythagorean Theorem and its converse, the 30-60-90 Triangle Theorem, and the Isosceles Right Triangle Theorem. These problems regarding the measurement and area of right triangles contain some of the most essential elements of Euclidian Geometry.

Teaching Suggestions

9.1 Students may be interested to learn that the literal translation of *polygon* from the Greek is "many angles," not "many sides" as it is frequently misused. Students should understand that the terms "area of the polygonal region" and "area of the triangular region" are hereafter shortened to "area of the polygon" and "area of the triangle" for convenience and brevity, *not* because they mean the same thing. Any polygon, including a triangle, is the union of segments, which have no area. It may be useful to draw chalkboard examples showing how figures like those on p. 277 may be divided into triangular regions. Oral Exercise 8 should alert students that the area of the union of overlapping polygonal regions is not equal to the sum of the areas of the regions.

9.2 Students should recognize that the area of a figure will always be a positive real number. In this respect, Postulate 20 relates to the Distance Postulate and the Angle Measurement Postulate, because the lengths of the base and altitude are real numbers. Whether the term "height" or "altitude" is used, the notation "h" will be preferred in the text. Oral Exercises 1-4 provide students with a short cut for computing the area of some similar figures. Stress should be placed on expressing written answers in the units given. Some students also may forget to express their answers in square units.

9.3 Students should recognize that the area theorem holds for all triangle types. Establish that triangles that have the same area may have equal bases and altitudes but are not necessarily congruent. Point out that altitudes and bases may be segments, distances, or both. Establish the concept that the ratio of areas between triangles with congruent bases is related to the ratio of their altitudes. Some students attempting C-level exercises will need to be reminded to divide figures into triangular regions when necessary.

9.4 Because standard textbook figures are presented with altitudes oriented upright, some students may not readily grasp that one altitude of a parallelogram may be oriented horizontally. The proof for Written Exercise 19 employs the converse of Theorem 8.25, so it may be useful to review this theorem. In developing the proof of Theorem 9.6 discuss the bimedian (the segment joining the midpoints of the two nonparallel sides) as an average of the two bases. This concept is useful when using the Mean Value Theorem in calculus to find the area under a curve.

Also, consider if the product of the altitude and bimedian will give the area for other figures such as triangles, squares, parallelograms, and so on.

Self-Quiz Exercise 5 should be solved by adding the areas of the triangular regions, since it is not indicated that the figure is a rhombus.

9.5 The demonstration of the Pythagorean Theorem in the chapter opener photo on p. 275 is thought to be one used by Pythagoras, or his students, the Pythagoreans. The proof probably used by Pythagoras appears on Enrichment page E6 in the Teacher's Resource Book. Many students do not realize that Pythagoras' work predated Euclid's by about 200 years. Pythagoras was not the first to discover this triangle relationship; evidence exists that it was known by the Chinese and others long before his time. However, since the Pythagoreans were among the first to actively teach the theorem, it has been named in his honor. There are nearly 400 different proofs of this theorem, which may convey to students some sense of why it, together with its converse, is a cornerstone of plane geometry. An excellent reference for these proofs is *The Pythagorean Proposition,* by Elisha Scott Loomis, which has been republished by the National Council of Teachers of Mathematics. You also may wish to introduce the concept of *Pythagorean Triples* at this time—those positive integers that determine the sides of a right triangle, such as 3:4:5, 5:12:13, 8:15:17, 15:10:25, and so on. These may be derived from the formula $(a^2 - b^2, 2ab, a^2 + b^2)$, where a and b are positive integers and $a > b$. Students should learn that any triangle in which the length of the sides have the same ratio as a known Pythagorean Triple will also be right: 6:8:10, 10:24:26, 16:30:34, 30:40:50, and so on. You may wish to have students identify members of the set of *primitive triples*—those triples which have no greater common factor than 1. Examples are 3:4:5, 5:12:13, 7:24:25, 8:15:17, and 20:21:29.

Challenge Students will need to apply both Theorems 9.1 and 9.7 to solve this ratio problem. Some students may not be able to visualize the four right triangles.

9.6 Students should master the application of Theorems 9.9 and 9.10 in this section. Many of the subsequent proofs and exercises in this text are dependent on students recognizing 30-60-90 and 45-45-90 triangles within figures. With this recognition, they will be able to derive the lengths of two unknown sides of such triangles from a given side, such as in Written Exercise 35, where the altitude must be found. 30-60-90 triangles occur in regular hexagons, where the diameter forms the hypotenuese, and a side forms the base. 45-45-90 triangles are always formed on the diagonal of a square. Students should be made aware that questions involving these triangles invariably occur in standardized tests.

Careers You may wish to pose a practice problem drawn from surveying. For example, a building is to be oriented diagonally on a square lot. The length of the building requires the lot's diagonal to be 60 yards. Given the location of the ends of the diagonal, what must the surveyor do to stake out the other two corners? *Answer:* The surveyor would sight along a 45° angle on either side of each end of the diagonal. The intersection of these sight lines will determine the other two corners. By the Isosceles Right Triangle Theorem, the edges of the lot will each measure $\frac{60\sqrt{2}}{2} = 30\sqrt{2}$, approximately 42.43 yards.

Computer Students must remember to input values for a true triangle. For example, $a = 2$, $b = 3$, and $c = 6$ cannot be the lengths of the sides of a triangle.

10 • Similarity

Overview Similarity is defined and there is stress on having the correct correspondence between the figures. The development of this topic was left until after the unit on area so that area could be used to establish The Basic Proportionality Theorem. The ideas developed in this chapter will be used and reviewed in the trigonometry work in Chapter 16. In Lesson 10.1.

Teaching Suggestions

10.1 It is worthwhile to give a proportion and then to develop the many different equations that can be derived from the proportion. Emphasize area ratios in the final proportion. Students should grasp the distinction between an *arithmetic mean,* as learned in algebra (the sum of all values divided by the number of values), and the *mean of a proportion* as used in this lesson. They should further distinguish that a *geometric mean* must be a single value occurring in both ratios of a proportion—as the value for both means. In algebra, as illustrated in Oral Exercise 23, students will have used negative numbers in a proportion. They should be reminded that by the Distance Postulate, the means and extremes of a *geometric* proportion must be *positive* real numbers. Some students may need to be reminded to convert measurements in the exercises into compatible units and to express ratio answers in their simplest terms. For convenience, the answers to Written Exercises 40 and 41 assume that the edges of the drawing paper and board can be used.

10.2 Students need to clearly understand the distinctions between similarity and congruence. Congruent figures are always similar, but similar figures are not necessarily congruent. Similarity among figures requires both congruent angles and proportionate sides. The same notation convention used for congruence is used for similarity—the vertices of similar figures should be named in the same clockwise or counterclockwise order. Unlike congruence, however, angles and sides of similar figures are not noted separately. Some students may misinterpret similarly named figures as being geometrically similar. Point out that rectangles, parallelograms, trapezoids, acute and scalene triangles, or *n*-gons can have different shapes within the bounds of their definitions. Squares, regular pentagons, regular hexagons, and equilateral triangles are always similar because both conditions for similarity exist in these figures. Though not implicitly stated in the text, students should recognize that Theorem 10.2 is the converse of Theorem 10.1. You may wish to discuss the concept of scale in connection with problems like Written Exercise 16. The enlarged photo is 160% of the size of the original, so the ratio between the two photos is 1.6:1. This discussion can be extended to the precise meanings of the words *model* and *replica*.

10.3 The proof of the AAA Similarity Theorem is necessary primarily as a lemma for proving the AA Corollary, which is more useful in subsequent problem solving. Because of the "alphabet soup" names ascribed to congruence theorems such as ASA, LL, HL, SSS, and SAA, and the SAS congruence postulate, some students may later mistakenly recall AAA, and AA as reasons supporting congruence. This problem is aggravated by the next lesson, which introduces SAS and SSS *similarity* theorems. Students will need to clearly recall which acronyms relate to congruence and which relate to similarity.

10.4 Some students may ask why there are no ASA or SAA similarity theorems in addition to those for SAS and SSS. Point out that the AA similarity corollary already covers ASA and SAA, so they are unnecessary. As with proving congruence, SSA could not be used to prove triangle similarity except in the special case of right triangles. Some students may be interested to learn how the ancient Greeks applied similar triangles to solving work problems. For example, if Sally can reorganize the reference section of the library in 6 hours, and Angie can do the same job in 3 hours, how long will the job take if they work together? Algebraically, the solution would be as follows: Sally can do $\frac{1}{6}$ of the work in 1 hour, and Angie can do $\frac{1}{3}$ of the work in 1 hour, so together they can do $\frac{1}{x}$ of the work in 1 hour.

$$\frac{1}{3} + \frac{1}{6} = \frac{1}{x}$$
$$6x\left(\frac{1}{3} + \frac{1}{6}\right) = 6x \cdot \frac{1}{x}$$
$$\frac{6x}{3} + \frac{6x}{6} = \frac{6x}{x}$$
$$2x + x = 6$$
$$3x = 6$$
$$x = 2 \text{ hr}$$

The Greeks, possessing a limited algebra, solved such problems as shown in the left-hand figure. Two parallel perpendiculars, representing the times, were connected with diagonals, thus forming two triangles, similar by AAA. The height of a perpendicular dropped from the triangles' common vertex represented the combined work rate. The problem can be altered as shown in the right-hand figure. If Paul needs 8 hours to type a term paper by himself, but with Ali's help finishes the job in 3 hours, how long would it have taken Ali typing alone? ($4\frac{4}{5}$ hr)

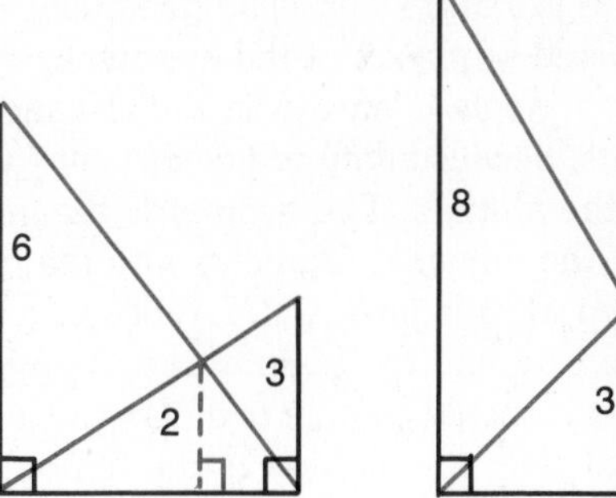

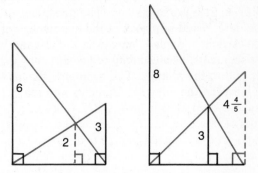

This type of problem-solving is not as accurate as the algebraic solution, but it is a quick way of estimating combined work rates. You may wish to have students try it on graph paper as a prelude to working with coordinates in the next chapter.

10.5 After a brief explanation, students will realize that Theorem 10.6 allows endless repetition; that is, any right triangle may be subdivided into infinitely many right triangles, all similar to each other and to the original. Another way of stating part 1 of Corollary 10.6.1 is "The altitude to the hypotenuse of a right triangle is the geometric mean of the segments determined." Students should understand that the ratios containing geometric means are constant in similar triangles, even if the scale of the triangle and the numerical values of the means change. The geometric means in an $2\frac{1}{4}:3:3\frac{3}{4}$ right triangle are in the same ratio when the lengths are doubled to $4\frac{1}{2}:6:7\frac{1}{2}$. Use of Pythagorean Triples may make this clearer to students. The geometric mean (the altitude to the hypotenuse) between the determined segments on the hypotenuse of a 3:4:5 triangle will always be in a $1\frac{1}{3}:1$ ratio with those segments. The geometric means (the lengths of the adjacent legs) of the determined segments and the hypotenuse will be in $1\frac{2}{3}:1$ and $1\frac{1}{4}:1$ ratios, respectively. All 6:8:10, 15:20:25, and 30:40:50 triangles have geometric means in the same ratios. For a 5:12:13 right triangle, the ratios involving geometric means as just described are $2\frac{2}{5}:1$ for the altitude and $2\frac{3}{5}:1$ and $1\frac{1}{12}:1$ for the legs. These ratios are preserved in $1\frac{1}{12}:1$ for the legs. These ratios are preserved in 10:24:26 triangles and so on. The geometric mean of the determined segments of the hypotenuse of an isosceles right triangle is always in a 1:1 ratio with those segments, because they are congruent to each other and to the altitude. The geometric means (the legs) between the adjacent segments and the hypotenuse are both always in a $\sqrt{2}:1$ ratio. Given the lengths of one side and the hypotenuse of any right triangle, students should be able to derive the lengths of the adjacent side, the altitude to the hypotenuse, and the segments determined by that altitude, using only Corollary 10.6.1 and subtraction. Previously, these lengths could be found only by use of the Triangle Area Theorem with the Pythagorean Theorem. Now students have two independent methods, and as shown in Written Exercise 33, Corollary 10.6.1 can be used to prove the Pythagorean Theorem. However, whereas the Triangle Area Theorem and the Pythagorean Theorem can be used to find the measures of a right triangle whose legs are the only knowns, Corollary 10.6.1 is insufficient for this purpose.

10.6 In developing Theorem 10.7, intuitively extend the discussion to volume ratios in solid figures. Using similar cubes is easy for students to understand and gives a base for future work. The written exercises are extensive and some may be used during later chapters for review.

Skills Maintenance Various methods for solving quadratic equations are used. Point out the benefits of using the formula.

Career: Diamond Cutter This discussion can be extended to the regular or Platonic polyhedra.

Computer The SSS Similarity Theorem is used. Students could develop a program to check similarity when angles are input.

---

11 • Coordinate Geometry of the Plane

Overview Once similar triangles and the Pythagorean Theorem are established, elementary coordinate geometry can be developed. The spiraling of topics in mathematics leads to better student mastery, and this section will help review Algebra I and prepare for Algebra II. René Descartes' (1596–1650) development of the coordinate plane gives us the chance to explore the relationships between algebra and geometry. (It was this interrelation that provided the foundation for Gottfried Wilhelm Leibnitz and Issac Newton to develop the calculus.) After the development of the coordinate plane, the slope, distance, and midpoint formulas are developed. The formulas are used to prove geometric theorems. Some of the theorems have been proved by synthetic methods in earlier chapters. The concluding sections discuss linear graphs and inequalities.

Teaching Suggestions

11.1 Stress the idea of projecting a point into the axes and finding the coordinates of the images. Some of the problems can be extended as in Written Exercise 30 "What is BC?"

11.2 Slope will probably be new to the students and the use of rise over run and uphill and downhill are helpful. Better students may relate slope to the tangent function. Assign the graphs of lines with equal slopes or slopes that will make the lines be perpendicular.

11.3 Note again that the use of "two" in Oral Exercise 1 means two *distinct* lines. Make students aware that vertical and horizontal lines are perpendicular to each other because they are parallel to the axes. Written Exercises 16–22 are pre-work for proving theorems in Lesson 11.6.

11.4 Stress the importance of the Pythagorean Theorem and its converse in mathematics. It is helpful if the students develop a list of integral triples and the special triangle triples. Since most of the written answers have irrational values for answers, you may want to review simplification of radical expressions. Written Exercise 24 extends the distance formula to three dimensions. A similar discussion could be used for distances in higher dimensions.

Self-Quiz Most results are irrational.

11.5 Written Exercises 11–26 are a prelude to the proofs in Section 11.6. Exercises 27–30 should not be overstressed. Students will probably gain more knowledge by using common sense to trisect segments. No three-dimensional midpoint problems are given, but you may want to create some.

11.6 While doing the proof of the bimedian theorem, recall and discuss the proof of Theorem 8.22. In the model for the proof, you may wish to place one vertex at the origin. In each of the exercises briefly discuss the synthetic proof when applicable. Oral Exercise 6 can be further developed to eliminate *c* as a variable in a rhombus. Written Exercise 6 should receive attention. A similar theorem, "The segment joining the midpoints of the diagonals of a trapezoid is parallel to the bases and equals one-half of their difference," is easily proved by analytic methods and difficult in synthetic geometry.

11.7 As preparation for work in Algebra II, assign a series of graphs of the form $y + a = b\,|x + c|$ to develop the concept of translations of the absolute value function.

11.8 The theorems here are logically presented, but some students may profit from a lighter treatment. Keep reminding students that the point-slope form of the equation is derived from the definition of slope.

Exploration Similar triangles are used for the proof. This is a good extra for expert students.

Math Heritage: Grace Hopper Students might explore the language ADA and its future impact on programming.

Computer Demonstrates the use of a computer to solve a minimum value problem by brute calculation.

12 • Circles and Spheres

Overview This chapter is another that can be separated into three major sections. Since the proofs and ideas about circles and spheres are analogous, both topics are treated together. After the basic definitions and relations are established, numerical applications of angle measure and segment length are explored. The ideas in this chapter are widely used in contests and standardized tests. The final section concerns the coordinate geometry of the circle in a plane.

Teaching Suggestions

12.1 This section could be done as a reading assignment and the students should be able to master much of the material on their own. The true/false questions develop some subtle nuances that you will need to explain. Treat this section as two different assignments to be sure that all of the concepts are understood.

Calculator Circumference has not yet been formally defined, but students will have no trouble with the discussion.

12.2 This section includes three theorems and six corollaries. Most students will prove Corollaries 12.2.3 through 12.2.5 by using congruent triangles and avoid the use of the more elegant perpendicular bisector theorem. The Pythagorean Theorem will be used extensively and the true/false questions are a quick way to confirm mastery of the ideas presented.

12.3 The theorems for spheres, analogous to those for circles in Section 12.2, are developed. Written Exercise 24 can be extended to prove that circle *D* is congruent to circle *E*.

12.4 Arcs and central angles are new to the students. Theorem 12.6 would be a very technical, and perhaps impossible, proof with the postulates and definitions of this course. Have the students treat it as a postulate.

12.5–12.6 The distinction between inscribed angles and intercepted arcs frequently confuses students. Be sure to use good models during the discussion. Attention to the true/false items in the exercises can help to develop the concepts.

12.7 This section contains several powerful theorems that can save time on tests such as SAT. Theorems 12.13, 12.14, and 12.15 can all be combined by considering that the product of the distance to the nearest side and the distance to the far side of any circle is constant for any point in the plane. For tangent segments the two distances are the same, and for a point on the circle one of the distances is zero. A similar treatment can be given to Theorems 12.16 and 12.17 where an interior point is the average of the arc measures, an exterior point is the average of the differences, and a point on the circle could be either.

12.8 This section reviews perfect square trinomials and the manipulation of equations to put them into a standard form.

In Other Fields: Astronomy Erastosthenes was known as Beta, the second letter of the Greek alphabet, due to his accomplishments in areas such as poetry, drama, mathematics, and astronomy. He was outstanding in many—but never the best in any one.

Computer Have students confirm the values for x and y in the equations by doing a two-column proof. Superior students could consider a similar approach to the intersection of three planes in three-space.

13 • Constructions

Overview Most students have had some experience with constructions. This chapter has been left until sufficient theorems, postulates, and definitions have been developed to justify or prove the validity of the constructions. The term *locus of points* is best represented by the perpendicular bisector of a segment in a plane or the angle bisector. Students who are studying Latin could research the meaning of *locus, lemma* and *pons asinorum.* The concurrency theorems in Lesson 13.2 are followed by the basic compass and straightedge constructions.

Teaching Suggestions

13.1 The idea of sketching several points that meet a condition is a good discovery exercise for the students. The treasure problem anticipates the Two Circle Theorem necessary for constructions. Extension of Written Exercise 13 could lead better students to the study of the necessary conditions for hyperbolas and ellipses.

13.2 Some points of concurrency will be identified in section 13.4 but you may wish to use them now. The centroid or the point of concurrency of the medians of the triangle is found two-thirds of the way from the vertex to the corresponding midpoint. Have students consider the ingenious selection of ΔDEF to simplify the proof of Theorem 13.3.

13.3 The seven constructions in this section are all standard and essential. Students should apply their past postulates and theorems to show the validity of the constructions. The most difficult for the students to do correctly will be Construction 7. You may wish to discuss various types and proper use of the compasses.

Self-Quiz The answer to Exercise 1 should exclude the midpoint of the segment.

Exploration Students in computer classes could have a similar contest using high resolution graphics.

13.4 Constructions 8, 9, and 10 complete the development of this chapter. Have students write the proofs. In the "Impossible Constructions," stress that the construction tools are limited to a compass and an *unmarked* straightedge.

Calculator Several classic stories that rely on power series exist. An analysis of the "Towers of Hanoi" problem works well at this level.

Skills Maintenance This is a review of some of the similarity concepts from Chapter 10.

Calculator This topic will be extended in Lesson 14.2 in Written Exercises 24 and 25.

Computer In addition to a valuable list of triples the students are introduced to permutations and combinations.

Exploration Have students develop a sequence of numbers similar to the Fibonacci set by starting with their month and day of birth. For example: 3, 2, 5, 7, 12, 19, . . . 898, 1453. The quotient of the four-digit number and the number that precedes it will approach 1.618 to the nearest one-thousandth as a limit. If students get 1.618 assure them that they have a golden birthday.

14 • Area and Volume

Overview Using regular polygons as a criterion, the measure of circumference, area, and the related parts of circles are established. Formulas are developed to find the length of arcs and the area of sectors. Prisms, pyramids, and their related area and volume formulas are developed. The concept of volume is developed with a limited postulational system. This intuitive approach is adequate since a more formal approach would require rigor beyond the grasp of many students.

Teaching Suggestions

14.1 The definition of polygons is long but serves the purpose. A more simplistic but less sound definition of a convex polygon is to state that all of the diagonals lie in the interior of the figure. The remaining sections of the chapter deal primarily with convex polygons that are regular. Students with computer experience can write programs to find the various angle measures using the formulas developed in this section for 3-gons to *n*-gons. Now is a good time to remind students that the special triangles will be widely used for problem solving.

14.2 Although it is not in a definition box, *pi* is defined to be the ratio of the circumference to the diameter. The use of limits to define circumference is informal, since a full development would require too much time and sophistication for this course. The "area of a circle" is again a convenient short-hand for "the area of the circular region." An interesting approach to determine the area of a circle is to take small pie-shaped wedges from the circle and alternatively place them point up and point down. The resulting figure will be a parallelogram with a base that is one-half the circumference and a height equal to the radius. The resulting area would be $\frac{1}{2}Cr$ or πr^2. Another approach would be to rotate a radius one turn to sweep out the interior area. The outer

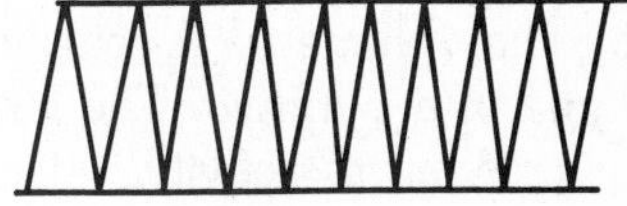

end travels C and the inner end zero for an average of $\frac{1}{2}$C. This times the sweeper (r) yields $\frac{1}{2}$Cr. One suggested exercise for this section would be to create a four-column chart headed by radius, diameter, circumference, and area. Provide one of the measurements in its proper column and have the student determine the missing measurements. Exercises 24 and 25 are extensions of the Exploration in the last chapter.

14.3 Question the students on the difference between arc measure and arc length. The formula in Theorem 14.4 is good for computer programming. You may want to show your students the following alternative method for finding the length of an arc: take the ratio of the arc measure over 360 times the circumference. The majority of the answers are expressed in terms of pi. Have the students approximate the answers using pi to be 3.14.

14.4 When discussing segments, have the students decide which arc measures will be most likely used and why they will be used.

14.5 Determine how rigorously you wish to discuss this section. Be sure to include cubes and rectangular parallelepipeds.

14.6 Develop the idea that area ratios are the squares of linear ratios. Students should be aware that the selection of bases will be largely limited to figures for which theorems have been proved.

14.7 Postulation of Cavalieri's Principle allows the development of formulas from the unit volume postulate. It is difficult for the students to see the three pyramids in Theorem 14.15. The Oral Exercises should be done by all students. Written Exercise 8 is not intuitively acceptable to students.

14.8 If you treated the area of a circle by sweeping with a radius, you can sweep out the volume of a cylinder by sweeping a circle from the bottom to the top. The volume of a cone follows easily from the volume of a pyramid. The large choice of problems requires your selectivity.

14.9 This treatment of sphere volume dates back to the work of Archimedes. Most students will find the proof difficult. The development of the surface area of a sphere anticipates the type of reasoning used in calculus.

Exploration Consider the results when the strip is cut down the center and when it is cut one-third of the way in from the left edge.

15 • Transformations

Overview Transformations are considered as mappings on the Cartesian plane. After the definitions of relations and functions, *one-to-one* and *onto* are used to develop the mappings. Included among the transformations are:

1. Reflections
2. Translations
3. Rotations
4. Glide reflections
5. Isometries
6. Dilations

The last section considers transformations as similarities. This material is difficult for a student to master without your help. The best use of this chapter is as a preparation for functions and analysis or Advanced Placement Mathematics. It is recommended that students do at least the Oral Exercises and some items from the A and B sections of the Written Exercises.

Teaching Suggestions

15.1 The Cartesian product of sets is used to establish relations, functions, domain, and range. Inverse functions are defined in terms of one-to-one relations. The conventional "$^{-1}$" superscript is used to name inverse functions. The assignment section is long and you should use only part of the items. The omitted items can be assigned as supplemental homework for later lessons and will help the students master the ideas in this chapter.

15.2 One-to-one and onto mappings are used to define a transformation. Again, the long assignment section can be used over a period of time while doing other sections of the chapter.

15.3 Reflections and lines of symmetry are sometimes confusing for secondary students. Piaget's ideas of conservation probably apply here. This section should convince students that an inverse function is a reflection in the line $y = x$. Again the assignment section is long and selectivity must be used. It is worthwhile to start a chart for Written Exercises 28 to 33 to be used with similar questions in the following sections.

15.4 The definition of translations is a case where equal lines are considered to be parallel. Have the students note how this definition is built on the last section. Add the answers to Written Exercises 20–25 to the chart started in the last section.

Self-Quiz Have students add Exercises 14–19 to the chart started in Section 15.3.

15.5 The definition of rotations as a composition of two reflections in intersecting lines includes direction and magnitude. Consideration is given to rotational symmetries that are also point symmetries. Have students add the answers to Written Exercises 13–18 to the chart started in Section 15.3.

15.6 Glide reflection and isometry are both defined. *Group* and *Abelian group* are developed and provide a source for further exploration by the better students. Have students add the answers to Oral Exercises 6–11 to the chart started in Section 15.3. The concepts in this section could provide an excellent science fair project for a motivated student who is willing to analyze various tranformations as groups.

15.7 Dilations can serve as a review of the work on similar triangles. Again, some of the exercise set could be reserved for review work. Linear, area, and volume ratios in Written Exercises 18 and 19 should be discussed.

15.8 The composition of transformations is considered as similarities. Have students complete the chart started in Section 15.3 by adding the answers to Written Exercises 11 to 16.

Computer For the better students, suggest finding and graphing a parabola that would show the minimum surface area.

16 • Trigonometry and Vectors

Overview The final chapter introduces students to the elementary trigonometry of the right triangle and the beginning concepts of vectors, including the parallelogram method of solution. An average or better student should be able to do most of the sections on trigonometry with little help. The two sections on vectors require more aid, but they are important to those students who plan to take a course in secondary physics. Degree measure is used in the trigonometry sections and angle measures are kept between 0 and 90. In the vector sections measures greater than 90 are used but are restricted to the first and second quadrants. The calculator topics introduce radian measure.

Teaching Suggestions

16.1 This section reviews and shows the use of similar triangles. Extensive use is made of Pythagorean Triples. A mnemonic such as "Oscar Had A Heap Of Apples" (OH/AH/OA; opp. - hyp., adj. - hyp., opp. - adj.) may help the students remember the ratios for the three basic functions. Encourage the students to use a calculator to find solutions. Begin the discussion with a set of several similar triangles such as 3:4:5, 6:8:10, 12:16:20, and so on, to compare the ratios for the functions. Written Exercise 34 anticipates the identity in Theorem 16.2.

16.2 Stress the importance of the special triangles, 30-60-90 and 45-45-90. When solving the triangles in section B have the students estimate each answer before beginning calculation. The text will use the sign "$\approx$" to indicate an approximate answer.

16.3 The exercises in this section are reasonable applications of right triangle trigonometry. The introduction to trigonometric identities includes three theorems. In section C, seven identities are presented for the better students to prove. Be sure to emphasize Theorem 16.1 (The Pythagorean Identity).

16.4 Although this section is not usually required in secondary geometry, it is a good base for students who will be taking a physics course in following years. The Cartesian plane is used, and initial and terminal points are introduced without fuss. Angle measures are less than 180. The teacher can consider angles in the third and fourth quadrants if desired.

16.5 Addition of vectors is introduced and the parallelogram method is developed. Students will need help to select the best arrangement of vectors.

16.6 Standard position and vector components are defined. Trigonometric functions are used to determine the magnitude and direction of resultant vectors. With a calculator, most students will find this problem set easy to do.

Exploration This topic can be extended to consider all subsets of a set of elements, truth tables, or the probability of binary events.

Career Triangulation is often used in park and forest management as well.

Computer Very superior students could use the ARC(X) to create a formula for the arcsine and arccosine.

ENRICHMENT ACTIVITIES

Enrichment Activity 1

Have students supply the reasons for each statement below and find the fault in the reasoning.

1. $a = b$ Given
2. $a^2 = ab$ Multiplication Property of Equality
3. $a^2 - b^2 = ab - b^2$ Subtraction Property of Equality
4. $(a + b)(a - b) = b(a - b)$ Factoring and Distributive Property
5. $a + b = b$ Division Property of Equality
6. $2b = b$ Substitution Property of Equality
7. $2 = 1$ Division Property of Equality

Solution: The 'fault' is division by zero in step 5.

Enrichment Activity 2

The Pythagoreans believed that all important relationships in nature could be expressed by groups of whole numbers. The triangular numbers were 1, 3, 6, 10, 15, etc. The square numbers were 1, 4, 9, 16, 25, etc.

Triangular

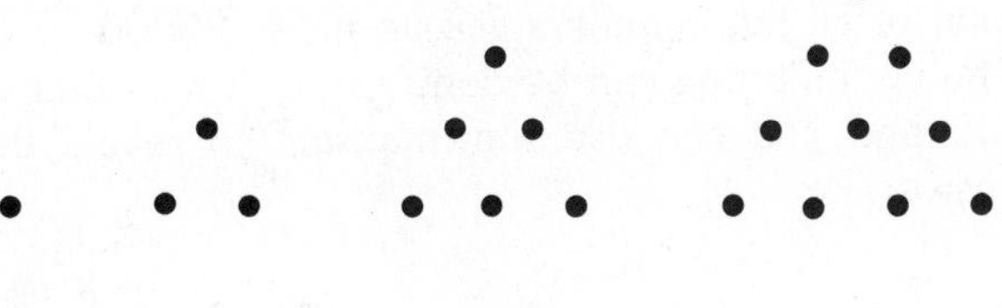

Square

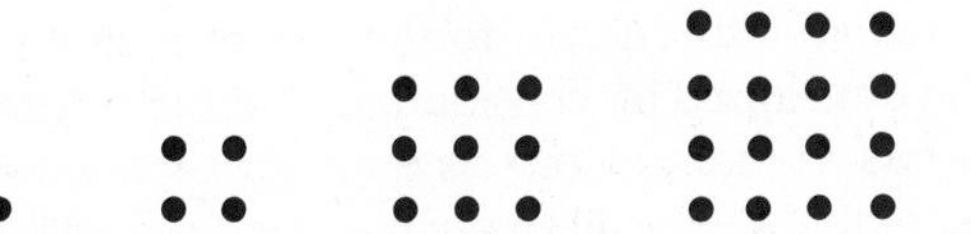

Oblong numbers 2, 6, 12, 20 etc. are the product of two successive whole numbers.

Oblong

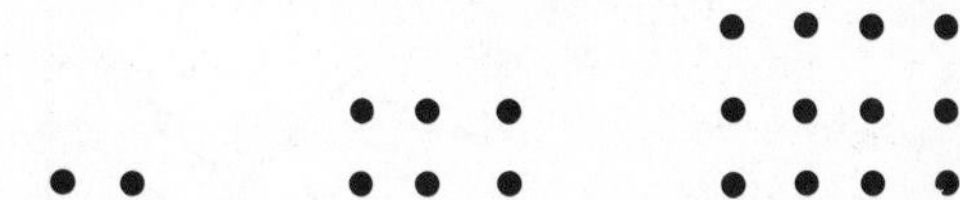

The prime numbers were called linear numbers since they could best be shown in a one line array.

Other number form classifications included pentagonal, hexagonal and heptagonal numbers.

Certain numbers were thought to represent specific characteristics. The number one signified unity and was considered the "nomad of intelligent fire in the dark of unlimit." Odd numbers were masculine and even numbers were feminine. Since five is the sum of the first odd and even numbers greater than one, it was associated with marriage. For similar reasons the three-four-five right triangle was called "the figure of the bride."

Enrichment Activity 3

Choose a three digit number. Write it down and repeat the digits in the same order. For example if you picked 123 you would write 123,123.

Since 7 is a lucky number, divide your 6 digit number by 7 and it might come out even. 11 is lucky so divide your result by 11 and see if it still divides evenly. After two lucky divisions try an unlucky 13 into the last result. What is your result?

Solution: The original 3 digit number.

123×1001
$= 123{,}123$ and $7 \times 11 \times 13 = 1001$.

Enrichment Activity 4

1. Connect the nine points below with four line segments drawn without lifting the pencil from the paper or retracing any line.

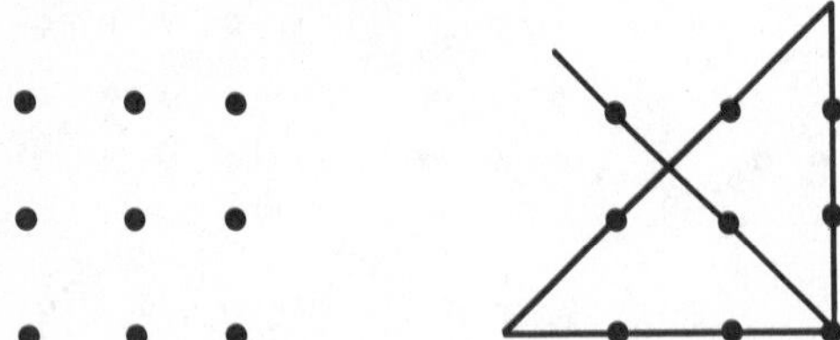

2. Connect each utility to each house without having any of the utility lines cross each other.

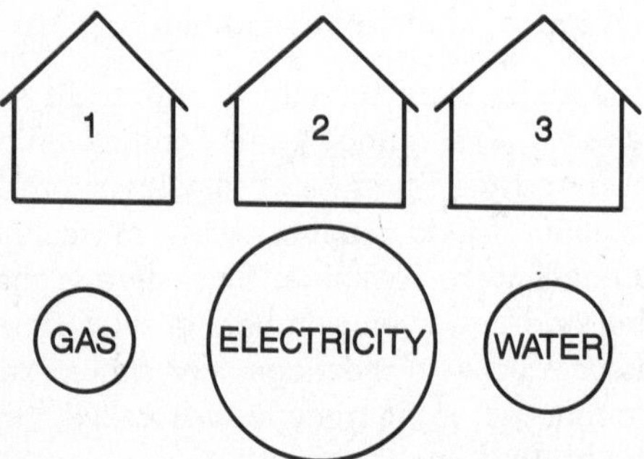

Solution: This problem is impossible on a plane unless one utility line goes through a house.

3. Other problems from graph theory to trace the pattern without lifting the pencil or retracing over any segment include:

a.
possible

b.
impossible, unless the paper is folded to allow one escape to do the last segment.

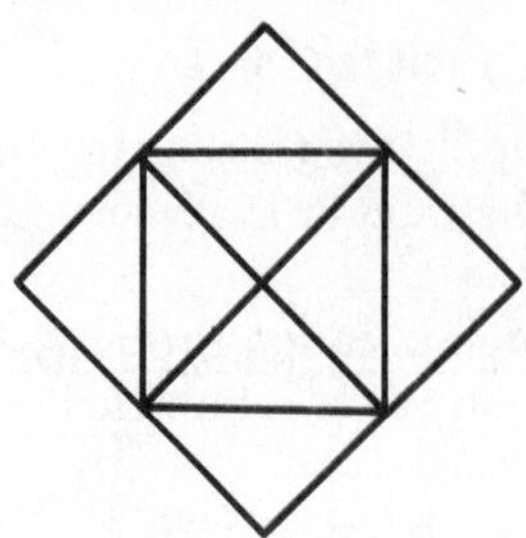

Enrichment Activity 5

A number trick using simple computations.

1. Have student number one select a four-digit number. 2345 n_1

2. Have student number two write a four-digit number beneath the first 4263 n_2

3. You write 5736 n_3

4. Have student number three write a four-digit number 2675 n_4

5. You write 7324 n_5

and tell the class that the sum is 22343.

The number you select for $n_3 = 9999 - n_2$ and the number you select for $n_5 = 9999 - n_4$ making the sum of $n_2 + n_3 + n_4 + n_5 = 2000 - 2$ and the total of all five numbers will be $n_1 + 20000 - 2$. The computation can be done easily in a second or two and you can use showmanship to reveal the answer.

Enrichment Activity 6

An intuitive introduction to the use of indirect proof can be developed by considering whether a short segment has as many points as a longer segment. Draw two segments parallel to each other. ($\overline{AB}$ and $\overline{CD}$)

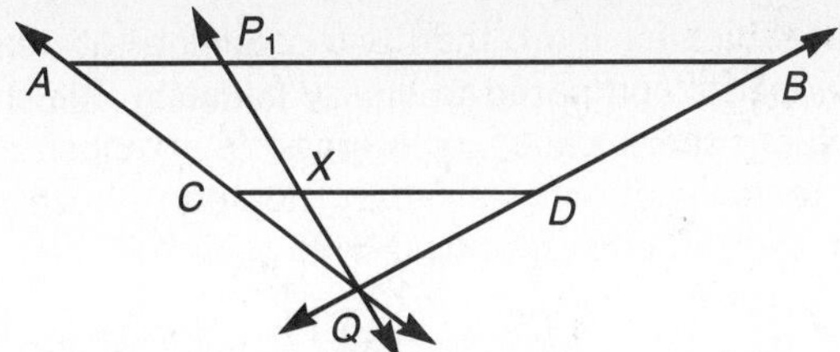

Draw line $\overleftrightarrow{AC}$ and $\overleftrightarrow{BD}$. Since $AB \neq CD$ it is presumed that the lines will intersect at some point Q. (This is intuitively acceptable to the students without the rigorous development of the separation properties of a plane.)

Select a point P, between A and B and draw $\overleftrightarrow{P_1Q}$, that will intersect $\overline{CD}$ at X. Select P_2 on $\overline{AB}$ between A and B. Draw $\overleftrightarrow{P_2Q}$ that will intersect $\overline{CD}$ at Y. Regardless of how close P_1 is to P_2, X and Y must be different points. If they were not different points, then the two lines $\overleftrightarrow{P_1Q}$ and $\overleftrightarrow{P_2Q}$ would have two points (Q and X/Y) in common, which would contradict Postulate 1. Therefore $\overline{CD}$ has as many points as $\overline{AB}$.

Enrichment Activity 7

While crossing a railroad tressle, Denny Doppler heard a train approaching at 60 mph. He was exactly $\frac{3}{8}$ of the way across the tressle and had exactly enough time to get to either end of the bridge safely if he ran at a certain speed. What was that speed?

Solution:

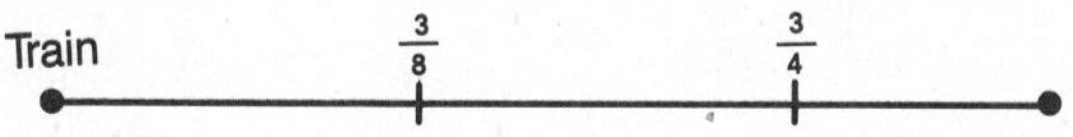

By the time the train reaches the left end of the tressle Denny can be at the $\frac{3}{4}$ mark and will have to travel $\frac{1}{4}$ the distance that the train travels and $\frac{1}{4}$ the speed. Therefore he must run 15 mph.

Most secondary students find this problem difficult and try to do too much calculation. Providing a length for the bridge will only confuse the issue.

Enrichment Activity 8

Perfect numbers are numbers whose factors total twice the number. Six is the first perfect number since 1, 2, 3, and 6 total 12, or 2×6. Other perfect numbers include 28,496 and 8,128. The search for more of these is a good exercise in computer programming.

Amicable, or friendly, numbers are a pair of numbers where the divisors (the factors excluding the number itself) add up to the other number and vice versa. The first pair discovered by the Pythagoreans was 220 and 284. The next pair found by Pierre de Fermat more than 2000 years later was 17,296 and 18,416.

Enrichment Activity 9

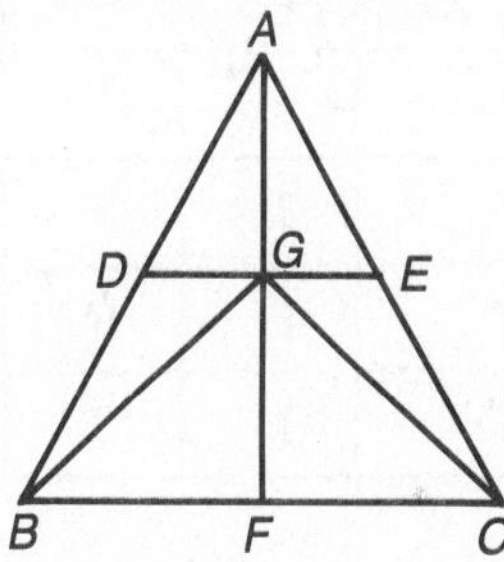

If $\overline{AB} \cong \overline{AC}$ and $\overline{GB} \cong \overline{GC}$ list and prove all of the conclusions that you can find.

Solution:

1. $AB = AC$ because congruence of segments is an equivalence relation
2. $GB = GC$ because congruence of segments is an equivalence relation
3. $\triangle AGB \cong \triangle AGC$ by SSS
4. $\angle ABC \cong \angle ACB$ by the Isosceles Triangle Theorem

5. $\angle GBF \cong \angle GCF$ by the Isosceles Triangle Theorem
6. $\angle ABG \cong \angle ACG$ by the Angle Addition Postulate or CPCTC
7. $\angle BAF \cong \angle CAF$ by CPCTC
8. $\triangle BAF \cong \triangle CAF$ by SAS
9. $BF = FC$ by CPCTC
10. $\angle AGB \cong \angle AGC$ by CPCTC
11. $\triangle GBF \cong \triangle GCF$ by SSS or SAS
12. $\angle BFG \cong \angle CFG$ by CPCTC
13. $\angle BFG$ & $\angle CFG$ are right $\angle$s by Theorem 3.4
14. $AB \perp BC$ by Def. of $\perp$ lines

Enrichment Activity 10

To prove a theorem, $A \rightarrow B$, by indirect proof we start by assuming the negation of B ($\sim B$) and reason until we reach a contradiction. A demonstration of why this method of reasoning works is the truth values for the contrapositive of an implication.

For $A \rightarrow B$ the contrapositive is $\sim B \rightarrow \sim A$.

A	B	A → B	~B	~A	~B → ~A
T	T	T	F	F	T
T	F	F	T	F	F
F	T	T	F	T	T
F	F	T	T	T	T

The truth values for $A \rightarrow B$ and $\sim B \rightarrow \sim A$ are identical, so both arguments are logically equivalent. This is called a *tautology*.

The isosceles triangle theorem states that "If two sides of a triangle are congruent, then the angles opposite these sides are congruent." The contrapositive is "If two angles of a triangle are not congruent, then the sides opposite these angles are not congruent." In the chapter on inequalities we prove this theorem by direct proof so that we can also show which side is greater.

Truth tables for more than two conditions are easily developed if compared to binary counting. For three conditions there are 2^3, or 8, possible arrangements. The table below shows binary notation for zero to eight and the corresponding truth table.

000	TTT
001	TTF
010	TFT
011	TFF
100	FTT
101	FTF
110	FFT
111	FFF

Using this method, complicated combinations of several statements can be considered on a truth table.

Enrichment Activity 11

On the SAT and similar examinations students frequently miss the easiest items.

If Sam drives from town A to town B at 20 mph and makes the return trip at an average of 30 mph what is his average speed for the round trip?

a. 22 **b.** 24 **c.** 25 **d.** 26 **e.** 28

Most students will select **c** and be confident that they got "at least one question right." The correct answer **b** can be found by selecting an arbitrary distance such as 60, 120, or 180 miles to solve the problem.

Similar problems can be developed by raising and lowering the price of an article by a percentage of the article's value.

Enrichment Activity 12

A customer went into a hardware store to buy something. The clerk told him that it would cost 25¢. He then asked how much would 19 cost, and the clerk said 50¢. The man decided to buy 1251 and paid the clerk $1.00. What did he buy?

Solution: Numerals for a house number.

Enrichment Activity 13

Three men are each to be asked a single question that can be answered either yes or no. One always tells the truth, another always lies, and the third randomizes his answers, sometimes lying and sometimes not. How can you identify each person by asking only three yes-or-no questions?

There are six possible arrangements of the men.

	A	*B*	*C*
1	T	L	R
2	T	R	L
3	L	T	R
4	L	R	T
5	R	T	L
6	R	L	T

Ask *A*, "Is *B* more likely to tell the truth than *C*?" A "yes" answer eliminates cases 1 and 3, and *C* is not the randomizer. A "no" answer eliminates cases 2 and 4 and *B* is not the randomizer.

Now ask the man who is not the randomizer "Are you the randomizer?" His answer will identify him as either a truthteller or liar. Knowing this, ask him if a certain one of the other two is randomizer. His answer will help to identify the other two.

Enrichment Activity 14

There are several perpendicular relations a roofing contractor would deal with to construct rafters and roofs. In the gable-end view of a roof shown below, each rafter is part of a right triangle. The rafter ($\overline{AB}$ or $\overline{DB}$) is the hypotenuse, a joist of the attic floor ($\overline{AC}$ or $\overline{DC}$) is the base, and the distance to the center peak (CB) is the altitude. $\angle ACB$ and $\angle DCB$ will always be right angles. Roofers call the base ($\overline{AC}$) the *run*, and the altitude ($\overline{CB}$) the *rise*. The *slant* of the rafter (and of the plane of the attached roof) is the relation between the rise and the run. For example, if CB = 6 ft and $\overline{AC}$ = 12 ft, the *rise per foot of run* is 6 in. to 1 ft. The slant of a roof also can be given as the *pitch* of the roof. When the rise is $\times \frac{1}{2}$, $\times \frac{1}{4}$, or $\times 1$ of the *full width* of the building ($\overline{AD}$), the roof is called *half pitch, quarter pitch,* or *full pitch,* respectively. Pitch for intermediate relations are given as their fractions. For example, if the run is 12 ft and the rise is 10 ft, the pitch is $\frac{5}{12}$. ($\frac{10}{12 \cdot 2} = \frac{10}{24} = \frac{5}{12}$)

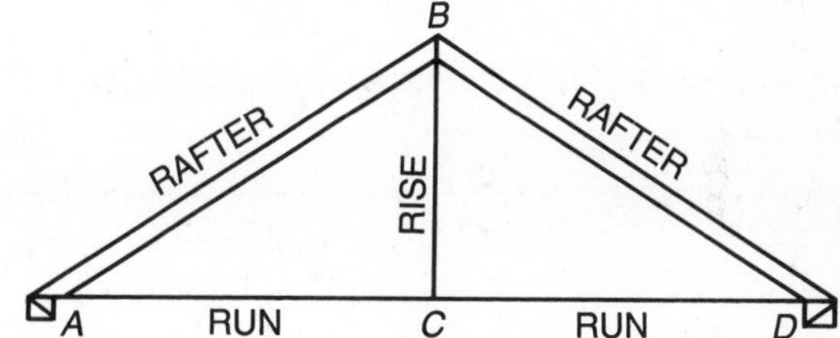

Have students determine the following relations:

1. the rise per foot of run for a roof with a run of 8 ft and a rise of 3 ft
2. the rise per foot of run for a roof with a run of 10 ft and a rise of 6 ft
3. the pitch of a roof with a run of 12 ft and a rise of 15 ft
4. the pitch of a roof with a run of 9 ft and a rise of 15 ft

Solutions:

1. $4\frac{1}{2}$ in. to 1 ft
2. $7\frac{1}{5}$ in. to 1 ft
3. $\frac{5}{8}$
4. $\frac{5}{6}$

Enrichment Activity 15

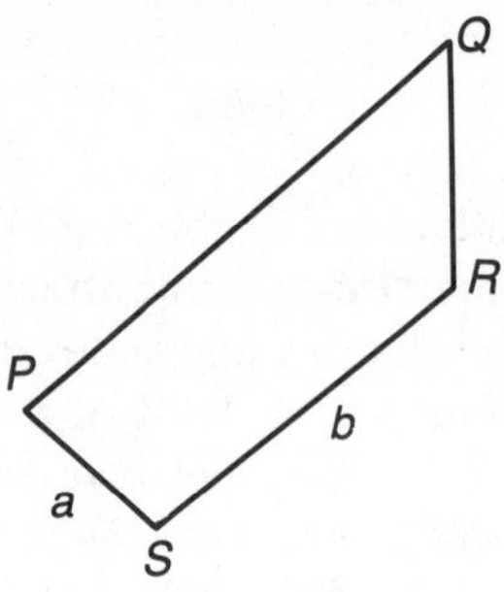

$\overline{PQ}$ and $\overline{RS}$ are parallel. The $m\angle S = 2(m\angle Q)$. $PS = a$ and $SR = b$.

Find PQ.

a. $\frac{1}{2}a + 2b$ **b.** $\frac{3}{2}b + \frac{3}{4}a$

c. $2a - b$ **d.** $4b - \frac{1}{2}a$

e. $a + b$

Solution: **a.** Let the bisector of $\angle S$ intersect $\overline{PQ}$ at A.

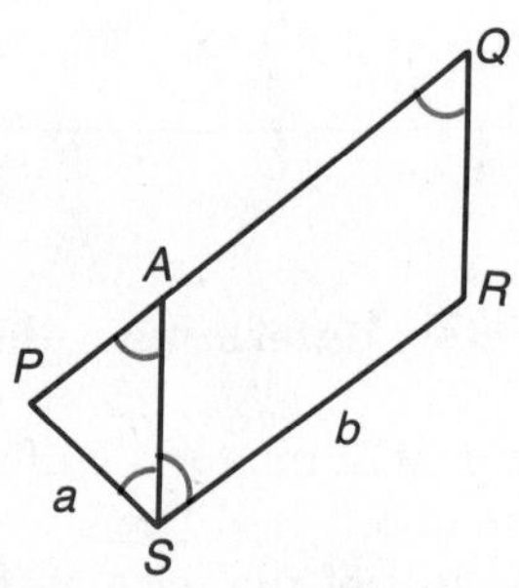

Then $\angle PAS \cong \angle ASR \cong \angle Q \cong \angle ASP$. $\triangle ASP$ is isosceles with $PA = PS = a$. Since quadrilateral $ASRQ$ is a parallelogram, $QA = RS = b$. So $PA + AQ = PQ = a + b$.

Enrichment Activity 16

The word paradox comes from the Greek word paradoxus, meaning "contrary to opinion or expectation."

1. In Buttermore's Landing there is a barber who shaves all those people, and only those people, who do not shave themselves.

2. | The statement in this box is false. |
|---|

3. Every generalization is false.

These three statements are generally known as liar's paradoxes.

The most widely known paradoxes are those of Zeno the Stoic.

4. If a runner is to cover a set distance she must first cover half of this distance in one half of the time. To do this she must first cover one-fourth the distance in one-fourth the time. Continuing the reasoning she must cover an infinite set of sub-intervals $\frac{1}{2}, \frac{1}{4}, \frac{1}{8} \cdots \cdot \frac{1}{2n}$.

To do this the runner would have to run for an eternity and could never complete the distance.

5. If Achilies runs 10 times faster than a tortoise and starts 1000 stadia behind the tortoise he can never catch the tortoise. When Achilles has covered the 1000 stadia the Tortoise will be 100 stadia ahead. When Achilles has covered the 100 stadia the tortoise will be 10 stadia ahead. Achilles can get closer and closer but never reach the tortoise, since each time he reaches the tortoise's last position he will have moved a small distance ahead.

6. Finally, consider a card with the first side having the statement "The statement on the other side is false." The reverse side states "The statement on the other side is true."

Enrichment Activity 17

Matthew Stewart's theorem circa 1745.

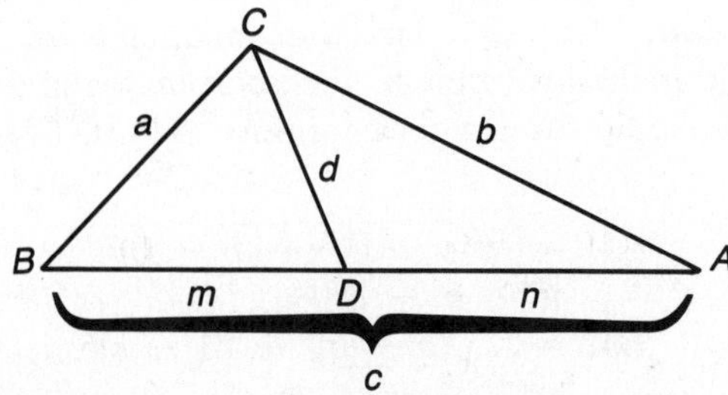

Using the letters in the figure Stewart proved that $a^2n + b^2m = c(d^2 + mn)$ regardless of where D fell on $\overline{BA}$. This describes the relationship of any internal line segment ($\overline{CD}$) to the two parts of the intercepted side ($\overline{BA}$) and the other two sides. Complete the proof.

Solution: Drop the perpendicular from C to $\overline{BA}$. Let this altitude $\overline{CE} = h$.

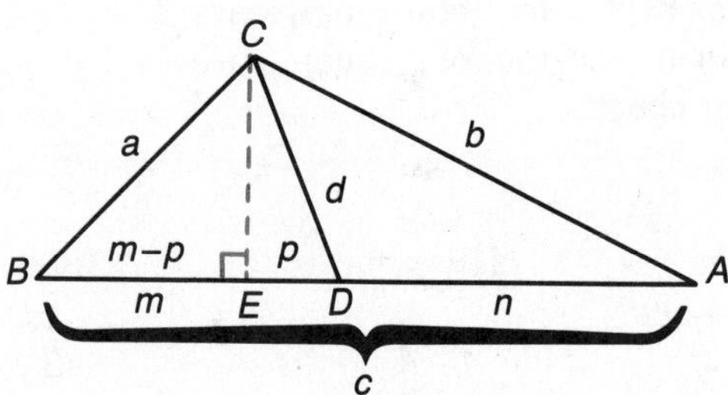

By the Pythagorean theorem in $\triangle CEB$, $a^2 = h^2 + (m - p)^2$ (1). In $\triangle CED$, $h^2 = d^2 - p^2$. Substitute for h^2 in equation (1) to get $a^2 = d^2 - p^2 + m^2 - 2mp + p^2$. Therefore $a^2 = d^2 + m^2 = 2mp$ (2). In $\triangle CDA$, similarly prove: $b^2 = d^2 - p^2 + n^2 + 2np + p^2$ or $b^2 = d^2 + n^2 + 2np$ (3).

Multiply equation (2) by n and equation (3) by m to get $a^2n = d^2n + m^2n - 2mnp$ (4) and $b^2m = d^2m$ $n^2m + 2mnp$ (5).

Add equations (4) and (5) together and substitute c for $m + n$ to get $a^2n + b^2m = c(d^2 + mn)$.

Enrichment Activity 18

Are there more ways to order 30 points on a line from left to right than there are drops of water in all of the oceans of the world?

Consider:

Points	Orders	Factorials
1	1	1
2	2	$2 \cdot 1$
3	6	$3 \cdot 2 \cdot 1$
4	24	$4 \cdot 3 \cdot 2 \cdot 1$
.	.	
.	.	
.	.	
n	$n!$	$n(n - 1)\ (n - 2) \cdots (1)$

For 30 points there are 30! or about 2.65×10^{32} possible arrangements. Using a standard eyedropper, we will find that it takes 10 drops to make a cubic centimeter or 10^7 drops per cubic meter or 10^{16} drops per cubic kilometer.

Given the radius of the earth is about 6.37×10^3 kilometers and considering that the oblate spheroid is a sphere. The volume would be $\frac{4}{3}\pi r^3$ or $1.333 \times 3.142 \times (6.37 \times 10^3)$ or $1.08 \times 10^{12} \times 10^{16}$ or 1.08×10^{28} drops if the entire earth is water.

There are 20,000 times as many arrangements as there are drops of water.

Enrichment Activity 19

In the diagram (not drawn to scale) figures A and C are equilateral triangles with areas of $32\sqrt{3}$ and $8\sqrt{3}$ in.^{2}. Figure B is a square with area of 32 in.^{2}. MQ is reduced by $12\frac{1}{2}$% of itself, while MN and PQ remain unchanged.

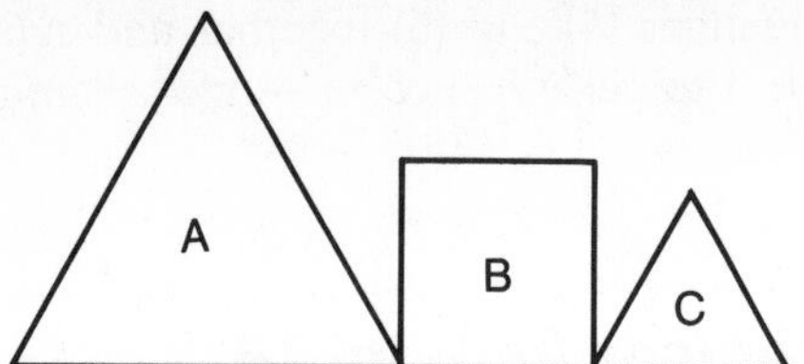

The percent of decrease in the area of the square is:
a. 12 **b.** 25 **c.** 50 **d.** 75 **e.** 87

Solution: **d.** From the areas of the equilateral triangles $MN = 8\sqrt{2}$ and $PQ = 4\sqrt{2}$. $NP = 4\sqrt{2}$ so $MQ = 16\sqrt{2}$. The reduction from NP would be $2\sqrt{2}$ and would leave $2\sqrt{2}$ or $\frac{1}{2}$ of its first value. This would leave an area of $\frac{1}{4}$ of the original or a reduction of 75%.

Enrichment Activity 20

Leonardo of Pisa is supposed to have posed the following problem: Two towers, one 30 and the other 40 cubits high, are 50 cubits apart. There is a marker on the line between the bases of these towers. Two crows fly from the top of each tower at the same time and at the same speed. If both of them reach the marker at the same time how far is the marker from each tower?

Solution: Since the crows reach the marker at the same time the hypotenuses must be of equal length a.

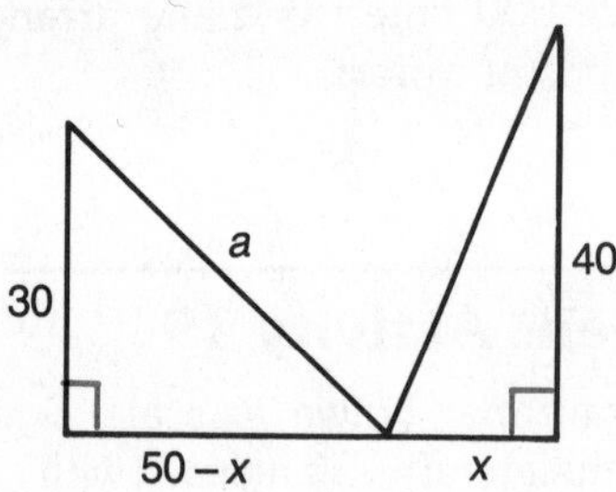

Solve the equation: $30^2 + x^2 = 40^2 + (50 - x)^2$ to find $x = 18$ and $50 - x = 32$.

Enrichment Activity 21

Prove that the midpoint of the hypotenuse of a right triangle is equidistant from the vertices of the triangle. Use $A(0, 0)$, $B(2a, 0)$ and $C(0, 2b)$ for $\triangle ABC$.

Solution: Let M be the midpoint of $\overline{BC}$. By the midpoint formula, the coordinates of M are (a, b). Apply the distance formula to AM, BM, and CM.

$$\begin{aligned} AM &= \sqrt{(a - 0)^2 + (b - 0)^2} \\ &= \sqrt{a^2 + b^2} \\ BM &= \sqrt{(2a - a)^2 + (0 - b)^2} \\ &= \sqrt{a^2 + b^2} \\ CM &= \sqrt{(0 - a)^2 + (2b - b)^2} \\ &= \sqrt{a^2 + b^2} \end{aligned}$$

Thus the midpoint is equidistant from all three vertices.

Enrichment Activity 22

Find the pattern for the total number of squares of all sizes generated by a square of side n where n is a positive integer.

1. For example if $n = 1$ the total of squares is 1
2. For $n = 2$ the total squares are 5
3. For $n = 3$ the total squares are 14

Make a chart:

n	New squares	Total
1	0	1
2	4	5
3	9	14
.	.	.
.	.	.
.	.	.

Have students experiment by drawing the figures and counting possible squares in an organized manner to discover the patterns, and see if they can find the formula

$$\frac{n(n + 1)\ (2n + 1)}{6}$$

Enrichment Activity 23

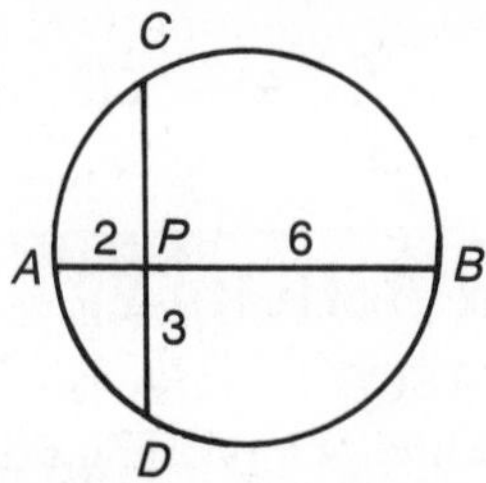

Chords $\overline{CD}$ and $\overline{AB}$ intersect at P. $\overline{CD} \perp \overline{AB}$.

With $AP = 2$, $PB = 6$, and $PD = 3$, find the diameter of the circle.

a. $4\sqrt{5}$ **b.** $\sqrt{65}$ **c.** $2\sqrt{17}$

d. $3\sqrt{7}$ **e.** $6\sqrt{2}$

Solution: **b.** By the power of a point, $AP \cdot PB = CP \cdot PD$. or $CP \cdot 3 = 2 \cdot 6$ so $CP = 4$. Therefore $AB = 8$ and $CD = 7$.

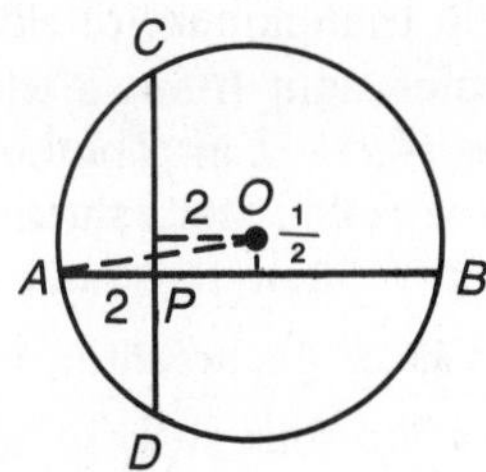

The center of the circle, O, will be on the perpendicular bisectors of $\overline{AB}$ and $\overline{CD}$ which is $\frac{1}{2}$ unit above and 4 units to the right of A.

By the Pythagorean theorem the radius $OA = \frac{\sqrt{65}}{2}$ and the diameter is $\sqrt{65}$.

Enrichment Activity 24

Given a regular polygon of n sides of length l, inscribed in a circle of radius r, the length of each side of a regular polygon of $2n$ sides inscribed in the same circle is:

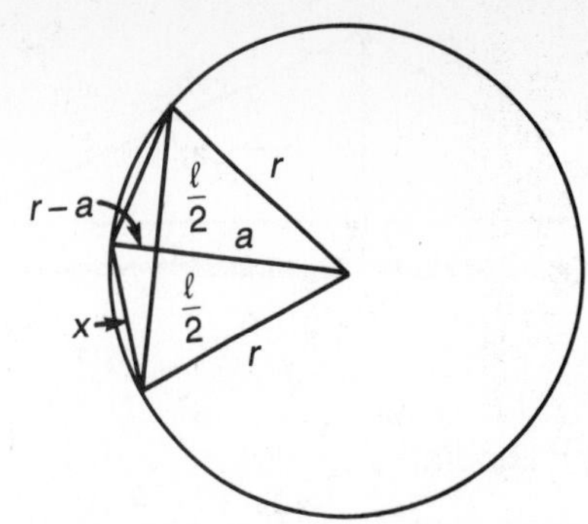

$$l_{2n} = \sqrt{2r^2 - r\sqrt{4r^2 - l^2}}$$

$$a^2 = r^2 - \frac{l^2}{4}$$

$$x^2 = \frac{l^2}{4} + r^2 - 2ra + a^2$$

$$x^2 = \frac{l^2}{4} + r^2 - \frac{2r\sqrt{4r^2 - l^2}}{2} + r^2 - \frac{l^2}{4}$$

$$x^2 = 2r^2 - r\sqrt{4r^2 - l^2}$$

and $x = \sqrt{2r^2 - r\sqrt{4r^2 - l^2}}$

where $x =$ the length of each side of the polygon of $2n$ sides.

This formula can be used to generate values for pi in a computer program using a radius of 1 and a regular polygon such as a square or a hexagon where the edge can be determined. For example:

n	Formula	l	Perimeter	$\frac{\text{Perimeter}}{\text{Diameter}}$
6		1	6	3
12	$2 - 4 - 1$	.517	6.212	3.106

r will remain one and l will be redefined each time the loop is completed. By printing the ratio of $n \cdot l$ to the diameter (two) you will approach pi as a limit.

Enrichment Activity 25

Prove that the square of the side opposite an acute angle of a triangle is equal to the sum of the squares of the other two sides minus twice the product of one of the two sides and the projection of the other upon it.

Prove: $b^2 = a^2 + c^2 - 2xc$

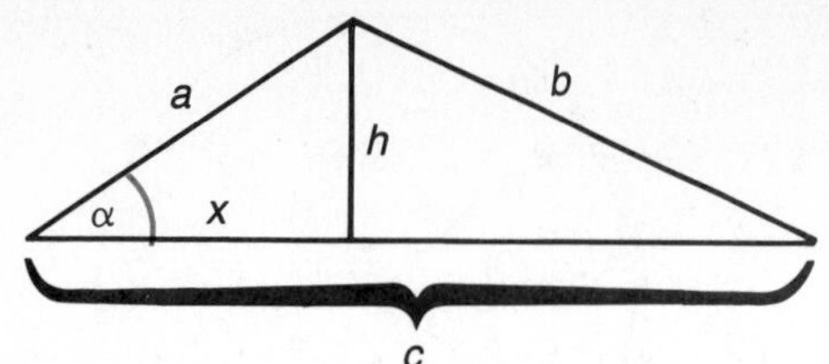

By the Pythagorean Theorem

$$h^2 = a^2 - x^2 \text{ and } h^2 = b^2 - (c - x)^2$$

By substitution

$$\begin{aligned} b^2 - (c - x)^2 &= a^2 - x^2 \\ b^2 &= a^2 - x^2 + (c - x)^2 \\ &= a^2 - x^2 + c^2 - 2cx + x^2 \\ &= a^2 + c^2 - 2cx \end{aligned}$$

In trigonometry this is usually given as

$$b^2 = a^2 + c^2 - 2ac \text{ Cos } \alpha$$

and is called the *Law of Cosines.*

Enrichment Activity 26

Prove that the bisector of the right angle of a right triangle bisects the angle included by the altitude and median to the hypotenuse.

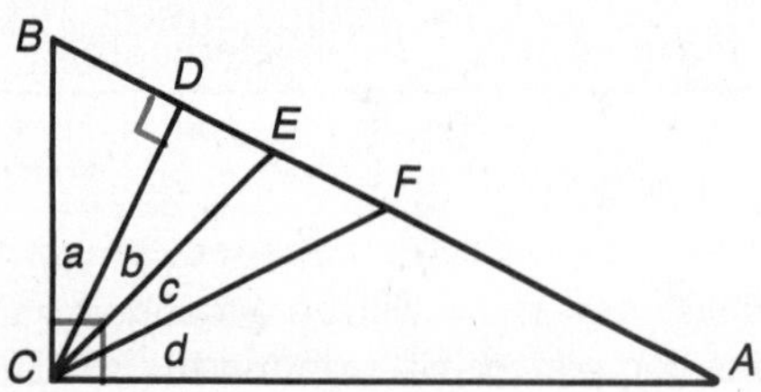

Solution: In right $\triangle ABC$, let $\overline{CE}$ be the angle bisector, $\overline{CD}$ the altitude, and $\overline{CF}$ the median. As you've learned from Chapter 13, the midpoint of the hypotenuse of a right triangle is the center of the circumscribed circle of the triangle, thus the midpoint is equidistant from the vertices of the triangle, so $CF = FA$, and $\triangle CFA$ is isosceles. Thus $\angle A \cong \angle d$. $\angle a$ and $\angle B$ are complementary, and $\angle A$ and $\angle B$ are complementary (Corollary 8.13.2), thus $\angle a \cong \angle A$ (Theorem 3.3 and Theorem 3.6). Then $\angle a \cong \angle d$ because congruence of angles is transitive. $\angle BCE \cong \angle ACE$ by the Definition of angle bisector and $\angle b \cong \angle c$ by the Angle Addition Postulate.

Enrichment Activity 27

In this figure, $ABCD$ is a square whose side is 8 inches. With the mid-points of the sides of the square as center, arcs are drawn tangent to the diagonals. Find the area enclosed by the four arcs.

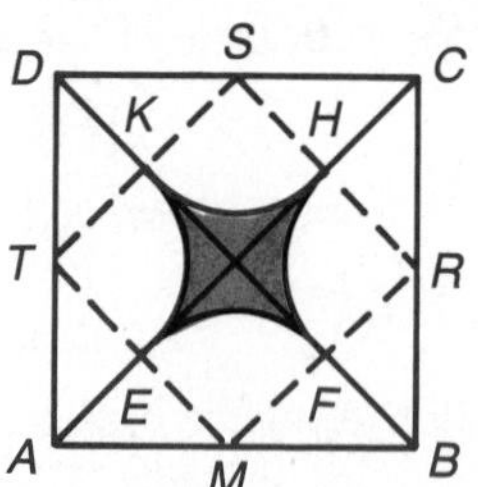

Solution: Each triangle SCR, RBM, MAT, and TDS is an isosceles right triangle with legs $= 4$ in. and hypotenuses $= 4\sqrt{2}$ in. The hypotenuses form the sides of square $SRMT$, thus the area of $SRMT = (4\sqrt{2})^2 = 32$ in.^{2}. Then the radii of the arcs $= 2\sqrt{2}$ and the area of each sector $= \frac{\pi}{360}(90)(2\sqrt{2})^2 = 2\pi$ in.^{2}. There are four such sectors, so the area of the shaded region $=$ the area of square $SRMT$ $-$ the area of the four sectors $= 32 - 8\pi$ in.^{2}.

Enrichment Activity 28

If Noca wishes to water the lawn and it takes her three hours with a $\frac{3}{8}$-inch diameter hose, how much time will she save by using a $\frac{5}{8}$-inch hose? Assume that the water pressure for both hoses is constant and that the smaller hose will deliver 9 gallons per minute.

Solution: With constant water pressure the amount delivered will be determined by the area of the hose openings.

$$a_1 = \frac{9\pi}{16^2} \text{ and } a_2 = \frac{25\pi}{16^2}, \text{ so}$$

their ratio is $\frac{9}{25}$. Therefore it will take $\frac{9}{25}$ of 3 hours or 64 minutes and 48 seconds. She will save 115 minutes and 12 seconds.

Enrichment Activity 29

If a quadrilateral is inscribed in a circle, the sum of the products of the opposite sides is equal to the product of the length of the diagonals.

For the figure below, prove:

$$BC \cdot AD + AB \cdot CD = AC \cdot BD$$

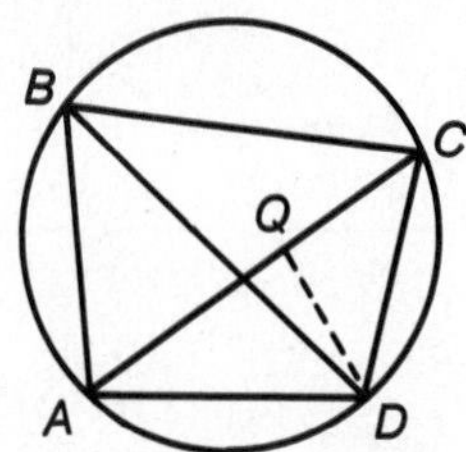

Solution: Select point Q on $\overline{AC}$ so that $\angle ADQ \cong \angle BAC$

Proof: $\triangle ADQ \sim \triangle BDC$ by AA ($\angle QAD \cong \angle CBD$ by Corollary 12.7.1 and $\angle ADQ \cong \angle BDC$.) So $\frac{AQ}{BC} = \frac{AD}{DB}$ or $AQ = \frac{BC \cdot AD}{DB}$.

Proof: $\triangle ADB \sim \triangle QDC$ by AA ($\angle ABD \cong \angle QCD$ by Corollary 12.7.1 and $m\angle ADQ = m\angle BDC$, $m\angle ADB + m\angle BDQ = m\angle ADQ$ and $m\angle BDQ + m\angle QDC = m\angle BDC$ by Angle Addition Postulate; then $m\angle ADB = m\angle QDC$ by Subtraction property of equality.)

So $\frac{QC}{AB} = \frac{CD}{DB}$ or $QC = \frac{AB \cdot CD}{DB}$.

Then $AQ + QC = AC = \frac{BC \cdot AD}{DB} + \frac{AB \cdot CD}{DB}$

and $AC \cdot DB = BC \cdot AD + AB \cdot CD$

Enrichment Activity 30

In a closed $16 \times 16 \times 60$ inch shipping carton a fly who is 2 inches from the top of the middle of the front (16×16) wall becomes paralyzed by fear when he sees a tarantula 2 inches from the bottom of the rear wall. What is the shortest path that the tarantula can travel to reach the fly? HINT: What would you have to do to the box to use the Pythagorean theorem?

Solution: Unfold the box.

$FX = 48$
$XT = 64$
$FT = 80$

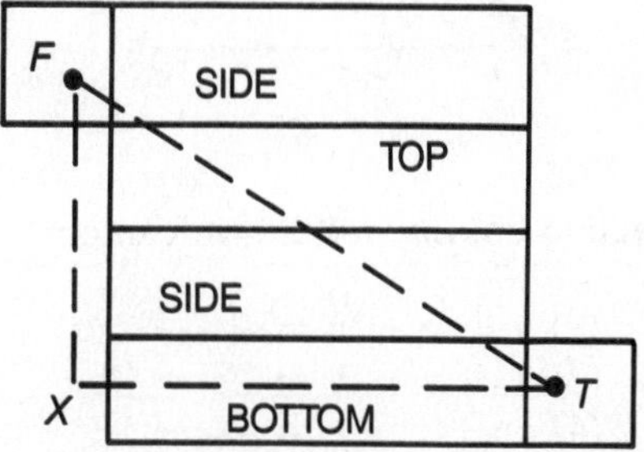

Enrichment Activity 31

Given right triangle ABC with the right angle at C, prove:

$$\sin(A + B) = \sin A \cos B + \cos A \sin B.$$

Solution: Since the acute angles of a right triangle are complementary, $m\angle A + m\angle B = 90$, so $\sin(A + B) = \sin 90 = 1$, so $1 = \sin A \cos B + \cos A \sin B$.

From the definitions of sine and cosine, $\sin A = \frac{a}{c}$, $\cos A = \frac{b}{c}$, $\sin B = \frac{b}{c}$, and $\cos B = \frac{a}{c}$. Substituting these into the identity,

$$1 = \frac{a}{c} \cdot \frac{a}{c} + \frac{b}{c} \cdot \frac{b}{c}$$

$$1 = \frac{a^2 + b^2}{c^2}$$

and $c^2 = a^2 + b^2$ which you know to be true by the Pythagorean Theorem, thus the identity is true.

Enrichment Activity 32

If s equals one half of the perimeter of a triangle with sides of a, b and c, then prove:

$$\text{the area of a } \triangle = \sqrt{s(s-a)(s-b)(s-c)}$$

Solution:

$$s = \tfrac{1}{2}(a+b+c)$$
$$\text{or (1) } 2s = a+b+b+c$$

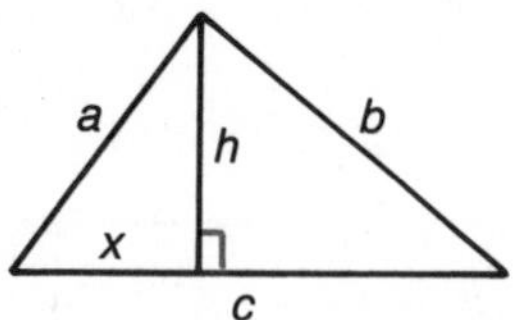

By subtracting $2a$, $2b$, and $2c$ we can get

$$(2)\ b+c-a = 2s-2a$$
$$(3)\ a+c-b = 2s-2b$$
$$(4)\ a+b-c = 2s-2c$$

Recall that the law of cosines problem in Enrichment Activity 25 stated:

$$b^2 = a^2 + c^2 - 2xc$$

Solve for x:

$$x = \frac{a^2+c^2-b^2}{2c}$$

By the Pythagorean Theorem:

$$h^2 = a^2 - x^2 \text{ and substituting}$$
$$h^2 = a^2 - \left(\frac{a^2+c^2-b^2}{2c}\right)$$

Factoring the difference of two squares yields

$$h^2 = \left(a + \frac{a^2+c^2-b^2}{2c}\right)\left(a - \frac{a^2+c^2-b^2}{2c}\right)$$

Adding

$$h^2 = \left(\frac{2ac+a^2+c^2-b^2}{2c}\right)\left(\frac{2ac-a^2-c^2+b^2}{2c}\right)$$
$$h^2 = \left(\frac{(a+c)^2-b^2}{2c}\right)\left(\frac{b^2-(a-c)^2}{2c}\right)$$
$$h^2 = \left(\frac{(a+c-b)(a+c+b)}{2c}\right)\left(\frac{(b+a-c)(b-a+c)}{2c}\right)$$

By substituting equations 1, 2, 3 and 4

$$h^2 = \frac{(2s-2b)(2s)(2s-2a)(2s-2c)}{4c^2}$$
$$h^2 = \frac{16(s-b)(s)(s-a)(s-c)}{4c^2}$$
$$h = \frac{2\sqrt{s(s-a)(s-b)(s-c)}}{c}$$

Since the area of a triangle is $\frac{1}{2}$ · base · height, the area of the triangle

$$= \tfrac{1}{2} \cdot c \cdot \sqrt{s(s-a)(s-b)(s-c)}$$
$$= \sqrt{s(s-a)(s-b)(s-c)}\,.$$

PERFORMANCE OBJECTIVES

This list of course goals includes objectives for every section of Laidlaw Geometry

Chapter 1

The student can do the following:

1.1 Name, describe and draw models for points, lines, and planes.
1.2 Identify real numbers and their properties.
1.3 Use the definitions of $>$ and $<$ to complete an inequality.
Identify the properties of inequalities.
1.4 Given an implication, give its converse and biconditional statements and determine whether given statements are true or false.
1.5 Find the distance between two points on a number line, given their coordinates.
1.6 Identify line segments, rays, opposite rays, endpoints, and midpoints.
Determine the midpoint of a segment, given its endpoints.

Chapter 2

The student can do the following:

2.1 Identify collinear and coplanar points and intersecting lines and planes.
2.2 Tell if a figure is a convex set.
Given an appropriate figure, tell if two points are on the same side or on opposite sides of a line in a plane or of a plane in space.
2.3 Identify sides, vertices, interiors, and exteriors of angles and triangles and name angles and triangles.
Determine the perimeter of a triangle.
2.4 Identify congruent angles.
Use a protractor to measure angles.

Chapter 3

The student can do the following:

3.1 Identify adjacent and supplementary angles.
Given the measure of an angle, find the measure of its supplement.
3.2 Identify acute, right, and obtuse angles and triangles, perpendicular lines, and complementary angles.
Given the measure of an angle, find the measure of its complement.
3.3 Identify vertical angles.
Given the measure of one angle in a figure, determine the measure of another angle using supplements, complements, or congruence.
3.4 Identify congruent figures and their corresponding parts.
3.5 Identify congruent triangles, their corresponding parts, and included and opposite sides and angles.
3.6 Identify equivalence relations and use the properties of equality in proofs involving algebraic equations.
3.7 Identify medians and angle bisectors.
Given the measure of a line segment or an angle, determine the measure of another line segment or angle using medians or angle bisectors.

Chapter 4

The student can do the following:

4.1 Use SAS or LL to prove two triangles congruent.
4.2 Use ASA to prove two triangles congruent.
4.3 Identify scalene, isosceles, and equilateral triangles.
Use the Isosceles Triangle Theorem and its converse and corollaries to prove parts of a triangle congruent.

4.4 Use SSS to prove two triangles congruent.
4.5 Use congruent triangles to prove statements involving quadrilaterals and other polygons.

Chapter 5

The student can do the following:

5.1 Given a conditional statement, give its negation, inverse and contrapositive and determine whether given statements are true or false.
5.2 Identify a perpendicular bisector and use its definition, theorems, and corollaries in proofs.
5.3 Supply reasons in direct and indirect proofs involving perpendicular bisectors.
5.4 Justify the use of auxiliary sets.
5.5 Use the definitions and theorems on betweenness and separation in proofs.

Chapter 6

The student can do the following:

6.1 Distinguish between reason, conjecture, chance discovery, and intuition.
6.2 Apply the order reversal rule and use the properties of inequalities to solve inequalities.
6.3 Identify remote interior and exterior angles of a triangle.
Use the Exterior Angle Theorem and its corollary to determine the relationship of the measures of the angles of a figure.
6.4 Use SAA and HL in proofs.
6.5 Use the Triangle Inequality Theorem and Theorems 6.4 and 6.5 to answer questions involving inequalities in a triangle.
6.6 Use the Hinge Theorem and its converse to answer questions regarding triangles and use these theorems in proofs.
6.7 Identify the altitudes of a triangle.

Chapter 7

The student can do the following:

7.1 Identify perpendicular relationships between lines and planes.
7.2 Use Theorems 7.2 and 7.3 in proofs.
7.3 Use Theorems 7.4-7.7 to answer questions regarding perpendicular lines and planes.
7.4 Use Theorems 7.8-7.11 to answer questions regarding perpendicular lines and planes and use these theorems in proofs.

Chapter 8

The student can do the following:

8.1 Use Theorems 8.1-8.5 in proofs and use alternate interior angles of parallel lines to find the measure of an angle.
8.2 Use Theorems 8.6 and 8.7 in proofs and use corresponding angles of parallel lines to prove lines parallel.
8.3 Use the Parallel Postulate and Theorems 8.8-8.12 in proofs and to find angle measure.
8.4 Use Theorems 8.13 and its corollaries to find the measure of an angle of a triangle.
8.5 Identify opposite sides and vertices, consecutive sides and vertices, and diagonals of quadrilaterals and identify trapezoids and parallelograms.
Use Theorems 8.14-8.22 to answer questions regarding parallelograms.
8.6 Identify rhombuses, rectangles, and squares.
Use Theorems 8.23-8.26 to find missing measures in figures and use these theorems in proofs.
8.7 Use Theorems 8.27-8.31 to answer questions regarding parallel lines and planes and use these theorems in proofs.
8.8 Identify a dihedral angle, its parts in figures, and its characteristics.
8.9 Identify projections into a plane.

Chapter 9

The student can do the following:

9.1 Use Postulate 18 to determine the area of a polygonal region.
9.2 Use Postulate 20 to determine the area of a rectangle.
9.3 Use Theorems 9.1 and 9.2 to determine the area of a triangle.

9.4 Use Theorem 9.5 to determine the area of a parallelogram and Theorem 9.6 to determine the area of a trapezoid.

9.5 Use the Pythagorean Theorem to solve problems regarding right triangles.

9.6 Use Theorems 9.9 and 9.10 to determine the lengths of sides of special right triangles.

Chapter 10

The student can do the following:

10.1 Write ratios and proportions, solve proportions, and identify the properties of proportions.

10.2 Use the Basic Proportionality Theorem to find the length of a side of a triangle.

10.3 Use AAA, AA, and ASA in proofs.

10.4 Use SAS and SSS in proofs and to find a measure of a triangle.

10.5 Use Theorem 10.6 and its corollary to find a measure of a triangle.

10.6 Use Theorem 10.6 to find a measure of a triangle.

Chapter 11

The student can do the following:

11.1 Graph and locate points in the coordinate plane.

11.2 Find the slope of a line.

11.3 Use slopes to determine whether two lines are parallel, perpendicular, or neither.

11.4 Use the distance formula to determine the distance between two points, given their coordinates.

11.5 Use the midpoint formula to determine the coordinates of the midpoint of a segment, given the coordinates of its endpoints.

11.6 Use the coordinate plane, the distance formula, and slope to prove theorems involving figures in a plane.

11.7 Graph algebraic equations and inequalities in the coordinate plane.

11.8 Write and graph equations in point-slope form, y-intercept form, or standard form.

Chapter 12

The student can do the following:

12.1 Identify circles, spheres, radii, interior and exterior of circles, great circle, concentric circles, tangents, secants, and chords.

12.2 Use Theorem 12.2 and its corollaries and Theorems 12.3 and 12.4 to answer questions regarding tangents and chords and to find the length of segments in circles.

12.3 Use Theorem 12.5 and its corollaries to answer questions regarding tangents and chords and to find the length of segments in spheres.

12.4 Identify major and minor arcs, semicircles, and central angles and find their measures.

12.5 Identify inscribed angles and inscribed polygons.
Use Theorem 12.7 and its corollaries and Theorems 12.8 and 12.9 to find the measure of an arc or an angle.

12.6 Use Theorems 12.9–12.11 to find the measure of an arc or an angle.

12.7 Use Theorems 12.12–12.17 to find the measure of an arc or an angle.

12.8 Given the equation of a circle, write the equation in standard form, determine the center and the radius, and graph the circle.

Chapter 13

The student can do the following:

13.1 Describe and sketch geometric figures that satisfy a given condition.

13.2 Use Theorems 13.1–13.4 to answer questions regarding angle bisectors, points of concurrence, and set characterizations.

13.3 Use compass and straightedge to perform Constructions 1–7, the basic geometric constructions.
Apply Theorem 13.5 to the construction of a perpendicular bisector of a segment.

13.4 Use compass and straightedge to perform Constructions 8–10, regarding circles.
Recognize and identify impossible constructions.

Chapter 14

The student can do the following:

14.1 Identify polygons, their vertices, sides, angles, apothems, and perimeters.
Determine central angles of a polygon.
Use formulas for deriving angles of a polygon.

14.2 Use Theorems 14.1 and 14.2 to answer questions regarding circles and their arcs.

14.3 Use Theorems 14.3 and 14.4 to answer questions regarding the lengths of arcs.

14.4 Use formulas derived from Theorems 14.5 and 14.6 to find the areas of sectors and segments of circles.

14.5 Identify prisms, their bases, altitudes, cross sections, lateral edges, and lateral faces.
Use Theorems 14.7–14.9 and Corollaries 14.7.1 and 14.8.1 to answer questions regarding the lateral surface areas and total surface area of prisms.

14.6 Identify pyramids, their bases, vertices, altitudes, slant heights, and cross sections.
Use Theorems 14.10–14.12 to answer questions regarding the areas of lateral surfaces and cross sections of pyramids.

14.7 Identify polyhedral regions.
Use Postulates 21 and 22, and Theorems 14.13–14.16, to find the volumes of polyhedral regions.

14.8 Identify cylinders and cones and their cross sections.
Use Theorems 14.17–14.21 to find the volumes of cylinders and cones.

14.9 Identify the annulus of a sphere and a spherical shell.
Use Theorems 14.22 and 14.23 to find the volume and area of a sphere.

Chapter 15

The student can do the following:

15.1 Find the Cartesian product of two sets.
Identify a relation, its domain, range, inverse, function, and inverse function.

15.2 Identify the domain and codomain of a mapping.
Identify and graph a transformation.

15.3 Identify line reflections and lines of symmetry.
Graph lines and their reflections.

15.4 Identify and plot translations and determine their rules and magnitudes.

15.5 Identify rotations and determine their center, magnitudes, and directions.

15.6 Identify glide reflections and isometries.
Identify Abelian groups.

15.7 Identify dilations and determine their centers and magnitudes.

15.8 Identify similarity transformations and their properties.

Chapter 16

The student can do the following:

16.1 Identify sine, cosine, and tangent values given the measures of the sides of a right triangle.
Establish that complementary angles have equal cofunctions and reciprocal tangents.

16.2 Find trigonometric ratios for special right triangles (30-60-90, 45-45-90). Use trigonometric table and calculator to
(1) determine trigonometric ratios, given angle measures;
(2) determine angle measures given ratios;
(3) determine area of a figure given a side and an angle.

16.3 Apply trigonometric ratios to practical problem solving.
Prove identities 16.1–16.3.

16.4 Identify quantities expressed to vectors.
Find magnitude and direction of a given vector and graph it on the coordinate plane.

16.5 Add vectors.
Find net velocity and force by parallelogram method.

16.6 Add and subtract nonperpendicular vectors.
Find vectors components.
Find magnitude and direction of resultant vector.

ADDITIONAL ANSWERS

The following answers are those which could not be accommodated in the daily lesson margins.

Written Exercises, Page 69, Lesson 3.2

30. *1.* $\angle 1 \cong \angle 2$, $\angle 1$ and $\angle 2$ are supp. (Given); *2.* $m\angle 1 = m\angle 2$ (Def. of $\cong$ $\angle$s); *3.* $m\angle 1 + m\angle 2 = 180$ (Def. of supp. $\angle$s); *4.* $m\angle 1 + m\angle 1 = 180$ (Subst.); *5.* $2 \cdot m\angle 1 = 180$ (Distributive); *6.* $m\angle 1 = 90$ (Division prop. of equality); *7.* $m\angle 2 = 90$ (Transitive prop. of equality); *8.* $\angle 1$ and $\angle 2$ are right $\angle$s (Def. of right angles).

32. *1.* $m\angle 1 + m\angle 2 = 180$ (Def. of supp. $\angle$s); *2a.* If $\angle 1$ is acute, $0 < m\angle 1 < 90$ (Def. of acute angles); *2b.* $90 < m\angle 1 + 90 < 180$ (Addition prop. of inequality); *2c.* $m\angle 1 + 90 < m\angle 1 + m\angle 2$ (Substitution); *2d.* $90 < m\angle 2$ (Subtraction prop. of inequality); *2e.* $\angle 2$ is obtuse (Def. of obtuse $\angle$s); *3a.* If $\angle 1$ is a right $\angle$, $m\angle 1 = 90$ (Def. of right $\angle$s); *3b.* $m\angle 2 = 90$ (Steps *1*, *3a*, and subst. prop. of inequality); *3c.* $\angle 1$ and $\angle 2$ are right $\angle$s (Def. of right $\angle$s); *4a.* If $\angle 1$ is obtuse, $90 < m\angle 1 < 180$ (Def. of obtuse $\angle$s); *4b.* $180 < m\angle 1 + 90$ (Addition prop. of inequality); *4c.* $m\angle 1 + m\angle 2 < m\angle 1 + 90$ (Steps *1*, *4b*, and substitution); *4d.* $m\angle 2 < 90$ (Subtraction prop. of inequality); *4e.* $\angle 2$ is acute (Def. of acute $\angle$s); *5.* At most $\angle 1$ or $\angle 2$ may be obtuse, but not both (Steps *2d*, *3b*, and *4d*).

Written Exercises, Page 134, Lesson 5.1

17. *1.* Scalene $\triangle ABC$ and $\overline{BD}$ bisects $\angle ABC$ (Given); *2.* $\angle ABD \cong \angle CBD$ (Def. of $\angle$ bisector); *3.* $\overline{BD} \cong \overline{BD}$ (Congruence of segments is reflex.); *4.* Let $\overline{BD} \perp \overline{AC}$ (Indirect assump.); *5.* $\angle BDA$ and $\angle CBD$ are rt. $\angle$s (Def. of $\perp$); *6.* $\angle BDA \cong \angle BDC$ (All rt. $\angle$s are $\cong$); *7.* $\triangle ABD \cong \triangle CBD$ (ASA); *8.* $\overline{AB} \cong \overline{CB}$ (CPCTC)

Contradiction: $\triangle ABC$ is scalene.
Therefore, $\overline{BD}$ is not $\perp \overline{AC}$.

19. *1.* Scalene $\triangle ABC$, $\overline{AD}$ and $\overline{CD}$ are bisectors (Given); *2.* $\angle BAD \cong \angle DAC$, $\angle BDC \cong \angle DCA$ (Def. of bisector); *3.* $m\angle BAD = m\angle DAC$, $m\angle BCD = m\angle DCA$ (Def. of $\cong$ $\angle$s); *4.* Let $\overline{AD} \cong \overline{CD}$ (Indirect assump.); *5.* $\angle DAC \cong \angle DCA$ (Isos. $\triangle$ Theorem); *6.* $m\angle DAC = m\angle DCA$ (Def. of $\cong$ $\angle$s); *7.* $m\angle BAD = m\angle BCD$ (Trans. prop.); *8.* $m\angle BAD + m\angle DAC = m\angle BCD + m\angle DCA$ (Addition prop. of equality); *9.* $m\angle BAC \cong m\angle BCA$ (Post. 13); *10.* $\angle BAC \cong \angle BCA$ (Def. of $\cong$ $\angle$s); *11.* $\overline{BA} \cong \overline{BC}$ (Theorem 4.4); 12. $\triangle ABC$ is isosceles (Def. of isosceles).

Contradiction: $\triangle ABC$ is scalene, so $\overline{AD} \not\cong \overline{CD}$.

Written Exercises, Page 140, Lesson 5.2

15. 1. $\triangle ABC$ is scalene, AD is bisector of $\angle BAC$ (Given); 2. $\overline{AD} \perp \overline{BC}$ by (Indirect assump.); 3. $\angle ADB$ and $\angle ADC$ are right angles (Def. of $\perp$); 4. $\angle BAD \cong \angle CAD$ (Def. of bisector); 5. $\overline{AD} \cong \overline{AD}$ (Congruence of segments is reflex.); 6. $\triangle ABD \cong \triangle ACD$ (Steps 3, 4, 5 and ASA); 7. $\overline{AB} \cong \overline{AC}$ (CPCTC).

Contradiction: $\triangle ABC$ is scalene, it cannot have two congruent sides; therefore, indirect assumption is false: $\overline{AD}$ is not $\perp$ to $\overline{BC}$.

17. 1. $\triangle ABC$, $\overline{BC} \cong \overline{AC} \not\cong \overline{AB}$, $\overline{AD}$ bisects $\angle CAB$ (Given); 2. $\angle CAD = \angle BAD$ (Def. of $\angle$ bisector); 3. $AD \perp BC$ (Indirect assump.); 4. $\angle ADB$ and $\angle ADC$ are rt. $\angle$s (Def. of $\perp$); 5. $\angle ADB \cong \angle ADC$ (All rt. $\angle$s are $\cong$.); 6. $\overline{AD} \cong \overline{AD}$ (Congruence of segments is reflex.); 7. $\triangle ACD \cong \triangle ABD$ (Steps 2, 5, 6, and ASA); 8. $\overline{AC} \cong \overline{AB}$ (CPCTC).

Contradiction: This isosceles $\triangle$ is not equilateral, so the indirect assumption must be false. Hence, $\overline{AD}$ is not $\perp$ to $\overline{BC}$.

Written Exercises, Page 144, Lesson 5.3

19. Direct proof: 1. $\overline{RS} \cong \overline{RT}$ (Def. of isosceles $\triangle$); 2. $\overline{RY} \cong \overline{RY}$ (Congruence of segments is reflex.); 3.

$\overline{SY} \cong \overline{TY}$ (Def. of median); 4. $\triangle RYS = \triangle RYT$ (SSS); 5. $\angle RYS = \angle RYT$ (CPCTC); 6. $\angle RYS$ and $\angle RYT$ are rt. $\angle$s. (Theorem 3.4); 7. $\overline{RY} \perp \overline{ST}$ (Def. of $\perp$).

21. **Given:** Quadrilateral $ABCD$, $\overline{AC}$ bisects $\angle A$ and $\angle C$, $\overline{AC}$ and $\overline{BD}$ intersect at point E.
Prove: $\overline{AC}$ bisects $\overline{BD}$.
Direct proof: 1. $\triangle ABC \cong \triangle ADC$ (ASA); 2. $\overline{AB} \cong \overline{AD}$ (CPCTC); 3. $\triangle ABE = \triangle ADE$ (SAS); 4. $\overline{BE} \cong \overline{DE}$ (CPCTC); 5. $\overline{AC}$ bisects $\overline{BD}$ (Def. of bisector).

Written Exercises, Page 150, Lesson 5.4

35. Givens; Let B and D determine $\overleftrightarrow{BD}$ and let A and C determine $\overleftrightarrow{AC}$ by Post. 1; $\triangle ABD \cong \triangle DCA$ by SAS; $\overline{BD} = \overline{CA}$ by CPCTC; $\triangle BCD \cong \triangle CBA$ by SSS; $\angle ABC \cong \angle DCB$ by CPCTC.

37. (noncoplanar) Givens; W is in a different plane F by Postulate 7; let X and W determine $\overleftrightarrow{XW}$ by Post. 1; $\triangle XYW \cong \triangle XZW$ by SSS Theorem 4.5; $\angle XZW$ by CPCTC

Written Exercises, Page 190, Lesson 6.7

13. **Proof 1:** Congruent altitudes → isosceles triangle: The altitudes create two right triangles that are congruent by HL. Then the base angles of the larger triangle are congruent by CPCTC, and the triangle is isosceles by Theorem 4.4.

Proof 2: Isosceles triangle → congruent altitudes: If the triangle is isosceles, its base angles are congruent by Theorem 4.3. Then the triangles formed by the altitudes are congruent by SAA, and the altitudes are congruent by CPCTC.

Challenge, Page 215

16. **Given:** $\overline{PA} \perp E$ at A

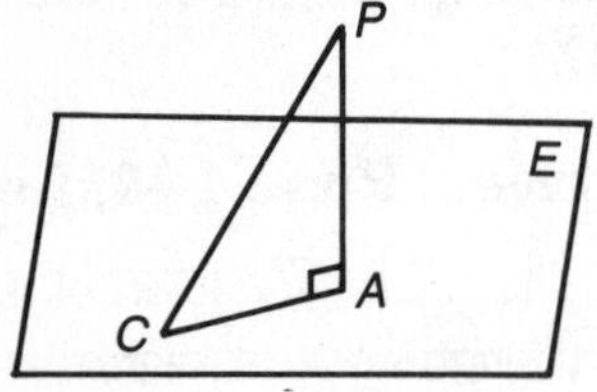

Prove: $PA < PC$ for any other point C in A
Proof: Assume $PA > PC$. This is impossible because $\overline{PA}$ is the leg of right $\triangle PAC$ (opposite an acute $\angle$) and $\overline{PC}$ is the hypotenuse (opposite the rt. $\angle$). By Theorem 6.5, the longer side of a triangle is opposite the larger angle.

Written Exercises, Page 238, Lesson 8.4

17. **Statement:** Two acute angles of a triangle are complementary if the triangle is a right triangle.

(1) Given: $\triangle ABC$, $m\angle A + m\angle B = 90$
Prove: $\triangle ABC$ is a right $\triangle$.
Proof: $m\angle A + m\angle B + m\angle C = 180$ (Thm. 8.13); $90 + m\angle C = 180$ (Substitution); $m\angle C = 90$ (subtraction); $\triangle ABC$ is a right $\triangle$ (Def. of right $\triangle$).
(2) Given: Right $\triangle ABC$, right $\angle$ at C
Prove: $m\angle A + m\angle B = 90$
Proof: $m\angle A + m\angle B + m\angle C = 180$ (Thm. 8.13); $m\angle C = 90$ (Def. of right $\angle$); $m\angle A + m\angle B = 90$ (Subtraction).

Written Exercises, Page 250, Lesson 8.6

19. Draw auxiliary line $\overline{DB}$ with midpoint K. In $\triangle ABD$, $\overline{PK}$ joins the midpoints of sides $\overline{AD}$ and $\overline{BD}$. By Thm. 8.22, $\overline{PK} \parallel \overline{AB}$ and $PK = \frac{1}{2}AB$. Likewise, in $\triangle CDB$, $\overline{QK} \parallel \overline{DC}$ and $QK = \frac{1}{2}DC$. Because $\overline{DC} \parallel \overline{AB}$, then by Thm. 8.11, $\overline{QK} \parallel \overline{AB}$. By the Parallel Postulate, Q, K, and P must be collinear. Therefore $\overline{PQ} \parallel \overline{AB} \parallel \overline{DC}$. Furthermore, since $PK = \frac{1}{2}AB$ and $QK = \frac{1}{2}DC$, and $PK + QK = PQ$, $PQ = \frac{1}{2}(AB + DC)$ by the Addition prop. of equality.

Written Exercises, Page 255, Lesson 8.7

15.

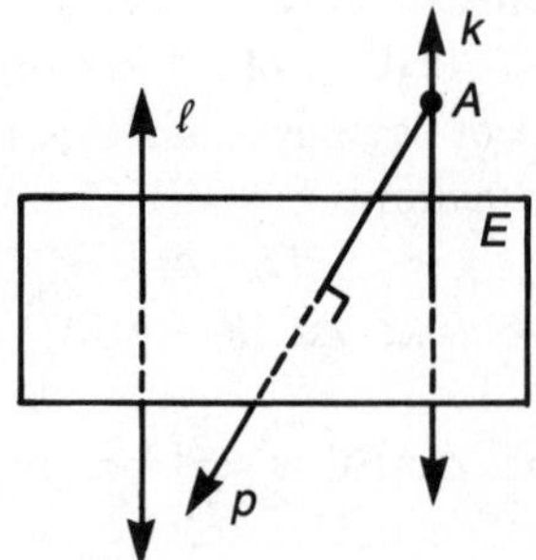

Given: lines l and k, plane E
$l \parallel k$, $l \parallel E$
Prove: $k \perp E$
Proof: Let p be a line perpendicular to E through any point A of k, by Theorem 7.10. Then by Theorem 8.30, $l \parallel p$. Hence, by the Parallel Postulate, k and p are the same line, so $k \perp E$.

Written Exercises, Page 255, Lesson 8.7

17. By Theorem 8.28, $\overline{PQ}$ and $\overline{RS}$ are each perpendicular to both E and F. By Theorem 8.30, $\overline{PQ} \parallel \overline{RS}$, so by Theorem 8.1, $\overline{PQ}$ and $\overline{RS}$ determine a plane G. By Theorem 8.27, $\overline{QR} \parallel \overline{PS}$. Therefore, $PQRS$ is a ▱. Because opposite sides of a ▱ are ≅ (Theorem 8.15), planes E and F are equidistant, and $PQ = RS$.

Written Exercises, Page 366, Lesson 11.3

1.

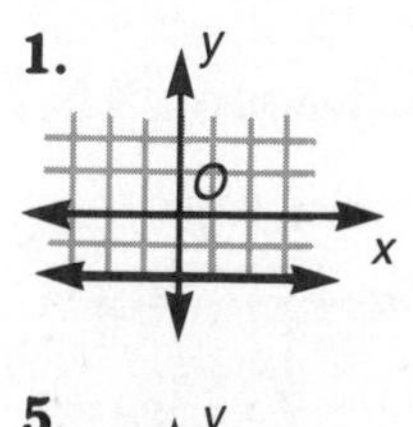

3.

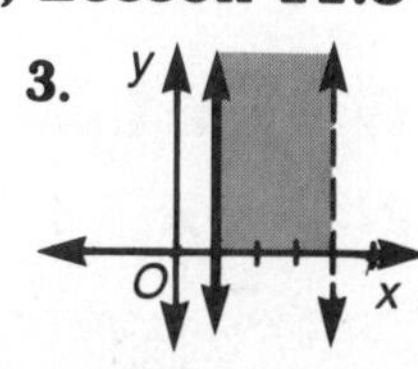

5.

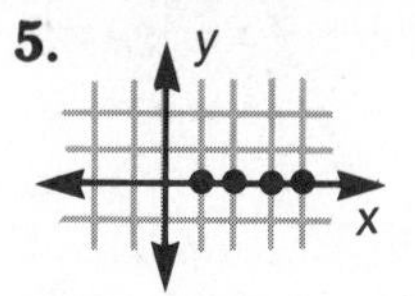

7.

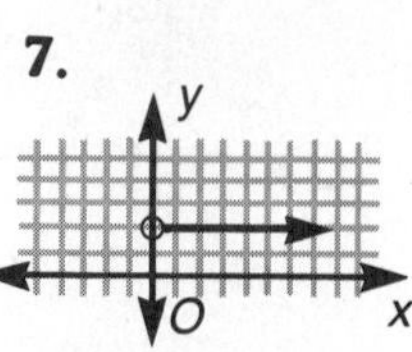

9.

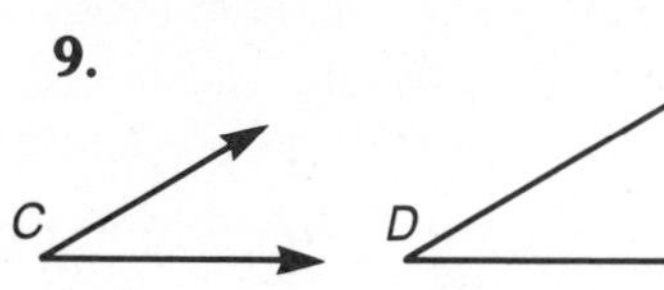

11.

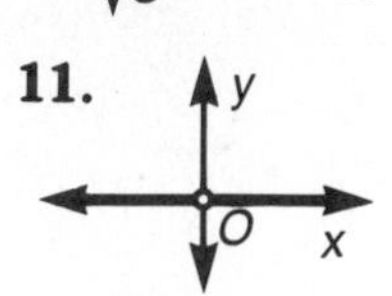

13.

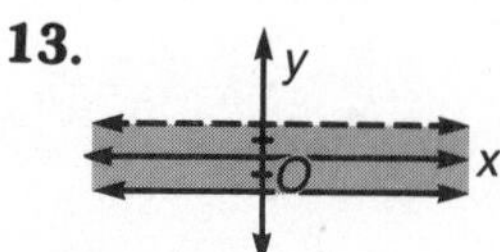

15.

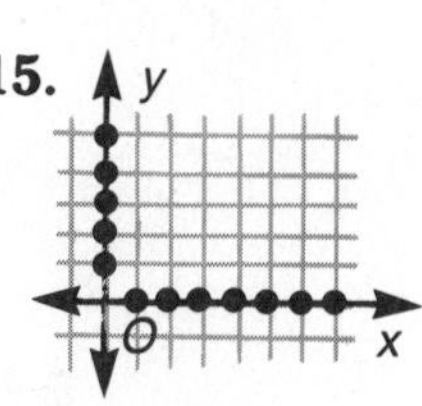

17.

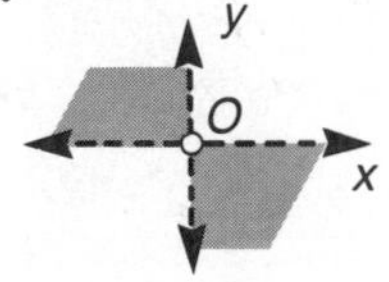

19.

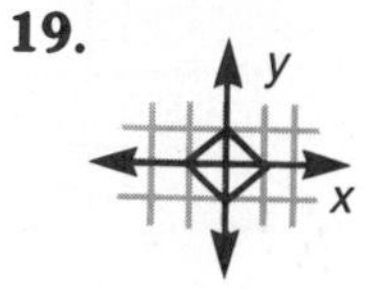

Written Exercises, Page 371, Lesson 11.8

17.

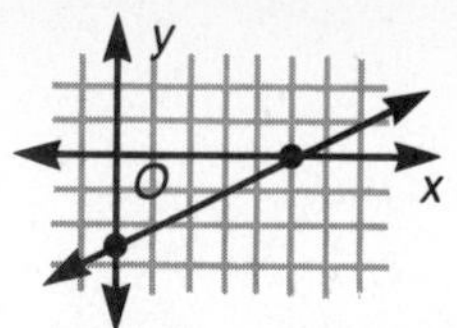

19.

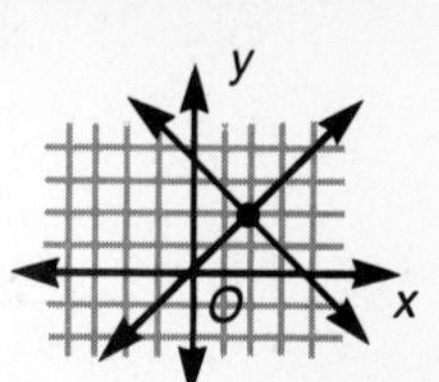

Written Exercises, Page 390, Lesson 12.2

27. *1.* $\overline{CD} \perp \overline{BC}$ (Given); *2.* $\overline{AB} \perp \overline{BC}$ (Cor. 12.2.1); *3.* $\overline{AB} \parallel \overline{CD}$ (2 lines ⊥ to the same line are ∥.); *4.* $\overline{BC} \perp \overline{CD}$ (Given); *5.* $\overline{AD} \perp \overline{CD}$ (Cor. 12.2.1); *6.* $\overline{AD} \parallel \overline{BC}$ (2 lines C to the same line are ∥); *7.* Quad. $ABCD$ is a ▱ (def. of ▱); *8.* ▱ $ABCD$ has 4 rt. ∠s def. of ⊥); *9.* ▱ $ABCD$ is a rectangle (Def. of a rectangle); *10.* $\overline{AB} \cong \overline{AD}$ (Radii of the same circle are ≅.); *11.* ▱ $ABCD$ is a rhombus (2 consecutive sides are ≅.); *12.* ▱ $ABCD$ is a square (Def. of square as both a rectangle and a rhombus)

Written Exercises, Page 416, Lesson 12.7

43.

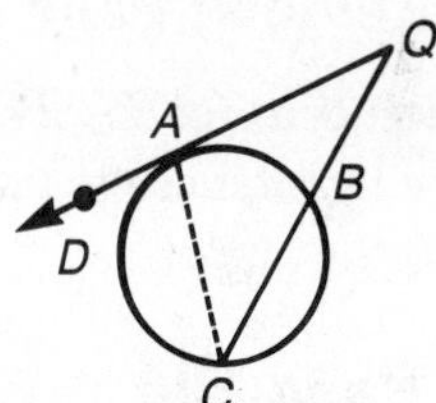

Tangent $\overline{QD}$ and secant $\overline{QC}$ intersect a circle as shown (given); Draw $\overline{AC}$; $m\angle Q + m\angle QAC + m\angle QCA = 180$;

$$\begin{aligned} m\angle Q &= 180 - m\angle QAC - m\angle QCA \\ &= m\angle DAC - m\angle QCA \\ &= \tfrac{1}{2}mAC - \tfrac{1}{2}mAB \\ &= \tfrac{1}{2}(mAC - mAB). \end{aligned}$$

6–8.

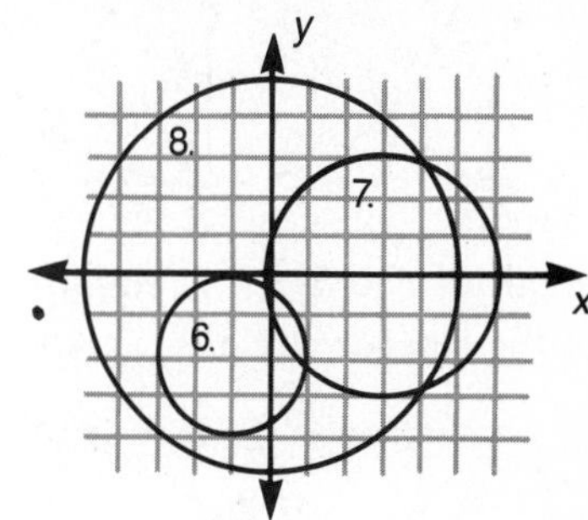

9–10.

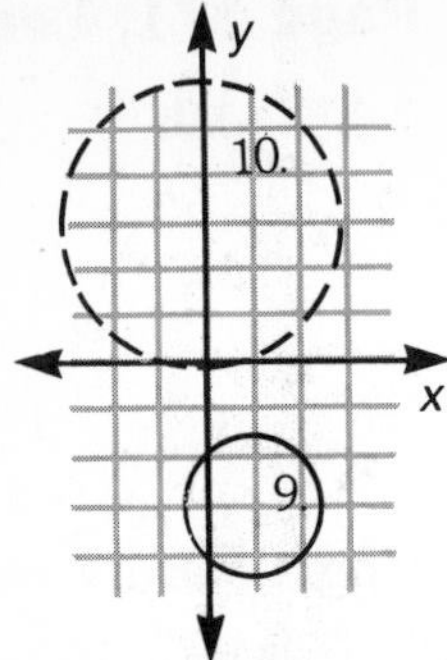

Written Exercises, Page 451, Lesson 13.4

17. Let r be the distance between 2 marks on the straightedge. Draw $\odot$ B with radius r intersecting the angle at A and C. Use the straightedge to locate P on $\overline{AB}$ such that $QP = r$, Q is on $\odot$ B, and $\overline{QP}$ passes through C. Then by the Ext. Angle Thm., $w = u + v = 2u$ (because $u = v$), $z = x + u = w + u$ (because $x = w$), so $z = 3u$. Thus, $m\angle CBA = 3m\angle P$. Copy $\angle P$ twice to trisect $\angle CBA$

Chapter 13, Review, Page 457

25. Follow construction for Ex. 24, but connect the endpoints of the hypotenuse to the intersection of its $\perp$ bisector and the circle.

Exploration, Page 504

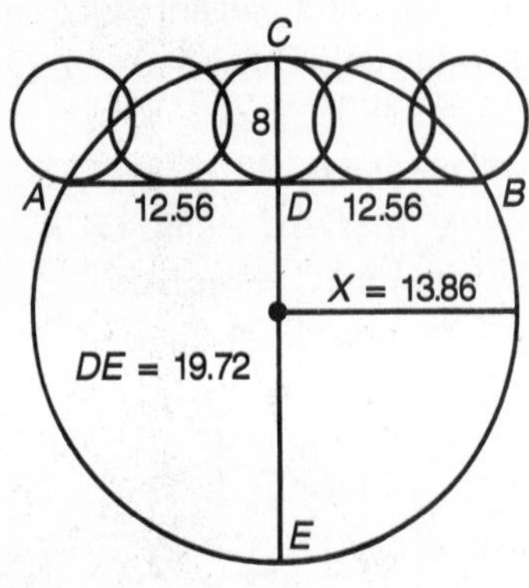

The length of chord $\overline{AB}$ is equal to the circumference of the smaller circle,

$$2\pi r = 2\pi 4 = 25.12$$

$\overline{CD}$ is the perpendicular bisector of chord $\overline{AB}$, so $AD = DB = \frac{1}{2}AB = 12.56$.
Since by Theorem 12.15, the product of the segments of intersecting chords within a circle are equal, assume some point E lies on the circle such that $AD \cdot DB = CD \cdot DE$. So,

$$\begin{aligned} DE &= \frac{12.56 \cdot 12.56}{8} \\ &= \frac{157.7536}{8} \\ &= 19.7192 \end{aligned}$$

Thus, the diameter of the circle $= CD + DE = 8 + 19.7192 = 27.7192$, which when halved gives a radius of 13.86. So,

$$\begin{aligned} A &= \pi r^2 \\ &= 3.14 \cdot 13.86^2 = 603.19 \end{aligned}$$

which is a 12:1 ratio thus the area of the smaller circle is 50.24.

Written Exercises, Page 516, Lesson 15.1

27.

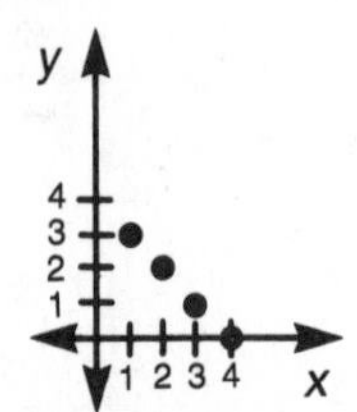

29.

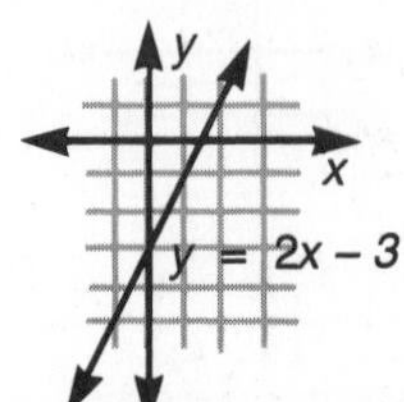

31.

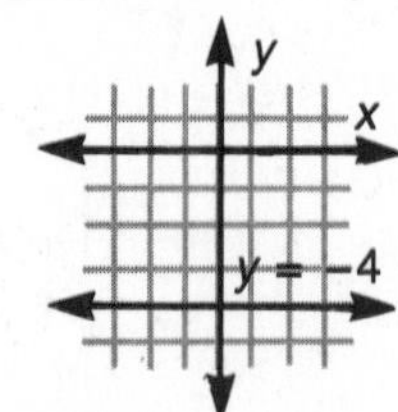

33.

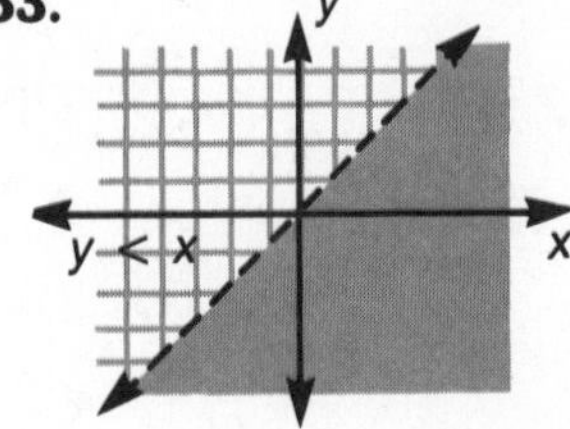

Written Exercises, Page 529, Lesson 15.4

13. 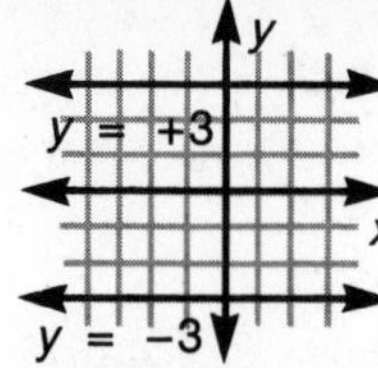

15. 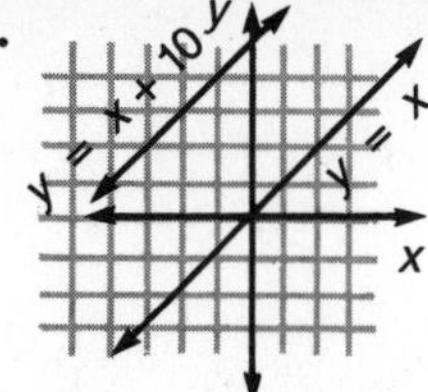

17. 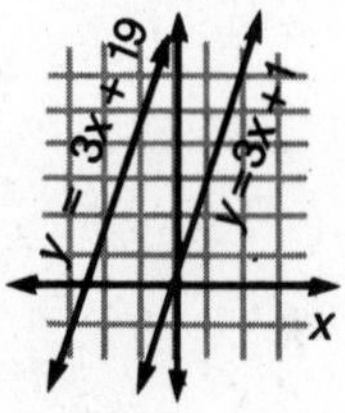

GEOMETRY

Kenneth J. Travers
Professor of
Mathematics Education
University of Illinois
Urbana, Illinois

LeRoy C. Dalton
Mathematics Area
Chairperson
Wauwatosa School District
Wauwatosa, Wisconsin

Katherine P. Layton
Mathematics Teacher
Beverly Hills High School
Beverly Hills, California

Laidlaw Brothers • Publishers
A Division of Doubleday & Company, Inc.
River Forest, Illinois

Sacramento, California • Chamblee, Georgia
Dallas, Texas • Toronto, Canada

ACKNOWLEDGMENTS

Development and Production by Educational Challenges, Inc., in cooperation with Laidlaw Brothers, Publishers.

Development Team: Laidlaw Brothers—Max V. Lyles and Mary Fraser
Educational Challenges, Inc.—David A. Keckler, Donald O. Buttermore, Deborah K. Nagy, and Nancy Estler.

Educator/ Contributors: Darlyn J. Counihan, Beverly J. Ferrucci, Cathy Graf, Michael R. Makynen, Ann Cate Miller, Thomas J. Moriarty Jr., James O'Donnell, Linda P. Rosen, John W. Totten, Pamela C. Walpole, and Rosabelle G. Wynn.

Design: Lynne C. Miller/Miller & Seper

Art Direction: Fred C. Pusterla

Educator/ Reviewers: Gerald T. Cowles—Oak Park and River Forest High School; Oak Park, Illinois
Arthur C. Dotterweich—School Board of Manatee County; Bradenton,, Florida
Ruth Ellen Doane, S.P.—Our Lady of the Westside Catholic School; Chicago, Illinois
Donna Gabanski—Homewood-Flossmoor High School; Flossmoor, Illinois
Robert Gyles—Community School District 4; New York, New York
George Levine—Nyack Public Schools; Nyack, New York
Deborah Neuman-Oak Park and River Forest High School; Oak Park, Illinois

---

ISBN 0-8445-1842-5

Printed in the United States of America
123456789 10 11 12 13 14 15 32109876

CONTENTS

1 Introduction to Geometry

2 Lines, Angles, Planes, and Space

3 Angles, Triangles, and Congruence

4 Congruent Triangles

5 Thinking and Proving

6 Inequalities in Geometry

7 Perpendicular Relationships

8 Parallels

9 Area and the Pythagorean Theorem

10 Similarity

11 Coordinate Geometry of the Plane

12 Circles and Spheres

13 Constructions

14 Area and Volume

15 Transformations

16 Trigonometry and Vectors

A Appendix

PHOTO CREDITS

Chapter Openers:

Chapter 1 Fred C. Pusterla

Chapter 2 Fred C. Pusterla

Chapter 3 Courtesy of National Aeronautics and Space Administration

Chapter 4 Fred C. Pusterla

Chapter 5 Don Carstens/Folio Inc.

Chapter 6 Fred C. Pusterla

Chapter 7 James Sawders-Cushing

Chapter 8 Courtesy of Sears Roebuck & Co.

Chapter 9 Tom Russoniello

Chapter 10 Educational Challenges Inc.

Chapter 11 The Smithsonian Institution

Chapter 12 D. A. Keckler

Chapter 13 Tom Russoniello

Chapter 14 Courtesy of American Airlines

Chapter 15 Courtesy of Consulate General of Japan, Chicago

Chapter 16 Courtesy of Pacific Gas & Electric Co.

Color Section:

p. A Brent Bear/West Light

p. B Shostal Associates

p. C (top) Shostal Associates; (bottom) John Gerlach/DRK Photo

p. D J. A. L. Cooke/Animals, Animals

p. E (top) Herbert Lanks/Shostal Associates; (background) H. Abernatly/H. Armstrong Roberts

p. F Wolfgang Hoyt/Esto Photographics Inc.

p. G (top) Adolph F. Rohrer/Shostal Associates; (bottom) James F. Pribble/Taurus; (background) Ed Cooper Photo

p. H Ed Cooper Photo

p. I J. Moss/H. Armstrong Roberts

p. J (top) John Curtis/Taurus; (background) Robert Frerck

p. K John Zoiner/Peter Arnold, Inc.

p. L (top) Frost Publishing Group, Ltd.; (bottom) Bill Barley/Shostal Associates

p. M Camerique

p. N Manfred Kage/Peter Arnold, Inc.

p. O Schecter Me Sun Lee/Esto Photographics

p. P (top) Jed Clark/Royce Bair & Associates; (bottom left) Graham Gund/Art Resource; (bottom right) Art Resource

Full-color section designed by Lynne C. Miller and Victor F. Seper, Jr./Miller & Seper

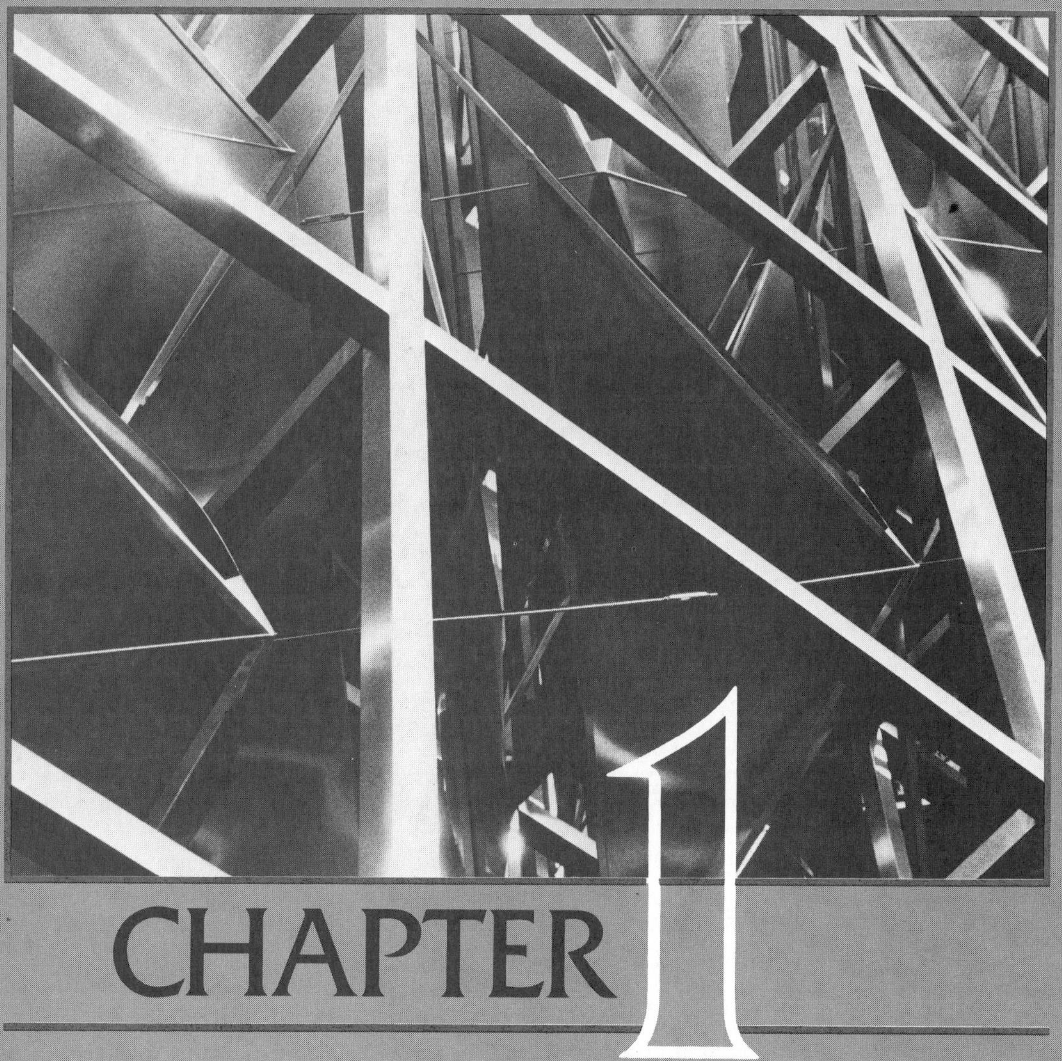

CHAPTER 1

Introduction to Geometry

OBJECTIVE

Name, describe, and draw models for points, lines, and planes.

TEACHER'S NOTES

See p. T24

MIXED REVIEW

1. Add $\frac{2}{7} + \frac{1}{5}$. $\frac{17}{35}$
2. Multiply $\frac{3}{4} \cdot \frac{16}{21}$. $\frac{4}{7}$
3. Divide $8 \div \frac{1}{2}$. 16
4. Solve $3x + 2 = 11$. $x = 3$
5. Multiply $a(b + c)$. $ab + ac$

TEACHER'S RESOURCE MASTERS

Practice Master 1, Part 1

1.1 Geometry and Problem Solving

Geometry is the study of the relationships among points, lines, angles, surfaces, and solids. Just as important, geometry is a mathematical system that uses logical reasoning, building upon known and accepted facts, to discover new properties.

Geometry is a science in which not only "the answer" is important, but also *how* and why you arrived at that answer.

With this text, you will start with a few undefined terms, add some definitions, and make a few assumptions. You will prove certain statements as true, and build upon these statements to prove even more statements. But there must be a starting place, and that is with three undefined terms: **point, line,** and **plane.**

A *point* is a place in space. It has no length, nor any thickness. A pinhole or a pencil dot can serve as a physical model. A point is represented with a dot that is labeled with a capital letter.

A *line* is a set of points with length but no width. A tightly stretched thread or one rail of a straight railroad track can serve as a physical model. A line is represented with arrowheads on each end to indicate that the line extends without end.

To name a line, you can pick any two points on the line, or you can use a lowercase letter. When you use two points, you list the two letters with a line symbol above them. The line shown above can be named $\overleftrightarrow{AB}$, $\overleftrightarrow{BA}$, $\overleftrightarrow{AC}$, or line *l*. Are there any other names for this same line? $\overleftrightarrow{AD}$, $\overleftrightarrow{BC}$, $\overleftrightarrow{BD}$, $\overleftrightarrow{CA}$, $\overleftrightarrow{CB}$, $\overleftrightarrow{CD}$, $\overleftrightarrow{DA}$, $\overleftrightarrow{DB}$, $\overleftrightarrow{DC}$

Now, think of the surface of a table top, and mentally extend that surface in all directions. That will give you the idea of a *plane*. It extends without end but has no thickness.

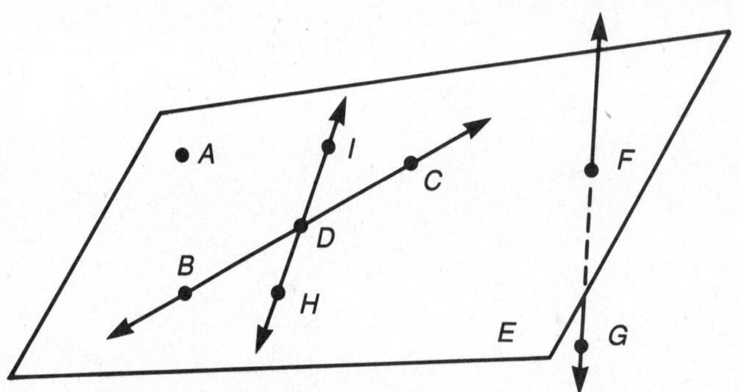

In the figure at the left, point *A* is "contained in," or "lies in," plane *E*. $\overleftrightarrow{BC}$ and $\overleftrightarrow{HI}$ "intersect" or pass through each other, at point *D*. $\overleftrightarrow{FG}$ intersects plane *E* at point *F*. Plane *E* contains points *A* and *F*, and $\overleftrightarrow{BC}$ and $\overleftrightarrow{HI}$. Notice that planes are also labeled with capital letters.

Remember that drawings are models and only represent the *concepts* of geometric figures. For example, when you let a pencil dot represent a point, the dot really "covers up" an infinite number of points, because the dot can never be small enough to be a perfect model. Lines and planes extend without end, so they are impossible to picture, too.

Based on the undefined terms, *point, line,* and *plane*, you will begin to use

Definitions—statements describing certain figures and conditions

Postulates—statements assumed to be true without proof

Theorems—statements proven on the basis of definitions, postulates, and previously proven theorems

ASSIGNMENT GUIDE

Minimum 1-14
Regular 1-18
Maximum 1-18

ORAL EXERCISES

1. The three undefined terms are _____, _____, and _____.
2. A line has _____, but no _____.
3. Drawings of points, lines, and planes are _____ that represent geometric _____.

Using objects in the classroom (walls, floor, thumbtacks, and so on), describe models for the following figures:

4. a point
5. a line
6. a plane
7. two lines that intersect
8. two lines that do not intersect
9. two planes that intersect
10. two planes that do not intersect
11. a plane and a line that intersect in only one point
12. a plane, and a line not on the plane

Oral Exercises

1. point, line, plane
2. length, width
3. models, concepts

4.-12. Answers will vary.

WRITTEN EXERCISES

A. Refer to the figure at the right for Exercises 1-15.

1. Another name for line l is _____.
2. Plane E (does or does not) contain $\overleftrightarrow{TY}$.
3. Point Q is contained in _____.
4. $\overleftrightarrow{AB}$ lies in both _____ and _____.

B.

5. The intersection of plane E and plane M is _____.
6. $\overleftrightarrow{TY}$ and line l intersect at _____.

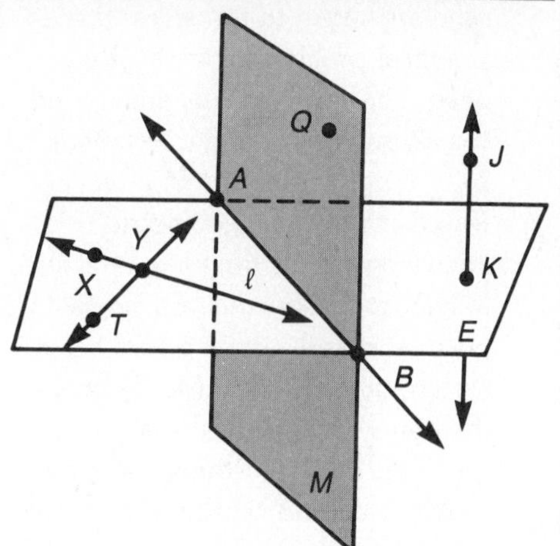

Written Exercises

1. $\overleftrightarrow{XY}$
2. does
3. plane M
4. plane M, plane E
5. $\overleftrightarrow{AB}$
6. point Y

7. plane E

8. no

9. yes

10. yes

11. no

12. They both lie in plane M.

13. one

14. an endless number

15.–18. Drawings will vary.

7. $\overleftrightarrow{JK}$ intersects ______.

8. Does $\overleftrightarrow{JK}$ intersect $\overleftrightarrow{AB}$?

9. Does $\overleftrightarrow{XY}$ intersect $\overleftrightarrow{AB}$?

10. Does plane M intersect $\overleftrightarrow{TY}$?

11. If a line were drawn through point T and Q, would $\overleftrightarrow{TQ}$ intersect $\overleftrightarrow{AB}$?

12. What do $\overleftrightarrow{AB}$ and point Q have in common?

13. How many labeled lines pass through point B?

14. How many lines *can* pass through point B?

C. Draw and label the following:

15. Line l intersects $\overleftrightarrow{AB}$ at point X.

16. $\overleftrightarrow{CD}$ contained in plane E.

17. Points, A, B, and C in plane E, and a point D not on the plane.

18. Three intersecting lines, $\overleftrightarrow{AT}$, $\overleftrightarrow{BT}$, and $\overleftrightarrow{TC}$.

MATH HERITAGE/Euclid

Geometry is perhaps the most enduring of the sciences. You may be surprised as you learn how much fine art, architecture, engineering, and many other arts and sciences rely on geometry. As long ago as 3000 B.C. the Sumerians used geometry to build temples. The early Egyptians used it to compute the amount of grain they could store in a bin of a given size and shape.

In the sixth century B.C. Greek scholars began to transform these practical problems into theoretical ones. The most famous among the Greek scholars was Euclid (about 300 B.C.), a mathematician and teacher who combined the geometric knowledge of his time into one system. In his book, *Elements,* Euclid listed postulates and axioms as his basic assumptions. From these he proved theorems, using logical reasoning. *Elements* has been the world's most widely used and reprinted textbook.

1.2 The Real Numbers

In geometry, **real numbers** are used to express size and distance. The real numbers are made up of the rational and the irrational numbers, which you have studied in algebra. A **rational number** is any number that can be written in the form $\frac{a}{b}$, where a and b are integers $(\ldots, -3, -2, -1, 0, 1, 2, 3, \ldots)$ and $b \neq 0$. You usually think of the rational numbers as fractions. Examples are $\frac{2}{3}$, $-\frac{1}{2}$, 6, 0, 1.4, -2.3, and $-5\frac{1}{2}$. The **irrational numbers** are those numbers that cannot be expressed as rational numbers. Examples are $\sqrt{2}$, $-\sqrt{5}$, π, and $\sqrt[3]{26}$.

Every real number is either a rational or an irrational number. The points on a line can be paired with the real numbers to form the real number line:

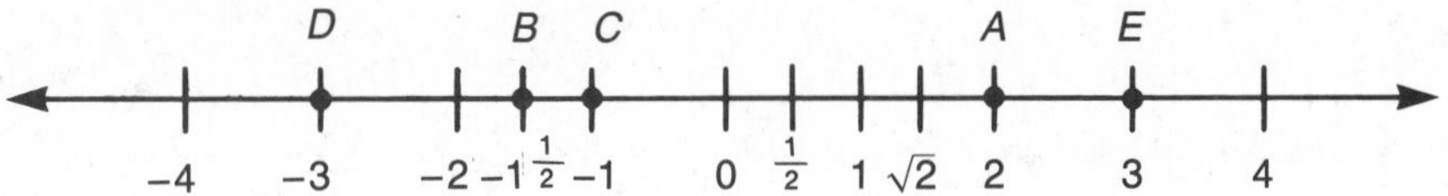

The number associated with each point on the line is called its **coordinate.** Therefore, the coordinate of A is 2 and the coordinate of B is $-1\frac{1}{2}$. What point is associated with -1? Are there any coordinates, identified or not identified in the figure, for which there are no points on the line? Are there any points on the line, identified or not identified in the figure, that do not have corresponding coordinates?

The following are some of the real number properties you studied in algebra [a, b, c, d and $e \in$ (is an element of) R, where $R =$ the set of real numbers]:

NAME	PROPERTY
Closure properties of addition and multiplication	$a + b$ is a real number $a \cdot b$ is a real number
Commutative properties of addition and multiplication	$a + b = b + a$ $a \cdot b = b \cdot a$
Associative properties of addition and multiplication	$(a + b) + c = a + (b + c)$ $(a \cdot b) \cdot c = a \cdot (b \cdot c)$
Identity property of addition	$a + 0 = a$
Identity property of multiplication	$a \cdot 1 = a$
Inverse property of addition	$a + (-a) = 0$
Multiplicative property of zero	$a \cdot 0 = 0$
Inverse property of multiplication	$a \cdot \frac{1}{a} = 1$

OBJECTIVE

Identify real numbers and their properties.

TEACHER'S NOTES

See p. T24

MIXED REVIEW

1. Add $\frac{3}{8} + \frac{1}{3}$. $\frac{17}{24}$
2. Find $\sqrt{400}$. 20
3. Subtract $16 - (-10)$. 26
4. Subtract $-16 - (-10)$. -6
5. Multiply $-8 \cdot (-4.2)$. 33.6

TEACHER'S RESOURCE MASTERS

Practice Master 1, Part 2

C

no

no

NAME	PROPERTY
Distributive property of multiplication over addition	$a \cdot (b + c) = (a \cdot b) + (a \cdot c)$
Reflexive property of equality	$a = a$
Symmetric property of equality	If $a = b$, then $b = a$
Transitive property of equality	If $a = b$ and $b = c$, then $a = c$
Substitution property	If $a = b$, then a may be substituted for b
Addition property of equality	If $a = b$, then $a + c = b + c$
Subtraction property	$a - b = a + (-b)$
Subtraction property of equality	If $a = b$, then $a - c = b - c$
Multiplication property of equality	If $a = b$, then $c \cdot a = c \cdot b$
Division property of equality	If $a = b$ and $c \neq 0$, then $\frac{a}{c} = \frac{b}{c}$

These properties can be used to solve equations in algebra. For example, solving the equation

$$4(3x + 2) = 32$$

involves the following steps:

STATEMENTS	REASONS
$4(3x + 2) = 32$	Given equation
$4(3x) + 4 \cdot 2 = 32$	Distributive property
$12x + 8 = 32$	Number fact
$12x + 8 + (-8) = 32 + (-8)$	Addition property of equality
$12x + 0 = 32 + (-8)$	Inverse property of addition
$12x = 32 + (-8)$	Identity property of addition
$12x = 24$	Number fact
$\frac{1}{12} \cdot 12x = \frac{1}{12} \cdot 24$	Multiplication property of equality
$(\frac{1}{12} \cdot 12)\, x = \frac{1}{12} \cdot 24$	Associative property of multiplication
$1 \cdot x = \frac{1}{12} \cdot 24$	Inverse property of multiplication
$x = \frac{1}{12} \cdot 24$	Identity property of multiplication
$x = 2$	Number fact

Showing all these steps may be cumbersome and unnecessary, but you can see how the properties are used to verify each step in solving an equation.

Two definitions from algebra are also necessary at this time:

Absolute value—
$|a| = a$ if $a \geq 0$, $|a| = -a$ if $a < 0$

The absolute value of a number is the distance of that number from zero on the number line.

$$|7| = 7 \qquad |-2| = 2 \qquad |0| = 0$$

Principal square root—
$\sqrt{a^2} = |a|$

The principal square root of a number is its positive square root. The radical sign ($\sqrt{\ }$) always indicates a positive number.

$$\sqrt{4} = 2 \qquad \sqrt{49} = 7 \qquad -\sqrt{25} = -5$$

Now suppose you wanted to prove some statement about the real numbers. For example, suppose you wanted to prove that the sum of two odd numbers is always an even number. You might try to justify this statement by testing some examples. This type of logical thinking, called **inductive reasoning,** would require you to continue to test examples. But since the set of odd numbers is infinite, this method is not useful here.

Deductive reasoning, a logical sequence of steps that are justified by postulates, theorems, and definitions, is the process usually employed to prove mathetical statements. Before applying deductive reasoning to the problem of summing two odd numbers, two more specific definitions are needed:

Even number—any number that can be expressed as $2x$, where x is an integer.

Odd number—any number that can be expressed as $2x + 1$, where x is an integer.

Now you can restate the problem using variables for the numbers.

Given: $2a + 1$ and $2b + 1$ are any two odd numbers and $(2a + 1) + (2b + 1) = c$

Prove: c is an even number

Proof:

STATEMENTS	REASONS
1. $(2a + 1) + (2b + 1) = c$	1. Given
2. $(2a + 1) + (1 + 2b) = c$	2. Commutative property of addition
3. $2a + (1 + 1) + 2b = c$	3. Associative property of addition
4. $2a + 2 + 2b = c$	4. Number fact
5. $2(a + 1 + b) = c$	5. Distributive property
6. c is even	6. Closure property of addition and definition of even numbers

The above example is a simple **two-column proof,** in which statements are made in one column and justified in the other, using *deductive reasoning.* Remember, inductive reasoning, or seeing a trend through many examples, does not "prove" many statements *true.* To prove a statement is *false,* however, you need only one false example.

ORAL EXERCISES

Tell whether each of the following statements is true or false.

1. A number written in the form $\frac{a}{b}$, where a and b are integers and $b \neq 0$, is a rational number.
2. $\sqrt{3}$ is an example of a rational number
3. -5.8 is an example of a rational number
4. Every point of a number line has a coordinate.
5. $-7 = -7$
6. $-\sqrt{9} = -3$
7. $4 \cdot \frac{1}{4} = 2$
8. $12 \cdot 0 = 12$
9. $(7 + 3) \cdot 2 = 14 + 6$
10. $|-8| = -2 \cdot -4$
11. $(12 \cdot 13) \cdot 14 = 12 \cdot (13 \cdot 14)$
12. $\sqrt{2} + 7\frac{5}{8}$ is a real number.
13. The distance between $|-7|$ and $|3|$ is 10.
14. $\sqrt{81} = 9$
15. $-\sqrt{36} = 6$
16. $-\sqrt{25} + \sqrt{25} = 0$

WRITTEN EXERCISES

A. State the properties demonstrated in Exercises 1–16.

1. $6 + a$ is a real number.
2. $4 + a = a + 4$
3. $4a + 5a = (4 + 5)a$
4. $6 = 6 \cdot 1$
5. If $x = 3$, then $3 = x$
6. $15 \cdot (3 \cdot x) = (15 \cdot 3) \cdot x$
7. If $x - 2 = 4$, then $x - 2 + 2 = 4 + 2$
8. If $5y = 10$, then $y = 2$

B.

9. $(6x + 5) + 0 = 6x + 5$
10. $x \cdot 3y = 3y \cdot x$
11. $3 + 5 + x = 5 + x + 3$
12. If $x = 5$ and $5 = y$, then $x = y$
13. $(6x - 1) \cdot \frac{1}{(6x - 1)} = 1$
14. $2(6 + x) = 2(x + 6)$
15. $219 \cdot 6 \cdot x \cdot 0 \cdot 24 \cdot 18 = 0$
16. $-65 + 65 = 0$

Solve for x in each of the following open sentences.

17. $|x| > 11$
18. $|x - 2| = 7$
19. $|x + 5| = 3$
20. $|x + 4| > 5$
21. $|x \cdot 1| = 12$
22. $|x - 2| < 6$

Find each square root.

23. $\sqrt{169}$
24. $\sqrt{\frac{16}{49}}$
25. $\sqrt{\frac{1}{16}}$

ASSIGNMENT GUIDE

Minimum 1-27 odd
Regular 1-27 odd, 29-38
Maximum 1-27 odd, 29-40

Oral Exercises

1. T 2. F 3. T 4. T
5. T 6. T 7. F 8. F
9. T 10. T 11. T 12. T
13. F 14. T 15. F 16. T

Written Exercises

1. closure property of addition
2. commutative property of addition
3. distributive property
4. identity property of multiplication
5. symmetric property of equality
6. associative property of multiplication
7. addition property of equality
8. division property of equality
9. identity property of addition
10. commutative property of multiplication
11. commutative property of addition
12. transitive property of equality
13. inverse property of multiplication
14. commutative property of addition
15. multiplication property of zero
16. inverse property of addition
17. $x > 11$ or $x < -11$
18. $x = -5$ or $x = 9$
19. $x = -2$ or $x = -8$
20. $x < -9$ or $x > 1$

26. $-\sqrt{64}$ **27.** $\sqrt{8^2}$ **28.** $\sqrt{4^3}$

Supply the reasons for each statement in the following proof.

Given: $3x + 7 = 16$

Prove: $x = 3$

Proof:

STATEMENTS	REASONS
1. $3x + 7 = 16$	1. Given
2. $(3x + 7) + (-7) = 16 + (-7)$	2. **29.**
3. $3x + [7 + (-7)] = 16 + (-7)$	3. **30.**
4. $3x + 0 = 16 + (-7)$	4. **31.**
5. $3x = 16 + (-7)$	5. **32.**
6. $3x = 9$	6. **33.**
7. $\frac{1}{3}(3x) = \frac{1}{3}(9)$	7. **34.**
8. $(\frac{1}{3} \cdot 3)\, x = \frac{1}{3}(9)$	8. **35.**
9. $1x = \frac{1}{3}(9)$	9. **36.**
10. $x = \frac{1}{3}(9)$	10. **37.**
11. $x = 3$	11. **38.**

C. 39. Prove that the product of two odd numbers is an odd number. (HINT: Express an odd number as $2x + 1$.)

40. Use the following facts to find the coordinates for points A, B, C, D, and E on the number line below, represented by a, b, c, d, and e, respectively.

$$e \cdot b = 0$$
$$|a| = d$$
$$\sqrt{c^2} = \frac{1}{2}d$$
$$d - e = a$$
$$e = \sqrt{64} - b$$
$$a < 0$$
$$c^3 = e$$

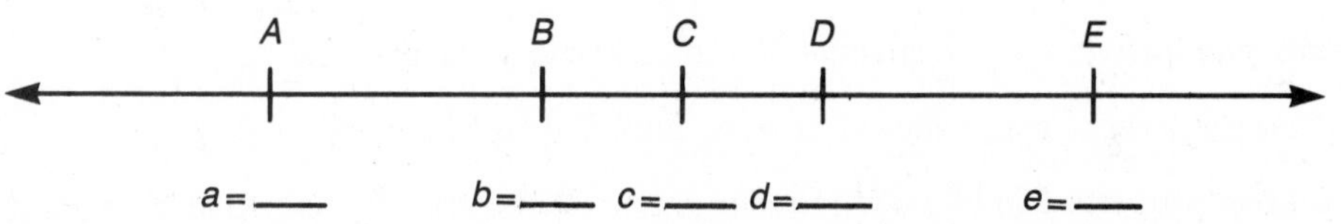

21. $x = 12$ or $x = -12$
22. $-4 < x < 8$
23. 13 24. $\frac{4}{7}$
25. $\frac{1}{4}$
26. -8 27. 8 28. 8
29. addition property of equality
30. associative property of addition
31. inverse property of addition
32. identity property of addition
33. number fact
34. multiplication property of equality
35. associative property of multiplication
36. inverse property of multiplication
37. identity property of multiplication
38. number fact

39. $(2x + 1) \cdot (2y + 1)$ $= 4xy + 2(x + y) + 1$ $= 2(2xy + x + y) + 1$ $= 2x + 1$ (definition of an odd number)

40. $a = -4$
$b = 0$
$c = 2$
$d = 4$
$e = 8$

OBJECTIVES

Use the definitions of $>$ and $<$ to complete an inequality.

Identify the properties of inequalities.

TEACHER'S NOTES

See p. T24

MIXED REVIEW

1. Solve $3x + 2(4 - x) = 12$. $x = 4$
2. Solve $4x - 8 = 12 - x$. $x = 4$
3. Find $\sqrt{196}$. 14
4. Find $\sqrt{1444}$. 38
5. Divide $\frac{7}{8} \div \frac{1}{4}$. $3\frac{1}{2}$

TEACHER'S RESOURCE MASTERS

Practice Master 2, Part 1

1.3 Real Number Relationships

A new real number property you will use is the **trichotomy property,** which claims that for any two real numbers, x and y, exactly one of the following is true:

$$x = y \ (x \text{ equals } y),$$
$$x > y \ (x \text{ is greater than } y),$$
$$\text{or } x < y \ (x \text{ is less than } y).$$

The statement $x < y$ means x lies to the left of y on the number line. You can reverse this statement and declare $y > x$, meaning y lies to the right of x. This gives a geometric picture for an algebraic concept. The symbols "$<$" and "$>$" mean "is not less than" and "is not greater than."

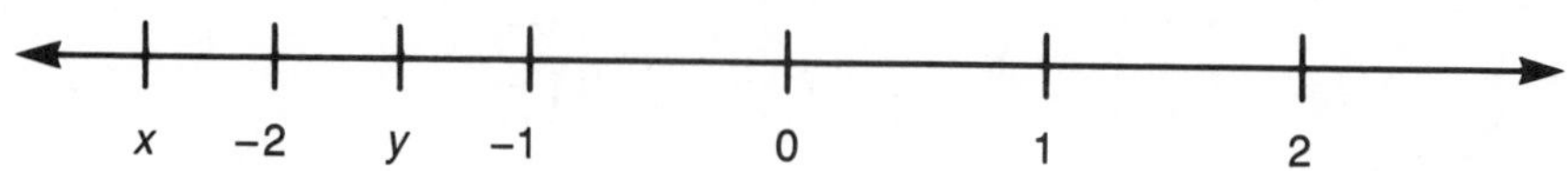

You can see that any negative number is less than any positive number, because on the number line the negative numbers are to the left of the positive numbers. The statement $-10 < 2$ is true since -10 is to the left of 2. A compound statement, such as $x \leq y$, is read "x is less than or equal to y." Expressions using $<$ or $>$ are called **order relations** or **inequalities.** Here are some examples of inequalities represented graphically:

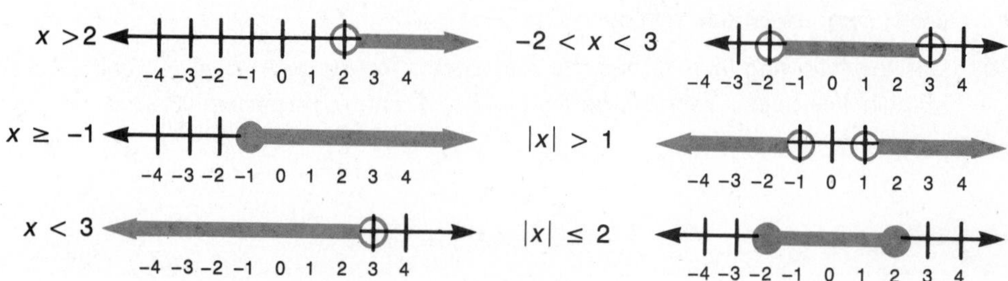

Inequalities also have several fundamental properties:

Transitive property of inequality—If $x < y$ and $y < z$, then $x < z$.

Multiplication property of inequality—If $x < y$ and $a > 0$, then $ax < ay$.

Addition property of inequality—If $x < y$, then $x + a < y + a$.

The transitive property can be used to make the addition property of inequality more useful:

Given: $x < y$ and $a < b$

Prove: $x + a < y + b$

Proof:

STATEMENTS	REASONS
1. $x < y$	1. Given
2. $x + a < y + a$	2. Addition property of inequality
3. $a < b$	3. Given
4. $a + y < b + y$	4. Addition property of inequality
5. $y + a < y + b$	5. Commutative property of addition
6. $x + a < y + b$	6. Transitive property, steps 2 and 5

Therefore, the addition property may be restated as follows: If $x < y$ and $a < b$, then $x + a < y + b$ (letting you add inequalities the same way you add equations).

The relation "=" has three properties that make it an **equivalence relation.** The three properties are the **reflexive property** ($a = a$), the **symmetric property** (if $a = b$, then $b = a$), and the **transitive property** (if $a = b$, and $b = c$, then $a = c$). Any relationship possessing these three properties is called an equivalence relation.

ASSIGNMENT GUIDE

Minimum 1-23
Regular 1-33 odd
Maximum 1-25 odd, 26-33

ORAL EXERCISES

Indicate whether each statement is true or false for every value of x and y.

1. $-x \leq 0$

2. $\sqrt{x}$ is always positive.

3. $\sqrt{x}$ is always nonnegative.

4. $\sqrt{x^2} = |x|$

5. $\sqrt{x^2} = x$

6. $|x - y| = |y - x|$

7. $|x| - |y| \geq |x - y|$

8. $|xy| \geq |x| \cdot |y|$

Oral Exercises

1. F 2. F
3. T 4. T
5. F 6. T
7. F 8. T

WRITTEN EXERCISES

A. State the property that is demonstrated or makes the statement true.

1. If $5 < 9$, then $10 < 18$.

2. If $-6 < 5$, and $5 < 14$, then $-6 < 14$.

3. If $x > 2$, and $-4 > -9$, then $x + (-4) > -7$.

4. If $x < -2$, then $x \neq -2$.

5. $x = x$

6. Name the three properties of an equivalence relation.

Written Exercises

1. multiplication property of inequality
2. transitive prop. of inequality
3. addition property of inequality
4. trichotomy property
5. reflexive prop. of inequality
6. reflexive, symmetric, transitive

7. $<$ 8. $>$
9. $=$ 10. $\leq$
11. $\geq$ 12. $\geq$
13. $=$ 14. $>$
15. $\leq$ 16. $=$

17. no, reflexive, symmetric
18. no, symmetric
19. no, reflexive
20. no, reflexive, symmetric
21. 13
22. 3
23. 15
24. -18
25. 0
26. -55
27. Answers will vary.

28.
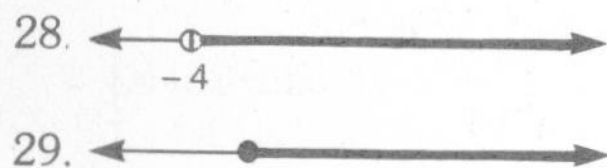

29.

30.
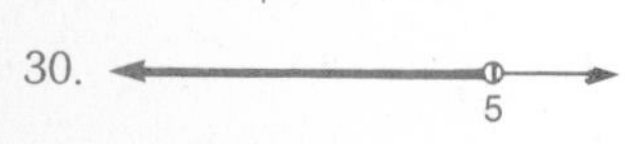

31. -1 4

32. -2 2

33. -1 1

Error Search

1. $3 \cdot (5 + 7) = (3 \cdot 5) + (3 \cdot 7) = 36$
2. $|a + b| = |a + b|$
3. $\sqrt{4} \cdot 4^2 = \frac{4^3}{\sqrt{4}}$
4. $4x^2 - 3x^2 \geq \sqrt{x^2}$ allowing for the cases $x = 1$, or 0.
5. $\sqrt{\frac{1}{2}} + \sqrt{\frac{1}{3}} > \sqrt{\frac{1}{4}} + \sqrt{\frac{1}{5}}$
6. $7\,(4 \cdot \sqrt{\frac{1}{4}}) = \sqrt{\frac{1}{4}}\,(7 \cdot 4)$

B. Replace the circle with $<$, $>$, $\leq$, $\geq$, or $=$ to make each statement true.

7. $3(2 + 7)$ ● 28

8. 120 ● $(5 + 6 \cdot 3) + 2 + 15 \cdot 4$

9. $8 + 9 \cdot 3 - 8 + 1$ ● 28

10. 0 ● $\sqrt{x}$

11. $|x|$ ● 0

12. x^2 ● 0

13. $|6 - 8|$ ● $|8 - 6|$

14. $|8| - |6|$ ● $|6| - |8|$

15. $-\sqrt{x}$ ● 0

16. 4_2 ● $4 \cdot 4$

Determine which of the following are equivalence relations. If any are not, state the property that does not hold.

17. is less than

18. is greater than or equal to

19. is a reciprocal of

20. is a brother to

Simplify the following expressions:

21. $\sqrt{169}$

22. $-\sqrt{144} + |-15|$

23. $|-\sqrt{36} - \sqrt{81}|$

24. $-\sqrt{121} - |-\sqrt{49}|$

25. $|2 + (-2)|$

26. $-5 \cdot |2 - 13|$

C. 27. Show that for the set of human beings the relation "has the same color eyes as" is an equivalence relation. (HINT: The fact that you have the same color eyes as yourself shows the reflexive property.)

Graph each of the following.

28. $x > -4$

29. $-1 \leq x$

30. $x < 5$

31. $-1 < x < 4$

32. $|x| \geq 2$

33. $|x| < 1$

ERROR SEARCH

Correct the error in each exercise.

1. $3 \cdot (5 + 7) = (3 \cdot 5) + 7 = 36$

2. $|a + b| = |a| + |b|$

3. $\sqrt{4} \cdot 4^2 > \frac{4^3}{\sqrt{4}}$

4. $4x^2 - 3x^3 > \sqrt{x^2}$

5. $\sqrt{\frac{1}{2}} + \sqrt{\frac{1}{3}} < \sqrt{\frac{1}{4}} + \sqrt{\frac{1}{5}}$

6. $7\,(4 \cdot \sqrt{\frac{1}{4}}) < \sqrt{\frac{1}{4}}\,(7 \cdot 4)$

1.4 Logic in Mathematics

In an effort to make the study of geometry more orderly and concise, this lesson introduces some formal logic terms and techniques that will be used in later chapters.

Any statement that can be written in "if—then" form is called an **implication,** or a **conditional statement.** For example, "If it is raining, then I will get wet" is an implication. The statement "Water freezes below 0°C" can be made into an implication by saying, "If the temperature is below 0°C, then water will freeze." The part that follows "if" is called the **hypothesis,** and the statement that follows "then" is called the **conclusion.** In the first example, "it is raining" is the hypothesis, and the conclusion is "I will get wet."

Now, let A be "it is raining," and let B be "I will get wet." The English sentence transforms into *If A then B.* An implication symbol ($\rightarrow$) can be used to abbreviate this to the even shorter expression $A \rightarrow B$. The notation $A \rightarrow B$ can be read in many ways: "A implies B," "if A then B," "B if A," "B follows from A," or "A only if B."

Let C be "$x = 4$" and D be "$x^2 = 16$." $C \rightarrow D$ now translates to "If $x = 4$, then $x^2 = 16$," which is a true statement. Interchanging the hypothesis and the conclusion forms the **converse,** $D \rightarrow C$, creating the new statement "If $x^2 = 16$, then $x = 4$." As you can see, the converse may be false even though the original implication is true. If $x^2 = 16$, x could be either 4 or -4. To prove a statement is false, you need show only one contradiction. The converse of a true statement may be true or false. A statement and its converse must be proven *separately.* Can you think of an implication that is true and has a true converse?

Consider the following implication and its converse:

If $a \geq 0$, then $|a| = a$.
If $|a| = a$, then $a \geq 0$.

Since both of these statements are true, they can be combined into one compound statement, called a **biconditional,** that claims "$|a| = a$ if and only if $a \geq 0$." You may use the abbreviation **iff** for "if and only if." The statement "Today is Wednesday iff tomorrow is Thursday" is actually two statements in one:

If today is Wednesday, then tomorrow is Thursday, and
If tomorrow is Thursday, then today is Wednesday.

Every definition is a biconditional and can be written in iff form, making it two implications in one statement. For example, the definition of a right triangle as a triangle that contains a right angle yields both of the following statements:

If a triangle is right, then it has a right angle, and
If a triangle has a right angle, then it is a right triangle.

OBJECTIVE

Given an implication, give its converse and biconditional statements and determine whether given statements are true or false.

TEACHER'S NOTES

See p. T24

MIXED REVIEW

1. Solve $3x - 2 < 4$. $x < 2$
2. Simplify $|-8 - (-3)|$. 5
3. Find $-\sqrt{169}$. -13
4. Solve $|x| = 2$. $\{2, -2\}$
5. Subtract $\frac{1}{2} - \frac{1}{3}$. $\frac{1}{6}$

TEACHER'S RESOURCE MASTERS

Practice Master 2, Part 2
Quiz 1

ASSIGNMENT GUIDE

Minimum 1-27 odd
Regular 1-31 odd
Maximum 1-25 odd, 26-31

Oral Exercises

1. implications
2. hypothesis, conclusion
3. converse
4. true or false
5. one
6. if and only if (iff)
7. two
8. truth tables

Written Exercises

1-10. The hypothesis follows "if", the conclusion follows "then." Reversing the two forms the converse.

1. T, F
2. F, F
3. T, F
4. T, F
5. F, T
6. T, F
7. T, F
8. T, T
9. T, F
10. T, T

11.-14. Answers will vary.

Examples:

11. If today is Monday, then tomorrow is Tuesday.
12. If the sun is visible, then it is daytime.
13. If April follows May, then Memorial Day follows April Fool's Day.
14. If water can be poured into a glass, then the glass is empty.

Logicians make charts called **truth tables** to determine the truth or falsity of compound statements. The table at the right shows that the compound statement *A* and *B* is true if *both A* and *B* are true. The truth table for *A or B* is as follows:

A	*B*	*A* and *B*
T	T	T
T	F	F
F	T	F
F	F	F

A	*B*	*A* or *B*
T	T	T
T	F	T
F	T	T
F	F	F

If either *A* or *B* is true, then the compound statement *A or B* is true. Try substituting some English phrases for *A* and *B* to verify for yourself that the table is valid.

ORAL EXERCISES

1. If—then statements ($A \rightarrow B$) are called _____.

2. In an if—then statement, the _____ follows "if," and the _____ follows "then."

3. Interchanging the hypothesis and the conclusion ($B \rightarrow A$) forms the _____.

4. The converse of a statement may be _____. It must be proved on its own.

5. To prove that a statement is false, you need show only _____ false example.

6. A true statement with a true converse can be written as a biconditional using _____.

7. A biconditional statement has _____ implications.

8. _____ may be used to decide if a compound statement is true or false.

WRITTEN EXERCISES

A. Copy each of the following implications and: a) label the hypothesis and the conclusion; b) determine whether the implication is true or false; c) write the converse; and d) determine if the converse is true or false.

1. If today is Saturday, then there is no school.

2. If the air conditioner is on, then it is summer.

3. If you rode the bus to school, then you didn't drive there.

4. If $x = 3$, then $x^2 = 9$.

5. If $|x| = 7$, then $x = 7$.

6. If you live in Virginia, then you live in the United States.

7. All integers are real numbers. (HINT: Convert the definition to if—then form first.)

8. If x^2 is an odd number, then x is an odd number.

9. A square is a rectangle.

10. $3x + 7 = 13 \rightarrow x = 2$.

B. Give an example of each of the following:

11. A true implication with a true converse.

12. A true implication with a false converse.

13. A false implication with a false converse.

14. A false implication with a true converse.

Change each statement to if—then form, adding your own words where needed to make sense. The new statement may be false.

15. All snakes lay eggs.

16. There are four periods of play in a basketball game.

17. Permanent-press shirts do not need ironing.

18. All microwave ovens cook by a timer.

19. The postal service returned the letter because of insufficient postage.

20. Coffee contains caffeine.

21. Fillet of fish is on Wednesday's menu.

22. Brazilians speak Portuguese.

23. After every home game we have a dance.

24. $\sqrt{2}$ is an irrational number.

25. Prime numbers are only divisible by themselves and 1.

Combine the following implications using iff:

26. If points lie on the same line, then they are collinear.
If points are collinear, then they lie on the same line.

27. If $x \geq 0$, then $|x| = x$.
If $|x| = x$, then $x \geq 0$.

C. Prove that the following statements are false:

28. To complete a telephone call, you must dial at least seven numbers.

29. A square house cannot be located so that every side has a northern exposure.

30. Two identical twins cannot have different birthdays.

31. A person who lives in Texas cannot get up at 7:00 A.M., eat breakfast, and arrive at work in New Mexico by 7:01 A.M. the same day.

15. If an animal is a snake, then it lays eggs.

16. If a game has four periods of play, then the game is basketball.

17. If a shirt is permanent-press, then it does not need ironing.

18. If an oven is a microwave, then it cooks by a timer.

19. If the postal service returns a letter, then it has insufficient postage.

20. If a beverage is coffee, then it contains caffeine.

21. If fillet of fish is on the menu, then it must be Wednesday.

22. If a person is Brazilian, then that person speaks Portuguese.

23. If there is a home game, then we will have a dance afterward.

24. If a number is $\sqrt{2}$, then that number is irrational.

25. If a number is prime, then that number is only divisible by itself and the number 1.

26. Points are collinear iff they lie on the same line.

27. $|x| = x$ iff $x \geq 0$

28. You may dial "0" for the operator, "911" for emergency, etc.

29. A house located at the south pole would have four sides facing the north.

30. One twin could be born at 11:59 P.M. of one day, and the second at 12:01 A.M. the next day, two minutes apart.

31. A person who lives on one side of the Texas/New Mexico border and works on the other crosses into another time zone.

Self-Quiz

1. point, line, plane
2. $\overleftrightarrow{EG}$, $\overleftrightarrow{GE}$
3. a plane
4. positive square root
5. coordinate
6. 14
7. −7
8. 3
9. −24
10. trichotomy
11. 

12. reflexive, symmetric, transitive
13. February has 28 days iff it is not a leap year.

Challenge

1. If a number is rational, then it is an integer.
   Implication: T
   Converse: F
2. If a number is irrational, then it is a fraction.
   Implication. F
   Converse: F
3. If the inverse property of mult. holds, the numbers are rational.
   Implication: T
   Converse: F
4. If an equation involves only integers, the substitution property can be applied.
   Implication: F
   Connverse: T

SELF-QUIZ

1. Name the three undefined terms of geometry.

2. Give two different names for this line: 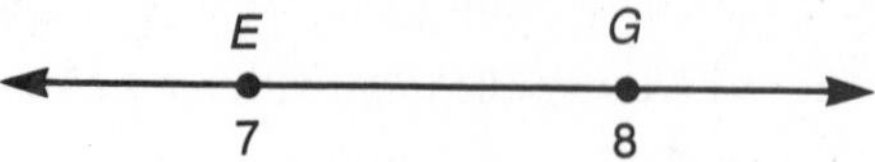

3. The ceiling of a room could be a physical model for what geometric figure?

4. The principal square root of a number is its _____.

5. The number of a labeled point on a number line is that point's _____.

Simplify the expressions in Exercises 10–13.

6. $\sqrt{196}$

7. $-\sqrt{225} + |-8|$

8. $|-5 - (-2)|$

9. $-4 \cdot \sqrt{36}$

10. The _____ property claims that for any two real numbers, x and y, $x = y$, $x > y$, or $x < y$.

11. Graph $x \leq -1$ on a number line.

12. Name the three properties that make up an equivalence relation.

Give the biconditional for the following pair of statements:

13. If February has 28 days, then it is not a leap year.
If it is not a leap year, then February has 28 days.

CHALLENGE

For each statement below, state the converse and determine whether the original statement and the converse are true or false.

1. Integers are rational numbers.

2. Fractions are irrational numbers.

3. Rational numbers obey the inverse property of multiplication.

4. If the substitution property can be applied, then the equation involves only integers.

1.5 Measuring Distance

Previously in this chapter, you learned how important it is for geometry to be logically organized, with established definitions and properties that lead to new ones. This might lead you to think that *every* statement or property used should first be proved. This is not always possible. You know that proofs of new properties, or *theorems,* are based on those already proved. But what about the very first theorem? Like the undefined terms you learned in the first lesson, a starting point is needed as a basis for the theorems. Thus, in geometry, some statements, called *postulates,* are accepted without proof. Postulates lead to theorems, which in turn lead to more theorems.

It is important to realize that postulates serve as the foundation of geometry, the "rules of the game." In volleyball or chess, everyone who plays must agree on the same set of rules, or arguments will result. In geometry, everyone must accept a common set of postulates, or they will reach different conclusions.

Have you ever watched a carpenter "snap a chalk line" on a floor or roof? To make a straight line joining two points that are far apart, a carpenter will stretch a chalked string tightly between the two points, raise the string slightly in the middle, then allow it to snap back against the surface. If done properly, a long, visible, straight line will result. Snapping a chalk line suggests the first postulate for geometry:

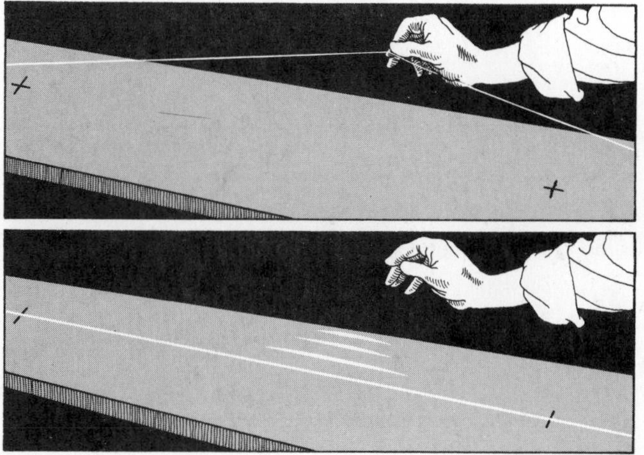

POSTULATE 1
Given any two different points, there is exactly one line that contains both of them.

After the first carpenter has snapped a chalk line between the two points, you would not expect a second carpenter to be able to snap a different straight line between the same two points. So, in geometry, Postulate 1 asserts that if line l contains points A and B, there can be no other line containing them both. Another way to say this is that two given points *uniquely determine* a line, meaning that those two points establish the location of one and only one line.

OBJECTIVE

Find the distance between two points on a number line, given their coordinates.

TEACHER'S NOTES

See p. T24

MIXED REVIEW

1. Solve $2x - 3(2 - x) = 19$. $x = 5$
2. Multiply $(x + 3)(x + 5)$. $x^2 + 8x + 15$
3. Multiply $(x - 3)(x + 4)$. $x^2 + x - 12$
4. Solve $4x - 3 \geq 17 - x$. $x \geq 4$
5. Factor $x^2 + 7x + 10$. $(x + 2)(x + 5)$

TEACHER'S RESOURCE MASTERS

Practice Master 3, Part 1

When you are constructing a number line by assigning the real numbers to the points on a line, you have a certain amount of freedom in doing it. One person may do it like this:

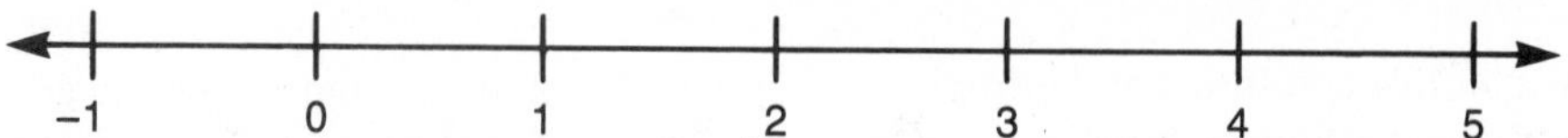

Another person may do it like this:

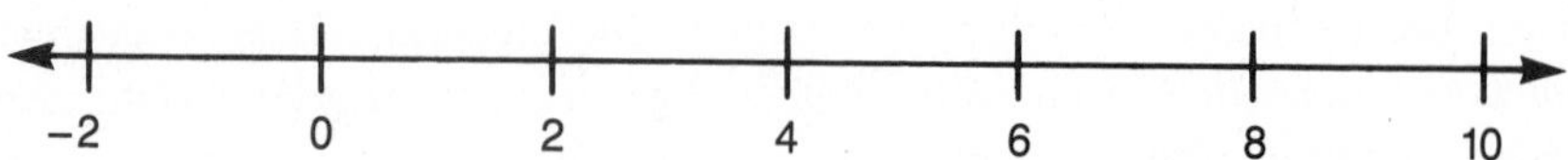

Suppose that you are to find the **distance** (that is, count the number of units) between two points, *A* and *B*. If you use the first person's numbering of the scale, it would appear that the distance between *A* and *B* is 3 units:

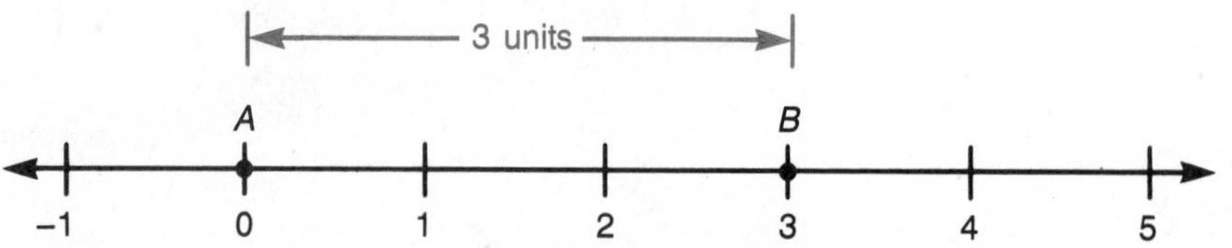

If you use the second person's numbering, the distance is 6 units:

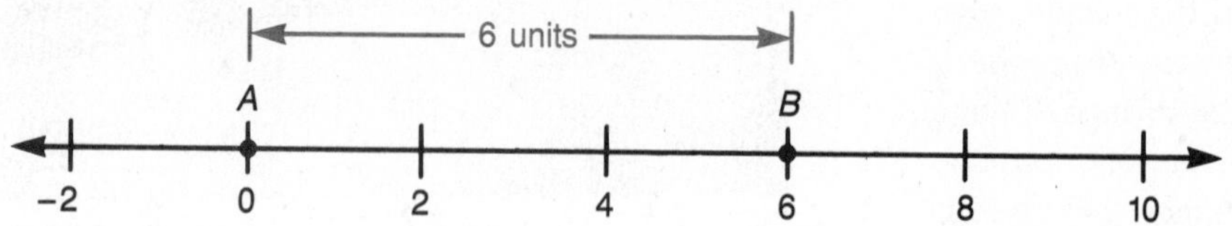

Obviously, the distance has not changed; it is the *scale* that has changed. In order to avoid confusion whenever you deal with distance, the following agreement must be observed: in a given problem, the scale on the number line used must remain constant. When you go on to another problem, the scale may be changed if you desire. The agreement to use a constant scale in a given problem leads to the second postulate:

POSTULATE 2 (The Distance Postulate)
To every pair of different points, there corresponds a unique positive real number.

Next, you shall see that Postulate 3 completes your ability to deal with measurements of line segments.

POSTULATE 3 (The Ruler Postulate)
The points of a line can be placed in correspondence with the real numbers in such a way that:

1. to every point of the line there corresponds exactly one real number;
2. to every real number there corresponds exactly one point of the line; and
3. the distance between two points is the absolute value of the difference of the corresponding numbers.

You already know that a line is a set consisting of an infinite number of points. You also know that the set of real numbers is infinite. The Ruler Postulate states that it is possible to establish a **one-to-one correspondence** between the elements of these two sets. This means that each real number can be matched with exactly one point on the line, and each point on the line can be matched with exactly one real number. Here is a number line with some typical coordinates (real numbers):

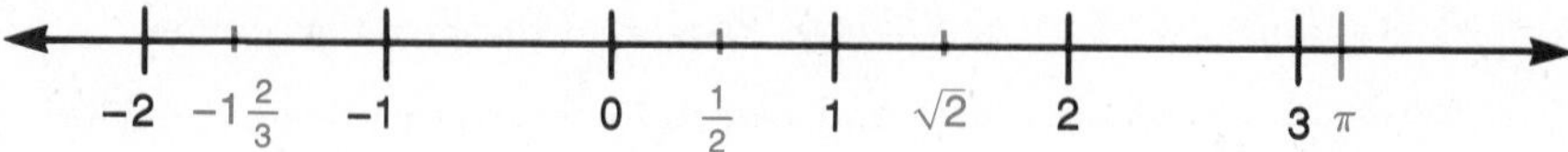

Parts 1 and 2 of the Ruler Postulate describe how to set up a number line. Part 3 tells how to use the number line as a measuring device. When you measure the length of an object, you usually put one end of the ruler against one end of the object you are measuring, as in the first figure below. Then you look at the other end of the object to see the corresponding measurement on the ruler.

Suppose the ruler you are using is damaged at one end, so that you cannot line it up with the object. Must you use another ruler? No, it is still possible to make the measurement with the damaged ruler as shown in the second figure. You must simply remember to subtract the number matched with the left end of the object from the number matched with the right end, so the measurement is three centimeters and not four centimeters.

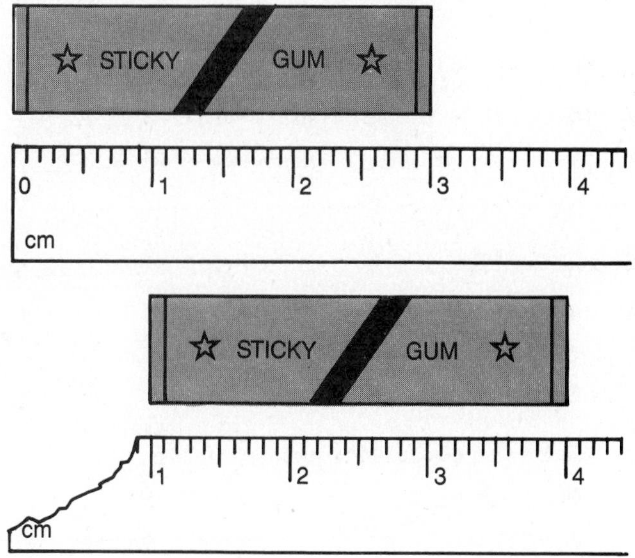

The same principle is used to find the distance between any two points on a number line, even if one or both of them have negative coordinates.

Every point on a number line has both a name and a coordinate. You know from the first lesson that the names shall be capital letters of the alphabet. The coordinates are, of course, the real numbers.

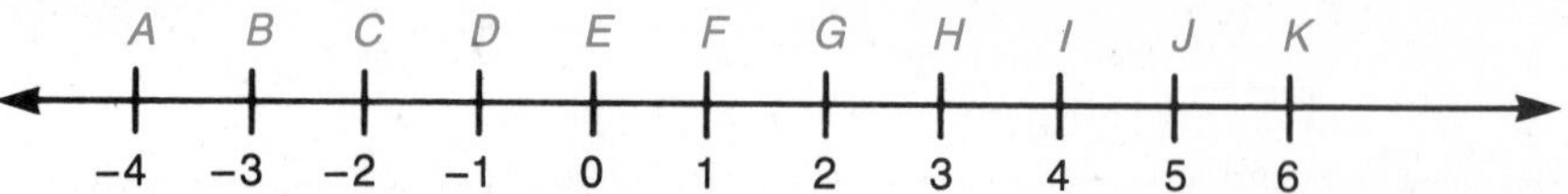

The symbol AB shall be used to mean the *distance* between points A and B. Thus, in the figure above, $FJ = |5 - 1| = 4$ and $EH = |3 - 0| = 3$. Consider some points with negative coordinates: $CG = |2 - (-2)| = |2 + 2| = 4$.

There is one more question to settle. Sometimes the coordinates are variables that can take on both positive and negative values. Consider A and B with coordinates x and y, respectively. If you said the distance between A and B always meant $y - x$, you would sometimes get a negative number. For example, suppose the coordinate of point A is $x = 8$ and that of point B is $y = 3$. Then $y - x = 3 - 8 = -5$. But according to Postulate 2, distance is always a *positive* number. A simple solution is to take the *absolute value* of $y - x$. You can say that $AB = |y - x|$ or $AB = |x - y|$ and always know that the result is positive.

ASSIGNMENT GUIDE

Minimum 1-16 odd
Regular 1-19 odd
Maximum 1-23 odd

Example: Suppose the coordinates of A and B are 3 and -7, respectively. Then the distance $AB = |y - x| = |(-7) - 3| = |-10| = 10$. Even if you say $AB = |x - y|$, you still get 10. Thus, the distance between two points on a number line is defined as the *absolute value of the difference of their coordinates.*

ORAL EXERCISES

Oral Exercises
1. positive
2. 3
3. 3
4. 2
5. 7
6. 15
7. 2
8. 6
9. 6
10. 16

1. The number representing the distance between two different points is always _____.

2. $|6 - 3| =$ _____ **3.** $|3 - 6| =$ _____ **4.** $|-4 + 2| =$ _____

5. $|6 - 13| =$ _____ **6.** $|-15| =$ _____ **7.** $|-2 - (-4)| =$ _____

8. $|-2 - 4| =$ _____ **9.** $|-4 - 2| =$ _____ **10.** $|-7 + (-9)| =$ _____

WRITTEN EXERCISES

Written Exercises
1. 9
2. 3
3. 7
4. 3
5. 3
6. 4
7. 8
8. 5
9. 5
10. 9

A. **1.** If $P = 16$ and $R = 7$, then $PR =$ _____.

2. If $P = 12$ and $R = 15$, then $PR =$ _____.

3. $2 + |-8| - |3| =$ _____.

4. $|2 + (-8)| - |-3| =$ _____

B. Given the coordinate system below:

R S N T B P M Q A C
−5 −4 −3 −2 −1 0 1 2 3 4

5. $PA =$ _____

6. $TQ =$ _____

7. $SC =$ _____

8. $PR =$ _____ **9.** $NQ =$ _____ **10.** $RB + BC =$ _____

Given the coordinate system below:

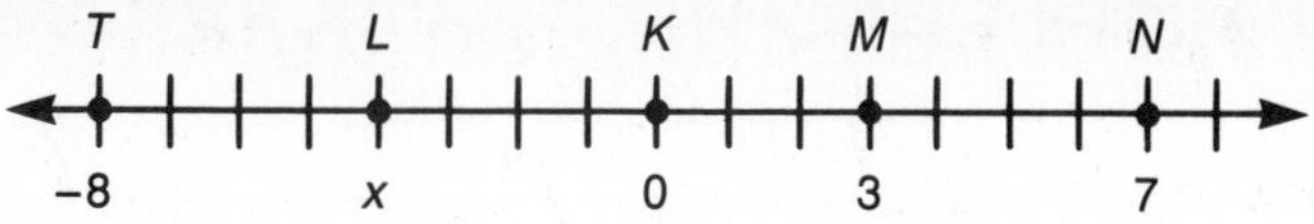

11. TM = ____

12. TK = ____

13. KN = ____

14. KL = ____ **15.** ML = ____ **16.** NL = ____

C. Given the coordinate system below:

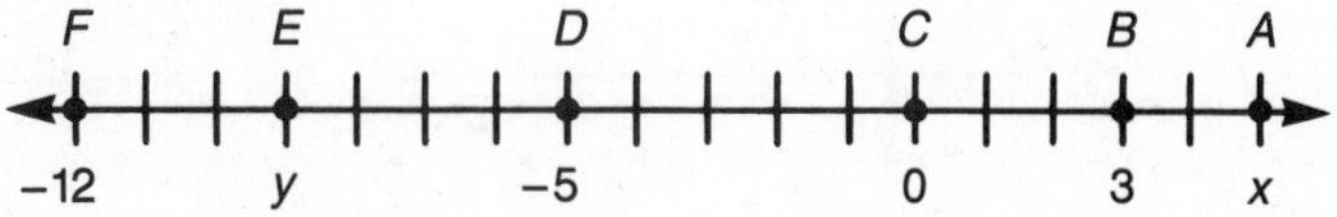

17. CD = ____

18. CF = ____

19. BC = ____

20. AF = ____ **21.** BE = ____ **22.** AE = ____

23. If the coordinate of A is x, and the coordinate of B is y, which lettered examples below would represent AB?

a. $x - y$ **b.** $y - x$ **c.** $|x - y|$ **d.** $|y - x|$ **e.** $|x| - |y|$

MATH HERITAGE/Hypatia

Among the many brilliant minds produced by ancient Greek civilization was Hypatia (about 370–415 A.D.), the first woman known to have made important contributions to mathematics. Hypatia was the daughter of the mathematician Theon, whose version of Euclid's *Elements* became the traditional geometry textbook. She taught at the famous Library of Alexandria, Egypt, the learning center of the ancient world.

Hypatia wrote commentaries on the works of Appollonius, the mathematician, and Ptolemy, the scientist. She was interested in astronomy and philosophy as well. Hypatia was a popular and respected teacher and lecturer, who attracted many distinguished students, such as the astronomer Synesius.

Because of her importance among scholars, Hypatia eventually became a target of criticism for fanatics who equated science with paganism. They thought her prominence was politically dangerous. In March of 415, Hypatia was brutally murdered by an angry mob. Her death foreshadowed the beginning of the end for Alexandria as the cultural hub of the ancient world. The library itself was soon destroyed, and the Dark Ages began, limiting mathematical studies for the next 500 years.

11. 11
12. 8
13. 7

NOTE: Students should be made aware in Exercises 14–16 that x may or may not be 4. Therefore, their answers should be in terms of x.

14. $|x - 0|$, $|-x|$, x
15. $|x - 3|$, $3 - x$
16. $|x - 7|$, $7 - x$

17. 5
18. 12
19. 3
20. $|-12 - x|$, $x + 12$
21. $|y - 3|$, $|3 - y|$
22. $|x - y|$, $|y - x|$
23. c, d

1.6 Selecting an Infinite Ruler

OBJECTIVES

Identify line segments, rays, opposite rays, endpoints, and midpoints.

Determine the midpoint of a segment, given its endpoints.

TEACHER'S NOTES

See p. T24

MIXED REVIEW

1. Solve $x + y = 7$
   $x - y = 3$. (5, 2)
2. Solve $x - 4(3 - x) = 18$. $x = 6$
3. Mulitply $(2x + 1)(3x + 2)$. $6x^2 + 7x + 2$
4. Average -8 and 20. 6
5. Solve $|x - 3| = 5$. $\{8, -2\}$

TEACHER'S RESOURCE MASTERS

Practice Master 3, Part 2
Quiz 2

The Ruler Postulate allows you to create a coordinate system on a line. This can be accomplished in many ways. One way is to choose any point P to be zero. Then label the positive coordinates in either direction:

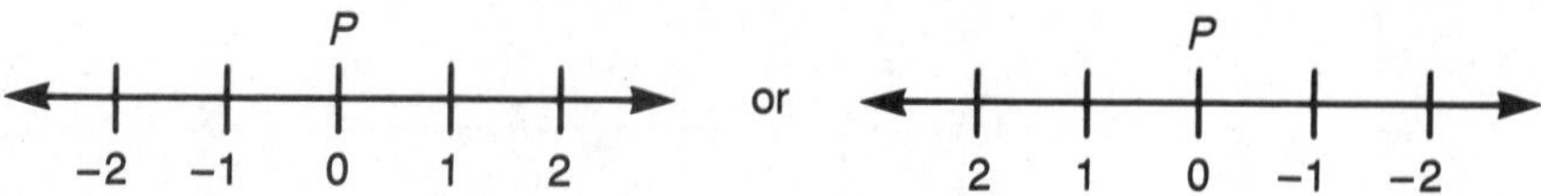

This is formally stated in the Ruler Placement Postulate:

> **POSTULATE 4 (The Ruler Placement Postulate)**
> Given two points P and Q of a line, the coordinate system can be chosen in such a way that the coordinate of P is zero and the coordinate of Q is positive.

You already have some concept of the term *between,* but a formal definition is needed:

> **DEFINITION: betweenness of points**
> Given three points A, B, and C, B is between A and C if and only if
> 1. A, B, and C are on the same line, and
> 2. $AB + BC = AC$

Y is clearly not between X and Z, but it appears that B is between A and C. Therefore, if a point is between two other points, the three points lie on the same line. You would also expect the distance AC to be equal to AB plus BC, or $AB + BC = AC$. These statements formalize the definition of between.

You now have the basis for the first theorem:

> **THEOREM 1.1**
> Let A, B, and C be three points of a line, with coordinates x, y, and z, respectively. If $x < y < z$, then B is between A and C.

The proof for this theorem can be given in a *narrative,* or *paragraph, proof,* which is a written description of the deductive steps.

Given: A, B, and C lie on the same line and have coordinates x, y, and z, respectively. $x < y < z$

Prove: B is between A and C.

Proof: From the givens, you know that A, B, and C are collinear, and that $x < y < z$. By the Ruler Postulate (Postulate 3), $AB = |y - x|$ and $BC = |z - y|$, so that $AB + BC = |y - x| + |z - y|$. Since the absolute value of a number is defined as its distance from zero, the statement becomes $AB + BC = y - x + z - y$. By the inverse property for addition, $y + (-y) = 0$, so the statement may be simplified as $AB + BC = -x + z$, or $AB + BC = |z - x|$. Again, by the Ruler Postulate, $|z - x|$ is the distance between points A and C, so that $AB + BC = AC$. Thus, by the definition of between, B is between A and C.

THEOREM 1.2
Of three different points of the same line, exactly one is between the other two.

Given: A, B, and C are three points on the same line.

Prove: Either A, B, or C lies between the other two.

Proof: From the definition of between, you know that at least one of the following is true: $AB + BC = AC$, $AC + CB = AB$, or $BA + AC = BC$. It is necessary to show that one of these statements is true. If the first one is true, then AC is the largest distance of AB, AC, and BC; if the second statement is true, then AB is the largest. Likewise, if the third equation is true, then BC is the largest distance. By the trichotomy property, only one of these three numbers can be the largest, and therefore only one of the statements can be true. Therefore, only one point can be between the other two.

Consider now a portion of a line, called a **line segment.**

DEFINITION: line segment
A set of points is a **line segment** if and only if the set contains two points and all the points between them.

Line segments are labeled by naming the two **endpoints** and placing a horizontal bar over the two letters. The segment at the right can be called either $\overline{AB}$ or $\overline{BA}$.

The **length** of $\overline{AB}$ is the distance determined from the Distance Postulate. Therefore, every segment has a positive number associated with it, and that number is its length. The length of $\overline{AB}$ is AB (no horizontal bar in the symbol). Remember that AB represents a real number, not the segment AB.

You cannot call two segments equal unless they are the same set of points. The term **congruent** is used to indicate different segments of equal length.

DEFINITION: congruent segments
Two or more line segments are congruent if and only if they have the same length.

Congruent segments are said to have a congruence. The symbol "$\cong$" is used to mean "is congruent to," and the symbol "$\ncong$" is used to mean "is not congruent to."

THEOREM 1.3
Congruence between segments is an equivalence relation.

Many times in proving a theorem, it is helpful to restate the theorem in an if—then form. The "given" represents the hypothesis, or "if" component. The "prove" represents the conclusion, or "then" component. Thus, the proof of Theorem 1.3 would read:

Given: $\overline{AB}$, $\overline{CD}$, and $\overline{EF}$
$\overline{AB} \cong \overline{CD}$; $\overline{CD} \cong \overline{EF}$

Prove: $\overline{AB} \cong \overline{AB}$ (reflexive); $\overline{CD} \cong \overline{AB}$ (symmetric); $\overline{AB} \cong \overline{EF}$ (transitive)

Proof: Restating the theorem in if—then form, if $\overline{AB} \cong \overline{CD}$ and $\overline{CD} \cong \overline{EF}$, then $\overline{AB} \cong \overline{AB}$, $\overline{CD} \cong \overline{AB}$, and $\overline{AB} \cong \overline{EF}$. By the Ruler Postulate, you know a segment, $\overline{AB}$, corresponds to a distance, AB, which is a real number, so by the reflexive property, $AB = AB$. By the definition of congruent, if $AB = AB$, then $\overline{AB} \cong \overline{AB}$. Likewise, given $\overline{AB} \cong \overline{CD}$, then $AB = CD$ and by the symmetric property, $CD = AB$, which defines the congruence $\overline{CD} \cong \overline{AB}$. In the same manner, if $\overline{AB} \cong \overline{CD}$ and $\overline{CD} \cong \overline{EF}$, then $AB = CD$ and $CD = EF$. By the transitive property, $AB = EF$, which defines the congruence $\overline{AB} \cong \overline{EF}$. Since the congruences among $\overline{AB}$, $\overline{CD}$, and $\overline{EF}$ are reflexive, symmetric, and transitive, congruence between segments fulfills the definition of an equivalence relation.

As you can see in this proof, the rules of logic do not allow a real number property to be used as a reason for a congruence relation. Segments are first converted to their corresponding distances, which are real numbers, and a real number property is used to establish an equality, which is then converted back into a congruence.

Now consider a set of points, with one endpoint, extending infinitely in one direction. Such a figure is called a **ray** and is labeled $\overrightarrow{KL}$.

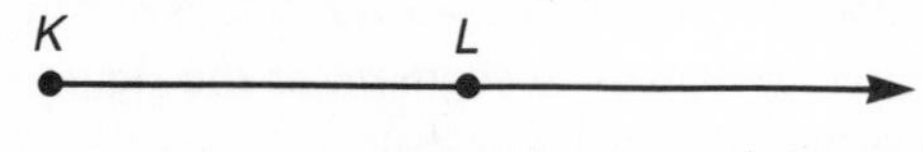

DEFINITION: ray
Ray AB ($\overrightarrow{AB}$) is the figure that contains A and every point on the same side of A as B.

Let A and B be points of line l. The set of points is ray AB if and only if the set of points is the union of (1) the segment AB and (2) the set of all points C for which it is true that B is between A and C.

The first letter is the endpoint of the ray and the second letter is any other point on the ray. The ray symbol (→) always points to the right, regardless of the actual direction of the ray. The ray at the right is named $\overrightarrow{FG}$.

DEFINITION: opposite rays
$\overrightarrow{AB}$ and $\overrightarrow{AC}$ are called **opposite rays** if and only if A is between B and C.

$\overrightarrow{AB}$ and $\overrightarrow{AC}$ are opposite rays.

The next theorem follows from the Ruler Placement Postulate and the definition of ray.

THEOREM 1.4 (The Point Plotting Theorem)
Let $\overrightarrow{AB}$ be a ray, and let x be a positive number. Then there is exactly one point P of $\overrightarrow{AB}$ such that $AP = x$.

Given: $\overrightarrow{AB}$ and a positive number x

Prove: There is exactly one point P on $\overrightarrow{AB}$ such that $AP = x$.

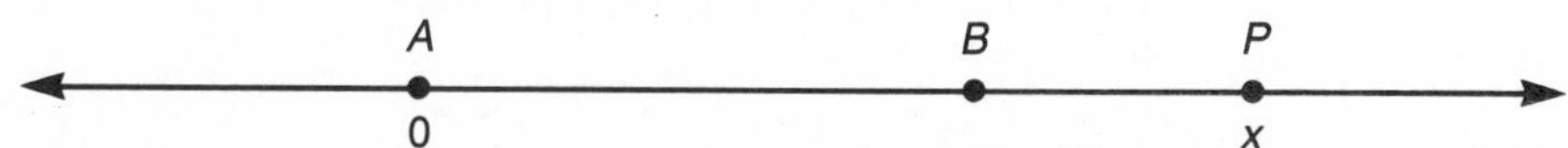

Proof: By the Ruler Postulate, choose a coordinate system on $\overleftrightarrow{AB}$ such that A has the coordinate 0 and B is positive. Let P be the point with coordinate x. Since $x > 0$, P must be on $\overrightarrow{AB}$, and since only one point can have the coordinate x, and $AP = |x - 0| = x$, then P is the only point that lies at a distance of x from A.

Note that the same pair of points may be used to name several geometric figures, $\overleftrightarrow{AB}$, $\overline{AB}$, $\overrightarrow{AB}$, $\overrightarrow{BA}$, as well as a distance that is a number, AB.

Lines, segments, and rays may intersect each other variously in a figure. To explore these relations, you will need two new terms, **midpoint** and **bisect.**

DEFINITION: midpoint
A point B is called the **midpoint** of $\overline{AC}$ if and only if (1) B is between A and C and (2) $AB = BC$.

THEOREM 1.5
Every segment has exactly one midpoint.

Given: Points A and C

Prove: There is exactly one point B on $\overline{AC}$ such that (1) B is between A and C and (2) $AB = BC$.

A B C

Proof: Since $AB + BC = AC$, and $AB = BC$, by substituting AB for BC and solving for AB you obtain $AB = \frac{1}{2}AC$. By the Point Plotting Theorem, there is exactly one point B of $\overline{AC}$ that lies at a distance $\frac{1}{2}AC$ from A. Therefore, $\overline{AC}$ has exactly one midpoint.

DEFINITION: bisect; bisector
A point, line, segment, ray, or plane **bisects** a segment if and only if it intersects the segment at only the segment's midpoint. Any figure that bisects $\overline{AC}$ is called a **bisector** of $\overline{AC}$.

ASSIGNMENT GUIDE

Minimum 1-19
Regular 1-23 odd
Maximum 1-19 odd, 20-23

ORAL EXERCISES

Name a physical model in your classroom for Exercises 1-3.

1. a segment
2. a ray
3. opposite rays
4. If $AB = BC$, is B the midpoint of $\overline{AC}$? Why or why not?
5. L, M, and N are three points on a line with coordinates 5, -3, and 8, respectively. Which point is between the other two?
6. Q is the midpoint of $\overline{PR}$. The coordinate of P is 6 and the coordinate of Q is -1. What is the coordinate of R?
7. B is the midpoint of $\overline{AC}$. B lies on $\overleftrightarrow{EF}$. Is $\overleftrightarrow{EF}$ always a bisector of $\overline{AC}$?
8. How can you compute the coordinate of the midpoint?
9. If $\overrightarrow{RS}$ and $\overrightarrow{RT}$ are opposite rays, is R the midpoint of $\overline{ST}$? Why or why not?
10. Why can't a line have a midpoint?
11. If $\overline{AB}$ bisects $\overline{XY}$ at P, and $\overline{XY}$ also bisects $\overline{AB}$ at P, which is the relation between the distances AP and XP if $AB = XY$?

Oral Exercises
1-3. Answers will vary.
4. No; B may not be between A and C.
5. L
6. -8 or 13
7. only if $\overleftrightarrow{EF}$ does not contain $\overline{AC}$
8. Average the coordinates of the endpoints.
9. No; RS may not be equal to RT.
10. Because a line's infinite length is not measurable.
11. $AP = XP$

WRITTEN EXERCISES

A. **1.** Is $\overline{AB} = AB$? Why? **2.** Is $AB = BA$? Why? **3.** Is $\overline{AB} \cong \overline{BA}$? Why?

4. Is $\overleftrightarrow{AB} \cong \overleftrightarrow{BA}$? Why? **5.** Is $\overrightarrow{AB} \cong \overrightarrow{BA}$? Why? **6.** Is $\overline{AX} \cong \overline{XB}$? Why?

B. **7.** What is the coordinate of the midpoint of $\overline{RS}$ if the coordinate of R is 6 and the coordinate of S is 15?

8. What is the coordinate of the midpoint of a segment whose endpoint coordinates are -5 and -11?

9. If the coordinate of a segment's midpoint is -3 and that of one endpoint is 0, what is the coordinate of the other endpoint?

10. If the coordinate of endpoint A of $\overline{AC}$ is -5 and the coordinate of midpoint B is 3, then $AC =$ ______.

11. R, S, and T are three points. How many segments do they determine? Name them.

12. U, V, and W are three points not on the same line. How many lines do they determine? Name them.

13. How many lines do three points determine if they are collinear?

14. In the figure at the right, how many different rays can you name that have A, B, or C as endpoints? Name them.

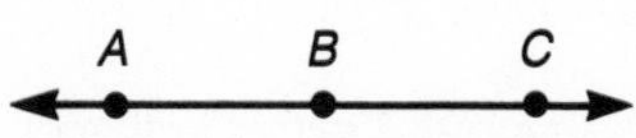

15. If A, B, and C are not on the same line, how many different rays can you name that have A, B, or C as endpoints? Name them.

16. A segment may be bisected in how many points?

17. How many bisectors can a segment have?

18. Draw a figure of two rays that have a common endpoint, but are not opposite rays.

19. Draw a figure of two opposite rays, $\overrightarrow{BA}$ and $\overrightarrow{BC}$, so that $\overline{AB} \cong \overline{BC}$. Draw another ray, $\overrightarrow{BD}$, such that D is not on $\overleftrightarrow{AC}$. If $BD = BC$, what real number property tells you that $AB = BD$?

20. Draw a figure of three intersecting rays, $\overrightarrow{PQ}$, $\overrightarrow{RQ}$, and $\overrightarrow{SQ}$.

C. **21.** How many rays can have a common endpoint?

22. How many collinear rays can have a common endpoint?

23. A, C, and E are three points not on the same line. Draw a figure showing the segments they determine. Now indicate the midpoint of each segment and label them B, D, and F. How many segments can you name that are determined by this set of points?

Written Exercises

1. No; a segment cannot equal a number.
2. Yes; the distance is the same.
3. Yes; they are the same set of points.
4. Yes; they are the same set of points.
5. No; the rays go in opposite directions.
6. No; their lengths are unknown.
7. $10\frac{1}{2}$ 8. -8 9. -6
10. 16
11. three; $\overline{RS}$, $\overline{RT}$, and $\overline{ST}$
12. three; $\overleftrightarrow{UV}$, $\overleftrightarrow{UW}$, and $\overleftrightarrow{VW}$
13. one
14. four; $\overrightarrow{AC}$, $\overrightarrow{CA}$, $\overrightarrow{BA}$, and $\overrightarrow{BC}$
15. six; $\overrightarrow{AB}$, $\overrightarrow{AC}$, $\overrightarrow{BA}$, $\overrightarrow{BC}$, $\overrightarrow{CA}$, and $\overrightarrow{CB}$
16. one
17. an infinite number
18.

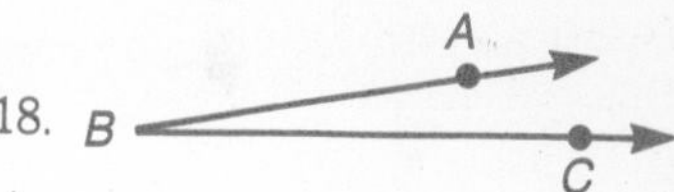

19. transitive property

20.

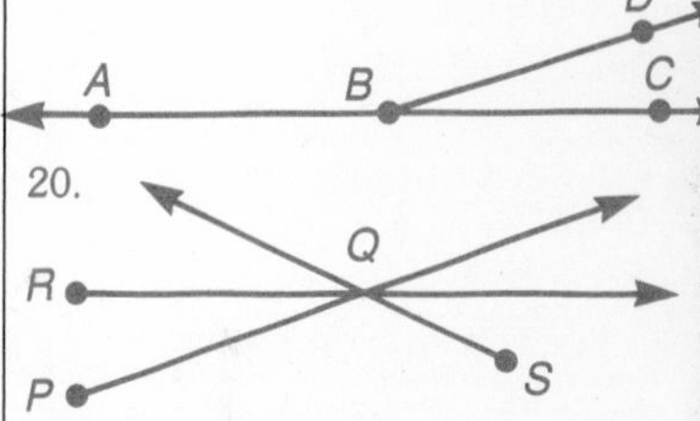

21. an infinite number
22. two
23. 15

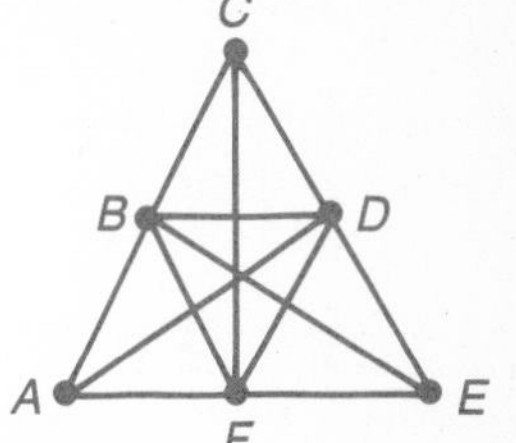

SKILLS MAINTENANCE
1. e, f
2. c, e
3. e
4. b, c, d, e, f, g, h
5. F
6. T
7. F
8. F
9. 6, 12, 18, 24, . . .
10. 15, 30, 45, . . . , 90
11. 30, 60, 90
12. F
13. T
14. F
15. the set of positive multiples of 3
16. 2, 4, 6, 8, . . .

Exploration
1. 0
2. 3
3. 3
4. Yes; 1 and 4, 2 and 3, and 0 is its own inverse

SKILLS MAINTENANCE

Refer to the figure to name the elements in each set described.

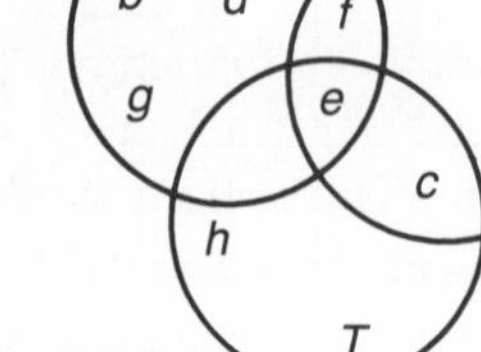

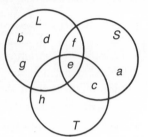

1. $L \cap S$ **2.** $T \cap S$

3. $L \cap T \cap S$ **4.** $L \cup T$

Tell whether each statement about the figure is *true* or *false*.

5. $L \cup S = \{f\}$ **6.** $S \cap T = \{e, c\}$

7. $d \in T$ **8.** $T \subset S$

Given $M = \{3, 6, 9, 12, \ldots\}$, $N =$ positive even numbers, and $O = \{$multiples of 5 between 5 and 100, inclusive$\}$, name the elements in each set described.

9. $M \cap N$ **10.** $M \cap O$ **11.** $M \cap N \cap O$

Tell whether each statement about sets *M*, *N*, and *O* is *true* or *false*.

12. $M \subset N$ **13.** $\{6, 12, 18, 24\} \subset M$ **14.** $M \cup O = \varnothing$

15. Describe set M in words. **16.** Give a roster of the elements of set N.

EXPLORATION
Mod Math

Modular arithmetic is widely used in computer work. At the right is an addition table for "mod five." Notice that the set of elements in mod five consists of the numbers 0 through 4. What set of numbers would be used in mod eight? Modular arithmetic is also called "clock arithmetic," because operating in a mod is similar to moving around the face of a clock. On a five-minute clock, if you start at 4 and move one unit clockwise, you arrive at 0. Therefore, 4 + 1 = 0. To subtract, You move counterclockwise.

⊕	0	1	2	3	4
0	0	1	2	3	4
1	1	2	3	4	0
2	2	3	4	0	1
3	3	4	0	1	2
4	4	0	1	2	3

Use the table to determine the following sums in mod five.

1. 3 + 2 **2.** 1 + 4 + 3 **3.** 3 + 3 + 2

4. Are there additive inverses in mod five? If so, name all such pairs.

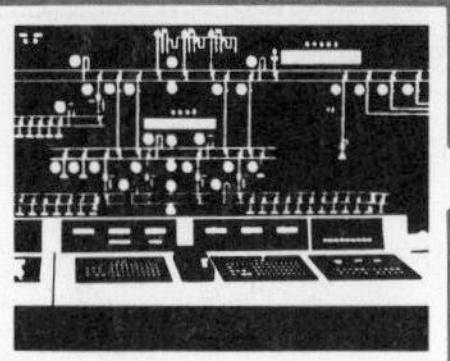

COMPUTER

Computer programming, the process of giving instructions to a computer so that it will perform as desired, often depends on a deductive approach to problem solving. Each new program step should be a logical progression from the preceding steps to the desired goal. One method used to design logical programs is the **flowchart.**

The answer to a decision question determines which path to follow. The answer can only be yes or no, hence two paths. For example, demonstrating that the sum of two odd integers is an even integer can be represented by the flowchart shown below.

Start or Stop	(rounded rectangle)
Input information	(rectangle with cut corner)
Instruction or Operation	(rectangle)
Decision points	(diamond)
Output information	(parallelogram)

START → Choose any integer, x → Choose any integer, y → Let $z = x + y$ → Does $\text{INT}\left(\frac{z}{2}\right) = \frac{z}{2}$? → YES: The sum of $x + y$ is even → STOP; NO: The sum of $x + y$ is odd → STOP

Number the program lines below from 1 to 8 to show their correct order as shown in the flowchart.

_____ LET Z = X + Y
_____ PRINT"THE SUM OF"X"+"Y"IS ODD"
_____ PRINT"ENTER FIRST INTEGER":INPUT X
_____ IF INT(Z/2) <> (Z/2) THEN GOTO 7
_____ END
_____ PRINT"THE SUM OF"X"+"Y"IS EVEN":GOTO 8
_____ PRINT"ENTER SECOND INTEGER":INPUT Y
_____ IF INT(Z/2) = (Z/2) THEN GOTO 6

TEACHER'S RESOURCE MASTERS

Computer Master 1

Computer

Program steps: 3, 7, 1, 5, 8, 6, 2, and 4

It may be helpful to some students to point out that the BASIC abbreviation "INT" is used to find the integer of a number and that the greater than and less than symbols are combined to mean "is not equal to."

TEACHER'S RESOURCE MASTERS

Enrichment Master 1

ENRICHMENT

See Activities 1-2, p. T43

Chapter 1 Review

1. $\overleftrightarrow{PQ}$ 2. $\overleftrightarrow{SP}$
3. R 4. P
5. Sketches will vary.
6. commutative prop. of multiplication
7. associative property of addition
8. distributive property
9. reflexive property
10. symmetric property
11. transitive property
12. addition property of equality
13. multiplication property of equality
14. 2
15. −2
16. −4

CHAPTER 1 REVIEW

VOCABULARY

absolute value (1.2)
between-ness of points (1.6)
biconditional (1.4)
bisect (1.6)
bisector (1.6)
conclusion (1.4)
conditional statement (1.4)
congruent segments (1.6)
converse (1.4)
coordinate (1.2)
deductive reasoning (1.2)
definition (1.1)
distance (1.5)
endpoint (1.6)
equivalence relation (1.3)
even number (1.2)
hypothesis (1.4)
iff (1.4)
implication (1.4)
inductive reasoning (1.2)
inequalities (1.3)
irrational numbers (1.2)
length (1.6)
line (1.1)
line segment (1.6)
midpoint (1.6)
odd number (1.2)
one-to-one correspondence (1.5)
opposite rays (1.6)
order relations (1.3)
plane (1.1)
point (1.1)
postulate (1.1, 1.5)
principal square root (1.2)
rational number (1.2)
ray (1.6)
real number (1.2)
reflexive property (1.3)
symmetric property (1.3)
theorem (1.1, 1.5)
transitive property (1.3)
trichotomy property (1.3)
truth table (1.4)
two-column proof (1.2)

REVIEW EXERCISES

1.1

1. Name the intersection of planes X and Y.

2. Name a line that does not lie in plane X.

3. Name a point not contained in plane Y.

4. Name a point that is the intersection of three lines.

5. Draw a model of the following:
Lines x and y in plane E intersect in point K. Point J is not contained in plane E.

S R P Y X Q

1.2 **Given that x and y are real numbers, name the property demonstrated.**

6. $y(2x) = (2x)y$

7. $x + (y + 3) = (x + y) + 3$

8. $3x + 5x = (3 + 5)x$

9. $x = x$

10. If $x = y$, then $y = x$.

11. If $x = 6$ and $6 = y$, then $x = y$.

12. If $x = y$, then $x + \frac{1}{2} = y + \frac{1}{2}$

13. If $x = y$, then $3x = 3y$.

Simplify each expression.

14. $|8 - 10|$

15. $|8| - |10|$

16. $-\sqrt{16}$

17. Solve $3x - 16 = 20$ using a two-column proof to show each step.

1.3 18. Graph the solution of $x - 2 \leq 4$.

Given that a and b are real numbers, name the property of inequality demonstrated.

19. If $a < 7$ and $7 < b$, then $a < b$.

20. If $a < b$ and $x > 0$, then $ax < bx$.

21. If $a > b$, then $a + 11 > b + 11$.

22. If $a < b$, then $a \neq b$.

Complete each expression by inserting >, <, or =.

23. $|12 - 8|$ ● $|8 - 12|$

24. $|12 - 8|$ ● $|8| - |12|$

25. If $x < y$ and $a < b$, then $x + a$ ● $y + b$.

26. Is > an equivalence relation? Support your answer.

1.4 27. a. Express the following statement as an implication. Label the hypothesis and conclusion and then state the converse: *In a leap year, the month of February has 29 days.* Is the implication true? Is the converse true?

b. Form a biconditional from the implication and its converse. Is the biconditional true?

28. Give one example to disprove the following statement: *The converse of a true statement must also be true.*

1.5 **Refer to the figure to complete each statement below.**

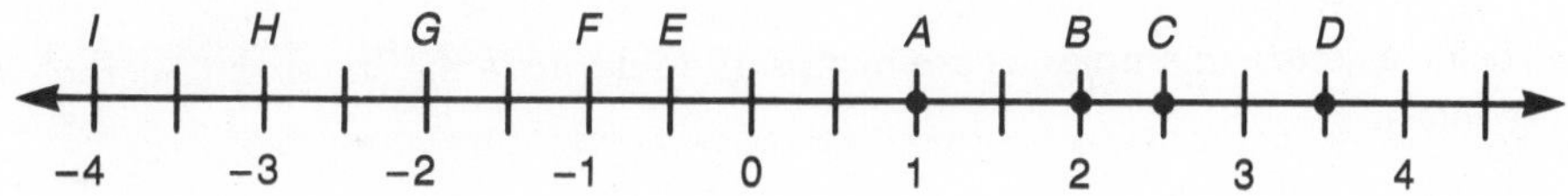

29. The coordinate of G is _____.

30. The coordinate of is $2\frac{1}{2}$.

31. AF = _____

32. AD = _____

33. CE = _____

34. HE = _____

35. GB = _____

36. BF = _____

1.6 37. The coordinate of the midpoint of $\overline{GI}$ is _____.

38. The coordinate of the midpoint of $\overline{FD}$ is _____.

39. What is the coordinate of the midpoint of $\overline{RS}$ if the coordinate of R is -11 and the coordinate of S is 5?

40. Draw and label a model of opposite rays that share the common endpoint W.

17. *1.* $3x - 16 = 20$ (Given); *2.* $3x - 16 + 16 = 20 + 16$ (Addition prop.); *3.* $3x + 0 = 20 + 16$ (Inverse prop. of addition); *4.* $3x = 20 + 16$ (Identity of prop. of addition); *5.* $3x = 36$ (Number fact); *6.* $\frac{1}{3}(3x) = \frac{1}{3}(36)$ (Mult. prop.); *7.* $(\frac{1}{3} \cdot 3)x = \frac{1}{3}(36)$ (Assoc. prop. of mult.); *8.* $1x = \frac{1}{3}(36)$ (Inverse prop. of mult.); *9.* $x = \frac{1}{3}(36)$ (Identity prop. of mult.); *10.* $x = 12$ (Number fact).

18. $x \leq 6$ 6

19. transitive property of inequality

20. mult. property of inequality

21. addition property of inequality

22. trichotomy property

23. = 24. > 25. <

26. No; it is neither symmetric nor reflexive.

27. a. (H) *If it is a leap year,* then (C) *February has 29 days.* Conv: *If February has 29 days, then it is a leap year.* Both are true.

b. *It is a leap year if and only if February has 29 days.* True.

28. Answers will vary. For example, if $x^2 = 16$, then $x = 4$.

29. −2 30. *C* 31. 2

32. $2\frac{1}{2}$ 33. 3 34. $2\frac{1}{2}$

35. 4 36. 3 37. −3

38. $1\frac{1}{4}$ 39. −3

40. *W*

TEACHER'S RESOURCE MASTERS

Chapter 1 Test
Multiple Choice Test—Chapter 1

Chapter 1 Test

1. T 2. F
3. F 4. T
5. F 6. T
7. T 8. F
9. $\geq$

10. 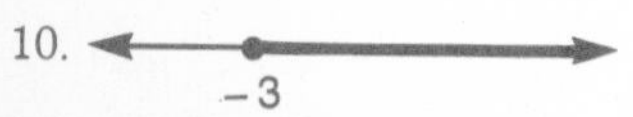

11. multiplication property of inequality
12. reflexive, symmetric, transitive
13. (H) If x is an even number, then (C) $3x$ is an even number.
14. If 3x is an even number, then x is an even number.
15. x is an even number if and only if $3x$ is an even number. Yes.
16. Only one example is needed of a fractional real number.
17. 13 18. 3
19. 2 20. 2
21. x
22. $|y - x|$ or $|x - y|$
23. $\overleftrightarrow{AC}$, $\overleftrightarrow{AB}$, or $\overleftrightarrow{BC}$
24. $\overrightarrow{BA}$ and $\overrightarrow{BC}$
25. $\overline{AB}$, $\overline{BC}$, or $\overline{AC}$
26. C 27. 5

CHAPTER 1 TEST

True or false?

1. Point, line, and plane are undefined in geometry.

2. Points differ in size.

3. Theorems are accepted as true without proof.

4. $\overleftrightarrow{AB}$ names a line that contains points A and B.

5. $\frac{7}{8}$ is an irrational number.

6. Every point on the number line has a real number associated with it.

7. The associative property of addition states that $2 + (3 + x) = (2 + 3) + x$.

8. $\sqrt{25} + |-15| = -10$

9. Supply the symbol of inequality that makes the statement true: $|x| \bigcirc 0$.

10. Graph the inequality $-3 \leq x$.

11. Which property states that if $x < y$, then $6x < 6y$?

12. Name the three properties that determine an equivalence relation.

13. Label the hypothesis and conclusion of the following implication: *If x is an even number, then 3x is an even number.*

14. State the converse of the implication in Exercise 13.

15. Form a biconditional from the implication and its converse in Exercise 13 and 14. Is the biconditional true?

16. Provide as many examples as are necessary to disprove the statement *All real numbers are integers.*

Find *AB* given the following coordinates of *A* and *B*.

17. 9 and -4 **18.** -3 and 0 **19.** -5 and -7

20. $\frac{1}{2}$ and $\frac{5}{2}$ **21.** $2x$ and $3x$ **22.** x and y

Refer to the figure to name an example of each.

23. a line **24.** two opposite rays

25. a line segment **26.** the endpoint of $\overrightarrow{CX}$

A B C

27. Q is the midpoint of $\overline{PR}$. If the coordinate of P is 2 and the coordinate of R is 8, what is the coordinate of Q?

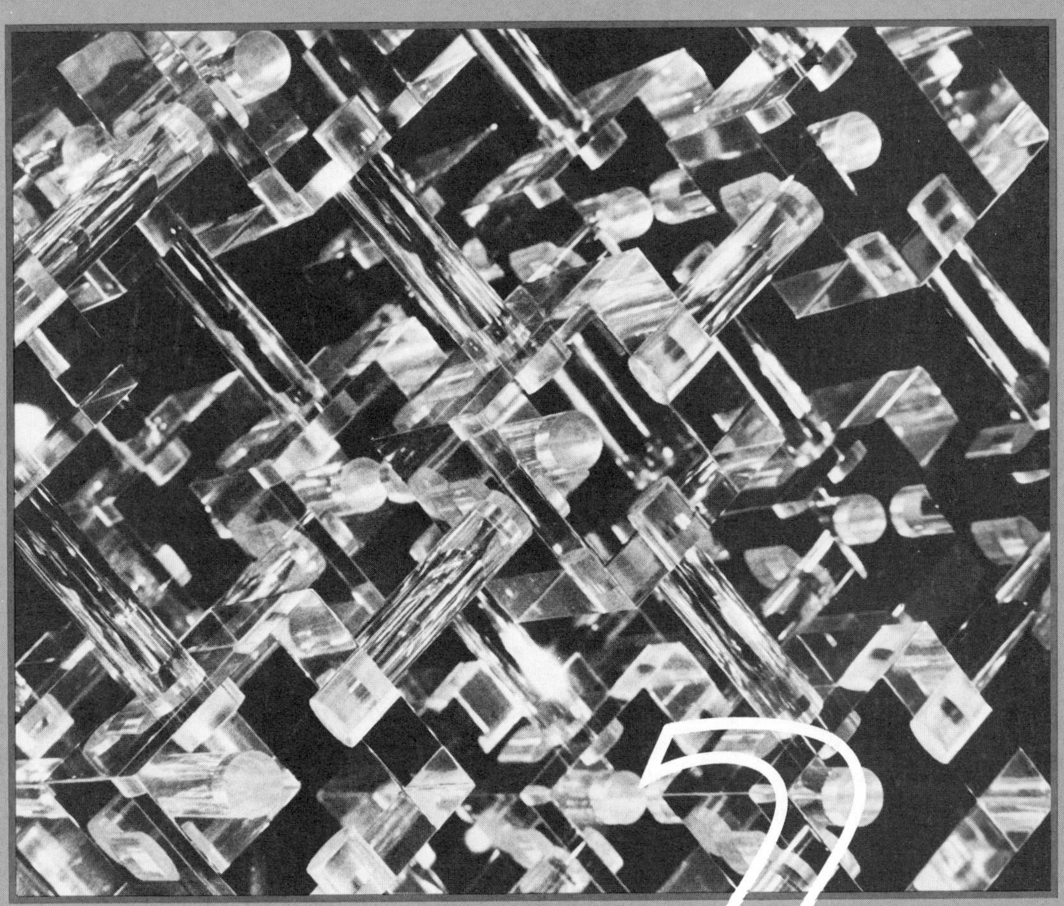

CHAPTER 2

Lines, Angles, Planes, and Space

2.1 Lines and Planes in Space

OBJECTIVE

Identify collinear and coplanar points and intersecting lines and planes.

TEACHER'S NOTES

See p. T25

MIXED REVIEW

1. What are the three undefined terms in our geometry? point, line, plane
2. Simplify $|-9 - 2|$. 11
3. Solve $16 - 3(4 - x) = 1$. $x = -1$
4. Solve $x + 2y = 9$
   $2x - 2y = 6$. (5, 2)
5. Factor $x^2 - 5x + 6$. $(x - 2)(x - 3)$

TEACHER'S RESOURCE MASTERS

Practice Master 4, Part 1

In the last chapter, you were introduced to points, lines, and planes, the three fundamental, undefined terms upon which Euclidian geometry is based. Throughout this book, you will study points, lines, planes, and their relationships.

> **DEFINITIONS: collinear; coplanar**
> Points are **collinear** if and only if there is a line that contains all of them. Points are **coplanar** if and only if there is a plane that contains all of them.

In the figure at the right, points A and C are collinear. Other collinear pairs of points are A, D and D, E, although the lines connecting them are not drawn in the figure. Points B, D, and E are coplanar since they all lie in plane G. Points A, B, and D are also coplanar, because there is a plane (not shown) that could contain them all.

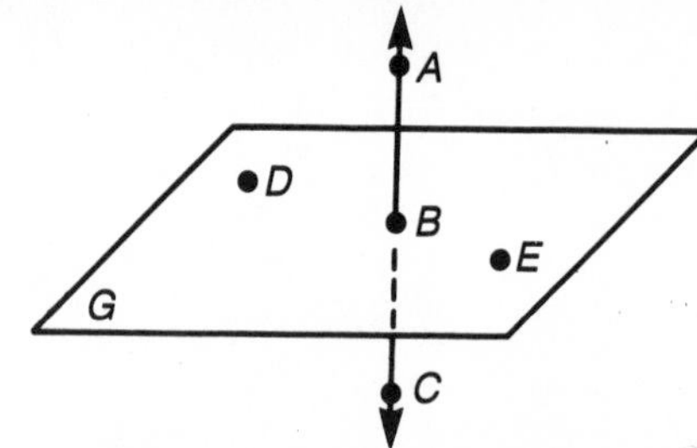

Look at this book page, and let any two letters or punctuation marks on it represent two points. You can always find a line that will contain them both. Now let any two words represent line segments. Is there *always* a line that would contain them? Two points must be collinear, but two segments are not always collinear. no

Going back to the two points (letters) you chose, now imagine an additional point anywhere on or off the page. The three points may not be collinear; however, a flat sheet of paper, representing a plane, could be positioned to contain all three points. What happens if you add a fourth point? Any two points must be collinear, and any three points must be coplanar, but four points may be neither.

> **DEFINITION: space**
> **Space** is the set of all points.

How many points are in space? Choose any two; there will be at least one point between them. Though it should be clear that the number of points in space is infinite, the smallest number necessary will be postulated.

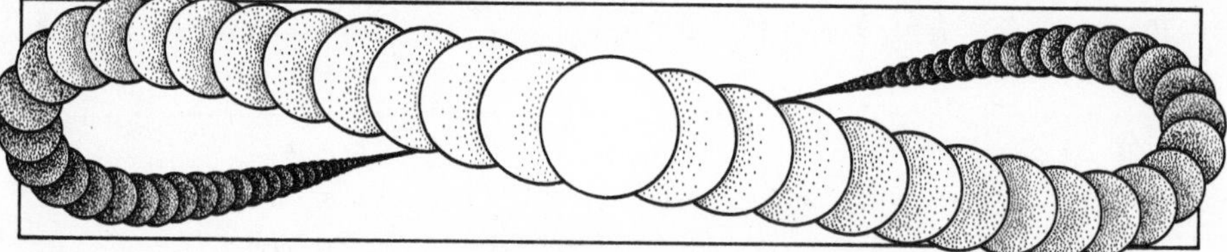

POSTULATE 5
a. Every plane contains at least three noncollinear points.
b. Space contains at least four noncoplanar points.

Refer again to any two points on this page. Is it possible to move your finger in a straight line from one point to the other if you lift your finger from the plane surface created by the page? no

POSTULATE 6
If two points lie in a plane, then the line containing these points lies in the same plane.

Now consider a door (a plane) attached to a wall by three hinges (three collinear points). Each slight opening or closing of the door (rotation) about the hinges determines a new plane containing the same three hinge points. Now imagine that one of the points is moved a foot or two away from the wall. If the plane must still contain all three points, it can now assume only one position.

POSTULATE 7
Any three points lie in at least one plane; any three noncollinear points lie in exactly one plane.

Imagine the two open book pages facing you are two planes. Position the planes at any angle you wish. Their intersection is always the line created by the spine of the book. The planes created by two adjacent walls also intersect in a line.

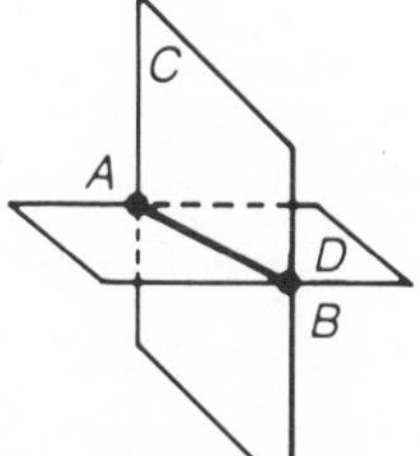

POSTULATE 8
If two planes intersect, then their intersection is a line.

Use two pencils and the top of your desk to represent two lines and a plane. Crossing the pencils illustrates the new theorems that follow from the preceding postulates:

THEOREM 2.1
Two lines intersect in at most one point.

Hold the end of one pencil up so that only the tip touches the plane of the desk top. This illustrates the next theorem suggested by the postulates:

THEOREM 2.2
If a given line intersects a plane not containing it, then their intersection is a single point.

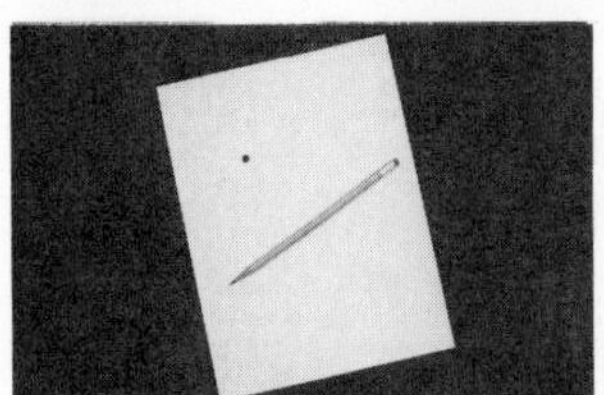

Take a sheet of paper (which can be moved to represent all possible planes) and mark a dot on it. Lay the pencil near the dot. This illustrates another new theorem:

THEOREM 2.3
Given a line and a point not on the line, there is exactly one plane containing them both.

Finally, cross the two pencils on the paper. Note that when one is lifted, it leaves the plane. This illustrates the next theorem:

THEOREM 2.4
Given two intersecting lines, there is exactly one plane containing them both.

Later in this course, you will be asked to prove some of the theorems as they are introduced. For now, remember that theorems are developed from postulates and therefore can be proven true. Postulates are always assumed true without proof.

ASSIGNMENT GUIDE

Minimum 1-17, 23
Regular 1-23
Maximum 1-24

ORAL EXERCISES

1. What are the three fundamental undefined terms of geometry?
2. Two points determine a _____.
3. Three noncollinear points determine a _____.
4. Four noncoplanar points determine _____.
5. Points contained in one line are _____.
6. If one plane contains all the points in a set, then the points are _____.
7. Space is the _____ of all points.
8. _____ can be proven true; _____ are assumed true without proof.

Oral Exercises

1. point, line, and plane
2. line
3. plane
4. space
5. collinear
6. coplanar
7. set
8. Theorems, postulates

WRITTEN EXERCISES

A. Supply the correct number missing from each sentence.

1. Space contains at least _____ noncoplanar points.
2. Any _____ points must be collinear.
3. Any _____ points must be coplanar.
4. _____ intersecting lines determine a plane.
5. The intersection of two lines contains at most _____ point(s).
6. The intersection of a line and a plane that does not contain it contains _____ point(s).

B. Answer the following questions with choices from this list: *a point, a line, a plane.* Some questions may have more than one correct answer.

7. If two lines intersect, the intersection is _____.
8. If two planes intersect, the intersection is _____.
9. If a point and a line intersect, the intersection is _____.
10. If a line and a plane intersect, the intersection is _____.

Written Exercises

1. 4
2. 2
3. 3
4. 2
5. 1
6. 1
7. a point
8. a line
9. a point
10. a point; a line

11. a plane

12. coplanar
13. coplanar
14. both
15. coplanar
16. neither
17. coplanar

18. A
19. S
20. A
21. S
22. A
23. False; because there are an infinite number of points, there would be an infinite number of divisions.
24. F; Postulate 7

CALCULATOR

1. 42
2. 0.2
3. $6 + 8 = 14$
4. 10
5. 10
6. 5
7. 2
8. 3
9. 1.41421356

11. If space and a plane intersect, the intersection is ______.

Refer to the figure for Exercises 12–17 and state whether the elements in each of the following sets are <u>collinear</u>, <u>coplanar</u>, <u>both collinear and coplanar</u>, or <u>neither</u>.

12. A, B, and E

13. A, B, and C

14. G and D

15. A, B, D, and E

16. B, C, D, and E

17. C, D, E, and F

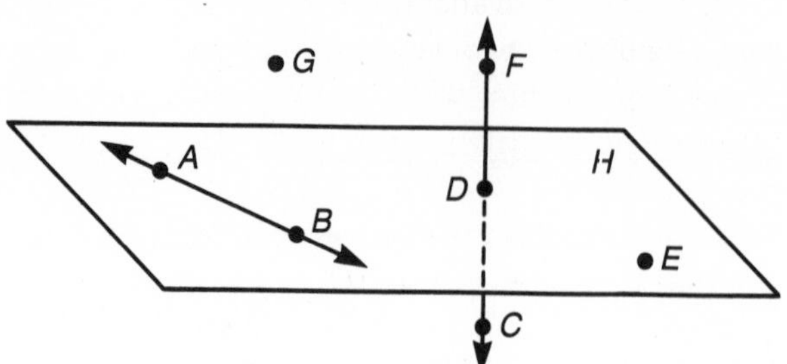

Indicate if the statement is <u>always</u>, <u>sometimes</u>, or <u>never</u> true.

18. Collinear points are also coplanar.

19. A segment and a ray are collinear.

20. A point and a ray are coplanar.

21. The intersection of two lines is a point.

22. Two points are coplanar.

C. State whether each statement is <u>true</u> or <u>false</u>, and why.

23. If a segment is cut in half, then in half again, continuously, you will eventually end up with a single point.

24. If three points are noncollinear, they may also be noncoplanar.

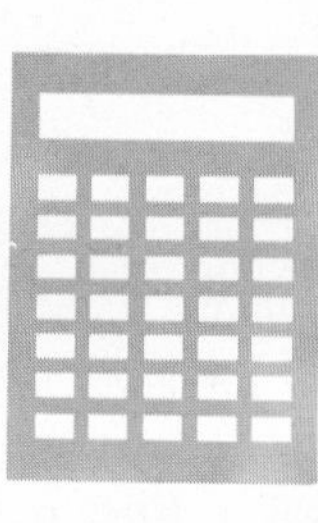

CALCULATOR

Most calculators have a square root key $\sqrt{}$ When this key is pressed, the calculator finds the square root of the number in the display.
Use a calculator to simplify each expression.

1. $\sqrt{1764}$ **2.** $\sqrt{0.04}$ **3.** $\sqrt{36} + \sqrt{64}$

4. $\sqrt{36 + 64}$ **5.** $\sqrt{\sqrt{10{,}000}}$ **6.** $\sqrt{\sqrt{625}}$

7. $\sqrt{\sqrt{\sqrt{256}}}$ **8.** $\sqrt{\sqrt{\sqrt{6561}}}$ **9.** $\sqrt{2}$

2.2 Convex Sets and Separation

Having formulated some of the conditions necessary to determine geometric relationships (for example, in Theorem 2.4, you found that two intersecting lines determine a unique plane), you will now work with separations of these sets. The specific sets you will be dealing with are called **convex** sets. You may have heard the terms convex and concave applied to shapes, such as the lenses at the right. Notice that no matter where a segment is drawn in the convex figure, all of the segment lies within the figure. A segment connecting two points in the concave figure may not lie completely in the figure. In geometry, sets are also referred to as convex or nonconvex.

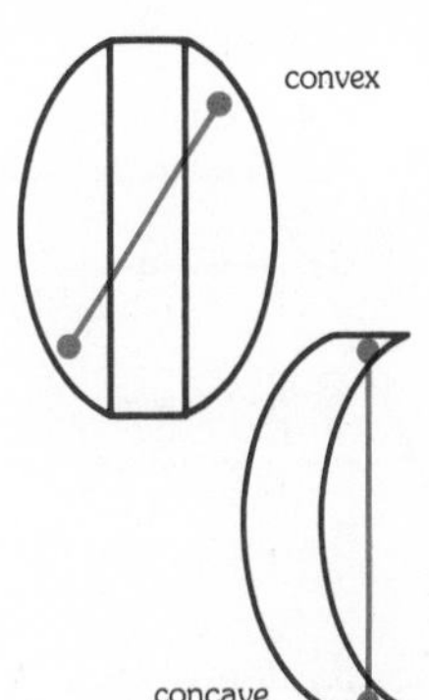

DEFINITION: convex
A set is called **convex** if, for every two points P and Q of the set, the entire segment PQ lies within the set.

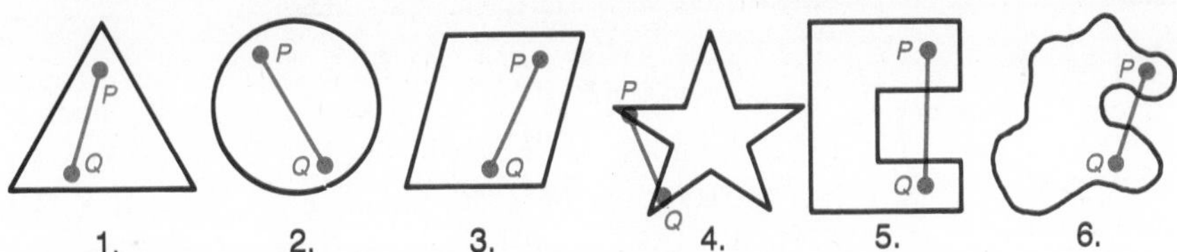

The sets of points within figures 1, 2, and 3 above are convex. The sets of points within figures 4, 5, and 6 are nonconvex. Notice that at least one segment in figures 4, 5, and 6 does not lie entirely within the figure. Lines, planes, and space are all convex sets.

In the figure below, point A separates $\overleftrightarrow{AB}$ into two half-lines. Remember that the arrows indicate that the model of a line extends without end in two directions.

OBJECTIVES

Tell if a figure is a convex set.
Given an appropriate figure, tell if two points are on the same side or on opposite sides of a line in a plane or of a plane in space.

TEACHER'S NOTES

See p. T25

MIXED REVIEW

1. What is the coordinate of the midpoint of $\overline{AB}$ if the coordinate of A is 7 and the coordinate of B is -15? (-4)
2. Solve $5x - 6(4 + x) = -12$. $x = -12$
3. Solve $x + 2y = 9$
   $x - y = 6$. $(7, 1)$
4. Factor $x^2 - x - 42$. $(x - 7)(x + 6)$
5. Simplify $|-27 - 4|$. 31

TEACHER'S RESOURCE MASTERS

Practice Master 4, Part 2
Quiz 3

DEFINITIONS: half-plane; edge
Given a line and the plane containing it, the two sets separated by the line are called **half-planes.** The line that determines two half-planes is called an **edge** of each.

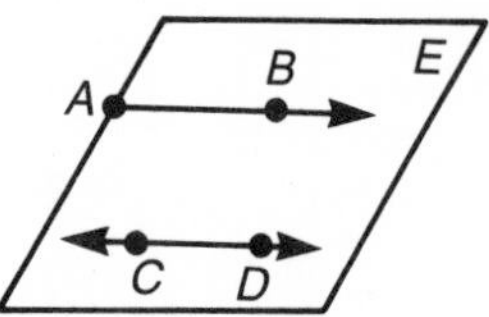

Imagine now that a plane E contains both $\overrightarrow{AB}$ and $\overleftrightarrow{CD}$, as in the figure at the left. Because plane E extends without end in all directions while $\overrightarrow{AB}$ extends without end in only one direction, $\overrightarrow{AB}$ does not separate plane E. Remember that figures can be misleading; point A is not on the border of plane E, because planes have no "border." $\overleftrightarrow{CD}$, however, extends without end, along the plane, so $\overleftrightarrow{CD}$ does separate plane E.

Every line drawn in any plane separates that plane. When a plane is separated, a situation is set up that requires a new postulate:

POSTULATE 9 (The Plane Separation Postulate)
Given a line and a plane containing it, the points of the plane that do not lie on the line form two half-planes, such that:
a. each of the half-planes is a convex set, and
b. if P is in one half-plane and Q is in the other, then $\overline{PQ}$ intersects the line.

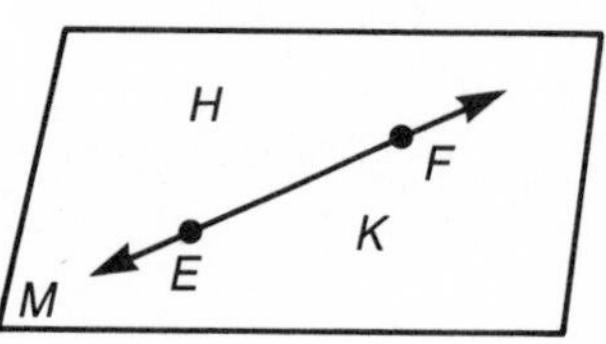

Suppose that $\overleftrightarrow{EF}$ separates plane M into half-planes of which $\overleftrightarrow{EF}$ is the edge, as shown at the left. If H and K are the two half-planes, then M is the union of H, $\overleftrightarrow{EF}$, and K. The edge $\overleftrightarrow{EF}$ is not considered to be a part of either half-plane; therefore, the union of H and K is the plane *minus* the edge, not the complete plane itself.

A similar postulate and similar definitions hold if you expand your initial set from a plane to space itself. While a point is sufficient to separate a line into two half-lines, and a line is sufficient to separate a plane into two-half planes, a plane is required to separate space into two **half-spaces.** Depending on which plane is chosen, an endless variety of half-spaces is possible.

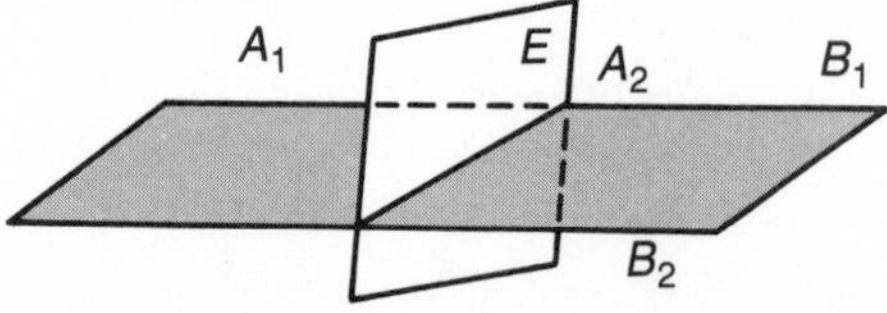

For example, the vertical plane E, at the left, separates space into the half-spaces A_1 and A_2. The horizontal plane F separates space into the half-spaces B_1 and B_2. As an *edge* is to a *plane*, a **face** is to *space*.

DEFINITION: face
A **face** is a plane that separates space into two half-spaces, yet is a part of neither half-space.

The subdivisions made when a line separates a plane, or a plane separates space, are called regions. In the preceding figure, A_1, B_1, A_2, and B_2 are all **regions** of space.

POSTULATE 10 (The Space Separation Postulate)
The points of space that do not lie in a given plane form two half-spaces such that:
a. each half-space is a convex set, and
b. if point P is in one half-space and point Q is in the other, then $\overline{PQ}$ intersects the plane.

The figure at the right suggests that a given edge (here, line l) separates an infinite number of planes into half-planes. Points are said to be on *opposite sides* of an edge if they are coplanar and if the segment they determine intersects the edge. While points A and B are in different half-planes, they are not on opposite sides of edge l, because the segment they determine does not intersect l. Points A and C, however, are on opposite sides, as are points B and D.

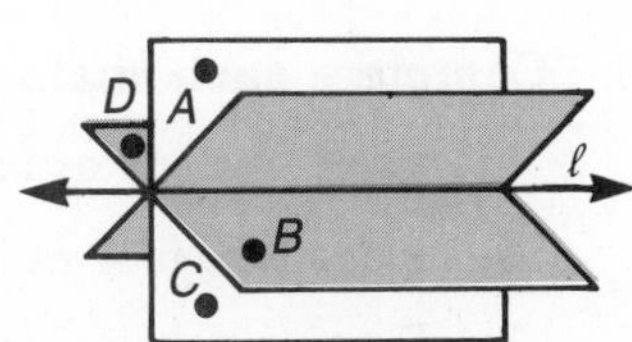

While a given edge creates an infinite number of half-planes, a given face cannot create an infinite number of half-spaces. An infinite number of spaces does not exist. Since there is but one set called space, a face separates it into exactly two half-spaces.

ASSIGNMENT GUIDE
Minimum 1-15
Regular 1-16
Maximum 1-18

ORAL EXERCISES

Supply the missing word(s) in each definition.

1. If the segment joining any two points of a set lies entirely within the set, the set is ______.
2. Two ______ are created when a plane is separated by a line.
3. The ______ between two half-planes is not considered a part of either half-plane.
4. Any plane separates space into exactly two ______.
5. A ______ is a plane that separates ______ into two half-spaces.

Oral Exercises
1. convex
2. half-planes
3. edge
4. half-spaces
5. face; space

6. convex 7. convex

8. convex 9. nonconvex

10. nonconvex

Written Exercises

1. $\overleftrightarrow{EF}$ 2. plane M

3. I; J or G

4. $\overline{GJ}$ doesn't intersect edge $\overleftrightarrow{EF}$

5. plane 6. edge

7. half-space union face union half-space

8. face

9. space

10. False; postulates are not proved.

11. False; the segments must be adjacent.

12. False; the face is not part of either half-space.

13. T 14. T

15. b; d

State whether each of the following is a convex or nonconvex set.

6. the surface of a chalkboard
7. the region enclosed by a circle
8. the region enclosed by a triangle
9. the surface of a coffee mug
10. the region enclosed by a five-pointed star

WRITTEN EXERCISES

A. Refer to the figure.
(Points *E, F, G, I,* and *J* lie in plane *M*.)

1. The drawn edge is _____.

2. The face is _____.

3. Two points on opposite sides of the edge are _____ and _____.

4. Points G and J are not on opposite sides of the edge because _____.

B. Complete each analogy.

5. Point is to line as edge is to _____.

6. Plane is to face as line is to _____.

7. Plane is to half-plane union edge union half-plane as space is to _____.

8. Edge is to plane as _____ is to space.

9. Three noncollinear points are to plane as four noncoplanar points are to _____.

Tell whether each statement is true or false. If it is false, explain why.

10. The Plane Separation Postulate can be proven.

11. Two collinear segments form a convex set.

12. The intersection of two half-spaces is a face.

13. The three undefined terms of geometry are all convex sets.

14. The half-planes created by an edge must be coplanar.

C. Use the figure below to list all correct answers for multiple-choice Exercises 15–18.

15. Two points on opposite sides of $\overleftrightarrow{AB}$ are

a. A and B. **b.** E and G.
c. F and G. **d.** G and D.

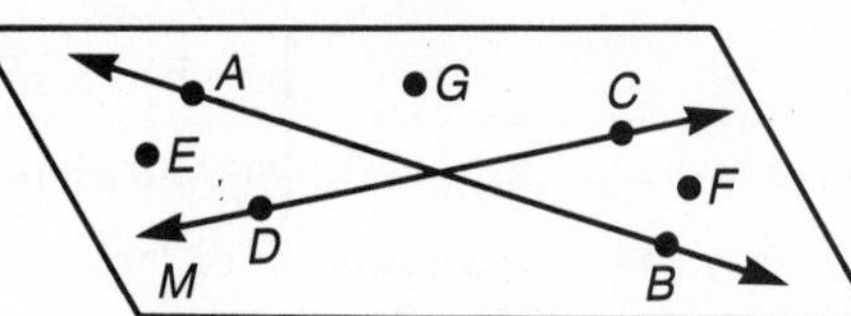

16. An example of an edge is

a. $\overleftrightarrow{AB}$. **b.** $\overrightarrow{DC}$. **c.** $\overrightarrow{AB}$. **d.** $\overleftrightarrow{DC}$.

17. Plane *M* is

a. a convex set. **b.** the union of two half-planes.

c. the union of two half-planes and an edge. **d.** a face.

18. Points *G* and *F* are

a. collinear. **b.** coplanar.

c. on opposite sides of $\overleftrightarrow{CD}$. **d.** on edge $\overleftrightarrow{GF}$.

16. a; d

17. a; c; d

18. a; b; c; d

SELF-QUIZ

Fill in the blanks.

1. All points contained in one line are ______.

2. All points contained in one plane are ______.

3. The set of all points is ______.

4. The intersection of two planes is a(n) ______.

5. Two lines intersect in a(n) ______.

6. If a line intersects a plane not containing it, the intersection is a(n) ______.

Identify each set as convex or nonconvex.

7. the letter J **8.** the surface of a stop sign

9. the surface of a fire hydrant **10.** the surface of a maple leaf

11. an edge **12.** a half-plane

Use the figure to answer Exercises 13–16. $\overleftrightarrow{PQ}$ separates the plane into two half-planes *M* and *N*.

13. Is $\overrightarrow{PQ}$ an edge?

14. In which half-plane do the points on $\overleftrightarrow{PQ}$ lie?

15. What is the edge of half-plane *N*?

16. Name two points in opposite half-planes.

M
Q
N
X
W
P
Y

Plane *F* is a face separating space into two half-spaces. Points *A* and *B* lie in opposite half-spaces of plane *F*.

17. Describe the intersection of $\overleftrightarrow{AB}$ and *F*.

18. Describe the intersection of *F* and any plane containing $\overleftrightarrow{AB}$.

Self-Quiz

1. collinear 2. coplanar
3. space 4. line
5. point 6. point
7. nonconvex 8. convex
9. nonconvex 10. nonconvex
11. convex 12. convex
13. no 14. neither
15. $\overleftrightarrow{PQ}$
16. *X* and *W* or *X* and *Y*
17. a point
18. a line

2.3 Angles and Triangles

OBJECTIVES

Identify sides, vertices, interiors, and exteriors of angles and triangles and name angles and triangles.

Determine the perimeter of a triangle.

TEACHER'S NOTES

See p. T25

MIXED REVIEW

1. What are the three properties of an equivalence relation?
   symmetric, reflexive, transitive
2. Solve $9x + 7 = 4x - 6$.
   $x = \frac{-13}{5}$
3. Multiply $(2x - 3)(x + 4)$.
   $2x^2 + 5x - 12$
4. Factor $x^2 + 7x + 12$.
   $(x + 3)(x + 4)$
5. Add $\sqrt{16} + \sqrt{9}$. 7

TEACHER'S RESOURCE MASTERS

Practice Master 5, Part 1

As students read the definition, encourage them to draw and label a model for what is stated. If they do this throughout the year, it will help to clarify definitions that are mathematically precise yet difficult to understand on first reading.

While you probably are comfortable with the term **angle,** a formal definition is now needed.

> **DEFINITIONS: angle; side of an angle; vertex**
> An **angle** is the union of two noncollinear rays with the same endpoint. The two rays are called the **sides** of the angle; their common endpoint is the **vertex.**

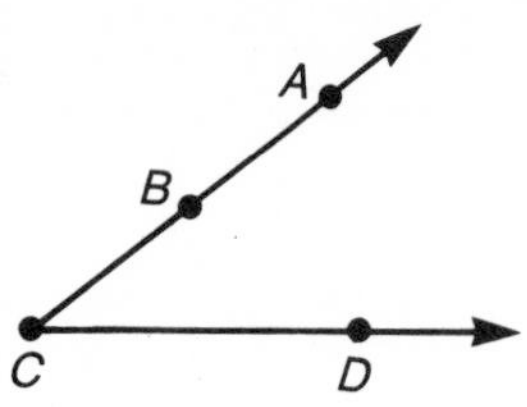

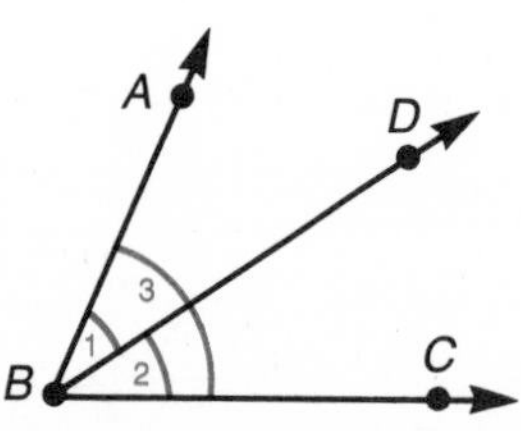

In the top figure at the left, $\overrightarrow{CA}$ and $\overrightarrow{CD}$ form an angle. To name the angle using three letters, you name a point on one side, followed by the vertex and a point on the other side. Note that $\angle ACD$ and $\angle BCD$ are names for the same angle. Would $\angle DCA$ be the same as $\angle ACD$? You may also simply call the angle $\angle C$, since it is clear from the model that only one angle could be $\angle C$. yes

Contrast $\angle C$ with the angle below it. Because B is the endpoint of three rays, $\angle B$ could mean $\angle ABD$, $\angle DBC$, or $\angle ABC$. Numbers can be used to distinguish angles as follows: $\angle 1$ is $\angle ABD$; $\angle 2$ is $\angle DBC$; and $\angle 3$ is $\angle ABC$. Naming an angle by using three letters (with the vertex in the middle) is always correct. Using one letter (corresponding to the vertex) is correct *if* there is no possibility of confusion. Numbers are also used to name angles.

The **interior** of an angle consists of all the points inside the angle; the **exterior** consists of all the points outside the angle. The points on the sides of the angle are not considered to be in either the interior or the exterior (much as an edge is not considered to be in either half-plane).

> **DEFINITIONS: interior; exterior**
> Let $\angle BAC$ be an angle lying in plane E. A point P of E lies in the **interior** of $\angle BAC$ if and only if **(1).** P and B are on the same side of $\overleftrightarrow{AC}$, and **(2).** P and C are on the same side of $\overleftrightarrow{AB}$. The **exterior** of $\angle BAC$ is the set of all points of E that do not lie in the interior and do not lie on the angle itself.

Some of the vocabulary you have learned for angles can now be extended to cover triangles as well.

DEFINITIONS: triangle; vertices; sides; angles of a triangle
If A, B, and C are any three noncollinear points, then the union of $\overline{AB}$, $\overline{AC}$, and $\overline{BC}$ is called a **triangle** and is denoted as $\triangle ABC$. The points A, B, and C are called its **vertices** (the plural of **vertex**), and the segments $\overline{AB}$, $\overline{AC}$, and $\overline{BC}$ are called its **sides.** The **angles of the triangle** are the three angles determined by the sides and vertices of the triangle.

The figure at the right shows $\triangle ABC$; the angles of the triangle are $\angle A$, $\angle B$, and $\angle C$. How could you name $\angle A$ using three letters? While $\triangle ABC$ *determines* three angles, it does not *contain* them. If, for example, $\angle A$ is drawn to show its sides as the rays they actually are, you can see that the sides of a triangle do not contain the rays of an angle but only determine them.

$\angle BAC$ or $\angle CAB$

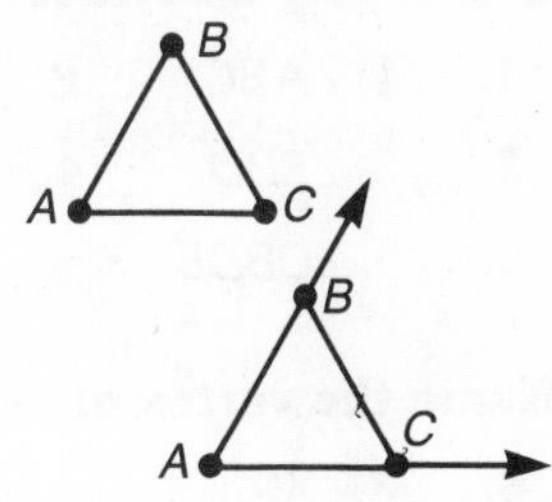

DEFINITIONS: interior/exterior of a triangle
A point lies in the **interior** of a triangle if and only if it lies in the interior of each angle of the triangle. A point lies in the **exterior** of the triangle if and only if it is coplanar with the triangle but is a part of neither the triangle nor its interior.

In the figure at the right, point X lies in the interior of $\triangle PQR$ and point Z lies in the exterior of $\triangle PQR$. Point Y does not lie in either the interior or the exterior of the triangle.

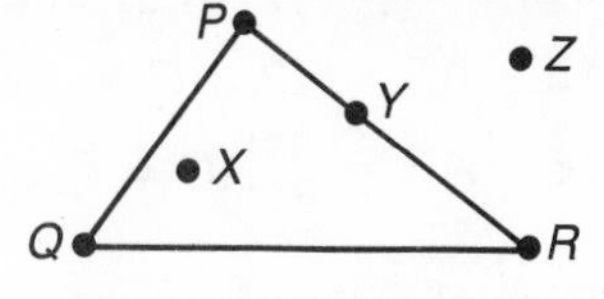

Is the interior of a triangle a convex set? Is the exterior? Is the triangle itself a convex set?

yes
no
no

Many times during the study of geometry, you will be concerned with the lengths of the sides of a triangle. The concept of perimeter will be introduced now.

DEFINITION: perimeter
The **perimeter** of a triangle is the sum of the lengths of its three sides.

Example: In $\triangle JEB$ at the right, JE is 5, BE is 9, and JB is 8. Find the perimeter of $\triangle JEB$.

$$\begin{aligned}\text{perimeter } \triangle JEB &= JE + JB + BE \\ &= 5 + 8 + 9 \\ &= 22\end{aligned}$$

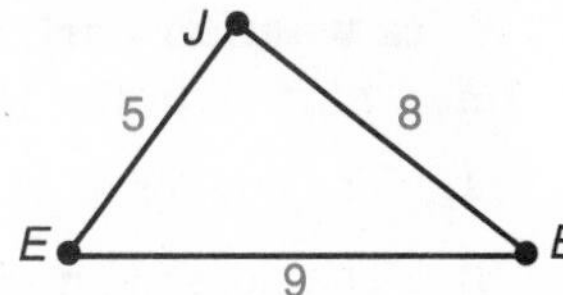

ASSIGNMENT GUIDE

Minimum 1-10, 14-18
Average 1-12, 14-20
Maximum 1-22

Oral Exercises

1. yes
2. no, ∠CBD or ∠DBC
3. yes
4. no, ∠ABE or ∠EBA
5. no, ∠CBE or ∠EBC
6. M, $\overrightarrow{MX}$, $\overrightarrow{MW}$
7. T
8. R
9. V, $\overrightarrow{VN}$, $\overrightarrow{VB}$
10. $\overline{AB}$, $\overline{AC}$, $\overline{BC}$, ∠A, ∠B, ∠C
11. $\overline{DE}$, $\overline{EF}$, $\overline{DF}$, ∠D, ∠E, ∠F
12. $\overline{GH}$, $\overline{HI}$, $\overline{GI}$, ∠G ∠H, ∠I
13. yes
14. 17
15. 98
16. $\frac{67}{8}$
17. 9x + 12
18. 13x + 2
19. 6x − 3
20. 6x − 6

Written Exercises

1. T
2. F; coplanar

ORAL EXERCISES

For Exercises 1–5, refer to the figure and state whether or not each numbered angle is matched with a correct letter name for the same angle. If it is not, supply a correct letter name.

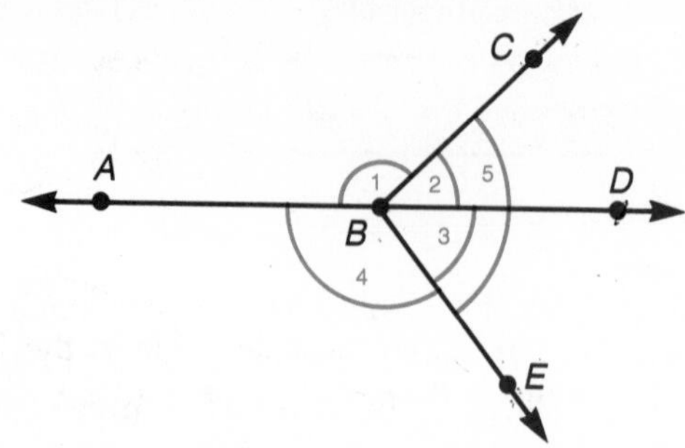

1. ∠1, ∠ABC **2.** ∠2, ∠B

3. ∠3, ∠EBD **4.** ∠4, ∠BEA

5. ∠5, ∠CBDE

Name the vertex of each of the following angles. If possible, also name the sides.

6. ∠XMW **7.** ∠T **8.** ∠R **9.** ∠NVB

Name the three sides and three vertices of each of the following triangles.

10. △ABC **11.** △DEF **12.** △GHI

13. Two identical triangles would have equal perimeters. Could the perimeters of two differently shaped triangles still be equal?

Find the perimeter of △*ABC* if

14. $AB = 3$, $AC = 8$, and $BC = 6$

15. $AB = 17$, $AC = 39$, and $BC = 42$

16. $AB = \frac{5}{8}$, $AC = \frac{9}{2}$, and $BC = \frac{13}{4}$

Give the simplest polynomial expression for the perimeter of △*SET* if

17. $SE = 2x + 3$, $ST = 4x + 5$, and $ET = 3x + 4$

18. $SE = 5x$, $ST = 7x - 1$, and $ET = x + 3$

19. $SE = 2x + 8$, $ST = x - 5$, and $ET = 3x - 6$

20. $SE = 14$, $ST = 2x - 20$, and $ET = 4x$

WRITTEN EXERCISES

A. Write whether each statement is true or false. If it is false, rewrite the underlined part to make it true.

1. The interior of an angle is a convex set.

2. The sides of an angle are collinear.

3. $\angle RMT$ is the same angle as $\angle TMR$.

4. If R and W are collinear, then $\angle RWT$ is the same as $\angle WRT$.

5. If the perimeter of a triangle and the lengths of two of its sides are known, the length of the third side cannot be determined.

6. A theorem is a statement accepted as true without proof.

7. There are ten numbered angles in the figure. Name each one in order by using letters instead of numbers.

8. Which is the only angle in the figure that can be named with one letter?

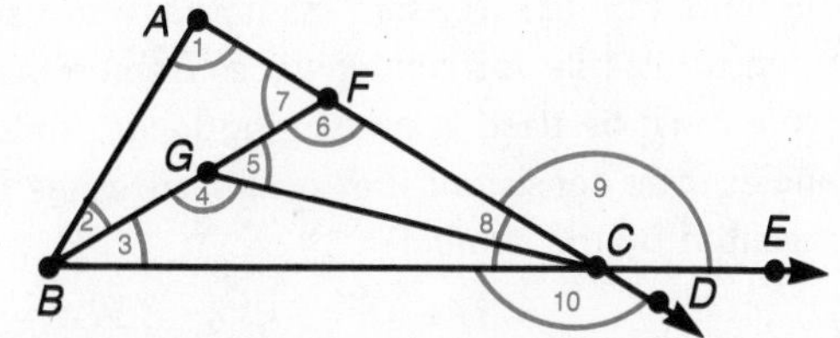

B. Find the length of each side of $\triangle MRT$ if its perimeter is 60 and

9. $MR = 3x + 5$, $MT = 3x - 1$, and $RT = 2x - 8$.

10. $MR = x + 14$, $MT = 5x - 10$, and $RT = 3x + 2$.

11. $MR = 3x + 7$, $MT = 6x - 11$, and $RT = x + 4$.

12. $MR = 17$, $MT = 3x + 1$, and $RT = 2x - 3$.

13. $MR = x - 4$, $MT = 4x$, and $RT = 5x - 6$.

Refer to the figure at the right to determine if the following statements are true or false.

14. B is in the exterior of $\triangle ACD$.

15. $\angle ABC$ contains $\angle ADC$.

16. $\triangle ADC$ and $\triangle ABC$ share two vertices.

17. All points in the interior of $\triangle ACD$ are also in the interior of $\angle B$.

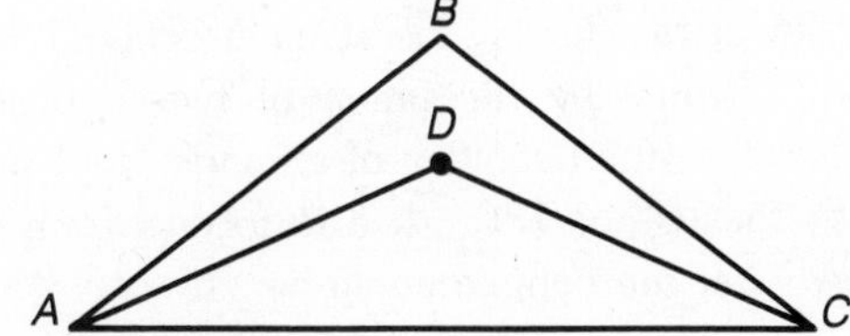

18. The perimeter of $\triangle ACD$ could be equal to the perimeter of $\triangle ABC$.

19. All points in the exterior of $\triangle ABC$ are also in the exterior of $\triangle ADC$.

20. All points in the exterior of $\triangle ADC$ are also in the exterior of $\triangle ABC$.

C. 21. In $\triangle XYZ$, $XY = 7x - 6$, $XZ = 3x + 4$, and the perimeter is $15x - 8$. If $YZ = 14$, find the lengths of $\overline{XY}$ and $\overline{XZ}$.

22. In the figure, B is the midpoint of $\overline{AC}$, $\overline{DA} \cong \overline{DC}$, and $DA = 10$. The perimeter of $\triangle ACD$ is 34. $AB = 4x - 1$, and $DB = 7x - 5$. Give the value of x and the perimeter of $\triangle DBC$.

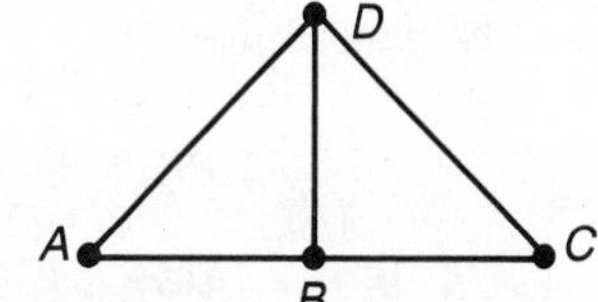

3. T
4. F; $\angle TWR$ or $\angle W$
5. F; can
6. F; a postulate
7. $\angle 1$ is $\angle A$; $\angle 2$ is $\angle ABF$; $\angle 3$ is $\angle FBC$; $\angle 4$ is $\angle BGC$; $\angle 5$ is $\angle FGC$; $\angle 6$ is $\angle BFC$; $\angle 7$ is $\angle AFB$; $\angle 8$ is $\angle ACB$; $\angle 9$ is $\angle ACE$; $\angle 10$ is $\angle BCD$. Other names are possible; hence, $\angle 8$ is also $\angle BCA$, $\angle BCF$, $\angle FCB$, and so on.
8. $\angle 1$
9. 29, 23, 8
10. 20, 20, 20
11. 25, 25, 10
12. 17, 28, 15
13. 3, 28, 29
14. T
15. F
16. T
17. T
18. F
19. T
20. F
21. $x = 4$; $XY = 22$, $XZ = 16$
22. $x = 2$, perimeter is 26

OBJECTIVES

Identify congruent angles.
Use a protractor to measure angles.

TEACHER'S NOTES

See p. T25

MIXED REVIEW

1. Must three points be coplanar? yes
2. Graph $x + 2 \leq 5$.

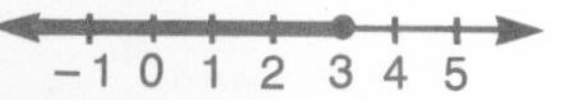

Find *AB* if the coordinates of *A* and *B* are:

3. −7 and 20. 27
4. 6*x* and 2*x*. 4 |*x*|
5. −13 and −19. 6

TEACHER'S RESOURCE MASTERS

Practice Master 5, Part 2
Quiz 4

2.4 Angles and Their Measure

The study of angles is important in geometry. Especially important is the idea of congruent angles. In order to define congruent angles, it is necessary to learn how angles are measured.

All units of measure, such as hours, meters, and gallons, are units that people have agreed upon arbitrarily for convenience. Remember that in Chapter 1 it was agreed that the same scale must be used in measuring length to avoid confusion. To avoid confusion in measuring angles, one consistent unit of measure has been used for hundreds of years: **degrees,** represented by the symbol "°."

POSTULATE 11 (The Angle Measurement Postulate)
To every ∠*BAC* there corresponds a real number between 0 and 180.

You may wonder why the numbers range from 0 to 180, instead of to 200, 300, 1000, or some other rounder number. One of the primary reasons the ancients developed geometry was to study the heavens. They divided up the sky based on the constellations they could see, and the result was a system of measurement based on 180 units.

Remember that the definition of *angle* is "the *union* of two *noncollinear* rays." An angle of 0° would be the union of two collinear rays having the same direction. Likewise, an angle of 180° would be the union of two opposite *collinear* rays. Therefore the definition of an angle does not allow for angles of either 0° or 180°. It also follows from the definition that ∠*ABC* at the right can only be ∠1.

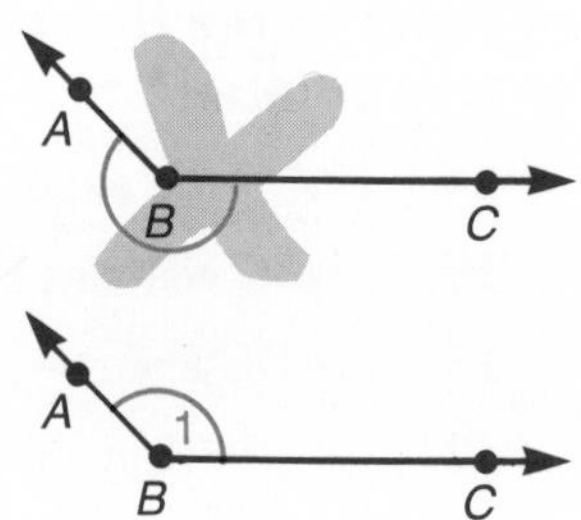

Using algebraic symbols, you may condense the statement "the measure of any angle *A* is between 0° and 180°" to read: $0 < m\angle A < 180$. When a degree measure is used in an algebraic statement, the degree symbol (°) is omitted. An "*m*" is written in front of the angle symbol so "*m*∠*A*" is read as "the measure of angle *A*." Thus, you would write "$m\angle ABC = 30$," *not* $\angle ABC = 30$ or $m\angle ABC = 30°$. ∠*ABC names* an angle, while *m*∠*ABC* is a number representing the *measure* of the angle. The statement $\angle ABC \cong \angle XYZ$ means that the angles have the same measure.

DEFINITION: congruent angles
Congruent angles are angles of the same degree measure.

If $m\angle X = 25$ and $m\angle Y = 25$, it follows that $\angle X \cong \angle Y$. Remember that rays extend in one direction without end; hence the size of an angle is not dependent on the lengths of the rays. In the figure at the right, $\angle C$ and $\angle D$ are congruent because they both measure 30.

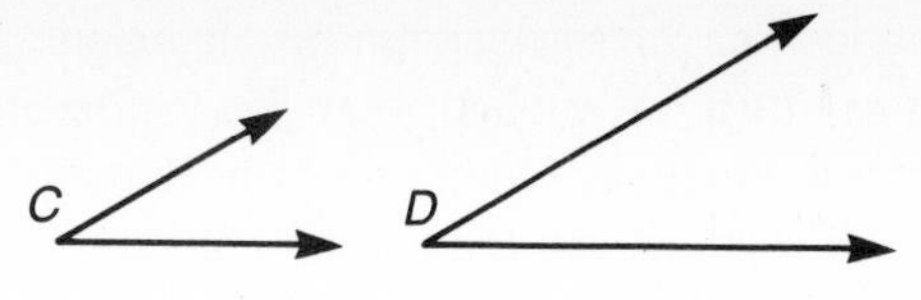

In order to determine the exact measure of an angle accurately and consistently, you will need to become familiar with a **protractor.** A protractor is divided into 180 units representing degrees. One set of numbers reads clockwise and a second set reads counterclockwise so both "left-hand" and "right-hand" angles may be measured. To measure an angle, first place the notch or mark in the center of the protractor's bottom edge at the vertex of the angle. Next, adjust the protractor so that one ray is aligned with the the bottom edge. The point where the other ray intersects the protractor is the measure of the angle. Always read the number from the same set as the 0 aligned with the bottom edge. Use a protractor to confirm that the angle shown measures 35.

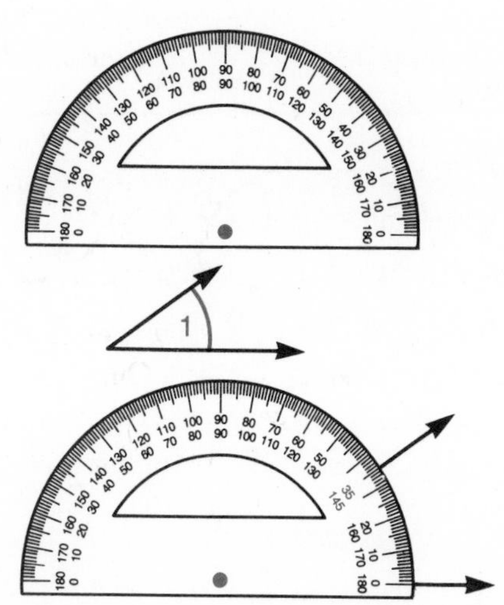

In Chapter 1, an equivalence relation was defined as any relation that is reflexive, symmetric, and transitive. Equality was shown to be an equivalence relation. To determine whether or not the congruence of angles is also an equivalence relation, consider the following:

$\angle X \cong \angle X$	(reflexive property)
If $\angle X \cong \angle Y$, then $\angle Y \cong \angle X$	(symmetric property)
If $\angle X \cong \angle Y$ and $\angle Y \cong \angle Z$, then $\angle X \cong \angle Z$	(transitive property)

Because congruent angles are defined as angles with equal measures, you can translate the statements above with no loss of meaning:

$m\angle X = m\angle X$	(reflexive property)
If $m\angle X = m\angle Y$, then $m\angle Y = m\angle X$	(symmetric property)
If $m\angle X = m\angle Y$ and $m\angle Y = m\angle Z$, then $m\angle X = m\angle Z$	(transitive property)

Since $m\angle X$, $m\angle Y$, and $m\angle Z$ are all numerical values, and since you already know that equality of numbers is an equivalence relation, it follows that congruence of angles is an equivalence relation as well.

Now look at the two-column proofs below. Although this proof does not specifically refer to angles, it will be applied to angles in Chapter 3. To prove $x = y + z$ iff $x - y = z$, two proofs are actually required, one beginning with the first equation and proving the second, the other beginning with the second equation and proving the first:

Given: $x = y + z$

Prove: $x - y = z$

Proof:

STATEMENTS	REASONS
1. $x = y + z$	1. Given
2. $x + (-y) = y + z + (-y)$	2. Addition property of equality
3. $x + (-y) = z + y + (-y)$	3. Commutative property of addition
4. $x + (-y) = z + 0$	4. Inverse property of addition
5. $x + (-y) = z$	5. Identity property of addition
6. $x - y = z$	6. Definition of subtraction

Now for the second proof:

Given: $x - y = z$

Prove: $x = y + z$

Proof:

STATEMENTS	REASONS
1. $x - y = z$	1. Given
2. $x + (-y) = z$	2. Definition of subtraction
3. $x + (-y) + y = z + y$	3. Addition property of equality
4. $x + 0 = z + y$	4. Inverse property of addition
5. $x = z + y$	5. Identity property of addition
6. $x = y + z$	6. Commutative property of addition

The statement you have just proved, $x = y + z$ iff $x - y = z$, may seem obvious, especially if you replace x, y, and z with real numbers. The concept is particularly useful, however, when applied to angle measure, as you will see in the next chapter.

ORAL EXERCISES

Refer to the figure to complete each statement.

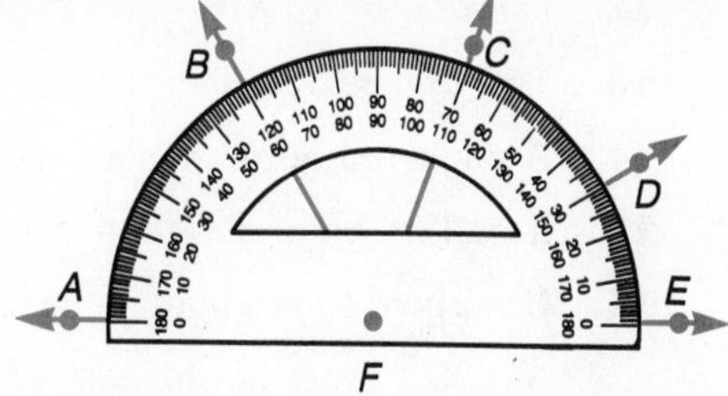

1. $m\angle AFB$ = ____. **2.** $m\angle AFC$ = ____.
3. $m\angle AFD$ = ____. **4.** $m\angle EFD$ = ____.
5. $m\angle EFC$ = ____.
6. $m\angle DFB$ = ____.
7. What are the three properties necessary to determine an equivalence relation?
8. State the difference between $\angle XYZ$ and $m\angle XYZ$.
9. What is wrong with the statement $\angle X \cong 50$?
10. Explain why two angles with sides of apparently different lengths can be congruent?

WRITTEN EXERCISES

A. Each statement below is written *incorrectly*. Correct the error.

1. $m\angle X \cong m\angle Y$ **2.** $m\angle A = 30°$ **3.** $\angle W \cong 20$
4. $0 \leq m\angle A \leq 180$
5. Without using a protractor, sketch angles of approximately 30°, 100°, and 170°.
6. Referring to the protractor at the right, name two pairs of congruent angles.

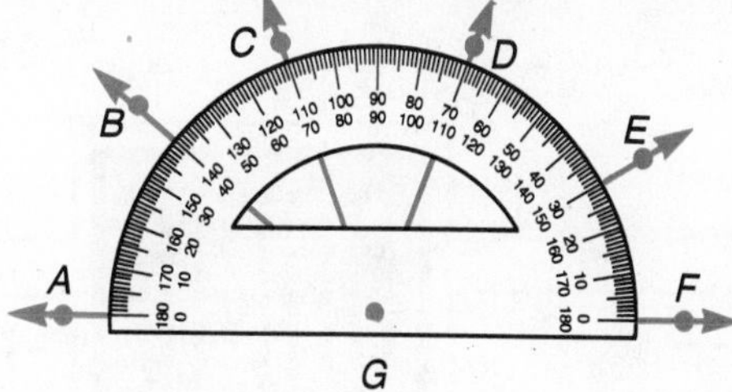

B. Use your protractor to determine the measure of each angle below within 5 degrees.

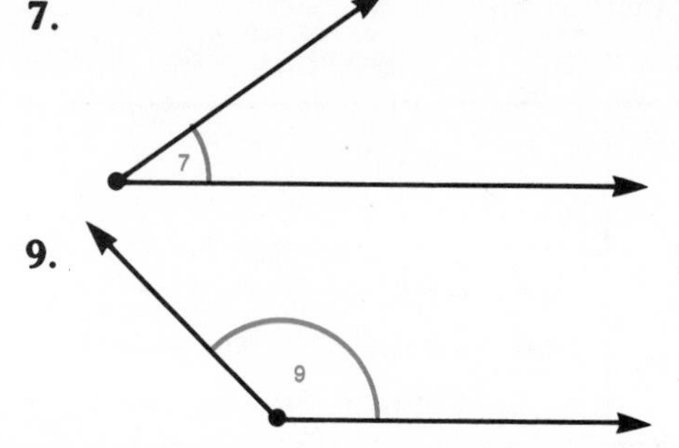

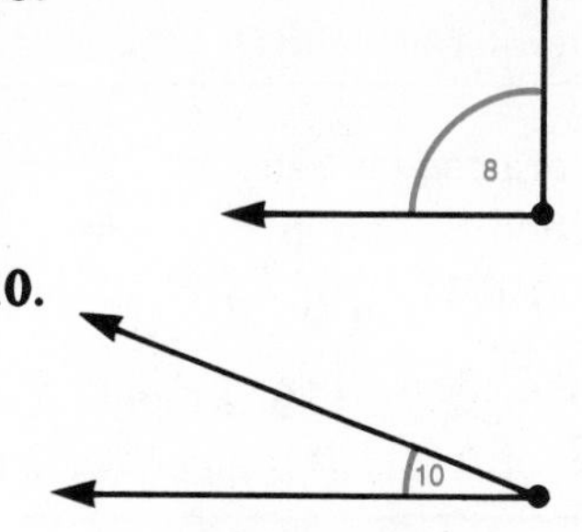

ASSIGNMENT GUIDE

Minimum 1-17
Regular 1-21
Maximum 1-24 odd

Oral Exercises

1. 60 2. 110
3. 150 4. 30
5. 70 6. 90
7. reflexive, symmetric, transitive
8. $\angle XYZ$ is an angle; $m\angle XYZ$ is a number.
9. $\angle X$ names an angle, not a measure.
10. The side of an angle is a ray, and all rays have the same "length" even though they may be depicted differently.

Written Exercises

1. $m\angle X = m\angle Y$ or $\angle X \cong \angle Y$
2. $m\angle A = 30$ 3. $m\angle W = 20$
4. $0 < m\angle A < 180$
5.

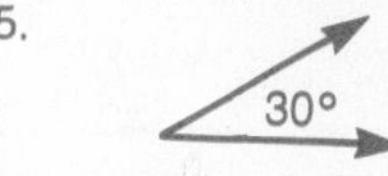

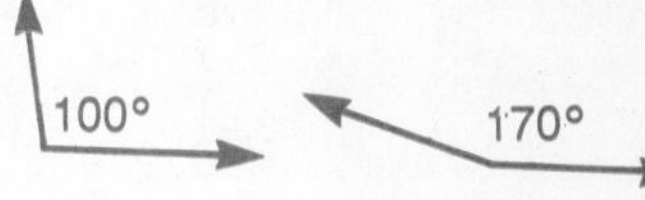

6. $\angle AGC \cong \angle FGD$, $\angle AGD \cong \angle CGF$
7. 35° 9. 135°
8. 90° 10. 20°

11. F 12. T

13. F 14. F

15. T 16. T

17. 40 18. 150

19. 90

20.

X A T M R

21. 35 22. 85

23. 60

24. *1.* $x \cdot y = w$ (Given); *2.* $x \cdot y(\frac{1}{y}) = w(\frac{1}{y})$ (Mult. prop. of equality); *3.* $x \cdot 1 = w(\frac{1}{y})$ (Inverse prop. of mult.); *4.* $x = w(\frac{1}{y})$ (Identity prop. of mult.); *5.* $x = w \div y$ (Def. of division).
The reverse of this proof is necessary to show $x = w \div y \rightarrow x \cdot y = w$.

Error Search

1. S: Q is in A and B.
2. R: Def. of convex set
3. S: $\overline{PQ}$ is in the intersection . . .
4. S: The intersection of A and B . . .

Tell whether each statement in Exercises 11–16 is <u>true</u> or <u>false</u>.

11. $m\angle MRT = 40$ and $\angle MRT \cong 40$ mean the same thing.

12. $m\angle MRT = m\angle XWA$ and $\angle MRT \cong \angle XWA$ mean the same thing.

13. Two opposite rays form an angle of 180°.

14. A single ray represents an angle of 0°.

15. If $m\angle 1 = 80$ and $m\angle 2 = 80$, then $\angle 1 \cong \angle 2$.

16. Congruent angles may be noncoplanar.

$\overrightarrow{QP}$ and $\overrightarrow{QS}$ are noncollinear rays. Point R is in the interior of $\angle PQS$. Using this information, complete each statement below.

17. If $\angle PQR \cong \angle RQS$, and $m\angle PQS = 80$, $m\angle RQS =$ ____.

18. If $m\angle PQR = 100$, and $m\angle RQS = \frac{1}{2}m\angle PQR$, $m\angle PQS =$ ____.

C. 19. If $\angle R \cong \angle W$, $m\angle R = 4x + 10$, and $m\angle W = 6x - 30$, find $m\angle R$.

20. Draw a figure to match the following description: $m\angle AMR = 60$; point T is in the interior of $\angle AMR$ such that $m\angle RMT = 25$; and point X is in the exterior of $\angle AMR$ such that $\angle AMX \cong \angle RMT$.

Refer to the figure you drew for Exercise 20 to complete the following statements.

21. $m\angle TMA =$ ____.

22. $m\angle XMR =$ ____.

23. $m\angle XMT =$ ____.

24. Prove $x \cdot y = w$ iff $x = w \div y$.

ERROR SEARCH

Given that A and B are convex sets having at least two points, P and Q, in common, it can be proven that the intersection of A and B is also a convex set. Correct the error in each step of the proof that follows:

Proof:

STATEMENTS	REASONS
1. A and B are convex sets; P is in A and B; Q is in B.	*1.* Given
2. $\overline{PQ}$ is in A; $\overline{PQ}$ is in B.	*2.* Definition of between
3. PQ is in the intersection of A and B.	*3.* Definition of intersection
4. The union of A and B is a convex set.	*4.* Definition of a convex set

SKILLS MAINTENANCE

What is the first step in solving each equation below?

1. $x + 6 = 2$ **2.** $2x + x = 3$ **3.** $3k - 2 = k + 6$

4. $6x + 7 = x$ **5.** $\frac{2}{3}y = \frac{5}{2}$ **6.** $\frac{(x + 2)}{2} = 5$

For Exercises 7–12, solve each equation above.
Solve each equation.

13. $4(x - 5) + 2 = 3x + 7$ **14.** $0.3(x + 3) = 0.2(x + 3) + 0.6$

15. $\frac{x}{2} = \frac{5}{7}$ **16.** $\frac{1}{2}y + \frac{3}{2} = \frac{5}{4}$

For each equation below, if the replacement set is the real numbers, state whether the solution set is (*a*) empty, (*b*) real numbers, or (*c*). a proper subset of the set of real numbers.

17. $x + 1 = x - 1$ **18.** $x^2 = -2$ **19.** $3x + 5 = 2x$

20. $6(\frac{2}{3}x - 1) = 4x - 6$ **21.** $2x(\frac{12}{6} - 2) = 7$ **22.** $5 - x = 2 + x$

Solve for *x*.

23. $t - rx = d$ **24.** $ax - b = cx + d$ **25.** $fx + ghx = j + kx$

EXPLORATION/
Base Systems

The base ten number system uses ten number symbols: 0, 1, 2, 3, 4, 5, 6, 7, 8, and 9. These symbols assume different values according to the position they occupy in a numeral. The numeral 56 means five groups of ten and six ones.

Base two, the binary system used by computers, uses only two number symbols: 0 and 1. These correspond to open and closed circuits within the computer. 1011_{two} means $(1 \times 2^3) + (0 \times 2^2) + (1 \times 2^1) + (1 \times 2^0)$. The first six numerals in base two are 1, 10, 11, 100, 101, and 110. Can you perform the following operations in base two?

a. $\begin{array}{r} 1101 \\ \times 111 \end{array}$ **b.** $\begin{array}{r} 111 \\ +101 \end{array}$ **c.** $\begin{array}{r} 101 \\ \times 11 \end{array}$ **d.** $\begin{array}{r} 1011 \\ \times 111 \end{array}$

If you wanted to work with a base twelve system, what would you have to invent?

Skills Maintenance

1. Add −6 to both sides.
2. Combine x and $2x$.
3. Add 2 and $-k$ to both sides.
4. Add −7 and $-x$ to both sides.
5. Multiply both sides by $\frac{3}{2}$.
6. Multiply both sides by 2.

7. $x = -4$ 8. $x = 1$
9. $k = 4$ 10. $x = \frac{-7}{5}$
11. $y = \frac{15}{4}$ 12. $x = 8$
13. $x = 25$ 14. $x = 3$
15. $x = \frac{10}{7}$ 16. $y = -\frac{1}{2}$
17. a 18. a
19. c 20. b
21. a 22. c
23. $x = \frac{t - d}{r}$
24. $x = \frac{b + d}{a - c}$
25. $x = \frac{j}{f + gh - k}$

Exploration

a. 10100
c. 1111
b. 1100
d. 1001101

symbols for ten and eleven

IN OTHER FIELDS/ Navigation

Picture a large ship sailing beyond the sight of land on a vast expanse of water in 300 BC. Now, picture yourself as captain of this ship! How are you to determine your location and the time?

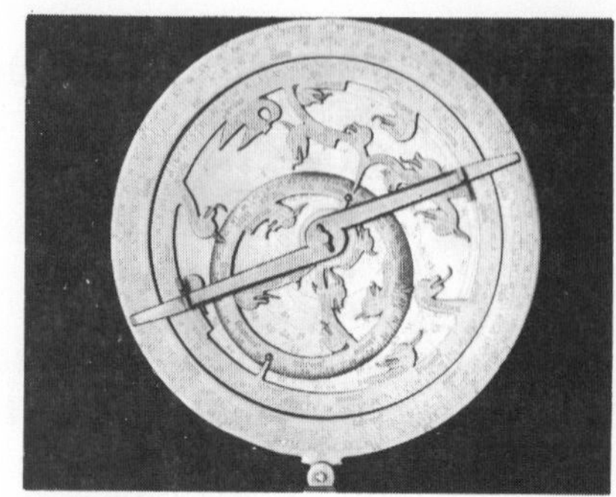

Using what you already know of these voyages, you might turn to the sky, stars, and sun to help determine your direction.

By 539 BC, Babylonian astronomers had divided the sky into twelve constellations, 30° apart, in a circle of 360°. Later, the Persians added more scientific observations to these Babylonian ideas.

The Greek Ptolemy produced a star table listing 1022 stars and their positions as seen from Alexandria, Egypt. Constructing this table required accuracy in measuring degrees of position and minutes of time. The Greeks invented an instrument called the *astrolabe* (above). This balanced disk of wood or metal was graduated in degrees, like a protractor, and used in measuring the altitude of the sun or stars. From these measurements, sailors could calculate time and latitude.

For 2000 years, sailors used the astrolabe, possibly making it the oldest scientific instrument in the world. In the 1700's it was replaced by the *sextant* (left). The sextant got its name from the framework of brass (ABC) that forms a 60° angle. Its purpose is the same as the astrolabe, but the sextant is more accurate.

The sextant was adapted for use on land and in the air, and is still used at sea as a backup instrument and for teaching basic navigational principles.

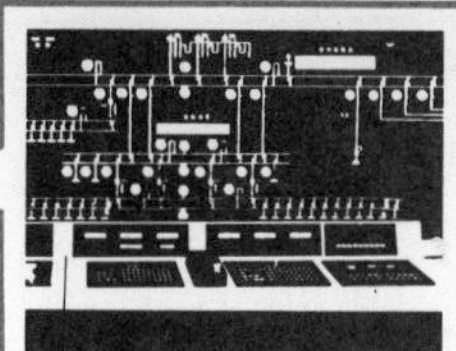

COMPUTER

The FOR-NEXT command is useful when certain steps in a computer program must be applied repeatedly. For example, suppose you are designing a program that requires computing the square roots of all integers between 1 and 100. BASIC has a built-in square root function (SQR), but to input manually 100 integers would be a tedious task. The computer can perform this task for you by what is called a *loop,* using the FOR-NEXT command. A loop is a self-contained part of a program that is reapplied according to the number of intervals, or *increments,* you designate. The loop for calculating square roots would look like this:

```
60  FOR X = 1 TO 100
70  LET S = SQR(X)
80  PRINT S
90  NEXT X
```

After the SQR(100) is printed, the program exits the loop and executes the statement immediately, following the NEXT X statement. Any number of calculations or decisions may occur within a loop, but once a program exits a loop, it can reenter that loop only through the original FOR statement.

The figure shows a triangle whose sides are expressed in terms of any number x. The program below uses a FOR-NEXT loop to calculate the perimeter of the triangle for every value of x between 1 and 15. For each x, the program prints the lengths of the three sides and the perimeter. Supply the missing steps.

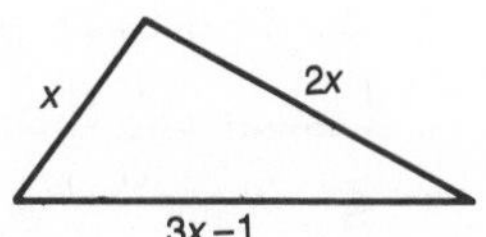


```
10    REM CALCULATE THE PERIMETER OF A TRIANGLE WITH SIDES
      X,2X,3X − 1
20    FOR X = 1 TO __1.__
30    PRINT "THE SIDES OF THE TRIANGLE HAVE LENGTHS";X;
      ","  __2.__ ",";"AND";3 * X − 1
40    LET P = __3.__
50    PRINT "THE PERIMETER OF THE TRIANGLE IS"; __4.__
60    NEXT __5.__
70    END
```

TEACHER'S RESOURCE MASTERS

Computer Master 2

Computer Skills

1. 15
2. 2 * X
3. 6 * X − 1
4. P
5. X

TEACHER'S RESOURCE MASTERS

Enrichment Master 2

ENRICHMENT

See Activities 3-4, p. T43

TEACHER'S NOTES

See p. T26

Chapter 2 Review

1. A
2. S
3. A
4. N
5. N
6. S
7. N
8. T
9. F
10. T
11. F
12. T
13. c
14. a

CHAPTER 2 REVIEW

VOCABULARY

angle (2.3)
angle of a triangle (2.3)
collinear (2.1)
congruent angles (2.4)
convex (2.2)
coplanar (2.1)
degrees (2.4)
edge (2.2)
exterior of a triangle (2.3)
exterior of an angle (2.3)
face (2.2)
half-plane (2.2)
half-space (2.2)
interior of a triangle (2.3)
interior of an angle (2.3)
perimeter of a triangle (2.3)
protractor (2.4)
region (2.2)
side of a triangle (2.3)
side of an angle (2.3)
space (2.1)
triangle (2.3)
vertex of a triangle (2.3)
vertex of an angle (2.3)

REVIEW EXERCISES

2.1 Are the following true always, sometimes, or never?

1. Two points are collinear.
2. Three points are collinear.
3. The intersection of two planes is a line.
4. $\overleftrightarrow{AB}$ and $\overleftrightarrow{CD}$ are two different lines. Their intersection is points A and C.
5. Noncoplanar lines intersect in a point.
6. Four points determine space.
7. Postulates can be proven.

2.2 Answer the following exercises with true or false.

8. A line is a convex set.
9. A triangle is a convex set.
10. The interior of an angle is a convex set.
11. A ray separates a plane into two half-planes.
12. The points on the edge of a half-plane are not contained in the half-plane.

Refer to the figure at the right.

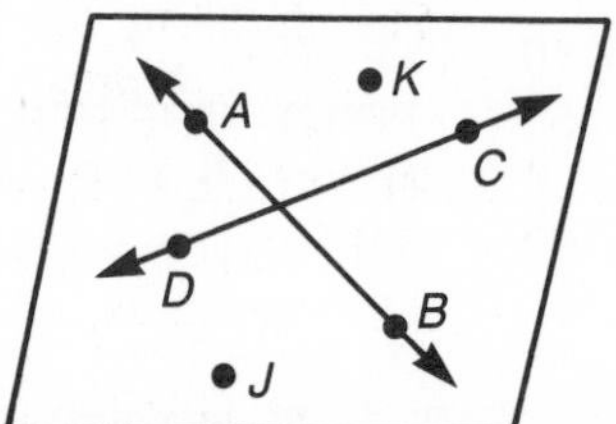

13. Two points on the same side of $\overleftrightarrow{AB}$ are

a. D, K **b.** D, C **c.** D, J **d.** K, J

14. Two points on opposite sides of $\overleftrightarrow{AB}$ are

a. D, K **b.** A, D **c.** D, J **d.** K, C

For Exercises 15–16, refer to the figure at the right.

15. Two points in the same half-plane are
   a. X, Y. b. R, S.
   c. V, J. d. V, R.

16. Two points in opposite half-planes are
   a. X, Y. b. V, J.
   c. T, S. d. X, K.

2.3 17. In all cases, another name for $\angle BAC$ is
   a. $\angle A$. b. $\angle CAB$. c. $\angle ABC$. d. $\angle CBA$.

Refer to the figure at the right for Exercises 18–20.

18. Which of the following is NOT a side of $\triangle CDB$?
   a. $\overline{DB}$ b. $\overline{DA}$ c. $\overline{BC}$ d. $\overline{CD}$

19. Which of the following is NOT an angle of $\triangle ADB$?
   a. $\angle ADB$ b. $\angle DAB$ c. $\angle AED$ d. $\angle ABD$

20. Which of the following does not have A as a vertex?
   a. $\angle BAE$ b. $\angle CAB$ c. $\angle DAE$ d. $\angle CDB$

21. In $\triangle EBA$, $EA = 4x + 1$, $AB = 7x + 21$, and $EB = 9x - 3$. The perimeter is 279. Find the length of each side.

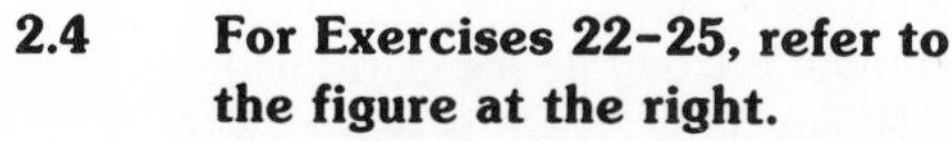

2.4 **For Exercises 22–25, refer to the figure at the right.**

22. What angles are congruent to $\angle BYX$?

23. What is $m\angle XYB$?

24. What is $m\angle BYC$?

25. What angle is congruent to $\angle EYZ$?

For Exercises 26–28, refer to the figure at the right.

26. If $\angle BAC \cong \angle DAE$ and $m\angle DAB = 30$, what is $m\angle EAC$?

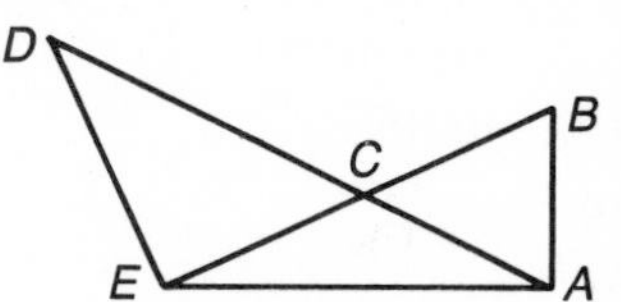

27. If $m\angle ACB = 4x + 6$, $m\angle DEC = 46$, and $\angle ACB \cong \angle DEC$, find x.

28. If $\angle EDC \cong \angle CAE$, $m\angle EDA = 38$, and $m\angle DAE = 7x - 11$, find x.

15. d
16. a
17. b
18. b
19. c
20. d
21. $EA = 53$, $AB = 112$, $EB = 114$
22. $\angle DYZ$, $\angle BYE$
23. 75
24. 10
25. $\angle BYD$
26. 30
27. $x = 10$
28. $x = 7$

TEACHER'S RESOURCE MASTERS

Chapter 2 Test
Multiple Choice Test-Chapter 2

Chapter 2 Test

1. T
2. T
3. F
4. T
5. T
6. T
7. F
8. T
9. F
10. E
11. 13
12. 4
13.

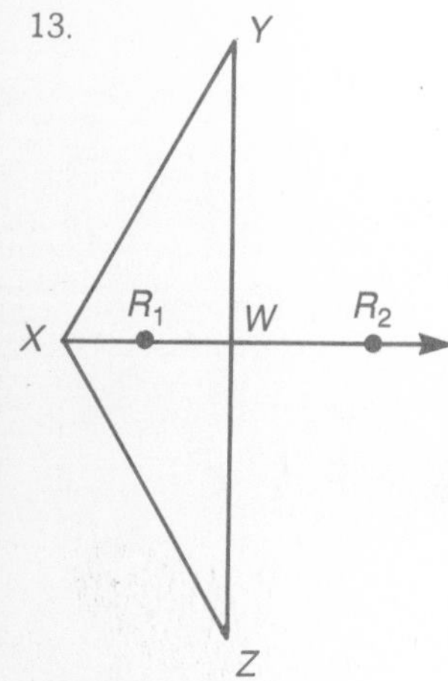

14. $\frac{5}{6}$
15. ∠DFE, ∠CFB
16. ∠AFB, ∠CFD
17. ∠CFA, ∠BFD, ∠CFE
18. 120
19. AFD
20. $\overrightarrow{FA}$

CHAPTER 2 TEST

Refer to the figure for Problems 1-9 and determine whether each statement is *true* or *false*.

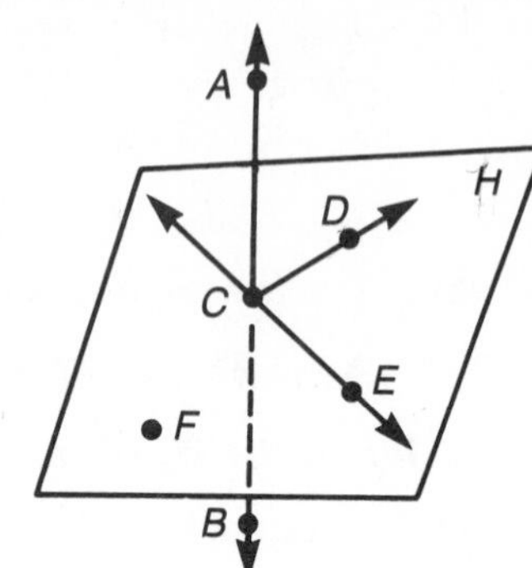

1. Points *B*, *F*, and *E* are coplanar.

2. Points *B* and *D* are collinear.

3. The intersection of $\overleftrightarrow{AB}$ and plane *H* is $\overrightarrow{CA}$.

4. Plane *H* divides space into two half-spaces.

5. $\overleftrightarrow{CE}$ is an edge separating plane *H*.

6. Points *D* and *F* are on opposite sides of $\overleftrightarrow{CE}$.

7. Point *F* is in the interior of ∠*DCE*.

8. The interior of ∠*DCE* is a convex set.

9. ∠*DCE* can also be called ∠*C*.

Refer to the figure for Exercises 10-12.

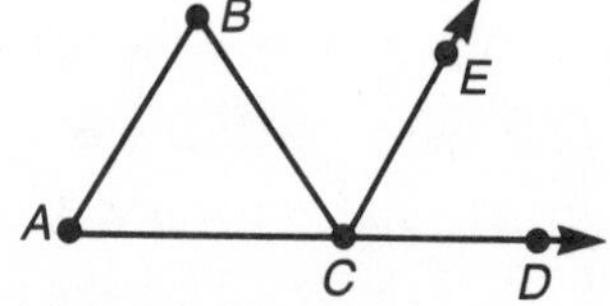

10. Name a point in the interior of ∠*A*.

11. If the perimeter of △*ABC* = 38, *AB* = 12, and $\overline{BC} \cong \overline{AC}$, how long is *BC*?

12. If $AB = 8x + 6$, $BC = 4x - 2$, $AC = 13x - 9$, and the perimeter of △*ABC* = 95, find *x*.

13. Draw a figure that matches this description (Estimate the degree measures without a protractor.): In △*XYZ*, *m*∠*YXZ* = 120; point *W* lies on $\overline{YZ}$ such that *m*∠*YXW* = *m*∠*ZXW* = 60; point *R*, on $\overrightarrow{XW}$, is in the interior of ∠*YXZ*.

14. If ∠*A* ≅ ∠*B*, *m*∠*A* = $12x + 32$, and *m*∠*B* = 42, find *x*.

Refer to the figure for Exercises 15-20:

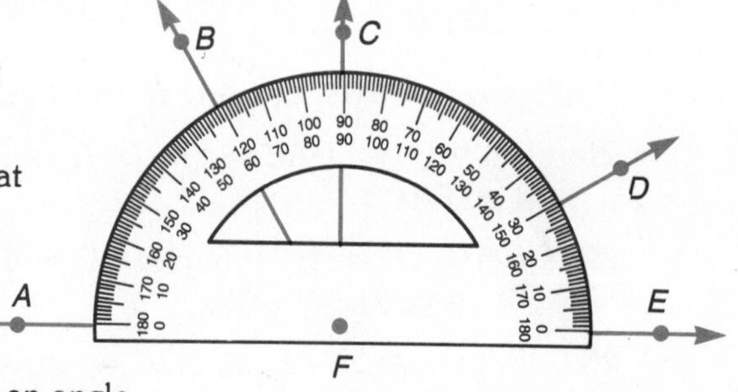

15. Name the two congruent angles that measure 30.

16. Name the two congruent angles that measure 60.

17. Name the three congruent angles that measure 90.

18. *m*∠*BFE* = _____.

19. Angle _____ measures 150.

20. The rays $\overrightarrow{EF}$ and _____ do not form an angle.

CHAPTER 3

Angles, Triangles, and Congruence

3.1 The Supplement Postulate

OBJECTIVES

Identify adjacent and supplementary angles.
Given the measure of an angle, find the measure of its supplement.

TEACHER'S NOTES

See p. T26

MIXED REVIEW

1. Is the union of two half-planes a plane?
   No; edge is missing.
2. Factor $2x^2 - 5x - 12$.
   $(2x + 3)(x - 4)$
3. Solve $x^2 = 9$. $\{3, -3\}$
4. If $(x - 2)(x - 5) = 0$, then $x =$ ______ or ______.
   2; 5
5. Solve $2x - 3y = 4$
   $2x + y = 12$. $(5, 2)$

TEACHER'S RESOURCE MASTERS

Practice Master 6

In Chapter 1 you learned that postulates are statements accepted as true without a proof. The list of postulates is becoming more complete, and you will soon be able to combine these postulates with the defined and undefined terms to prove more theorems about angles, triangles, and congruence.

Before you can continue, it is necessary to discuss angles and their measures. As you saw in the previous chapter, every angle is associated with a unique real number between 0 and 180. This number is referred to as its measure. When an angle is said to have a measure of 45, this means that it contains 45 degrees. Remember that $\angle ABC$ is the symbol used to name the angle itself, where $m\angle ABC$ is the number of degrees in the angle.

POSTULATE 12 (The Angle Construction Postulate)
Let $\overrightarrow{AB}$ be a ray on the edge of the half-plane H. For every number r between 0 and 180 there is exactly one ray $\overrightarrow{AP}$ with P in H such that $m\angle PAB = r$.

POSTULATE 13 (The Angle Addition Postulate)
If D is a point in the interior of $\angle BAC$, then $m\angle BAC = m\angle BAD + m\angle DAC$.

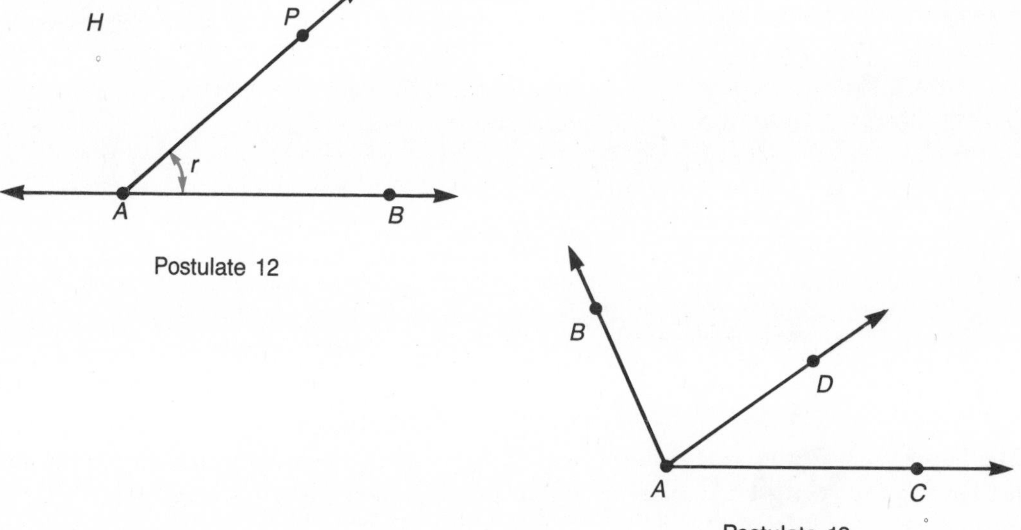

Postulate 12

Postulate 13

For example, if $m\angle BAD = 25$ and $m\angle DAC = 80$ then $m\angle BAC = 105$. Angles that are "next to" each other, like $\angle BAD$ and $\angle DAC$, are called **adjacent angles.**

DEFINITION: adjacent angles
Two coplanar angles are **adjacent** if and only if they have a common side, but no points in the interior of one angle are in the interior of the other.

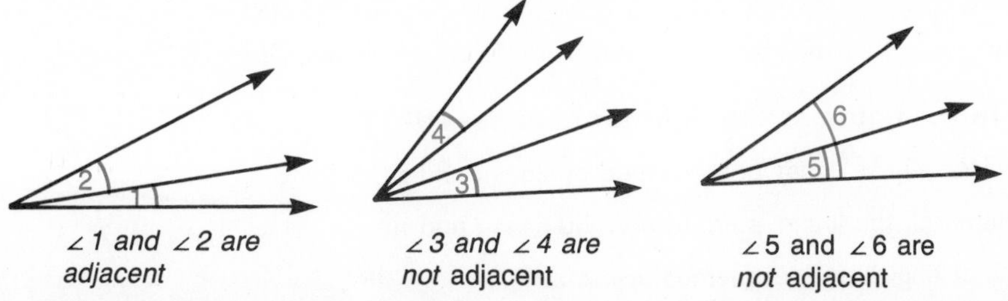

∠1 and ∠2 are *adjacent*

∠3 and ∠4 are *not* adjacent

∠5 and ∠6 are *not* adjacent

DEFINITION: supplementary angles
Two angles are **supplementary** if and only if the sum of their measures is 180.

Each angle, ∠*ABC* and ∠*DEF*, is called a **supplement** of the other. The two angles are then referred to as *supplementary angles.*

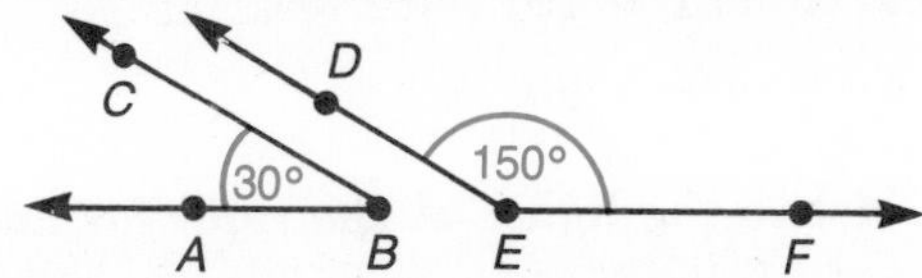

DEFINITION: linear pair
Two angles form a **linear pair** if and only if they are adjacent angles and the noncommon sides are opposite rays.

POSTULATE 14 (The Supplement Postulate)
If two angles form a linear pair, then they are supplementary.

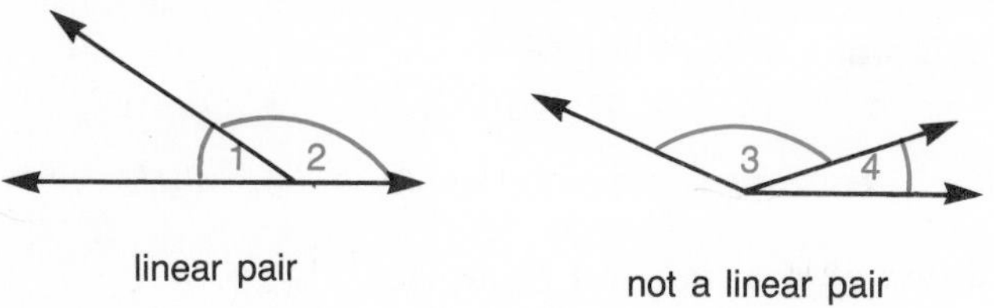

linear pair

not a linear pair

The Supplement Postulate is always true, but its converse is not. Supplementary angles do not have to form a linear pair or even be located in the same plane. Two angles are supplementary as long as the sum of their measure is 180.

ASSIGNMENT GUIDE

Day 1
Minimum 1-23 odd
Regular 1-23 odd
Maximum 1-27 odd

Day 2
Minimum 2-24 even
Regular 6-32 even
Maximum 12-28 even, 31-35

Oral Exercises

1. 58 2. 141
3. 63 4. 18
5. 140 6. 99
7. $180 - a$ 8. $187 - 3b$
9. ∠1, ∠2; ∠1, ∠4; ∠3, ∠4; ∠2, ∠3
10. ∠5, ∠6; ∠5, ∠8; ∠6, ∠7; ∠7, ∠8
11. ∠2, ∠4
12. ∠5, ∠7
13. ∠1, ∠2; ∠1, ∠4; ∠3, ∠4; ∠2, ∠3
14. 79 15. 96
16. 90 17. 112
18. *m*∠*AOC* 19. *m*∠*AOD*
20. 95 21. $5x$

Written Exercises

1. 160 2. 66
3. $90 + x$ 4. $90 - x$
5. x 6. $200 - 3x$
7. $180 - 5x$ 8. $230 - 2x$
9. 63 10. 137
11. 12
12. ∠*DPC*, ∠*CPA*; ∠*DPB*, ∠*BPA*; ∠*CPB*, ∠*BPF*; ∠*CPA*, ∠*APF*; ∠*BPA*, ∠*APE*; ∠*BPF*, ∠*FPE*; ∠*APF*, ∠*FPD*; ∠*APE*, ∠*EPD*; ∠*FPE*, ∠*EPC*; ∠*FPD*, ∠*DPC*; ∠*EPD*, ∠*DPB*; ∠*EPC*, ∠*CPB*
13. ∠*APE*, ∠*BPD*
14. ∠*CPA*, ∠*DPF* 15. See #12.
16. *m*∠*FPB* 17. *m*∠*CPE*

ORAL EXERCISES

Name the supplement of each angle.

1. 122 **2.** 39 **3.** 117 **4.** 162
5. 40 **6.** 81 **7.** a **8.** $3b - 7$

Refer to the figure at the right for Exercises 9-17.

9. Name all the linear pairs formed by lines *l* and *m*.

10. Name all the linear pairs formed by lines *l* and *n*.

11. What angles are supplementary to ∠3?

12. What angles are supplementary to ∠8?

13. Name all the pairs of supplementary angles formed by lines *l* and *m*.

14. If *m*∠1 = 101, *m*∠2 = _____.

15. If *m*∠8 = 84, *m*∠7 = _____.

16. If *m*∠6 = 90, *m*∠5 = _____.

17. If *m*∠4 = 68, *m*∠3 = _____.

Refer to the figure at the right for Exercises 18-21.

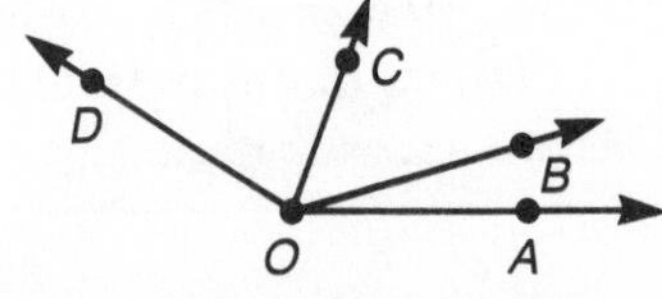

18. *m*∠*AOB* + *m*∠*BOC* = _____

19. *m*∠*AOC* + *m*∠*COD* = _____

20. If *m*∠*AOB* = 40 and *m*∠*AOD* = 135, then *m*∠*DOB* = _____.

21. If *m*∠*AOC* = $3x$ and *m*∠*COD* = $2x$, then *m*∠*AOD* = _____.

WRITTEN EXERCISES

A. Name the supplement of each angle.

1. 20 **2.** 114 **3.** $90 - x$ **4.** $90 + x$ **5.** $180 - x$
6. $3x - 20$ **7.** $5x$ **8.** $2x - 50$ **9.** 117 **10.** 43

B. Refer to the figure at the right for Exercises 11-19.

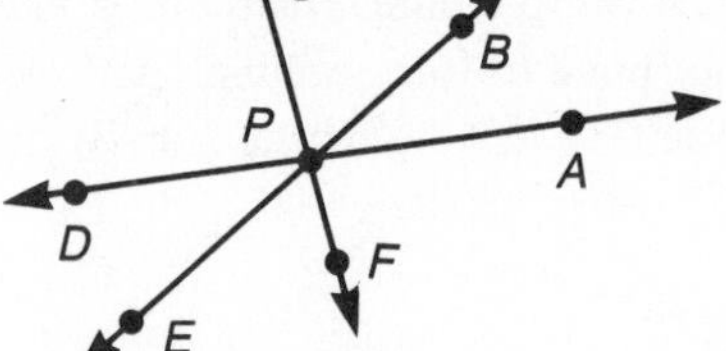

11. How many linear pairs are shown in the diagram?

12. Name all possible linear pairs.

13. Name two supplements of ∠*APB*.

14. Name two supplements of ∠*DPC*.

15. Name five pairs of supplementary angles.

16. *m*∠*FPA* + *m*∠*APB* = _____

17. *m*∠*CPD* + *m*∠*DPE* = _____

18. $m\angle BPA +$ ____ $= m\angle BPF$ **19.** ____ $+ m\angle EPF = m\angle DPF$

Example: The measure of $\angle A$ is 12 more than the measure of its supplement. Find $m\angle A$.

Let $m\angle A = x$. Then the measure of its supplement is $180 - x$.

$$\begin{aligned} \text{Thus, } x &= 12 + (180 - x) \\ 2x &= 192 \\ x &= 96 \\ m\angle A &= 96 \end{aligned}$$

20. The measures of two supplementary angles differ by 24. Find the measure of each angle.

21. $\angle A$ and $\angle B$ are supplementary and $m\angle A$ is four times $m\angle B$. Find the measure of each angle.

22. Find an angle whose measure is equal to that of its supplement.

23. The measure of an angle is 34 more than the measure of its supplement. Find the measure of each angle.

24. The measure of an angle is 11 times the measure of its supplement. Find the measure of each angle.

If $\angle 1$ and $\angle 2$ are a linear pair as shown at the right below, find their measures.

Example: $m\angle 1 = 2x - 2$; $m\angle 2 = 20x + 28$
Find $m\angle 1$ and $m\angle 2$.
Because $\angle 1$ and $\angle 2$ are a linear pair they are supplementary, so $m\angle 1 + m\angle 2 = 180$.

$$\begin{aligned} \text{Thus, } 2x - 2 + 20x + 28 &= 180 \\ 22x + 26 &= 180 \\ 22x &= 154 \\ x &= 7 \\ \text{So } m\angle 1 = 2 \cdot 7 - 2 &= 12 \\ m\angle 2 = 20 \cdot 7 + 28 &= 168 \end{aligned}$$

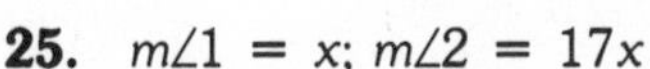

25. $m\angle 1 = x$; $m\angle 2 = 17x$ **26.** $m\angle 1 = 3x$; $m\angle 2 = 57x$

27. $m\angle 1 = 2x + 2$; $m\angle 2 = 30x + 18$ **28.** $m\angle 1 = 2x - 5$; $m\angle 2 = 16x + 5$

29. $m\angle 1 = 3x - 1$; $m\angle 2 = 20x + 66$ **30.** $m\angle 1 = 2(x - 3)$; $m\angle 2 = 15x - 18$

C. Refer to the figure for Exercises 31–35. Find $m\angle RSV$ and $m\angle TSV$.

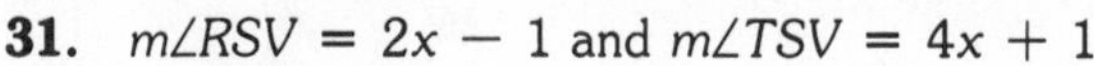

31. $m\angle RSV = 2x - 1$ and $m\angle TSV = 4x + 1$

32. $m\angle RSV = 10x - 10$ and $m\angle TSV = 15x - 10$

33. $m\angle RSV = 4x + 8$ and $m\angle TSV = 8x - 20$

34. $m\angle RSV = x + 52$ and $m\angle TSV = x^2 + 2x + 20$

35. $m\angle RSV = 6x + 40$ and $m\angle TSV = x^2 + 100$

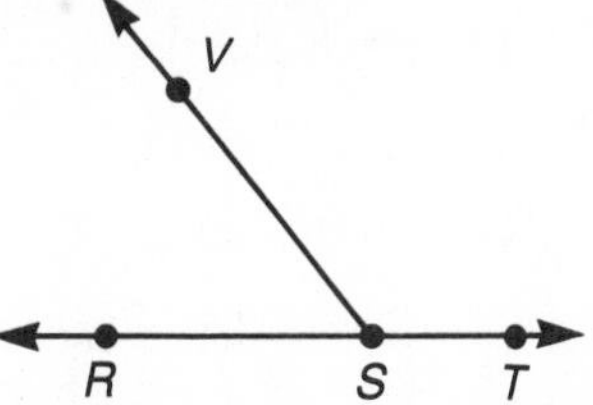

18. $m\angle APF$
19. $m\angle DPE$
20. 78, 102
21. $m\angle A = 144$, $m\angle B = 36$
22. 90
23. 73, 107
24. 15, 165
25. 10, 170 26. 9, 171
27. 12, 168 28. 15, 165
29. 14, 166 30. 18, 162
31. 59, 121
32. 70, 110
33. 72, 108
34. 61, 119; 40, 140
35. 64, 116; extraneous root

3.2 Special Angles

OBJECTIVES

Identify acute, right, and obtuse angles and triangles, perpendicular lines, and complementary angles.

Given the measure of an angle, find the measure of its complement.

TEACHER'S NOTES

See p. T26

MIXED REVIEW

1. Solve $7x + 4(x - 12) = 7$. $x = 5$
2. State the Plane Separation Postulate. See Section 2.2.
3. If $x^2 - 5 = 11$, then $x =$ ______ or ______. 4; -4
4. If $(x - 7)(x + 2) = 0$, then $x =$ ______ or ______. 7; -2
5. If $2|x - 3| = 8$, then $x =$ ______ or ______. 7; -1

TEACHER'S RESOURCE MASTERS

Practice Master 7, Part 1

The postulates you learned in the preceding sections will be used to prove theorems about special angles and their relationships. But first, it is necessary to define some more terms:

> **DEFINITIONS: acute angle; right angle; obtuse angle**
> An angle is **acute** if and only if it has a measure greater than 0 and less than 90. An angle is a **right angle** if and only if it has a measure of 90. An angle is **obtuse** if and only if it has a measure greater than 90 but less than 180.

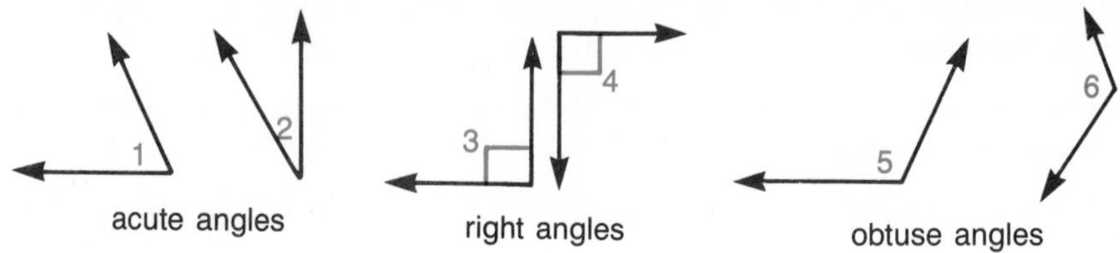

Note that in angles 3 and 4 above a right angle is indicated by drawing a square in its interior, near the vertex (r). Triangles may now be described according to the types of angles they contain.

> **DEFINITIONS: acute triangle; obtuse triangle**
> A triangle is **acute** if and only if it has three acute angles. A triangle is **obtuse** if and only if it has one obtuse angle.

In the figure below, $\triangle ABC$ is an acute triangle, and $\triangle JKL$ is an obtuse triangle. $\triangle XYZ$ contains one right angle and is called a **right triangle.**

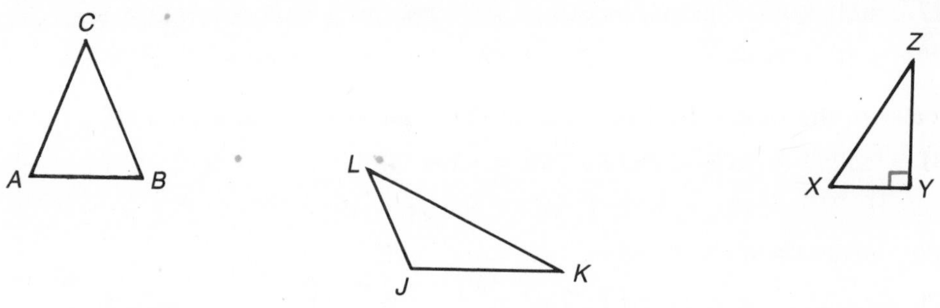

DEFINITIONS: right triangle; hypotenuse; leg
A triangle is a **right triangle** if and only if it has one right angle. The side opposite the right angle is called the **hypotenuse.** The other two sides are called the **legs.**

In $\triangle XYZ$, if $\angle X$ is a right angle, $\overline{YZ}$ is the hypotenuse and $\overline{XY}$ and $\overline{XZ}$ are the legs.

DEFINITION: perpendicular lines
Two lines are **perpendicular** if and only if they intersect and form a right angle.

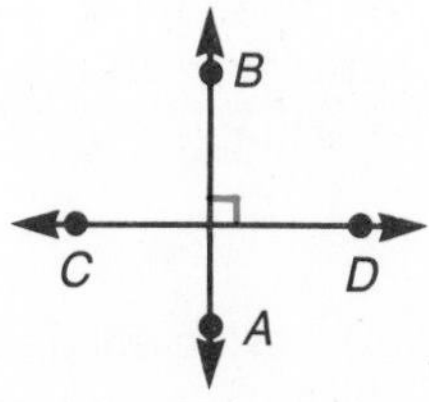

The symbol $\perp$ is read "is perpendicular to." In the figure at the right, $\overleftrightarrow{AB} \perp \overleftrightarrow{CD}$. Segments contained in perpendicular lines are also perpendicular. Therefore, $\overline{AB} \perp \overline{CD}$.

DEFINITION: complementary angles
Two angles are **complementary** if and only if the sum of their measures is 90.

Each angle, $\angle JHG$ and $\angle KLM$, is called a **complement** of the other. The two angles are then referred to as *complementary angles.* As with supplementary angles, it is not necessary for complementary angles to be adjacent or coplanar.

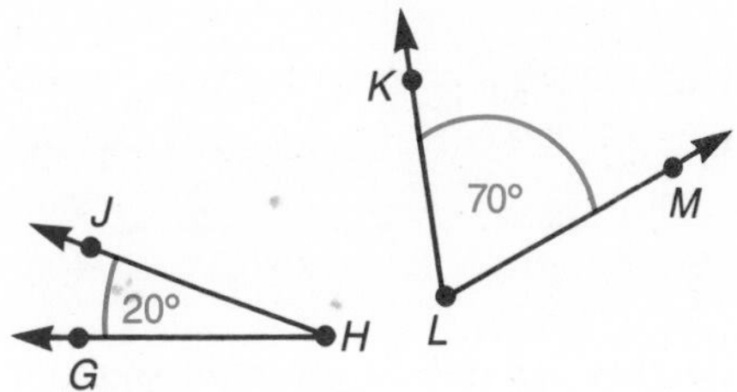

It is important to distinguish between the terms *equal* and *congruent* when you are referring to angles. Angles are *congruent* if and only if they have the same measure. Congruent angles are not necessarily *equal.*

DEFINITION: equal angles
Two angles are **equal** (=) if and only if they are the *same* angle.

Because $m\angle ABC = m\angle DEF = m\angle GHI$, $\angle ABC \cong \angle DEF \cong \angle GHI$. But $\angle ABC = \angle CBA = \angle B$.

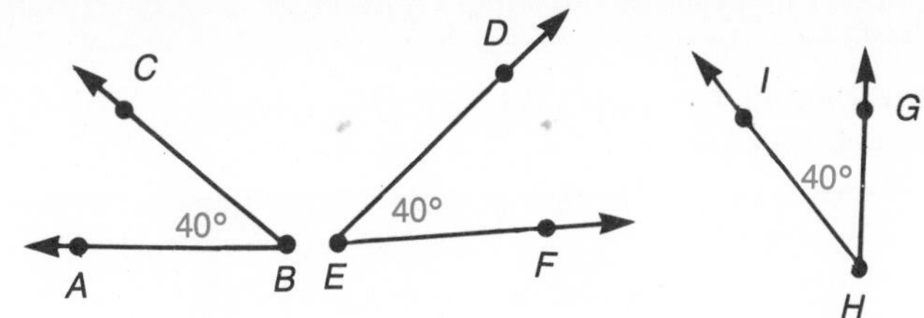

THEOREM 3.1
If two angles are complementary, then both of them are acute.

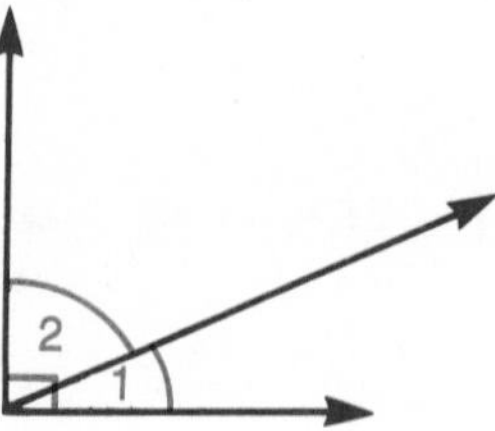

Given: $\angle 1$ and $\angle 2$ are complementary angles

Prove: $m\angle 1 < 90$ and $m\angle 2 < 90$

Proof: By definition of complementary, the sum of the measures of $\angle 1$ and $\angle 2$ is 90. That is possible only if each angle has a measure less than 90. In other words, both angles must be acute.

Section 2.4 established that congruence of angles is an equivalence relation. The next theorem follows logically from that statement and is therefore presented without proof.

THEOREM 3.2
Every angle is congruent to itself.

THEOREM 3.3
All right angles are congruent.

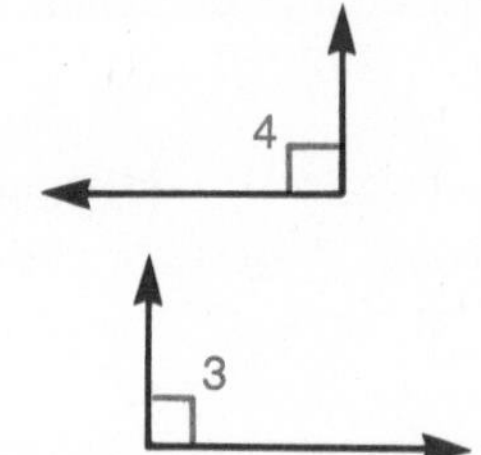

Given: $\angle 3$ and $\angle 4$ are right angles

Prove: $\angle 3 \cong \angle 4$

Proof: According to the definition of a right angle, both $\angle 3$ and $\angle 4$ have measures of 90. Their measures are therefore equal, and by the definition of congruence, $\angle 3 \cong \angle 4$.

THEOREM 3.4
If two angles are both congruent *and* supplementary, then each of them is a right angle.

The proof of Theorem 3.4 is left as an exercise.

THEOREM 3.5
Supplements of congruent angles are congruent.

Theorem 3.5 can be proved using the figure below and the definitions of supplementary and congruent angles.

Given: $\angle 1 \cong \angle 2$; $\angle 3$ is supplementary to $\angle 1$; $\angle 4$ is supplementary to $\angle 2$.

Prove: $\angle 3 \cong \angle 4$

Proof:

STATEMENTS	REASONS
1. $\angle 1 \cong \angle 2$; $\angle 3$ is supplementary to $\angle 1$; $\angle 4$ is supplementary to $\angle 2$.	1. Given
2. $m\angle 3 + m\angle 1 = 180$	2. Definition of supplementary angles
3. $m\angle 4 + m\angle 2 = 180$	3. Definition of supplementary angles
4. $m\angle 3 + m\angle 1 = m\angle 4 + m\angle 2$	4. Transitive property of equality
5. $m\angle 1 = m\angle 2$	5. Definition of congruent angles
6. $m\angle 3 + m\angle 1 = m\angle 4 + m\angle 1$	6. Substitution property
7. $m\angle 3 = m\angle 4$	7. Subtraction property of equality
8. $\angle 3 \cong \angle 4$	8. Definition of congruent angles

THEOREM 3.6
Complements of congruent angles are congruent.

The proof of Theorem 3.6 is left as an exercise.

ORAL EXERCISES

Complete each statement.

1. Lines that form a linear pair of congruent adjacent angles are _____.

2. Two angles with the same measure are _____.

3. Two complementary angles are each _____.

4. If two angles are both complementary *and* congruent, the measure of each is _____.

ASSIGNMENT GUIDE

Minimum 1-22
Regular 1-22, 23-27 odd
Maximum 15-32

Oral Exercises

1. perpendicular
2. congruent
3. acute
4. 45

5. 90

6. The complement of $\angle ABC$ is greater than that of $\angle QRS$.

7. 50, 140 8. 63, 153

9. $90 - x$, $180 - x$

10. x, $90 + x$

11. hypotenuse 12. hypotenuse

13. leg 14. hypotenuse

15. leg

Written Exercises

1. acute 2. right

3. acute 4. obtuse

5. obtuse

6. $\angle BPC$, $\angle APE$, $\angle APD$

7. $\angle DPA$, $\angle APB$, $\angle BPC$, $\angle CPD$

8. $\angle EPB$, $\angle CPE$

9. any combination of $\angle DPA$, $\angle APB$, $\angle BPC$, $\angle CPD$

10. $\angle DPE$, $\angle EPA$

11. $\angle ABC$, $\angle CDE$; $\angle AEF$, $\angle AED$; $\angle AED$, $\angle BCD$

12. $\angle BAE$

13. $\angle CDE$

14. $\overline{AB} \perp \overline{BC}$, $\overline{DC} \perp \overline{DE}$, $\overline{DC} \perp \overline{DF}$

5. If two angles are both supplementary *and* congruent, the measure of each is ____.

6. If $\angle ABC$ and $\angle QRS$ are acute, and $m\angle ABC$ is less than $m\angle QRS$, what can you conclude about their complements?

Name the complement and supplement of each angle.

7. 40 **8.** 27 **9.** x **10.** $90 - x$

In the figure below, $\triangle ABC$ is a right triangle with right $\angle ABC$ and $\overline{BD} \perp \overline{AC}$. Tell whether each of the following sides is a hypotenuse or a leg.

11. $\overline{AC}$ is called the ____ of $\triangle ABC$.

12. $\overline{AB}$ is called the ____ of $\triangle ADB$.

13. $\overline{AB}$ is called the ____ of $\triangle ABC$.

14. $\overline{BC}$ is called the ____ of $\triangle BDC$.

15. $\overline{BD}$ is called the ____ of $\triangle ADB$.

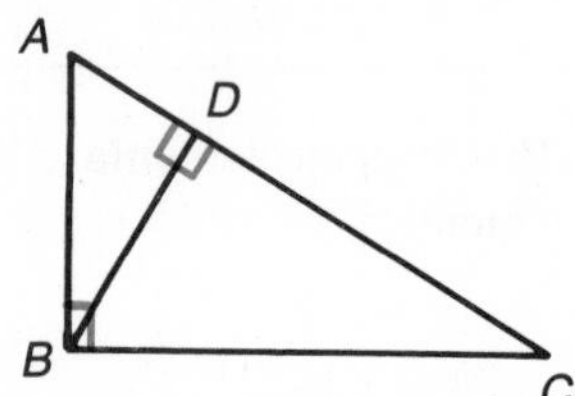

WRITTEN EXERCISES

A. Classify each angle as acute, obtuse, or right.

1. 35 **2.** 90 **3.** 16 **4.** 162 **5.** 95

Refer to the figure at the right for Exercises 6–10.

6. Name two angles adjacent to $\angle APB$.

7. Name two right angles.

8. Name two obtuse angles.

9. Name two congruent angles.

10. Name two acute angles.

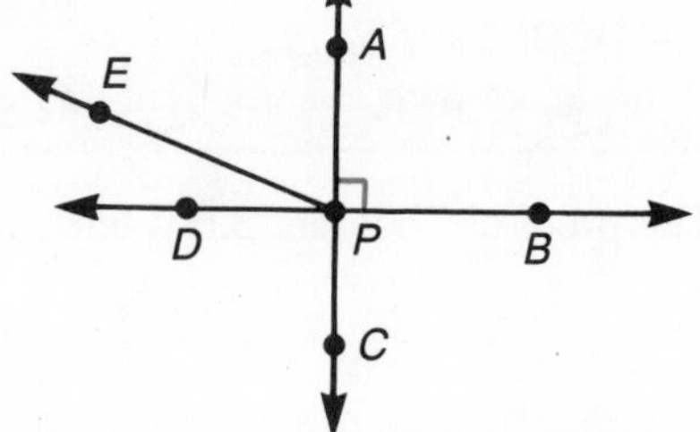

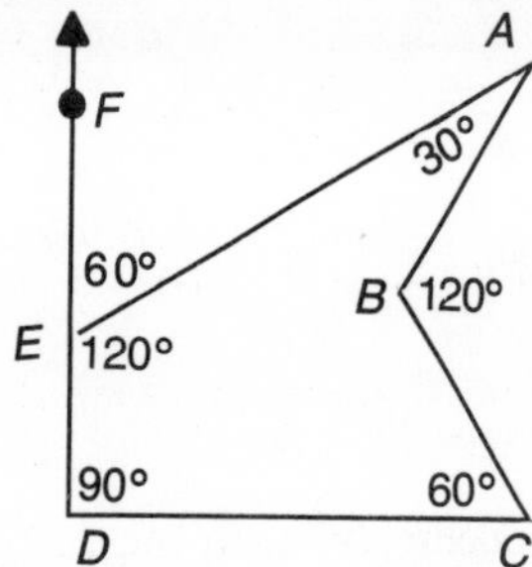

Refer to the figure at the left for Exercises 11–14.

11. Name two supplementary angles.

12. Name a complement of $\angle AEF$.

13. Name a supplement of $\angle B$.

14. Name two pairs of perpendicular segments.

B. Use the figure to complete the proof of Theorem 3.6 (Complements of congruent angles are congruent). (HINT: Review the proof of Theorem 3.5).

Given: $\angle 1 \cong \angle 2$; $\angle 1$ is complementary to $\angle 3$.
$\angle 2$ is complementary to $\angle 4$.

Prove: $\angle 3 \cong \angle 4$

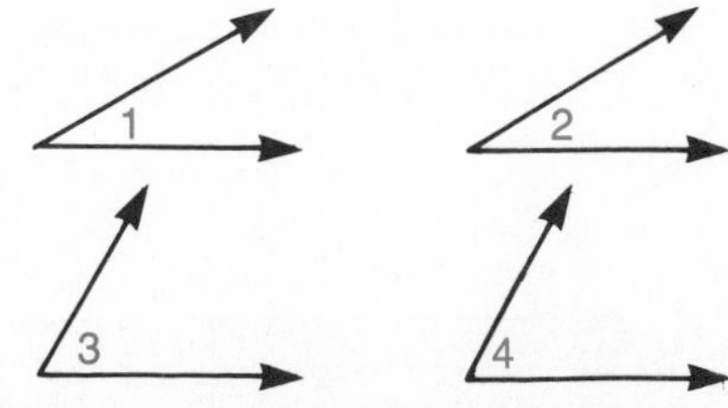

Proof:

STATEMENTS	REASONS
1. **15.** ____	*1.* Given
2. **16.** ____	*2.* Definition of complementary angles
3. **17.** ____	*3.* Definition of complementary angles
4. **18.** ____	*4.* Transitive property of equality
5. **19.** ____	*5.* Definition of congruent angles
6. **20.** ____	*6.* Substitution property
7. **21.** ____	*7.* Subtraction property of equality
8. **22.** ____	*8.* Definition of congruent angles

23. The measures of two complementary angles differ by 20. Find the measure of each angle.

24. The measure of one angle is four times the measure of its complement. Find the measure of each angle.

25. $\angle A$, which has a measure of $36 + 6x$, is a right angle. Find x.

26. $\angle B$, which has a measure of $10 + 4x$, is acute. Find the solution set for x.

27. $\angle Y$, which has a measure of $3x - 15$, is obtuse. Find the solution set for x.

28. The measure of an angle is 18 more than 5 times its supplement. Find the measure of each angle.

29. Two supplementary angles have measures of $3x + 35$ and $4x + 12$. Find the measure of each angle.

C. 30. Prove Theorem 3.4. (If two angles, $\angle 1$ and $\angle 2$, are both congruent and supplementary, then each of them is a right angle.)

31. The sum of an angle's complement and supplement is 186. Find the measure of all three angles.

32. Prove that if two angles, $\angle 1$ and $\angle 2$, are supplementary, at most one is obtuse.

15. $\angle 1 \cong \angle 2$; $\angle 1$ is complementary to $\angle 3$; $\angle 2$ is complementary to $\angle 4$.
16. $m\angle 1 + m\angle 3 = 90$
17. $m\angle 2 + m\angle 4 = 90$
18. $m\angle 1 + m\angle 3 = m\angle 2 + m\angle 4$
19. $m\angle 1 = m\angle 2$
20. $m\angle 1 + m\angle 3 = m\angle 1 + m\angle 4$
21. $m\angle 3 = m\angle 4$
22. $\angle 3 \cong \angle 4$
23. 35, 55
24. 18, 72
25. $x = 9$
26. $-2.5 < x < 20$
27. $35 < x < 65$
28. 27, 153
29. 92, 88
30. See *Teacher's Manual,* p. T59
31. 42, 48, 138
32. See *Teacher's manual,* p. T59

3.3 Congruence of Angles

OBJECTIVES

Identify vertical angles.

Given the measure of one angle in a figure, determine the measure of another angle using supplements, complements, or congruence.

TEACHER'S NOTES

See p. T26

MIXED REVIEW

1. If $|x - 3| = 9$, then $x =$ ______ or ______.
   12; −6
2. Factor $2x^2 - 11x + 12$.
   $(2x - 3)(x - 4)$
3. Solve $2x + 3y = -4$
   $x + y = 1$.
   (7, −6)
4. Solve $2x + 3 \leq 5x - 12$.
   $x \geq 5$
5. If $x^2 - 2x - 3 = 0$, then x = ______ or ______.
   3; −1

TEACHER'S RESOURCE MASTERS

Practice Master 7, part 2
Quiz 5

In the preceding lesson, you proved theorems that identify some of the attributes of congruent angles. In this lesson, you will prove congruence relations for right angles and **vertical angles.**

DEFINITION: vertical angles
Two angles are **vertical** if and only if their sides form two pairs of opposite rays.

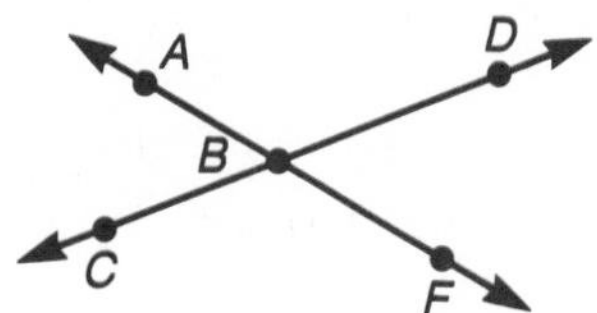

In the figure at the left, $\angle ABC$ and $\angle DBF$ are vertical angles. Another pair of vertical angles is $\angle ABD$ and $\angle CBF$.

This definition leads to the following theorems.

THEOREM 3.7
Vertical angles are congruent.

Given: Vertical angles 1 and 2

Prove: $\angle 1 \cong \angle 2$

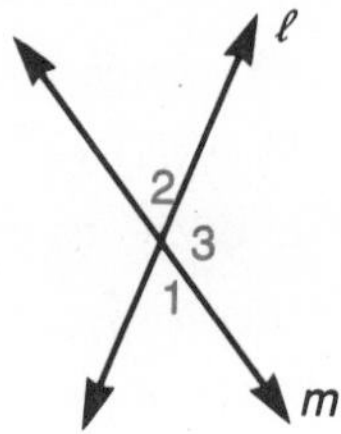

Proof: In the figure at the right, $\angle 1$ and $\angle 2$ are vertical angles. $\angle 1$ and $\angle 2$ are both supplementary to $\angle 3$ by the Supplement Postulate. By Theorem 3.2, you know that $\angle 3$ is congruent to itself. By Theorem 3.5 you know that supplements of congruent angles are congruent. Therefore $\angle 1 \cong \angle 2$.

This deductive reasoning can be translated into a two-column format. When your purpose is to prove a relation, such as $\angle 1 \cong \angle 2$, you must review what situations define that relation and apply them. Remember that the reason for each statement must be a postulate, a theorem, or a definition.

Given: Lines l and m intersect to form angles 1, 2, and 3 as shown.

Prove: $\angle 1 \cong \angle 2$

Proof:

STATEMENTS	REASONS
1. Lines l and m intersect to form $\angle$s 1, 2, and 3.	1. Given
2. $\angle 1$ is supplementary to $\angle 3$. $\angle 2$ is supplementary to $\angle 3$.	2. Postulate 14 (The Supplement Postulate)
3. $\angle 3 \cong \angle 3$	3. Theorem 3.2 (Every angle is congruent to itself.)
4. $\angle 1 \cong \angle 2$	4. Theorem 3.5 (Supplements of congruent angles are congruent.)

THEOREM 3.8
If two intersecting lines form one right angle then they form four right angles.

Given: Lines l and m intersect to form angles 1, 2, 3, and 4; $\angle 1$ is a right angle.

Prove: $\angle 2$, $\angle 3$, and $\angle 4$ are right angles.

Proof: In the figure at the right, $\angle 1$ is a right angle. $\angle 1$ and $\angle 3$ are vertical angles, so $\angle 1 \cong \angle 3$. Thus $\angle 3$ must be a right angle. $\angle 2$ and $\angle 4$ are each supplementary to $\angle 1$ by the Supplement Postulate, so they must be right angles as well.

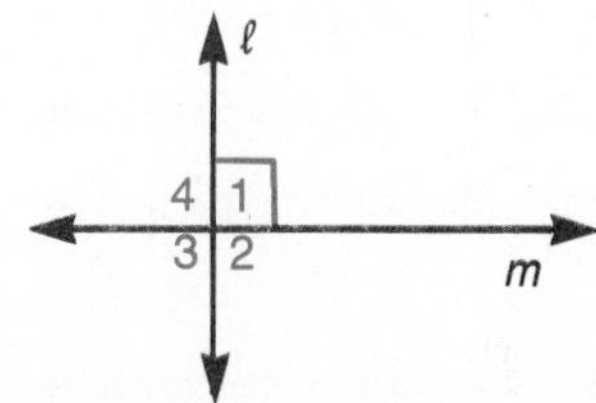

ASSIGNMENT GUIDE

Minimum 1-25 odd
Regular 1-29 odd
Maximum 1-35 odd

ORAL EXERCISES

Using the figure at the right for Exercises 1–5, name the following:

1. Two pairs of vertical angles
2. Two pairs of adjacent acute angles
3. Two right angles
4. Two pairs of congruent angles
5. Two pairs of complementary angles

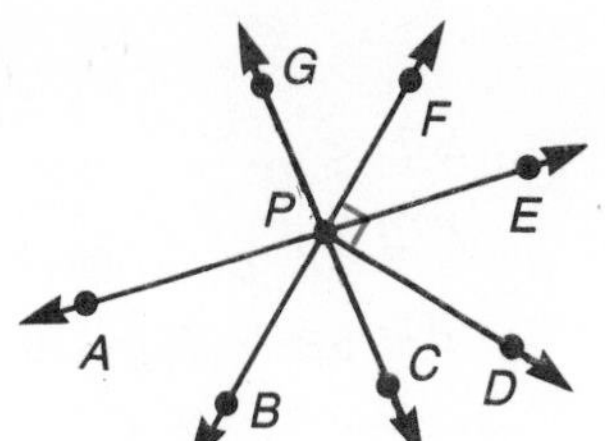

Oral Exercises

1. $\angle GPF$, $\angle BPC$; $\angle FPE$, $\angle APB$; $\angle GPE$, $\angle APC$; $\angle APG$, $\angle EPC$; $\angle APF$, $\angle EPB$
2. $\angle APG$, $\angle GPF$; $\angle GPF$, $\angle FPE$; $\angle FPE$, $\angle EPD$; $\angle EPD$, $\angle DPC$; $\angle DPC$, $\angle CPB$; $\angle CPB$, $\angle BPA$; $\angle BPA$, $\angle APG$
3. $\angle DPF$, $\angle DPB$
4. $\angle FPD$, $\angle DPB$ and answers to Exercise 1.
5. $\angle FPE$, $\angle EPD$; $\angle DPC$, $\angle CPB$; $\angle BPA$, $\angle EPD$; $\angle GPF$, $\angle DPC$

6. 35 7. 140
8. 74 9. 110
10. 60

Written Exercises

1. 145 2. 29
3. 144 4. 54
5. 42 6. 30
7. 159 8. 22
9. 45 10. 150
11. 9 12. 20
13. $53\frac{1}{3}$ 14. 30
15. $43\frac{1}{3}$ 16. $16\frac{1}{2}$
17. $x = 49$, $m\angle 4 = 131$, $m\angle 5 = 49$, $m\angle 6 = 131$
18. $x = 20$, $m\angle 7 = m\angle 9 = 20$, $m\angle 10 = 70$
19. $x = 20$, $m\angle 4 = 130$, $m\angle 5 = 50$, $m\angle 6 = 130$
20. $x = 45$, $m\angle 3 = 60$, $m\angle 5 = 60$, $m\angle 6 = 120$
21. $x = 8$, $m\angle 3 = 65$, $m\angle 4 = 115$, $m\angle 5 = 65$
22. $x = 65$, $m\angle 3 = 44$, $m\angle 4 = 136$, $m\angle 6 = 136$
23. $x = 6$, $m\angle 3 = 50$, $m\angle 4 = 130$, $m\angle 5 = 50$, $m\angle 6 = 130$
24. $x = 12\frac{1}{2}$, $m\angle 3 = 52$, $m\angle 4 = 128$, $m\angle 5 = 52$, $m\angle 6 = 128$
25. $x = 15$, $m\angle 3 = 60$, $m\angle 4 = 120$, $m\angle 5 = 60$, $m\angle 6 = 120$
26. $x = 18\frac{1}{3}$, $m\angle 8 = 65$, $m\angle 9 = 25$, $m\angle 10 = 65$
27. $x = \pm 12$, $m\angle 6 = m\angle 4 = 140$, $m\angle 3 = m\angle 5 = 40$

Use the figure at the left for Exercises 6–10.

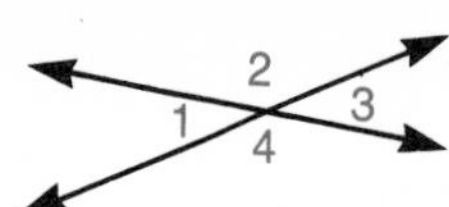

6. Find $m\angle 1$ if $m\angle 3 = 35$.

7. Find $m\angle 2$ if $m\angle 1 = 40$.

8. Find $m\angle 3$ if $m\angle 4 = 106$.

9. Find $m\angle 4$ if $m\angle 2 = 110$

10. Find $m\angle 1$ if $m\angle 2 = 2 \cdot m\angle 1$.

WRITTEN EXERCISES

A. Refer to the figure at the right for Exercises 1–16.

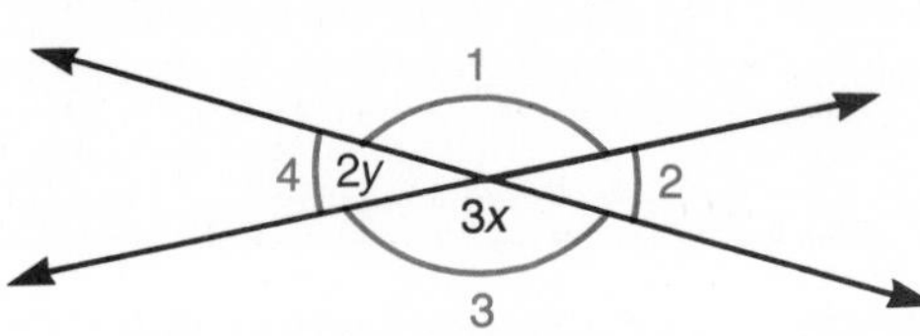

1. Find $m\angle 3$ if $m\angle 1 = 145$.

2. Find $m\angle 2$ if $m\angle 4 = 29$.

3. Find $m\angle 1$ if $m\angle 4 = 36$.

4. Find $m\angle 4$ if $m\angle 3 = 126$.

5. Find $m\angle 3$ if $m\angle 1 = 2x + 14$.

6. Find $m\angle 4$ if $m\angle 3 = 5 \cdot m\angle 4$.

7. Find $m\angle 1$ if $x = 53$.

8. Find $m\angle 2$ if $y = 11$.

9. Find $m\angle 2$ if $x = 45$.

10. Find $m\angle 1$ if $y = 15$.

11. Find y if $m\angle 2 = 18$.

12. Find y if $m\angle 1 = 140$.

13. Find x if $m\angle 2 = 20$.

14. Find y if $x = 40$.

15. Find x if $y = 25$.

16. Find y if $x = 49$.

B. Using the figures below, solve for x to find the unknown angle measures.

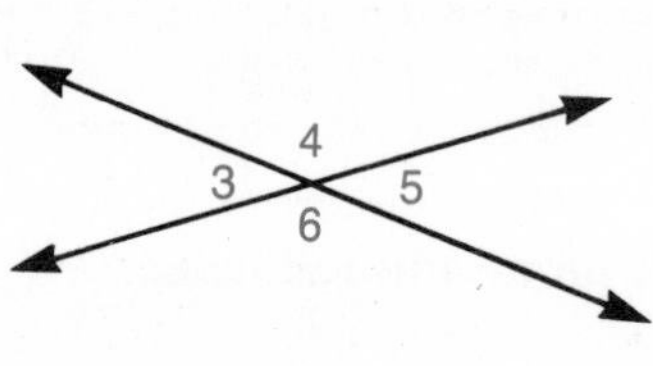

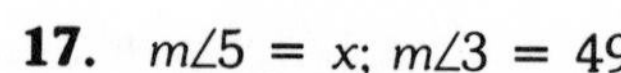

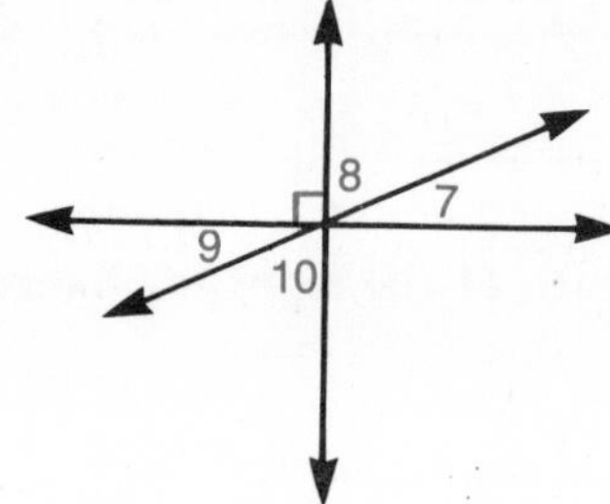

17. $m\angle 5 = x$; $m\angle 3 = 49$

18. $m\angle 7 = x$; $m\angle 8 = 70$

19. $m\angle 5 = 2x + 10$; $m\angle 3 = 50$

20. $m\angle 6 = 3x - 15$; $m\angle 4 = 120$

21. $m\angle 3 = 5x + 25$; $m\angle 6 = 115$

22. $m\angle 4 = 2x + 6$; $m\angle 5 = 44$

23. $m\angle 5 = 8x + 2$; $m\angle 4 = 25x - 20$

24. $m\angle 3 = 4x + 2$; $m\angle 5 = 2x + 27$

25. $m\angle 4 = 6x + 30$; $m\angle 6 = 10x - 30$

26. $m\angle 7 = 25$; $m\angle 10 = 3x + 10$

C. 27. $m\angle 6 = x^2 - 4;\ m\angle 4 = 140$

28. $m\angle 3 = 2x^2 + 22;\ m\angle 4 = 140$

29. $m\angle 4 = 3x^2 + 60;\ m\angle 3 = 45$

30. $m\angle 7 = 2x;\ m\angle 10 = 5x + 27$

31. $m\angle 9 = 4x + 3;\ m\angle 8 = 10x + 31$

32. $m\angle 9 = x;\ m\angle 8 = 4x$

33. $m\angle 3 = x^2 + 23x;\ m\angle 5 = 30x - 10$

34. $m\angle 4 = x^2 + x;\ m\angle 6 = 10x + 22$

35. $m\angle 7 = x;\ m\angle 10 = x^2$

SELF-QUIZ

Give the complement of each angle for Exercises 1–8.

1. 79 **2.** x **3.** $x - 9$ **4.** $3a$

5. 24 **6.** $18\frac{1}{2}$ **7.** $53\frac{3}{8}$ **8.** $2a - 9b$

Give the supplement of each angle for Exercises 9–16.

9. 37 **10.** a **11.** $2b + 10$ **12.** 118

13. $4y$ **14.** $102\frac{1}{4}$ **15.** $32\frac{4}{11}$ **16.** $7k - g$

Classify each angle measurement as *acute, obtuse,* or *right*.

17. 132 **18.** 77 **19.** 20 **20.** 90

21. Name two pairs of perpendicular lines in the figure at the right.

22. Name the hypotenuse of $\triangle HCE$.

23. Name the legs of $\triangle CHA$.

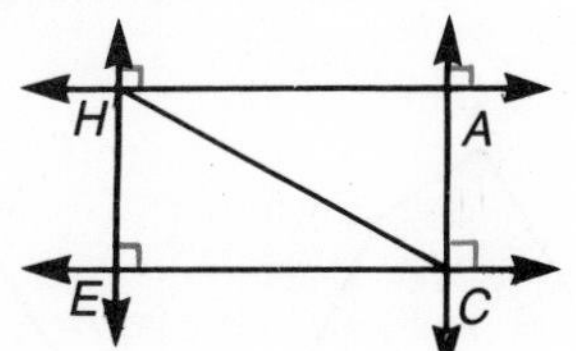

Refer to the figure at the left for Exercises 24–27.

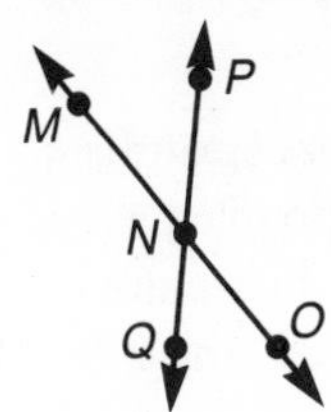

24. Name two pairs of vertical angles.

25. Name two linear pairs.

26. Name two pairs of congruent angles.

27. Name two pairs of supplementary angles.

28. $x = \pm 3$, $m\angle 3 = m\angle 5 = 40$, $m\angle 4 = m\angle 6 = 140$
29. $x = \pm 5$, $m\angle 4 = m\angle 6 = 135$, $m\angle 3 = m\angle 5 = 45$
30. $x = 9$, $m\angle 7 = m\angle 9 = 18$, $m\angle 8 = m\angle 10 = 72$
31. $x = 4$, $m\angle 7 = m\angle 9 = 19$, $m\angle 8 = m\angle 10 = 71$
32. $x = 18$, $m\angle 7 = m\angle 9 = 18$, $m\angle 8 = m\angle 10 = 72$
33. $x = 2$, $m\angle 3 = m\angle 5 = 50$, $m\angle 4 = m\angle 6 = 130$; or $x = 5$, $m\angle 3 = m\angle 5 = 140$, $m\angle 4 = m\angle 6 = 40$
34. $x = 11$, $m\angle 4 = m\angle 6 = 132$; $m\angle 3 = m\angle 5 = 48$; or $x = -2$, $m\angle 4 = m\angle 6 = 2$; $m\angle 3 = m\angle 5 = 178$
35. $x = 9$, $m\angle 7 = m\angle 9 = 9$, $m\angle 8 = m\angle 10 = 81$

Self-Quiz

1. 11 2. $90 - x$
3. $99 - x$ 4. $90 - 3a$
5. 66 6. $71\frac{1}{2}$
7. $36\frac{5}{8}$
8. $90 - 2a + 9b$
9. 143 10. $180 - a$
11. $170 - 2b$ 12. 62
13. $180 - 4y$ 14. $77\frac{3}{4}$
15. $147\frac{7}{11}$
16. $180 - 7k + g$
17. obtuse 18. acute
19. acute 20. right
21. $\overline{HA}, \overline{HE}; \overline{HA}, \overline{AC}; \overline{EC}, \overline{HE}; \overline{EC}, \overline{AC}$
22. $\overline{HC}$
23. $\overline{HA}, \overline{AC}$
24. $\angle MNP, \angle QNO; \angle PNO, \angle MNQ$
25. $\angle MNP, \angle PNO; \angle PNO, \angle ONQ; \angle ONQ, \angle QNM; \angle QNM, \angle MNP$
26. $\angle MNP, \angle QNO; \angle PNO, \angle MNQ$
27. See #25.

3.4 Congruence of Figures

OBJECTIVE

Identify congruent figures and their corresponding parts.

TEACHER'S NOTES

See p. T26

MIXED REVIEW

1. Subtract $\frac{2}{3} - \frac{1}{5}$. $\frac{7}{15}$
2. Add $\frac{a}{b} + \frac{c}{b}$. $\frac{a+c}{b}$
3. Add $\frac{a}{b} + \frac{c}{d}$. $\frac{ad+bc}{bd}$
4. Add $\frac{2}{x+2} + \frac{x}{x+2}$. 1
5. If $\frac{4}{x} = \frac{x}{9}$, then $x =$ _____ or _____.
   6; −6

TEACHER'S RESOURCE MASTERS

Practice Master 8, Part 1

Chapter 1 established that congruent segments have the same length. This section deals with the concept of congruence of geometric figures.

> **DEFINITION: congruent figures**
> Geometric figures are **congruent** if and only if they have the same size and shape.

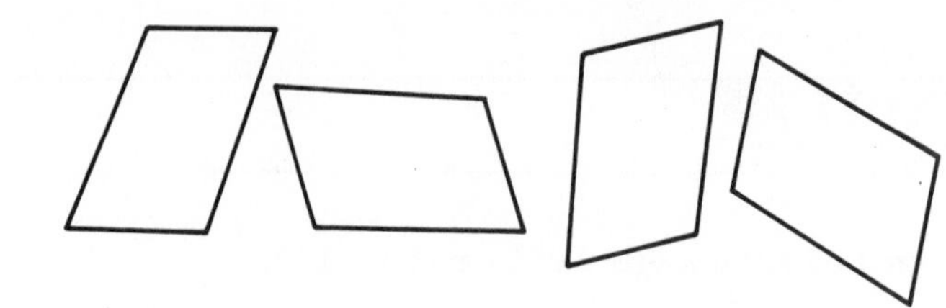

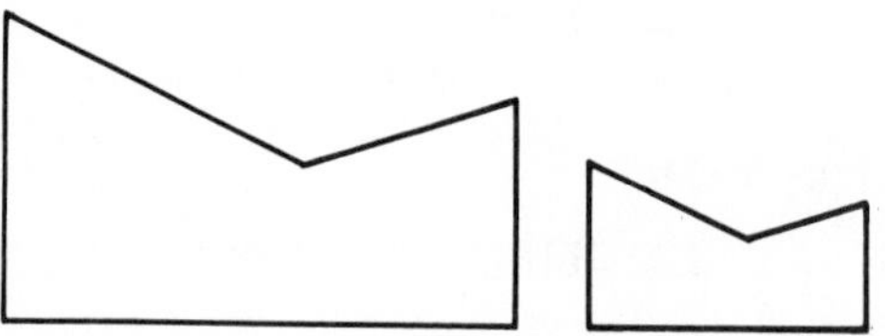

The figures above are all congruent because they have the same size and shape. The figures at the left are not congruent. Although they have the same shape, they cannot be considered congruent because they are not the same size.

While the definition of congruence requires figures to have the same size and shape, it does not restrict them to being positioned in the same way. If two figures can be moved in space so that one figure fits exactly over the other, then they are congruent. Congruent figures may be either planar (two-dimensional) or three-dimensional.

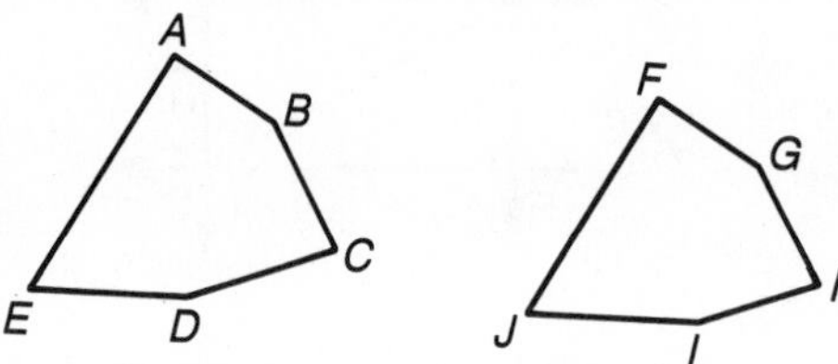

Examples of planar figures are figure *ABCDE* and figure *FGHIJ* shown at the left. Because these two figures are exactly the same size and shape, the following notation is used to denote their congruence; figure *ABCDE* ≅ figure *FGHIJ*.

When two figures are congruent, the sides and angles that coincide are called **corresponding sides and angles.** For example, the previous figure shows five pairs of corresponding sides (namely, $\overline{AB}$ and $\overline{FG}$; $\overline{BC}$ and $\overline{GH}$; $\overline{CD}$ and $\overline{HI}$; $\overline{DE}$ and $\overline{IJ}$; $\overline{EA}$ and $\overline{JF}$) and five pairs of corresponding angles (namely, $\angle A$ and $\angle F$; $\angle B$ and $\angle G$; $\angle C$ and $\angle H$; $\angle D$ and $\angle I$; $\angle E$ and $\angle J$).

A special notation is used for corresponding parts in congruent triangles. Write $\overline{AB} \leftrightarrow \overline{FG}$ to show that side $\overline{AB}$ corresponds to side $\overline{FG}$. Write $\angle C \leftrightarrow \angle H$ to show that $\angle C$ corresponds to $\angle H$. Thus, the ten correspondence relationships described above can be summarized:

sides:	$\overline{AB} \leftrightarrow \overline{FG}$	$\overline{BC} \leftrightarrow \overline{GH}$	$\overline{CD} \leftrightarrow \overline{HI}$	$\overline{DE} \leftrightarrow \overline{IJ}$	$\overline{EA} \leftrightarrow \overline{JF}$
angles:	$\angle A \leftrightarrow \angle F$	$\angle B \leftrightarrow \angle G$	$\angle C \leftrightarrow \angle H$	$\angle D \leftrightarrow \angle I$	$\angle E \leftrightarrow \angle J$

Congruence applies to three-dimensional figures as well. Examples of congruent three-dimensional objects are pennies, cereal boxes, milk cartons, and plastic spoons manufactured in mass production.

ASSIGNMENT GUIDE

Minimum 1-16
Regular 1-18
Maximum 1-15, 21-22

ORAL EXERCISES

Oral Exercises
For students unfamiliar with the geoboard, instructors may want to clarify that the points mark off equal distances.

Refer to the figures on the geoboard to answer Exercises 1–3.

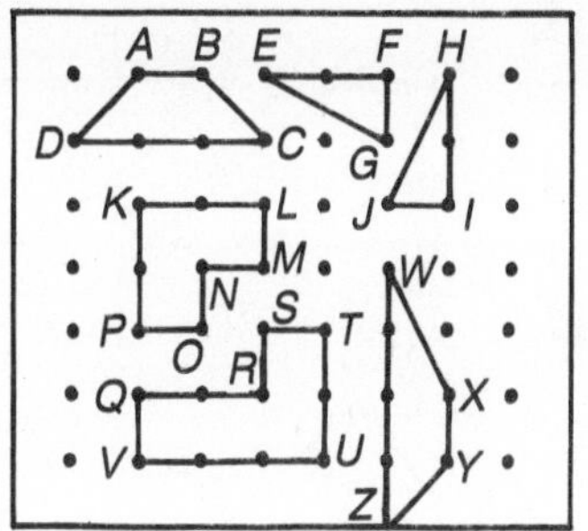

1. Which figure has only one pair of congruent sides?
2. Which figures have three or more pairs of congruent sides?
3. Name all pairs of congruent figures shown.

1. figure *ABCD*
2. figures *KLMNOP* and *QRSTUV*
3. $\triangle EFG \cong \triangle HIJ$

Given $\triangle ABC \cong \triangle RPL$, name the corresponding part for each side and angle.

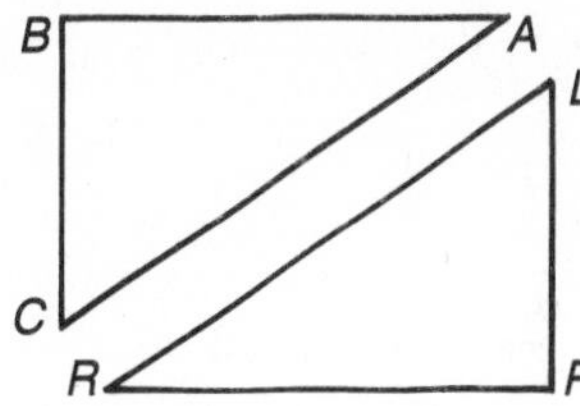

4. $\angle A \leftrightarrow$ ____
5. $\angle B \leftrightarrow$ ____
6. $\angle C \leftrightarrow$ ____
7. $\overline{AB} \leftrightarrow$ ____
8. $\overline{BC} \leftrightarrow$ ____
9. $\overline{CA} \leftrightarrow$ ____
10. Can two triangles be congruent if they are not coplanar?
11. Are all squares congruent?
12. Can a rectangle be congruent to a triangle?

4. $\angle R$ 5. $\angle P$
6. $\angle L$ 7. $\overline{RP}$
8. $\overline{PL}$ 9. $\overline{LR}$
10. Yes
11. No
12. No

Written Exercises

1. $\angle G$ 2. $\angle GSF$

3. $\overline{SF}$ 4. $\angle E$

5. $\overline{GS}$ 6. $\overline{GF}$

7. $\angle X$ 8. $\angle ADC$

9. $\angle B$ 10. $\angle YCD$

11. $\overline{DC}$ 12. $\overline{DX}$

13. $\overline{CB}$ 14. $\overline{XY}$

15. $\angle D \leftrightarrow \angle U$; $\angle C \leftrightarrow \angle T$; $\angle A \leftrightarrow \angle R$; $\angle B \leftrightarrow \angle S$; $\overline{DC} \leftrightarrow \overline{UT}$; $\overline{AD} \leftrightarrow \overline{RU}$; $\overline{AB} \leftrightarrow \overline{RS}$; $\overline{BC} \leftrightarrow \overline{ST}$

16. $\angle A \leftrightarrow \angle D$; $\angle B \leftrightarrow \angle E$; $\angle C \leftrightarrow \angle F$; $\overline{AB} \leftrightarrow \overline{DE}$; $\overline{AC} \leftrightarrow \overline{DF}$; $\overline{CB} \leftrightarrow \overline{FE}$

17. $\angle A \leftrightarrow \angle J$; $\angle B \leftrightarrow \angle K$; $\angle C \leftrightarrow L$; $\angle D \leftrightarrow \angle M$; $\angle E \leftrightarrow \angle N$; $\overline{AB} \leftrightarrow \overline{JK}$; $\overline{BC} \leftrightarrow \overline{KL}$; $\overline{CD} \leftrightarrow \overline{LM}$; $\overline{DE} \leftrightarrow \overline{MN}$; $\overline{EA} \leftrightarrow \overline{NJ}$

18. $\angle 1 \leftrightarrow \angle 4$; $\angle 3 \leftrightarrow \angle 2$ $\angle H \leftrightarrow \angle R$; $\overline{HL} \leftrightarrow \overline{RK}$; $\overline{HK} \leftrightarrow \overline{RL}$; $\overline{LK} \leftrightarrow \overline{KL}$

19. $\angle A \leftrightarrow \angle J$; $\angle B \leftrightarrow \angle K$; $\angle C \leftrightarrow \angle L$; $\angle D \leftrightarrow \angle M$; $\angle E \leftrightarrow \angle N$; $\angle F \leftrightarrow \angle O$; $\overline{AB} \leftrightarrow \overline{JK}$; $\overline{BC} \leftrightarrow \overline{KL}$; $\overline{CD} \leftrightarrow \overline{LM}$; $\overline{DE} \leftrightarrow \overline{MN}$; $\overline{EF} \leftrightarrow \overline{NO}$; $\overline{FA} \leftrightarrow \overline{OJ}$

20. $\angle F \leftrightarrow \angle D$; $\angle A \leftrightarrow \angle C$; $\angle 1 \leftrightarrow \angle 2$; $\angle 3 \leftrightarrow \angle 4$; $\overline{FE} \leftrightarrow \overline{DE}$; $\overline{AF} \leftrightarrow \overline{CD}$; $\overline{EB} \leftrightarrow \overline{EB}$; $\overline{BA} \leftrightarrow \overline{BC}$

21. 17 22. 120

WRITTEN EXERCISES

A. Given that $\triangle DES \cong \triangle GFS$, supply the missing correspondences.

1. $\angle D \leftrightarrow$ _____ **2.** $\angle DSE \leftrightarrow$ _____

3. $\overline{SE} \leftrightarrow$ _____ **4.** $\angle F \leftrightarrow$ _____

5. $\overline{DS} \leftrightarrow$ _____ **6.** $\overline{DE} \leftrightarrow$ _____

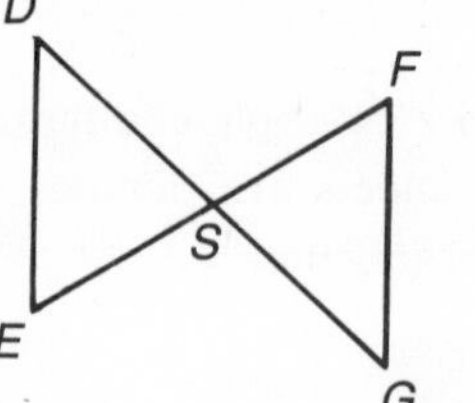

Given that figure $ABCD \cong$ figure $XYCD$, supply the missing correspondences.

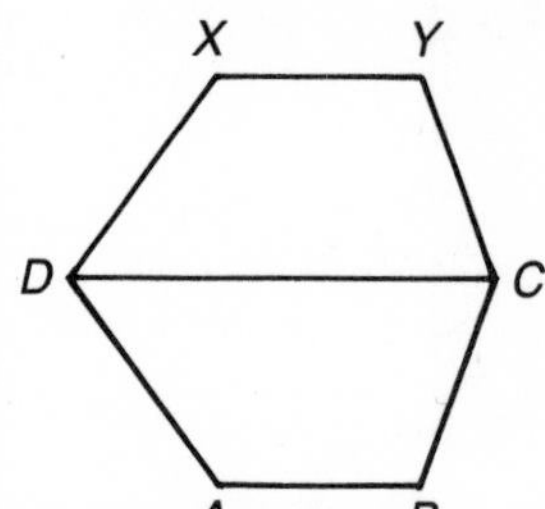

7. $\angle A \leftrightarrow$ **8.** $\angle XDC \leftrightarrow$

9. $\angle Y \leftrightarrow$ **10.** $\angle BCD \leftrightarrow$

11. $\overline{DC} \leftrightarrow$ **12.** $\overline{DA} \leftrightarrow$

13. $\overline{CY} \leftrightarrow$ **14.** $\overline{AB} \leftrightarrow$

B. The pair of figures in each exercise is congruent. List the corresponding pairs of congruent sides and angles.

15.

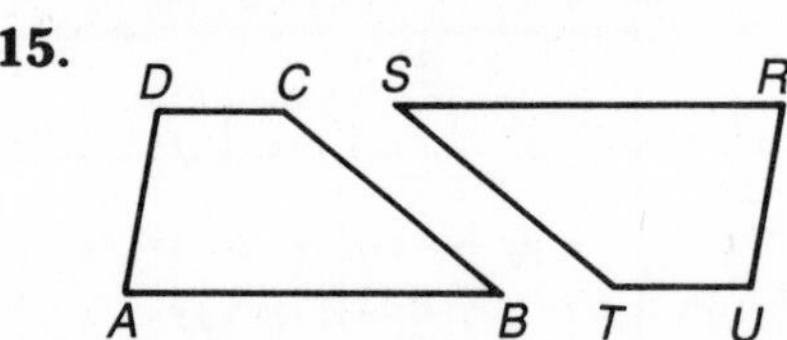

16.

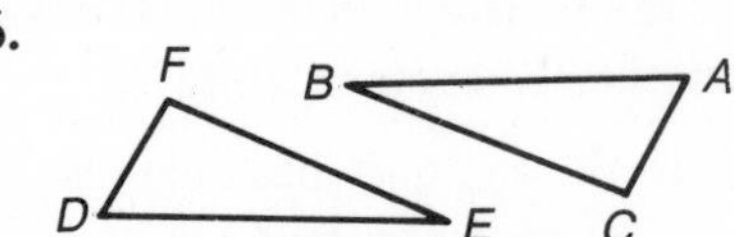

17.

D E C A B M N L J K

18.

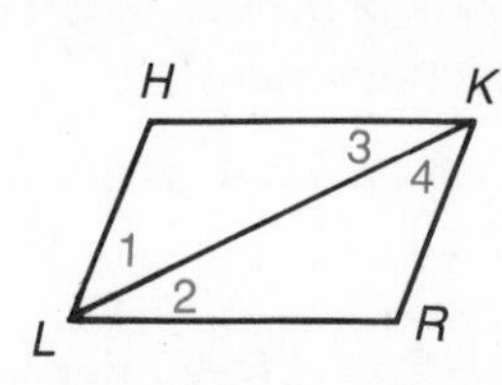

19.

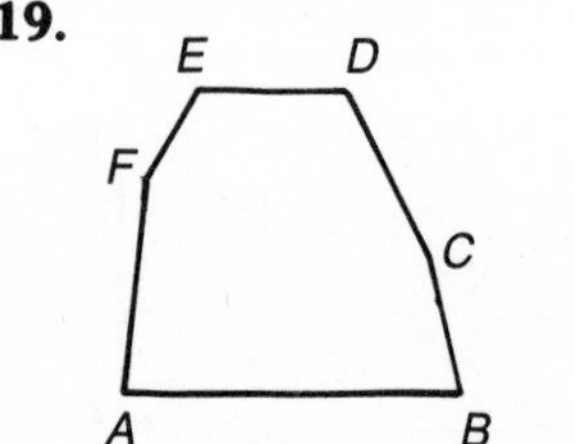

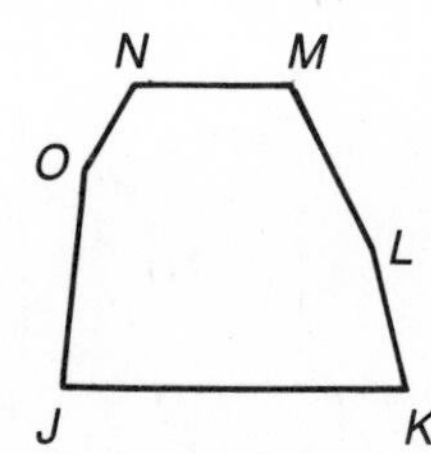

20.

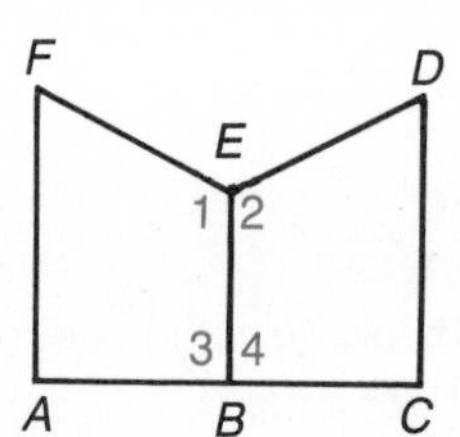

C. 21. Given that $\triangle LMN \cong \triangle PQR$, $LM = 3x + 2$, and $PQ = 5x - 8$, find LM.

22. Given that $\triangle DBF \cong \triangle KJC$, $m\angle F = 5x + 30$, and $m\angle C = \frac{20}{3}x$, find $m\angle F$.

3.5 Congruence Between Triangles

In the previous section, you learned that congruent figures have the same size and shape. This concept will now be examined with respect to triangles.

The following six conditions must be met to make $\triangle ABC \cong \triangle MLN$:

$\angle A \cong \angle M$ $\overline{AB} \cong \overline{ML}$
$\angle B \cong \angle L$ $\overline{BC} \cong \overline{LN}$
$\angle C \cong \angle N$ $\overline{CA} \cong \overline{NM}$

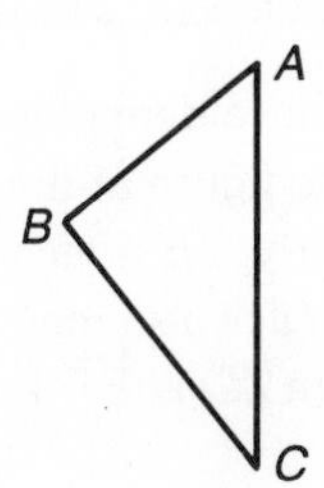

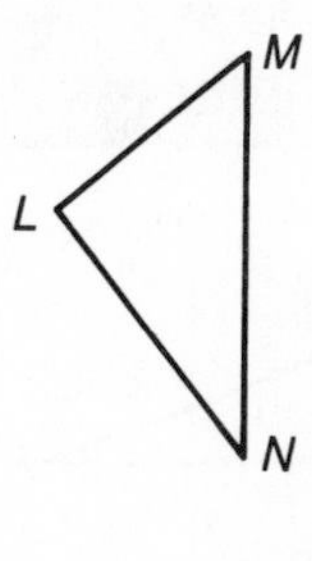

When naming vertices of congruent triangles, it is important to pair the vertices in order of their correspondence. $\triangle ABC \cong \triangle MLN$ implies $\angle A \cong \angle M$, $\angle B \cong \angle L$, and $\angle C \cong \angle N$.

The definition of congruence between two triangles will now be stated more formally:

DEFINITION: congruent triangles
Given a correspondence $ABC \leftrightarrow DEF$ between the vertices of two triangles, if the corresponding *sides* are congruent, and the corresponding *angles* are congruent, then the correspondence $ABC \leftrightarrow DEF$ is called a **congruence** between the two triangles.

Two triangles are congruent if and only if their corresponding sides have the same length and their corresponding angles all have the same measure. The correspondence between parts of congruent triangles is more widely known by the phrase *corresponding parts of congruent triangles are congruent.*

When drawing congruent triangles, you can mark corresponding parts to show which parts are congruent. In the figures at the right, the markings show that

$\angle B \cong \angle L$ $\overline{AC} \cong \overline{MN}$
$\angle A \cong \angle M$ $\overline{BC} \cong \overline{LN}$
$\angle C \cong \angle N$ $\overline{AB} \cong \overline{ML}$

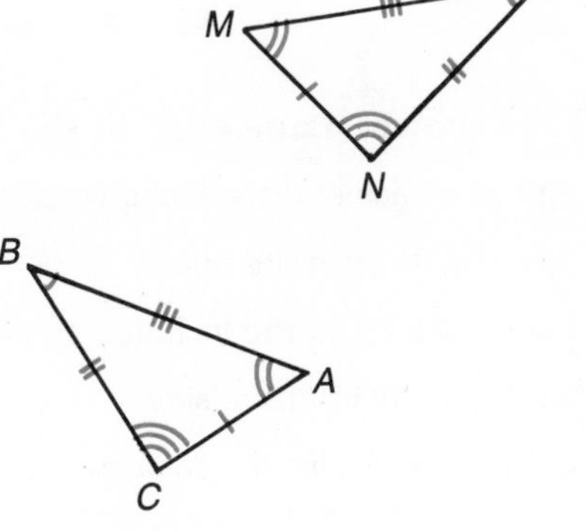

OBJECTIVE

Identify congruent triangles, their corresponding parts, and included and opposite sides and angles.

TEACHER'S NOTES

See p. T27

MIXED REVIEW

1. What angle has a supplement that is three times its complement? 45
2. Subtract $\frac{4}{5} - \frac{1}{3}$. $\frac{7}{15}$
3. Factor $x^2 - 8x + 15$. $(x - 3)(x - 5)$
4. Solve $|x + 4| = -3$. $\varnothing$
5. If $x^2 - x - 20 = 0$, then $x =$ _____ or _____. 5; -4

TEACHER'S RESOURCE MASTERS

Practice Master 8, Part 2

This is abbreviated as CPCTC in the *Teacher's Edition.*

ASSIGNMENT GUIDE

Day 1
Minimum 1-15 odd
Regular 1-19 odd
Maximum 1-23 odd

Day 2
Minimum 2-24 even
Regular 8-26 even
Maximum 16-24 even, 25-30

> **DEFINITIONS: included side; included angle; opposite angle; opposite side**
> A **side** of a triangle is said to be **included between two angles** if and only if the vertices of the angles are the endpoints of the segment. An **angle** of a triangle is said to be **included between two sides** of the triangle if and only if the sides of the angle contain the two sides of the triangle. A side of a triangle is said to be **opposite an angle** if and only if the side does not contain the vertex of that angle. This angle is also said to be **opposite the side.**

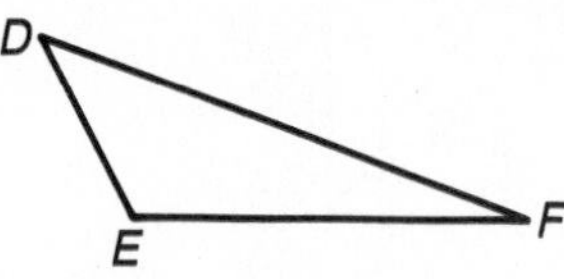

These definitions will be made clearer by observing $\triangle DEF$ in the figure at the left. $\overline{DE}$ is included between $\angle D$ and $\angle E$. Similarly, $\angle E$ is included between $\overline{DE}$ and $\overline{EF}$. Opposite sides and angles also may be shown by the same figure. The side opposite $\angle D$ is $\overline{EF}$, and the angle opposite $\overline{DE}$ is $\angle F$.

ORAL EXERCISES

For $\triangle ABC$, as shown, identify each of the following:

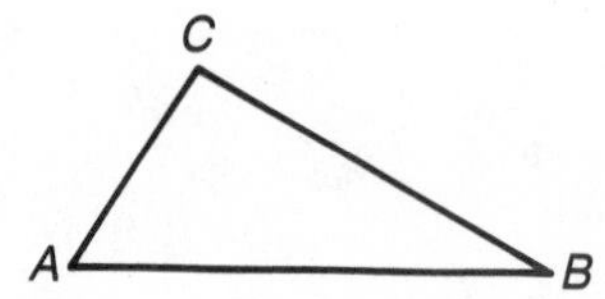

1. The angle included between $\overline{AB}$ and $\overline{BC}$.

2. The side included between $\angle C$ and $\angle A$.

3. The angle opposite side $\overline{BC}$.

4. The side opposite $\angle A$.

Oral Exercises

1. $\angle B$
2. $\overline{CA}$
3. $\angle A$
4. $\overline{BC}$

For $\triangle LMT$, as shown, identify each of the following:

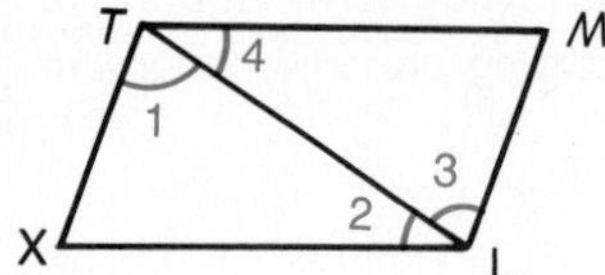

5. The angle opposite $\overline{LT}$.

6. The side opposite $\angle 4$.

7. The angle included between $\overline{TL}$ and $\overline{LM}$.

8. The side included between $\angle 4$ and $\angle M$.

5. $\angle M$
6. $\overline{ML}$
7. $\angle 3$
8. $\overline{TM}$

For $\triangle XLT$, as shown, name each of the following:

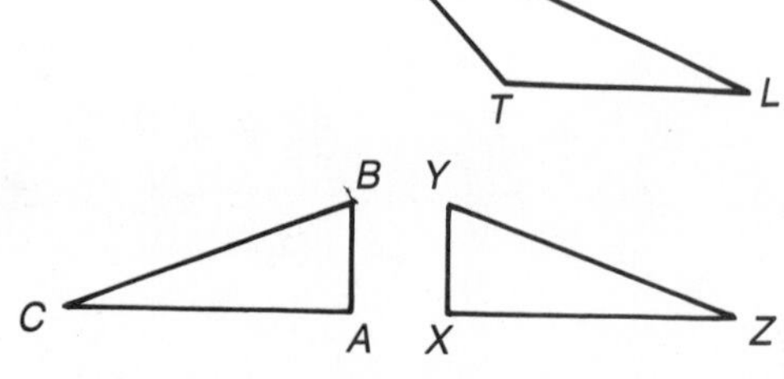

9. One pair of angles and the included side.

10. One side and its opposite angle.

11. One pair of sides and the included angle.

12. One angle and its opposite side.

13. If $\triangle ABC \cong \triangle XYZ$, list the corresponding pairs of congruent sides and angles.

9. $\angle L, \angle T, \overline{TL}$; $\angle T, \angle X, \overline{XT}$; $\angle X, \angle L, \overline{XL}$;
10. $\overline{XL}, \angle T$; $\overline{TL}, \angle X$; $\overline{XT}, \angle L$
11. $\overline{XT}, \overline{LT}, \angle T$; $\overline{XL}, \overline{LT}, \angle L$; $\overline{XL}, \overline{XT}, \angle X$
12. See #10.
13. $\angle A \cong \angle X$; $\angle B \cong \angle Y$, $\angle C \cong \angle Z$, $\overline{AC} \cong \overline{XZ}$, $\overline{CB} \cong \overline{ZY}$, $\overline{AB} \cong \overline{XY}$

14. If $\triangle ACT \cong \triangle TSA$, at the right, list the corresponding pairs of congruent sides and angles.

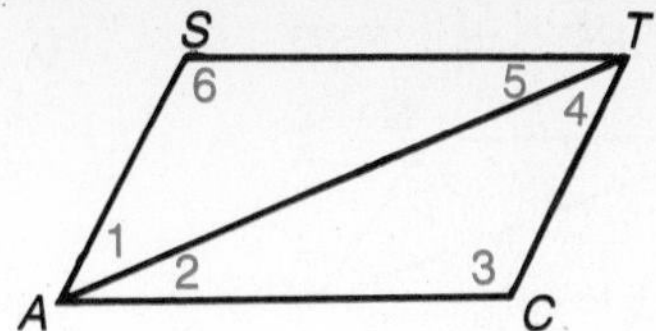

WRITTEN EXERCISES

A. For each pair of sides, name the included angle.

1. $\overline{XW}$ and $\overline{XY}$ **2.** $\overline{WY}$ and $\overline{YZ}$

3. $\overline{WZ}$ and $\overline{WY}$ **4.** $\overline{WX}$ and $\overline{WZ}$

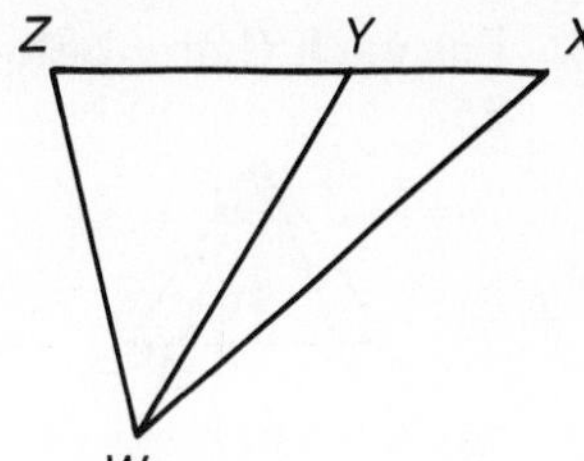

For each pair of angles, name the included side.

5. $\angle X$ and $\angle Z$ **6.** $\angle YWZ$ and $\angle ZYW$

7. $\angle Z$ and $\angle ZWY$ **8.** $\angle YWX$ and $\angle YXW$

For each angle, name the opposite side.

9. In $\triangle XYW$, $\angle X$ **10.** In $\triangle XZW$, $\angle X$ **11.** In $\triangle XWZ$, $\angle XWZ$

For each side, name the opposite angle.

12. In $\triangle WYZ$, $\overline{YZ}$ **13.** In $\triangle XYW$, $\overline{WY}$ **14.** In $\triangle XWZ$, $\overline{WZ}$

B. Each of the following pairs of triangles are congruent. List the corresponding pairs of congruent sides and angles.

15. $\triangle ABD \cong \triangle CBD$

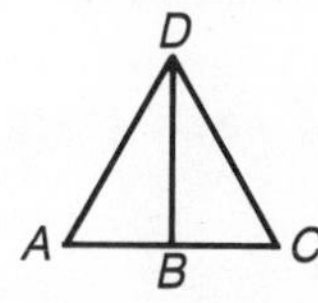

16. $\triangle AXY \cong \triangle BZY$

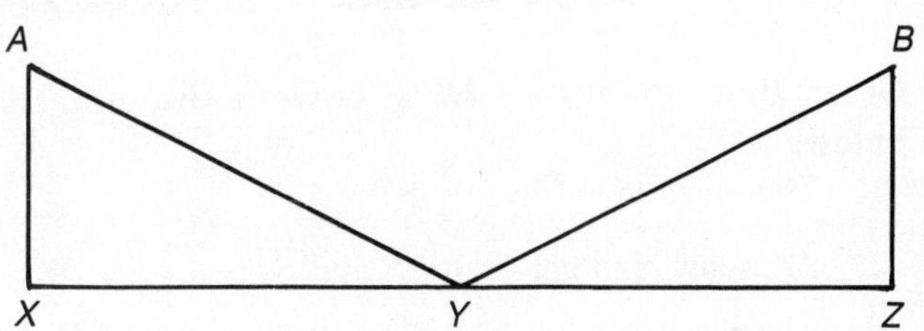

17. $\triangle PRX \cong \triangle PLX$

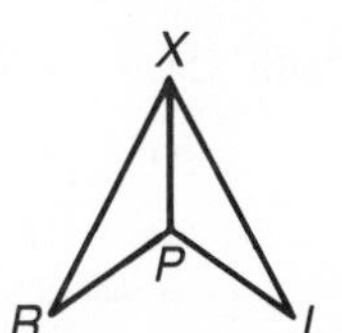

18. $\triangle ADC \cong \triangle CBA$

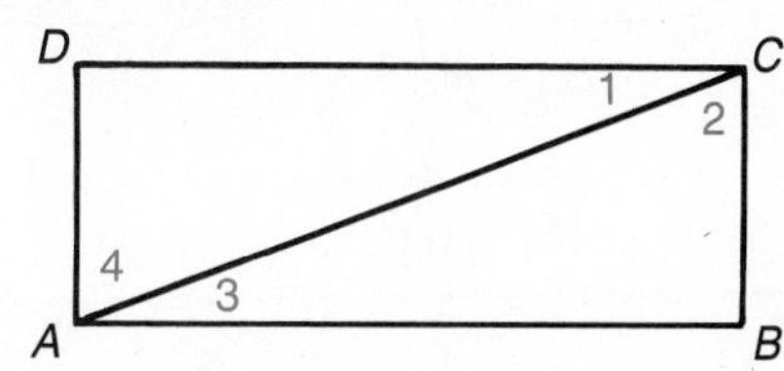

14. $\angle 1 \cong \angle 4$, $\angle 6 \cong \angle 3$, $\angle 5 \cong \angle 2$, $\overline{ST} \cong \overline{CA}$, $\overline{SA} = \overline{CT}$, $\overline{AT} \cong \overline{TA}$

Written Exercises

1. $\angle X$ 2. $\angle WYZ$
3. $\angle ZWY$ 4. $\angle XWZ$

5. $\overline{XZ}$ 6. $\overline{WY}$
7. $\overline{ZW}$ 8. $\overline{WX}$

9. $\overline{WY}$
10. $\overline{WZ}$
11. $\overline{ZX}$
12. $\angle YWZ$
13. $\angle X$
14. $\angle X$

15. $\angle A \cong \angle C$, $\angle ADB \cong \angle CDB$, $\angle DBA \cong \angle DBC$, $\overline{AD} \cong \overline{CD}$, $\overline{DB} \cong \overline{DB}$, $\overline{BA} \cong \overline{BC}$
16. $\angle A \cong \angle B$, $\angle X \cong \angle Z$, $\angle AYX \cong \angle BYZ$, $\overline{AY} \cong \overline{BY}$, $\overline{AX} \cong \overline{BZ}$, $\overline{XY} \cong \overline{ZY}$

17. $\angle R \cong \angle L$, $\angle RXP \cong \angle LXP$, $\angle XPR \cong \angle XPL$, $\overline{XR} \cong \overline{XL}$, $\overline{XP} \cong \overline{XP}$, $\overline{PR} \cong \overline{PL}$
18. $\angle 1 \cong \angle 3$, $\angle 2 \cong \angle 4$, $\angle D \cong \angle B$, $\overline{DC} \cong \overline{BA}$, $\overline{AD} \cong \overline{CB}$, $\overline{AC} \cong \overline{CA}$

19. $\angle Q \cong \angle S$, $\angle QRT \cong \angle STR$, $\angle QTR \cong \angle SRT$, $\overline{RQ} \cong \overline{TS}$, $\overline{RT} \cong \overline{TR}$, $\overline{RS} \cong \overline{TQ}$

20. $\angle L \cong \angle M$, $\angle T \cong \angle R$, $\angle LXT \cong \angle MXR$, $\overline{LT} \cong \overline{MR}$, $\overline{LX} \cong \overline{MX}$, $\overline{RX} \cong \overline{TX}$

21. $\angle CAD \cong \angle CBD$, $\angle CDA \cong \angle CDB$, $\angle ACD \cong \angle BCD$, $\overline{CA} \cong \overline{CB}$, $\overline{CD} \cong \overline{CD}$, $\overline{DA} \cong \overline{DB}$

22. $\angle DAE \cong \angle BCE$, $\angle ADE \cong \angle CBE$, $\angle DEA \cong \angle BEC$, $\overline{DA} \cong \overline{BC}$, $\overline{EA} \cong \overline{EC}$, $\overline{ED} \cong \overline{EB}$

23. $\angle CAE \cong \angle CED$, $\angle CEA \cong \angle CDE$, $\angle ACE \cong \angle ECD$, $\overline{CA} \cong \overline{CE}$, $\overline{CE} \cong \overline{CD}$, $\overline{AE} \cong \overline{ED}$

24. $\angle A \cong \angle D$, $\angle AEC \cong \angle DEB$, $\angle ECA \cong \angle EBD$, $\overline{EA} \cong \overline{ED}$, $\overline{EC} \cong \overline{EB}$, $\overline{AC} \cong \overline{DB}$

25. $\triangle ABC \cong \triangle AED$, $\triangle ADB \cong \triangle ACE$

26. $\triangle FEG \cong \triangle GHF$, $\triangle FEJ \cong \triangle GHJ$

27. $\triangle PQL \cong \triangle NMJ$, $\triangle PQO \cong \triangle NMO$, $\triangle JQK \cong \triangle LMK$, $\triangle JOM \cong \triangle LOQ$

28. $\triangle WXZ \cong \triangle WVY$, $\triangle YZX \cong \triangle ZYV$, $\triangle YTX \cong \triangle ZTV$

29. $\triangle KHG \cong \triangle HKJ$, $\triangle KLG \cong \triangle HMJ$, $\triangle HLG \cong \triangle KMJ$

30. $\triangle ADC \cong \triangle DCB \cong \triangle CBA \cong \triangle BAD$, $\triangle ADE \cong \triangle DCE \cong \triangle CBE \cong \triangle BAE$

Error Search

1.	$\angle R$	2.	HF
3.	$\overline{RT}$	4.	$\angle H$
5.	$\angle S$	6.	$\angle G$
7.	$\angle S$ and $\angle T$	8.	$\overline{RS}$
9.	$= m\angle H$	10.	$\overline{FG}$

19. $\triangle RQT \cong \triangle TSR$

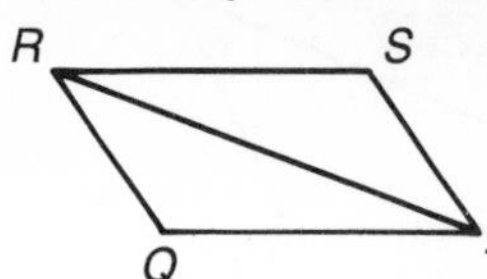

20. $\triangle XMR \cong \triangle XLT$

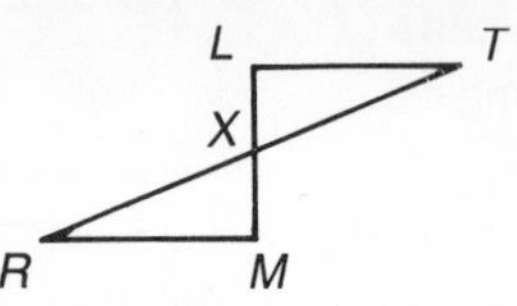

21. $\triangle ADC \cong \triangle BDC$

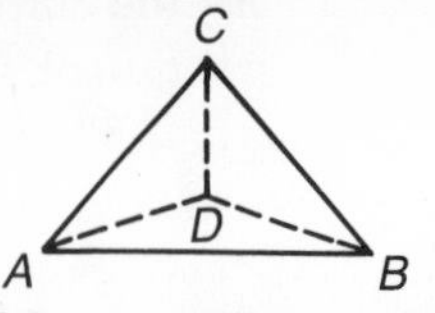

22. $\triangle AED \cong \triangle CEB$

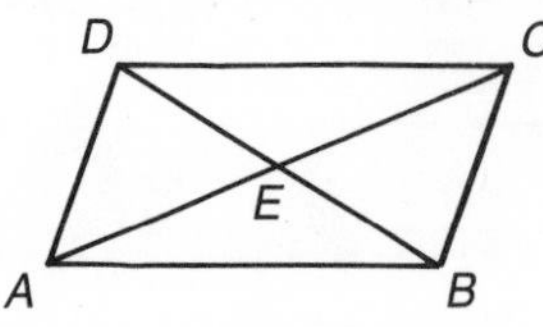

23. $\triangle AEC \cong \triangle EDC$

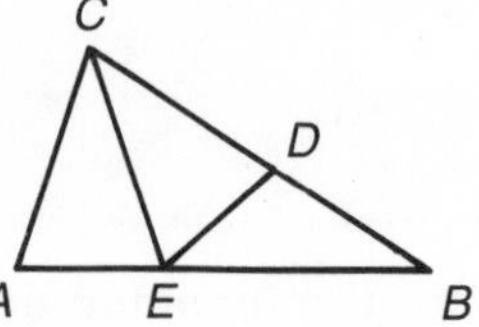

24. $\triangle ACE \cong \triangle DBE$

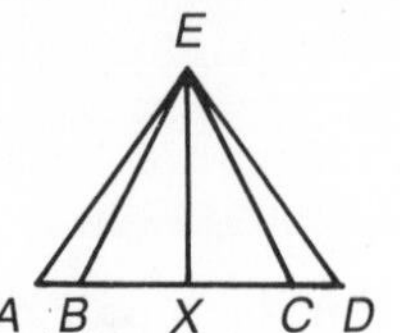

C. For each figure below, name all the pairs of congruent triangles.

25.

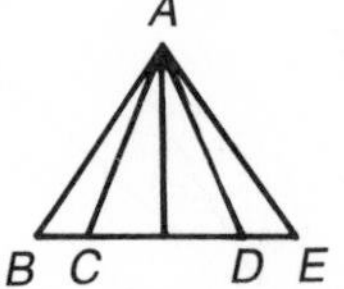

26.

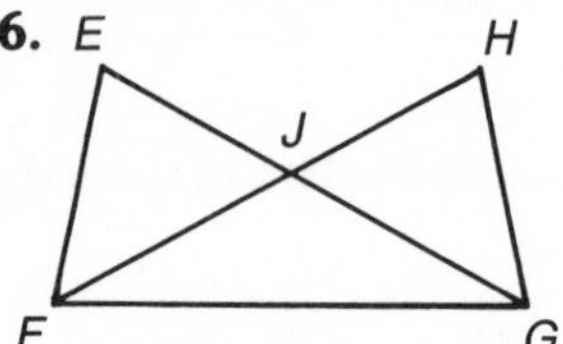

27.

28.

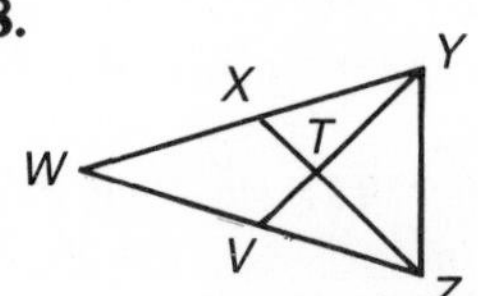

29.

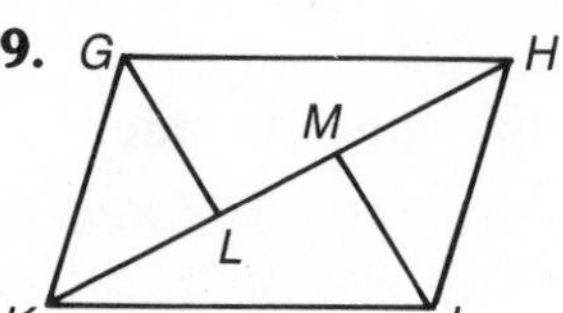

30.

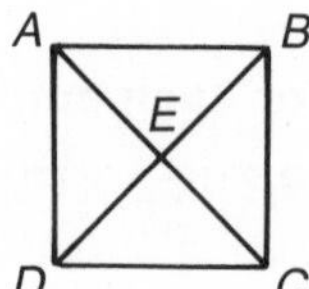

ERROR SEARCH

Given that $\triangle STR \cong \triangle HFG$, correct the underlined part of each statement below.

1. The angle opposite side $\overline{ST}$ is $\underline{G}$.
2. $ST \leftrightarrow \underline{FH}$.
3. $\angle T$ is included between $\underline{\overline{RS}}$ and $\overline{ST}$.
4. $\underline{\angle F} \cong \angle S$.
5. The side opposite $\underline{\angle R}$ is $\overline{RT}$.
6. $\angle R \cong \underline{\angle T}$.
7. $\underline{\overline{ST}}$ is included between $\underline{\angle T \text{ and } \angle R}$.
8. $\underline{\overline{RT}} \cong \overline{GH}$.
9. $m\angle S \underline{\cong m\angle H}$.
10. $\underline{\overleftrightarrow{FG}}$ is opposite $\angle H$.

3.6 Triangle Congruence as an Equivalence Relation

In previous sections you have learned that congruence of segments and congruence of angles are both equivalence relations (Section 1.6, Section 2.4). These statements can be summarized as follows:

Segments

Reflexive: $\overline{AB} \cong \overline{AB}$

Symmetric: If $\overline{AB} \cong \overline{CD}$, then $\overline{CD} \cong \overline{AB}$

Transitive: If $\overline{AB} \cong \overline{CD}$ and $\overline{CD} \cong \overline{EF}$, then $\overline{AB} \cong \overline{EF}$

Angles

Reflexive: $\angle 1 \cong \angle 1$

Symmetric: If $\angle 1 \cong \angle 2$, then $\angle 2 \cong \angle 1$

Transitive: If $\angle 1 \cong \angle 2$ and $\angle 2 \cong \angle 3$, then $\angle 1 \cong \angle 3$

The reflexive properties for congruent segments and congruent angles will be particularly important in proving later theorems about triangles. These properties have therefore been singled out for separate, formal statements as theorems. For angles, Theorem 3.2 stated that every angle is congruent to itself. The next theorem makes the same formal statement for segments. Remember that the proof has already been presented as part of the proof of Theorem 1.3 (Congruence between segments is an equivalence relation.).

THEOREM 3.9
Every segment is congruent to itself.

Because the congruence of triangles depends on the congruence of segments and angles, both of which are equivalence relations, you might expect that congruence of triangles is an equivalence relation also. This is intuitively apparent from the definition of congruent triangles; that is, they have the same size and shape. The relationship of "having the same size and shape" is reflexive, symmetric, and transitive.

THEOREM 3.10
Congruence of triangles is an equivalence relation.

The proof of Theorem 3.10 is left as an exercise.

OBJECTIVE

Identify equivalence relations and use the properties of equality in proofs involving algebraic equations.

TEACHER'S NOTES

See p. T27

MIXED REVIEW

1. Add $\frac{x+2}{x-3} + \frac{x-1}{x-3}$. $\frac{2x+1}{x-3}$
2. Add $\frac{x-1}{x+2} + \frac{x+1}{x-2}$. $\frac{2x^2+4}{(x+2)(x-2)}$
3. Solve $\frac{3}{x} = \frac{5}{x+7}$. $10\frac{1}{2}$
4. If $x^2 + 4x - 5 = 0$, then $x =$ ______ or ______. -5; 1
5. If $\frac{x}{1} = \frac{5}{x-4}$, then $x =$ ______ or ______. -5; 1

TEACHER'S RESOURCE MASTERS

Practice Master 9, Part 1

ASSIGNMENT GUIDE

Minimum 1-25
Regular 1-35
Maximum 1-15 odd, 16-37

Oral Exercises

1. R 2. T 3. R
4. S 5. R 6. T
7. S 8. T 9. S
10. R

Written Exercises

1. S 2. T
3. R, S, T 4. T
5. R, S, T 6. T
7. S, T 8. R, S, T
9. T 10. R, S, T
11. R, S, T 12. R, T
13. R, S, T 14. R, S, T
15. 3, 5, 8, 10, 11, 13, 14

ORAL EXERCISES

Identify each relationship shown as *reflexive, symmetric,* or *transitive.*

1. $x = x$

2. If $a = b$ and $b = c$, then $a = c$.

3. $\triangle ABC \cong \triangle ABC$

4. If $x = 5$, then $5 = x$.

5. $m\angle 3 = m\angle 3$

6. If $a > b$ and $b > 2$, then $a > 2$.

7. If Pam is related to John, then John is related to Pam.

8. If Ted is older than Karen, and Karen is older than Maria, then Ted is older than Maria.

9. If $25 = 2x^2 - 3x$, then $2x^2 - 3x = 25$.

10. $a + b = a + b$

WRITTEN EXERCISES

A. Examine each relationship to determine if it is *reflexive, symmetric,* or *transitive.*

Example: is younger than

Reflexive: For any person A, is it true that A "is younger than" A? No. Therefore, the relationship is not reflexive.

Symmetric: For any two people A and B, is it true that if A "is younger than" B, then B "is younger than" A? No. Therefore, the relationshiop is not symmetric.

Transitive: For any three people A, B, and C, is it true that if A "is younger than" B, and B "is younger than" C, then A "is younger than" C? Yes. Therefore, the relationship is transitive.

1. is next to

2. is older than

3. is the same color as

4. is heavier than

5. is the same age as

6. is brother of

7. is sibling of

8. costs the same as

9. is less than

10. has the same area as

11. is equal to

12. is a subset of

13. is in the same geometry class as

14. has exactly the same number of pages as (with respect to books)

15. Which of the relationships in Exercises 1-14 are equivalence relations?

B. Supply the reason for each step in the following proof.

Given: $3x + 20 = 140$

Prove: $x = 40$

Proof:

STATEMENTS	REASONS
1. $3x + 20 = 140$	1. **16.**
2. $20 = 20$	2. **17.**
3. $3x + 20 - 20 = 140 - 20$	3. **18.**
4. $3x + 0 = 140 - 20$	4. **19.**
5. $3x = 140 - 20$	5. **20.**
6. $3x = 120$	6. **21.**
7. $\frac{3x}{3} = \frac{120}{3}$	7. **22.**
8. $1x = \frac{120}{3}$	8. **23.**
9. $x = \frac{120}{3}$	9. **24.**
10. $x = 40$	10. **25.**

Supply the reason for each step in the following proof.

Given: $65 = 2x - 5$

Prove: $x = 35$

Proof:

STATEMENTS	REASONS
1. $65 = 2x - 5$	1. **26.**
2. $2x - 5 = 65$	2. **27.**
3. $2x - 5 + 5 = 65 + 5$	3. **28.**
4. $2x + 0 = 65 + 5$	4. **29.**
5. $2x = 65 + 5$	5. **30.**
6. $2x = 70$	6. **31.**
7. $\frac{2x}{2} = \frac{70}{2}$	7. **32.**
8. $1x = \frac{70}{2}$	8. **33.**
9. $x = \frac{70}{2}$	9. **34.**
10. $x = 35$	10. **35.**

C. 36. Given $20 = 7x - 8$ and $y = 4$, prove $x = y$. **37.** Prove Theorem 3.10.

16. Given
17. Reflex. prop. of equality
18. Subtraction prop. of equality
19. Inverse prop. of addition
20. Identity prop. of addition
21. Number fact
22. Division prop. of equality
23. Inverse prop. of mult.
24. Identity prop. of mult.
25. Number fact
26. Given
27. Sym. prop. of equality
28. Addition prop. of equality
29. Inverse prop. of addition
30. Identity prop. of addition
31. Number fact
32. Division prop. of equality
33. Inverse of mult.
34. Identity prop. of mult.
35. Number fact
36. *1.* $20 = 7x - 8$, $y = 4$ (Given); *2.* $8 = 8$ (Reflex.); *3.* $20 + 8 = 7x - 8 + 8$ (Addition prop.); *4.* $20 + 8 = 7x + 0$, (Inverse of addition); *5.* $20 + 8 = 7x$ (Identity of addition); *6.* $28 = 7x$ (Number fact); *7.* $\frac{28}{7} = \frac{7x}{7}$ (Division prop.); *8.* $\frac{28}{7} = 1x$ (Inverse of mult.); *9.* $\frac{28}{7} = x$ (Identity of mult.); *10.* $4 = x$ (Number fact); *11.* $x = 4$ (Sym.); *12.* $4 = y$, (Sym.); *13.* $x = y$ (Trans.).
37. Given $\triangle ABC \cong \triangle DEF \cong \triangle GHI$, all corresp. segments and angles in the three $\triangle$s are $\cong$. Since these congruences are equiv. relations, it can be shown that (1) $\triangle ABC \cong \triangle ABC$, (Reflex.) (2) $\triangle DEF \cong \triangle ABC$ (Sym.), and (3) $\triangle ABC \cong \triangle GHI$ (Trans.).

3.7 Medians and Bisectors

OBJECTIVES

Identify medians and angle bisectors.

Given the measure of a line segment or an angle, determine the measure of another line segment or angle using medians or angle bisectors.

TEACHER'S NOTES

See p. T27

MIXED REVIEW

1. If an angle is four times its complement, what is the measure of the angle? 72
2. What condition for x would guarantee that $2x - 18$ is the measure of an obtuse angle? $54 < x < 99$
3. In $\triangle ABC$, which side is opposite $\angle B$? $\overline{AC}$
4. Add $|8 - (-3)| + |-8 + 3|$. 16
5. If $5x - 3(4 - x) = 12 - (x + 2)$, then $x =$ ______. $\frac{22}{9}$

TEACHER'S RESOURCE MASTERS

Practice Master 9, Part 2
Quiz 6

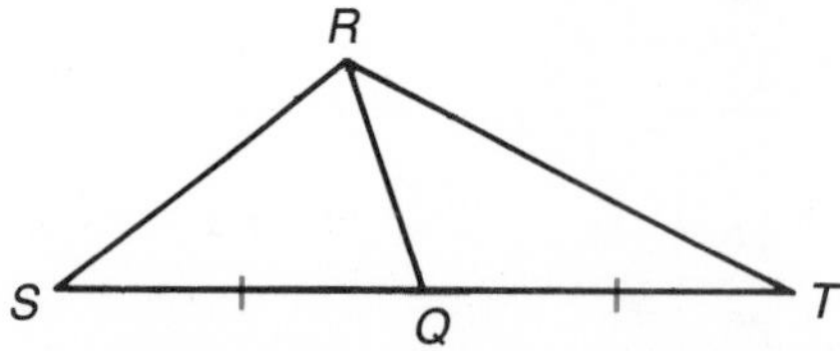

In $\triangle SRT$ at the left, $\overline{RQ}$ is the **median** of $\triangle SRT$. One endpoint of $\overline{RQ}$, R, is a vertex of the triangle, and the other endpoint, Q, is the midpoint of $\overline{ST}$.

DEFINITION: median
A segment is a **median** of a triangle if and only if its endpoints are a vertex of the triangle and the midpoint of the opposite side.

Another segment having special properties is an **angle bisector.**

DEFINITION: angle bisector
If T lies in the interior of $\angle XYZ$, and $\angle XYT \cong \angle TYZ$, then $\overrightarrow{YT}$ *bisects* $\angle XYZ$ and is called the **angle bisector** of $\angle XYZ$.

DEFINITION: angle bisector of a triangle
A segment is an **angle bisector of a triangle** if and only if it *bisects* an angle and its endpoints are the vertex of the angle and a point on the opposite side.

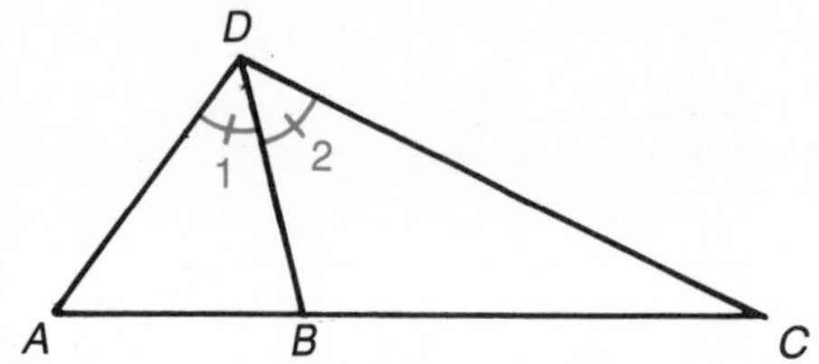

In $\triangle ADC$ at the left, $\overline{DB}$ divides $\angle ADC$ into two congruent angles ($\angle 1$ and $\angle 2$), as indicated by the marked angle arcs. The endpoints of $\overline{DB}$ are the vertex of $\angle ADC$ and a point on the opposite side ($\overline{AC}$). Therefore, $\overline{DB}$ is an angle bisector of $\triangle ADC$.

Every triangle has exactly three medians and exactly three angle bisectors.

In previous lessons, you learned about corresponding sides and corresponding angles. Now you will investigate similar properties involving medians and bisectors. In the figure at the right, in which $\triangle ABD \cong \triangle WXZ$, the medians $\overline{AC}$ and $\overline{WY}$ are **corresponding medians.** Corresponding medians are medians drawn from corresponding vertices.

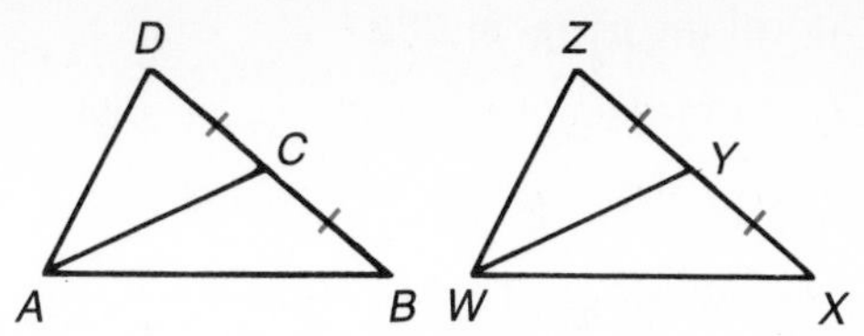

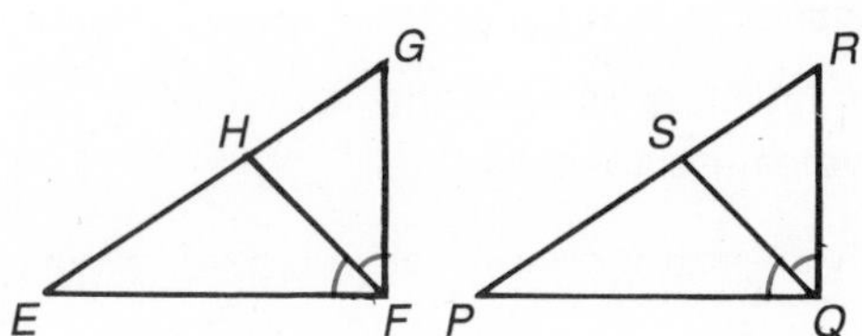

Similarly, **corresponding angle bisectors** are angle bisectors drawn from corresponding vertices. In the figure at the left, in which $\triangle EFG \cong \triangle PQR$, the angle bisectors $\overline{HF}$ and $\overline{SQ}$ are corresponding angle bisectors.

The following theorems will now be stated without proof:

THEOREM 3.11
Corresponding medians of congruent triangles are congruent.

THEOREM 3.12
Corresponding angle bisectors of congruent triangles are congruent.

ORAL EXERCISES

Complete the statements below with always, sometimes, or never.

1. A triangle ____ has three medians.
2. A triangle ____ has three angle bisectors.
3. From a given vertex of a triangle, the median and the angle bisector are ____ the same segment.
4. A median of a triangle is ____ the same segment as one of the sides of the triangle.
5. The three medians of a triangle ____ have the same length.

ASSIGNMENT GUIDE

Minimum 1-16
Regular 1-23 odd
Maximum 1-15 odd, 19-26

Oral Exercises

1. A
2. A
3. S
4. N
5. S

6. S
7. S
8. S

Written Exercises

1. Answers will vary.
2. Answers will vary.

3. 6 4. 18
5. 35 6. 50
7. $8\frac{1}{2}$ 8. 13
9. $19\frac{1}{2}$ 10. 25
11. $7\frac{1}{3}$ 12. 10
13. $6\frac{2}{3}$ 14. $17\frac{1}{2}$
15. 4 16. 8
17. $12\frac{1}{3}$ 18. 2
19. 15 20. 7
21. 10
22. 7
23. 2
24. 6
25. 7
26. $AD = 36$

6. An angle bisector of a triangle _____ connects one vertex of a triangle to the midpoint of the opposite side.

7. A median of a triangle _____ divides the triangle into two congruent triangles.

8. An angle bisector of a triangle _____ divides the triangle into two congruent triangles.

WRITTEN EXERCISES

A. 1. Draw two triangles, one whose three medians all have the same length, and another whose three medians all have different lengths.

2. Draw two triangles, one whose three angle bisectors all have the same length, and another whose three angle bisectors all have different lengths.

B. Refer to the figures for Exercises 3–26. Assume that $\overline{CD}$ is a median of $\triangle ABC$ and $\overline{XZ}$ is an angle bisector of $\triangle WXY$.

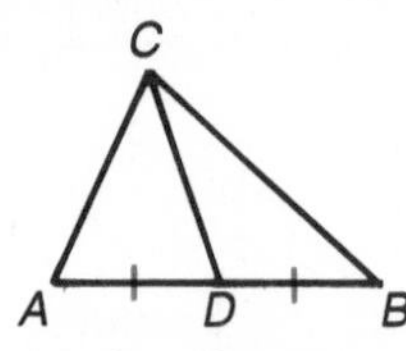

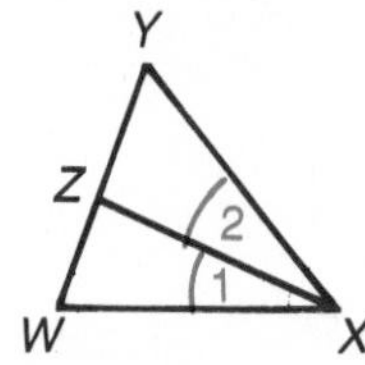

3. If $AB = 12$, find AD.

4. If $AD = 9$, find AB.

5. If $m\angle WXY = 70$, find $m\angle 1$.

6. If $m\angle 2 = 25$, find $m\angle WXY$.

7. If $AB = 17$, find DB.

8. If $m\angle 1 = 13$, find $m\angle 2$.

9. If $m\angle WXY = 39$, find $m\angle 1$.

10. If $AD = 25$, find DB.

11. If $m\angle WXY = 44$ and $m\angle 1 = 3a$, find a.

12. If $m\angle 1 = 24$ and $m\angle 2 = 3b - 6$, find b.

13. If $AD = 20$ and $AB = 6a$, find a.

14. If $DB = 35$ and $AD = 2y$, find y.

15. If $AB = 80$ and $DB = 10a$, find a.

16. If $AD = 2y + 4$ and $DB. = 3y - 4$, find y.

17. If $AB = 37$ and $AD = \frac{3y}{2}$, find y.

18. If $AD = 14$ and $DB = 5x + 4$, find x.

19. If $m\angle 1 = 31$ and $m\angle WXY = 4x + 2$, find x.

20. If $m\angle WXY = 78$ and $m\angle 2 = 7k - 10$, find k.

21. Find a if $m\angle 1 = 2a$ and $m\angle WXY = 3a + 10$.

22. Find b if $AD = 5b - 2$ and $AB = 9b + 3$.

C. 23. Find y if $m\angle 1 = 7y + 10$ and $m\angle 2 = 9(y + 1) - 3$.

24. Find c if $m\angle 2 = 4c + 7$ and $m\angle WXY = 5(c + 5) + 7$.

25. Find x if $AD = x^2 - 5x + 1$ and $BD = x^2 - x - 27$.

26. Find AD if $DB = x^2 + 2x + 1$ and $AB = 2x^2 + 3x + 7$.

SKILLS MAINTENANCE

To solve each of the following systems of equations, would it be easier to use substitution or addition and multiplication?

1. $x - y = 0$, $x + y = 4$

2. $2x + y = 7$, $x = y + 2$

3. $3a + 3b = 15$, $2a + 6b = 22$

Solve each system of equations below by the indicated method. Be sure to check your solution in *both* equations.

Solve by substitution:

4. $2y + x = 7$, $y = x - 4$

5. $2y + 3x = 12$, $x = 4y - 10$

6. $a = 3b$, $2a = -2b + 16$

7. $x - 2y = 2$, $3x - 6y = 6$

Solve by addition and multiplication:

8. $5c + 3d = 17$, $-5c + 2d = 3$

9. $3b - 2c = 0$, $3b - 4c = -1$

10. $20x + 10y = 40$, $2x - y = 0$

11. $3x + 2y = -7$, $3x + 2y = 7$

12. How can you tell if a system of equations is dependent? inconsistent?

CHALLENGE

A logic problem is solved by stating a conclusion that uses information in the given statements, or *premises*. For example, consider the three premises:

1. *Everyone who is sane can use logic.*
2. *No lunatics are fit to serve on a jury.*
3. *None of your sons can use logic.*

The only conclusion that can be drawn from all three premises is: *None of your sons is fit to serve on a jury.* Now try these:

A.
1. No one takes the *Times* who is not well educated.
2. No hedgehogs can read.
3. Those who cannot read are not well educated.

B.
1. No experienced person is incompetent.
2. Jenkins is always blundering.
3. No competent person is always blundering.

Skills Maintenance

1. addition and multiplication
2. subtraction
3. either
4. 5, 1
5. 2, 3
6. 6, 2
7. Dependent equations; the solution is an infinite set of real no. prs. that satisfy the condition $y = \frac{x-2}{2}$.
8. 1, 4
9. $\frac{1}{3}, \frac{1}{2}$
10. 1, 2
11. Inconsistent equations; $\varnothing$.
12. If the slopes and y-intercepts are the same, the equations are dependent. When solving, you will get a statement that is always true, such as $0 = 0$. If the equations have the same slope but different y-intercepts, they are inconsistent. Solving them will provide a statement that is never true, such as $0 = -7$.

Challenge

These logic problems were created by Charles Dodgson (1832–1898), a storyteller and mathematics teacher at Oxford University. Mr. Dodgson may be known to students by his pseudonym, Lewis Carroll.

A. No hedgehogs take the *Times*.

B. Jenkins is not experienced.

EXPLORATION
Finite Geometry

The geometry presented in this book is Euclidean, considered for hundreds of years to be the only possible geometry. Non-Euclidean geometry was discovered when someone suggested that since postulates are unproven, they could be changed. It would simply mean that the theorems based on those changed postulates might not be the same as Euclid's.

Finite geometry is one type of non-Euclidean geometry that satisfies some of Euclid's postulates. On the left is a typical Euclidean model, and on the right is a possible non-Euclidean model. Using the pyramid as a model, *point* is defined as one of the four corners, *line* as one of the six edges, *plane* as one of the four sides, and *space* as the pyramid itself.

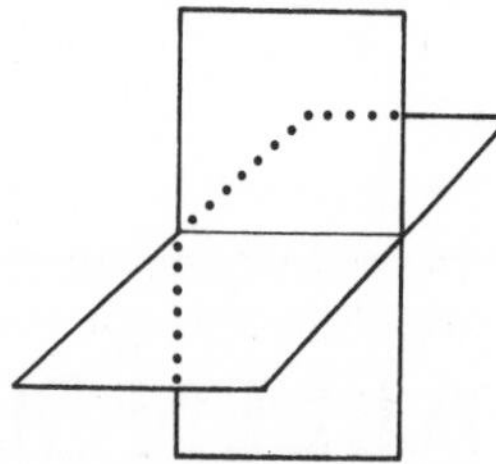

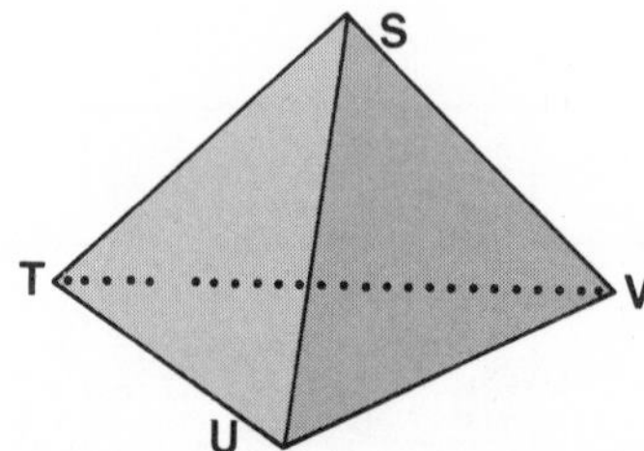

Now recall some of Euclid's first postulates:

- Given two points, there is exactly one line that contains both of them.
- Every plane contains at least three noncollinear points. Space contains at least four noncoplanar points.
- If two points lie in a plane, then the line containing these points lies in the same plane.
- If two planes intersect, then their intersection is a line.

Now substitute the new interpretations of point, line, plane, and space. The first postulate would be "Given two *corners,* there is exactly one *edge* that contains both of them." Do this for the other three postulates. Other postulates cannot be rephrased in these terms. The Ruler Postulate calls for infinite points, but the pyramid model has a finite number of corners. This model satisfies some, but not all, of Euclid's postulates.

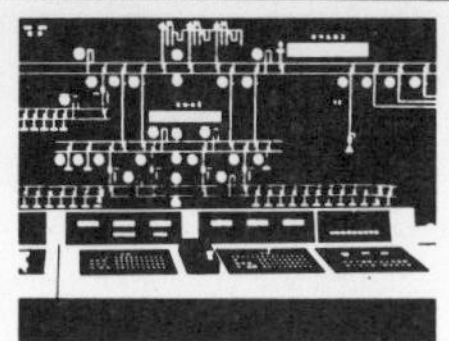

COMPUTER

When a computer program does not require special data, the computer can generate data at random, much as you would obtain random results by tossing a coin. The function RND (1), will produce nine-digit decimals between 0 and 1. A simple program to generate and print five random numbers would look like this:

```
10 FOR X = 1 TO 5
20 PRINT RND(1)
30 NEXT X
40 END
```

The result of this program might be the numbers .766524553, .132572496, .368149568, .926387247, and .045226966. Suppose, however, you need random integers. Then you could combine the RND (X) and INT (X) commands as follows:

```
20 PRINT INT(10*RND(1))
```

This instruction multiplies each random decimal by 10 and then reduces the product to an integer. Thus, the decimals generated above would yield 7, 1, 3, 9, and 0. Notice that neither program will produce the number 10. To obtain integers between 1 and 10, you could give the command INT (10*RND (1) + 1). Now your list of decimals would become 8, 2, 4, 10, and 1. In general, to produce integers between 1 and any integer Y, use the command INT (Y*RND (X) + 1).

The function ABS(A − B), which finds the absolute value of the difference between two values A and B, is useful for determining distance or length. Supply the missing steps in the following program, which randomly generates two endpoints of a segment and computes the distance between them.

```
10 REM RANDOMLY GENERATE TWO ENDPOINTS OF A SEGMENT
20 LET X = INT(10*RND(1) + 1)
30 LET Y = __1.__
40 PRINT "THE ENDPOINTS OF THE SEGMENT ARE : "; __2.__
50 REM NOW COMPUTE THE LENGTH OF THE SEGMENT
60 LET D = ABS __3.__
70 PRINT "THE LENGTH OF THE SEGMENT IS"; __4.__
```

TEACHER'S RESOURCE MASTERS

Computer Master 3

Computer

1. 30 INT(10*RND(1) + 1)
2. 40 X;Y
3. 60 (X − Y)
4. 70 D

CHAPTER 3 REVIEW

TEACHER'S RESOURCE MASTERS

Enrichment Master 3

ENRICHMENT

See Activities 5-6, p. T44

Chapter 3 Review

1. ∠2, ∠3 2. ∠1, ∠4
3. No; they are not adjacent.
4. 168 5. 43
6. $180 - a$ 7. $185 - 2x$
8. 70, 110
9. ∠BCF, ∠BDE, ∠DEA
10. ∠EAB, ∠ABD, ∠FCD
11. ∠AFC, ∠EFC
12. 47 13. 8
14. $90 - x$ 15. $89 - 3y$
16. 10, 80

VOCABULARY

acute angle (3.2)
acute triangle (3.2)
adjacent angles (3.1)
angle bisector (3.7)
angle bisector of a triangle (3.7)
complement (3.2)
complementary angles (3.2)
congruent figures (3.4)
congruent triangles (3.5)
corresponding angles (3.4)
corresponding angle bisectors (3.7)
corresponding medians (3.7)
corresponding sides (3.4)
equal angles (3.2)
hypotenuse (3.2)
included angle (3.5)
included side (3.5)
leg (3.2)
linear pair (3.1)
median (3.7)
obtuse angle (3.2)
obtuse triangle (3.2)
opposite angle (3.5)
opposite side (3.5)
perpendicular lines (3.2)
right angle (3.2)
right triangle (3.2)
supplement (3.1)
supplementary angles (3.1)
vertical angles (3.3)

REVIEW EXERCISES

3.1 **Refer to the figure for Exercises 1–3.**

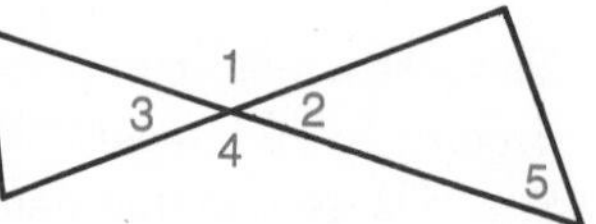

1. Name all the angles supplementary to ∠4.

2. Name all the angles adjacent to ∠3.

3. Do ∠2 and ∠5 form a linear pair? Explain.

Name the supplement of each angle.

4. 12 **5.** 137 **6.** a **7.** $2x - 5$

8. The measures of two supplementary angles differ by 40. Find the measures.

3.2 **Refer to the figure for Exercises 9–11.**

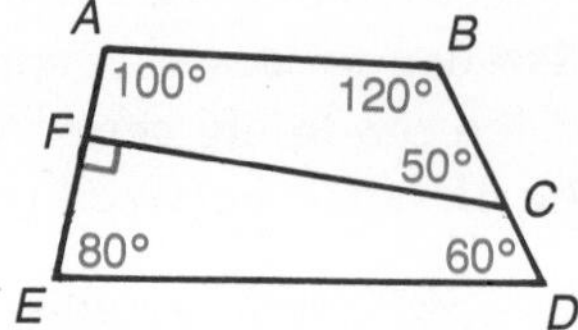

9. Name the acute angles.

10. Name the obtuse angles.

11. Name the right angles.

Name the complement of each angle.

12. 43 **13.** 82 **14.** x **15.** $3y + 1$

16. The measure of an angle is eight times the measure of its complement. Find the measure of each angle.

3.3 **17.** In the figure, $\angle 1$ has a measure of $4x + 43$ and $\angle 3$ has a measure of $7x - 20$. Find the measure of $\angle 2$.

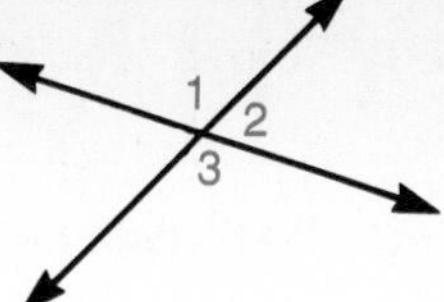

18. How can two angles be both vertical and supplementary to each other?

3.4 **In the figure $\triangle ABC \cong \triangle ADC$ and $\triangle ABE \cong \triangle ADE$. Name the corresponding part for each side or angle.**

19. $\angle BAC \leftrightarrow$ _____ **20.** $\overline{BE} \leftrightarrow$ _____

21. $\angle CDE \leftrightarrow$ _____ **22.** $\overline{CD} \leftrightarrow$ _____

3.5 **For the figure above, name the following:**

23. The angle included between $\overline{AB}$ and $\overline{BE}$. **24.** The angle opposite $\overline{BC}$.

25. The side included between $\angle EAD$ and $\angle EDA$. **26.** The side opposite $\angle DEC$.

3.6 **27.** If $x*y$ means that x is evenly divisible by y, is $*$ an equivalence relation?

Supply the reason for each step in the following proof:

Given: $40 = 3x - 50$

Prove: $x = 30$

Proof:

STATEMENTS	REASONS
1. $40 = 3x - 50$	1. **28.**
2. $50 = 50$	2. **29.**
3. $40 + 50 = 3x - 50 + 50$	3. **30.**
4. $40 + 50 = 3x + 0$	4. **31.**
5. $40 + 50 = 3x$	5. **32.**
6. $90 = 3x$	6. **33.**
7. $\frac{90}{3} = \frac{3x}{3}$	7. **34.**
8. $\frac{90}{3} = 1x$	8. **35.**
9. $\frac{90}{3} = x$	9. **36.**
10. $30 = x$	10. **37.**
11. $x = 30$	11. **38.**

3.7 **In the figure at the right, $\overline{UX}$ is an angle bisector, $m\angle UVX = 48$, $m\angle VUW = 84$, and $VW = 12$.**

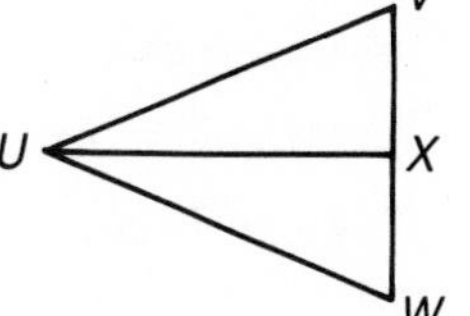

39. Find $m\angle XUW$. **40.** If $\overline{UX}$ is a median, find WX.

17. 53
18. They are right angles.
19. $\angle DAC$ 20. $\overline{DE}$
21. $\angle CBE$ 22. $\overline{CB}$
23. $\angle ABE$ 24. $\angle BEC$
25. $\overline{AD}$ 26. $\overline{DC}$
27. No; it is not symmetric.
28. Given
29. Reflex. prop. of equality
30. Add. prop. of equality
31. Inverse of addition
32. Identity of addition
33. Number fact
34. Division prop. of equality
35. Inverse of mult.
36. Identity of mult.
37. Number fact
38. Sym. prop. of equality
39. 42
40. 6

TEACHER'S RESOURCE MASTERS

Chapter 3 Test
Multiple Choice Test-Chapter 3

Chapter 3 Test

1. $200 - 3x$
2. No; the angles could be right angles.
3. $22\frac{1}{2}$, $157\frac{1}{2}$
4. 33, 57
5. 41, 49
6. 90
7. $\angle CXD$, $\angle DXE$, $\angle EXA$
8. $\overline{CD}$
9. $\angle ADC$
10. $\overline{AD}$
11. $\angle ACD$
12. $\overline{AB}$
13. $\angle D$
14. $\angle BAC$
15. $\overline{AC}$
16. Reflexive
17. Transitive
18. Symmetric
19. 5
20. 3
21. $4\frac{3}{5}$

CHAPTER 3 TEST

1. If an angle has a measure of $3x - 20$, what is its supplement?
2. Must one angle of a pair of supplementary angles always be obtuse?
3. $\angle ABC$ and $\angle DEF$ form a linear pair. $m\angle ABC$ is seven times $m\angle DEF$. Find the measure of each angle.
4. The measure of an angle is 24 less than its complement. Find the measure of each angle.
5. Two complementary angles have measures of $3x + 20$ and $4x + 21$. Find the measure of each angle.

Use the figure at the right for Questions 6–7. $\angle AXB$ and $\angle BXC$ are complementary.

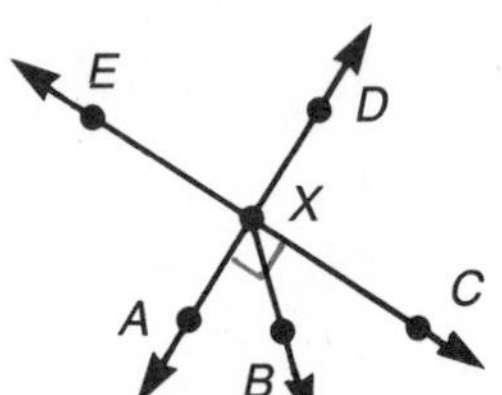

6. What is the measure of $\angle EXD$?
7. Name all the angles congruent to $\angle AXC$.

In the figure at the left, $\triangle ABC \cong \triangle CDA$. Identify the corresponding parts.

8. $\overline{AB} \leftrightarrow$ _____
9. $\angle CBA \leftrightarrow$ _____
10. $\overline{CB} \leftrightarrow$ _____
11. $\angle CAB \leftrightarrow$ _____
12. Name the side included between $\angle CAB$ and $\angle ABC$.
13. Name the angle included between $\overline{CD}$ and $\overline{AD}$.
14. Name the angle opposite $\overline{BC}$.
15. Name the side opposite $\angle ABC$.

Identify the relationship (*reflexive, symmetric,* or *transitive*) illustrated in each statement for Questions 16–18.

16. $m\angle UVX = m\angle UVX$.
17. If Tammy is older than Pedros, and Pedros is older than Chen, then Tammy is older than Chen.
18. If $XY = BC$ then $BC = XY$.

In the figure at the right, $\overline{AD}$ is an angle bisector and median of $\triangle ABC$.

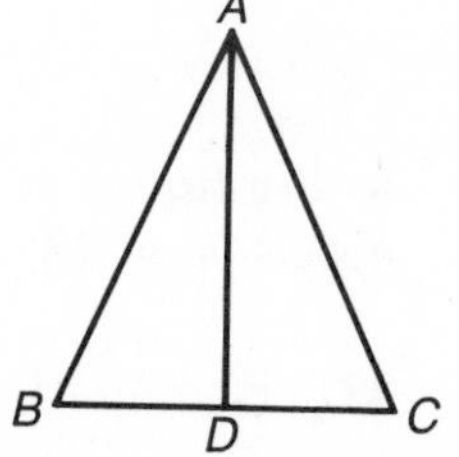

19. If $m\angle BAD = 27$ and $m\angle BAC = 11x - 1$, find x.
20. If $BD = 73$ and $DC = 22x + 7$, find x.
21. If $m\angle BAC = 69$ and $m\angle DAC = \frac{15x}{2}$, find x.

CHAPTER 4

Congruent Triangles

OBJECTIVE

Use SAS or LL to prove two triangles congruent.

TEACHER'S NOTES

See p. T27

MIXED REVIEW

1. If the measures of two angles are equal, what do you know about the measures of their supplements? Why? Equal Supp. of ≅ ∠s ≅
2. Solve $3(x - 7) = 14 + 2(5 - x)$. $x = 9$
3. Multiply $(2x - 3)(4x + 1)$. $8x^2 - 10x - 3$
4. Factor $3x^2 - 5x - 28$. $(3x + 7)(x - 4)$
5. What are the three properties of an equivalence relation? symmetric, reflexive, transitive

TEACHER'S RESOURCE MASTERS

Practice Master 10

4.1 The Basic Congruence Postulate

In the previous chapter, you learned that two triangles are congruent if and only if *all* pairs of corresponding parts are congruent. In this chapter you will learn under what conditions two triangles are congruent if only *some* of the corresponding sides and angles are known to be congruent.

In the table below, different pairs of corresponding parts are given as congruent. Determine if the triangles are necessarily congruent.

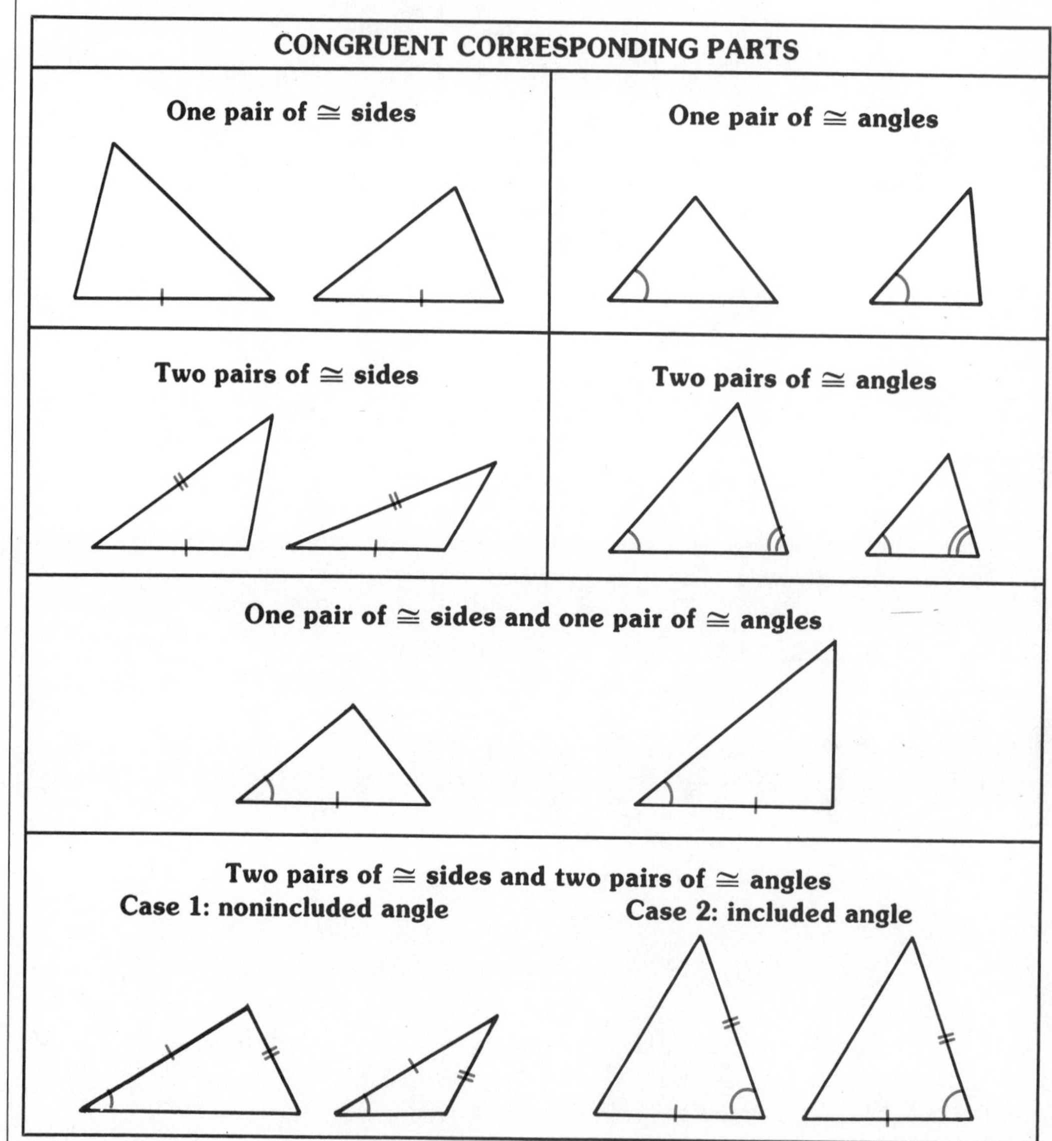

The last correspondence in the table appears to establish a congruence between two triangles, while the others do not. This correspondence is called a Side-Angle-Side (SAS) correspondence; two sides and the included angle of one triangle are congruent to the corresponding parts of a second triangle. One true example should not convince you, but if you were to draw many other pairs of triangles with an SAS correspondence you would find every correspondence a congruence. This fact is stated formally as the **basic congruence postulate.**

> **POSTULATE 15 [The Side-Angle-Side (SAS) Postulate]**
> Given a correspondence between two triangles (or between a triangle and itself), if two sides and the included angle of the first triangle are congruent to the corresponding parts of the second triangle, then the correspondence is a congruence.

The SAS postulate may be used to prove a congruence between two triangles:

Given: $\triangle AEC \leftrightarrow \triangle BED$
$\overline{AB}$ and $\overline{CD}$ bisect each other at E.

Prove: $\triangle AEC \cong \triangle BED$

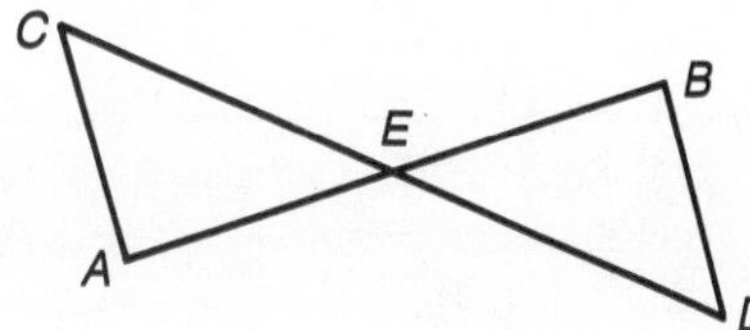

Proof:

STATEMENTS	REASONS
1. $\overline{AB}$ and $\overline{CD}$ bisect each other at E.	1. Given
2. $CE = DE$; $AE = BE$	2. Definition of segment bisector
3. $\overline{CE} \cong \overline{DE}$; $\overline{AE} \cong \overline{BE}$	3. Definition of $\cong$ segments
4. $\angle AEC \cong \angle BED$	4. Vertical $\angle$s are $\cong$.
5. $\triangle AEC \cong \triangle BED$	5. Steps 3, 4, and SAS

When you have proved $\triangle AEC \cong \triangle BED$, you may also state that $\angle A \cong \angle B$, $\angle C \cong \angle D$, and $\overline{AC} \cong \overline{BD}$, because the definition of congruence states that *all* pairs of corresponding parts of congruent triangles are congruent. You can now prove two angles or two segments congruent by showing that they are corresponding parts of congruent triangles.

The following example involves overlapping triangles. Sometimes it helps to redraw overlapping triangles as separate figures to see their relations more clearly.

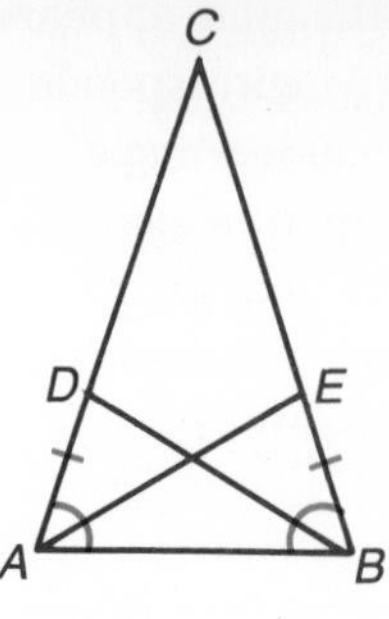

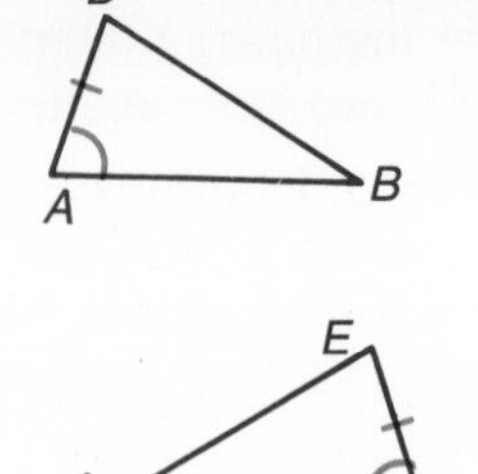

Given: ΔABC
$\overline{AD} \cong \overline{BE}$
$\angle DAB \cong \angle EBA$

Prove: $\overline{AE} \cong \overline{BD}$

Proof:

STATEMENTS	REASONS
1. $\overline{AD} \cong \overline{BE}$; $\angle DAB \cong \angle EBA$	1. Given
2. $\overline{AB} \cong \overline{BA}$	2. Congruence of segments is reflexive.
3. $\Delta ABD \cong \Delta BAE$	3. Steps *1, 2,* and SAS
4. $\overline{AE} \cong \overline{BD}$	4. Corresponding parts of $\cong$ Δs are $\cong$.

Finally, the SAS postulate may be used to prove the following theorem that establishes a congruence between two right triangles:

THEOREM 4.1 [The Leg-Leg (LL) Theorem]
Given a correspondence between two right triangles (or between a right triangle and itself), if the legs of the first right triangle are congruent to the corresponding legs of the second right triangle, then the correspondence is a congruence.

Given: Right triangles *RST* and *XYZ*
$\overline{RS} \cong \overline{XY}$, $\overline{ST} \cong \overline{YZ}$

Prove: $\Delta RST \cong \Delta XYZ$

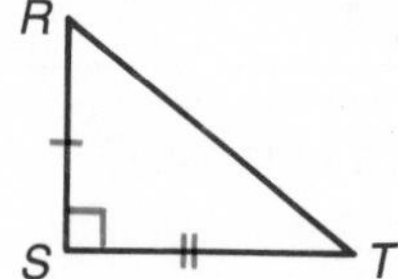

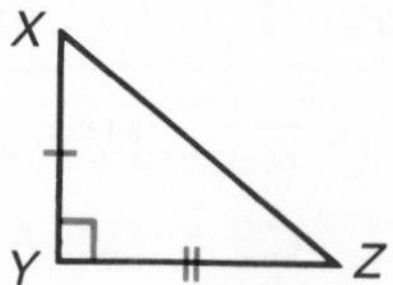

Proof:

STATEMENTS	REASONS
1. ΔRST and ΔXYZ are right triangles.	1. Given
2. $\angle S \cong \angle Y$	2. Any 2 right $\angle$s are $\cong$.
3. $\overline{RS} \cong \overline{XY}$, $\overline{ST} \cong \overline{YZ}$	3. Given
4. $\Delta RST \cong \Delta XYZ$	4. Steps *2, 3,* and SAS

You must remember that the LL Theorem applies only to right triangles. If you wish to use it in a proof, you must first show that the triangles involved are right triangles.

ORAL EXERCISES

A pair of triangles in each figure is congruent by SAS. Complete the congruence statement $\Delta ABC \cong$ _____ for each.

1.

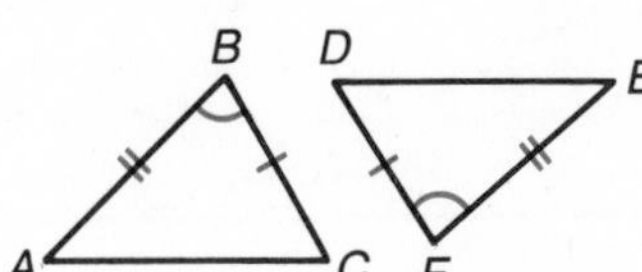

2.

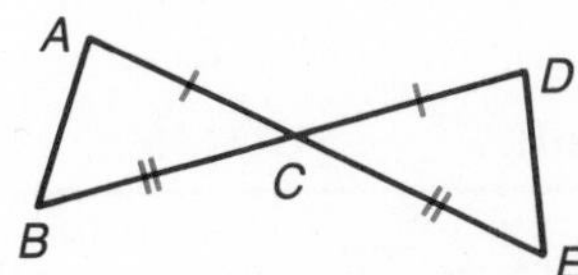

For each of the following pairs of triangles, are the triangles congruent by SAS?

3.

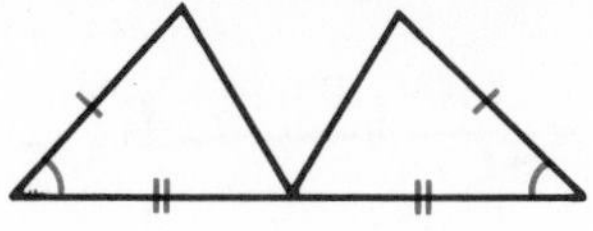

4.

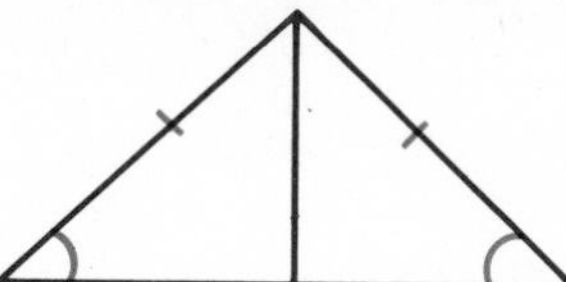

5.

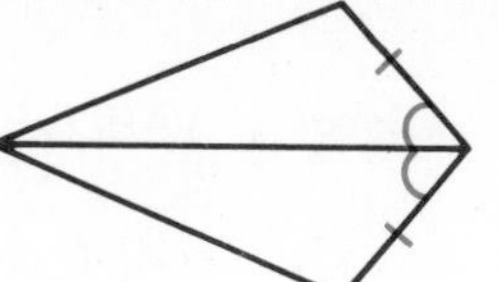

6.

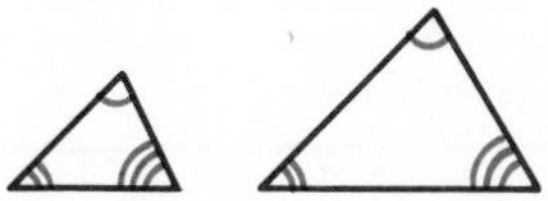

7.

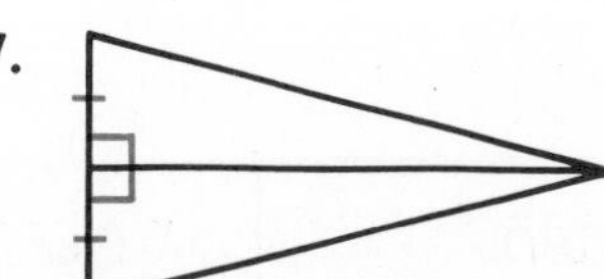

8.

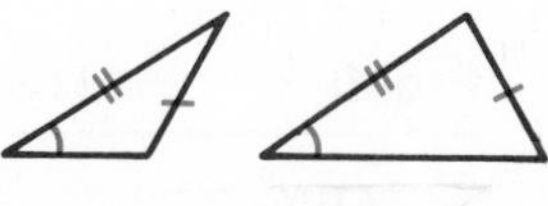

9.

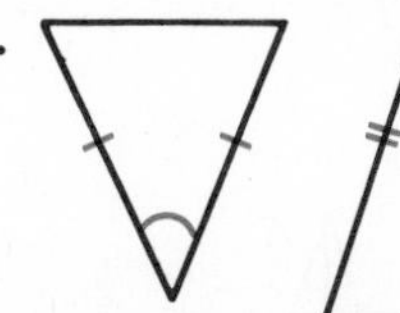

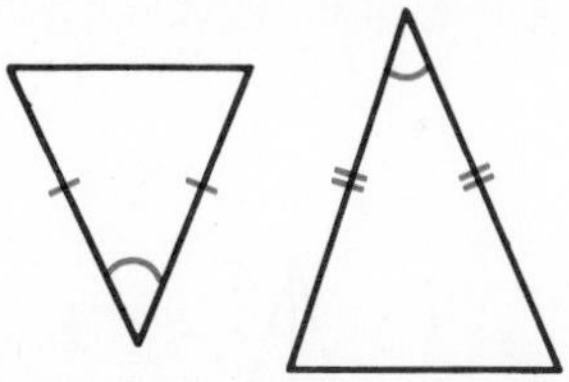

10.

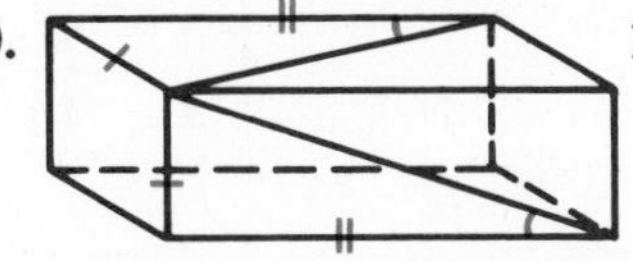

11.

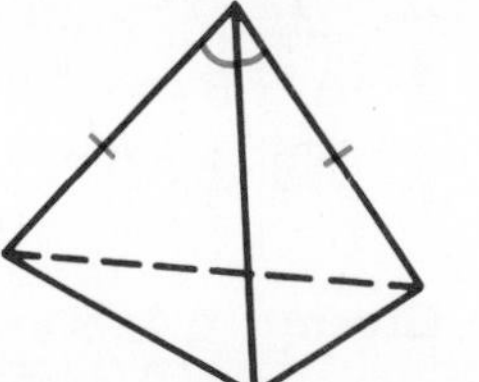

WRITTEN EXERCISES

A. Each pair of triangles at the right has two pairs of congruent corresponding parts. What other pair of corresponding parts is needed to prove the triangles congruent by SAS?

1.

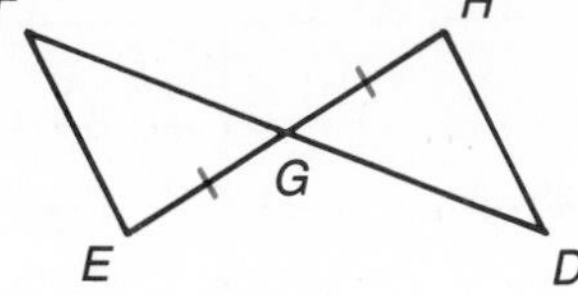

2.

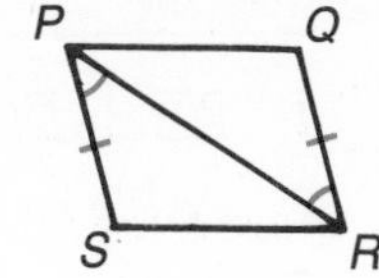

3.

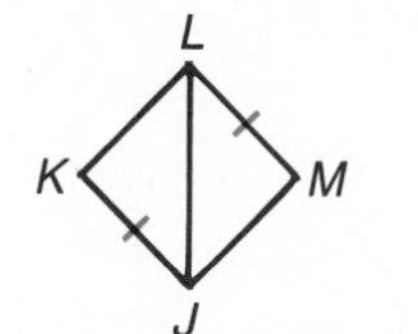

4.

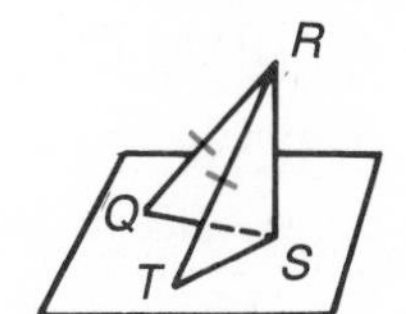

ASSIGNMENT GUIDE

Minimum 1-25
Regular 1-26
Maximum 1-25 odd, 27-29

Oral Exercises

1. ΔEFD
2. ΔDEC
3. yes
4. no
5. yes
6. no
7. yes
8. no
9. no
10. no
11. yes

Written Exercises

1. $\overline{FG} \cong \overline{DG}$
2. $\overline{PR} \cong \overline{RP}$
3. $\angle KJL \cong \angle MLJ$
4. $\angle QRS \cong \angle TRS$

Supply the missing statements and reasons to complete each proof.

Given: ΔPAC and ΔQAC
$\angle PAC \cong \angle QAC$
$\overline{PA} = \overline{QA}$

Prove: $\Delta PAC \cong \Delta QAC$

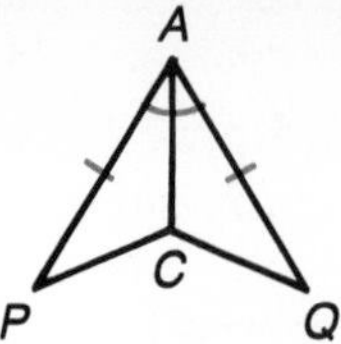

Proof:

STATEMENTS	REASONS
1. $\overline{PA} \cong \overline{QA}$, $\angle PAC \cong \angle QAC$	1. Given
2. $\overline{AC} \cong \overline{AC}$	2. **5.**
3. $\Delta PAC \cong \Delta QAC$	3. **6.**

5. Congruence of segments is reflexive.
6. Steps *1*, *2*, and SAS

B. Given: ΔABD and ΔBCD
$\overline{BC} \cong \overline{DA}$
$\angle ADB \cong \angle CBD$

Prove: $\overline{AB} \cong \overline{CD}$

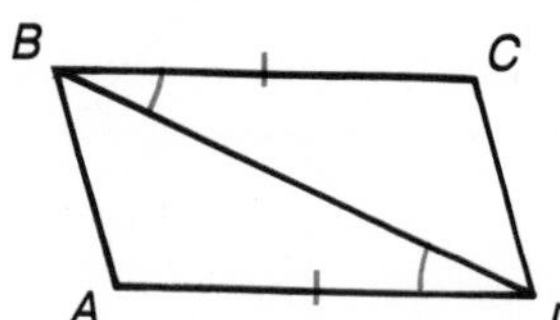

Proof:

STATEMENTS	REASONS
1. $\overline{BC} \cong \overline{DA}$, $\angle ADB \cong \angle CBD$	1. Given
2. **7.**	2. **8.**
3. $\Delta ADB \cong \Delta CBD$	3. **9.**
4. $\overline{AB} \cong \overline{CD}$	4. **10.**

7. $\overline{BD} \cong \overline{DB}$
8. Congruence of segments is reflexive.
9. Steps *1*, *2*, and SAS
10. Corres. parts of $\cong$ Δs are $\cong$.

Given: ΔABD and ΔABC
$\overline{AB} \perp \overline{DB}$, $\overline{AB} \perp \overline{CB}$
$\overline{DB} \cong \overline{CB}$

Prove: $\angle ADB \cong \angle ACB$

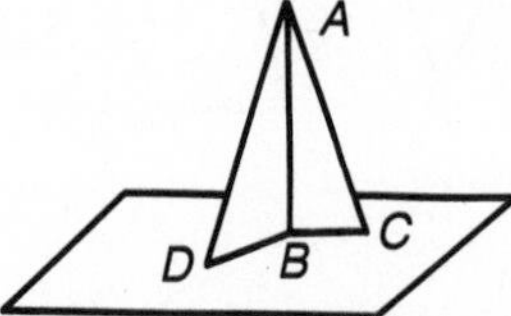

Proof:

STATEMENTS	REASONS
1. $\overline{AB} \perp \overline{DB}$, $\overline{AB} \perp \overline{CB}$	1. Given
2. $\angle ABD$ and $\angle ABC$ are right $\angle$s.	2. **11.**
3. **12.**	3. Definition of right Δ
4. $\overline{DB} \cong \overline{CB}$	4. **13.**
5. **14.**	5. **15.**
6. $\Delta ADB \cong \Delta ACB$	6. Steps *3*, *4*, *5*, and LL Theorem
7. **16.**	7. **17.**

11. Definition of $\perp$ lines
12. ΔABD and ΔABC are rt. Δs.
13. Given
14. $\overline{AB} \cong \overline{AB}$
15. Congruence of segments is reflexive.
16. $\angle ADB \cong \angle ACB$
17. Corres. parts of $\cong$ Δs are $\cong$.

Given: ΔAMC and ΔBMD
$\overline{AB}$ and $\overline{CD}$ bisect each other at M.

Prove: $\angle 1 \cong \angle 2$

Proof:

STATEMENTS	REASONS
1. $\overline{AB}$ and $\overline{CD}$ bisect each other.	1. Given
2. $AM = BM$, $CM = DM$	2. **18.** ______
3. $\overline{AM} \cong \overline{BM}$, $\overline{CM} \cong \overline{DM}$	3. **19.** ______
4. $\angle AMC \cong \angle BMD$	4. **20.** ______
5. $\Delta ACM \cong \Delta BDM$	5. **21.** ______
6. $\angle CAM \cong \angle DBM$	6. **22.** ______
7. $\angle 1$ and $\angle CAM$ form a linear pair. $\angle 2$ and $\angle DBM$ form a linear pair.	7. **23.** ______
8. $\angle 1$ and $\angle CAM$ are supplementary. $\angle 2$ and $\angle DBM$ are supplementary.	8. **24.** ______
9. $\angle 1 \cong \angle 2$	9. **25.** ______

C. Write a two-column proof for each of the following.

26. Given: ΔABM and ΔCDM
M is the midpoint of $\overline{BD}$.
$\overline{AB} \perp \overline{BD}$, $\overline{CD} \perp \overline{BD}$
$\overline{AB} \cong \overline{CD}$

Prove: $\Delta ABM \cong \Delta CDM$

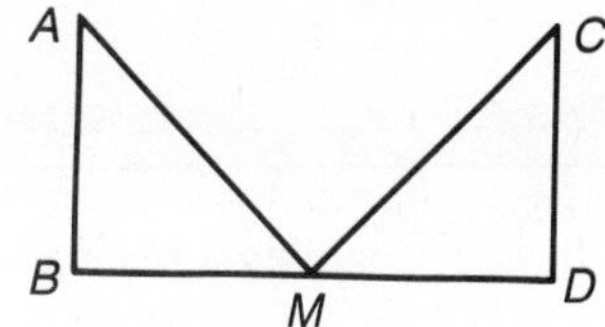

27. Given: ΔDAC and ΔBCA
$\overline{AD} \cong \overline{CB}$
$\angle DAC \cong \angle BCA$

Prove: $\angle DCA \cong \angle BAC$

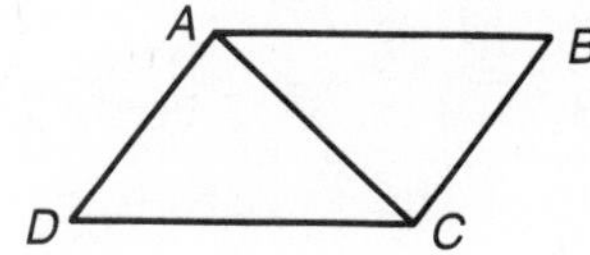

28. Given: ΔABD and ΔCBD
$\overline{AB} \cong \overline{CB}$
$\angle ABD \cong \angle CBD$

Prove: $\overline{AD} \cong \overline{CD}$

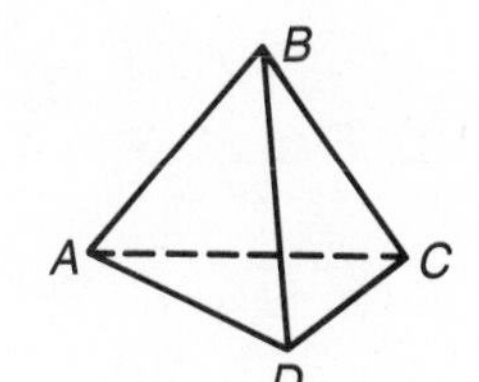

29. Given: ΔAMC and ΔBMC
M is the midpoint of $\overline{AB}$.
$\overline{CM} \perp \overline{AB}$ at M

Prove: $\angle ACM \cong \angle BCM$

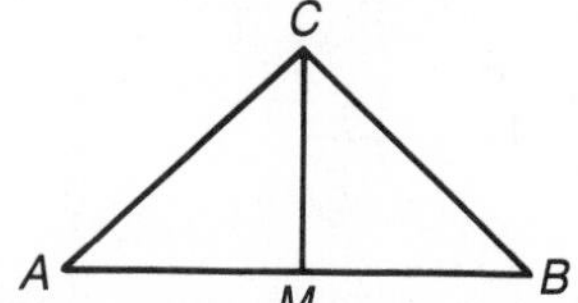

18. Definition of bisect
19. Definition of congruent segments
20. Verticals $\angle$s are $\cong$.
21. Steps 3, 4, and SAS
22. Corres. parts of $\cong$ Δs are $\cong$.
23. Definition of linear pair
24. The Supplement Postulate
25. Supplements of $\cong$ $\angle$s are $\cong$.
26. Definition of bisect and LL
27. Reflexive, SAS, CPCTC
28. Reflexive, SAS, CPCTC
29. Definition of midpoint, reflexive, LL, CPCTC

OBJECTIVE

Use ASA to prove two triangles congruent.

TEACHER'S NOTES

See p. T27

MIXED REVIEW

1. Solve $x^2 - 3x - 28 = 0$. $\{7, -4\}$
2. Add $\frac{2}{5} + \frac{4}{11}$. $\frac{42}{55}$
3. If two supplementary angles are adjacent, they form ____. a linear pair
4. If two angles are both congruent and supplementary, then they are ______. right angles
5. Solve $(x - 3)(x + 2)(x - 4) = 0$. $\{3, -2, 4\}$

TEACHER'S RESOURCE MASTERS

Practice Master 11, Part 1

4.2 The ASA Congruence Theorem

In the previous section you learned that every SAS correspondence between two triangles is a congruence. You used the SAS postulate to prove that every LL correspondence between two right triangles is also a congruence. In this lesson you will again employ the SAS postulate, this time to prove that every Angle-Side-Angle (ASA) correspondence is a congruence.

THEOREM 4.2 [The Angle-Side-Angle (ASA) Theorem]
Given a correspondence between two triangles (or between a triangle and itself), if two angles and the included side of the first triangle are congruent to the corresponding parts of the second triangle, then the correspondence is a congruence.

Given: $\triangle ABC$ and $\triangle DEF$
$\angle A \cong \angle D$
$\angle B \cong \angle E$
$\overline{AB} \cong \overline{DE}$

Prove: $\triangle ABC \cong \triangle DEF$

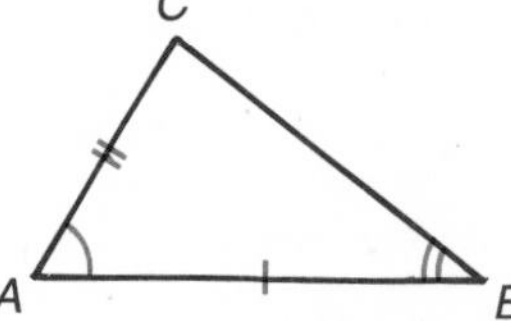

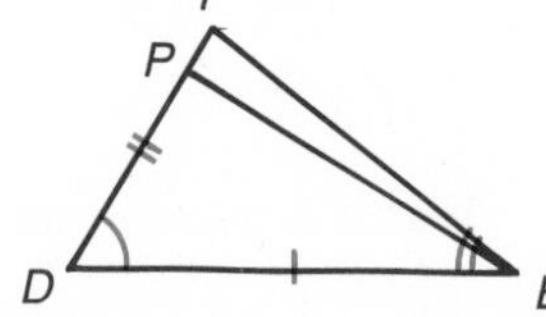

Proof:

STATEMENTS	REASONS
1. $\overrightarrow{DF}$ contains a point P such that $DP = AC$	1. The Point Plotting Theorem
2. $\overline{DP} \cong \overline{AC}$	2. Definition of $\cong$ segments
3. $\overline{AB} \cong \overline{DE}$, $\angle A \cong \angle D$	3. Given
4. $\triangle ABC \cong \triangle DEP$	4. Steps 2, 3, and SAS
5. $\angle ABC \cong \angle DEP$	5. Corres. parts of $\cong$ $\triangle$s are $\cong$.
6. $\angle ABC \cong \angle DEF$	6. Given
7. $\angle DEF \cong \angle DEP$	7. Steps 5, 6, and congruence of $\angle$s is transitive
8. $\overrightarrow{EF} = \overrightarrow{EP}$	8. Step 7 and the Angle Construction Postulate
9. P is on $\overleftrightarrow{DF}$ and $\overleftrightarrow{EF}$	9. Steps 1 and 8
10. F is on $\overleftrightarrow{DF}$ and $\overleftrightarrow{EF}$	10. Definition of vertex
11. $F = P$	11. Two different lines intersect in at most one point.
12. $\triangle ABC \cong \triangle DEF$	12. Steps 4 and 11

The two proofs that follow illustrate how the ASA Theorem may be applied to show triangles congruent. In the first example, you are given two pairs of congruent angles and a common, included side.

Given: ΔABC and ΔABD
$\angle CAB \cong \angle DAB$
$\angle CBA \cong \angle DBA$

Prove: $\Delta ABC \cong \Delta ABD$

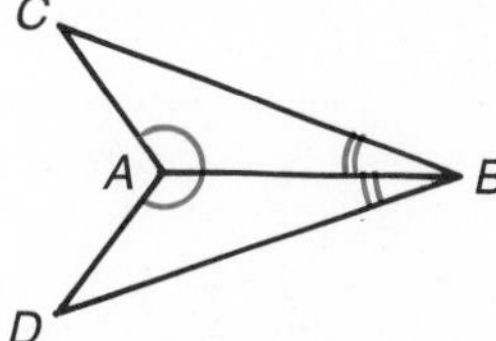

Proof:

STATEMENTS	REASONS
1. $\angle CAB \cong \angle DAB$, $\angle CBA \cong \angle DBA$	1. Given
2. $\overline{AB} \cong \overline{AB}$	2. Congruence of segments is reflexive.
3. $\Delta ABC \cong \Delta ABD$	3. Steps *1*, *2*, and ASA

The next example involves overlapping triangles that have two pairs of congruent angles and a shared segment between congruent parts.

Given: ΔABC and ΔDEF
$\angle B \cong \angle E$
$\overline{BF} \cong \overline{EC}$
$\angle ACB \cong \angle DFE$

Prove: $\overline{AB} \cong \overline{DE}$

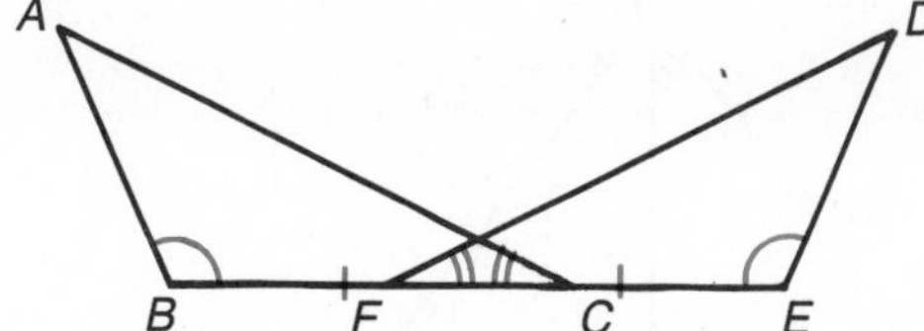

Proof:

STATEMENTS	REASONS
1. $\angle B \cong \angle E$, $\angle ACB \cong \angle DFE$	1. Given
2. $\overline{BF} \cong \overline{EC}$	2. Given
3. $BF = EC$	3. Definition of $\cong$ segments
4. $BF + FC = EC + FC$	4. Addition property of equality
5. $BF + FC = BC$, $EC + FC = EF$	5. Definition of between
6. $BC = EF$	6. Steps *4*, *5*, and substitution property
7. $\overline{BC} \cong \overline{EF}$	7. Definition of $\cong$ segments
8. $\Delta ABC \cong \Delta DEF$	8. Steps *1*, *7*, and ASA
9. $\overline{AB} \cong \overline{DE}$	9. Corres. parts of $\cong$ Δs are $\cong$.

ORAL EXERCISES

Each of the following exercises shows a pair of triangles which have congruent parts. If the triangles are congruent by either SAS or ASA, state the postulate or theorem that applies.

1.

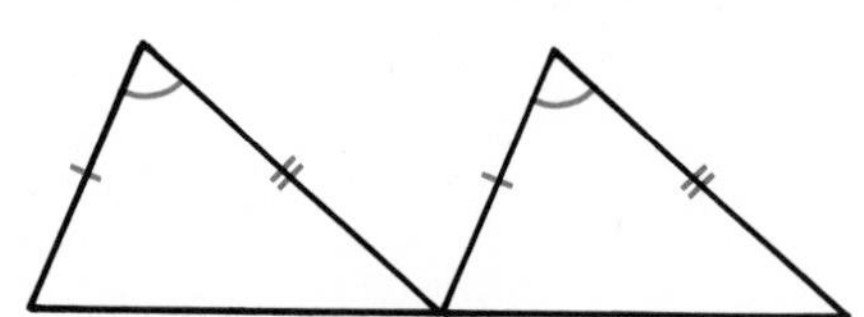

2.

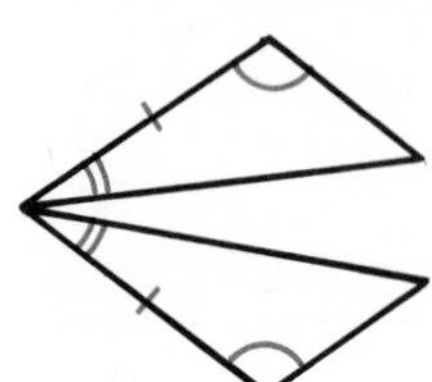

3.

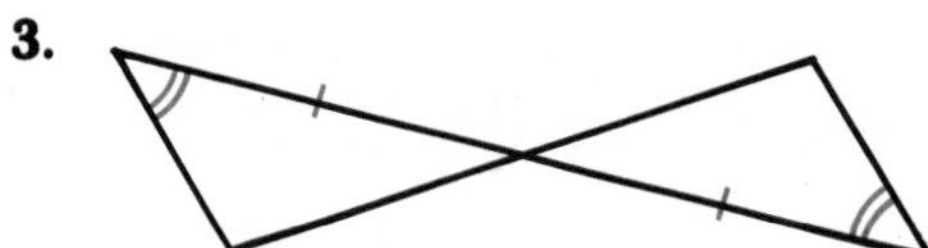

4.

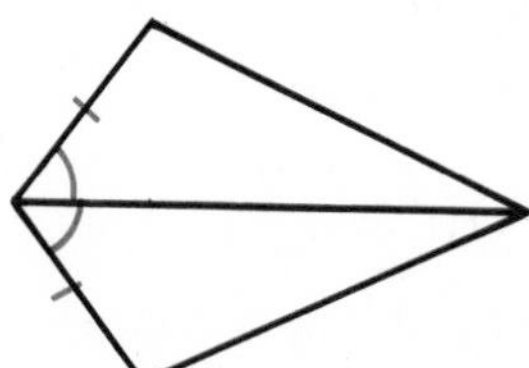

5.

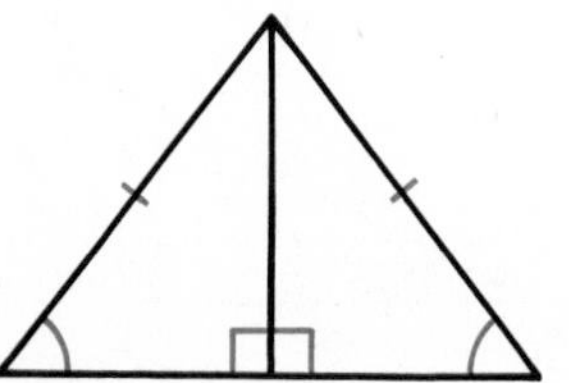

6.

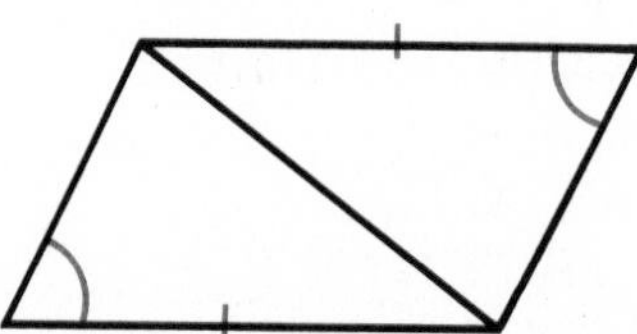

7.

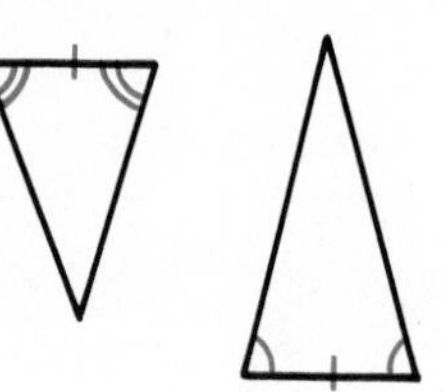

8.

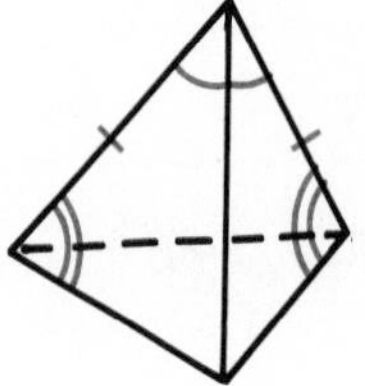

9.

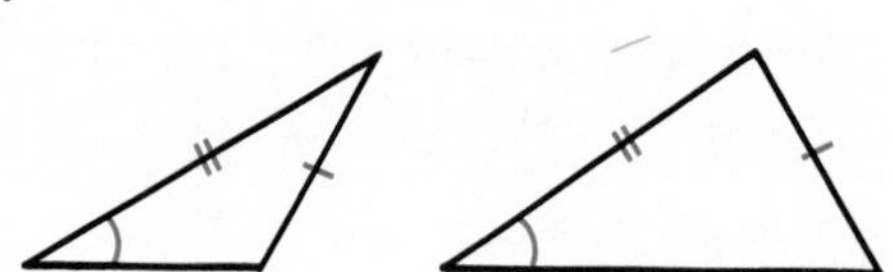

10.

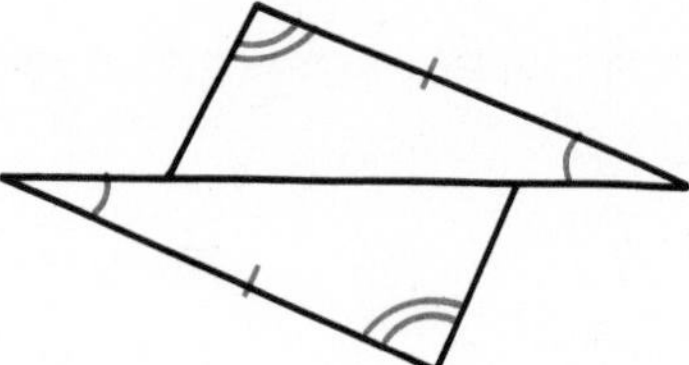

ASSIGNMENT GUIDE

Minimum 1-15
Regular 1-16
Maximum 1-15, 17-20

Oral Exercises

1. yes, SAS
2. yes, ASA
3. yes, ASA
4. yes, SAS
5. no
6. no
7. no
8. yes, ASA
9. no
10. yes, ASA

WRITTEN EXERCISES

A. Each pair of triangles shown has two pairs of corresponding parts marked congruent. What other pair of corresponding parts is needed in order to prove the triangles congruent by ASA?

1.

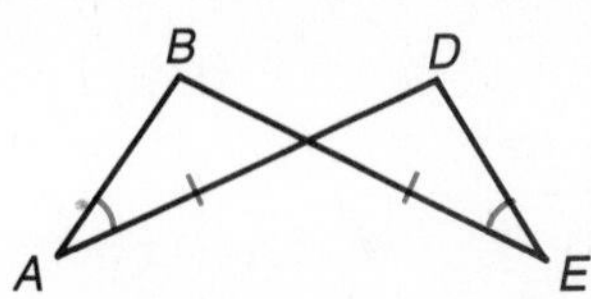

2.

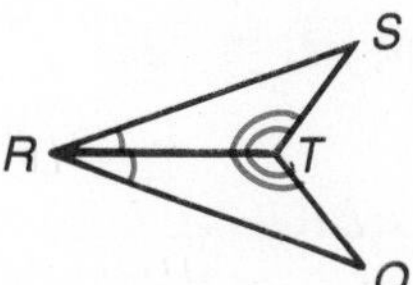

3.

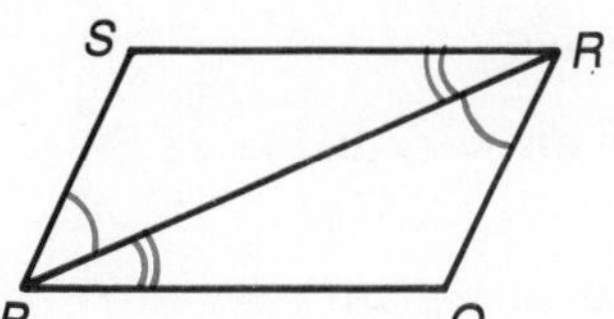

4.

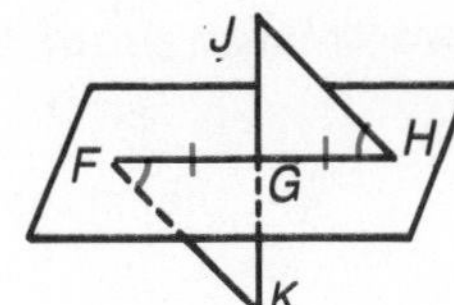

Supply the missing statements and reasons for each proof.

Given: $\triangle ABD$ and $\triangle CBD$
$\angle ABD \cong \angle CBD$
$\angle ADB \cong \angle CDB$

Prove: $\triangle ABD \cong \triangle CBD$

Proof:

STATEMENTS	REASONS
1. $\angle ABD \cong \angle CBD$	1. Given
2. $\overline{BD} \cong \overline{BD}$	2. **5.**
3. $\angle ADB \cong \angle CDB$	3. **6.**
4. $\triangle ABD \cong \triangle CBD$	4. Steps *1, 2, 3,* and ASA

B. Given: $\triangle ABC$ and $\triangle CDA$
$\angle BCA \cong \angle DAC$
$\angle BAC \cong \angle DCA$

Prove: $\triangle ABC \cong \triangle CDA$

Proof:

STATEMENTS	REASONS
1. $\angle BCA \cong \angle DAC$	1. **7.**
2. $\overline{AC} \cong \overline{AC}$	2. **8.**
3. $\angle BAC \cong \angle DCA$	3. **9.**
4. $\triangle ABC \cong \triangle CDA$	4. **10.**

Written Exercises

1. $\angle ACB \cong \angle ECD$
2. $\overline{RT} \cong \overline{RT}$
3. $\overline{PR} \cong \overline{RP}$
4. $\angle JGH \cong \angle KGF$
5. Congruence of segments is reflexive.
6. Given
7. Given
8. Congruence of segments is reflexive.
9. Given
10. Steps *1, 2, 3,* and ASA

11. Given

12. $\angle FHG \cong \angle KHJ$

13. Vertical $\angle$s are $\cong$.

14. Steps *1*, *2*, and ASA

15. Vertical angles, ASA, CPCTC

16. Reflexive, ASA, CPCTC

17. Reflexive, ASA

18. Supplements of $\cong$ $\angle$s, vertical angles, ASA

19. Addition, ASA

20. $\triangle ABE \cong \triangle CDE$ by ASA, $\triangle ADE \cong \triangle CBE$ by CPCTC, vertical angles, and SAS

Given: $\triangle FGH$ and $\triangle KJH$
$\overline{FH} \cong \overline{KH}$
$\angle F \cong \angle K$

Prove: $\triangle FGH \cong \triangle KJH$

Proof:

STATEMENTS	REASONS
1. $\angle F \cong \angle K$, $\overline{FH} \cong \overline{KH}$	*1.* **11.**
2. **12.**	*2.* **13.**
3. $\triangle FGH \cong \triangle KJH$	*3.* **14.**

Write a two-column proof for each of the following.

15. Given: $\angle C \cong \angle D$
M is the midpoint of $\overline{CD}$.

Prove: $\angle A \cong \angle B$

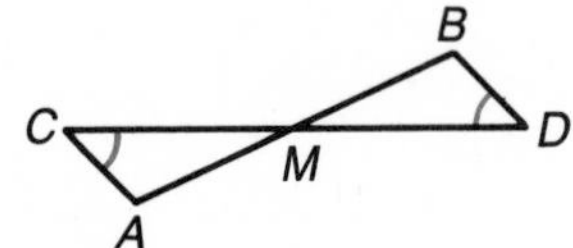

16. Given: $\angle ABD \cong \angle CBD$
$\angle ADB \cong \angle CDB$

Prove: $\angle BAD \cong \angle BCD$

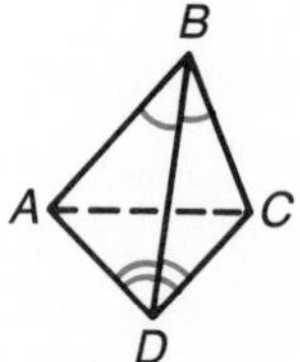

17. Given: $\overline{AB} \perp \overline{BD}$, $\overline{AB} \perp \overline{BC}$
$\angle DAB \cong \angle CAB$

Prove: $\triangle ADB \cong \triangle ACB$

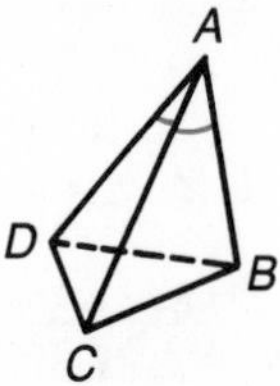

18. Given: $\angle 1 \cong \angle 2$
$\overline{MN} = \overline{RN}$

Prove: $\triangle MNP \cong \triangle RNQ$

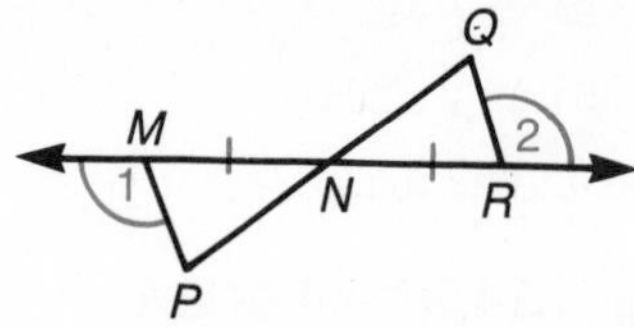

C. 19. Given: $\angle C \cong \angle BDF$, $\angle AEC \cong \angle F$
$\overline{CD} \cong \overline{EF}$

Prove: $\triangle CAE \cong \triangle DBF$

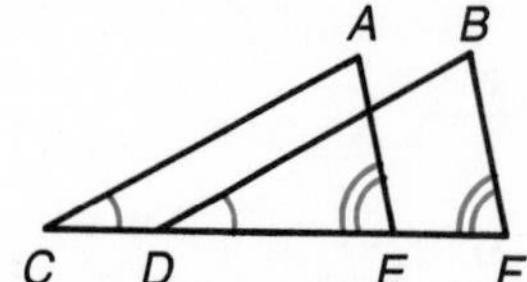

20. Given: $\angle 1 \cong \angle 2$
$\overline{BE} \cong \overline{DE}$

Prove: $\triangle ADE \cong \triangle CBE$

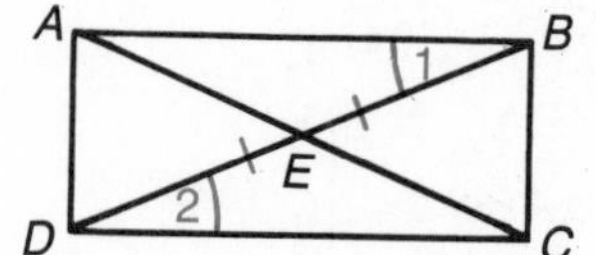

4.3 The Isosceles Triangle Theorem

Up to this point, you have been concerned with proving a congruence between two triangles when given a known correspondence between them. In this lesson you will look at correspondences between a triangle and itself to prove some theorems about special triangles.

A triangle may have no sides congruent, two sides congruent, or all three sides congruent. A triangle may be named according to the number of congruent sides it has.

DEFINITIONS: scalene; isosceles; equilateral
A triangle is **scalene** if and only if no two of its sides are congruent.
A triangle is **isosceles** if and only if at least two of its sides are congruent. The remaining side is the **base.** The two angles that include the base are the **base angles,** and the angle opposite the base is the **vertex angle.**
A triangle is **equilateral** if and only if all three of its sides are congruent.

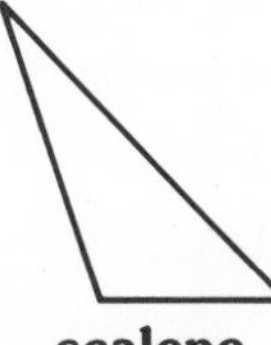
scalene

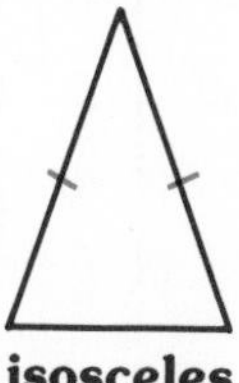
isosceles

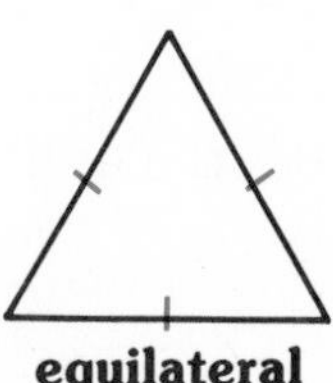
equilateral

According to the definitions, all equilateral triangles are also isosceles. In an isosceles triangle, the base, the base angles, and the vertex angle are defined with respect to the congruent sides.

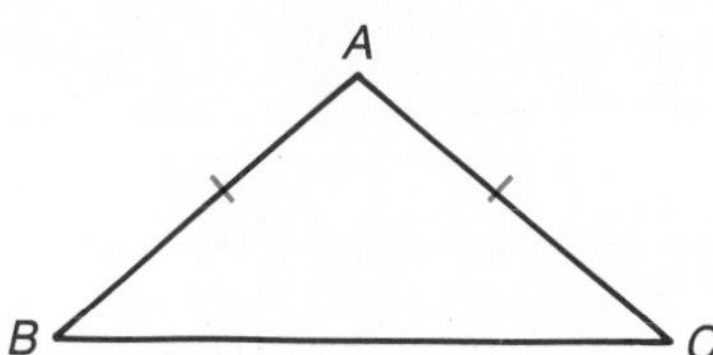

$\overline{AB} \cong \overline{AC}$

$\overline{BC}$ is the base.

$\angle B$ and $\angle C$ are the base angles.

$\angle A$ is the vertex angle.

$\overline{DE} \cong \overline{DF}$

$\overline{EF}$ is the base.

$\angle E$ and $\angle F$ are the base angles.

$\angle D$ is the vertex angle.

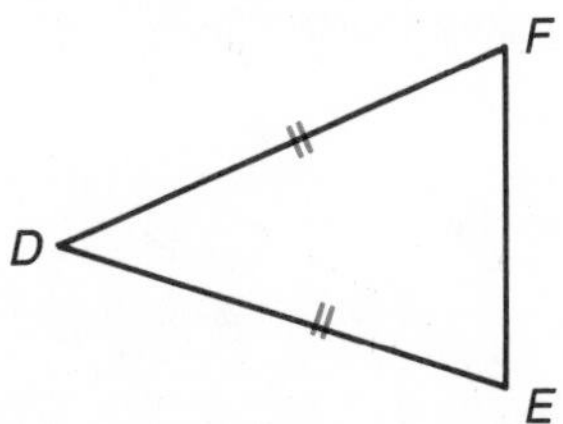

OBJECTIVES

Identify scalene, isosceles, and equilateral triangles.

Use the Isosceles Triangle Theorem and its converse and corollaries to prove parts of a triangle congruent.

TEACHER'S NOTES

See p. T27

MIXED REVIEW

1. What is the difference between postulates and theorems? Postulates are accepted without proof; theorems must be proved.
2. $\overrightarrow{BD}$ bisects $\angle ABC$ if D is in the interior of $\angle ABC$ and $\angle$__ $\cong \angle$_____. $\angle ABD$, $\angle DBC$
3. $|-9 - 7| =$ _____. 16
4. Factor $3x^3 - 9x^2 + 6x$. $3x(x - 1)(x - 2)$
5. Solve $x^2 - 3x = 0$. $\{0, 3\}$

TEACHER'S RESOURCE MASTERS

Practice Master 11, Part 2
Quiz 7

Theorem 4.3 is also called the **Pons Asinorum Theorem,** or "Bridge of Asses" Theorem. Some mathematicians and historians think the name derives from the figure that accompanied Euclid's proof of the theorem. Euclid's figure resembled a trestle bridge so steep that only a donkey could cross. Others have equated "ass" with "fool" and interpreted the name to mean that only poor geometricians have difficulty with such a simple proof. Students may wish to form their own interpretations after studying the theorem and its converse.

> **THEOREM 4.3 (The Isosceles Triangle Theorem)**
> If two sides of a triangle are congruent, then the angles opposite those sides are congruent.

In other words, the base angles of an isosceles triangle are congruent.

Given: ΔABC
$\overline{AB} \cong \overline{AC}$

Prove: $\angle B \cong \angle C$

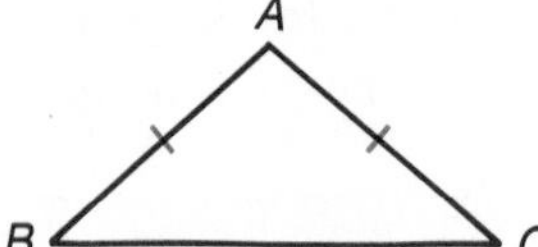

Consider the correspondence between the triangle and itself: $\Delta ABC \leftrightarrow \Delta ACB$. Therefore, $\overline{AB} \leftrightarrow \overline{AC}$, $\overline{AC} \leftrightarrow \overline{AB}$, and $\angle A \leftrightarrow \angle A$.

Proof:

STATEMENTS	REASONS
1. $\overline{AB} \cong \overline{AC}$	1. Given
2. $\overline{AC} \cong \overline{AB}$	2. Symmetric property of congruence
3. $\angle A \cong \angle A$	3. Congruence of angles is reflexive.
4. $\Delta ABC \cong \Delta ACB$	4. Steps *1, 2, 3,* and SAS
5. $\angle B \cong \angle C$	5. Corres. parts of $\cong$ Δs are $\cong$.

The next theorem is so readily proved by the Isosceles Triangle Theorem that it is called a **corollary** of the theorem. A corollary is a theorem that is directly and immediately proved from another.

> **COROLLARY 4.3.1**
> Every equi*lateral* triangle is equi*angular.*

That is, in an equilateral triangle, all three angles are congruent. The proof of the corollary is left as an exercise.

In previous lessons about conditional statements, you learned that the converse of a true conditional is not necessarily true. The converse of the Isosceles Triangle Theorem *is* true, however, and is stated below.

> **THEOREM 4.4**
> If two angles of a triangle are congruent, then the sides opposite those angles are congruent.

COROLLARY 4.3.1
Every equi*lateral* triangle is equi*angular*.

The proofs of Theorem 4.4 and Corollary 4.4.1 are left as exercises.

As you learned in Chapter 1, when a conditional and its converse are both true, they may be combined and written as a **biconditional.** All of the theorems and corollaries in this lesson can be expressed as biconditionals.

The Isosceles Triangle Theorem and its converse, for example, can be stated biconditionally as: *Two sides of a triangle are congruent if and only if the angles opposite them are congruent.* Corollary 4.3.1 and Corollary 4.4.1 can also be expressed in biconditional form.

ORAL EXERCISES

1. Define an equilateral triangle.

2. Define a scalene triangle.

3. Define an isosceles triangle.

4. If a triangle is equilateral, must it also be isosceles?

5. If a triangle is isosceles, must it also be equilateral?

6. If ΔABC is isosceles with base $\overline{AC}$, what are the base angles?

7. In ΔXYZ, if $\overline{XY} \cong \overline{YZ}$, which angles are congruent?

8. In ΔPQR, if $\angle P \cong \angle Q$, which sides are congruent?

9. If ΔABC is isosceles and $\angle A$ is the vertex angle, what are the legs?

10. What is a corollary?

11. Can all theorems be written as biconditionals? Explain.

12. If two coplanar isosceles triangles have the same base, must the triangles be congruent? Explain.

13. State the biconditional that combines Corollaries 4.3.1 and 4.4.1.

WRITTEN EXERCISES

A. Draw a figure to illustrate each of the following.

1. If two isosceles triangles have congruent bases, the triangles need not be congruent.

2. If two isosceles triangles have congruent legs, the triangles need not be congruent.

ASSIGNMENT GUIDE

Day 1
Minimum 1-15 odd
Regular 1-17 odd
Maximum 1-21 odd
Day 2
Minimum 2-14 even
Regular 2-16 even
Maximum 2-20 even

Oral Exercises

1. 3 ≅ sides 2. no ≅ sides
3. at least 2 ≅ sides 4. yes
5. no 6. $\angle A, \angle C$ 7. $\angle X \cong \angle Z$
8. $\overline{RP} \cong \overline{RQ}$ 9. $\overline{AB}, \overline{AC}$
10. a theorem that follows immediately from another
11. No; only those for which the converse is also true.
12. No; at least one other side and the included angle must be ≅, or the angles including the base.
13. A triangle is equilateral if and only if it is equiangular.

Written Exercises

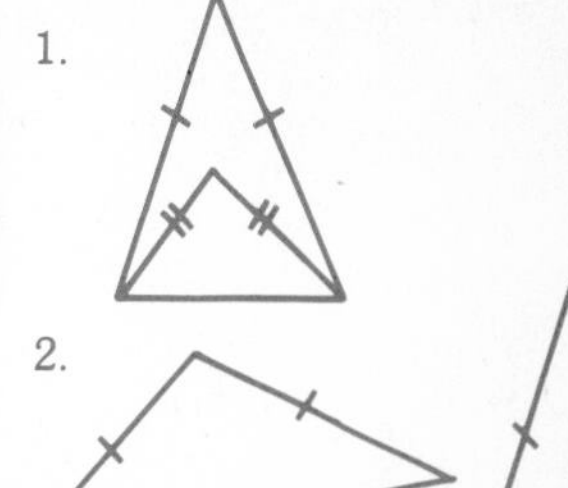

3. 

4. 6
5. 12
6. 13, 13, 5
7. 69, 69, 42
8. Isosceles Δ Thm., transitivity
9. Sym. prop. of ≅, reflexive prop. of ≅, ASA, CPCTC
10. Isosceles Δ Thm., transitivity
11. No; because two sides and an included angle determine a triangle.
12. Make $\Delta ABC \cong \Delta QPC$ and $\overline{PQ} \cong \overline{AB}$ by CPCTC
13. Thm. 4.3, transitivity
14. Thm. 3.5, Thm. 4.4
15. Addition prop., Thm. 4.3
16. SAS, CPCTC

---

3. If two isosceles triangles have congruent vertex angles, the triangles need not be congruent.

B.

4. ΔRST is isosceles with base $\overline{RT}$, $RS = 5x$, and $ST = 2x + 18$. Find x.
5. ΔJKL is isosceles with base $\overline{JK}$, $m\angle J = 5(x - 4)$ and $m\angle K = 40$. Find x.
6. ΔABC is isosceles with base $\overline{AC}$, $AB = 2x + 1$, $BC = 3x - 5$, and $AC = x - 1$. Find the measure of each side of the triangle.
7. ΔDEF is isosceles with base DF, $m\angle D = 4x + 13$, $m\angle E = x + 28$, and $m\angle F = 6x - 15$. Find the measure of each angle.

Prove each of the following.

8. Every equilateral triangle is equiangular (Corollary 4.3.1).
9. If two angles of a triangle are congruent, then the sides opposite those angles are congruent (Theorem 4.4).
10. Every equiangular triangle is equilateral (Corollary 4.4.1).
11. Suppose you nail two strips of wood together at an angle of 70°. If you want to attach a third strip of wood to form a triangle, can you use any length you wish? Explain.

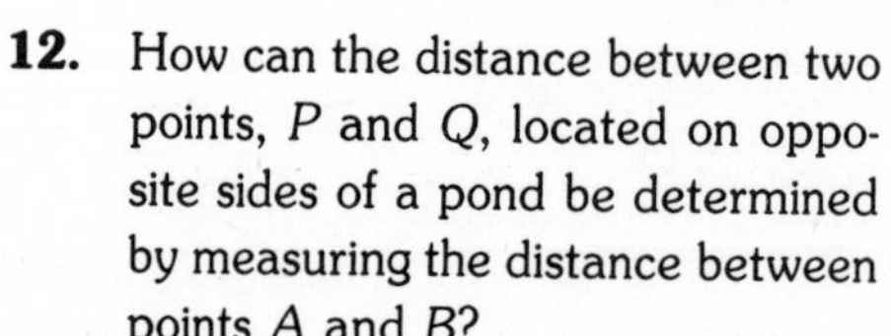

12. How can the distance between two points, P and Q, located on opposite sides of a pond be determined by measuring the distance between points A and B?

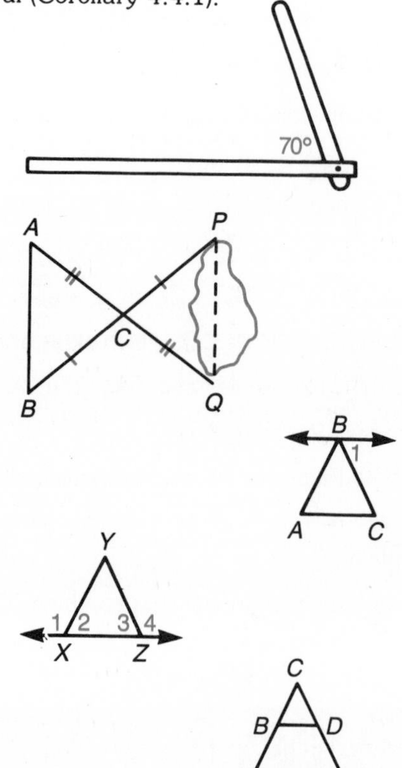

13. **Given:** ΔABC
$\angle C \cong \angle 1$, $\overline{AB} \cong \overline{BC}$
Prove: $\angle A \cong \angle 1$

14. **Given:** ΔXYZ, $\angle 1 \cong \angle 4$
Prove: ΔXYZ is isosceles

15. **Given:** ΔAEC
$\overline{BC} \cong \overline{DC}$, $\overline{AB} \cong \overline{ED}$
Prove: $\angle A \cong \angle E$

16. **Given:** ΔADC is isosceles with base $\overline{AC}$.
$\overline{DB}$ is a median of ΔADC.
Prove: $\angle 1 \cong \angle 2$

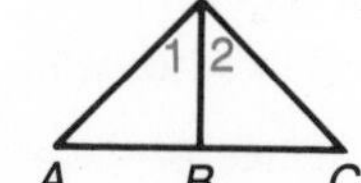

17. Given: ΔPRT
M is the midpoint of $\overline{PT}$,
$\overline{PR} \cong \overline{TR}$, $\overline{PQ} \cong \overline{TS}$

Prove: $\overline{QM} \cong \overline{SM}$

C. 18. Prove that no two angles of a scalene triangle are congruent. (HINT: Use an indirect argument.)

19. Prove that the medians to the legs of an isosceles triangle are congruent.

20. Prove that the triangle formed by joining the midpoints of the three sides of an equilateral triangle is also equilateral.

21. The plumb level, used by carpenters and stone masons before the more modern bubble level was invented, consists of a frame in the form of an isosceles triangle. The midpoint of the base, point M, is marked. A plumb line is suspended from the vertex angle. To use the instrument, you hold it upright with the base resting on the surface to be leveled. When the plumb line hangs directly over point M, the surface on which the base of the triangle rests is level. Explain why this instrument works.

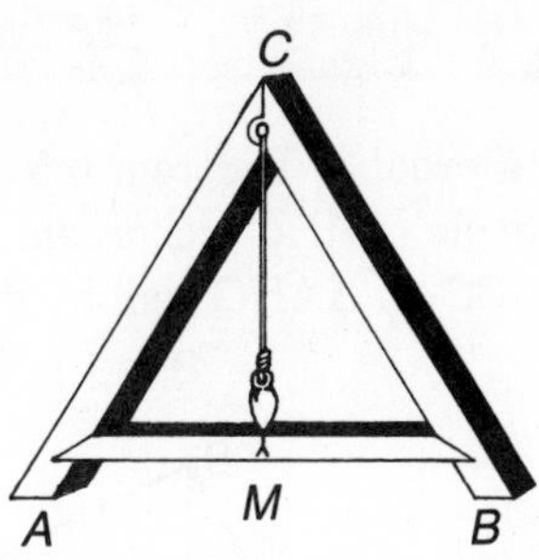

SELF-QUIZ

1. Which of the following cannot be used as a reason to prove that two triangles are congruent: ASA, SSA, or SAS?

2. Draw a figure to illustrate that although three angles of one triangle are congruent to the corresponding angles in another triangle, the triangles need not be congruent.

3. Given: ΔDAC, $\overline{AB} \perp \overline{DC}$
$\overline{AB}$ bisects $\overline{DC}$

Prove: $\angle DAB \cong \angle CAB$

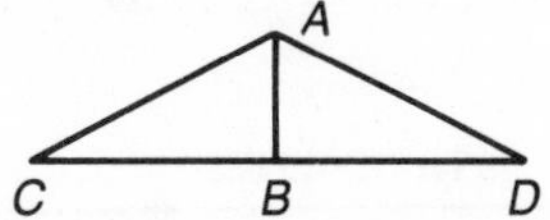

4. If a theorem and its converse are both true, then they can be combined to write what type of sentence?

5. If ΔPQR is isosceles with $\overline{PQ} \cong \overline{PR}$, name the base, the vertex angle, and the base angles.

6. State the definition of scalene triangle.

7. Write the converse of "Every equilateral triangle is equiangular."

8. Given: $\overline{AD} \cong \overline{DB} \cong \overline{BA}$
$\angle 1 \cong \angle 4$, $\angle 3 \cong \angle 2$

Prove: ΔBCD is equilateral

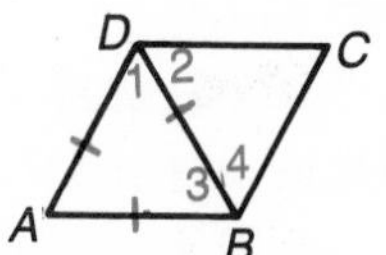

17. SAS, CPCTC
18. If $\cong$, then Δ is isosceles.
19. SAS, CPCTC
20. SAS, CPCTC
21. The median to the base of an isosceles Δ is $\perp$ to the base by SAS.

Self-Quiz

1. SSA
2. 
3. $\Delta DAB \cong \Delta CAB$ by SAS, $\angle DAB \cong \angle CAB$ by CPCTC
4. biconditional (iff)
5. $\overline{QR}$, $\angle P$, $\angle Q$ and $\angle R$
6. no two sides $\cong$
7. Every equiangular Δ is equilateral.
8. $\Delta ADB \cong \Delta CBD$ by ASA, $\overline{DC} \cong \overline{BA}$ and $\overline{AD} \cong \overline{CB}$ by CPCTC, so by transitivity, $\overline{AD} \cong \overline{DB} \cong \overline{BA} \cong \overline{DC} \cong \overline{CB}$.

OBJECTIVE

Use SSS to prove two triangles congruent.

TEACHER'S NOTES

See p. T27

MIXED REVIEW

1. Divide $8 \div \frac{1}{2}$. 16
2. What is the complement of $x - 30$? $120 - x$
3. If $\triangle ABC \cong \triangle RST$ list the six pairs of corresponding parts. $\overline{AB} \cong \overline{RS}$, $\overline{BC} \cong \overline{ST}$, $\overline{AC} \cong \overline{RT}$, $\angle A \cong \angle R$, $\angle B \cong \angle S$, $\angle C \cong \angle T$
4. $\frac{7}{x-2} + \frac{4}{x-2} =$ ______. $\frac{11}{x-2}$
5. $\frac{5}{x} + \frac{3}{2x} =$ ______. $\frac{13}{2x}$

TEACHER'S RESOURCE MASTERS

Practice Master 12, Part 1

4.4 SSS and the Angle Bisector Theorem

The next congruence theorem for triangles is the SSS (Side-Side-Side) Theorem.

THEOREM 4.5 [The Side-Side-Side (SSS) Theorem]
Given a correspondence between two triangles (or between a triangle and itself), if all three pairs of corresponding sides are congruent, then the correspondence is a congruence.

The proof of Theorem 4.5 differs somewhat from those you have studied previously. First a triangle (ΔAHC) congruent to ΔDEF is constructed below ΔABC. You will then prove that $\Delta ABC \cong \Delta AHC$ and, by the transitive property of congruence, $\Delta ABC \cong \Delta DEF$.

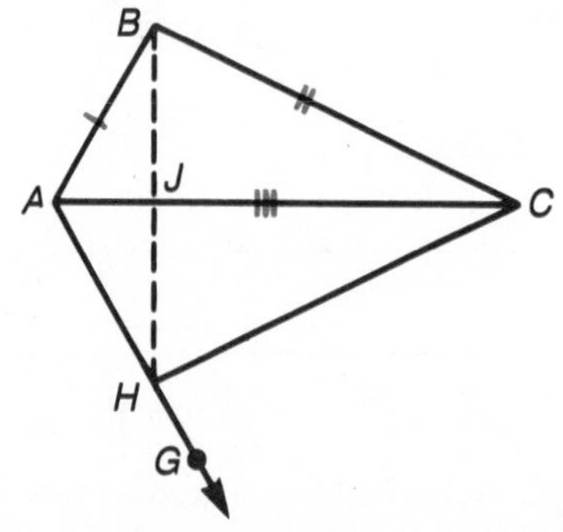

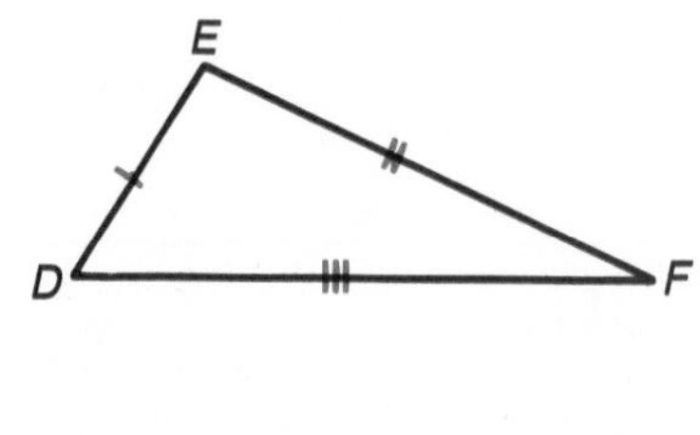

Given: $\overline{AB} \cong \overline{DE}$, $\overline{BC} \cong \overline{EF}$, $\overline{AC} \cong \overline{DF}$

Prove: $\Delta ABC \cong \Delta DEF$

Proof:

STATEMENTS	REASONS
1. $\overline{AB} \cong \overline{DE}$, $\overline{BC} \cong \overline{EF}$, $\overline{AC} \cong \overline{DF}$	1. Given
2. Construct a ray $\overrightarrow{AG}$, with G on the opposite side of $\overleftrightarrow{AC}$ from B, such that $m\angle CAG = m\angle D$	2. Angle Construction Postulate
3. $\angle CAG \cong \angle D$	3. Definition of $\cong$ $\angle$s
4. Find point H on $\overrightarrow{AG}$ such that $AH = DE$	4. Point Plotting Theorem
5. $\overline{AH} \cong \overline{DE}$	5. Definition of $\cong$ segments
6. $\Delta AHC \cong \Delta DEF$	6. Steps 1, 3, 5, and SAS
7. $\overline{AB} \cong \overline{AH}$	7. Steps 1, 5, and congruence of segments is transitive.

Proof: (continued)

STATEMENTS	REASONS
8. $\overline{HC} \cong \overline{EF}$	8. Corres. parts of $\cong$ Δs are $\cong$.
9. $\overline{BC} \cong \overline{HC}$	9. Steps 1, 8, and congruence of segments is transitive.
10. $\overleftrightarrow{BH}$ intersects $\overleftrightarrow{AC}$ at J	10. Plane Separation Postulate
11. ΔBAH and ΔBCH are isosceles.	11. Steps 7, 9, and definition of isosceles Δs
12. $\angle ABH \cong \angle AHB$; $\angle HBC \cong \angle BHC$	12. Isosceles Triangle Theorem
13. $m\angle ABH = m\angle AHB$, $m\angle HBC = m\angle BHC$	13. Definition of $\cong$ $\angle$s
14. $m\angle ABH + m\angle HBC = m\angle AHB + m\angle BHC$	14. Addition property of equality and substitution property
15. $m\angle ABH + m\angle HBC = m\angle ABC$ $m\angle AHB + m\angle BHC = m\angle AHC$	15. Angle Addition Postulate
16. $m\angle ABC = m\angle AHC$	16. Steps 14, 15, and substitution property
17. $\angle ABC \cong \angle AHC$	17. Definition of $\cong$ $\angle$s
18. $\Delta ABC \cong \Delta AHC$	18. Steps 7, 9, 17, and SAS
19. $\Delta ABC \cong \Delta DEF$	19. Steps 6, 18, and congruence of Δs is transitive.

The proof above is for the case in which $\overleftrightarrow{BH}$ intersects $\overleftrightarrow{AC}$ at a point between A and C. Two other cases illustrated below are possible: (1) $\overleftrightarrow{BH}$ intersects $\overleftrightarrow{AC}$ at A; and (2) $\overleftrightarrow{BH}$ intersects $\overleftrightarrow{AC}$ at a point outside $\overline{AC}$. The proofs of these cases are left as exercises.

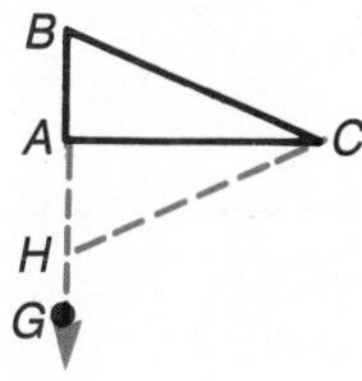

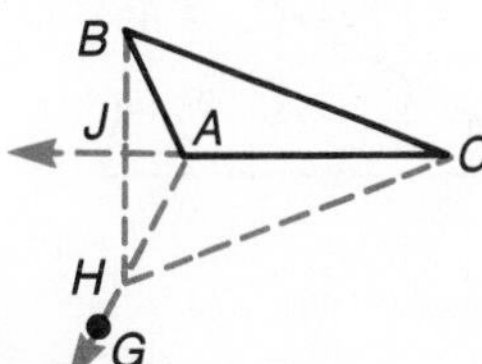

The SSS Theorem is used to prove another important theorem, the Angle Bisector Theorem.

THEOREM 4.6 (The Angle Bisector Theorem)
Every angle has exactly one bisector.

Theorem 4.6 makes two statements: (1) every angle has a bisector, and (2) the bisector is unique. The proof is therefore in two parts.

Given: $\angle B$

Prove: There exists a $\overrightarrow{BD}$ that bisects $\angle B$ and is unique.

Proof: (1) Choose points A and C on different sides of $\angle B$ such that $BA = BC$ (the Point Plotting Theorem). Let D be the midpoint of $\overline{AC}$ (Every segment has one midpoint) and draw $\overrightarrow{BD}$. By the SSS Theorem, $\triangle ABD \cong \triangle CBD$. So, $\angle ABD \cong \angle CBD$ by corresponding parts of congruent triangles. Therefore, $\overrightarrow{BD}$ is a bisector of $\angle ABC$ by the definition of angle bisector.

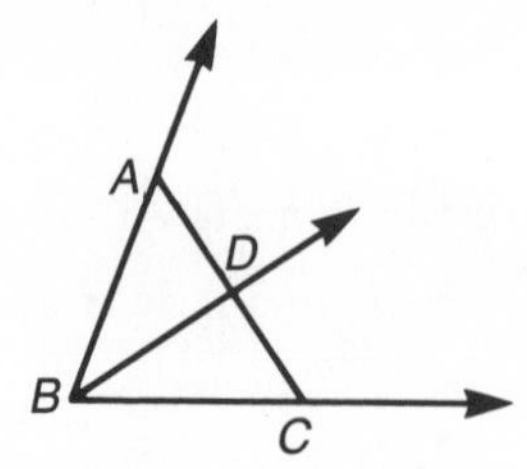

(2) Let $m\angle ABC = r$. Then $m\angle CBD = m\angle ABD = \frac{1}{2}r$. Let $\overrightarrow{BC}$ be a ray on the edge of a half-plane. By the Angle Construction Postulate, there is only one $\overrightarrow{BD}$ such that $m\angle CBD = \frac{1}{2}r$. Therefore, the angle bisector $\overrightarrow{BD}$ is unique.

ASSIGNMENT GUIDE

Day 1
Minimum 1-12
Regular 1-18
Maximum 1-19
Day 2
Minimum 13-20
Regular 19-21
Maximum 20-24

Oral Exercises

1. yes, SAS, $\triangle EBD$
2. yes, ASA, $\triangle EDC$
3. yes, SSS, $\triangle XCB$
4. yes, SSS, $\triangle ADC$
5. yes, ASA, $\triangle EDC$
6. no
7. yes, SAS, $\triangle ADC$
8. no

ORAL EXERCISES

Determine if each pair of triangles is congruent by SAS, ASA, or SSS. If so, state the postulate or theorem that applies and complete the congruence statement $\triangle ABC \cong$ _____. (NOTE: Some pairs may not be congruent.)

1.

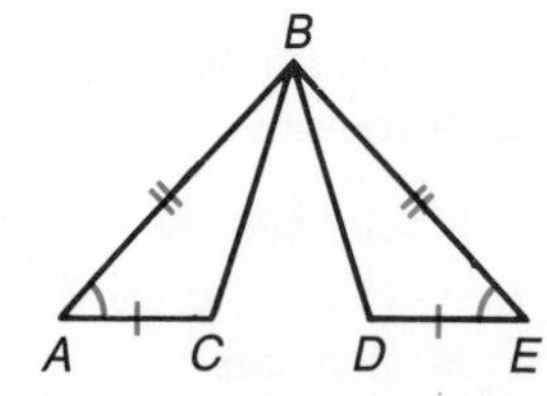

2.

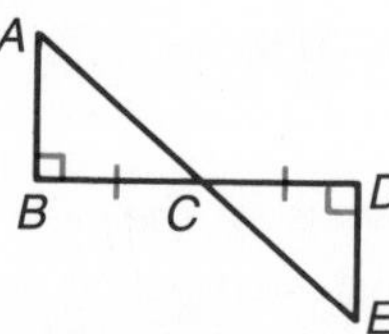

3.

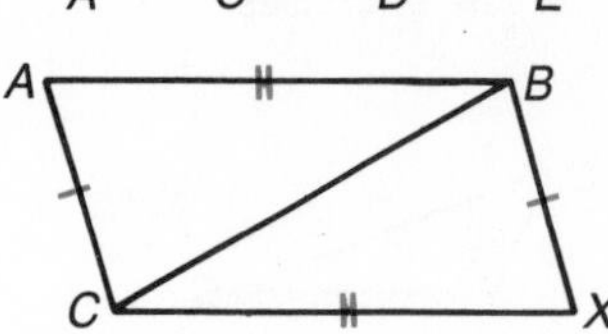

4.

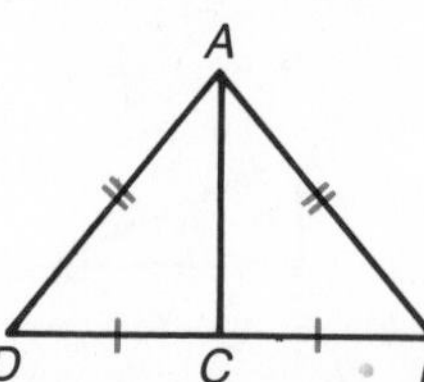

5.

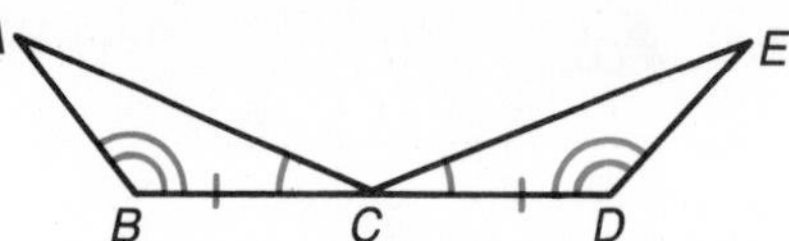

6.

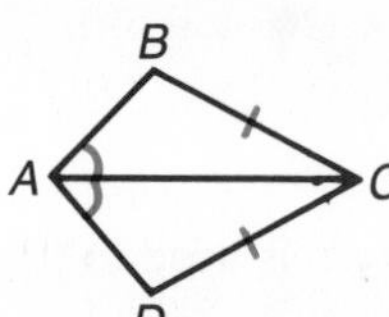

7.

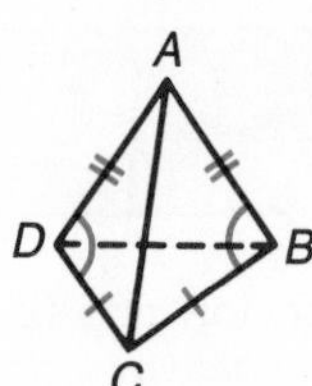

8.

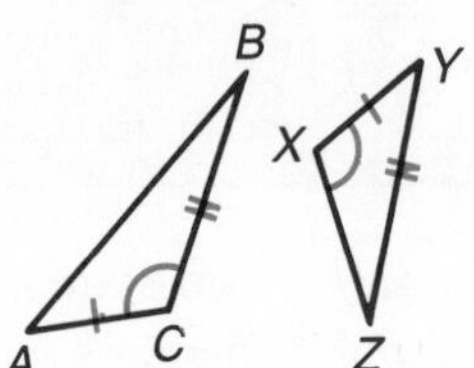

WRITTEN EXERCISES

A. Each pair of triangles shown has two pairs of corresponding parts marked congruent. What other congruence is needed in order to prove the triangles congruent by SSS?

1.

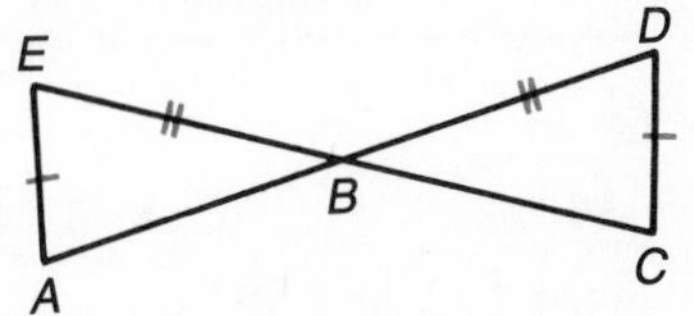

2.

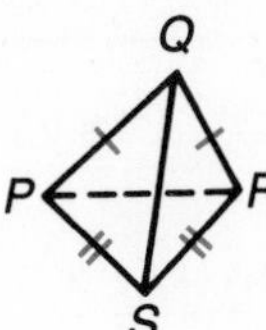

Supply the missing statements and reasons to complete each proof.

Given: $\overline{AF} \cong \overline{DE}$, $\overline{FC} \cong \overline{EB}$, $\overline{AB} \cong \overline{CD}$

Prove: $\Delta AFC \cong \Delta DEB$

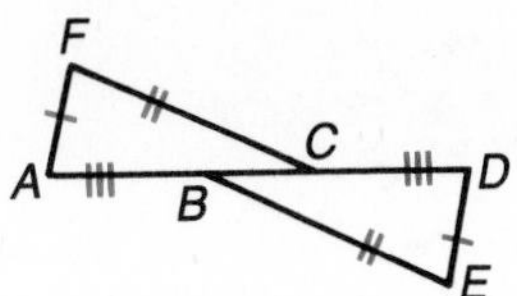

Proof:

STATEMENTS	REASONS
1. $\overline{AF} \cong \overline{DE}$, $\overline{FC} \cong \overline{EB}$, $\overline{AB} \cong \overline{CD}$	1. Given
2. $AB = CD$	2. **3.**
3. $AB + BC = CD + BC$	3. **4.**
4. $AB + BC = AC$, $BC + CD = BD$	4. **5.**
5. $AC = BD$	5. **6.**
6. $\overline{AC} \cong \overline{BD}$	6. **7.**
7. $\Delta AFC \cong \Delta DEB$	7. Steps *1*, *6*, and SSS

B. Given: $\overline{LM} \cong \overline{RM}$, $\overline{LK} \cong \overline{RS}$
M is the midpoint of $\overline{KS}$.

Prove: $\Delta LKM \cong \Delta RSM$

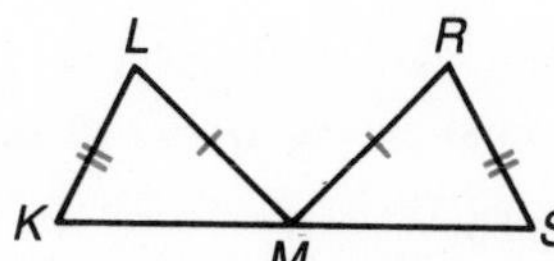

Proof:

STATEMENTS	REASONS
1. M is the midpoint of $\overline{KS}$.	1. **8.**
2. **9.**	2. **10.**
3. $\overline{LM} \cong \overline{RM}$, $\overline{LK} \cong \overline{RS}$	3. **11.**
4. $\Delta LKM \cong \Delta RSM$	4. **12.**

Written exercises

1. $\overline{AB} \cong \overline{CB}$
2. $\overline{QS} \cong \overline{QS}$
3. Definition of $\cong$ segments
4. Addition property of equality
5. Definition of between
6. Steps *3*, *4*, and substitution property
7. Definition of $\cong$ segments
8. Given
9. $\overline{KM} \cong \overline{SM}$
10. Definition of midpoint
11. Given
12. Steps *2*, *3*, and SSS

Given: $\overline{AB} \cong \overline{CB}$, $\overline{AD} \cong \overline{CD}$, $\angle 1 \cong \angle 2$

Prove: $\triangle ABE \cong \triangle CBE$

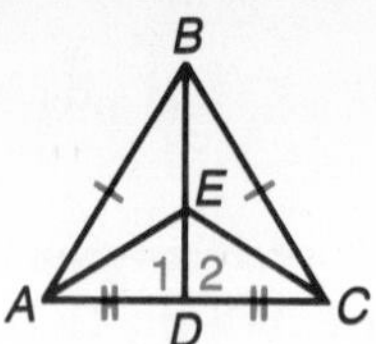

Proof:

STATEMENTS	REASONS
1. $\overline{AD} \cong \overline{CD}$, $\angle 1 \cong \angle 2$	1. Given
2. **13.**	2. **14.**
3. $\triangle ADE \cong \triangle CDE$	3. Steps *1, 2,* and SAS
4. $\overline{AE} \cong \overline{CE}$	4. **15.**
5. $\overline{AB} \cong \overline{CB}$	5. **16.**
6. **17.**	6. **18.**
7. $\triangle ABE \cong \triangle CBE$	7. Steps *4, 5, 6,* and SSS

Write a two-column proof for each of the following.

19. Given: $\overline{PQ} \cong \overline{PS}$
$\overline{PR}$ bisects $\overline{QS}$.

Prove: $\triangle QPR \cong \triangle SPR$

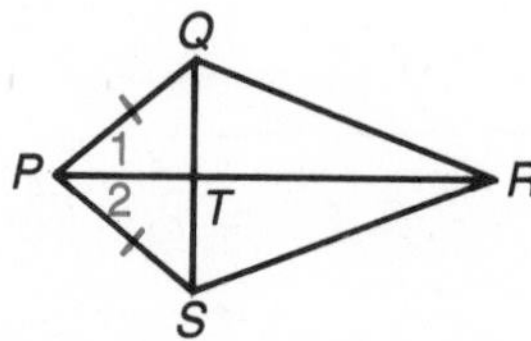

20. Given: $\overline{AB} \cong \overline{DC}$, $\overline{AG} \cong \overline{DE}$,
$\overline{GC} \cong \overline{EB}$

Prove: $\triangle AGC \cong \triangle DEB$

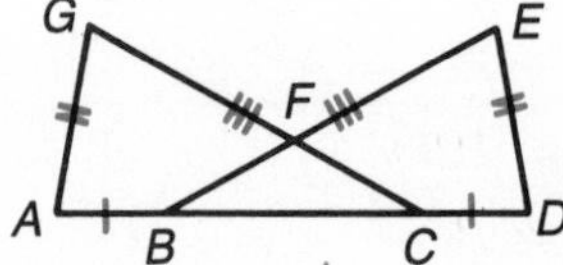

C. 21. Given: $\overline{AB} \cong \overline{CD}$, $\overline{AD} \cong \overline{BC}$
$\angle 1 \cong \angle 2$

Prove: $\triangle AXB \cong \triangle CYD$
(HINT: First prove $\triangle ABD \cong \triangle CDB$.)

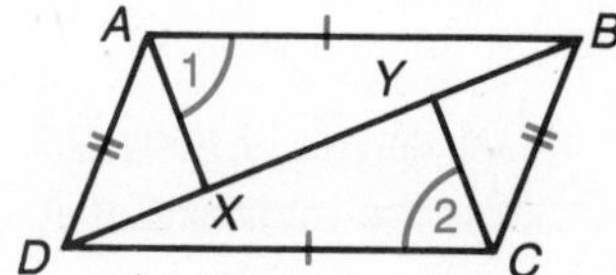

22. Given: $\overline{PT} \cong \overline{QR}$, $\overline{TS} \cong \overline{RS}$
$\overline{PS} \cong \overline{QS}$

Prove: $\triangle PTQ \cong \triangle QRP$

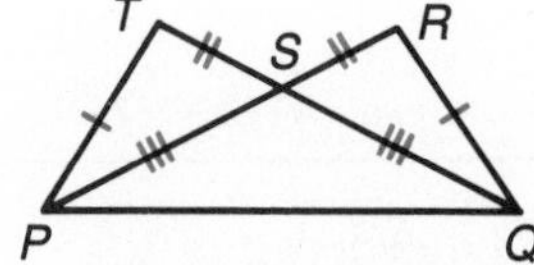

23. Prove that the bisector of the vertex angle of an isosceles triangle is perpendicular to the base.

24. Prove Case 2 and Case 3 of the SSS Theorem (Theorem 4.5).

13. $\overline{ED} \cong \overline{ED}$

14. Congruence of segments is reflexive.

15. Corres. parts of $\cong$ $\triangle$s are $\cong$.

16. Given

17. $\overline{BE} \cong \overline{BE}$

18. Congruence of segments is reflexive.

19. $\triangle QPT \cong \triangle SPT$ by SSS; $\angle 1 \cong \angle 2$ by CPCTC; $\triangle QPR \cong \triangle SPR$ by SAS

20. Reflexive; addition property; SSS

21. $\overline{DB} \cong \overline{DB}$; $\triangle ABD \cong \triangle CDB$ by SSS; $\angle BDC \cong \angle DBA$ by CPCTC; ASA

22. $\triangle PTS \cong \triangle QRS$ by SSS; $\angle T \cong \angle R$ by CPCTC; $\overline{PR} \cong \overline{QT}$ by addition prop.; SAS

23. ASA; CPCTC; supplementary and $\cong$ $\angle$s

24. Case 2: Follow first proof through Step *9;* then $\angle AHC \cong \angle ABC$ by Isos. $\triangle$ Thm.; $\triangle ABC \cong \triangle AHC$ by SAS; $\triangle ABC \cong \triangle DEF$ by transitivity. Case 3: Follow first proof through Step *13;* then use subtraction property to find $\angle ABC \cong \angle AHC$; $\triangle ABC \cong \triangle AHC$ by SAS; $\triangle ABC \cong \triangle DEF$ by transitivity.

4.5 Applying Congruent Triangles

Many of the proofs you have completed in this chapter have involved figures other than triangles. One of those figures is the **quadrilateral.**

> **DEFINITION: quadrilateral**
> Let A, B, C, and D be four coplanar points. If no three of these points are collinear, and the segments $\overline{AB}$, $\overline{BC}$, $\overline{CD}$, and $\overline{DA}$ intersect only at their endpoints, then the union of the four segments is a **quadrilateral.** The four segments are its sides, and the points A, B, C, and D are its vertices. $\angle DAB$, $\angle ABC$, $\angle BCD$, and $\angle CDA$ are its angles.

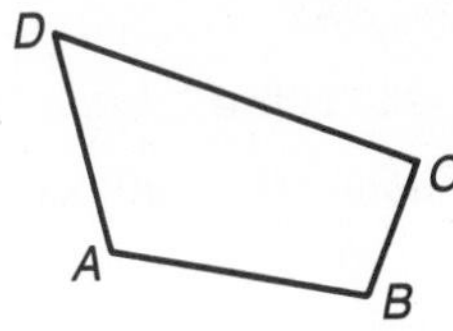

To name a quadrilateral, simply list its vertices in clockwise or counterclockwise order. The quadrilateral to the right can be named $ABCD$ or $CBAD$. How else can it be named?

The following example demonstrates how you can use congruent triangles in proofs involving quadrilaterals.

Given: Quadrilateral $ABCD$
$\overline{AB} \cong \overline{CD}$, $\overline{AD} \cong \overline{CB}$

Prove: $\angle A \cong \angle C$

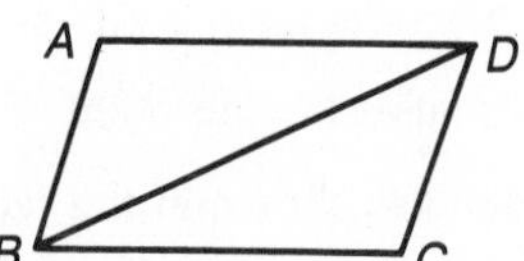

Proof:

STATEMENTS	REASONS
1. $\overline{AB} \cong \overline{CD}$, $\overline{AD} \cong \overline{CB}$	1. Given
2. There is a line $\overleftrightarrow{BD}$.	2. For every two points there is exactly one line that contains both points.
3. $\overline{BD} \cong \overline{DB}$	3. Congruence of segments is reflexive.
4. $\Delta BAD \cong \Delta DCB$	4. Steps 1, 3, and SSS
5. $\angle A \cong \angle C$	5. Corres. parts of $\cong$ Δs are $\cong$.

In the next example it is necessary to prove that one pair of triangles is congruent in order to prove that a second pair is congruent. Note that no two of the triangles are coplanar.

OBJECTIVE

Use congruent triangles to prove statements involving quadrilaterals and other polygons.

TEACHER'S NOTES

See p. T28

BCDA, CDAB, DABC, BADC, DCBA, ADCB

MIXED REVIEW

1. In an isosceles triangle, the base angles have measures of $2x - 10$ and $x + 5$. Find x. 15
2. Solve $3x - y = 10$
   $x + y = 6$. (4, 2)
3. Solve $x^2 - x - 20 = 0$. $\{5, -4\}$
4. Find the supplement of $x + 40$. $140 - x$
5. $\sqrt{2} \cdot \sqrt{8} =$ ______. 4

TEACHER'S RESOURCE MASTERS

Practice Master 12, Part 2
Quiz 8

Given: Points A, B, C, and D
$\overline{AB} \perp \overline{BC}$, $\overline{CD} \perp \overline{BC}$
$\overline{AB} \cong \overline{DC}$

Prove: $\Delta ACD \cong \Delta DBA$

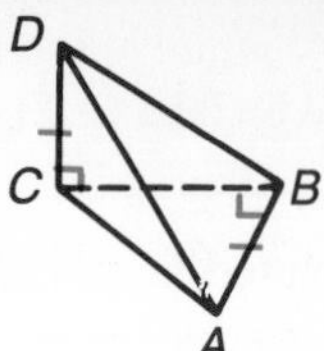

Proof:

STATEMENTS	REASONS
1. $\overline{AB} \perp \overline{BC}$, $\overline{CD} \perp \overline{BC}$	1. Given
2. $\angle ABC$ and $\angle DCB$ are right $\angle$s.	2. Definition of $\perp$
3. $\angle ABC \cong \angle DCB$	3. Any 2 rt. $\angle$s are $\cong$.
4. $\overline{AB} \cong \overline{DC}$	4. Given
5. $\overline{CB} \cong \overline{BC}$	5. Congruence of segments in reflexive.
6. $\Delta ABC \cong \Delta DCB$	6. Steps 3, 4, 5, and SAS
7. $\overline{AC} \cong \overline{DB}$	7. Corres. parts of $\cong$ Δs are $\cong$.
8. $\overline{AD} \cong \overline{DA}$	8. Congruence of segments is reflexive.
9. $\Delta ACD \cong \Delta DBA$	9. Steps 4, 7, 8, and SSS

ASSIGNMENT GUIDE

Minimum 1-7
Regular 1-8, 9-13 odd
Maximum 5-9 odd, 10-16

Oral Exercises

1. ΔCPB, ΔCAB
2. ΔABC, ΔABP, ΔABD
3. ΔADP, ΔAPB, ΔACB, ΔADB
4. ΔADP, ΔAPB, ΔACB, ΔADB, ΔCPB
5. ΔDPA, ΔCPB
6. ΔADB, ΔBCA
7. ΔABC, ΔAYP, ΔBXQ, and ΔXYZ
8. quad. $CPZQ$, quad. $AXZP$, quad. $YBQZ$
9. $AY = XB$
10. $\overline{AC} \cong \overline{BC}$, $\overline{AP} \cong \overline{YP}$, $\overline{QB} \cong \overline{QX}$, $\overline{XZ} \cong \overline{YZ}$

ORAL EXERCISES

Refer to the figure at the right for Exercises 1–6.

1. Name two triangles with a vertex at point C.

2. Name three triangles having $\overline{AB}$ as a side.

3. Name four triangles having point A as a vertex.

4. Name five triangles shown in the figure.

5. Name two nonoverlapping triangles that appear to be congruent.

6. Name two overlapping triangles that appear to be congruent.

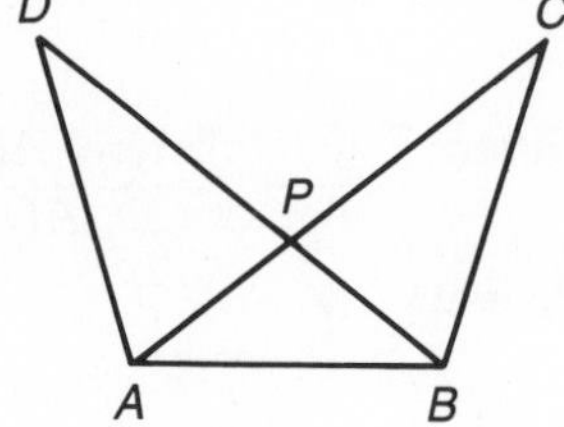

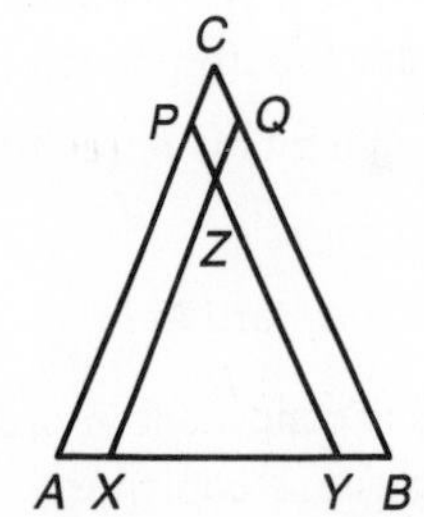

Refer to the figure at the left for Exercises 7–10.

7. Name four triangles in the figure.

8. Name three quadrilaterals in the figure.

9. If $AX = YB$, what else can be deduced?

10. Name all the pairs of congruent sides that can be deduced if $\angle A \cong \angle ZXY \cong \angle ZYX \cong \angle B$.

WRITTEN EXERCISES

A. Supply the missing reasons in the proof below.

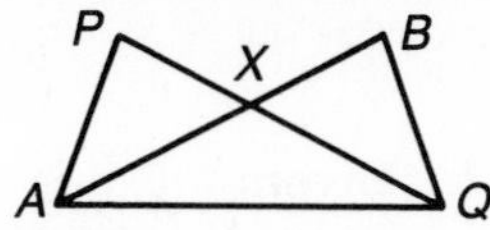

Given: $\triangle APQ$ and $\triangle QBA$
$\overline{PA} \cong \overline{BQ}$, $\overline{PQ} \cong \overline{BA}$

Prove: $\angle PQA \cong \angle BAQ$

Proof:

STATEMENTS	REASONS
1. $\overline{PA} \cong \overline{BQ}$, $\overline{PQ} \cong \overline{BA}$	1. **1.**
2. $\overline{AQ} \cong \overline{AQ}$	2. **2.**
3. $\triangle APQ \cong \triangle QBA$	3. **3.**
4. $\angle PQA \cong \angle BAQ$	4. **4.**

B. **5.** In $\triangle ABC$, $\overline{CA} \cong \overline{CB}$ and $m\angle 1 = 50$. Find $m\angle 3$.

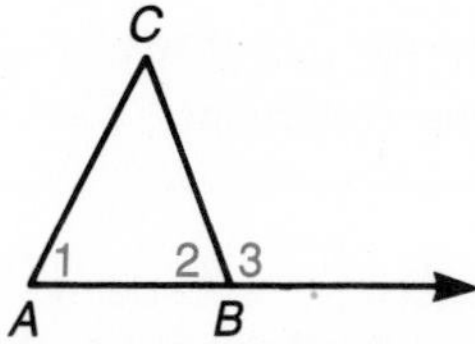

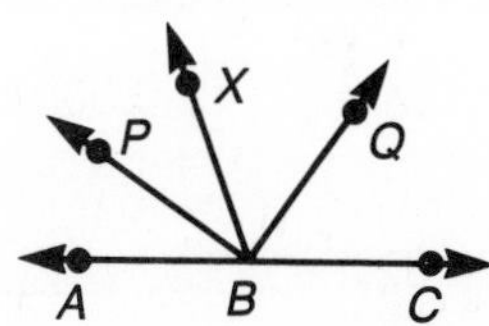

6. In the figure at the left, $m\angle ABX = 70$, $\overrightarrow{BP}$ bisects $\angle ABX$, and $\overrightarrow{BQ}$ bisects $\angle XBC$. Find $m\angle PBQ$.

7. Given: $\triangle ABC$ and $\triangle DCB$
$\overline{AB} \cong \overline{BC} \cong \overline{CD}$
$\overline{AB} \perp \overline{BC}$, $\overline{DC} \perp \overline{BC}$

Prove: $\overline{AC} \cong \overline{DB}$

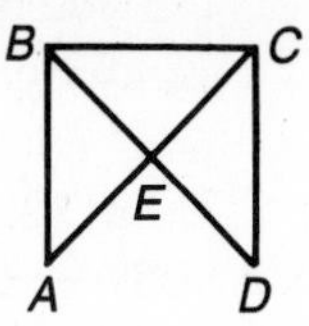

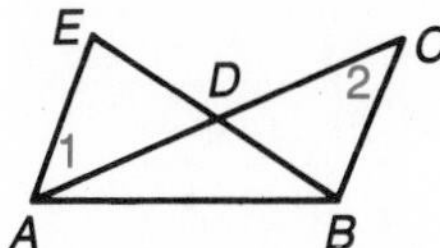

8. Given: Figure $ABCDE$
$\overline{EB}$ bisects $\overline{AC}$ at D.
$\angle 1 \cong \angle 2$

Prove: $\overline{AE} \cong \overline{CB}$

9. Given: Quadrilateral $ABCD$
$\overline{AD} \cong \overline{CB}$, $\overline{DC} \cong \overline{BA}$

Prove: $\angle DAB \cong \angle BCD$

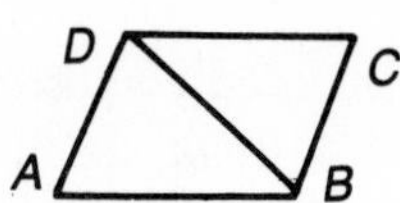

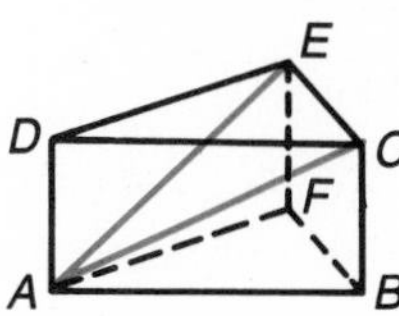

10. Given: Figure $ABCDEF$
$\overline{EF} \perp \overline{AF}$, $\overline{CB} \perp \overline{AB}$
$\overline{EF} \cong \overline{CB}$
$\triangle AFB$ is isosceles with base $\overline{BF}$.

Prove: $\angle AEC \cong \angle ACE$

Written Exercises

1. Given
2. Congruence of segments is reflexive.
3. Steps *1*, *2*, and SSS
4. Corres. parts of $\cong$ $\triangle$s are $\cong$.
5. 130
6. 90
7. $\triangle ABC \cong \triangle DCB$ by SAS, $\overline{AC} \cong \overline{DB}$ by CPCTC
8. $\triangle AED \cong \triangle CBD$ by ASA; $\overline{AE} \cong \overline{BC}$ by CPCTC
9. $\triangle DAB = \triangle BCD$ by SSS, then CPCTC
10. $\triangle EFA \cong \triangle CBA$ by LL; $\overline{AE} \cong \overline{AC}$ by CPCTC; then base $\angle$s $\cong$

11. $\Delta AXC \cong \Delta AYC$ by SAS; $\Delta ABC \cong \Delta ADC$ by ASA; CPCTC

12. $\Delta AEB \cong \Delta DEC$ by ASA so $\angle A \cong \angle D$ by CPCTC

13. **Given:** Isos. ΔABC; $\overline{AY}$ bisects $\angle CAB$; $\overline{BX}$ bisects $\angle ABC$; X lies between A and C; Y lies between B and C; $\angle CAB \cong \angle CBA$

Prove: $\overline{AY} \cong \overline{BX}$

Proof: $\overline{AB} \cong \overline{AB}$ by reflex.; $\angle YAB \cong \angle XBA$ by given and def. of bisect; $\Delta XBA \cong \Delta YAB$ by ASA; $\overline{AY} \cong \overline{BX}$ by CPCTC.

14. LL; CPCTC.

15. Def. of supp.; def. of bisector; Angle Addition Post.; Def. of $\perp$

16. ASA, CPCTC

Calculator

1. 4,485,600 2. 0.009387

3. 4891304.3 4. −31717

5. 68 6. 49.389

7. 1,793,760 8. 1

9. 2 10. 2.384

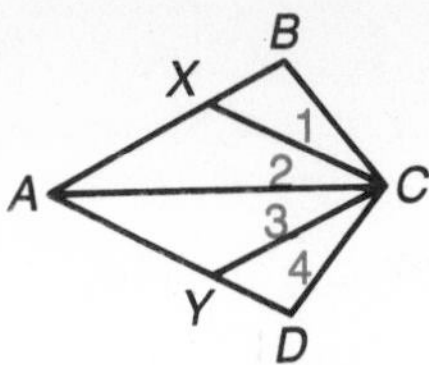

11. Given: Quadrilateral $ABCD$
$\angle 1 \cong \angle 2 \cong \angle 3 \cong \angle 4$
$\overline{XC} \cong \overline{YC}$

Prove: $\overline{BC} \cong \overline{DC}$

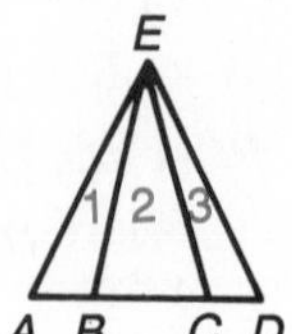

12. Given: Figure ADE
ΔBEC is isosceles with base $\overline{BC}$.
$\angle AEC \cong \angle BED$

Prove: ΔAED is isosceles.

C. 13. Prove that the bisectors of the base angles of an isosceles triangle are congruent.

14. Prove that if a median of a triangle is perpendicular to the opposite side, then the triangle is isosceles.

15. Prove that if two angles form a linear pair, then their bisectors are perpendicular.

16. Prove that if two triangles are congruent, then their corresponding angle bisectors are congruent.

1. 72,000,000 [×] 0.0623 **2.** 0.000987 [+] 0.0084

3. 45,000 [÷] 0.0092

4. −9087 [+] 7056 [−] 50,007 [+] 20,321

Did you have difficulty with number 4? You cannot use a negative sign for your first entry. You can enter one of the positive numbers first, then the negatives, or you can use the [+/−] key. Enter 9087, then press [+/−]. Your display will read −9087 or 9087−. Continue as usual with your entries.

5. 62 [−][(] 56 [÷] 7 [)][+] 14

6. [(] 50,006 [×] 0.001 [)][−][(] 1234 [÷] 2000 [)]

7. 4.44 [×] 10^2 [×] 4.04 [×] 10^3

8. 10^5 [×] 10^{-5}

Did you use the [x^2] key and the [y^x] key for Exercises 7 and 8? If not, try them again using these keys. Number 8 should be entered as follows:

10 [y^x] 5 [×] 10 [y^x] 5 [+/−] [=]

9. 2 [×] 10^3 [×] 10^0 [×] 10^{-3}

10. 0.298 [×] 10^{-2} [×] 0.008 [×] 10^5

SKILLS MAINTENANCE

When the same equation is used repeatedly in applied situations, it is often "formalized." That is, it is stated as a formula. Letters that help recall the quantities involved are used as variables instead of the usual x, y, or z.

The formulas below may be familiar to you. State each in words.

1. $A = lw$ **2.** $d = rt$ **3.** $I = prt$ **4.** $F = \frac{9}{5}C + 32$

Use the given formula to find each quantity described:

5. the voltage E in a circuit if current I is 7 amps and resistance R is 8 ohms; $E = IR$

6. the Fahrenheit temperature F if the Celsius temperature is 22; $F = \frac{9}{5}C + 32$

7. the interest I if principal p is \$5000, rate r is 12%, time t is 1 year; $I = prt$

8. the horsepower H of an engine if the number of cylinders n is 8 and the diameter d of each cylinder is 3 inches; $H = 0.4d^2n$

9. the volume V of a cone if the radius r is 10 and the height h is 8; $V = \frac{1}{3}\pi r^2 h$

Solve each formula below for the indicated variable:

10. $E = IR$ for R **11.** $A = p + prt$ for p **12.** $T^2 = 4\pi^2 \left(\frac{L}{g}\right)$ for g

EXPLORATION/Cubes

A cube, shown in the figure, is a solid that has the following properties:

1. All 12 edges are congruent.
2. All 6 faces are congruent squares.
3. All angles determined by the intersection of edges are right angles.

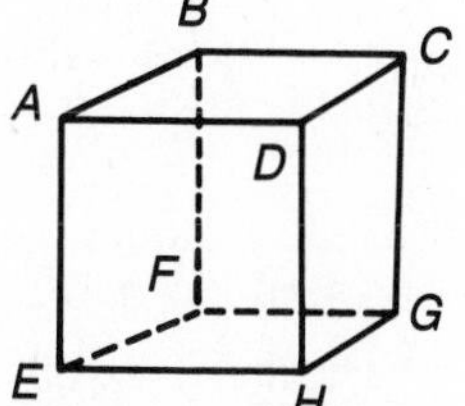

Given that the length of edge AB above is 10, test your memory of perimeter, area, volume, and right triangles by finding the following values of the cube.

1. the sum of the lengths of all the edges **2.** the area of one face

3. the surface area (all faces) **4.** the volume **5.** the length of $\overline{AC}$

Skills Maintenance

1. Area equals length times width.
2. Distance equals rate times time.
3. Interest equals principal times rate times time.
4. Fahrenheit degrees equals $\frac{9}{5}$ times Celsius degrees plus 32.
5. 56 volts 6. 71.6°F
7. \$600 8. 28.8 hp
9. $837\frac{1}{3}$ 10. $R = \frac{E}{I}$
11. $p = \frac{A}{1 + rt}$ 12. $g = \frac{4\pi^2 L}{T^2}$

Exploration

1. 120 2. 100
3. 600 4. 1000
5. $10\sqrt{2}$

CAREER/Technical Illustrator

More than any other drawing style, perspective drawings represent objects as we naturally perceive them. A correctly drawn perspective is the two-dimensional representation of what we see in three dimensions. Professionals in the art of drawing in perspective are **technical illustrators.**

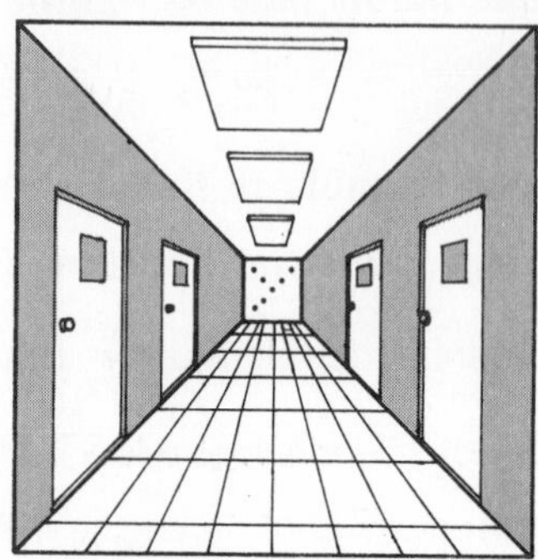

Among the principles that technical illustrators master is that congruent triangles are the basis for most perspective drawings. The picture above is a simple perspective drawing. When you look at it, you feel as if you are standing at one end of a long hall. The artist began by drawing two pairs of congruent triangles (one pair forms the ceiling and floor; one pair forms the two walls). The common vertex of the four triangles is called the *vanishing point.* Of course, in reality, the walls do not all meet at one point, but when you look down a long hallway, that is what you see. The figure below uses congruent triangles to depict a building in perspective. In this figure there are two vanishing points.

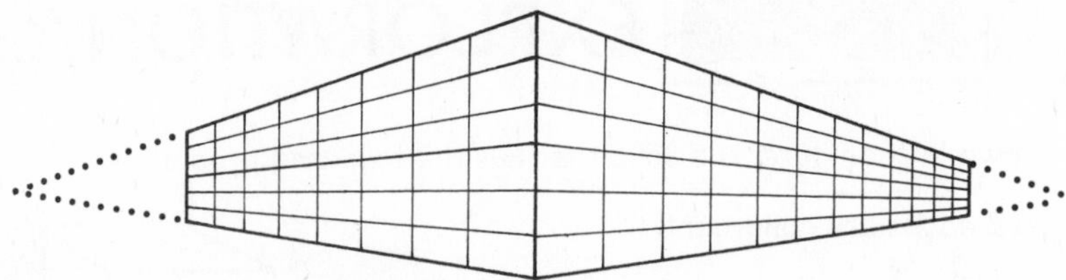

Technical illustrators must also understand *hidden lines,* the lines on the backside of an object that are blocked from view. The dotted lines in the figure at the right show hidden lines. Technical illustrators use these and other basic principles of geometry in their work.

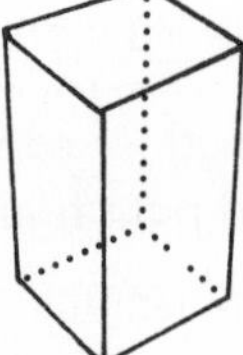

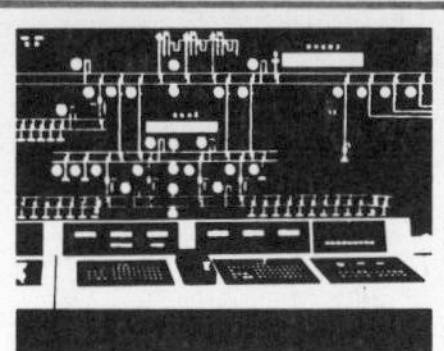

COMPUTER

A computer program is only as effective as the problem-solving approach used to write it. One method of problem analysis is the **top-down approach,** a device which divides a problem into subproblems, as illustrated below.

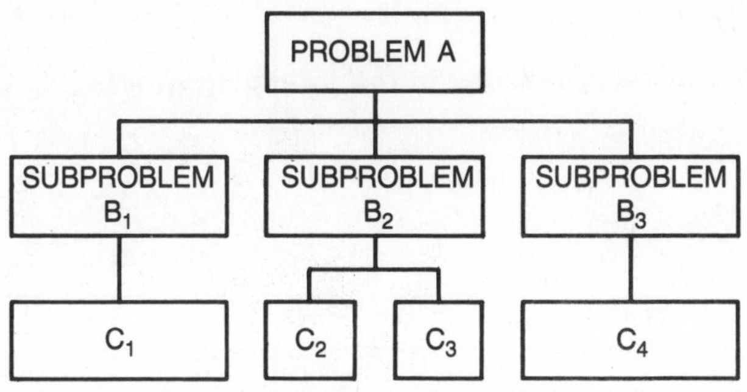

A programmer studies the main problem and decides what subproblems are needed at each level to find the solution on level A. Eventually a subroutine will be designed for each subproblem. This process is much like the reasoning you use in planning geometric proofs, when you mentally work backward from the prove statement without necessarily filling in each detail.

Complete the top-down analysis of two possible approaches to the following problem.

Given: $\angle 1 \cong \angle 2$, $\overline{CL} \cong \overline{CK}$

Prove: $\angle L \cong \angle K$

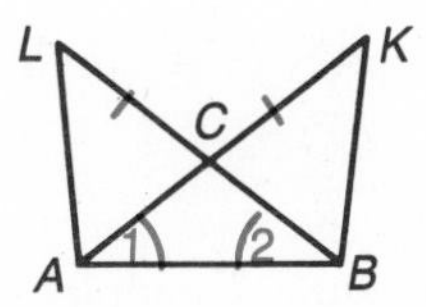

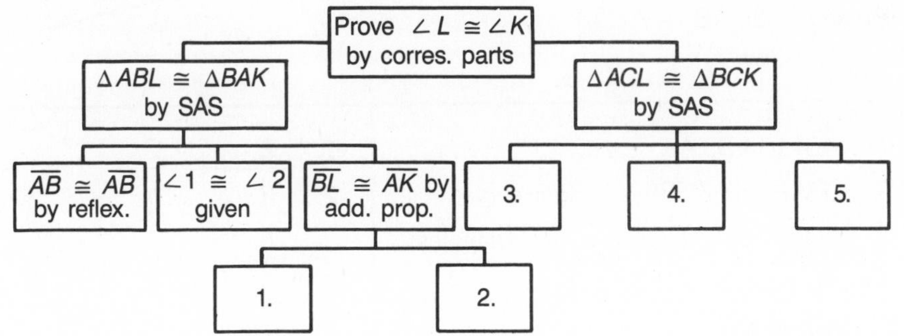

TEACHER'S RESOURCE MASTERS

Computer Master 4

Computer

1. $\overline{AC} \cong \overline{BC}$ (Thm. 4.4)
2. $\overline{CL} \cong \overline{CK}$ (Given)
3. $\overline{AC} \cong \overline{BC}$ (Thm. 4.4)
4. $\angle ACL \cong \angle BCK$ (Vert. $\angle$s)
5. $\overline{CL} \cong \overline{CK}$ (Given)

ENRICHMENT

See Activities 7–8, p. T45.

CHAPTER 4 REVIEW

VOCABULARY

base (4.3)
base angle (4.3)
basic congruence postulate (4.1)
biconditional (4.3)
corollary (4.3)
equilateral (4.3)
isosceles (4.3)
quadrilateral (4.5)
scalene (4.3)
vertex angle (4.3)

REVIEW EXERCISES

4.1 **Supply the missing reasons in the following proofs.**

Given: $\Delta ABC \cong \Delta DEF$
$\overline{CG}$ and $\overline{FH}$ are medians.

Prove: $\overline{CG} \cong \overline{FH}$

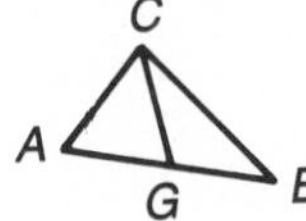

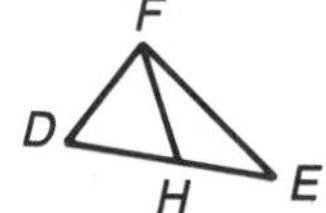

Proof:

STATEMENTS	REASONS
1. $\Delta ABC \cong \Delta DEF$	1. **1.** ____
2. $\overline{AC} \cong \overline{DF}$, $\angle A \cong \angle D$, $\overline{AB} \cong \overline{DE}$	2. **2.** ____
3. $AB = AG + GB$, $DE = DH + HE$	3. Definition of between
4. $AG = BG$, $DH = EH$	4. **3.** ____
5. $2AG = 2DH$	5. Substitution property of equality
6. $AB = DH$	6. Division property of equality
7. $\Delta ACG \cong \Delta DFH$	7. **4.** ____
8. $\overline{CG} \cong \overline{FH}$	8. **5.** ____

Given: Quadrilateral $ACBD$
$\overline{AB} \perp \overline{AD}$, $\overline{AB} \perp \overline{BC}$, $\overline{AD} \cong \overline{BC}$

Prove: $\Delta DAB \cong \Delta CBA$

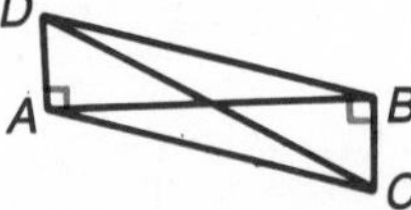

Proof:

STATEMENTS	REASONS
1. $\overline{AB} \perp \overline{AD}$, $\overline{AB} \perp \overline{BC}$	1. **6.** ____
2. $\angle DAB$ and $\angle CBA$ are right angles.	2. **7.** ____
3. ΔDAB and ΔCBA are right triangles.	3. **8.** ____
4. $\overline{AD} \cong \overline{BC}$	4. **9.** ____
5. $\overline{AB} \cong \overline{BA}$	5. **10.** ____
6. $\Delta DAB \cong \Delta CBA$	6. **11.** ____

Chapter 4 Review

1. Given
2. CPCTC
3. Def. of median
4. Steps *2*, *6*, and SAS
5. CPCTC
6. Given
7. Def. of perpendicular
8. Def. of right triangle
9. Given
10. Congruence of segments is reflexive.
11. Steps *4*, *5*, and LL Theorem

4.2 **Refer to the plane figure for Exercises 12–15. If the given information is sufficient to prove $\triangle RQP \cong \triangle RST$, name the postulate or theorem that supports your conclusion. If congruence cannot be shown, write "No."**

12. $\overline{QP} \cong \overline{ST}$, $\overline{RP} \cong \overline{RT}$, $\angle R \cong \angle R$

13. $\angle Q \cong \angle S$, $\overline{RQ} \cong \overline{RS}$, $\angle R \cong \angle R$

14. $\angle RTS \cong \angle RPQ$, $\overline{RP} \cong \overline{RT}$, $\angle R \cong \angle R$

15. $\overline{RQ} \cong \overline{RS}$, $\overline{QP} \cong \overline{ST}$, $\angle R \cong \angle R$

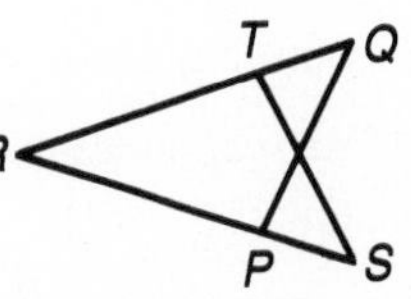

4.3 **Given $\triangle ABC$, fill in the blanks with the correct term.**

16. If $\overline{AB} \cong \overline{AC}$, then $\triangle ABC$ is a(n) ____ triangle.

17. If $\overline{AB} \ncong \overline{BC} \ncong \overline{CA}$, then $\triangle ABC$ is a(n) ____ triangle.

18. If $AB = BC = CA$, then $\triangle ABC$ is a(n) ____ triangle.

If $\overline{AC} \cong \overline{BC}$, then **19.** is the base, **20.** is the vertex angle, and **21.** and **22.** are the base angles.

23. A theorem that follows directly from another theorem is a(n) ____.

Refer to the figure of $\triangle ABC$ for Exercises 24–27. If the given information is sufficient to prove $\triangle ABE \cong \triangle ACD$, state the theorem or theorems that support your conclusions. If congruence cannot be shown, write "No."

24. $BD = CE$, $AD = AE$

25. $\angle B \cong \angle C$

26. $\angle ADE \cong \angle AED$, $\overline{BD} \cong \overline{CE}$

27. $\angle DAB \cong \angle EAC$, $\overline{BD} \cong \overline{CE}$

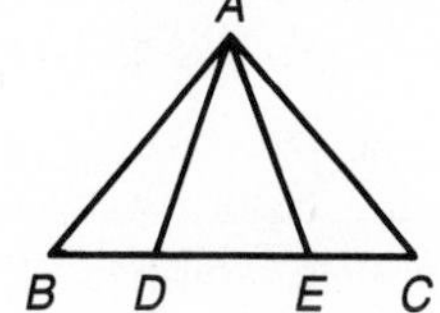

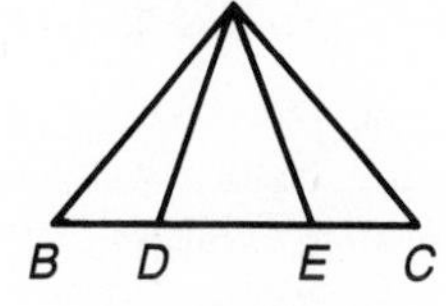

4.4 **28. Given:** $\triangle ABD$
$\overline{AB} \cong \overline{AE}$, $\overline{FB} \cong \overline{FE}$
$\angle B$ is a right angle

Prove: $\overline{FE} \perp \overline{AD}$

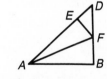

4.5 **29. Given:** Quadrilateral $ABCD$
$AB = CD$, $AD = CB$
F bisects $\overline{BD}$

Prove: $EF = GF$

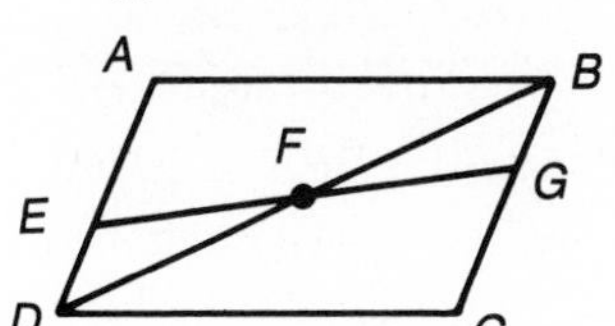

30. Given: Figure $ABCDEF$
$\overline{AB} \cong \overline{DE}$, $\overline{AF} \cong \overline{DC}$, $\overline{BC} \cong \overline{FE}$
$\angle 1 \cong \angle 2$

Prove: $\triangle ABF \cong \triangle DEC$

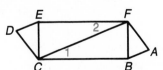

12. no
13. ASA
14. ASA
15. no
16. isosceles
17. scalene
18. equilateral
19. $\overline{AB}$ 20. $\angle A$
21. $\angle C$ 22. $\angle B$
23. corollary
24. Theorem 4.3 and SAS
25. no
26. Theorem 4.4 and SAS
27. no
28. SSS, CPCTC
29. SSS, vertical angles, ASA, CPCTC
30. SAS, CPCTC, SSS

TEACHER'S RESOURCE MASTERS

Chapter 4 Test
Multiple Choice Test—Chapter 4

Chapter 4 Test

1. T
2. T
3. F
4. T
5. F
6. F
7. F
8. T
9. T
10. $\Delta ABC \cong \Delta ABD$ by LL; $\overline{AC} \cong \overline{AD}$ by CPCTC
11. $\Delta AED \cong \Delta AEB$ by ASA; $\Delta DCE \cong \Delta BCE$ by SAS
12. $\overline{ED} \cong \overline{BD}$; $\angle FDE \cong \angle CDB$; $\Delta EFD \cong \Delta BCD$ by ASA; $\angle EFD \cong \angle BCD$ by CPCTC
13. $\Delta ABE \cong \Delta BEC$ by SSS; $\angle AEC \cong \angle CEB$ by CPCTC; $\angle DEA \cong \angle DEC$
14. $\angle AXB \cong \angle BXC \cong \angle CXD \cong \angle DXA$ by all right $\angle$s $\cong$; Δs $\cong$ by SAS; sides $\cong$ by CPCTC

CHAPTER 4 TEST

Are the following statements true or false?

1. Corresponding parts of congruent triangles are congruent.

2. If the corresponding legs of two right triangles are congruent, then the triangles are congruent.

3. All theorems can be written as biconditionals.

4. If a triangle is equilateral, then it is also equiangular.

5. If two isosceles triangles have the same base, then the triangles are congruent.

6. Each median of an isosceles triangle is perpendicular to a side of the triangle.

7. A scalene triangle may also be isosceles.

8. The base angles of an isosceles triangle are congruent.

9. A quadrilateral has four sides.

10. Given: Figure $ABCD$
$\overline{AB} \perp \overline{BC}$, $\overline{AB} \perp \overline{BD}$
$\overline{BC} \cong \overline{BD}$

Prove: ΔACD is isosceles.

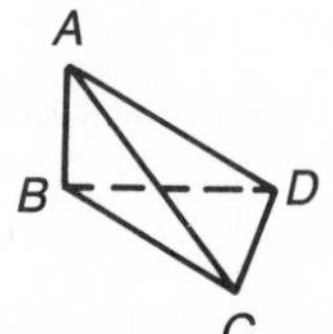

11. Given: Figure $ABCD$
$\angle 1 \cong \angle 2$, $\angle 3 \cong \angle 4$

Prove: $\Delta DCE \cong \Delta BCE$

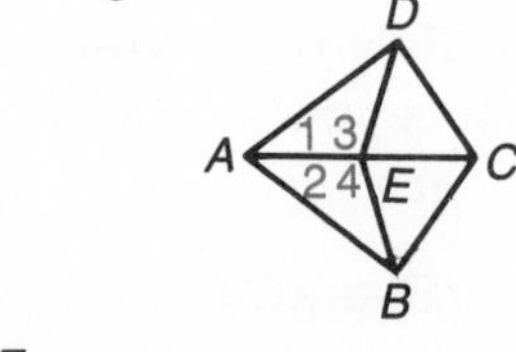

12. Given: Figure $ABCDE$
$\overline{FC}$ bisects $\overline{EB}$ at D.
$\angle E \cong \angle DBC$

Prove: $\angle EFD \cong \angle BCD$

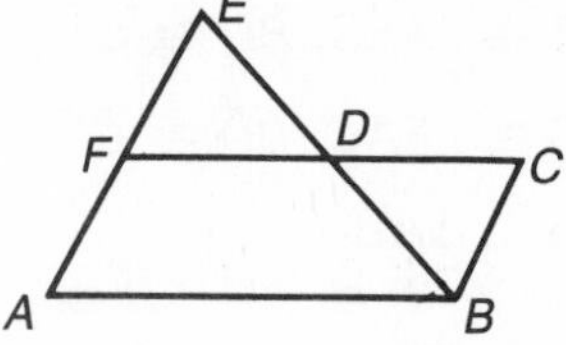

13. Given: Quadrilateral $ABCD$
$\overline{AB} \cong \overline{CB}$, $\overline{AE} \cong \overline{CE}$

Prove: $\angle DEA \cong \angle DEC$

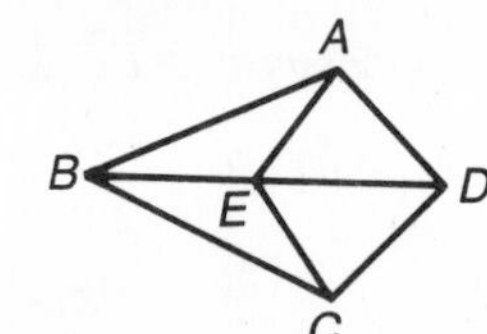

14. Given: Quadrilateral $ABCD$
X is the midpoint of $\overline{AC}$ and $\overline{BD}$.
$\overline{AC} \perp \overline{BD}$

Prove: $\overline{AB} \cong \overline{BC} \cong \overline{CD} \cong \overline{DA}$

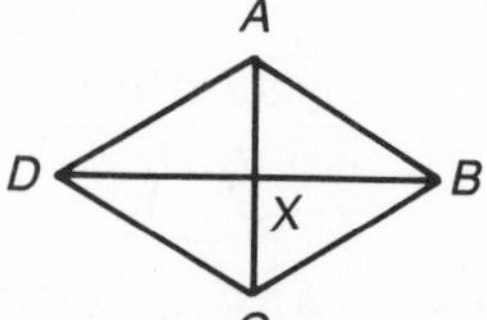

CUMULATIVE REVIEW: CHAPTERS 1–4

1. Which sentence best describes the figure?

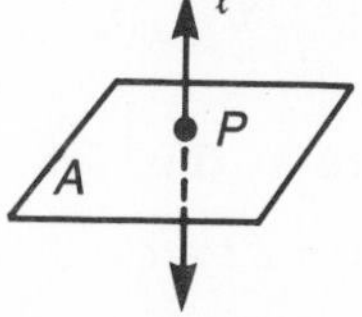

   a. Line l and point P intersect plane A.
   b. Plane A contains line l and point P.
   c. Point P on l lies in plane A.
   d. Line l intersects plane A in point P.

2. Which property of real numbers states that if $x = 2$, and $2 = y$, then $x = y$?

   a. reflexive b. transitive c. symmetric d. associative

3. Supply the missing symbol: If $x > 4$, then $x + 2$ ● 6.

   a. $<$ b. $=$ c. $>$ d. $\geq$

4. Select the converse of the implication "If they have gone to the beach, they will miss the party."

   a. If they miss the party, they have gone to the beach.
   b. They will miss the party if and only if they have gone to the beach.
   c. If they do not go to the beach, they will not miss the party.
   d. They have gone to the beach and missed the party.

5. Given line l as shown, what is the distance between A and H?

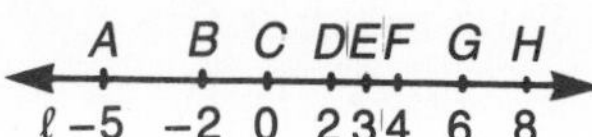

   a. 3 b. −13 c. 13 d. 9

Refer to the Figure at the right for Exercises 6 and 7.

6. What is the intersection of planes E and F?

   a. $\overleftrightarrow{PQ}$ b. T c. l d. $\overline{PQ}$

7. What point is not coplanar with R?

   a. P b. Q c. S d. T

8. An example of a convex set is

   a. three collinear points. b. a plane.
   c. a triangle. d. a line and an external point.

9. Another name for $\angle 1$, shown in the figure, is

   a. $\angle B$. b. $\angle DBA$.
   c. $\angle ABE$. d. $\angle DBC$.

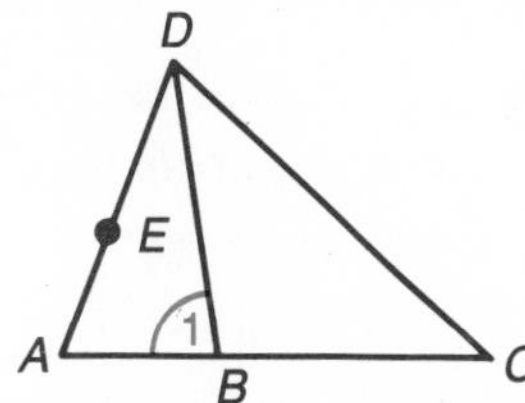

Cumulative Review: Chapters 1-4

1. d
2. b
3. c
4. a
5. c
6. a
7. d
8. b
9. b

TEACHER'S RESOURCE MASTERS

Cumulative Test—Chapters 1-4 Form A or Form B

TEACHER'S NOTES

See p. T28

10. b
11. a
12. d
13. b
14. a
15. b
16. a
17. c
18. b
19. d

Refer to the protractor figure for Exercises 10 and 11.

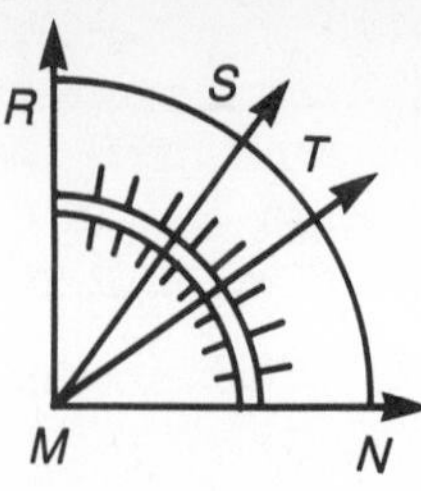

10. $m\angle SMR$ is

a. 25. **b.** 35. **c.** 70. **d.** 125.

11. An angle congruent to $\angle RMS$ is

a. $\angle TMN$. **b.** $\angle RMT$. **c.** $\angle LMQ$. **d.** $\angle QMR$.

Use the figure at the right for Exercises 12–14.

12. $\angle 1$ and $\angle 2$ are

a. adjacent. **b.** supplementary.

c. a linear pair. **d.** all of the above.

13. If $z \perp x$, then $\angle 3$ and $\angle 5$ are

a. obtuse. **b.** acute.

c. supplementary. **d.** right.

14. If $\angle 3 \cong \angle 5$, then

a. $\angle 1 \cong \angle 6$. **b.** $\angle 5 \cong \angle 7$. **c.** $\angle 1 \cong \angle 7$. **d.** $\angle 2 \cong \angle 6$.

15. If the figures shown are congruent, which correspondences are true?

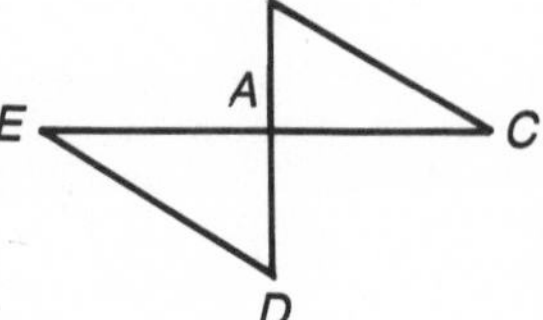

a. $\angle C \leftrightarrow \angle D$, $\overline{AE} \leftrightarrow \overline{AC}$ **b.** $\angle C \leftrightarrow \angle E$, $\overline{AB} \leftrightarrow \overline{AD}$

c. $\angle B \leftrightarrow \angle D$, $\overline{DE} \leftrightarrow \overline{AC}$ **d.** $\angle B \leftrightarrow \angle E$, $\angle C \leftrightarrow \angle D$

16. An equivalence relation is reflexive, transitive, and

a. symmetric. **b.** associative. **c.** commutative. **d.** distributive.

17. In ΔABC, if $\overrightarrow{AX}$ bisects $\angle A$, then

a. $\overrightarrow{AX}$ is a median of ΔABC. **b.** $\angle B \cong \angle C$.

c. $\angle CAX \cong \angle BAX$. **d.** $\overrightarrow{AX} \perp \overline{BC}$.

18. If M is the midpoint of $\overline{RS}$ and $\overline{PQ}$, how would you prove that $\Delta RPM \cong \Delta SQM$?

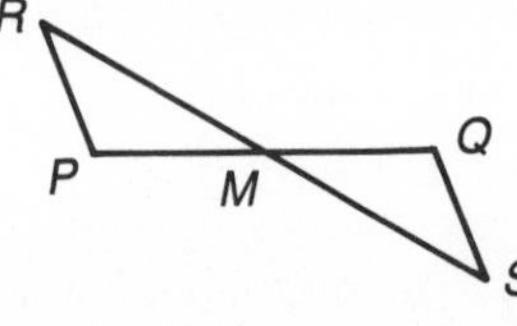

a. SSS **b.** SAS

c. LL **d.** ASA

19. Which statement about quadrilateral $ABCD$ can you prove using SSS?

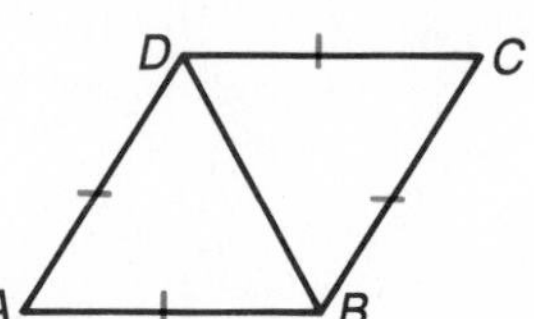

a. $\angle A \cong \angle C$ **b.** $\overline{DB}$ bisects $\angle ABC$.

c. $\angle ABC \cong \angle CDA$ **d.** all of the above

PREPARING FOR COLLEGE ENTRANCE EXAMS

Select the correct answer for each of the following questions.

1. C is the midpoint of $\overline{AE}$. B and D are on $\overline{AE}$ so that $AB = BC$ and $CD = DE$. What percent of AD is AC?

a. $33\frac{1}{3}$ **b.** 50 **c.** $66\frac{2}{3}$ **d.** 133 **e.** 150

2. For the figure shown, which statement is NOT true?

a. P, S, and R are coplanar.
b. P, Q, and R are collinear.
c. P and S are collinear.
d. P, S, R, and T are coplanar.
e. P, T, and R are coplanar.

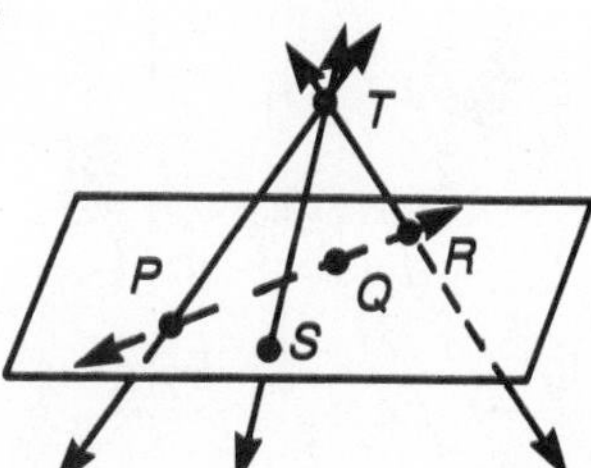

3. Which statement best expresses the relationship between a, b, and c if $a = b$?

a. $a + b > b + c$ **b.** $a + c > b + c$
c. $a - b - 2c = 0$ **d.** $a + 2c = b$
e. $a + c = b + c$

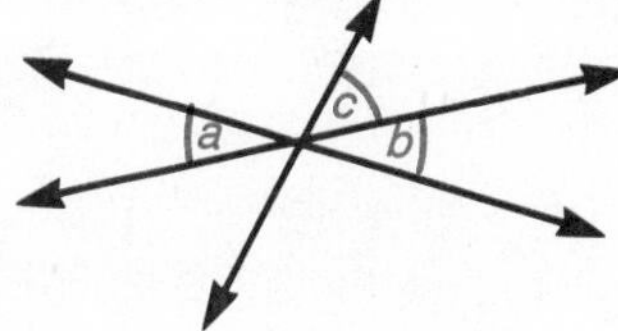

4. In the figure, $s = \frac{r}{3}$. Express $a + b$ in terms of r.

a. $\frac{r}{3} - 180$ **b.** $60 - \frac{r}{3}$
c. $180 - \frac{r}{3}$ **d.** $r - 180$
e. $180 - r$

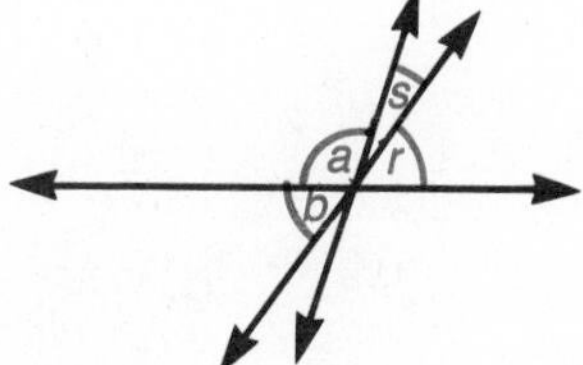

5. Which statement gives enough information to prove $\triangle ABC \cong \triangle QRS$?

I. $\overline{AB} \cong \overline{QR}$, $\overline{BC} \cong \overline{QS}$, $\angle B \cong \angle Q$ **II.** $\overline{BC} \cong \overline{QS}$, $\overline{AC} \cong \overline{RS}$
III. $\angle B \cong \angle Q$ **IV.** $\overline{AC} \cong \overline{RS}$, $\overline{BC} \cong \overline{QS}$, $\angle B \cong \angle Q$

a. I **b.** II **c.** III **d.** IV **e.** none

Preparing for College Entrance Exams

1. c
2. d
3. e
4. c
5. a

NOTE: Question 5 is representative of entrance exam questions where students must correctly match the numbering of answer choices with letters in the answer key. In this case, roman numerals become letter choices.

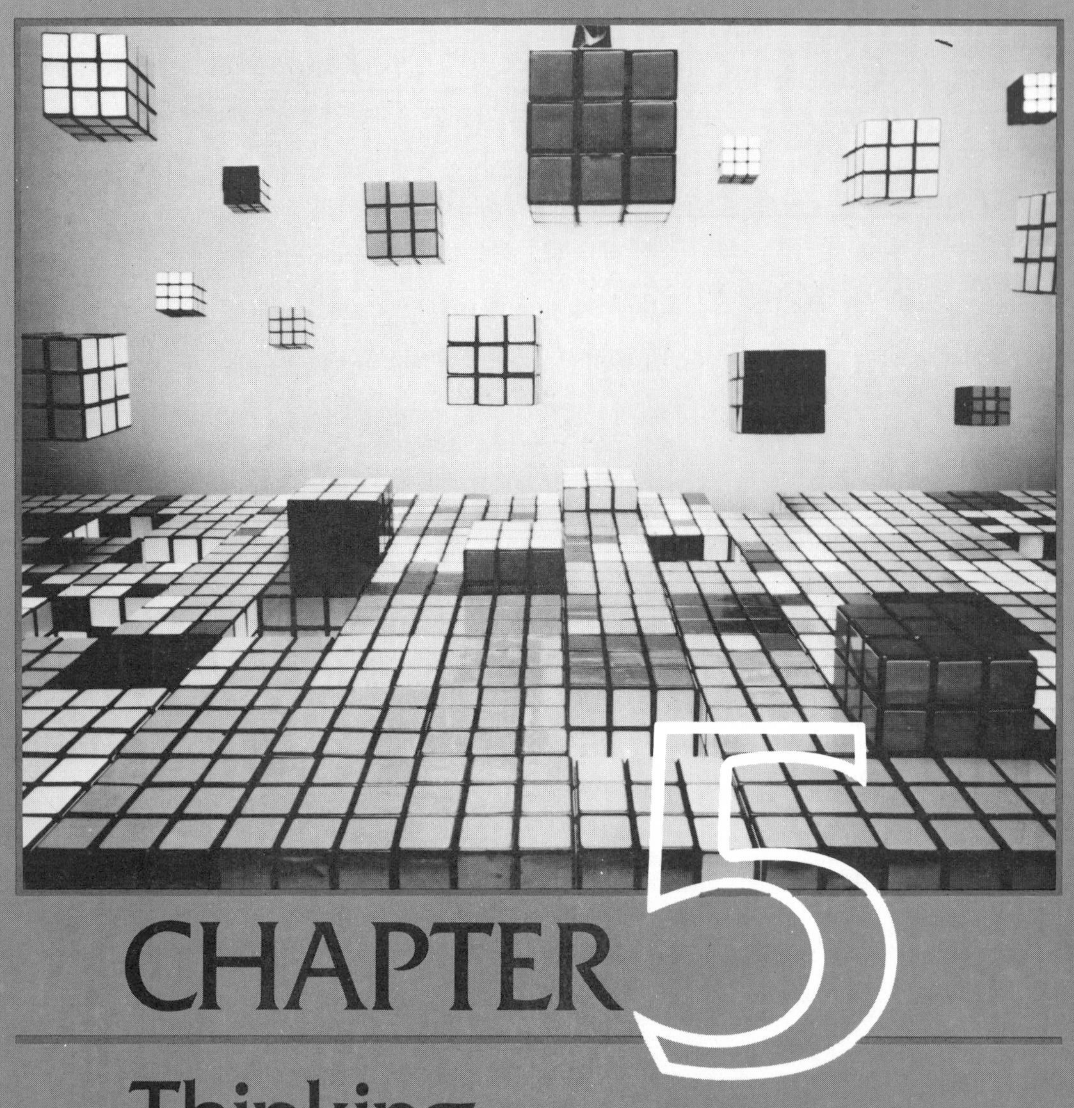

CHAPTER 5

Thinking and Proving

5.1 Logic and Deductive Proof

A deductive system requires a beginning. In Chapter 1, you began building your geometry vocabulary with three *undefined terms: point, line,* and *plane.* To relate these three terms, common-sense postulates were established. For example, Postulate 1 (Given any two different points, there is exactly one line that contains both of them.) relates *point* and *line.*

From this basis, your vocabulary has been extended to include *defined terms.* The definition of *segment length* from Chapter 1 is a good example: *"The length of a line segment is the distance determined from Postulate 2 (the Distance Postulate)."* These words make sense because you agreed to the meaning of *point* and *line,* and you built the definition of *line segment* from them. Applying the Distance Postulate to the idea of a line segment naturally suggests the definition of *length* of a segment.

You have proved about two dozen theorems and corollaries so far by a chain of reasoning that can be traced back to the earlier postulates, theorems, and terms (both defined and undefined). Thus, any time a theorem or definition is used in a proof, everything that preceded it can be deduced. For example, if you know that a triangle is isosceles, you can immediately deduce that it has two congruent sides (by definition) and that it has two congruent angles (by Theorem 4.3, the Isosceles Triangle Theorem). This is the logical process of *implication* that you learned in Chapter 1.

Implication alone is sometimes insufficient to deduce the information needed in a proof. In Chapter 1 you learned to change a statement to its *converse* and *biconditional* (if and only if) forms. These three logical concepts will now be extended to include three new concepts: **negation, inverse,** and **contrapositive.**

Negation is the easiest. To negate a statement, you add the word "not" (shown in notation as the symbol "$\sim$") to the main verb of the original statement. The truth value of the original statement is *opposite* the truth value of its negation.

For example, if a statement p, "Sally Ride was the first U.S. woman in space," is true, then its negation, $\sim p$, "Sally Ride was *not* the first U.S. woman in space," must be false. The truth table for negations is shown at the right.

p	$\sim p$
T	F
F	T

The *inverse* of a conditional statement, or implication, negates *both* the hypothesis and the conclusion. For an implication $p \rightarrow q$ (if p then q), the inverse would be $\sim p \rightarrow \sim q$ (if not p, then not q). Thus, given the implication "If a figure has three sides, then it is a triangle," the inverse is "If a figure does not have three sides, then it is not a triangle."

The *contrapositive* is another variation on a conditional statement. It negates the hypothesis and conclusion *and* reverses their positions. So, the contrapositive of $p \rightarrow q$ would be $\sim q \rightarrow \sim p$. Given the conditional statement "If it is dark outside, then it must be night," the contrapositive is "If it is not night, then it must not be dark outside."

OBJECTIVE

Given a conditional statement, give its negation, inverse, and contrapositive and determine whether given statements are true or false.

TEACHER'S NOTES

See p. T28

MIXED REVIEW

1. True or False: $|x| = x$. F
2. Add $\frac{2}{x-1} + \frac{3}{x+2}$. $\frac{5x+1}{(x-1)(x+2)}$
3. Factor $6x^2 + x - 1$. $(3x - 1)(2x + 1)$
4. Multiply $(x - 1)(x + 2)(x - 3)$. $x^3 - 2x^2 - 5x + 6$
5. Two lines are perpendicular if and only if ______. they form right angles

TEACHER'S RESOURCE MASTERS

Practice Master 13

The following statements review all the logical concepts you have learned and represent them symbolically.

Case 1

STATEMENT p:	Today is Wednesday (p).
STATEMENT q:	Tomorrow is Thursday (q).
NEGATION OF p:	Today is not Wednesday ($\sim p$).
NEGATION OF q:	Tomorrow is not Thursday ($\sim q$).
CONDITIONAL STATEMENT: (IMPLICATION)	If today is Wednesday, then tomorrow is Thursday ($p \rightarrow q$).
CONVERSE:	If tomorrow is Thursday, then today is Wednesday ($q \rightarrow p$).
BICONDITIONAL:	Today is Wednesday if and only if tomorrow is Thursday (p iff q).
INVERSE:	If today is not Wednesday, then tomorrow is not Thursday ($\sim p \rightarrow \sim q$).
CONTRAPOSITIVE:	If tomorrow is not Thursday, then today is not Wednesday ($\sim q \rightarrow \sim p$).

Case 2

STATEMENT p:	ΔABC is isosceles (p).
STATEMENT q:	ΔABC is equilateral (q).
NEGATION OF p:	ΔABC is not isosceles ($\sim p$).
NEGATION OF q:	ΔABC is not equilateral ($\sim q$).
CONDITIONAL STATEMENT:	If ΔABC is isosceles, then ΔABC is equilateral ($p \rightarrow q$).
CONVERSE:	If ΔABC is equilateral, then ΔABC is isosceles ($q \rightarrow p$).
BICONDITIONAL:	ΔABC is isosceles if and only if ΔABC is equilateral (p iff q).
INVERSE:	If ΔABC is not isosceles, then ΔABC is not equilateral ($\sim p \rightarrow \sim q$).
CONTRAPOSITIVE:	If ΔABC is not equilateral, then ΔABC is not isosceles ($\sim q \rightarrow \sim p$).

The given conditional statements and their contrapositives are logically equivalent; that is, either both are true or both are false. *This is true for all conditional statements.* You can substitute the contrapositive for the original statement whenever the substitution makes a proof easier. This process is called **indirect proof.** Consider the following example:

Let statement p be "$m\angle 1 \geq 90$" and let statement q be "$\angle 1$ is not an acute angle." Then $p \rightarrow q$ is the conditional statement "If $m\angle 1 \geq 90$, then $\angle 1$ is not an acute angle." To prove $p \rightarrow q$ is true, you might find it easier to prove the contrapositive true instead. Thus, assume that $\angle 1$ is an acute angle ($\sim q$). By definition of an acute angle, $m\angle 1 < 90$ ($\sim p$). Because the statement $\sim q \rightarrow \sim p$ is true (If $\angle 1$ is an acute angle, its measure is less than 90), you know that $p \rightarrow q$ is also true.

This method of indirect proof can be applied to theorems in Chapter 2 that were not formally proved before.

REVIEW: THEOREM 2.2
If a given line intersects a plane not containing it, then their intersection is a single point.

Given: Line l, not in plane E
l intersects E at point P.

Prove: P is the only point of intersection of l and E.

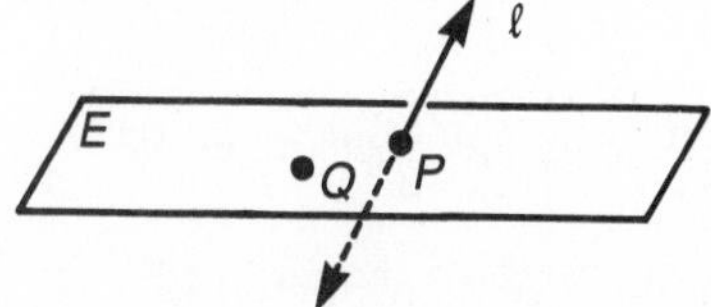

Proof: Let l intersect E at some other point, say point Q (indirect assumption). Then points P and Q lie on line l *and* in plane E. Then, by Postulate 6 (If two points lie in a plane, then the line containing these points lies in the same plane.), line l must lie in plane E. This deduction contradicts the original hypothesis that plane E does *not* contain line l. Because the contrapositive of the theorem holds true (If the intersection is not a single point, then the plane does contain the line.), the theorem itself must be true. Therefore, by the contrapositive, the intersection contains only one point.

To summarize, in a contrapositive proof you assume the opposite of what you want to prove ($\sim q$). If you can deduce from this the opposite of your given statement ($\sim p$), then the original implication ($p \rightarrow q$) is true.

As shown in the next proof, the word *exactly* has a particular meaning in geometry. In every day usage, *exactly* means "no more and no less" than some amount. So, in geometry, the phrase **exactly one** means that a specific geometrical relationship exists in only one way. The words **existence** and **uniqueness** describe this idea. To establish *existence,* you prove that there is *at least* one relationship of a particular kind. To establish *uniqueness,* you prove that there is *at most* one such relationship. The two proofs taken together allow you to deduce that there is *exactly one* relationship.

Uniqueness proofs almost always use an indirect approach. To prove that *at most* one geometrical configuration fits the given, try to prove that there are *two* different configurations. Then search for a contradiction of the postulates, theorems, and definitions,.

> **REVIEW: THEOREM 2.4**
> Given two intersecting lines, there is *exactly one* plane containing both of them.

Given: Line *l* intersects line *m*.

Prove: Exactly one plane contains both *l* and *m*.

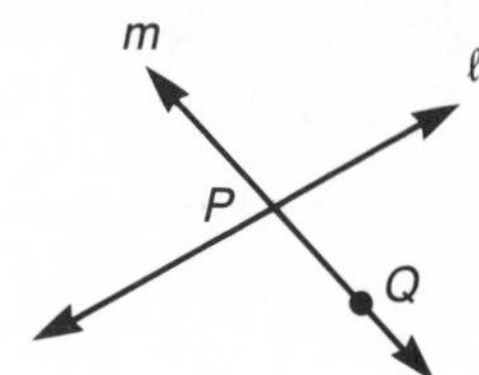

Existence proof:

STATEMENTS	REASONS
1. Line *l* intersects line *m*.	1. Given
2. *l* and *m* intersect at point *P*.	2. Two lines intersect in at most one point (Theorem 2.1).
3. Let *Q* be any other point on *m*.	3. A line contains infinitely many points (Postulate 3).
4. Plane *E* contains *Q* and *l*.	4. Given a line and a point not on the line, there is exactly one plane containing them both (Theorem 2.3).
5. *E* contains *m*.	5. Since *P* (as a point of *l*) and *Q* lie in *E*, line *m* containing *P* and *Q* is in *E* (Postulate 6).
Uniqueness proof:	
6. Let *F* be another plane that contains *l* and *m*.	6. Indirect assumption ($\sim q$)
7. *F* contains *Q*.	7. *Q* is a point of *m*.
8. Planes *E* and *F* both contain *Q* and *l*.	8. Steps 4, 6, and 7
9. *E* and *F* must name the same plane.	9. Given a line and a point not on the line, there is exactly one plane containing them both (Theorem 2.3).

The reason in Step 6, *indirect assumption,* introduces the contrapositive of the original conditional statement. (NOTE: The phrase *one and only one* is used interchangeably with the phrase *exactly one* in mathematics.)

ORAL EXERCISES

1. State the converse, inverse, and contrapositive of the following conditional statement: *If this exercise seems easy, then I understand alternate forms of conditional sentences.*

For Exercises 2–5, state the negation of each sentence and give the truth values for both the sentence and the negation.

2. A linear pair of angles are supplementary.
3. The measure of an obtuse angle is between 0 and 90.
4. Vertical angles are congruent.
5. ΔABC is equilateral.
6. State the indirect assumption that could be used to prove the following statement: *If a teenager earns more than $1200, then the teenager is required to file an income tax form.*

WRITTEN EXERCISES

A. For Exercises 1–8, tell whether each statement is always, sometimes, or never true.

1. A conditional sentence and its contrapositive are logically equivalent.
2. Two intersecting lines determine a plane.
3. An indirect assumption contradicts the given.
4. The angle bisector of an angle is unique to that angle.
5. Three points are collinear.
6. The phrase "if and only if" refers to existence and uniqueness.
7. Definitions are deduced from other definitions.
8. Uniqueness is proved by indirect logic.

B. For Exercises 9–10, identify (a) the given, (b) the "prove" statement for existence, (c) the "prove" statement for uniqueness, and (d) the indirect assumption.

9. From any vertex in an equilateral ΔABC, there is exactly one segment that is the median and the angle bisector.
10. In a plane, through a point on a line, there is *exactly one* line perpendicular to the given line.

ASSIGNMENT GUIDE

Day 1
Minimum 1-10
Regular 1-17
Maximum 1-18
Day 2
Minimum 11-18
Regular 18-19
Maximum 19-20

Oral Exercises

1. converse: If I understand . . . , then this exercise will seem . . . inverse: If this exercise does not seem easy, then I do not . . . contrapositive: If I do not . . . , then this exercise will not seem . . .
2. . . . are not . . . ; T, F
3. . . . is not . . . ; F, T
4. . . . are not . . . ; T, F
5. . . . is not . . . ; cannot determine truth value
6. A teenager is not required

Written Exercises

1. A	2. A	3. N
4. A	5. S	6. N
7. S	8. S	

9. (a) Given: equil. $\triangle ABC$; (b) Prove: $\overline{BD}$ is an $\angle$ bisector and a median; (c) Prove: $\overline{BD}$ is the only bisector and median of $\angle B$; (d) Assume: both $\overline{BD}$ and $\overline{BE}$ are angle bisectors and medians of $\angle B$.
10. (a) Given: P lies on l, l lies in plane E; (b) Prove: there is a line PQ in $E \perp l$; (c) $\overleftrightarrow{PQ}$ is the only line in $E \perp l$; (d) Assume: $\overleftrightarrow{PQ} \perp l$ and $\overleftrightarrow{PR} \perp l$.

Supply the missing reasons for the following proof, which uses indirect reasoning.

Given: $\overline{AB} \ncong \overline{DE}$

Prove: $\overline{AE}$ and $\overline{BD}$ do not bisect each other.

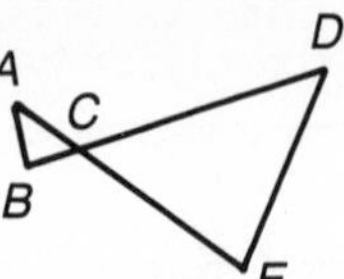

Proof:

STATEMENTS	REASONS
1. $\overline{AB} \ncong \overline{DE}$	1. Given
2. Let $\overline{AE}$ and $\overline{BD}$ bisect each other.	2. **11.**
3. $AC = EC$, $BC = DC$	3. **12.**
4. $\overline{AC} \cong \overline{EC}$, $\overline{BC} \cong \overline{DC}$	4. **13.**
5. $\angle ACB \cong \angle ECD$	5. **14.**
6. $\triangle ABC \cong \triangle ECD$	6. **15.**
7. $\overline{AB} \cong \overline{DE}$	7. **16.**

11. Indirect assumption
12. Definition of bisect
13. Definition of $\cong$ segments
14. Vertical $\angle$s are $\cong$.
15. SAS
16. Corres. parts of $\cong$ $\triangle$s are $\cong$.

Contradiction: From the given, these segments are *not* congruent. Therefore, $\overline{AE}$ and $\overline{BD}$ *cannot* bisect each other.

For Exercises 17–20, use indirect reasoning to prove each statement.

17. Given: $\triangle ABC$ is scalene.
$\overline{BD}$ is the bisector of $\angle ABC$.

Prove: $\overline{BD}$ is *not* $\perp$ to $\overline{AC}$.

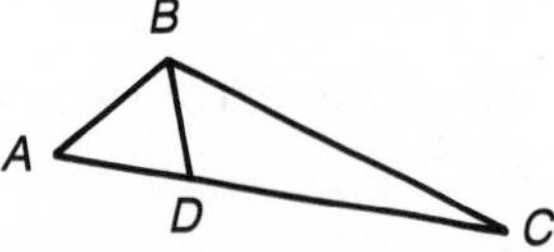

18. Given: $\overline{YW}$ bisects $\angle XYZ$.
$\overline{YW}$ is *not* a median.

Prove: $\overline{XY} \ncong \overline{ZY}$

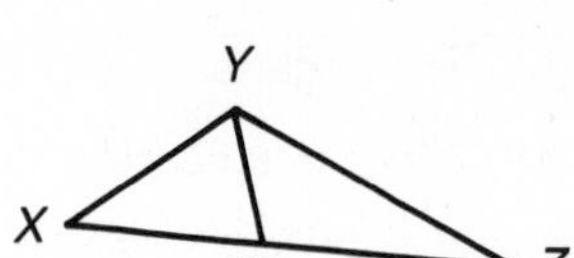

C. 19. Given: $\triangle ABC$ is scalene.
$\overline{AD}$ bisects $\angle BAC$.
$\overline{CD}$ bisects $\angle BCA$.

Prove: $\overline{AD} \ncong \overline{CD}$

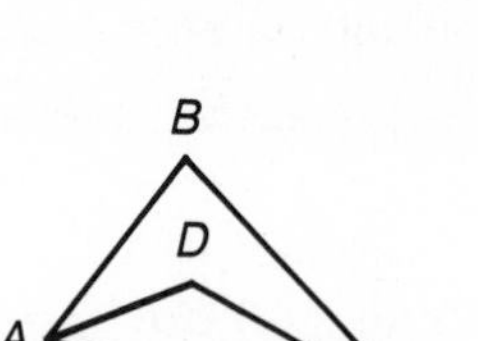

20. Given: $\overline{XY}$ bisects $\angle X$.

Prove: $\overline{XY}$ is the one and only one bisector of $\angle X$.

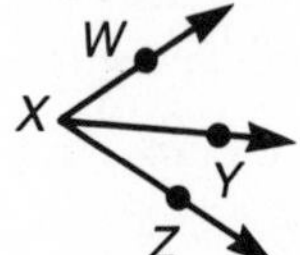

17. See *Teacher's Manual*, p. T59
18. See *Selected Answers*, p. 628
19. See *Teacher's Manual*, p. T59
20. See *Selected Answers*, p. 629

5.2 Indirect Proof

Indirect proofs are a powerful deductive tool. Certain theorems that seem obviously true are difficult to establish in a direct proof. Using the *contrapositive* in an indirect proof often overcomes this difficulty.

In Chapter 3, the definitions of *right angle* and *perpendicular lines* were introduced. If you choose a point on a line in a plane, you can draw a second line perpendicular to the first at that point.

REVIEW: THEOREM 2.2
If a given line intersects a plane not containing it, then their intersection is a single point.

Given: Line l in plane E, with P a point on l

Prove: There exists a unique line $\overleftrightarrow{PY} \perp$ to l at P.

Existence: Prove there *is* one line perpendicular to the given line at the given point.

Uniqueness: Prove there is *only* one line perpendicular to the given line at the given point.

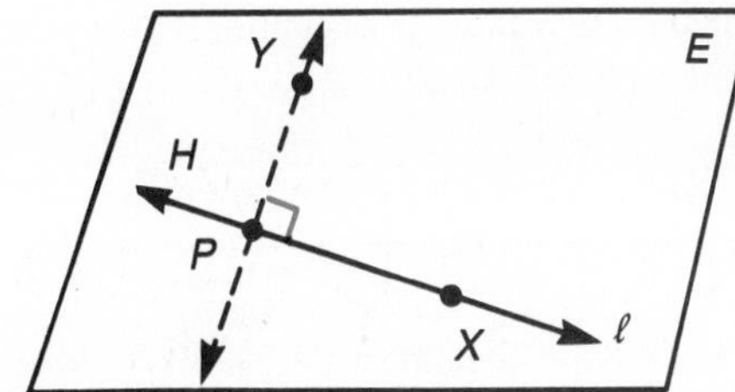

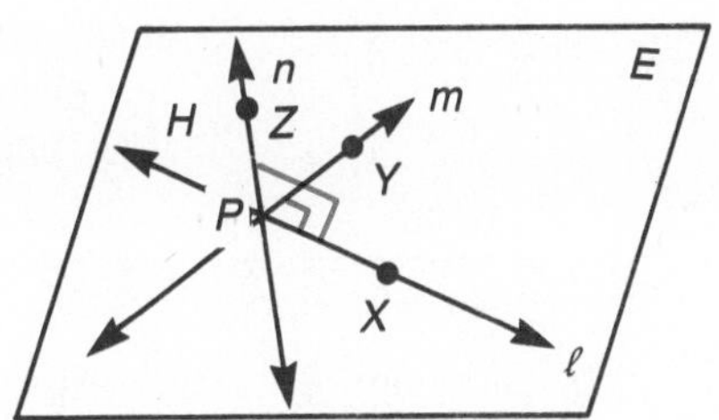

Existence proof:

STATEMENTS	REASONS
1. P on line l in plane E	1. Given
2. H is one of the half-planes in E determined by l.	2. Plane Separation Postulate
3. X is another point of l.	3. Ruler Postulate
4. $\overrightarrow{PY}$ lies in H so that $m\angle YPX = 90$.	4. Angle Construction Postulate
5. P and Y determine $\overleftrightarrow{PY}$.	5. Given any 2 different points, there is exactly 1 line that contains both of them (Postulate 1).
6. $\overleftrightarrow{PY} \perp l$	6. Definition of $\perp$

OBJECTIVE

Identify a perpendicular bisector and use its definition, theorems, and corollaries in proofs.

TEACHER'S NOTES

See p. T28

MIXED REVIEW

1. Can a line be bisected? no
2. What is the converse of $A \rightarrow B$? $B \rightarrow A$
3. What is the contrapositive of $P \rightarrow Q$? $\sim Q \rightarrow \sim P$
4. Add $\frac{x}{x-3} + \frac{3}{x-2}$. $\frac{x^2 + x - 9}{(x-3)(x-2)}$
5. Solve $2x + y = 7$, $3x + 2y = 13$ (1, 5)

TEACHER'S RESOURCE MASTERS

Practice Master 14, Part 1

Uniqueness Proof:

STATEMENTS	REASONS
7. Let lines m and n be $\perp$ to l at P in E, with point Z on n and point Y on m.	7. Indirect assumption
8. $\angle ZPX$ and $\angle YPX$ are rt. $\angle$s	8. Definition of $\perp$
9. $m\angle ZPX = 90$, $m\angle YPX = 90$	9. Definition of rt. $\angle$
10. $\overrightarrow{PY}$ and $\overrightarrow{PZ}$ must be the same ray.	10. Angle Construction Postulate
11. Lines m and n are the same.	11. m and n have more than one point in common (Postulate 1).

Remember that uniqueness of the perpendicular line in this theorem holds for one plane. Without such a restriction, you could find an endless number of lines in space that are perpendiculars to a line at a point.

DEFINITION: perpendicular bisector
In a given plane, the **perpendicular bisector** of a segment is *the* line that is perpendicular to the segment at its midpoint.

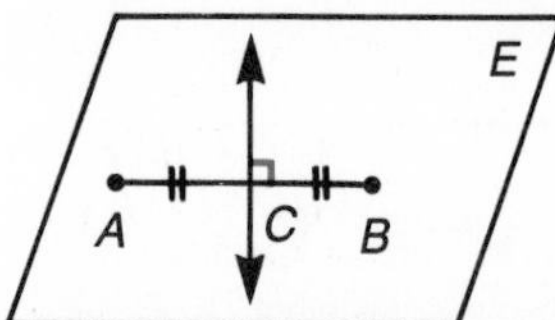

The existence and uniqueness of both the midpoint of a segment and the perpendicular to a line (or a segment) at a point in a plane guarantee the existence and the uniqueness of the perpendicular bisector.

DEFINITION: equidistant
Two points that are the same distance from a third point are **equidistant** from that point.

THEOREM 5.2 (The Perpendicular Bisector Theorem)
The perpendicular bisector of a segment *in a plane* is the set of all points of the plane that are equidistant from the endpoints of the segment.

The proof of Theorem 5.2 is also a two-part proof, although it is not as obvious as *if and only if, exactly one,* or *one and only one* proofs. When you characterize or describe something, you try to express its *special* qualities. The special quality of the perpendicular bisector is the property of being equidistant from the endpoints of a segment. So, in this theorem, the proof must first establish that *every* point on the perpendicular bisector is equidistant from the endpoints of the segment. But since the theorem describes the perpendicular bisector as the set of *all* such points, the second part of the proof must establish that any point equidistant from the endpoints of the segment lies on the perpendicular bisector. This set of points is called a **locus of points.**

Given: Line l is the $\perp$ bisector of AB at point C in plane E.

Prove: (1) If P is any point on l, then $PA = PB$, and
(2) if $QA = QB$ then Q is a point on l.

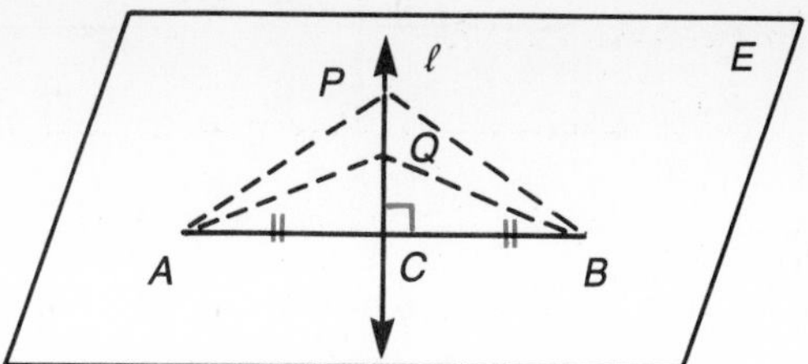

Proof:

Part 1 (Every point on l is equidistant from the endpoints of $\overline{AB}$.):

Let P be any point on l. Either P is the same point as C, or it is a different point on l. (a) If P is the same point as C, then $P = C$, and $PA = PB$ because C or P is the midpoint of $\overline{AB}$. (b) If P is not the same point as C, then $P \neq C$, and $\overline{PC} \cong \overline{PC}$ by the reflexive property, and $\overline{CA} \cong \overline{CB}$ from the definitions of midpoint and congruent segments. $\angle PCA$ and $\angle PCB$ are right angles from the perpendicular bisector. So, $\Delta PCA \cong \Delta PCB$ by SAS. Hence, $PA = PB$.

Part 2 (Any point equidistant from A and B lies on l.):

Let Q be any point in plane E such that $QA = QB$. Either Q is on $\overline{AB}$, or it is not. (a) If Q is on $\overline{AB}$, then Q and C are the same point and $Q = C$ because a line segment has exactly one midpoint. Since C is on l (definition of perpendicular bisector), Q must be on l. (b) If Q is not on $\overline{AB}$, draw the line determined by Q and C. Then, $\overline{QC} \cong \overline{QC}$, $\overline{CA} \cong \overline{CB}$, and $\overline{QA} \cong \overline{QB}$. By SSS, $\Delta QCA \cong \Delta QCB$. Thus, $\angle QCA$ and $\angle QCB$ form a linear pair of congruent angles. Hence, they are right angles. $QC \perp \overline{AB}$. But, by Theorem 5.1, perpendiculars in a plane at a point are unique. So, $\overleftrightarrow{QC}$ and l must be the same line. Therefore, Q is a point of l.

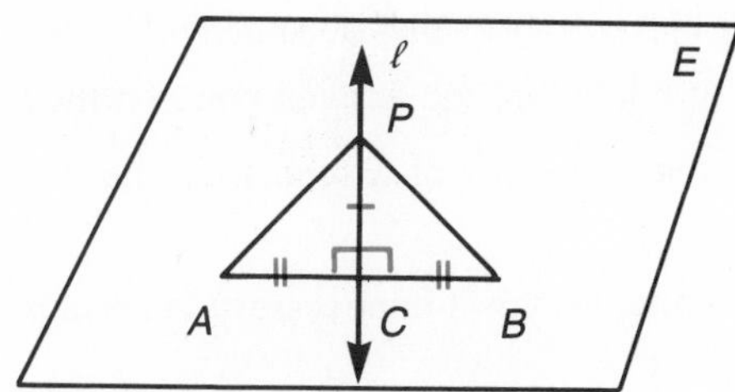

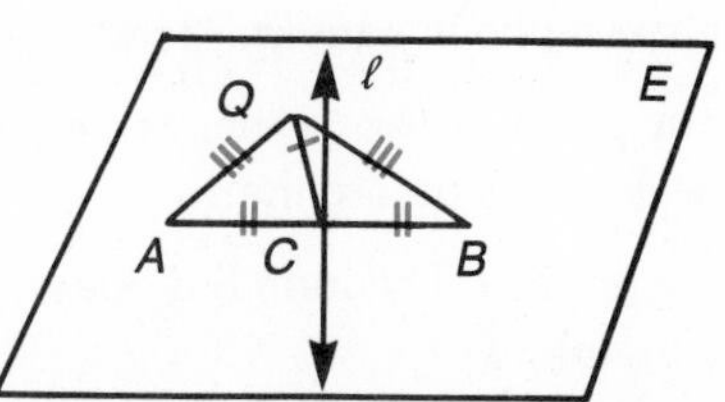

COROLLARY 5.2.1
Given a segment $\overline{AB}$ and a line l in a plane, if two points of l are equidistant from A and B, then l is the perpendicular bisector $\overline{AB}$.

The proof of this theorem is left as an exercise.

The next logical step in the deductive process is to establish theorems about a perpendicular to a line through a point *off* the line.

$\overline{QC} \cong \overline{QC}$, Reflexive
$\overline{CA} \cong \overline{CB}$, Definition of midpoint
$\overline{QA} \cong \overline{QB}$, Given

Proof of Theorem 5.3

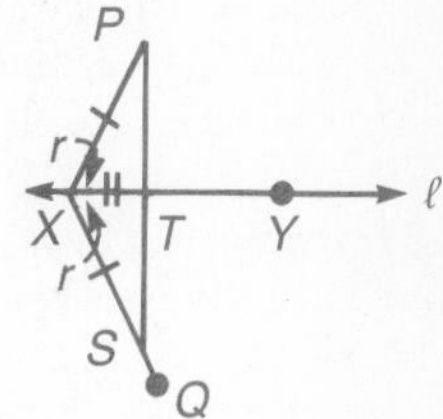

Given: Line l and a point P not on l

Prove: There exists a unique line perpendicular to l through P.

Proof:

Existence (There is *at least* one line perpendicular to l through P): Let X and Y be any two points on l such that $m\angle PXY = r$. Then by the Angle Construction Postulate, a point Q may be chosen in the opposite half-plane from P such that $m\angle QXY = r$. Therefore, $\angle PXY \cong \angle QXY$. Now if $XP = a$, then by the Ruler Postulate, a point S on $\overline{XQ}$ may be found in the same half-plane as Q such that $XS = a$, and $\overline{XP} \cong \overline{XS}$. Finally, let the line determined by P and S intersect l at T. Then $\overline{XT} \cong \overline{XT}$ and by SAS, $\Delta PXT \cong \Delta SXT$. This means that the corresponding angles PTX and STX are congruent *and* supplementary and are therefore right angles. So $\overline{PS}$ is perpendicular to l.

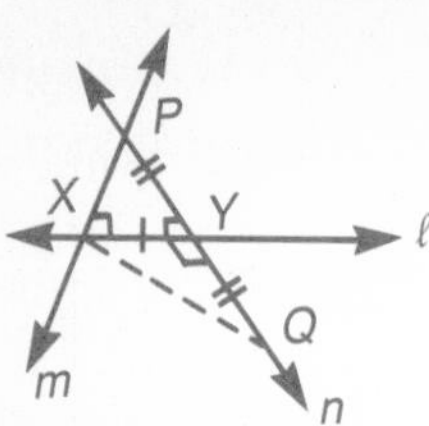

Uniqueness (There is *at most* one line perpendicular to l through P): By indirect assumption, suppose k and n are two lines perpendicular to l at X and Y, respectively. A point Q may then be found on n such that $\overline{PY} \cong \overline{QY}$ (the Point Plotting Theorem), and by Theorem 3.8, $\angle XYQ$ is a right angle. So, by Theorem 3.3, $\angle PXY \cong \angle QYX$. Now $\overline{XY} \cong \overline{XY}$, so $\Delta PYX \cong \Delta QYX$ by SAS. Corresponding angles PXY and QXY are therefore congruent and, because $\angle PXY$ is a right angle, $\angle QXY$ must also be a right angle. Thus $\overline{QX} \perp l$. This contradicts Theorem 5.1, because the proof shows that both k and $\overline{QX}$ are perpendicular to l at X. Therefore, the indirect assumption that there are two perpendiculars to l through P must be false.

ASSIGNMENT GUIDE

Minimum 1-13
Regular 1-17 odd
Maximum 1-17

Oral Exercises

1. 1
2. an endless number
3. the perpendicular bisector of the segment

THEOREM 5.3
Given a line and an external point, there is one and only one line perpendicular to the given line through the given point.

Theorem 5.3 must also be proved in two parts; both existence and uniqueness must be shown.

COROLLARY 5.3.1
At most one angle of a triangle can be a right angle.

The proof of this corollary is a good example of the occasional limitations of a direct proof. From the given, you can deduce three angles and three sides, but not much else. With an indirect proof, the result follows immediately.

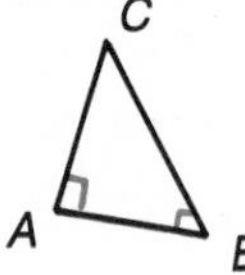

Given: ΔABC

Prove: Only one of $\angle A$, $\angle B$, or $\angle C$ may be a right angle.

Proof: Let $\angle A$ and $\angle B$ be right angles. Hence, there are two lines perpendicular to $\overline{AB}$ through point C. This contradicts Theorem 5.3. So, the assumption is false and $\angle A$ and $\angle B$ cannot both be right angles.

ORAL EXERCISES

1. In a plane, how many perpendiculars are there to a line through a given point on the line?
2. In space, how many perpendiculars are there to a line through a given point on the line?
3. In a plane, if two points are equidistant from the endpoints of a segment, what line do those points determine?
4. The proof of Theorem 5.3 does not mention a plane. Why is it unnecessary to use a plane in the proof?
5. Without using congruent triangles, show that the median to the base of an isosceles triangle is the same as the perpendicular bisector of the base.

In the figure at the right, l is the perpendicular bisector of $\overline{AB}$. $PA = 5$, $QB = 3$, $AM = 2$, $RA = 3x + 2$, and $RB = x + 12$.

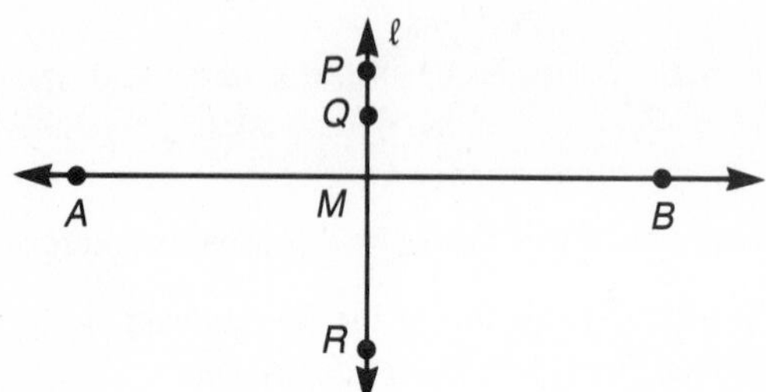

6. Find PB.
7. Find QA.
8. Find RA.
9. Find RB.

WRITTEN EXERCISES

A. For each of the implications in Exercises 1–3 write the given and an indirect assumption that could be used in a proof.

1. If ΔABC has no congruent angles, then it is not an isosceles triangle.
2. If ΔABC is scalene, then median $\overline{AD}$ is not the perpendicular bisector of $\overline{BC}$.
3. If lines m and n intersect, then their intersection is only one point.

B. Give all the possible correct answers for Exercises 4–8

4. Which terms imply both existence and uniqueness?
   a. more than one **b.** exactly one **c.** if and only if **d.** one and only one
5. All points on the perpendicular bisector of a segment are
   a. equidistant from the endpoints. **b.** the same distance from the midpoint.
   c. in the same plane as the segment. **d.** equidistant from the midpoint.
6. A "uniqueness" proof usually uses the
   a. direct approach. **b.** indirect approach. **c.** contrapositive. **d.** converse.
7. A right triangle has
   a. one hypotenuse. **b.** more than one hypotenuse. **c.** one leg. **d.** two legs.
8. The legs of a right triangle that is also isosceles are
   a. perpendicular. **b.** congruent. **c.** converse. **d.** inverse.

Tell whether each statement in Exercises 9–12 is *always, sometimes,* or *never* true.

9. The perpendicular bisector of a line intersects the line at its midpoint.
10. The perpendicular to a line from an external point is unique.
11. If a theorem cannot be proved with a direct approach, it can be proved with an indirect approach.
12. To prove a theorem indirectly, you assume the given information is false.
13. Refer to the figure at the right to prove Corollary 5.2.1.

Given: Line l and $\overline{AB}$ lie in plane E, points P and Q lie on l, $\overline{PA} \cong \overline{PB}$, $\overline{QA} \cong \overline{QB}$

Prove: l is the perpendicular bisector of $\overline{AB}$.

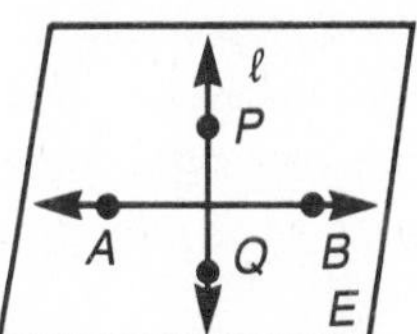

4. The given conditions determine a plane by Theorem 2.3.
5. The median contains the midpoint of the base; the other endpoint is equidistant from the endpoints of the base because the triangle is isosceles; then apply Corollary 5.2.1.

6. 5 7. 3
8. 17 9. 17

Written Exercises

1. $\angle A \ncong \angle B \ncong \angle C$, Given; Suppose ΔABC is isosceles, Indirect assumption.
2. ΔABC is scalene, $\overline{AD}$ is a median, Given; $\overline{AD}$ is $\perp$ bisector of $\overline{BC}$, Indirect assumption.
3. m intersects n, Given; m intersects n at points X and Y, Indirect assumption.
4. b, d 5. a, c
6. b, c 7. a, d
8. a, b
9. never 10. always
11. sometimes 12. never
13. *1.* $\overleftrightarrow{AB}$, l lie in plane E P, Q lie on l. $\overline{PA} \cong \overline{PB}$, $\overline{QA} \cong \overline{QB}$ (Given)
    2. $\overleftrightarrow{PQ}$ is $\perp$ bisector of $\overline{AB}$ (Theorem 5.2).
    3. $\overleftrightarrow{PQ}$ and l are the same line (Postulate 1).
    4. l must be the perpendicular bisector of $\overline{AB}$ (Steps *2* and *3*).

14. 1. $\angle BAC \cong \angle BCA$, $\angle DAC \cong \angle DCA$ (Given); 2. $\overline{AB} \cong \overline{CB}$, $\overline{AD} \cong \overline{CD}$ (Theorem 4.4); 3. $AB = CB$, $AD = CD$ (Def. of $\cong$ segments); 4. B is equidistant from A, C and D is equidistant from A, C (Def. of equidistant); 5. $\overleftrightarrow{BD}$ is the $\perp$ bisector of $\overline{AC}$ (Corollary 5.2.1); 6. $\overleftrightarrow{BD}$ intersects $\overline{AC}$ at point E (Theorem 2.1); 7. E is midpoint of $\overline{AC}$ (Def. of $\perp$ bisector).

15. See *Teacher's Manual*, p. T59

16. 1. Quadrilateral $ABCD$, $\angle 1 \cong \angle 2$, $\angle 3 \cong \angle 4$ (Given); 2. $\overline{AC} \cong \overline{AC}$ (Congruence of segments is reflex); 3. $\triangle ABC \cong \triangle ADC$ (Steps 1, 2, and ASA); 4. $\overline{AB} \cong \overline{AD}$, $\overline{CB} \cong \overline{CD}$ (Corres. parts of $\cong$ $\triangle$s are $\cong$); 5. $AB = AD$, $CB = CD$ (Def. of $\cong$ segments); 6. A, C equidistant from B and D (Def. of equidistant); 7. $\overline{AC}$ $\perp$ bisector of $\overline{BD}$ (Corollary 5.2.1).

17. See *Teacher's Manual*, p. T59

14. Given: $\angle BAC \cong \angle BCA$, $\angle DAC \cong \angle DCA$

Prove: E is the midpoint of $\overline{AC}$.

NOTE: Do not use congruent triangles.

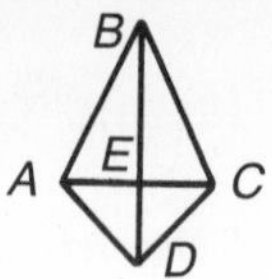

C. 15. Use an indirect method to prove the following.

Given: $\triangle ABC$ is scalene. $\overline{AD}$ is the angle bisector of $\angle BAC$.

Prove: $\overline{AD}$ is not perpendicular to $\overline{BC}$.

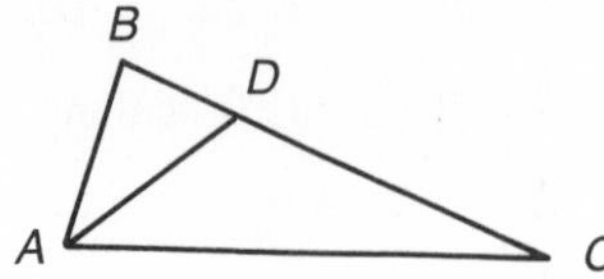

16. Given: Quadrilateral $ABCD$
$\angle 1 \cong \angle 2$, $\angle 3 \cong \angle 4$

Prove: $\overline{AC}$ is the perpendicular bisector of $\overline{BD}$.

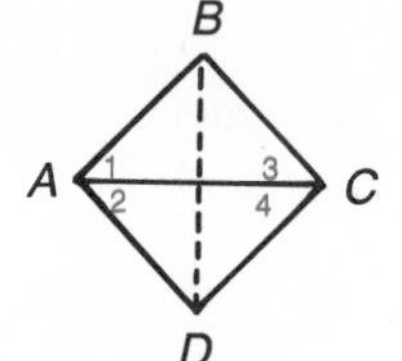

17. Use an indirect method to prove the following: In an isosceles triangle that is not equilateral, the bisector of a base angle is not perpendicular to the side opposite.

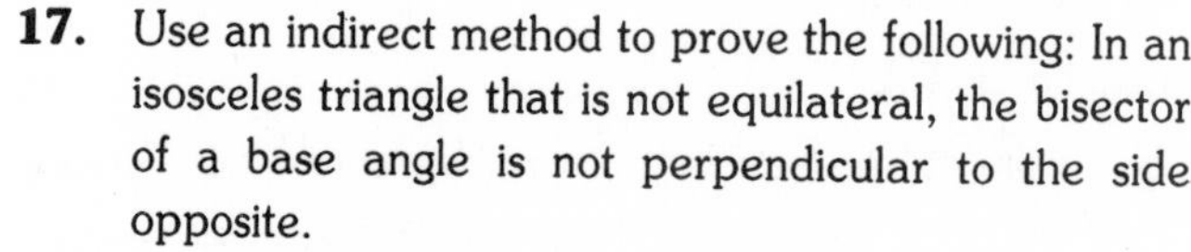

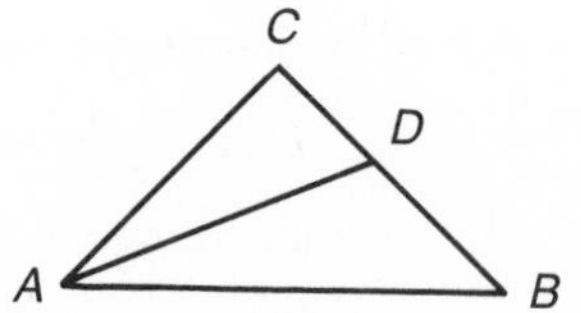

MATH HERITAGE/Right Triangles

Right angles are believed to have been used in construction long before they were formally identified. The pyramid builders of Egypt may have used a rope divided by eleven knots into twelve equal parts to form triangles with sides of 3, 4, and 5 units in length. When the rope was tied together, pulled taut, and pinned at the appropriate points, a triangle was formed with a "squared" angle at one vertex.

The question arose whether a "squared" triangle could be formed with sides of other measures, and mathematicians sought a general relationship among the sides of a right triangle. During his travels in Egypt, the Greek mathematician Pythagoras may have received instruction in the mysteries of the right triangle, allowing him to develop a famous theorem.

5.3 Indirect Proof and Triangle Relationships

The definition of a right triangle is a simple but important definition. Right angles, and by extension right triangles, provide the basis for many applications of mathematics to the real world. They are the foundation of trigonometry and such fields as astronomy, surveying, and architecture.

The idea that a right triangle exists depends on an indirect proof, as demonstrated in the previous section. Techniques of indirect proof provide a powerful tool for establishing theorems. The key is knowing when to use this tool. As you have seen, most *one and only one* proofs use an indirect approach. Indirect proof is also useful when the given information is sparse (as in Corollary 5.3.1) or when you are trying to show that something is different from something else, as in the following example:

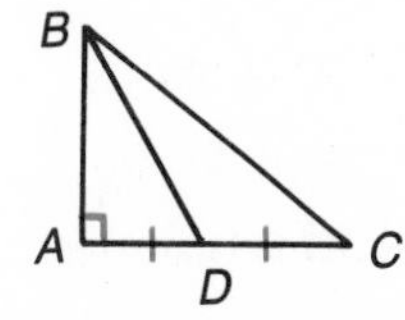

Given: Right ΔABC; $\angle A$ is a right $\angle$.

Prove: The median to leg $\overline{AC}$ is different from the $\perp$ bisector of $\overline{AC}$.

Proof:

STATEMENTS	REASONS
1. In ΔABC, $\overline{BD}$ is the median to $\overline{AC}$.	1. Given
2. Let $\overline{BD}$ be the $\perp$ bisector of $\overline{AC}$.	2. Indirect assumption
3. $\angle BDA$ is a right $\angle$.	3. Definition of $\perp$
4. $\angle A$ is a right $\angle$.	4. Given

Contradiction: Corollary 5.3.1 states that at most one angle of a triangle (ΔABD) can be a right angle. So, the assumption is false, and the median and perpendicular bisector of $\overline{AC}$ are different line segments.

The figure for the proof above suggests that $\overline{BD}$ is not the perpendicular bisector of $\overline{AC}$. It certainly doesn't *look* perpendicular. But because figures are only models, you must be careful not to base firm conclusions on "looks." Naming $\overline{BD}$ the perpendicular bisector of $\overline{AC}$ contradicts Theorem 5.3, which states that there is one and only one line perpendicular to $\overline{AC}$ through point B. That unique line is already given as $\overleftrightarrow{AB}$, because ΔABC is a right triangle.

Although there are times when neither a direct nor indirect approach will prove a statement or theorem, often you will find that both methods apply. The following statement, for example, can be proved by both direct and indirect methods: *If the median to the hypotenuse of a right triangle is perpendicular to the hypotenuse, then the right triangle is isosceles.*

OBJECTIVE

Supply reasons in direct and indirect proofs involving perpendicular bisectors.

TEACHER'S NOTES

See p. T29

MIXED REVIEW

1. Simplify $\frac{x^2 + 2x + 1}{x + 1}$. $x + 1$
2. Solve $x^2 - 9 = 0$. $\{3, -3\}$
3. Solve $4x - 3(x + 5) = 6 - 2x$. $x = 7$
4. Solve $2x - y = 1$, $x + 2y = 13$. $(3, 5)$
5. Multiply $(4x - 1)(3x + 2)$. $12x^2 + 5x - 2$

TEACHER'S RESOURCE MASTERS

Practice Master 14, Part 2
Quiz 9

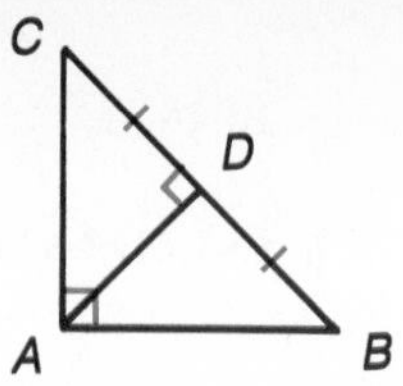

Given: Right $\triangle ABC$, as shown, with median $\overline{AD} \perp \overline{BC}$

Prove: $\triangle ABC$ is isosceles.

Direct proof:

STATEMENTS	REASONS
1. In right $\triangle ABC$, $\angle A$ is a right angle and median $\overline{AD} \perp \overline{BC}$.	1. Given
2. $\angle ADC$ and $\angle ADB$ are right $\angle$s.	2. Definition of $\perp$
3. $\triangle ADC$ and $\triangle ADB$ are right $\triangle$s.	3. Definition of right $\triangle$
4. $\overline{AD} \cong \overline{AD}$	4. Congruence of segments is reflexive.
5. $DC = DB$	5. Definition of median
6. $\overline{DC} \cong \overline{DB}$	6. Definition of $\cong$ segments
7. $\triangle ADC \cong \triangle ADB$	7. Steps 4, 6, and LL
8. $\overline{AC} \cong \overline{AB}$	8. Corres. parts of $\cong$ $\triangle$s are $\cong$.
9. $\triangle ABC$ is isosceles.	9. Definition of isosceles $\triangle$

Indirect proof:

STATEMENTS	REASONS
1. In right $\triangle ABC$, $\angle A$ is a right angle and median $\overline{AD} \perp \overline{BC}$.	1. Given
2. Assume $\triangle ABC$ is not isosceles.	2. Indirect assumption
3. $\overline{AB} \ncong \overline{AC}$	3. Definition of isosceles $\triangle$
4. $\overline{AD}$ is the $\perp$ bisector of $\overline{BC}$.	4. Step 1 and definition of $\perp$ bisector
5. A is equidistant from B and C.	5. The $\perp$ bisector of a segment in a plane is the set of all points equidistant from the endpoints of the segment (Theorem 5.2).
6. $AB = AC$	6. Definition of equidistant
7. $\overline{AB} \cong \overline{AC}$	7. Definition of $\cong$ segments

The last statement is a contradiction of Statement 3 if the assumption is true; therefore the assumption that $\triangle ABC$ is not isosceles must be false.

Opinions may differ on which proof is better. Sometimes finding the most logical proof may require that you try more than one method. Just remember that the most important discoveries in history have resulted from trial and error. It is the willingness to try another approach when the first have failed that often leads to success.

ORAL EXERCISES

State the indirect assumption you would use to prove each of the following:

1. If the temperature outside is freezing, there will be frost on the window.
2. If the lamp won't turn on, then the light bulb is burned out.
3. A right triangle has at least one acute angle.
4. Two lines intersect in no more than one point.
5. Zero has no reciprocal.

Describe a triangle in which the perpendicular bisectors of the sides intersect in

6. a point outside the triangle.
7. a point on the triangle.
8. a point inside the triangle.

WRITTEN EXERCISES

A. Supply the reasons for the following indirect proof.

Given: Scalene ΔABC
$\overline{BD} \perp \overline{AC}$

Prove: D is not the midpoint of $\overline{AC}$.

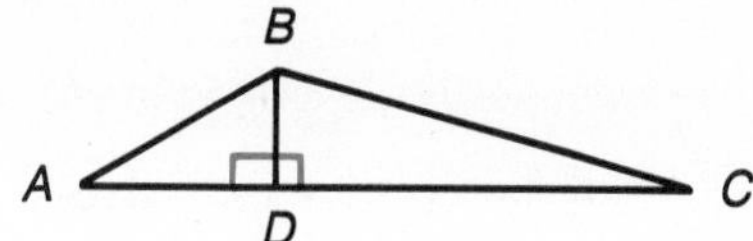

Proof:

STATEMENTS	REASONS
1. Scalene ΔABC, $\overline{BD} \perp \overline{AC}$	1. **1.**
2. D is the midpoint of $\overline{AC}$.	2. **2.**
3. $AD = CD$	3. **3.**
4. $\overline{AD} \cong \overline{CD}$	4. **4.**
5. $\angle BDA$ and $\angle BDC$ are right $\angle$s.	5. **5.**
6. $\angle BDA \cong \angle BDC$	6. **6.**
7. $\overline{BD} \cong \overline{BD}$	7. **7.**
8. $\Delta ABD \cong \Delta CBD$	8. **8.**
9. $\overline{AB} \cong \overline{CB}$	9. **9.**
10. ΔABC is isosceles.	10. **10.**

Contradiction: ΔABC is **11.** , so D is not the midpoint of $\overline{AC}$.

ASSIGNMENT GUIDE

Minimum 1-18
Regular 1-19
Maximum 1-22

Oral Exercises

1. There is no frost on the window.
2. The light bulb is not burned out.
3. A triangle has at most one acute angle.
4. Two lines intersect in more than one point.
5. Zero has a reciprocal.
6. obtuse triangles
7. right triangles
8. acute triangles

Written Exercises

1. Given
2. Indirect assumption
3. Def. of midpoint
4. Def. of $\cong$ segments
5. Def. of $\perp$
6. All rt. $\angle$s are $\cong$.
7. Congruence of segments is reflex.
8. SAS (Post. 15)
9. Corres. parts of $\cong$ Δs are $\cong$.
10. Def. of isosceles Δ
11. scalene

B. Supply the missing statements and reasons in the following indirect proof.

Given: In $\triangle ABC$, $\overleftrightarrow{DP}$, $\overleftrightarrow{EP}$, and $\overleftrightarrow{FP}$ are $\perp$ bisectors of $\overline{AB}$, $\overline{BC}$, and $\overline{AC}$, intersecting at P.

Prove: $PA = PB = PC$

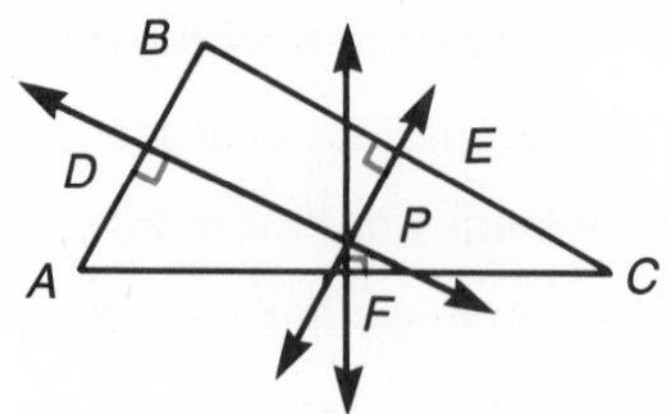

Indirect Proof:

STATEMENTS	REASONS
1. $\overleftrightarrow{DP}$ is the $\perp$ bisector of $\overline{AB}$. $\overleftrightarrow{FP}$ is the $\perp$ bisector of $\overline{AC}$.	1. **12.**
2. **13.**	2. Indirect assumption
3. P is not equidistant from A and B.	3. **14.**
4. **15.**	4. Definition of equidistant
5. P is not on the $\perp$ bisector of $\overline{AB}$. P is not on the $\perp$ bisector of $\overline{AC}$.	5. **16.**

Contradiction of given; therefore, **17.** .

18. Write a two-column, direct proof of the exercise above, using congruent triangles.

C. 19. Prove directly.

Given: Isosceles right $\triangle RST$, with $\overline{RY}$ the median to hypotenuse $\overline{ST}$

Prove: $\overline{RY} \perp \overline{ST}$

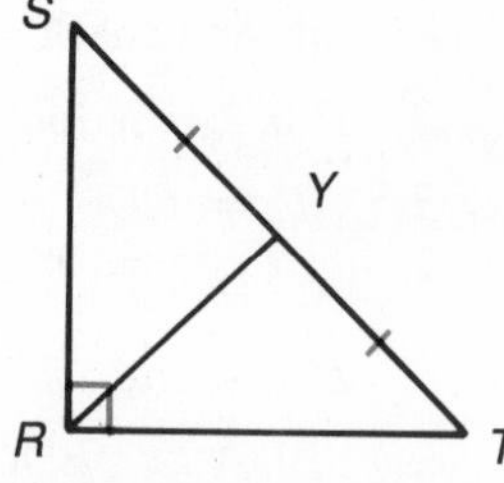

20. Prove Exercise 19 indirectly.

21. If one diagonal of a quadrilateral bisects two angles of the quadrilateral, prove that it bisects the other diagonal as well, using a direct proof.

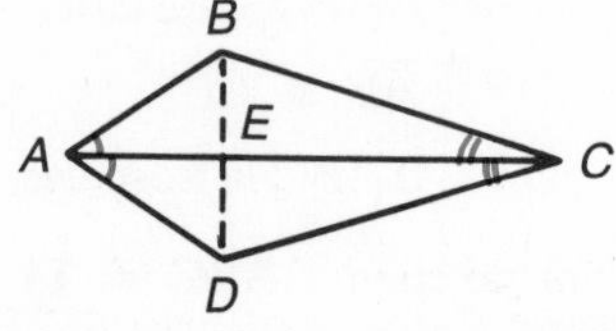

22. Prove Exercise 21 indirectly.

12. Given
13. $PA \neq PB \neq PC$
14. Definition of equidistant
15. P is not equidistant from A and C.
16. Theorem 5.2
17. $PA = PB = PC$

18. *1.* $\overline{DP}$ is the $\perp$ bisector of $\overline{AB}$ (Given); *2.* $AD = BD$ (Def. of bisector); *3.* $\overline{AD} \cong \overline{BD}$ (Def. of $\cong$ segments); *4.* $\angle BDP$ and $\angle ADP$ are rt. $\angle$s (Def. of $\perp$); *5.* $\angle BDP \cong \angle ADP$ (All rt. $\angle$s are $\cong$); *6.* $\overline{DP} = \overline{DP}$ (Congruence of segments is reflex.); *7.* $\triangle APD \cong \triangle BPD$ (SAS); *8.* $\overline{AP} \cong \overline{BP}$ (Corres. parts of $\cong$ $\triangle$s are $\cong$); *9.* $AP = BP$ (Def. of $\cong$ segments); *10.* $\overleftrightarrow{FP}$ is $\perp$ bisector of $\overline{AC}$ (Given); *11.* $\triangle APF \cong \triangle CPF$ (SAS); *12.* $\overline{AP} \cong \overline{CP}$ (Corres. parts of $\cong$ $\triangle$s are $\cong$; *13.* $AP = CP$ (Def. of $\cong$ segments); *14.* $AP = BP = CP$ (Congruence of segments is transitive).

19. See *Teacher's Manual*, p. T59

20. See *Selected Answers*, p. 628

21. See *Teacher's Manual*, p. T60

22. See *Selected Answers*, p. 629

SELF-QUIZ

Fill in the blanks for Exercises 1–6.

1. A conditional statement and its _____ are logically equivalent.

2. The inverse of a conditional statement $p \rightarrow q$ is expressed as _____.

3. The negation of "ΔABC is scalene" is _____.

4. "One and only one" means the same as _____ one.

5. "If and only if" combines a conditional statement and its _____.

6. A proof of _____ establishes that a certain geometric figure is possible.

7. State at least three conclusions you can deduce from the figure, given that $\overline{BD}$ is the perpendicular bisector of $\overline{AC}$.

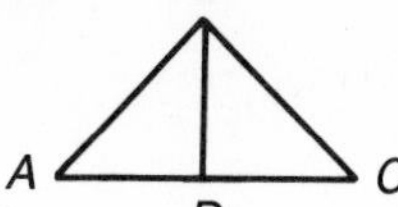

EXPLORATION/Conjunctions

Another term used in logic is the conjunction "and," denoted by "$\wedge$." The sentence $p \wedge q$ is true only when p and q are both true. Knowing this, complete the truth table below to determine whether the relationship "if—then" (denoted by "$\rightarrow$") is transitive. In other words, show "If $p \rightarrow q$ and $q \rightarrow r$, then $p \rightarrow r$" or $[(p \rightarrow q) \wedge (q \rightarrow r)] \rightarrow (p \rightarrow r)$. Note that the table has eight possible outcomes. Why?

p	q	r		$p \rightarrow q$	$q \rightarrow r$	$(p \rightarrow q) \wedge (q \rightarrow r)$	$p \rightarrow r$	$[(p \rightarrow q) \wedge (q \rightarrow r)] \rightarrow (p \rightarrow r)$
T	T	T		T	T	T	T	T
T	T	F		T	F	F	F	T
T	F	T	**1.**	___	___	___	___	___
T	F	F	**2.**	___	___	___	___	___
F	T	T	**3.**	___	___	___	___	___
F	T	F	**4.**	___	___	___	___	___
F	F	T	**5.**	___	___	___	___	___
F	F	F	**6.**	___	___	___	___	___

Self-Quiz

1. contrapositive
2. $\sim p \rightarrow \sim q$
3. ΔABC is not scalene.
4. exactly
5. converse
6. existence
7. $AC = CD$, $AB = CB$, $BD \perp AC$, $m\angle BDA = m\angle BDC = 90$, $\angle A \cong \angle C$, $\angle ABD \cong \angle CBD$.

Exploration

There are eight outcomes because you are considering all the true and false combinations of three statements, p, q, and r.

1. F, T, F, T, T
2. F, T, F, F, T
3. T, T, T, T, T
4. T, F, F, T, T
5. T, T, T, T, T
6. T, T, T, T, T

The last column shows that "$\rightarrow$" is transitive in all cases.

OBJECTIVE

Justify the use of auxiliary sets.

TEACHER'S NOTES

See p. T29

MIXED REVIEW

1. If B lies between A and C then ______. $AB + BC = AC$
2. If $PQ = 12$, $QR = 3$ and $PR = 9$ then ______. R lies between P and Q
3. Does the edge belong to the half-plane? no
4. Add $\frac{2x}{3y} + \frac{5x}{4y}$. $\frac{23x}{12y}$
5. Factor $6x^2 + 7x - 5$. $(3x + 5)(2x - 1)$

TEACHER'S RESOURCE MASTERS

Practice Master 15, Part 1

5.4 Auxiliary Sets

In a thought process called **closure,** the human brain automatically completes a partially drawn picture seen by the eye. The figures at right look like a square and triangle even though they are not completed. This phenomenon occurs with other geometric drawings as well. In each of the figures below, you can perceive relationships beyond the original drawing.

Closure is helpful in establishing geometric relationships, as shown in the example below.

Given: Quadrilateral $ABCD$ in plane E
$\overline{AB} \cong \overline{AD}$, $\overline{BC} \cong \overline{DC}$

Prove: $\angle B \cong \angle D$

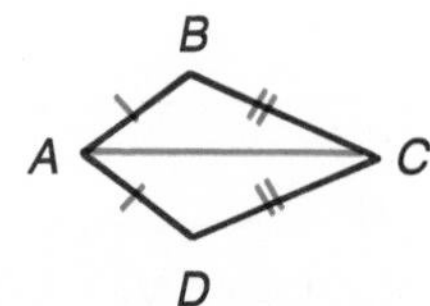

Proof: The given information does not seem to lead anywhere. An indirect proof, using the assumption that $\angle B \ncong \angle D$, leads nowhere. However, if you *close* the figure by drawing $\overline{AC}$, the proof follows easily. $\triangle ABC \cong \triangle ADC$ by SSS, and $\angle B \cong \angle D$ because corresponding parts of congruent triangles are congruent.

Is it "legal" to add a line segment in a deductive proof? The whole premise of deduction is that any step is permissible if it can be justified by an earlier theorem, postulate, or definition. Thus, you may add above "Let points A and C determine $\overleftrightarrow{AC}$," because Postulate 1 asserts that such a line exists and is unique. Such additions to diagrams are called **auxiliary sets.**

Any auxiliary set must satisfy two conditions: the set must logically exist, and it must be unique. For example, Thorem 1.5 says that every segment has *exactly* one midpoint. So, a unique midpoint exists on every segment in a given drawing, whether it is named or not.

How do you know *when* to use an auxiliary set and *which one* to use? An auxiliary set should be introduced only when necessary; there is no benefit in cluttering up a basic figure with irrelevant relationships. The first clue that an auxiliary set is needed is when it appears that you have insufficient information to prove a theorem. Another clue is when the given figure obviously needs to be closed. Deciding which auxiliary set would be helpful is often a trial and error process. Whatever looks plausible in the context of the problem is usually a good beginning. If one figure doesn't work, perhaps another will. Sometimes two different auxiliary sets will both work.

Look at the last problem using quadrilateral $ABCD$ with auxiliary set $\overleftrightarrow{BD}$ added, instead of $\overleftrightarrow{AC}$.

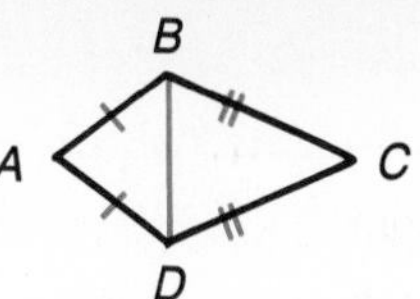

Given: Quadrilateral $ABCD$ in plane E
$\overline{AB} \cong \overline{AD}$, $\overline{BC} \cong \overline{DC}$

Prove: $\angle ABC \cong \angle ADC$

Proof:

STATEMENTS	REASONS
1. Quadrilateral $ABCD$ in plane E $\overline{AB} \cong \overline{AD}$, $\overline{BC} \cong \overline{DC}$	1. Given
2. Let B and D determine $\overleftrightarrow{BD}$.	2. Postulate 1
3. $\angle ABD \cong \angle ADB$; $\angle CBD \cong \angle CDB$	3. Isosceles Triangle Theorem
4. $m\angle ABD = m\angle ADB$; $m\angle CBD = m\angle CDB$	4. Definition of $\cong$ $\angle$s
5. $m\angle ABD + m\angle CBD = m\angle ADB + m\angle CBD$	5. Addition property of equality
6. $m\angle ABD + m\angle CBD = m\angle ADB + m\angle CDB$	6. Substitution
7. $m\angle ABD + m\angle CBD = m\angle ABC$ $m\angle ADB + m\angle CDB = m\angle ADC$	7. Angle Addition Postulate
8. $m\angle ABC = m\angle ADC$	8. Steps 6, 7, and substitution
9. $\angle ABC \cong \angle ADC$	9. Definition of $\cong$ $\angle$s

Although the first choice, $\overleftrightarrow{AC}$, leads to a shorter proof, both auxiliary sets provide easy solutions. An auxiliary set should serve only *one* purpose. Consider the following "theorem."

"THEOREM": The angle bisector of an angle of any triangle is the same segment as the median.

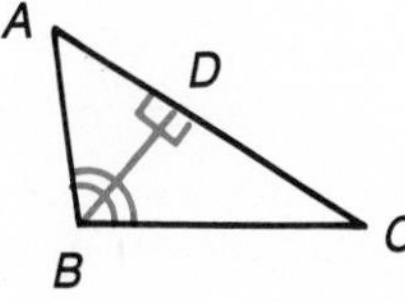

Given: In ΔABC, $\overline{BD}$ bisects $\angle ABC$.

Prove: $\overline{BD}$ is a median of ΔABC.

Proof: Let $\overline{BD}$ bisect $\angle ABC$ and be perpendicular to $\overline{AC}$. Then $\angle BDA \cong \angle BDC$ because all right angles are congruent, $\overline{BD} \cong \overline{BD}$, and $\angle ABD \cong \angle CBD$ by the definition of angle bisector. By ASA, $\Delta ABD \cong \Delta CBD$ and $AD = CD$. Therefore, D is the midpoint of $\overline{AC}$, which makes $\overline{BD}$ the median. This "theorem" cannot be true, so there must be an error in the proof. $\overline{BD}$ was drawn to serve two purposes; it was both the angle bisector of $\angle ABC$ and the perpendicular to $\overline{AC}$ from B. One auxiliary set cannot satisfy more than one characteristic.

For this "theorem," all that can be deduced is that $\overline{BD}$ is the angle bisector, and $\overline{BE} \perp \overline{AC}$. To prove the "theorem," you must show that D and E are the same point.

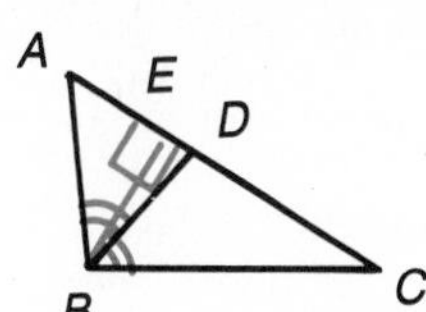

ASSIGNMENT GUIDE

Minimum 1-17
Regular 1-27
Maximum 14-26, 27-37 odd

Oral Exercises

1. Using $\overline{BD}$ in a new plane does not allow the Angle Addition Postulate. Using $\overline{AC}$ is allowed because you can have two $\cong$ Δs in two planes.
2. V is the midpoint of $\overline{XZ}$ and $\overline{YV} \perp \overline{XZ}$.
3. No, B and F determine $\overleftrightarrow{BF}$; there is no reason to assume $\perp$.
4. No, the angles are not vertical unless E is between A and C.
5. Yes, two distinct nonparallel lines intersect at a point.
6. No, there is insufficient information to draw this conclusion, even if $\overleftrightarrow{AC}$ is drawn.

Written Exercises

1. Theorem 1.5
2. Theorem 1.5
3. Postulate 1
4. Theorem 5.1
5. Theorem 5.1
6. Theorems 1.5 and 5.1
7. Theorem 5.3
8. Theorem 5.3
9. Postulate 7
10. Postulate 7
11. Theorem 4.6
12. Posts. 1, 2, and def. of segment

ORAL EXERCISES

1. Which of the two proofs about quadrilateral $ABCD$ in this lesson does not work if the points are not restricted to a single plane?

2. What two conditions have been placed on auxiliary set $\overline{YV}$ creating an error in the following "proof"? In any ΔXYZ, $\angle X \cong \angle Z$. Let V be the midpoint of $\overline{XZ}$ such that $\overline{YV} \perp \overline{XZ}$. Then $\angle XVY \cong \angle ZVY$ because both are right angles, $\overline{XV} \cong \overline{ZV}$, and $\overline{YV} \cong \overline{YV}$. So, $\Delta XYV \cong \Delta ZYV$ by SAS, and $\angle X \cong \angle Z$ because corresponding parts of congruent triangles are congruent.

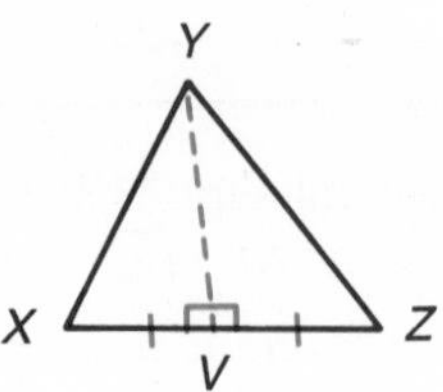

Use the figure at the right to explain why an auxiliary set can or cannot meet the conditions described in Exercises 3-6.

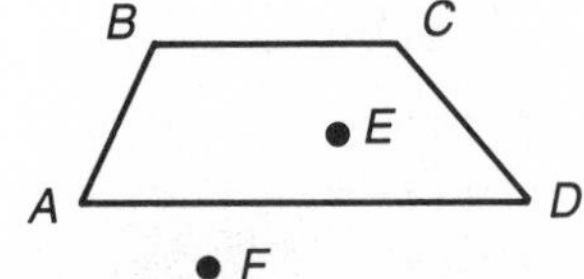

3. $\overline{BF} \perp \overline{AD}$

4. $\angle BEA \cong \angle CED$

5. $\overleftrightarrow{CE}$ intersects $\overleftrightarrow{AD}$ at G.

6. $\Delta ABC \cong \Delta DAC$

WRITTEN EXERCISES

A. Complete the following chart, which summarizes many of the acceptable justifications for the addition of auxiliary sets.

Geometric Set	Existence	Uniqueness
Point	Posts. 3 and 5	Theorems 1.4, 2.1, and 2.2
Midpoint	**1.**	**2.**
Line	Posts. 1 and 8	**3.**
Perpendicular at point on line, in plane	**4.**	**5.**
Perpendicular bisector, in plane	Theorems 1.5 and 5.1	**6.**
Perpendicular from external point	**7.**	**8.**
Plane	**9.**	**10.**
Ray, for angle measure	Post. 12	Post. 12
Bisector of an angle	**11.**	Theorem 4.6
Segment	Posts. 1, 2, and definition of segment	**12.**

B. Supply the missing statements and reasons for each proof.

Given: ΔABC and ΔEDC
$\overline{AB} \cong \overline{ED}$, $\overline{AD} \cong \overline{EB}$

Prove: $\angle A \cong \angle E$

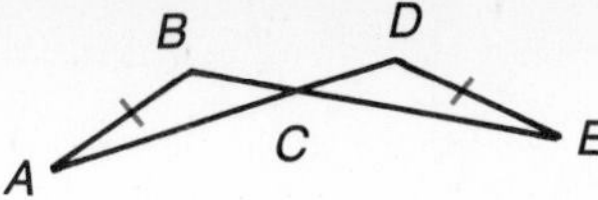

Proof:

STATEMENTS	REASONS
1. $\overline{AB} \cong \overline{ED}$, $\overline{AD} \cong \overline{EB}$	1. Given
2. **13.**	2. **14.**
3. $\overline{BD} \cong \overline{BD}$	3. **15.**
4. $\Delta ABD \cong \Delta EDB$	4. **16.**
5. $\angle A \cong \angle E$	5. **17.**

Given: Quadrilateral $ABCD$, M is the midpoint of $\overline{AB}$, $\overline{AD} \cong \overline{BC}$, $\angle A \cong \angle B$

Prove: $DM = CM$

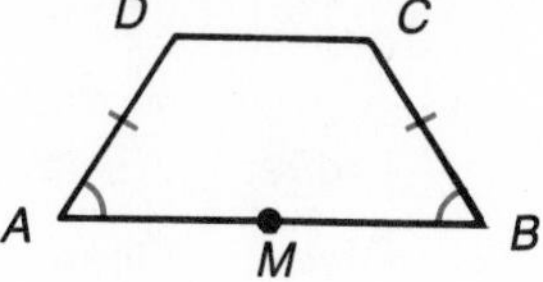

Proof:

STATEMENTS	REASONS
1. Quadrilateral $ABCD$, M is the midpoint of $\overline{AB}$, $\overline{AD} \cong \overline{BC}$, $\angle A \cong \angle B$	1. Given
2. Let D and M determine $\overleftrightarrow{DM}$. **18.**	2. **19.**
3. $AM = BM$	3. **20.**
4. **21.**	4. **22.**
5. $\Delta ADM \cong \Delta BCM$	5. **23.**
6. $\overline{DM} \cong \overline{CM}$	6. **24.**
7. **25.**	7. **26.**

27. Given: Figure $XYWZ$
$XY = XZ$, $YW = ZW$

Prove: $\angle Y \cong \angle Z$

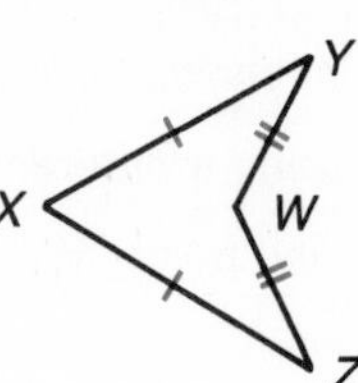

28. Given: Figure $ABCDE$
$\overline{AE} \cong \overline{BC}$, $\overline{ED} \cong \overline{CD}$
$\angle E \cong \angle C$.
G is the midpoint of $\overline{AB}$.

Prove: $\overline{DG}$ is $\perp$ bisector of AB.

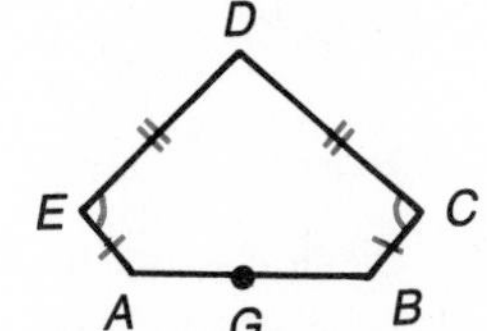

13. Let B and D determine $\overleftrightarrow{BD}$.
14. Postulate 1
15. $\cong$ of segments is reflexive.
16. SSS
17. Corres. parts of $\cong$ Δs are $\cong$.
18. Let C and M determine $\overleftrightarrow{CM}$.
19. Postulate 1
20. Def. of midpoint
21. $\overline{AM} \cong \overline{BM}$
22. Def. of $\cong$
23. SAS Post. 15
24. Corres. parts of $\cong$ Δs are $\cong$.
25. $DM = CM$
26. Definition of $\cong$
27. Givens; Let X and W determine $\overleftrightarrow{XW}$ by Post. 1; $\Delta XYW \cong \Delta XZW$ by SSS Theorem 4.5; $\angle Y \cong \angle Z$ by CPCTC.
28. Givens; Let D and A determine $\overleftrightarrow{DA}$, and let D and B determine $\overleftrightarrow{DB}$ by Post. 1; $\Delta DEA \cong \Delta DCB$ by SAS Post. 15; $\overline{DA} \cong \overline{DB}$ by CPCTC; D and G are equidistant from A and B by definition of equidistant; $\overline{DG}$ is $\perp$ bisector of $\overline{AB}$ by Theorem 5.2.

29. Givens; let B and D determine $\overleftrightarrow{BD}$ by Post. 1; $\angle ABD \cong \angle ADB$ by the Isosceles Triangle Theorem 4.3; $m\angle ABC = m\angle ABD + m\angle CBD$ and $m\angle ADC = m\angle ADB + m\angle CDB$ by Angle Addition Postulate (Post. 13); $m\angle CBD = m\angle CDB$ by subtraction property; $\overline{CB} \cong \overline{CD}$ by Theorem 4.4; $CB = CD$ by definition of congruence.

30. See *Selected Answers*, p. 529

31. Givens; Let A and Y determine $\overleftrightarrow{AY}$ and D and Z determine $\overleftrightarrow{DZ}$ by Post. 1; Let X be the intersection of $\overleftrightarrow{AY}$ and $\overleftrightarrow{DZ}$ by Thm 2.1; $\overline{AX} \cong \overline{DX}$ by Thm 4.4; $\angle 2 \cong \angle 3$ by Thm 3.5; $\angle XBC \cong \angle XCB$ by Thm 3.5; $BX = CX$ by Thm 4.4; $AB = CD$ by subtraction property of equality.

32. See *Selected Answers*, p. 630

33. Givens; Let A and D determine $\overline{AD}$ and B and C determine $\overline{BC}$ by Post. 1; $\Delta ADC \cong \Delta CBA$ by SAS; $\Delta ADF \cong \Delta CBE$ by SAS; $\overline{DF} = \overline{BE}$ by CPCTC; $\Delta CDF \cong \Delta ABE$ by SSS; $\angle CDF \cong \angle ABE$ by CPCTC.

34. See *Selected Answers*, p. 630

35. See *Teacher's Manual*, p. T60

36. See *Selected Answers*, p. 630

37. See *Teacher's Manual*, p. T60

29. Given: Quadrilateral $ABCD$ in plane E
$\overline{AB} \cong \overline{AD}$
$\angle B \cong \angle D$
Prove: $CB = CD$

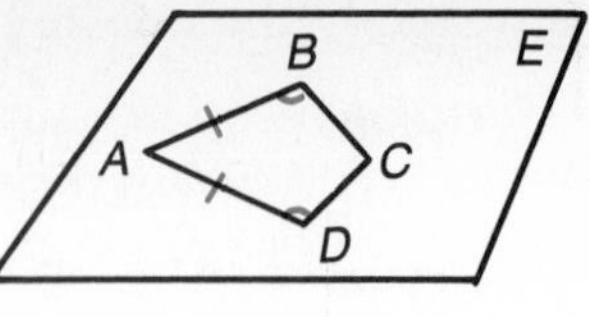

30. Given: ΔABC
$\angle A \cong \angle C$
Prove: The bisector of $\angle B$ is also a median to $\overline{AC}$.

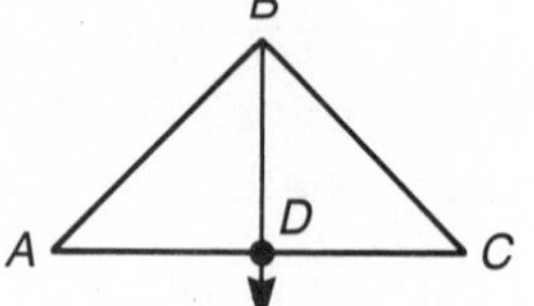

31. Given: Figure $ABCD$
$\angle 1 \cong \angle 4$
$\angle 1$ and $\angle 2$ are supplementary.
$\angle 4$ and $\angle 3$ are supplementary.
Prove: $\overline{AB} \cong \overline{CD}$

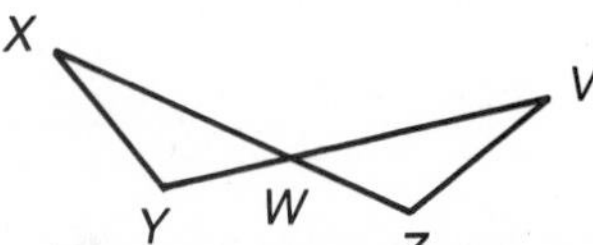

32. Given: Figure $XYWZV$
$\overline{XY} \cong \overline{VZ}$
$\overline{XZ} \cong \overline{VY}$
Prove: $\Delta XWY \cong \Delta VWZ$

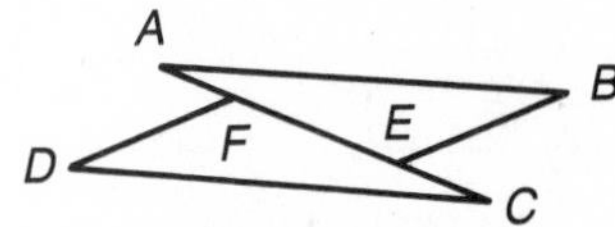

33. Given: ΔABE and ΔCDF
$\overline{AB} \cong \overline{CD}$, $\overline{AF} \cong \overline{CE}$
$\angle BAE \cong \angle DCF$
Prove: $\angle ABE \cong \angle CDF$

C. 34. Given: Quadrilateral $ABCD$
$\angle A \cong \angle D$
$\overline{AB} \cong \overline{DC}$
Prove: $\angle ABC = \angle DCB$
HINT: Name the point shown in red on the figure.

35. Prove Exercise 34 using a different auxiliary set.

36. Write a proof requiring points W, X, Y, and Z to be coplanar.

Given: ΔYXZ and ΔYWZ
$XY = XZ$, $WY = WZ$
Prove: $\angle XYW \cong \angle XZW$

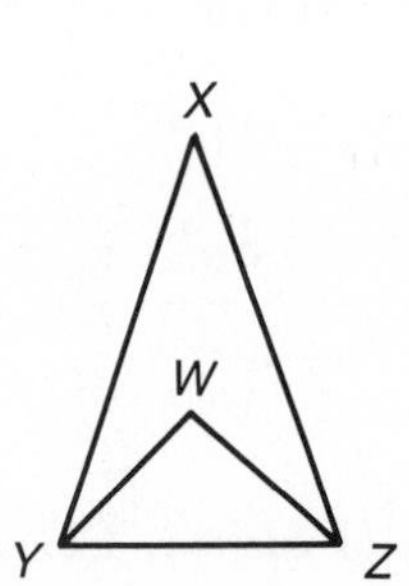

37. Write a proof for Exercise 36 in which points W, X, Y, and Z are noncoplanar.

5.5 Betweenness and Separation

This section may be considered optional for some classes.

OBJECTIVE

Use the definitions and theorems on betweenness and separation in proofs.

TEACHER'S NOTES

See p. T29

MIXED REVIEW

1. Solve for t if $d = rt$. $t = \frac{d}{r}$
2. Solve for x if $P = \frac{x + 2y}{3}$. $x = 3P - 2y$
3. What is the contrapositive of "If it is a cat then it is a feline"? If it is not a feline, then it is not a cat.
4. Solve $x - 3y = 2$; $4x + 2y = 22$ (5, 1)
5. Solve $2x^2 + 3x - 2 = 0$. $\left\{\frac{1}{2}, -2\right\}$

TEACHER'S RESOURCE MASTERS

Practice Master 15, Part 2
Quiz 10

The main objective of this chapter has been to expand and improve your deductive proof techniques. It is now possible to fill a gap in the deductive system developed thus far.

In Chapter 4, the proof of Theorem 4.6, which established that every angle has exactly one bisector, assumed that D is in the interior of $\angle ABC$. Certainly, it *appears* that D is in the interior of $\angle ABC$ from the figure. But figures are merely approximations of geometric relationships. Proofs derived from these relationships are easier to write with a figure for reference.

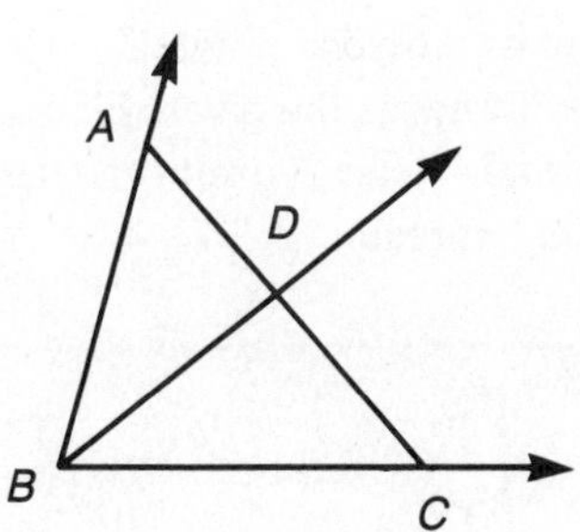

The figure above is one possible representation, but a proof must hold for *any* figure that meets the given criteria. Although they are helpful, figures do not provide evidence for a relationship.

It seems reasonable to locate point D within the interior of $\angle ABC$. The points A, B, and C determine exactly one plane, say plane E, so $\overline{AC}$ must lie in that plane. $\overline{AC}$ has exactly one midpoint, say D, which is also in E. So, it appears that D must lie in the interior of $\angle ABC$. But this analysis still does not follow from the formal defintion of the interior of an angle; it is simply based on intuition.

The same issue was glossed over in Section 5.4, where the Angle Addition Postulate (Post. 13) was applied to a coplanar figure. Euclid's *Elements* reveals many such logical defects because his deductive system included some assumptions not fully supported by his postulates. Still, many of his assumptions are intuitively acceptable and do not undermine the validity of the deductive system. In fact, it was not until the turn of this century that mathematicians were able to provide a revised postulate system for Euclidean geometry.

For a deductive system to be consistent, however, the *obvious* should be proven too. The following theorems could be used to establish that D is in the interior of $\angle ABC$, so that $\overrightarrow{BD}$ is an angle bisector.

> **THEOREM 5.4**
> If P is between X and Y on line l, then X and P are in the same half-plane created by any other line that contains Y.

Given: Point P between points X and Y on line l
Another line k containing Y

Prove: X and P are in the same half-plane created by k.

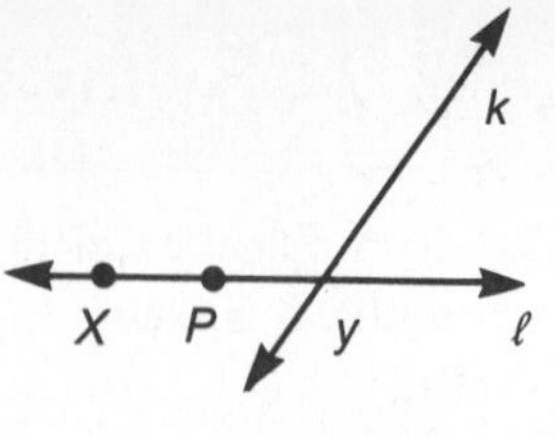

Proof (indirect): Assume that X and P are in opposite half-planes created by k. Lines l and k are coplanar, because two intersecting lines determine a plane (Theorem 2.4). Then, l intersects k at some point Z. So, Z is a point of l and k, and it is between X and P (indirect assumption). Since two lines intersect at exactly one point, $Z = Y$. So, Y is between X and P, which contradicts the given. Hence, the indirect assumption is invalid, and X and P are in the same half-plane created by any line that contains Y.

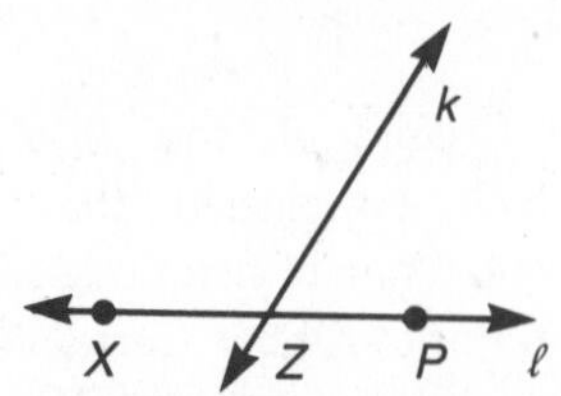

> **THEOREM 5.5**
> If D is between A and C, and B is any point not on $\overleftrightarrow{AC}$, then D is in the interior of $\angle ABC$.

Given: Point D between points A and C
Point B not on $\overleftrightarrow{AC}$

Prove: D is in the interior of $\angle ABC$.

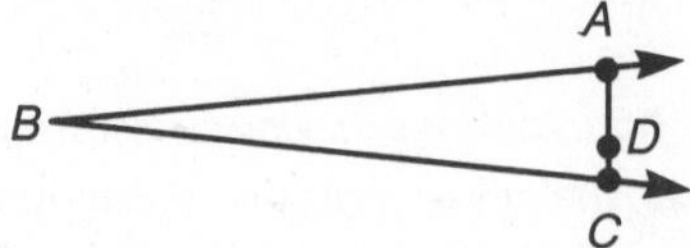

Proof: Apply Theorem 5.4 twice. That is, A and D are on the same side of $\overleftrightarrow{BC}$, and D and C are on the same side of $\overleftrightarrow{AB}$. Therefore, point D satisfies the definition of a point in the interior of an angle.

ORAL EXERCISES

Refer to the figure below to complete the following statements. Justify each answer with an acceptable deductive reason.

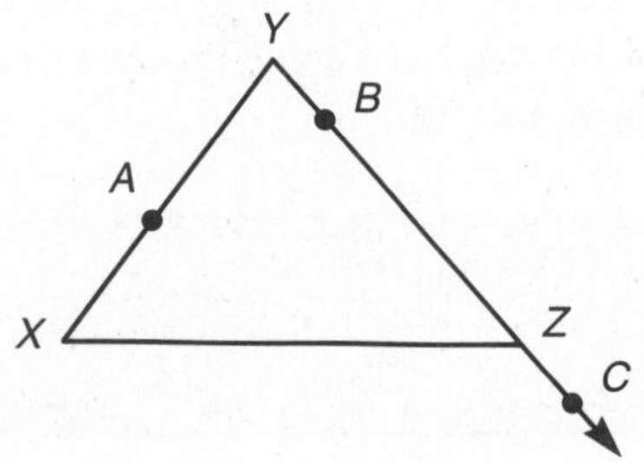

1. B is in the interior of ______.
2. A and B are in the same half-plane created by edge ______.
3. B and Z lie on the ______ side of $\overleftrightarrow{XY}$.
4. C and A lie on ______ sides of $\overleftrightarrow{XZ}$.
5. $\angle YZX$ and ______ form a linear pair.

ASSIGNMENT GUIDE

Minimum 1-10
Regular 1-10
Maximum 1-21, 24

Oral Exercises

1. $\angle YXZ$; Theorem 5.5
2. $\overleftrightarrow{XZ}$; Plane Separation Postulate
3. same; Theorem 5.4
4. opposite; Plane Sep. Post.
5. $\angle XZC$; Def. of linear pair

WRITTEN EXERCISES

A. Are the following conclusions acceptable, given the figure at the right? Write yes or no.

1. $\overline{AB} \cong \overline{CB}$
2. $\overline{BD} \perp \overline{AC}$
3. A and D are on the same side of $\overleftrightarrow{BC}$.
4. $\overrightarrow{BD}$ is the bisector of $\angle ABC$.
5. $\overline{BD}$ is a median of ΔABC.
6. $\Delta ABD \cong \Delta CBD$
7. $\angle EAB$ and $\angle FAD$ are vertical angles.
8. $\angle EAF \cong \angle GCH$

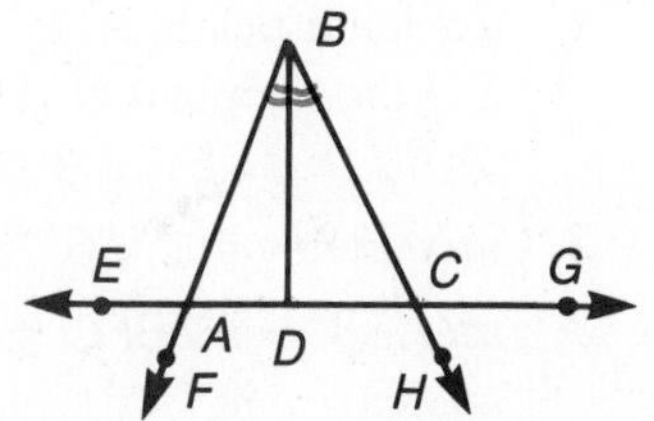

Written Exercises

1. no 2. no
3. yes 4. yes
5. no 6. no
7. yes 8. no

B. Sketch figures of an acute triangle, an obtuse triangle, and a right triangle. Refer to these figures for Exercises 9–10.

9. For which triangle types is the point of intersection of the medians of the triangle in the interior of the triangle?
10. From the vertex of each triangle, drawn the line perpendicular to the opposite side. For which triangle types is the point of intersection of these lines *not* in the interior of the triangle?

9. all types
10. obtuse, right

Supply the missing statements and reasons.

Given: Y is between X and Z on line l.

Prove: X and Z are in opposite half-planes created by any edge k containing Y.

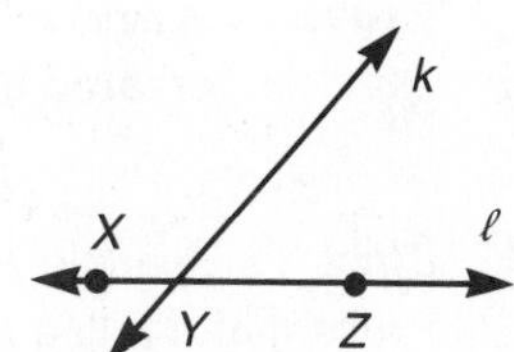

Proof:

STATEMENTS	REASONS
1. Y is between X and Z on line l.	1. **11.**
2. **12.**	2. Indirect assumption
3. $\overline{XZ}$ forms a convex set that does not contain Y.	3. **13.**

Contradiction: The definition of between says that Y lies on $\overline{XZ}$, so Step 3 contradicts **14.**. Therefore, X and Z are in opposite half-planes.

11. Given
12. X and Z are in the same half-plane created by line k through Y.
13. Plane Separation Postulate
14. the given

15. Definition of $\cong$ $\angle$s
16. Addition property of equality
17. Angle Addition Postulate, Post. 13
18. $\angle AEC \cong \angle DEB$
19. Definition of midpoint
20. ASA
21. Corres. parts of $\cong$ Δs are $\cong$.
22. X and W are in the same half-plane of $\overleftrightarrow{YZ}$ by Theorem 5.4, using point Y; W and U are in the same half-plane of $\overleftrightarrow{YZ}$ by Theorem 5.4, using point Z; so, X and U are in the same half-plane of $\overleftrightarrow{YZ}$.
23. Case 1: C lies on l. Then l intersects both $\overline{AC}$ and $\overline{BC}$. Case 2: C lies in H_1. Then by Plane Sep. Post., l intersects $\overline{AC}$. Case 3: C lies in H_2. Then by Plane Sep. Post., l interesects $\overline{BC}$.
24. Assume $\overline{EB} \perp \overline{AC}$. Then $\angle EBA$ and $\angle EBC$ are right angles. By the Isosceles Triangle Theorem, $\angle DBC \cong \angle DCB$. Given $\angle EBA \cong \angle DCB$, by transitivity $\angle EBA \cong \angle DBC$. So $\angle EBA$, $\angle DBC$, and $\angle DCB$ are all right angles, and ΔDBC has two right angles. This contradicts Cor. 5.3.1, so $EB \not\perp AC$.

Skills Maintenance

1. 0 4
$x < 4$

Given: Coplanar points A, B, C, D, and E
E is the midpoint of $\overline{AD}$.
$\angle AEB \cong \angle DEC$, $\angle A \cong \angle D$

Prove: $\angle B \cong \angle C$

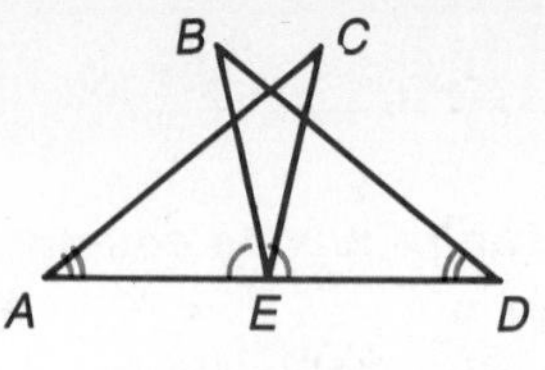

Proof:

STATEMENTS	REASONS
1. Coplanar points A, B, C, D, and E; E is the midpoint of $\overline{AD}$. $\angle AEB \cong \angle DEC$, $\angle A \cong \angle D$	1. Given
2. $m\angle AEB = m\angle DEC$	2. **15.**
3. $m\angle AEB + m\angle BEC = m\angle DEC + m\angle BEC$	3. **16.**
4. $m\angle AEB + m\angle BEC = m\angle AEC$; $m\angle DEC + m\angle BEC = m\angle DEB$	4. **17.**
5. $m\angle AEC = m\angle DEB$	5. Substitution property
6. **18.**	6. Definition of $\cong$ $\angle$s
7. $AE = DE$	7. **19.**
8. $\overline{AE} \cong \overline{DE}$	8. Definition of $\cong$ segments
9. $\Delta ACE \cong \Delta DBE$	9. Steps 1, 6, 8, and **20.**
10. $\angle B \cong \angle C$	10. **21.**

22. Given: X, Y, Z, U, V, and W are coplanar.
W is between U and Z.
Y is between V and Z.

Prove: X and U are in the same half-plane created by edge $\overleftrightarrow{YZ}$.

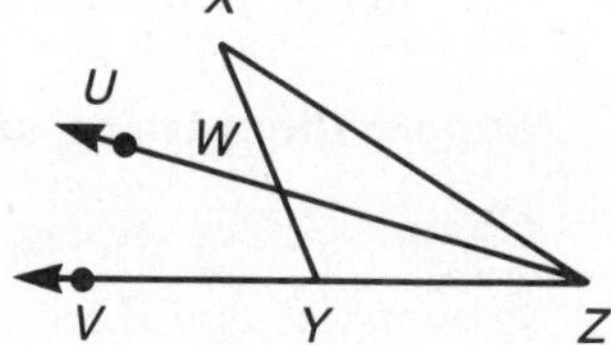

23. (Hilbert's Triangle Axiom)
Prove that if a line in the plane of ΔABC intersects a point between A and B, then the line intersects $\overline{AC}$ or $\overline{BC}$ or both. (HINT: With l as the edge, let H_1 and H_2 be two half-planes with point B in H_1. Therefore, C is either on l, in H_1, or in H_2.)

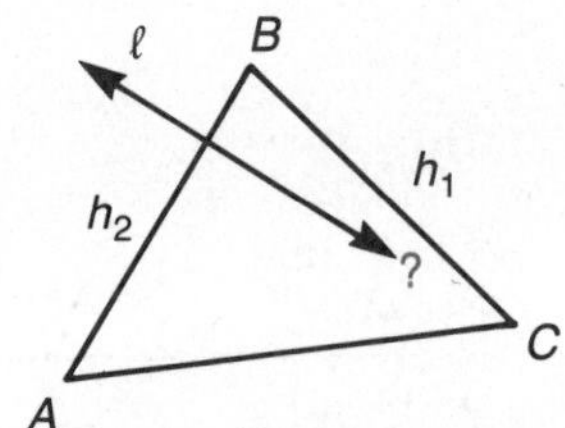

C. 24. Prove indirectly.

Given: B is between A and C on $\overleftrightarrow{AC}$; ΔBDC is an isosceles triangle; $\overline{BD} \cong \overline{CD}$; E is in the interior of $\angle ABD$; $\angle EBA \cong \angle DCB$.

Prove: $\overline{EB}$ is not perpendicular to $\overline{AC}$.

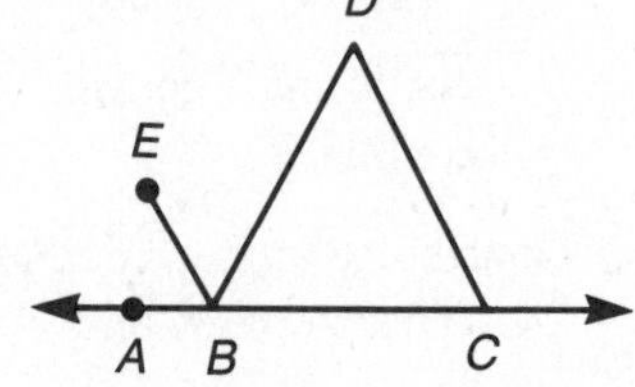

SKILLS MAINTENANCE

Solve and graph each equation or inequality.

1. $x + 3 < 7$ **2.** $y - 3 > 1$ **3.** $4x + 5 < 17$

4. $8 - 2x < 7x + 9$ **5.** $3y < 21$ **6.** $3 - 4t < 11$

7. $4 > x$ and $x > 2$ **8.** $y > 1$ or $y < -1$ **9.** $x \leq -2$

10. $1 < t < 3$ **11.** $|y| = 4$ **12.** $|x + 1| = 3$

13. If you are paid $3.50 an hour, how many hours must you work to make more than $50.00?

14. If 7 times a number is decreased by 8, the result is less than 27. Find the number.

15. If 3 times a number is increased by 5, the result is between 25 and 31. Find the number.

CHALLENGE

Mathematicians spend a great deal of time looking for and studying patterns. In the Skills Maintenance exercises in Chapter 1, you looked for a pattern to predict the number of subsets in a four-element set. This pattern-seeking procedure is common in mathematics.

Consider the following figure and the pattern suggested:

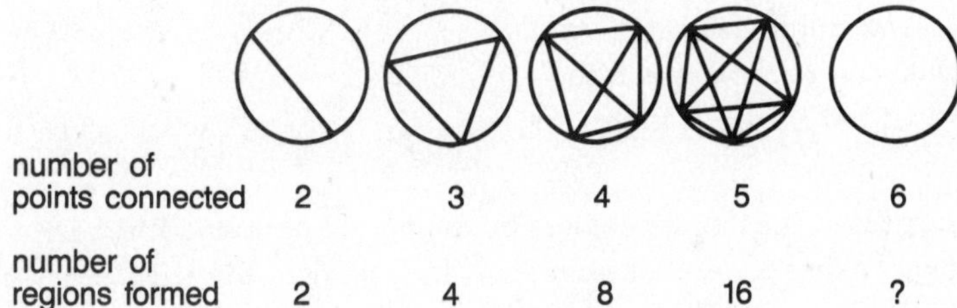

1. Replace the **?** under the 6 by the number you think belongs there.
2. Draw a circle and connect any six points on it in all possible ways. Count the regions thus formed. Does the result agree with your prediction?
3. What does this result indicate about predictions?

2. 0 4 $y > 4$

3. 0 3 $x < 3$

4. $-1\ -\frac{2}{3}\ -\frac{1}{3}\ 0\ \frac{1}{3}\ \frac{2}{3}$ $y > -\frac{1}{9}$

5. 0 7 $y < 7$

6. −2 0 $t > -2$

7. 0 2 4 $2 < x < 4$

8. −1 0 1 $y > 1$ or $y < -1$

9. −2 0 $x \leq -2$

10. 0 1 3 $1 < t < 3$

11. −4 0 4 $y = 4$ or $y = -4$

12. −4 0 2 $x = 2$ or $x = -4$

13. $n > 14\frac{2}{7}$ hr

14. $n < 5$

15. $\frac{20}{3} < n < \frac{26}{3}$

Challenge

1. 32

2. 30 or 31

3. They must be verified through proof.

MATH HERITAGE/Origins of Proof

Before the Greeks, civilizations otherwise highly advanced in the arts and sciences had not progressed far in mathematics, possibly due to their method. The Egyptians and Babylonians solved complicated problems through procedures based largely on trial and error. When they discovered the solution to a particular problem, they would record the steps they followed and then apply the same steps to solving other, similar problems.

Likewise, the Hindus and Arabs took an experimental or "empirical" approach to mathematics. They were the first to study irrational numbers expressed as roots, such as $\sqrt{5}$, but all their conclusions were drawn from comparisons. For instance, to determine if $\sqrt{2} + \sqrt{3} = \sqrt{2 + 3}$ or $\sqrt{5}$, they tested the more familiar case of $\sqrt{4} + \sqrt{9}$. Knowing that $\sqrt{4} = 2$ and $\sqrt{9} = 3$, they could state with certainty that $\sqrt{4} + \sqrt{9}$ did not equal $\sqrt{13}$. Thus, they concluded, $\sqrt{x} + \sqrt{y} \neq \sqrt{x + y}$ for any values of x and y. How would they have applied the same analogy to determine if $\sqrt{x} \cdot \sqrt{y} = \sqrt{xy}$?

Drawing general conclusions from specific observations, a method called *induction,* can produce incorrect conclusions. Based on observations of television alone, for example, you might easily conclude that all Texans live on ranches.

Similarly, in Euclidean geometry, you can draw an infinite number of examples to support the theory that every line in plane E intersects a given line x in E. Only one exception (which one?) proves that the theory is false.

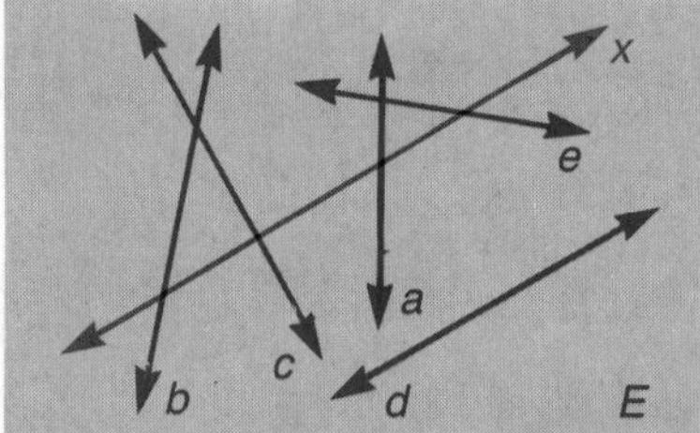

The Greeks surpassed their predecessors by taking the opposite approach to problem solving. Taking general observations, they worked toward a specific conclusion. Using *deduction,* they stated as "given" principles they accepted as true and, by combining and restating them, proceeded logically from one step to another until they concluded or "proved" something new. Their conclusion then became a new principle or theorem from which they could deduce further conclusions. With deductive reasoning, the Greeks opened the door to abstract theory and changed the way all future generations would study and use mathematics.

TEACHER'S RESOURCE MASTERS

Computer Master 5

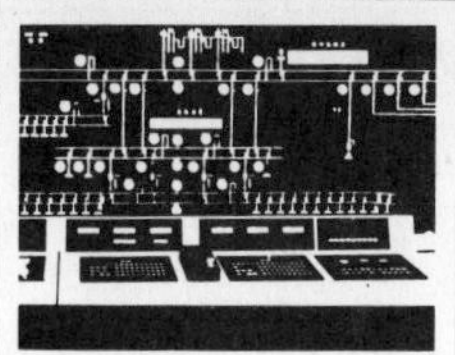

COMPUTER

The **Russian Peasant Multiplication Algorithm** is a procedure for performing multiplication problems quickly. Two examples are given below:

To apply this method, you continually halve the smaller factor, disregarding any remainder, and double the larger factor. When the result of halving is 1, you underline the values in the doubled column that correspond to odd numbers in the halved column. The sum of the underlined numbers is the final product.

$32 \times 14 = 448$		$19 \times 46 = 874$	
32	14	19	46
64	7	9	92
128	3	4	184
256	1	2	368
		1	736
448			874

Such procedures, called *algorithms,* are ideal for computer adaptation, as shown below. Run the program for five different pairs of factors. Check the answers by traditional multiplication.

```
10  REM RUSSIAN PEASANT MULTIPLICATION
20  INPUT "TYPE TWO NUMBERS.
    ENTER THE SMALLER      NUMBER FIRST."; A, B
30  REM INITIALIZE A TOTALER T
40  LET T = 0
50  IF A/2 = INT(A/2) THEN 130
60  LET T = T + B
70  LET A = INT(A/2)
80  IF A < 1 THEN 170
90  LET B = 2 * B
100 GOTO 110
110 PRINT "PRODUCT"; "="; T
120 END
```

TEACHER'S RESOURCE MASTER'S

Enrichment Master 4

ENRICHMENT

See Activities 9–10, p. T45–T46

Chapter 5 Review

1. T
2. False; $\sim p \rightarrow \sim q$ is the inverse, $q \rightarrow p$ is the converse.
3. False; its contrapositive
4. False; lie in two different planes
5. T
6. A
7. S
8. A
9. A
10. N
11. BX
12. $\angle C$

CHAPTER 5 REVIEW

VOCABULARY

auxiliary sets (5.4)
closure (5.4)
contrapositive (5.1)
equidistant (5.2)
exactly one (5.1)
existence (5.1)
indirect proof (5.1)
inverse (5.1)
locus of points (5.2)
negation (5.1)
perpendicular bisector (5.2)
uniqueness (5.1)

REVIEW EXERCISES

5.1 Indicate whether each of the following statements is true or false. If a statement is false, revise the underlined word(s) or phrase(s) to make the statement true.

1. The undefined terms point, line, and plane, together with the postulates, form an intuitive basis for geometry.
2. If $p \rightarrow q$ represents an implication, then $\sim p \rightarrow \sim q$ is the converse, $q \rightarrow p$ is the negation, and $\sim q \rightarrow \sim p$ is the contrapositive.
3. A conditional statement and its converse are logically equivalent.
4. To prove that two intersecting lines k and l lie in exactly one plane, you could make the indirect assumption that k and l lie in at most one plane.
5. If a set exists and is unique, then you can say that there is one and only one, or exactly one, such set.

5.2 Fill in the blanks with the word always, sometimes, or never.

6. In a given plane containing line x, with point R on x, there is _____ a line through R perpendicular to x.
7. The perpendicular bisector of a segment is _____ a line segment.
8. In a given plane, points on the perpendicular bisector of a segment are _____ equidistant from the endpoints of the segment.
9. In a given plane containing line x, with point S external to x, there is _____ a line through S perpendicular to x.
10. A triangle will _____ have two right angles.

5.3 Complete the indirect assumptions you would make in order to prove the following about scalene ΔABC.

11. To prove $\overline{AX}$ is not the perpendicular bisector of $\overline{BC}$, assume $CX =$ _____.
12. To prove $m\angle C \neq m\angle B$, assume $\angle B \cong$ _____.

13. To prove $\overline{AX} \not\cong \overline{AC}$, assume $AX =$ _____.

14. To prove $\overline{XY}$ is not a median of $\triangle ABX$, assume $\overline{AY}$ _____ $\overline{BY}$.

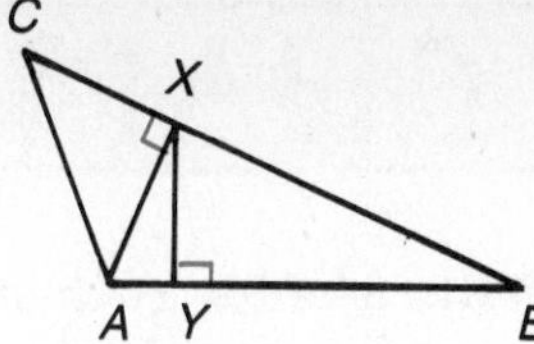

5.4 **Can auxiliary sets be drawn in the figure at the right to meet the following conditions?**

15. The angle bisector of $\measuredangle ACB$ also bisects $\angle FCE$.

16. $AF = BE$

17. $\overrightarrow{EG}$ bisects $\overline{CF}$.

18. $\overline{FG}$ bisects $\angle CFE$.

19. $\overline{CG} \perp \overline{FE}$

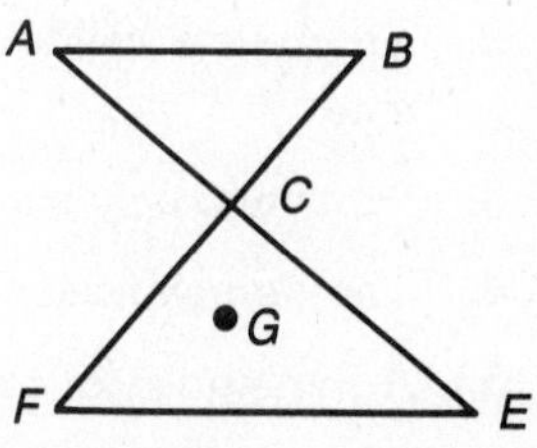

Complete the following proof.

Given: $\overleftrightarrow{AB}$ is the perpendicular bisector of $\overline{ST}$ and $\overline{RU}$.
$\overline{RS} \cong \overline{UT}$

Prove: $\angle R \cong \angle U$

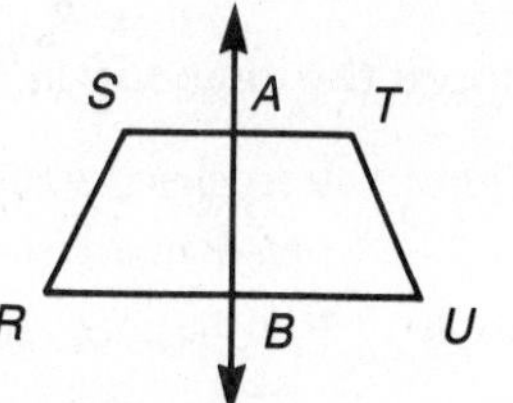

Proof:

STATEMENTS	REASONS
1. $\overline{RS} \cong \overline{UT}$	1. **20.**
2. Let S and B determine $\overline{SB}$. Let T and B determine $\overline{TB}$.	2. **21.**
3. $\overline{SB} \cong \overline{TB}$ **22.**	3. **23.**
4. $\triangle SRB \cong \triangle TUB$	4. **24.**
5. $\angle R \cong \angle U$	5. **25.**

5.5 **Refer to the figure at the right for Exercises 26–28.**

26. F and B are in the same half-plane created by

a. $\overleftrightarrow{AC}$. **b.** $\overleftrightarrow{AB}$. **c.** $\overleftrightarrow{BC}$. **d.** $\overleftrightarrow{DC}$.

27. A pair of points in opposite half-planes formed by $\overleftrightarrow{AC}$ are

a. A and B. **b.** B and D.

c. B and C. **d.** F and C.

28. F is in the interior of

a. $\angle AED$. **b.** $\angle ADB$. **c.** $\angle BDC$. **d.** $\angle ACB$.

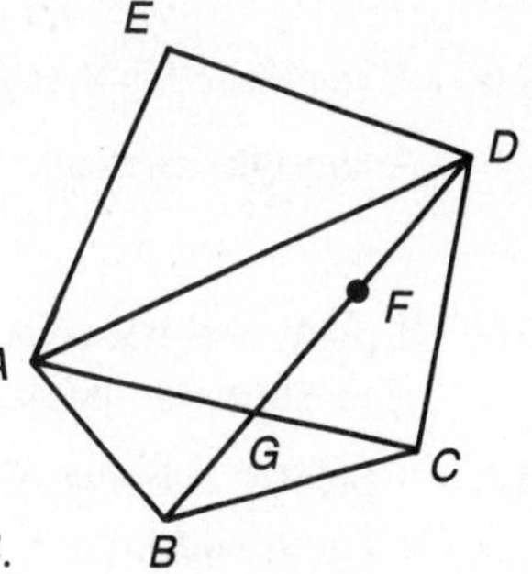

13. AC
14. $\cong$
15. yes
16. no
17. no
18. no
19. no
20. Given
21. Postulate 1
22. $\overline{RB} \cong \overline{UB}$
23. Theorem 5.2
24. SSS
25. Corres. parts $\cong \triangle$s are $\cong$.
26. d
27. b
28. a

TEACHER'S RESOURCE MASTERS

Chapter 5 Test
Multiple Choice Test—Chapter 5

Chapter 5 Test
1. F
2. T
3. F
4. T
5. F
6. F
7. Given
8. Indirect assumption
9. Theorem 5.2
10. Definition of congruent segments
11. Definition of an isosceles triangle
12. Step 5 contradicts the given; hence $\overleftrightarrow{BE}$ must not contain D.
13. Postulate 1
14. Theorem 4.6
15. Theorem 5.1
16. opposite
17. $\angle QSR$ or $\angle RSQ$

CHAPTER 5 TEST

Write whether each statement is true or false in Questions 1–6.

1. A uniqueness proof establishes that there is at least one.
2. To prove a conditional statement true, you can instead prove that its contrapositive is true.
3. "One and only one" has the same meaning as "if and only if."
4. The perpendicular bisector of a segment contains the midpoint.
5. A perpendicular to a line from an external point is not unique.
6. All points equidistant from two given points are collinear.

Supply the reasons in the following indirect proof.

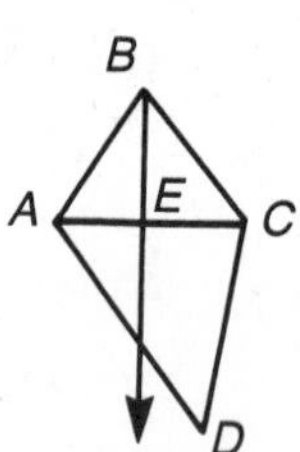

Given: Isosceles $\triangle ABC$, $\overline{AB} \cong \overline{CB}$, scalene $\triangle ADC$, $\overleftrightarrow{BE}$ is the perpendicular bisector of $\overline{AC}$.

Prove: $\overleftrightarrow{BE}$ does not contain D.

Proof:

STATEMENTS	REASONS
1. $\triangle ADC$ is scalene, $\overline{BE}$ is the $\perp$ bisector of $\overline{AC}$.	1. **7.**
2. Assume $\overleftrightarrow{BE}$ does contain D.	2. **8.**
3. $AD = CD$	3. **9.**
4. $\overline{AD} \cong \overline{CD}$	4. **10.**
5. $\triangle ADC$ is isosceles.	5. **11.**

Contradiction: **12.**

Give the reason justifying the auxiliary sets described in Questions 13–15.

13. A line, $\overleftrightarrow{AB}$, through points A and B.
14. A ray bisecting $\angle ACD$.
15. A line perpendicular to $\overleftrightarrow{BC}$ through point D.

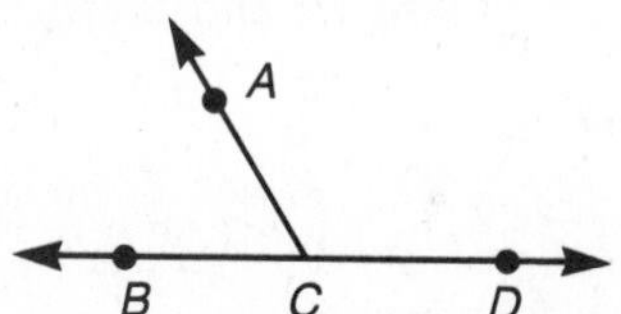

16. If point K is between points J and L on line x, then J and L are in _____ half-planes created by edge y which contains K.
17. If point P is between points Q and R, and point S does not lie on $\overleftrightarrow{QR}$, then P is in the interior of _____.

CHAPTER 6

Inequalities in Geometry

OBJECTIVE

Distinguish between reason, conjecture, chance discovery, and intuition.

TEACHER'S NOTES

See p. T29

MIXED REVIEW

1. What is the contrapositive of "If two sides of a triangle are congruent then the angles opposite these sides are congruent?" If two angles of a triangle are not congruent, then the sides opposite these angles are not congruent.
2. Solve $2x - 3 < 7$. $x < 5$
3. Solve $x + 7 < 2x - 5$. $x > 12$
4. Multiply $4x^2(3x^2 + 2x - 4)$. $12x^4 + 8x^3 - 16x^2$
5. Solve $14 - 3x = 2(x + 31)$. $x = -9\frac{3}{5}$

TEACHER'S RESOURCE MASTERS

Practice Master 16, Part 1

6.1 Conjectures from Experimentation

In previous chapters, your study of geometry has emphasized the idea of equality. Congruent segments and angles have *equal* measure. An isosceles triangle has two sides of *equal* measure. Real situations, however, often involve comparisons of measures that are not *equal*. For example, the flying distance from Houston to New York is *longer* if your plane makes a stop at Chicago. The angle of the sun is *smaller* in the early morning than at high noon.

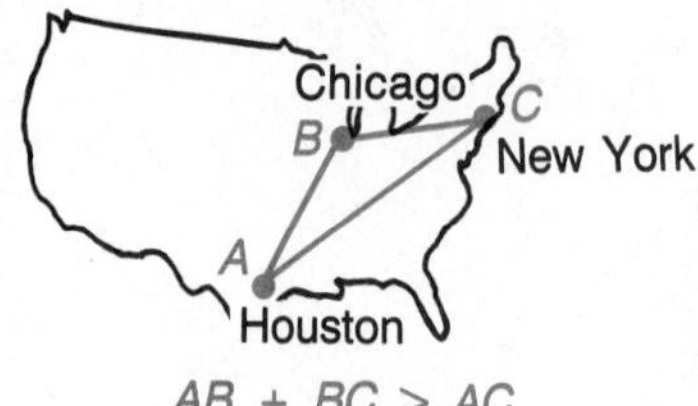

$AB + BC > AC$

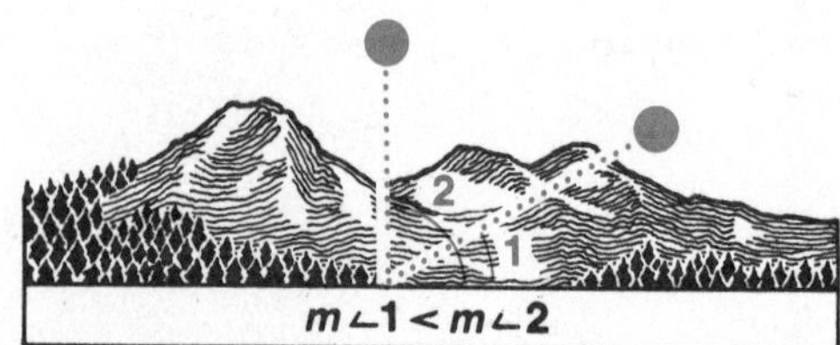

$m\angle 1 < m\angle 2$

As with congruence, you can deduce general conclusions about figures having unequal measure, and in this chapter you will prove some important theorems about inequalities. You can deduce a great deal about inequalities, though, just by conjecture, a reasonable guess. Once a conjecture has withstood a few tests, it can be added to your body of knowledge.

The Isosceles Triangle Theorem (Theorem 4.3) states that if two sides of a triangle are congruent, then the angles opposite those sides are congruent. What if you were to conjecture that the inverse of that theorem holds true? The inverse would read: *If two sides of a triangle are of unequal length, then the angles opposite them are of unequal measure.* Are you inclined to accept this conjecture?

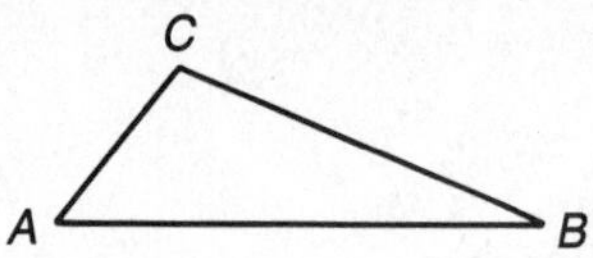

Look at $\triangle ABC$ at the left. You don't need a ruler to see that $\overline{CB}$ is longer than $\overline{CA}$. Now look at the angles opposite these segments. Clearly, $\angle A$ is larger than $\angle B$.

You may already be convinced that the conjecture is true. Perhaps you feel uncomfortable, though, about accepting *anything* on the basis of just one figure. So you sketch a few more pairs of triangles having pairs of unequal sides, and you become conviced that the statement is true. Understand that there has been no *proof,* but you are just as convinced as if there were.

Try another conjecture. You have accepted the SAS Postulate (Postulate 15), and you recall that the angle considered has to be the *included* angle. Suppose that two triangles have two pairs of sides and a pair of *non*included angles of equal measure. Are the two triangles then congruent? Your proposed "SSA Postulate" would state: *If two sides and a nonincluded angle of one triangle are congruent to the corresponding parts of a second triangle, then the triangles are congruent.*

Before deciding whether to accept or reject this conjecture, you would want to sketch several cases that fulfill the conditions. If the conclusion follows in every test, then you might be inclined to accept the proposed postulate. If, on the other hand, you can sketch just one exception, then you would have to reject the proposed rule. In logic, such an exception is called a **counterexample.**

Try to sketch a counterexample to the "SSA Postulate." In other words, try to draw two triangles with two pairs of sides and a pair of nonincluded angles congruent so that the triangles are not congruent. Only after you have decided whether or not to accept the proposed postulate should you proceed to the next paragraph.

Hopefully, you have decided to reject the "SSA Postulate." Observe that in ΔDAB and ΔDBC, $\overline{DB} \cong \overline{DB}$, $\angle D \cong \angle D$, and $\overline{BA} \cong \overline{BC}$. The condition SSA is satisfied, but the triangles are not congruent. This conjecture was not correct.

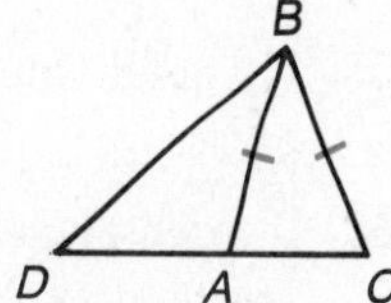

Reason and conjecture are not the only sources of knowledge. From the days of your infancy, you have learned much from **chance discovery.** A child on the playground, for example, may discover by chance that a ball strikes a wall and bounces off at the same angle.

You also gain knowledge from **intuition.** Using your intuition since an early age, you have acquired direct knowledge without conscious reasoning. Watch a child in a sandbox filling a bucket with sand. When the bucket is full, the child stops shoveling and dumps the sand, rather than attempting to force more into a bucket already full. The child intuitively understands a basic principle of physics: *Two things cannot occupy the same space at the same time.*

Intuition will often guide you correctly, but it can also be deceiving. Mathematicians therefore strive to support intuition by the use of inductive and deductive reasoning.

ASSIGNMENT GUIDE

Minimum 1-10
Regular 1-11
Maximum 1-11

ORAL EXERCISES

1. Name three things you know as a result of intuition.
2. Name three things you know as a result of chance discovery.
3. Name three things you know as a result of conjecture.
4. Name three things you know as a result of proof.
5. Other than chance discovery, proof, conjecture, and intuition, what are some other sources of knowledge?

Oral Exercises

1-4. Answers will vary.

5. Experience, hearsay, and revelation are three possible answers.

WRITTEN EXERCISES

A. **1.** A black bag contains 50 marbles. One by one, 49 are removed, and each is red in color. From this would you make the conjecture that the 50th marble is also red? Explain.

Written Exercises

1. A safe conjecture; the probability is high that the 50th marble is also red.

2. A poor conjecture; there could be many explanations for an all-girls class in a mixed population school.

3. false conjecture; sketches may vary.

4. no

5. yes

6. no

7. b

8. a

9. d

10. a or c

11. The conjecture would be wrong. The figure below shows one of the many circumstances in which the conditions are satisfied and the conjecture does not follow.

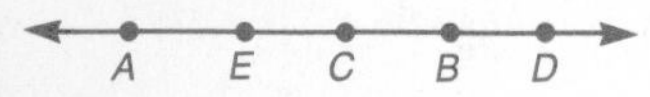

Calculator
An attempt at each of the three calculations on a hand calculator will produce an *error* display.

2. You walk into a strange school and, looking inside the first classroom you approach, observe that all the students in the class are girls? Is it reasonable to conjecture that the school is an all-girls school? Explain.

3. Test the conjecture *all isosceles right triangles are congruent* by making several sketches. On the strength of your sketches, are you willing to accept the conjecture?

B. Can the following conjectures be rejected using the sketch below?

4. Every quadrilateral has four right angles.

5. No quadrilateral has four right angles.

6. If three angles of a quadrilateral are right angles, then the fourth angles is also a right angle.

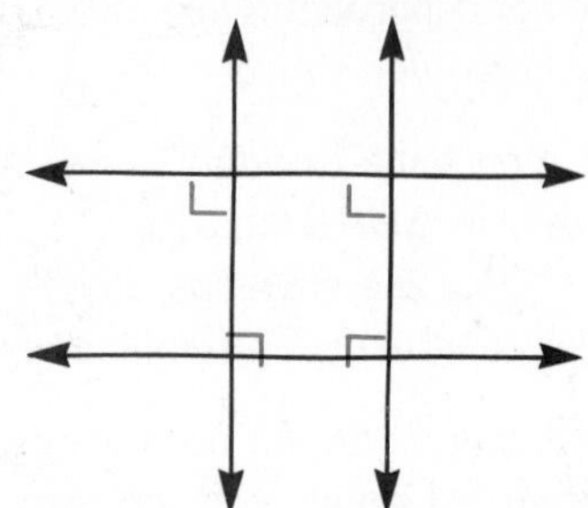

From the list on the right, choose the method by which you would be likely to acquire knowledge of the following:

7.	the quadratic formula	**a.**	discovery
8.	the law of gravity	**b.**	proof
9.	the infinity of space	**c.**	conjecture
10.	An isosceles triangle can be a right triangle.	**d.**	intuition

C. 11. A, B, C, and D are five integers. You are given that $A < B$, $E > A$, $D > B$, $C > A$, and $C < B$. Based on these facts, would you conjecture that $C < E$? If not, sketch a number line with these integers that serves as a counterexample.

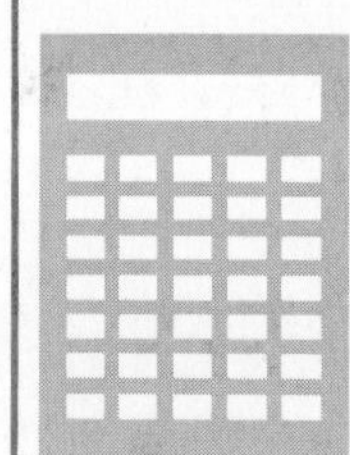

CALCULATOR

Use a calculator to disprove each of the following conjectures.

1. Any number can be divided by zero.

2. It is possible to find the square root of a negative number.

3. The number 0 has a reciprocal.

6.2 The Algebra of Inequalities

Before you consider geometric inequalities, it will be useful to review the properties of inequality you studied in algebra.

Looking at a number line, you can see the relationship between two coordinates. If a is to the left of b, then $a < b$. If c is to the right of b, then $c > b$.

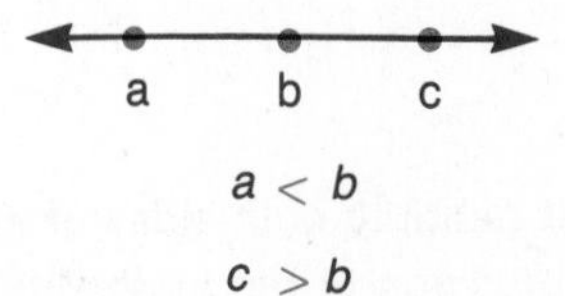

$a < b$

$c > b$

As you have learned, though, you cannot rely on visual props. The following definitions of **positive** and **negative numbers** provide a basis for defining inequality without figures.

> **DEFINITIONS: positive number, negative number**
> A **positive number** is a number greater than zero. A **negative number** is a number less than zero.

These definitions enable you to define the two inequality relationships, $\boldsymbol{a > b}$ and $\boldsymbol{a < b}$. In these definitions, a, b, and c represent real numbers.

> **DEFINITIONS:** $\boldsymbol{a > b, a < b}$
> $\boldsymbol{a > b}$ if and only if $a = b + c$ for some positive number c.
> $\boldsymbol{a < b}$ if and only if $a + c = b$ for some positive number c.

Therefore, $10 > 6$ because 6 plus the positive number 4 equals 10, and $-8 < -5$ because $-8 + 3$ (a positive number) $= -5$.

Now that you have formally defined $a > b$ and $a < b$, recall the properties of inequalities mentioned in Chapter 1. Though stated here for $>$, they are also true for $<$. Given $a > b$:

$a + c > b + c$	Addition property of inequality
$a - c > b - c$	Subtraction property of inequality
$ac > bc$, if $c > 0$	Multiplication property of inequality
$\frac{a}{c} > \frac{b}{c}$, if $c > 0$	Division property of inequality

These properties are like the properties of equality, which allow you to apply the same operation to both sides of an equation. You can do the same with algebraic inequalities, except for a restriction placed upon the multiplication and division properties.

OBJECTIVE

Apply the order reversal rule and use the properties of inequalities to solve inequalities.

TEACHER'S NOTES

See p. T29

MIXED REVIEW

1. What are the three properties of an equivalence relation? symmetric, reflexive, transitive
2. What kind of number is a if $a < -a$? negative
3. If $\frac{a}{b} = \frac{c}{d}$ then $a =$ ______. $\frac{bc}{d}$
4. Which is greater, $\frac{7}{8}$ or $\frac{8}{9}$? $\frac{8}{9}$
5. Factor $3x^2 - 19x - 14$. $(3x + 2)(x - 7)$

TEACHER'S RESOURCE MASTERS

Practice Master 16, Part 2

The following equation and inequality are similar in appearance:

$$-\tfrac{1}{2}x = 10 \qquad -\tfrac{1}{2}x > 10$$

To solve the equation, you would multiply both sides by -2 and obtain the solution $x = -20$. If you proceed the same way in solving the inequality, you would obtain $x > -20$. This solution is incorrect, as you see when you check for $x = 0$:

$$-\frac{1}{2} \cdot 0 = 0, \text{ and } 0 \not> 10.$$

When you multiply both sides of an inequality by a negative number, you must change the *sense* or *direction* of the inequality. Thus, the solution of the inequality above is $x < -20$. As another example, if $-3x$ is less than or equal to -15, written $-3x \leq -15$, then x is greater than or equal to 5 (or $x \geq 5$).

In previous mathematics courses, you have accepted this rule of algebra without questioning its validity. Here you will *prove* that it is valid. First express the rule symbolically: If $a > b$, then $-a < -b$. In other words, if you multiply both sides of an inequality by -1, you must change the direction of the inequality.

Any negative number is the product of -1 and the absolute value of that number, so the proof covers all cases.

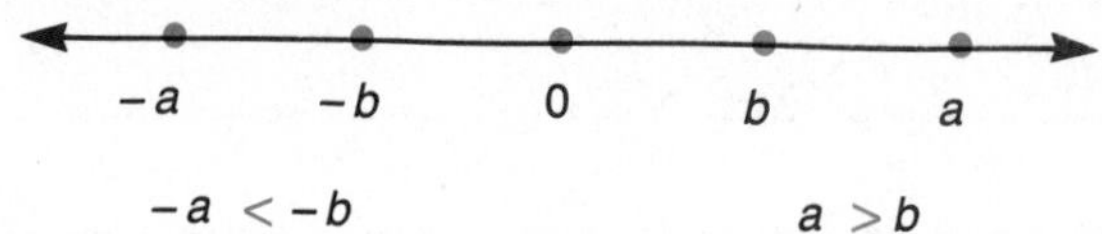

Next, recall the other properties of real numbers. For all real numbers a, b, and c:

$a < b$, $a = b$, or $a > b$	Uniqueness property of order (trichotomy)
If $a > b$, and $b > c$, then $a > c$	Transitive property of order
If $a < b$, then $b > a$	Relationship between > and <

Using these properties, you can now proceed with the proof.

Given: $a > b$

Prove: $-a < -b$

Proof:

STATEMENTS	REASONS
1. $a > b$	1. Given
2. $a + [-a + (-b)] > b + [-a + (-b)]$	2. Addition property of equality
3. $a + [-a + (-b)] > b + [-b + (-a)]$	3. Commutative property of addition
4. $[a + (-a)] + (-b) > [b + (-b)] + (-a)$	4. Associative property of addition
5. $0 + (-b) > 0 + (-a)$	5. Inverse property of addition
6. $-b > -a$	6. Identity property of addition
7. $-a < -b$	7. Relationship between > and <

The result of this proof is called the **rule for order reversal.**

ORAL EXERCISES

Using the definitions in this section, explain why:

1. $5 > 4$ **2.** $1 < 2$ **3.** $-3 > -12$ **4.** $-\frac{1}{2} < 0$

5. State four inequalities that can be deduced from the equation $2 + 3 = 5$.

Identify the property or definition that justifies each of the statements in Exercises 6–14.

6. If $x > 10$, then $x + 5 > 15$.

7. If $a < -b$, then $-a > b$.

8. If $a < b$, and $a + p = b$, then p is a positive number.

9. If $x < -3$, and $y > 0$, then $xy < -3y$.

10. If $7x > 21$, then $x > 3$.

11. If $a \ngtr b$, then $a < b$.

12. If $x < y$, then $x - 4 < y - 4$.

13. If a car is heavier than a bicycle, then a bicycle is lighter than a car.

14. If an elephant is stronger than a horse, and a horse is stronger than a goat, then an elephant is stronger than a goat.

If $a > b$, and $b > c$, then $a > c$.

WRITTEN EXERCISES

A. Solve the following inequalities.

1. $-x > 5$ **2.** $2x > -10$ **3.** $-x \leq 1$ **4.** $3 - (x + 2) < 7$

5. Consider this conjecture: if $a < b$, and $b > c$, then $a < c$. If you agree, draw several number lines that support the conjecture. If you disagree, draw one number line as a counterexample.

6. Give a counterexample to the conjecture that the sum of two odd numbers is odd.

B. 7. What restriction would have to be placed on a and b in order for this conjecture to be true: if $a > b$, then $a^2 > b^2$?

8. Write two equations that can be derived from the inequality $a > 5$. Let x represent a positive number.

ASSIGNMENT GUIDE

Minimum 1-9
Regular 1-10
Maximum 1-12

Oral Exercises

1. because $4 + 1 = 5$
2. because $1 + 1 = 2$
3. because $-12 + 9 = -3$
4. because $-\frac{1}{2} + \frac{1}{2} = 0$
5. $3 < 5$, $2 < 5$, $5 > 3$, $5 > 2$
6. addition property of inequality
7. order reversal
8. definition of $a < b$
9. multiplication property of inequality
10. division property of inequality
11. uniqueness of order
12. subtraction property of inequality
13. relationship between $>$ and $<$
14. transitivity of order

Written Exercises

1. $x < -5$ 2. $x > -5$

3. $x \geq -1$ 4. $x > -6$

5.

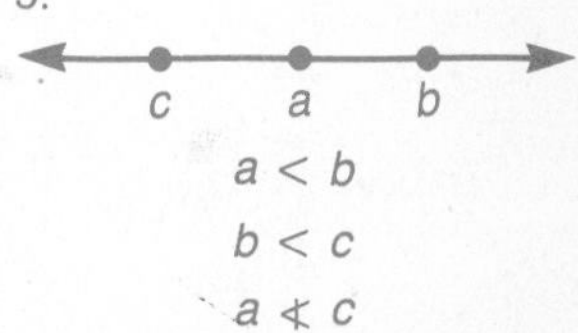

$a < b$
$b < c$
$a \nless c$

6. Answers will vary. As an example: $7 + 9 = 16$

7. Both a and b must be greater than 0.

8. $5 + x = a$
$5 = a - x$
$x = a - 5$

9. 1. $a + b > c$ (Given); 2. $a + b + (-b) > c + (-b)$ (Addition prop. of inequality); 3. $a + [b + (-b)] > c + (-b)$ (Assoc. prop. of addition); 4. $a + 0 > c + (-b)$ (Inverse prop. of addition); 5. $a > c + (-b)$ (Identity prop. of addition); 6. $a > c - b$ (Def. of subtraction)

10. It is given that $x < 1$. By the multiplication property of inequality, you can multiply both sides by x, since x is positive. The result is $x^2 < x$.

11. 1. $a > b$ (Given); 2. $\frac{a}{b} > \frac{b}{b}$ (Div. prop. of inequality); 3. $\frac{a}{b} > 1$ (Inverse prop. of mult.); 4. $(\frac{a}{b})n > 1$ (Given that n is a positive integer); 5. $\frac{a^n}{b^n} > 1$ (Prop. of powers); 6. $\frac{a^n}{b^n} \cdot b^n > 1 \cdot b^n$ (Mult. prop. of inequality); 7. $a^n > 1 \cdot b^n$ (Inverse prop. of mult.); 8. $a^n > b^n$ (Identity prop. of mult.)

12. Since $x \neq y$, $x - y = n$ $(n \neq 0)$. Hence, $x^2 - 2xy + y^2 = n^2$, and $x^2 - 2xy + y^2 > 0$. It follows that $x^2 + y^2 > 2xy$.

Write a two-column proof of the following.

9. Given: $a + b > c$

Prove: $a > c - b$

Write a *narrative*, or summary, proof of the following.

10. Given: $0 < x < 1$

Prove: $x^2 < x$

C. 11. Given that a and b are positive numbers, and n is a positive integer (1, 2, 3, . . .), write a two-column proof showing that if $a > b$, then $a^n > b^n$.

12. Given $x \neq y$, write a narrative proof showing that $x^2 + y^2 > 2xy$.

MATH HERITAGE/Systems of Measurement

Mankind's efforts to measure things accurately began with the most convenient instrument available: the human body. The distance between knuckles was called an *inch,* and the width of a hand was called a *hand* or *palm* (still used to measure the height of horses). A *span* was the distance between the tips of the thumb and little finger of a spread hand, and a *cubit* was the distance from the elbow to the tip of the longest finger. The length of a human *foot* eventually became a standard unit, and a *yard* was measured from the tip of the nose to the end of the thumb on an extended arm. Although imprecise, since no two people have exactly the same measurements, such methods were used for thousands of years. An advancement in the Middle Ages was the use of a metal bar with notches showing inches, feet, and yards.

As methods of measurement improved, special systems were developed for special purposes. At sea, depth is measured in *fathoms* (a fathom is about 6 feet) and distance in *nautical miles* (about 1.2 land miles). Lumber is measured in *board feet* (144 square inches) and piled wood in *cords* (128 cubic feet).

Modern scientists have their own language of measurement. Great distances in astronomy are measured in *light-years* or *parsecs,* and extremely small quantities are measured in *angstroms*. Today, almost any field of study or interest you can name uses a special system to measure some part of the world.

6.3 The Exterior Angle Theorem

You are now ready to consider some of the fundamental inequality theorems of geometry, beginning with ones involving a single triangle and its parts. From the definition of *interior of a triangle* stated in Chapter 2, you may be able to deduce the meaning of **interior angle of a triangle.**

In the triangle at the right, the interior angles are ∠1, ∠4, and ∠7. Where the sides of the triangle have been extended in the figure, six outside angles have been formed. These angles, ∠2, ∠3, ∠5, ∠6, ∠8, and ∠9, are the **exterior angles** of the triangle.

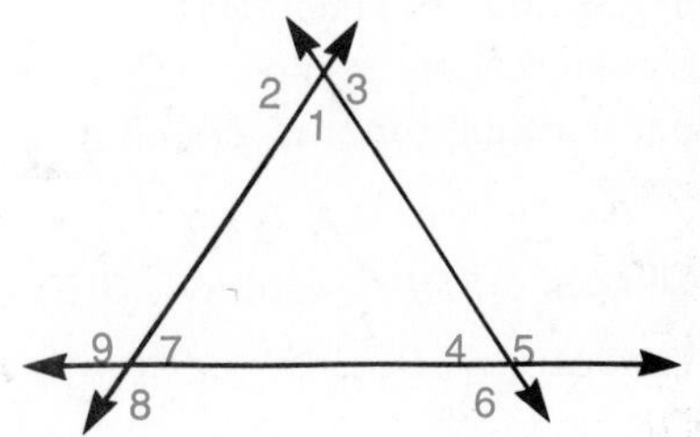

Note that the six exterior angles comprise three pairs of congruent vertical angles. The unnumbered vertical angles opposite the interior angles are *not* exterior angles. Note also that each exterior angle is *adjacent* to one of the interior angles. The other two interior angles are called **remote interior angles.** Thus, exterior ∠3 is adjacent to interior ∠1, and ∠7 and ∠4 are the remote interior angles with respect to ∠3.

DEFINITION: exterior angle
If *B* lies between *A* and *E*, then ∠*CBE* is an **exterior angle** of Δ*ABC*.

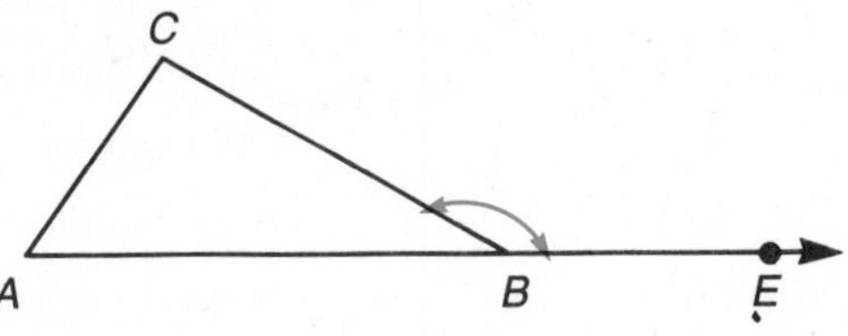

Now recall the Angle Addition Postulate (Postulate 13). If *D* is a point in the interior of ∠*BAC*, then *m*∠*BAC* = *m*∠*BAD* + *m*∠*DAC*. Applying the definition of $a > b$ and $a < b$, the postulate implies:

m∠*BAC* > *m*∠*BAD*   *m*∠*BAC* > *m*∠*DAC*
m∠*BAD* < *m*∠*BAC*   *m*∠*DAC* < *m*∠*BAC*

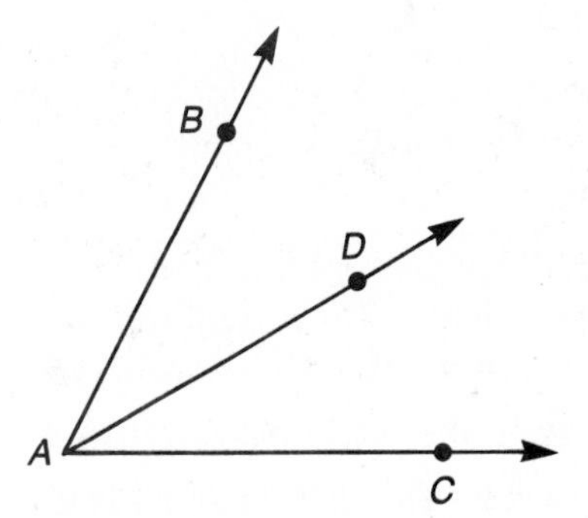

OBJECTIVES

Identify remote interior and exterior angles of a triangle.

Use the Exterior Angle Theorem and its corollary to determine the relationship of the measures of the angles of a figure.

TEACHER'S NOTES

See p. T29

The other exterior angles can be named by rearranging the letters of the definition.

MIXED REVIEW

1. If ∠*A* and *B* are supplements and *m*∠*A* = 2*x* − 3 and *m*∠*B* = 13 + 3*x*, find *x*. 34
2. Complementary and congruent angles measure ______? 45
3. Solve $\frac{2}{x+3} = \frac{7}{x-2}$. $x = -5$
4. What are the four ways to prove any triangles are congruent? SAS, ASA, SSS, and SAA
5. Solve for *P* if $Px - 2P = 3y$. $P = \frac{3y}{x-2}$

TEACHER'S RESOURCE MASTERS

Practice Master 17, Part 1
Quiz 11

Study these four inequalities in light of the last figure, and you will see that they can be summarized by the familiar statement, *the whole is greater than any of its parts.* You will use this concept in proving the first inequality theorem.

THEOREM 6.1 (The Exterior Angle Theorem)
An exterior angle of a triangle is larger than either remote interior angle.

The proof of Theorem 6.1 considers only remote $\angle B$, but it could apply to $\angle A$ as well.

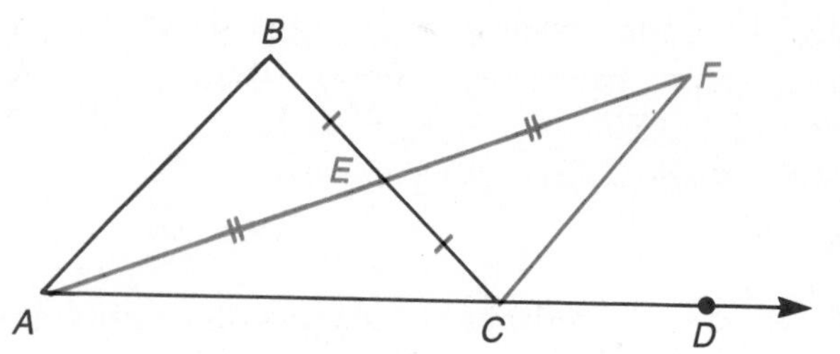

Given: $\triangle ABC$, exterior $\angle BCD$

Prove: $m\angle BCD > m\angle B$

Proof:

STATEMENTS	REASONS
1. Let E be the midpoint of $\overline{BC}$.	1. Every segment has exactly one midpoint (Theorem 1.5).
2. $\overline{BE} \cong \overline{CE}$	2. Definition of midpoint
3. Extend $\overrightarrow{AE}$ and let $EF = EA$.	3. Point Plotting Theorem (1.4)
4. $\angle BEA \cong \angle CEF$	4. Vertical $\angle$s are $\cong$ (Theorem 3.7).
5. $\triangle BEA \cong \triangle CEF$	5. SAS (Postulate 15)
6. $\angle B \cong \angle ECF$	6. Corres. parts of $\cong$ $\triangle$s are $\cong$.
7. $m\angle B = m\angle ECF$	7. Definition of $\cong$ $\angle$s
8. $m\angle BCD = m\angle ECF + m\angle FCD$	8. Angle Addition Postulate (13)
9. $m\angle BCD = m\angle B + m\angle FCD$	9. Steps 7, 8, and substitution
10. $m\angle BCD > m\angle B$	10. Definition of $a > b$

The Exterior Angle Theorem has an important corollary:

COROLLARY 6.1.1
If a triangle has a right angle, then the other two angles are acute.

The proof that follows shows that one angle ($\angle B$) is acute. Be extending another side ($\overrightarrow{CA}$), you can establish that the other angle ($\angle A$) is also acute.

Given: Right ΔABC with right angle at C

Prove: $\angle CBA$ is acute.

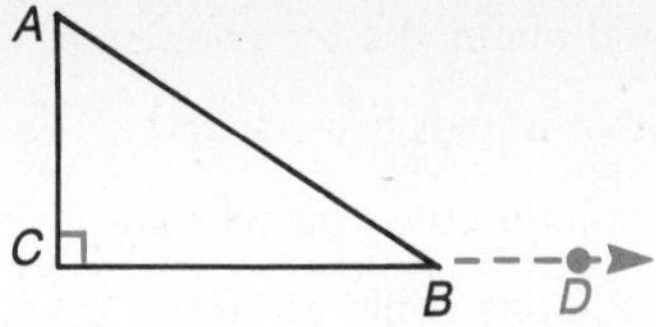

Proof:

STATEMENTS	REASONS
1. $\angle C$ is a rt. $\angle$.	1. Given
2. Extend $\overrightarrow{CB}$ to include point D.	2. Definition of ray
3. Form exterior $\angle ABD$.	3. Definition of exterior $\angle$
4. $m\angle C = 90$	4. Definition of right $\angle$
5. $m\angle ABD > m\angle C$	5. Exterior Angle Theorem (6.1)
6. $m\angle ABD > 90$	6. Steps 4, 5, and substitution
7. $\angle CBA$ and $\angle ABD$ form a linear pair.	7. Definition of linear pair
8. $\angle CBA$ and $\angle ABD$ are supplementary.	8. Supplement Postulate (14)
9. $m\angle CBA + m\angle ABD = 180$	9. Definition of supplementary $\angle$s
10. $m\angle CBA < 90$	10. Steps 6 and 9
11. $\angle CBA$ is acute.	11. Definition of acute $\angle$

ORAL EXERCISES

In the exercises below, refer to the three interior angles of ΔABC at the right as $\angle 1$, $\angle 2$, and $\angle 3$. Name all the other angles by using three letters.

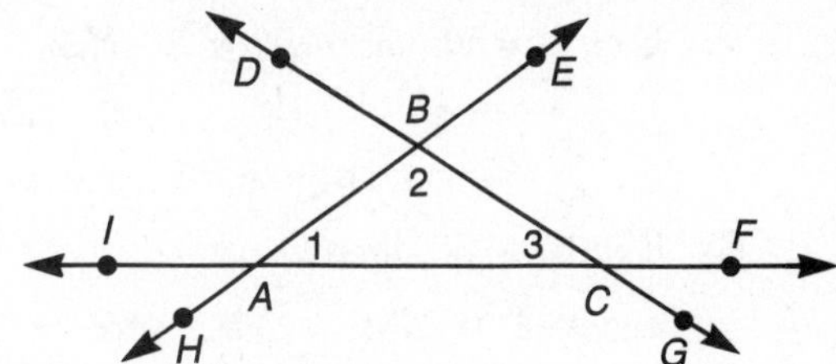

1. Name the exterior angles at vertex B.
2. Name the exterior angles at vertex A.
3. What is the relationship between $\angle 3$ and $\angle FCG$?
4. What is the relationship between each exterior angle and the interior angle adjacent to it?
5. Is $\angle DBE$ an exterior angle of ΔABC?
6. How many exterior angles are shown in the figure?

ASSIGNMENT GUIDE

Minimum 1-12
Regular 1-15 odd
Maximum 1-15 odd, 16-18

Oral Exercises

1. $\angle ABD$, $\angle CBE$
2. $\angle BAI$, $\angle HAC$
3. They are vertical angles.
4. They are supplementary.
5. no
6. 6

7. They are vertical angles.
8. ∠BCF or ∠ACG
9. if △ABC were equilateral
10. in a right △
11. ∠1, ∠3
12. ∠2, ∠3

Written Exercises

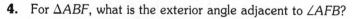

1. ∠FBA, ∠FCD,
2. ∠A, ∠AFC
3. △FBC, △ACF
4. ∠EFB
5. They are supplementary or adjacent angles.
6. ∠ABF and ∠CBF are right angles; △ABF and △CBF are right triangles; ∠A, ∠BFA, ∠BFC, and ∠BCF are acute angles.
7. b
8. d
9. b
10. a
11. c
12. a
13. No, the exterior angle must be the supplement of the interior angle, or 90°.
14. 4
15. Corollary 6.1.1
16. The conjecture is false. In the figure below, exterior ∠CBE is a right angle, but remote interior ∠D is obtuse.

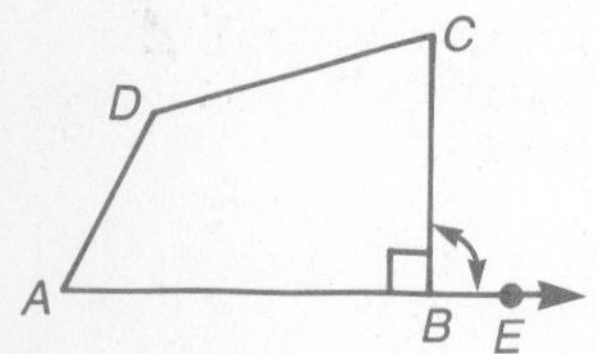

7. What can be said about the exterior angles at each vertex?

8. For which exterior angles are ∠1 and ∠2 remote interior angles?

9. Under what condition could all six exterior angles be congruent?

10. Under what conditions could an exterior angle be a right angle?

11. Name the remote interior angles of ∠EBC.

12. Name the remote interior angles of ∠IAE.

WRITTEN EXERCISES

A. Refer to the figure at the right for Exercises 1–6.

1. Name all the exterior angles for △BCF.

2. For △ACF, name the remote interior angles of ∠DCF.

3. ∠ACF is an interior angle of which triangle(s)?

4. For △ABF, what is the exterior angle adjacent to ∠AFB?

5. What is the relationship between ∠ABF and ∠CBF?

6. Given $\overline{FB} \perp \overleftrightarrow{AB}$, state three new conclusions you could deduce from the figure.

B. In Exercises 7–12, choose the answer that makes each statement correct, referring to the figure at the right.

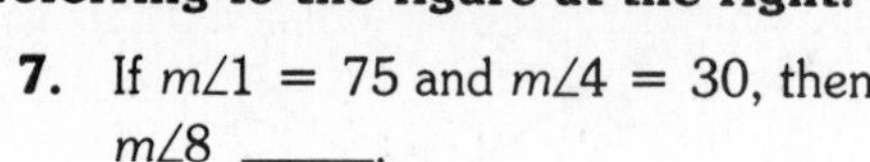

7. If m∠1 = 75 and m∠4 = 30, then m∠8 ____.

a. = 75 **b.** > 75 **c.** = 30 **d.** < 90

8. If m∠4 = 60, then ____.

a. m∠1 = 120 **b.** m∠6 = 30 **c.** m∠7 = 60 **d.** m∠5 = 120

9. If m∠6 = 50, then ____ equals 50.

a. m∠3 **b.** m∠4 **c.** m∠5 **d.** m∠7

10. If m∠1 = 90, then ∠7 and ∠4 ____.

a. are each acute **b.** are each obtuse **c.** have equal measures

d. have measures whose sum is greater than 90

11. If ∠2 is a right angle, then ____ is acute.

a. ∠1 **b.** ∠3 **c.** ∠4 **d.** ∠5

12. _____ exterior angles are numbered in the figure.

a. Four **b.** Five **c.** Six **d.** Seven

13. ΔXYZ is a right triangle with right $\angle X$. Is it possible for an exterior angle at vertex X to be an obtuse angle? Explain your answer.

14. ΔPQR has one obtuse angle. How many of its exterior angles are obtuse?

15. What argument would you use to refute the claim that a triangle can have more than one right angle?

16. Would you accept the following conjecture? *An exterior angle of a quadrilateral is greater than each of its remote interior angles.* If so, give a proof. If not, sketch a counterexample.

C. 17. Prove that a triangle cannot have two obtuse angles.

18. Prove that the sum of the measures of any two angles of a triangle is less than 180.

SELF-QUIZ

1. A _____ is one case that causes a proposed rule to be rejected.

2. Draw a counterexample figure to reject the conjecture "All four-sided polygons are convex sets."

3. When you multiply both sides of an inequality by _____, you must change the direction of the inequality.

4. The rule stated in Exercise 3 is called _____.

Identify the property that justifies each of the following statements.

5. If $k > j$ and $x = 4$, then $xk > xj$.

6. If $y > 5$, then $y - 5 > 0$.

7. If an ocean is deeper than a sea, and a sea is deeper than a bay, then an ocean is deeper than a bay.

8. If $k < 40$, then $7 + k < 47$.

9. If $14x < 7$, then $x < \frac{1}{2}$.

Solve the following inequalities.

10. $-3x < 12$ **11.** $36 > 5x + 11$ **12.** $\frac{1}{3}x > x$ **13.** $x - 32 > 17$

Refer to the figure at the right for Exercises 14–17.

14. Name the exterior angles at vertex A.

15. Name the remote interior angles of $\angle 10$.

16. If $m\angle 11$ is 115, what is $m\angle 10$?

17. If $m\angle 6 = 160$, what is $m\angle 10$?

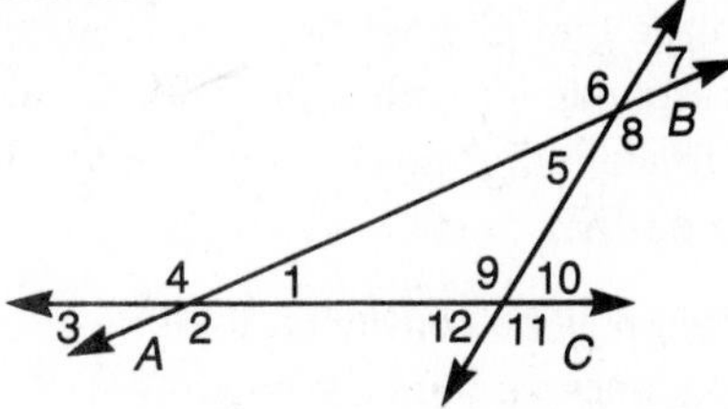

17. In the figure below, if $\angle 2$ and $\angle 3$ were obtuse, then $\angle 1$ and $\angle 4$ would also be obtuse, by Theorem 6.1. Thus, $m\angle 1 + m\angle 2 > 180$, and $m\angle 3 + m\angle 4 > 180$. This violates the Supplement Post. (Postulate 14).

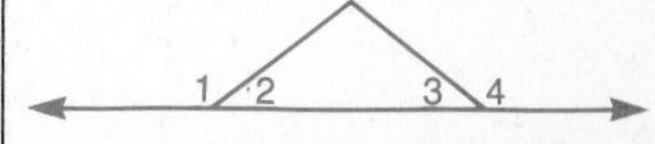

18. In the figure above, if $m\angle 2 + m\angle 3 \geq 180$, then $m\angle 1 + m\angle 4 \geq 180$ by Theorem 6.1. This violates Postulate 14.

Self-Quiz

1. counterexample
2.
3. a negative number
4. the rule of order reversal
5. Multiplication property of inequality
6. Subtraction property of inequality
7. Transition property of inequality
8. Addition property of inequality
9. Division property of inequality
10. $x > -4$
11. $x < 5$
12. $x < 0$
13. $x > 49$
14. $\angle 4$, $\angle 2$
15. $\angle 1$, $\angle 5$
16. 65
17. $m\angle 10 > 20$

OBJECTIVE

Use SAA and HL in proofs.

TEACHER'S NOTES

See p. T29

MIXED REVIEW

1. Simplify $\frac{42x^3y}{70x^2y^3}$. $\frac{3x}{5y^2}$
2. Explain the difference between $AB = CD$ and $\overline{AB} \cong \overline{CD}$. $AB = CD$ applies to real numbers that are the distances; $AB \cong CD$ applies to segments that are of equal length.
3. Solve $\frac{14}{12} = \frac{x-3}{5}$. $x = 8\frac{5}{6}$
4. Factor $12x^2 - 23x + 5$. $(3x - 5)(4x - 1)$
5. Use a ruler to measure and draw a triangle with sides of 2, 3 and 6 inches. impossible

TEACHER'S RESOURCE MASTERS

Practice Master 17, Part 2
Quiz 11

6.4 The Hypotenuse-Leg Theorem

From what you have learned in previous chapters, you know that three congruencies are indicated for the two triangles below:

$\angle A = \angle D \qquad \angle B = \angle E \qquad \overline{AC} \cong \overline{DF}$

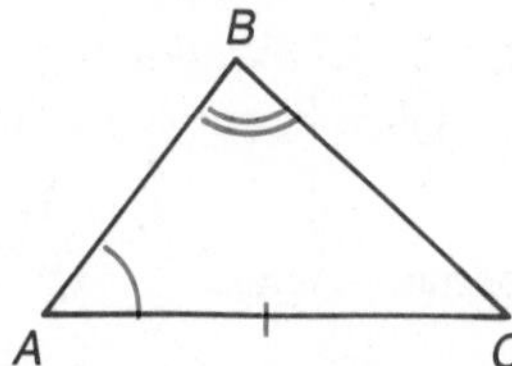

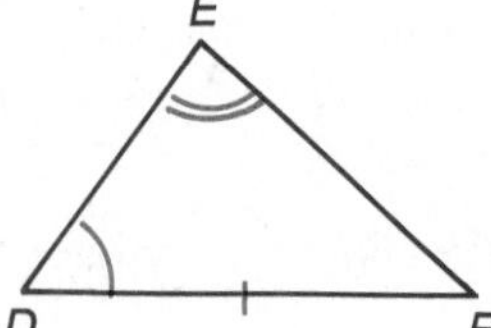

This is neither an ASA nor an SAS correspondence but rather an SAA correspondence. *Two angles and a side opposite one of the angles in one triangle are congruent to the corresponding parts of the other triangle.* The triangles *appear* to be congruent, but can you accept SAA as a valid congruence theorem?

Recall that in the first lesson of this chapter, you considered whether you should accept SSA as a theorem, and you decided against it. Could this be a similar case?

Before trying to prove an SAA theorem, see if you can sketch a counterexample: two triangles that satisfy the SAA condition but are obviously not congruent. Extend $\overrightarrow{AB}$ to the point B' and make $m\angle B' = m\angle B$, as shown in the left-hand figure below. In doing this, you retain the relationships $\angle A \cong \angle D$ and $\angle B' \cong \angle E$. In other words, you still have the AA part of the correspondence SAA. Now extend the side from B' until it intersects $\overrightarrow{AC}$, giving you the third vertex of the triangle, C', as shown in the right-hand figure below.

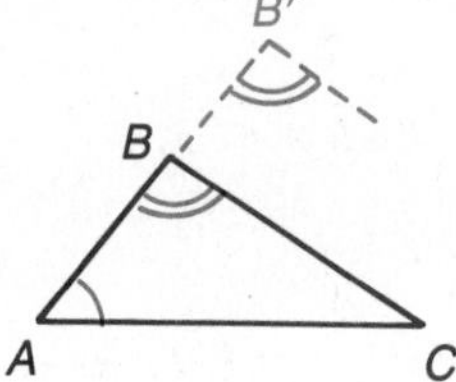

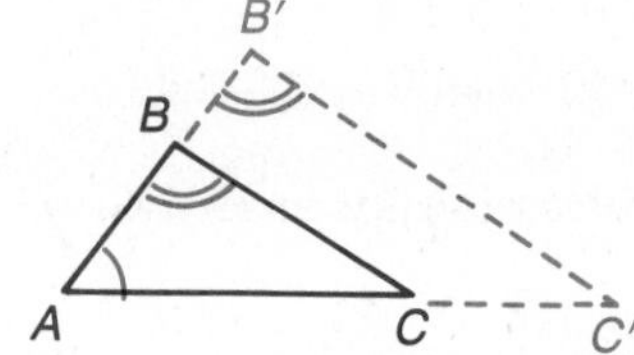

You can see that C' does not coincide with vertex C of the original triangle. You still have an AA correspondence with ΔDEF, but you no longer have an SAA correspondence. If you move point B to any other point on $\overrightarrow{AB}$ and keep $m\angle B$ the same, $\overline{AC}$ will no longer have the same measure as $\overline{DF}$.

You should now be convinced that it is impossible to sketch two triangles that satisfy the SAA correspondence and are not congruent. You are ready to accept and prove the SAA theorem.

THEOREM 6.2 [The Side-Angle-Angle (SAA) Theorem]
Given a correspondence between two triangles, if two angles and a side opposite one of them in one triangle are congruent to the corresponding parts of the second triangle, then the correspondence is a congruence.

Before plunging into the proof, a bit of planning is in order. Look again at ΔABC and ΔDEF. You might think to yourself how simple it would be if you knew that $\overline{AB} \cong \overline{DE}$, because then the two triangles would be congruent by ASA. So the proof takes on a new perspective. How might you prove that $\overline{AB} \cong \overline{DE}$? It turns out that an indirect proof is the best approach. Assume that the segments are not congruent, and see if you reach a contradiction.

The assumption $AB \neq DE$ yields two possibilities: $AB > DE$ or $AB < DE$. Your proof must cover both cases.

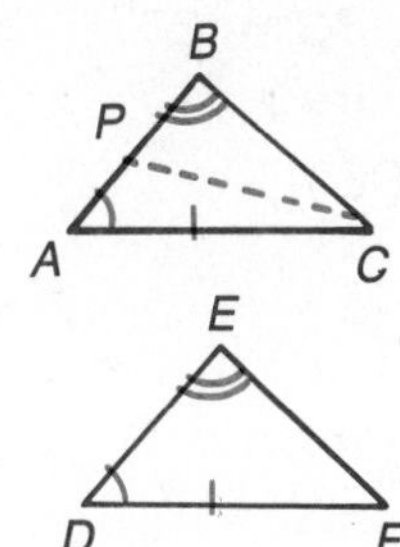

Given: ΔABC, ΔDEF
$\overline{AC} \cong \overline{DF}$
$\angle B \cong \angle E$, $\angle A \cong \angle D$

Prove: $\Delta ABC \cong \Delta DEF$

Proof: Case 1

Since $AB > DE$ (indirect assumption), there is a point P between A and B such that $AP = DE$, and $\Delta APC \cong \Delta DEF$ by SAS. Thus, $\angle APC \cong \angle E$ by corresponding parts of congruent triangles. It is given that $\angle E \cong \angle B$, so by transitivity $\angle APC \cong \angle B$. But this is impossible, because exterior $\angle APC$ is greater than remote $\angle B$ in ΔPBC (Theorem 6.1). Therefore, you must reject the possibility that $AB > DE$.

Case 2

The figure at the right illustrates the second case, $AB < DE$. The proof that this is also impossible is left as an exercise. It completes the indirect proof of Theorem 6.2.

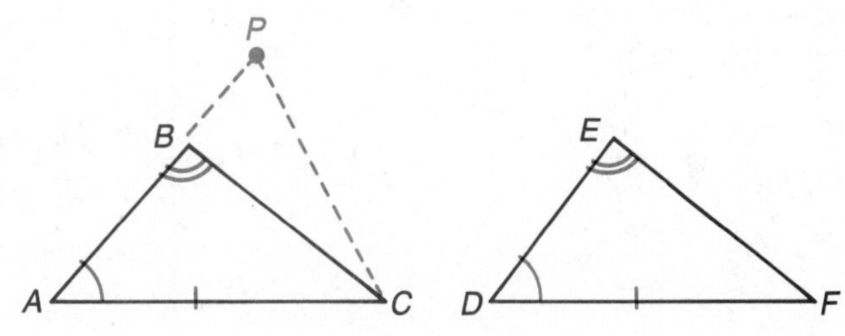

DEFINITION: lemma
A Greek word meaning *assumption.* A **lemma** is a theorem useful as an intermediate step toward proving another, more basic theorem.

It happens that the SAA Theorem is a lemma for the next theorem.

THEOREM 6.3 (The Hypotenuse-Leg [HL] Theorem)
Given a correspondence between two right triangles, if the hypotenuse and one leg of one triangle are congruent to the corresponding parts of the second triangle, then the correspondence is a congruence.

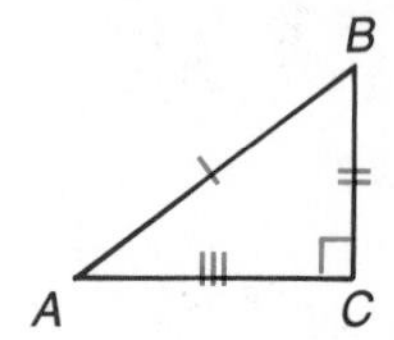

Given: ΔABC, ΔDEF
$AB = DE$, $BC = EF$
$\angle C$ and $\angle F$ are rt. $\angle$s.

Prove: $\Delta ABC \cong \Delta DEF$

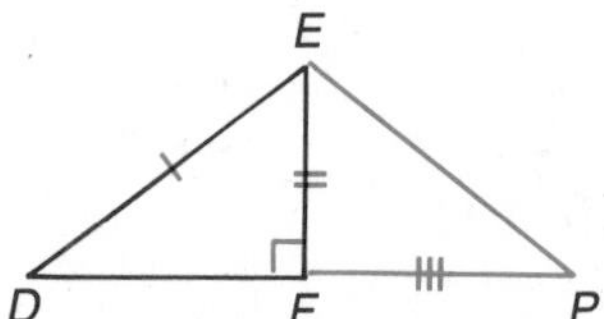

Proof:

STATEMENTS	REASONS
1. On the ray opposite $\overrightarrow{FD}$, choose P such that $FP = CA$.	1. Point Plotting Theorem
2. $\angle EFP$ is a rt. $\angle$.	2. If 2 intersecting lines form one rt. $\angle$ then they form 4 rt. $\angle$s (Theorem 3.8).
3. $\angle C$ is a rt. $\angle$.	3. Given
4. $\angle EFP \cong \angle C$	4. All rt. $\angle$s are $\cong$ (Theorem 3.3).
5. $BC = EF$	5. Given
6. $\Delta ABC \cong \Delta PEF$	6. Steps *1, 4, 5,* and SAS
7. $\overline{PE} \cong \overline{AB}$	7. Corres. parts of $\cong$ Δs are $\cong$.
8. $AB = DE$	8. Given
9. $\overline{AB} \cong \overline{DE}$	9. Def. of $\cong$ segments
10. $\overline{PE} = \overline{DE}$	10. Congruence of segments is transitive.
11. $\angle D \cong \angle P$	11. Isosceles Triangle Theorem
12. $\angle EFD$ is a rt. $\angle$.	12. Given
13. $\angle EFP \cong \angle EFD$	13. Theorem 3.3
14. $\Delta PEF \cong \Delta DEF$	14. Steps *10, 11, 13,* and SAA
15. $\Delta ABC \cong \Delta DEF$	15. Substitution prop.

ORAL EXERCISES

In Exercises 1–10, decide whether the triangles below are congruent on the basis of the given information. If your answer is *yes*, state the postulate or theorem that supports your answer.

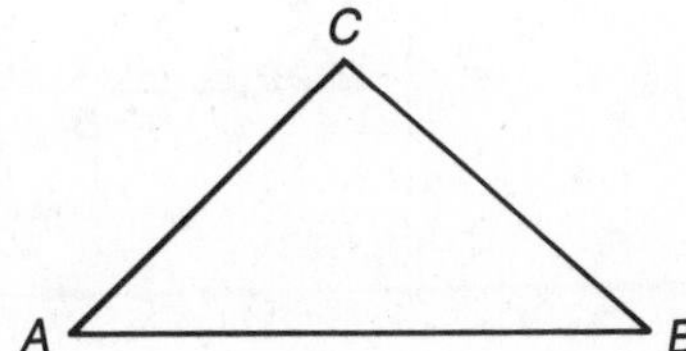

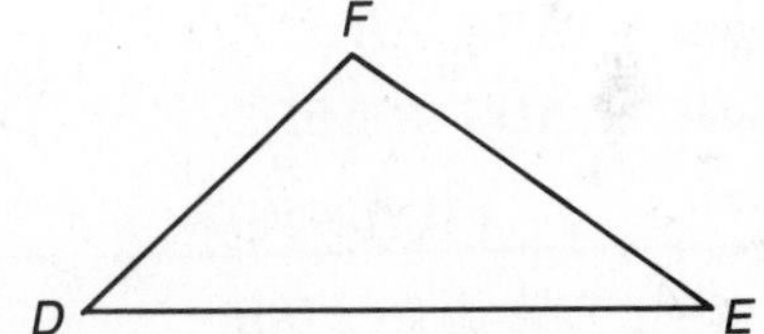

1. $m\angle A = m\angle D$; $m\angle F = m\angle C$, $CB = FE$

2. $m\angle A = m\angle D$, $m\angle E = m\angle B$, $AB = DE$

3. $m\angle C = 90$, $m\angle F = 90$, $FE = CB$, $AB = DE$

4. $AC = DF$, $BC = EF$, $m\angle C = m\angle F$

5. $AC = CB$, $DF = FE$, $m\angle C = m\angle F$

6. $CA = FD$, $m\angle D = m\angle A$, $m\angle E = m\angle B$

7. $CA = FD$, $FE = CB$, $m\angle B = m\angle E$

8. $\overline{CA} \perp \overline{BC}$, $\overline{FD} \perp \overline{FE}$, $AB = DE$, $CA = FD$

9. $AC = DF$, $CB = 2AC$, $FE = 2DF$, $AB = DE$

10. $m\angle A = m\angle D$, $m\angle C = m\angle F$, $m\angle B = m\angle E$

11. Which of the following correspondences can be used to prove congruence for any triangles?

a. SAS **b.** SAA **c.** HL **d.** SSA **e.** ASA **f.** SSS

12. Which term identifies a theorem useful in proving a new theorem?

a. corollary **b.** lemma **c.** hypotenuse **d.** biconditional

13. The proof of Theorem 6.2 uses which method?

a. indirect **b.** inductive **c.** converse **d.** transitive

14. If you use the HL Theorem to prove two isosceles triangles congruent, what must be true?

a. The triangles must also be adjacent.

b. The triangles must be equilateral.

c. The triangles must have corresponding right angles.

d. The bases of the triangles must be congruent.

ASSIGNMENT GUIDE

Minimum 1–12
Regular 1–13
Maximum 1–15 odd, 16

Oral Exercises

1. yes, SAA 2. yes, ASA
3. yes, HL 4. yes, SAS
5. no 6. yes, SAA
7. no 8. yes, HL
9. yes, SSS 10. no
11. a, b, e, f
12. b
13. a
14. c

WRITTEN EXERCISES

A. If $\triangle ABC \cong \triangle PDQ$, which parts correspond to the following?

1. $\overline{AC}$ **2.** $\angle B$ **3.** $\overline{BC}$ **4.** $\overline{DP}$

Supply the reasons in the proof below.

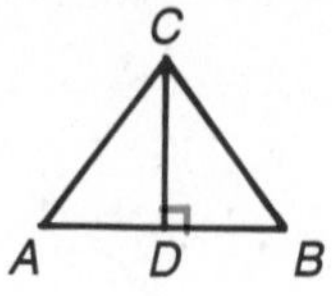

Given: $\triangle ABC$, $\overline{AB} \perp \overline{CD}$, $\overline{CA} \cong \overline{CB}$

Prove: $\triangle ADC \cong \triangle BDC$

Proof:

STATEMENTS	REASONS
1. $\overline{AB} \perp \overline{CD}$, $\overline{CA} \cong \overline{CB}$	1. **5.**
2. $\angle ADC$ and $\angle BDC$ are rt. $\angle$s.	2. **6.**
3. $\triangle ADC$ and $\triangle BDC$ are rt. $\triangle$s.	3. **7.**
4. $\overline{CD} \cong \overline{CD}$	4. **8.**
5. $\triangle ADC \cong \triangle BDC$	5. **9.**

B. 10. In $\triangle ABC$, $m\angle A = m\angle B$. $\overline{CD}$ is perpendicular to $\overline{AB}$ at point D. Write a two-column proof showing that $\triangle ADC \cong \triangle BDC$.

11. If two legs of a right triangle are congruent to the corresponding legs of a second right triangle, are the two triangles congruent? Give a reason for your answer.

12. Given: In the figure at right, $\overline{AP} \cong \overline{BP}$, $\angle C \cong \angle D$

Prove: $\overline{AC} \cong \overline{BD}$

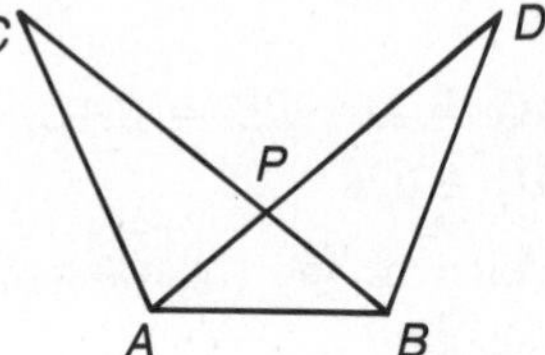

13. Given: $\overline{CE} \perp \overline{AB}$, $\overline{AC} \cong \overline{BC}$, $\angle ACD \cong \angle BCF$

Prove: $\triangle DEC \cong \triangle FEC$

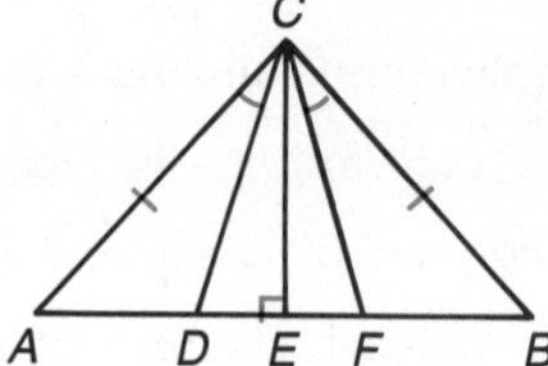

14. Prove Case 2 ($AB < DE$) of Theorem 6.2.

C. 15. Given: In $\triangle PQR$, $\overline{PT} \cong \overline{QS}$, $\overline{PT} \perp \overline{RQ}$, $\overline{QS} \perp \overline{RP}$

Prove: $\overline{PR} \cong \overline{QR}$

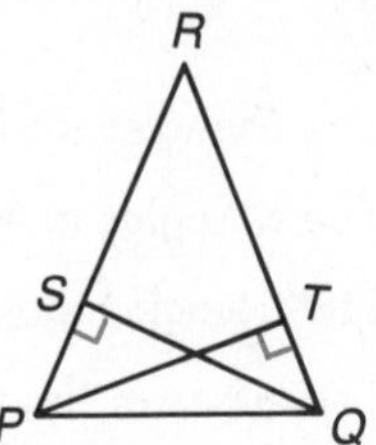

16. State the result of Exercise 15 as a conditional sentence.

Written Exercises

1. $\overline{PQ}$ 2. $\angle D$
3. $\overline{DQ}$ 4. $\overline{BA}$
5. Given 6. Def. of $\perp$
7. Def. of rt. $\triangle$
8. Congruence of segments is reflexive.
9. HL Theorem
10. See *Selected Answers*, p. 631
11. yes, LL or SAS
12. *1.* $\overline{AP} \cong \overline{BP}$ (Given); *2.* $\angle PAB \cong \angle PBA$ (Isos. $\triangle$ Theorem); *3.* $\angle C \cong \angle D$ (Given); *4.* $\overline{AB} \cong \overline{AB}$ (Congruence of segments is reflex.); *5.* $\triangle BCA \cong \triangle ADB$ (SAA); *6.* $\overline{AC} \cong \overline{BD}$ (CPCTC)
13. *1.* $\angle CEA$ and $\angle CEB$ are rt. $\angle$s, (Def. of $\perp$); *2.* $\triangle AEC$ and $\triangle BEC$ are rt. $\triangle$s (Def. of rt. $\triangle$); *3.* $\overline{CE} \cong \overline{CE}$ (Congruence of segments is reflex.); *4.* $\overline{AC} \cong \overline{BC}$ (Given); *5.* $\triangle AEC \cong \triangle BEC$ (HL); *6.* $\angle A \cong \angle B$ (CPCTC); *7.* $\triangle ADC \cong \triangle BFC$ (ASA); *8.* $\overline{CD} \cong \overline{CF}$ (CPCTC); *9.* $\triangle CDE \cong \triangle CFE$ (HL)
14. See *Selected Answers*, p. 631
15. *1.* $\overline{PT} \cong \overline{QS}$ (Given); *2.* $\overline{PQ} \cong \overline{PQ}$ (Congruence of segments is reflex.); *3.* $\triangle PTQ \cong \triangle QSP$ (HL); *4.* $\angle SPQ \cong \angle TQP$ (CPCTC); *5.* $\overline{PR} \cong \overline{QR}$ (Theorem 4.4)
16. If the perpendiculars connecting two vertices to the opposite sides of a triangle are congruent, then the triangle is isosceles.

6.5 Inequalities in a Single Triangle

In the first lesson of this chapter, the following conjecture was made: *If two sides of a triangle are of unequal length, then the angles opposite them are of unequal measure.* Since then, new theorems have been proved, and you are now equipped to establish your conjecture as a theorem. Note that it has been expanded.

THEOREM 6.4
If two sides of a triangle are not congruent, then the angles opposite those sides are not congruent, and the larger angle is opposite the larger side.

Given: ΔABC, $AB > AC$
Prove: $m\angle C > m\angle B$

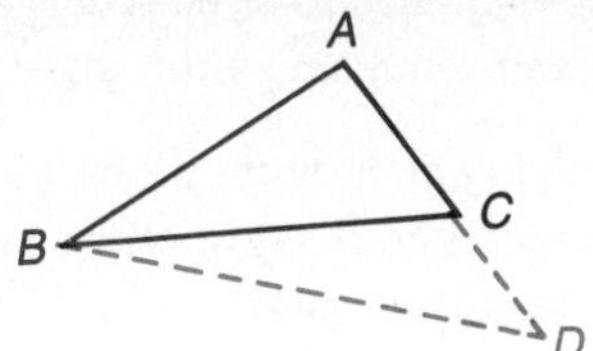

Proof: Let D be a point on $\overrightarrow{AC}$ such that $AD = AB$, as provided by the Point Plotting Theorem. Since the base angles of an isosceles triangle are congruent by Theorem 4.3, you know that $m\angle ABD = m\angle D$.

Now, because $AB > AC$, it follows by substitution that $AD > AC$. From Theorem 1.1 it follows that C lies between A and D. Next, Theorem 5.5 affirms that C lies in the interior of $\angle ABD$. You can therefore apply the Angle Addition Postulate and conclude that $m\angle ABD = m\angle ABC + m\angle CBD$.

From this and the definition of *greater than,* $m\angle ABD > m\angle ABC$. Substituting $m\angle D$ for $m\angle ABD$, you can conclude $m\angle D > m\angle ABC$. Finally, since $\angle ACB$ is an exterior angle of ΔBCD, $m\angle ACB > m\angle D$, and therefore $m\angle ACB > m\angle ABC$ by transitivity. Renaming the angles, $m\angle C > m\angle B$.

The following example illustrates an indirect approach sometimes used in the proof of geometric theorems.

A district attorney prosecuting a burglary suspect has established that the suspect could have been only three possible places at the time of the crime: at home, at work, or at the scene of the crime. The attorney proves that the suspect was not at home or at work. Is this sufficient to establish the suspect's presence at the scene of the crime? yes

The example illustrates that if there are a limited number of possible explanations, the true explanation can be found by eliminating all the others. This approach is useful in proving the next theorem.

OBJECTIVE

Use the Triangle Inequality Theorem and Theorems 6.4 and 6.5 to answer questions involving inequalities in a triangle.

TEACHER'S NOTES

See p. T29

MIXED REVIEW

1. What is a locus of points? See Section 5.2
2. What are the three undefined terms of geometry? point, line, plane
3. Solve $\frac{3x}{4} = \frac{12}{5}$. $x = 3\frac{1}{5}$
4. If the coordinates of R and S are -9 and 17, what is the coordinate of the midpoint of $\overline{RS}$. 4
5. Solve $3x^2 - 13x + 4 = 0$. $\{\frac{1}{3}, 4\}$

TEACHER'S RESOURCE MASTERS

Practice Master 17, Part 3

THEOREM 6.5
If two angles of a triangle are not congruent, then the sides opposite them are not congruent, and the longer side is opposite the larger angle.

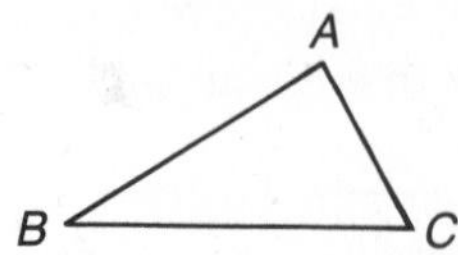

Given: ΔABC, $m\angle C > m\angle B$

Prove: $AB > AC$

Proof: There are three possibilities for $\overline{AB}$ and $\overline{AC}$: $AB < AC$, $AB = AC$, or $AB > AC$. If $AB < AC$, then $m\angle C < m\angle B$ from Theorem 6.4, but this contradicts the given. If $AB = AC$, then ΔABC is isosceles and $m\angle B = m\angle C$. This also contradicts the given. Therefore, the one remaining alternative, $AB > AC$, must be correct, and the theorem is proved.

Applying an indirect proof, you have assumed that two out of three possible options are true, and when both assumptions lead to contradictions, you must accept the remaining possibility as the correct one.

Theorem 6.5 leads to a theorem illustrated by the following problem. A farmer wants to run a waterline from the farmhouse to the road. The shorter the pipe, the less the cost. All other factors being equal, which path should the pipe follow: *a*, *b*, or *c*?

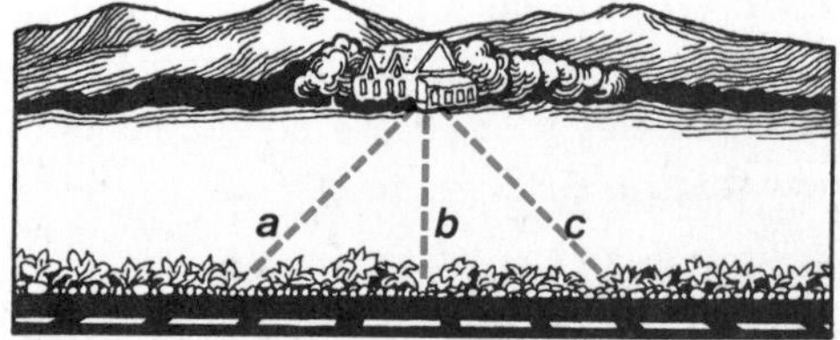

By measuring, you could confirm that *b* is the shortest segment, and *b* appears to be perpendicular to the road. From this, can you conclude that the shortest distance from a point (the farmhouse) to a line (the road) is measured on the perpendicular to the line? The next theorem proves this conjecture.

THEOREM 6.6
The shortest segment joining a point to a line is the perpendicular segment.

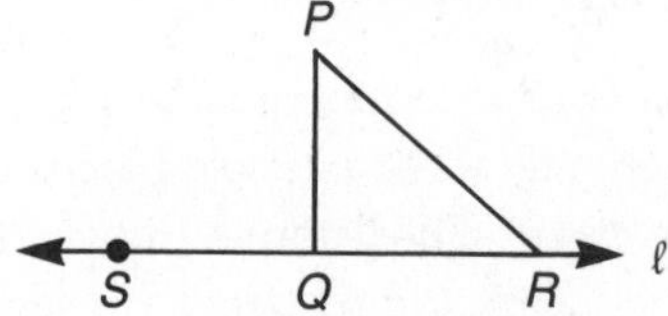

Given: Line l, external point P, point Q on l such that $PQ \perp l$, and R any other point on l

Prove: $PQ < PR$

Proof: Let S be a point on l such that Q is between S and R. Then $\angle PQS$ is an exterior angle of ΔPQR, and $m\angle PQS > m\angle R$. Since $\angle PQR \cong \angle PQS$, $m\angle PQR > m\angle R$. By Theorem 6.5 it follows that $PR > PQ$. Therefore, $\overline{PQ}$ is the shorter segment from P to l.

> **DEFINITION: distance between a line and a point**
> The **distance between a line and a point not on it** is the length of the perpendicular segment from the point to the line. The **distance between a line and a point on the line** is defined as zero.

In the first lesson of this chapter you observed that the flying distance from Houston to New York City is longer if you make a stop at Chicago. The next theorem formalizes that observation.

> **THEOREM 6.7 (The Triangle Inequality Theorem)**
> The sum of the lengths of any two sides of a triangle is greater than the length of the third side.

ASSIGNMENT GUIDE

Day 1
Minimum 1-14
Regular 1-16
Maximum 1-16
Day 2
Minimum 15-25
Regular 17-26
Maximum 17-27

Given: ΔABC
Prove: $AB + BC > AC$

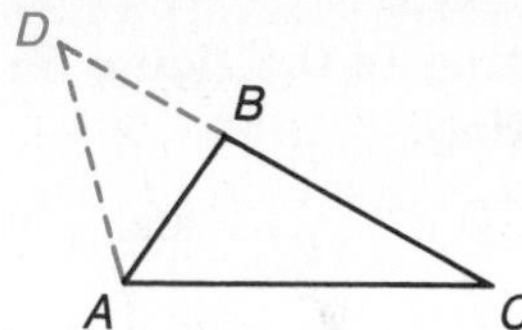

Proof:

STATEMENTS	REASONS
1. Let D be a point on $\overrightarrow{CB}$ such that B is between D and C and $DB = AB$.	1. The Point Plotting Theorem
2. $DC = DB + BC$	2. Definition of between
3. $DC = AB + BC$	3. Steps *1, 2,* and substitution
4. $m\angle DAB + m\angle BAC = m\angle DAC$	4. The Angle Addition Postulate
5. $m\angle DAB < m\angle DAC$	5. Definition of less than
6. $m\angle D = m\angle DAB$	6. Isosceles Triangle Theorem
7. $m\angle D < m\angle DAC$	7. Steps *5, 6,* and substitution
8. $DC > AC$	8. Theorem 6.5
9. $AB + BC > AC$	9. Steps *3, 8,* and substitution

ORAL EXERCISES

1. In proving Theorem 6.5, how can you be certain that there is no other possibility than $AB < CD$, $AB = CD$, or $AB > CD$?

2. In ΔPQR, $PR > QR$. Which angles can be compared, and how?

3. In ΔMNP, $m\angle M > m\angle P$. Which sides can be compared, and how?

Oral Exercises

1. uniqueness of order property
2. $m\angle Q > m\angle P$
3. $NP > MN$

4. No; if the ratio is 1:2:3, then the sum of the lengths of two sides will equal the length of the third, contrary to Theorem 6.7.

5. He can conclude that he scored a C by the process of elimination.

6. In a rigorous geometry, you never postulate a statement if it can be proved.

Written Exercises

1. CA, CB
2. CB, AB
3. Theorem 6.6
4. CD, CA, CB
5. Theorem 6.5 with or without Theorem 6.6
6. FE, DF, DE
7. Theorem 6.5 with or without Theorem 6.6
8. =
9. >
10. <
11. =
12. >, >
13. $\overline{ZY}$
14. $\overline{WZ}$

4. Can the lengths of the three sides of a triangle have the ratio 1:2:3? Support your answer.

5. A geometry teacher at a certain school posts two lists on the bulletin board the day after every test. One list, the honors list, names all students who received a score higher than C. The second list, a warning list, names all students who scored lower than C. Peter checks the bulletin board the day after a test and does not find his name on either list. What can he conclude, and what logical method has he applied?

6. Some of the theorems in this and other lessons are intuitively obvious. Why not accept them as postulates?

WRITTEN EXERCISES

A. Referring to the figure on the right, complete the following.

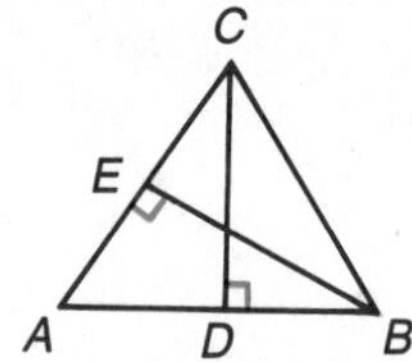

1. $CD <$ ____ and ____

2. $BE <$ ____ and ____

3. State the theorem that supports your conclusions in Exercises 1 and 2.

4. With angle measures as shown in the figure, insert CA, CB, and CD in correct order: ____ $<$ ____ $<$ ____.

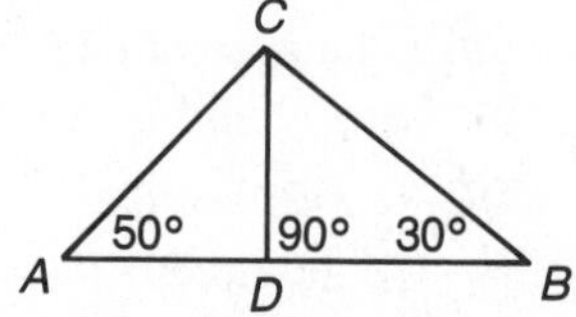

5. State the theorem or theorems that support your conclusion in Exercise 4.

6. In ΔDEF, not shown, $m\angle D = 30$, $m\angle E = 60$, and $m\angle F = 90$. Insert DE, FE, and DF in correct order: ____ $<$ ____ $<$ ____.

7. State the theorem or theorems that support your conclusion in Exercise 6.

B. Which symbol, $<$, $=$, or $>$, should replace the ●?

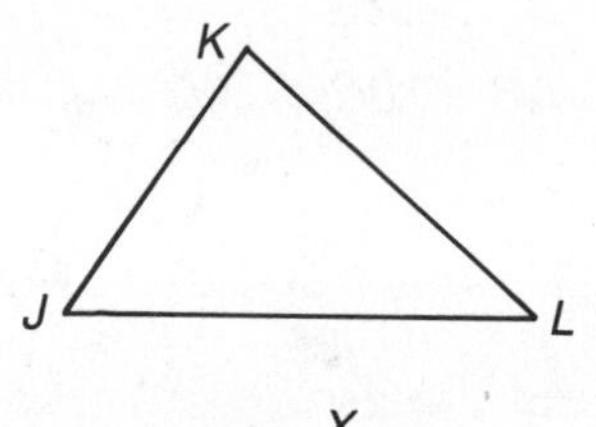

8. If $m\angle K = 80$ and $m\angle J = 50$, then JK ● KL.

9. If $m\angle J = 50$ and $m\angle L = 30$, then KL ● KJ.

10. If $m\angle K = 110$ and $m\angle L = 40$, then KJ ● LJ.

11. If $m\angle J = m\angle L$, then JK ● KL.

12. If $\angle K$ is obtuse, JL ● KL and JL ● JK.

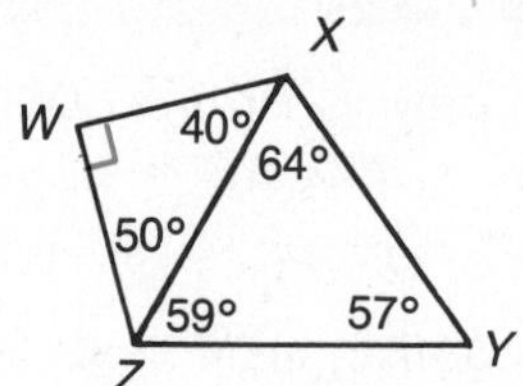

13. What is the longest segment in the figure?

14. What is the shortest segment in the figure?

15. Which of the following sets of numbers could be the lengths of the sides of a triangle? What theorem supports your answer? {3, 5, 8} {1, 6, 9} {3, 4, 6} {2, 2, 4}

16. What can you deduce about the measures of the three angles of a scalene triangle? What theorem supports your answer?

17. Fill in the blanks. If a triangle has two sides measuring 6 cm and 15 cm, the third must be greater than ____ and less than ____.

Supply the reasons in the following proof.

Given: $\triangle ABC$, M is the midpoint of $\overline{AC}$, $BM > AM$.

Prove: $m\angle A + m\angle C > m\angle ABC$

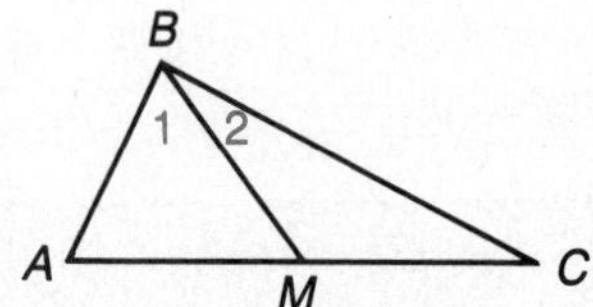

Proof:

STATEMENTS	REASONS
1. M is the midpoint of $\overline{AC}$.	1. **18.**
2. $AM = MC$	2. **19.**
3. $BM > AM$	3. **20.**
4. $BM > MC$	4. **21.**
5. In $\triangle AMB$, $m\angle A > m\angle 1$	5. **22.**
6. In $\triangle BMC$, $m\angle C > m\angle 2$	6. **23.**
7. $m\angle A + m\angle C > m\angle 1 + m\angle 2$	7. **24.**
8. $m\angle A + m\angle C > m\angle ABC$	8. **25.**

C. 26. Prove that the perimeter of a quadrilateral is greater than the sum of the lengths of the segments connecting its opposite vertices.

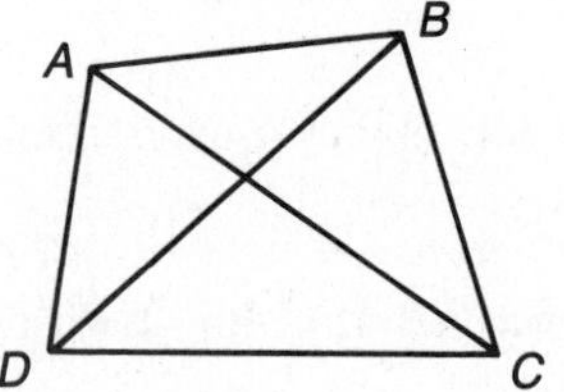

27. Line k is a straight shoreline and P and Q are two islands offshore. A skipper wants to go from island P to island Q, but first the skipper has to drop a passenger off on shore. Find the point on shore such that the entire trip is as short as possible. (Ignore tides, currents, wind, or any other extraneous factors.)

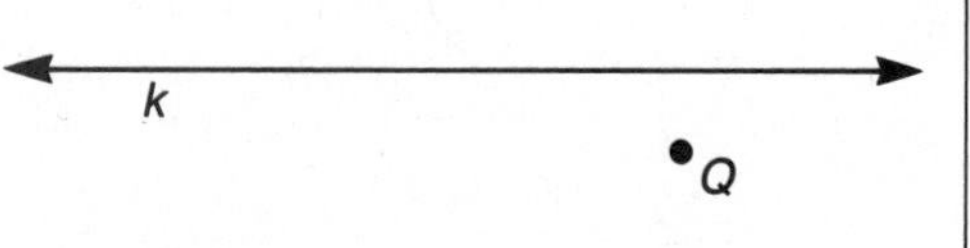

15. {3, 4, 6} by Theorem 6.7
16. They are unequal by Theorem 6.4.
17. 9, 21
18. Given
19. Def. of midpoint
20. Given
21. Steps *2, 3,* and substitution
22. Theorem 6.4
23. Theorem 6.4
24. Steps *5, 6,* and addition
25. Angle Addition Postulate and substitution
26. See *Selected Answers*, p. 631
27. Draw $\overline{QT}$ such that line k is the perpendicular bisector of $\overline{QT}$ at point X. Then $\triangle RXT \cong \triangle RXQ$ by SAS, and $RT = RQ$. By substitution, the distance from P to R to Q is the same as the distance from P to T. Thus, R is the point where the skipper should drop off the passenger. For any other point R', $PR' + R'T > PT$ (by Theorem 6.7) and therefore greater than $PR + RQ$.

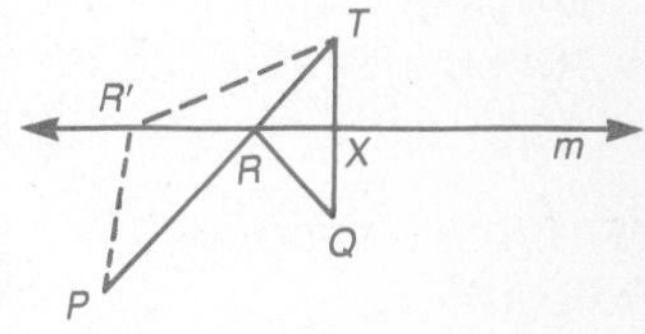

Note: The same point R can be found by drawing $\overline{PS}$ such that k is the perpendicular bisector of $\overline{PS}$. As an additional challenge, students might be asked to prove that $\overline{PT}$ and $\overline{SQ}$ will intersect in the same point on k whenever k is the perpendicular bisector of $\overline{PS}$ and $\overline{QT}$.

OBJECTIVE

Use the Hinge Theorem and its converse to answer questions regarding triangles and use these theorems in proofs.

TEACHER'S NOTES

See p. T30

Theorem 6.8 is also known as the Hinge Theorem.

MIXED REVIEW

1. The longest side of a right triangle is the ______. hypotenuse
2. Can a triangle have two obtuse angles? no
3. Solve $x^2 = x + 20$. $\{5, -4\}$
4. If $PM < PC$, which point cannot be between the other two points? C
5. Multiply $x^{-2} \cdot x^5 =$ x^3

TEACHER'S RESOURCE MASTERS

Practice Master 18, Part 1

6.6 Inequalities in Two Triangles

In the last lesson, you considered inequalities in a single triangle. Here you will look at inequalities that result from comparing *two* triangles.

The SAS Postulate gives you one way of comparing two triangles. You know that if the included angles in an SAS correspondence are not congruent, then the triangles are not congruent. Can anything further be deduced? The answer to that question lies in the next theorem.

THEOREM 6.8
If two sides of one triangle are congruent respectively to two sides of a second triangle, and the included angle of the first triangle is larger than the included angle of the second, then the opposite side of the first triangle is longer than the opposite side of the second.

To understand this theorem, imagine that two sides of a triangle are formed by two sticks hinged together. Think of the third side as an elastic band connecting the other ends of the two sticks. As you widen the interior angle formed by the two sticks, the elastic band stretches, making the side opposite the angle larger.

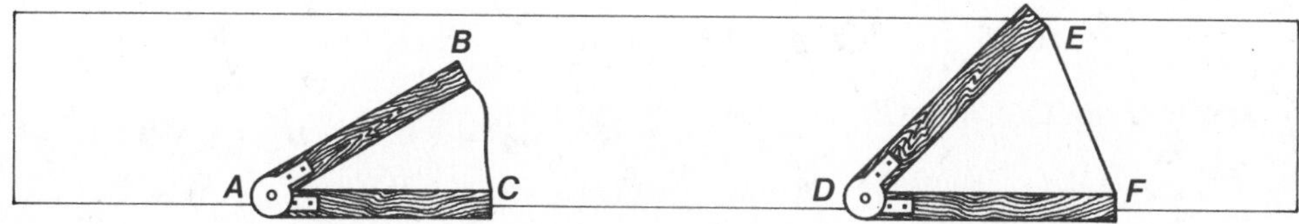

With this model in mind, you can now prove Theorem 6.8.

Given: ΔABC and ΔDEF, $AB = DE$, $AC = DF$, $m\angle A > m\angle D$
Prove: $BC > EF$

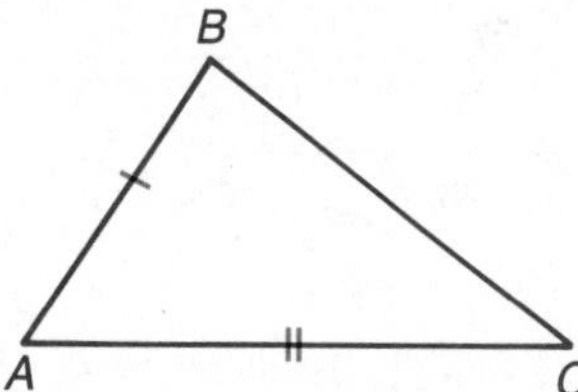

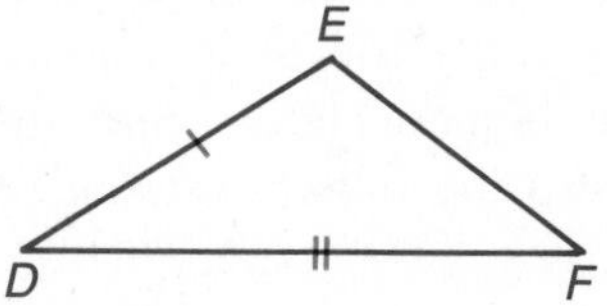

Proof: By the Angle Construction Postulate, there is a ray $\overrightarrow{AQ}$ such that $\angle QAC \cong \angle EDF$. By the Point Plotting Theorem, you can choose a point K on $\overrightarrow{AQ}$ such that $AK = DE$. It is given that $AC = DF$, so $\Delta AKC \cong \Delta DEF$ by SAS.

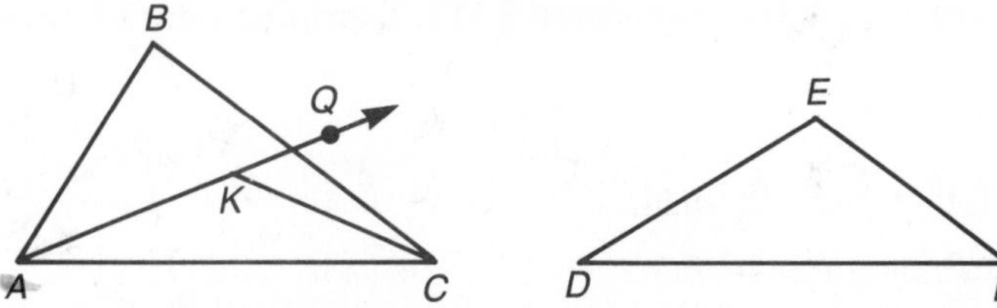

Note that K could be located on BC; the proof is still valid for this case.

Next, bisect $\angle BAK$ and let M be the point where the bisector intersects $\overline{BC}$.

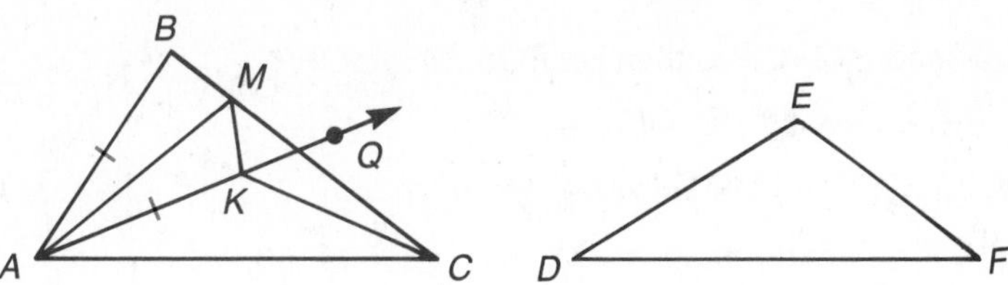

Since $AK = DE$ and $DE = AB$, it follows that $AK = AB$. By SAS, $\Delta AKM \cong \Delta ABM$, making $MK = MB$.

Looking at ΔCMK, you know from the Triangle Inequality Theorem that $CM + MK > CK$. Thus, by substitution, $CM + MB > CK$. Since $CK = EF$ by corresponding parts, and $CM + MB = BC$, make the necessary substitutions and conclude $BC > EF$.

The converse of Theorem 6.8 is also true and is presented as a new theorem.

THEOREM 6.9
If two sides of one triangle are congruent respectively to two sides of a second triangle, and the third side of the first triangle is longer than the third side of the second, then the included angle of the first triangle is larger than the included angle of the second.

Referring again to the hinge concept, Theorem 6.9 states that a larger side requires a larger hinge opening. Thus, in the figure below, if $BC > EF$, then $m\angle A > m\angle D$.

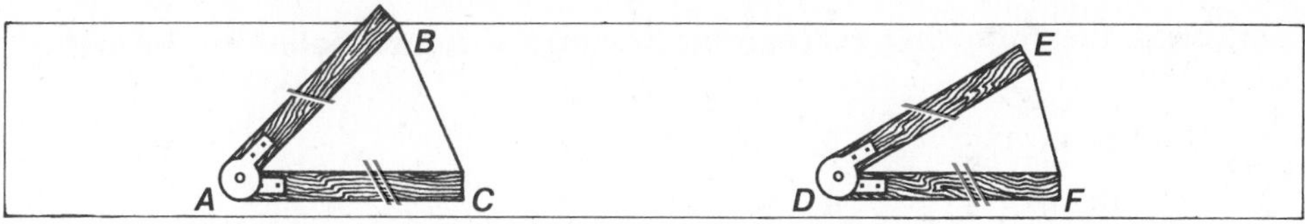

The proof of this theorem is similar to that of Theorem 6.5. There are only three possibilities: $m\angle A < m\angle D$, $m\angle A = m\angle D$, or $m\angle A > m\angle D$. Since you are trying to prove the last of these possibilities, eliminate the first two. The proof is left as an exercise.

ORAL EXERCISES

Refer to the figure below for Exercises 1–12. Complete each statement with $<$, $=$, or $>$.

1. MP ● RQ
2. If $PQ > RM$, then $m\angle 1$ ● $m\angle 4$
3. If $m\angle 1 > m\angle 2$, then PS ● PQ.
4. If $m\angle 4 = 45$, and $m\angle 2 = 60$, then RM ● PS.
5. If $PS = PQ$, then $m\angle 1$ ● $m\angle 2$.
6. If $PR = QS$, and $RQ < PS$, then $m\angle PQS$ ● $m\angle QPR$.
7. If $m\angle A < m\angle N$, then LT ● DK.
8. If $DK = 8$, and $LT = 11$, then $m\angle A$ ● $m\angle N$.
9. If $DK = 6$, $LT = 6$, and $m\angle A = 60$, then $m\angle N$ ● 60.
10. If $m\angle A = m\angle N = 50$, and $LT = 5$, then DK ● 5.
11. If $m\angle A = 32$, $m\angle N = 48$, and $DK = 15$, then LT ● 15.
12. If $m\angle A = m\angle N + 20$, then LT ● DK.
13. Given a correspondence between ΔABC and ΔDEF, if $AB > DE$ and $AC > DF$, what conclusion can you draw about $\angle A$ and $\angle D$?
14. Given a correspondence between ΔPQR and ΔXYZ, if $PR = PQ$ and $XZ = XY$, what conclusion can you draw about $\angle P$ and $\angle X$?
15. In ΔLMN and ΔSTU, $m\angle L > m\angle S$. What conclusion can you state about the relation of $\overline{MN}$ to $\overline{TU}$?
16. If the angles of a triangle have different measures, how would you describe the triangle?

WRITTEN EXERCISES

A. Complete the following statements about the figure below by inserting $>$, $=$, or $<$.

1. $m\angle P$ ● $m\angle TRS$
2. $m\angle S$ ● $m\angle P$
3. $m\angle T$ ● $m\angle S$
4. $m\angle P$ ● $m\angle T$
5. $m\angle Q$ ● $m\angle PRQ$
6. If $QT = 7$, $m\angle QRT$ ● $m\angle PRQ$.

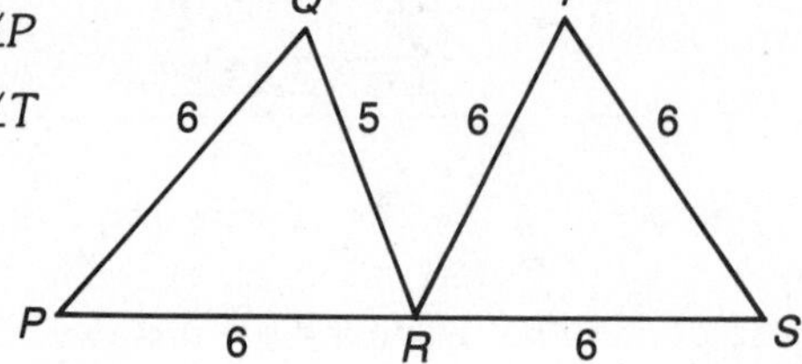

ASSIGNMENT GUIDE

Minimum 1-6
Regular 1-9
Maximum 1-7 odd, 8-12

Oral Exercises

1. = 2. >
3. < 4. <
5. = 6. >
7. < 8. >
9. = 10. =
11. < 12. >
13. none
14. only that they are vertex angles of two isosceles triangles
15. none
16. It is scalene.

Written Exercises

1. < 2. >
3. = 4. <
5. = 6. >

B. **7.** Given isosceles ΔABC with M not the midpoint of $\overline{AB}$, prove that $\overline{CM}$ is not the bisector of $\angle C$ using Theorem 6.9.

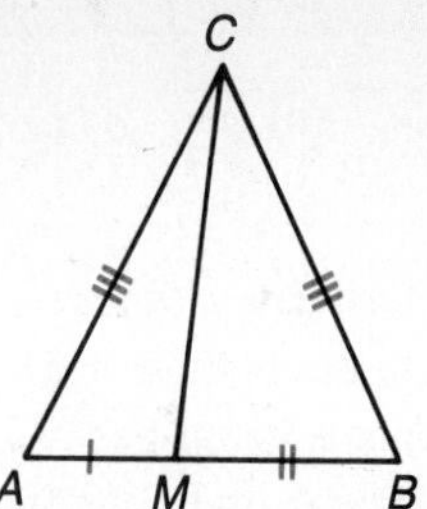

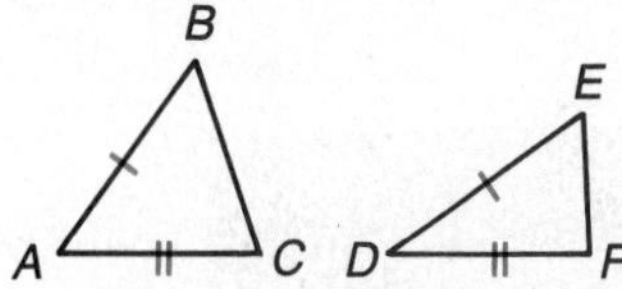

8. Use the figure at the left to prove Theorem 6.9.

9. **Given:** ΔCDE and ΔCDF, $EC = FC$
$m\angle ECD = m\angle ECF + m\angle FCD$

Prove: $ED > FD$

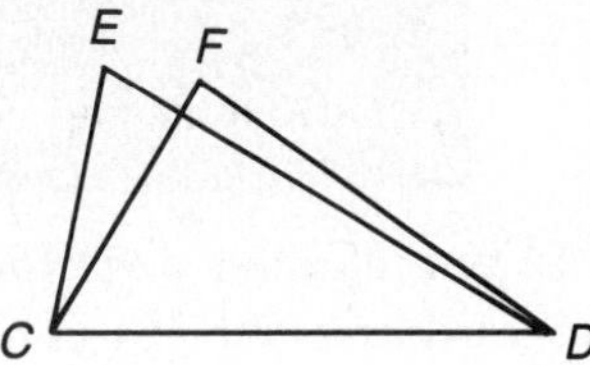

10. **Given:** ΔABC, $AB > AC$
$PC = MB$

Prove: $PB > CM$

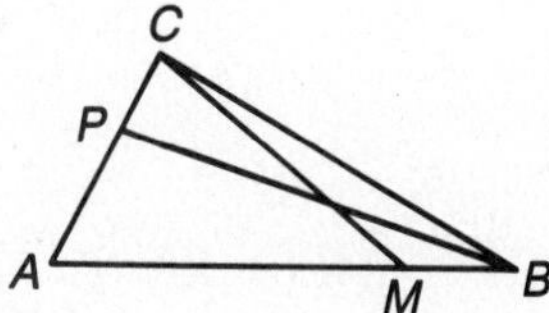

C. **11.** A *kite* is a nonequilateral quadrilateral having two pairs of congruent, adjacent sides. Prove that the measure of the angle included between the smaller sides is greater than the measure of the angle between the larger sides.

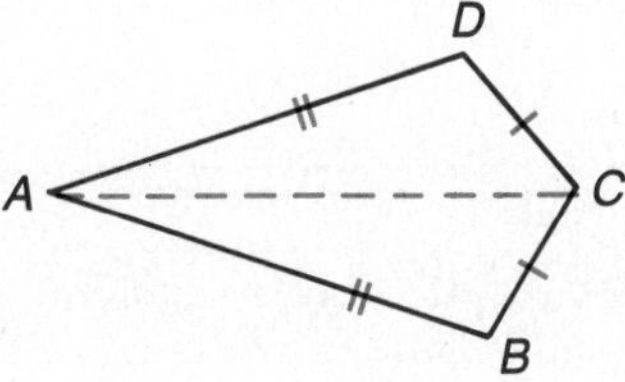

12. Prove the following: If a median of a triangle is not perpendicular to the side to which it is drawn, then the lengths of the other two sides of the triangle are unequal.

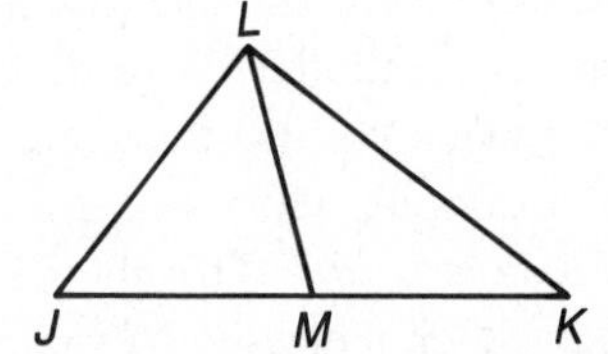

7. If M is not the midpoint, then $AM > BM$ or $AM < BM$. By Theorem 6.9, this means that either $m\angle ACM > m\angle BCM$ or $m\angle ACM < m\angle BCM$. In either case, $\overline{CM}$ does not bisect $\angle C$.

8. 1. ΔABC and ΔDEF, $AB = DE$, $AC = DF$, $BC > EF$ (Given); 2. Assume $m\angle A < m\angle D$ (Indirect assumption); 3. Then $BC < EF$ (Theorem 6.8), (Contradiction of given); 4. Assume $m\angle A = m\angle D$ (Indirect assumption); 5. Then $\Delta ABC \cong \Delta DEF$ (SAS); 6. $BC = EF$ (CPCTC), (Contradiction of given). The only other possibility, $m\angle A > m\angle D$, must therefore be true.

9. From the given, it can be deduced that $m\angle ECD > m\angle FCD$. By Theorem 6.8, therefore, $ED > FD$.

10. Since $AB > AC$, $m\angle ACB > m\angle CBA$ by Theorem 6.4. Applying Theorem 6.8 to ΔBPC and ΔCMB, $PB > CM$.

11. Draw auxiliary line $\overleftrightarrow{AC}$. In ΔADC, $m\angle DAC < m\angle DCA$, and in ΔABC, $m\angle CAB < m\angle ACB$, all by Theorem 6.4. By the addition property of inequality and the Angle Addition Postulate, $m\angle DAB < m\angle DCB$.

12. Since median $\overline{LM}$ is not perpendicular to side $\overline{JK}$, it forms unequal supplementary angles, $\angle LMJ$ and $\angle LMK$. Apply Theorem 6.8 to ΔJML and ΔKML, and LJ and LK are unequal.

OBJECTIVE

Identify the altitudes of a triangle.

TEACHER'S NOTES

See p. T30

MIXED REVIEW

1. Are all non-negative numbers positive? No
2. Solve $4x + 2y = 10$
   $3x + y = 9$ (4, −3)
3. Solve $5 - (x + 3) < 8$.
   $x > -6$
4. What type of triangle has all of its exterior angles obtuse? acute
5. When would $\overline{AB} = CD$? When they are both the same segment.

TEACHER'S RESOURCE MASTERS

Practice Master 18, Part 2
Quiz 12

6.7 Altitudes

The term altitude is a familiar one. Jets fly at high altitudes, and highway signs designating city limits often indicate a city's altitude or elevation. In both cases, altitude measures height from a given base. The altitude of a jet is its height above the ground below. The altitude of a city is its height above sea level.

When you refer to the **altitude of a triangle**, you mean the height of the vertex above the base. Looking at the figures below, you will see that the altitude of the same triangle changes, depending on how you position the figure. In fact, every triangle has three altitudes.

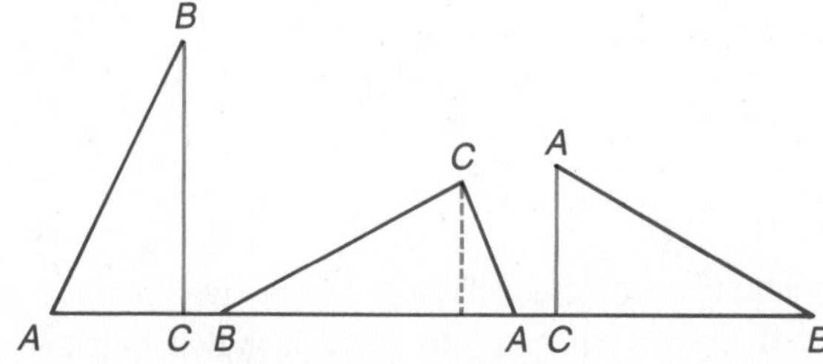

It is no coincidence that the altitudes of the triangles above appear to be perpendicular to the bases. The concept of altitudes follows directly from the definition of distance from a point to a line.

> **DEFINITION: altitude of a triangle**
> An **altitude of a triangle** is the perpendicular segment joining a vertex of the triangle to the line that contains the opposite side.

Because every triangle has three vertices, the definition implicitly states that every triangle has three altitudes. Note that the altitude of a triangle is defined as being a segment. Sometimes when you use the word *altitude,* you are referring rather to the measure of the segment. For example, when you are determining the area of a triangle, you may be told that "the altitude is 6 cm." This should cause no confusion, because the meaning of *altitude* in a given case will be indicated by the context.

It is important that the definition of altitude says that the vertex is joined "to the line that contains the opposite side." If it simply said "to the opposite side," ΔABC at the right would have no altitude from either vertex B or vertex C.

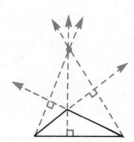

Sometimes altitude is defined as *the line containing the perpendicular segment,* so that you can accurately state an interesting property of altitudes. *For every triangle, the three altitudes meet at a point.* In the figure at the near right, the three *segments* meet at a point. In the figure at the far right, the three *lines containing the segments* meet at a point.

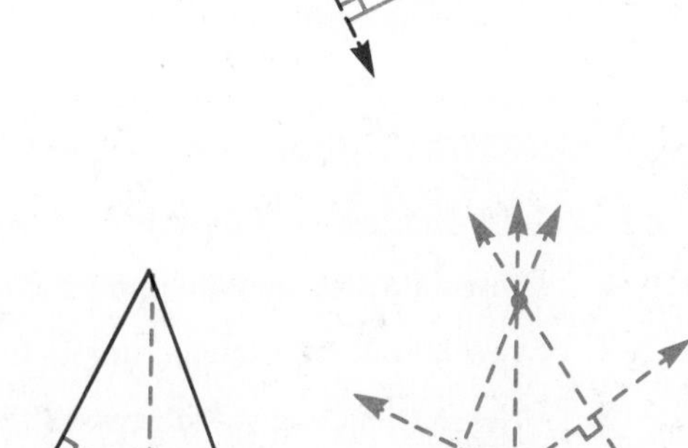

It will be useful to define a new term here to describe the intersection of lines at a common point.

> **DEFINITIONS: concurrent lines, point of concurrency**
> Two or more lines are **concurrent** if and only if there is a single point that lies on all of them. The common point is called the *point of* **concurrency.**

The proposition that the three altitudes of a triangle are concurrent at a point will be proved later.

ASSIGNMENT GUIDE

Minimum 1-11
Regular 1-12
Maximum 1-11 odd, 12-14

ORAL EXERCISES

1. Name the altitudes of ΔABC at the right.

2. Which altitude in the figure is also a median?

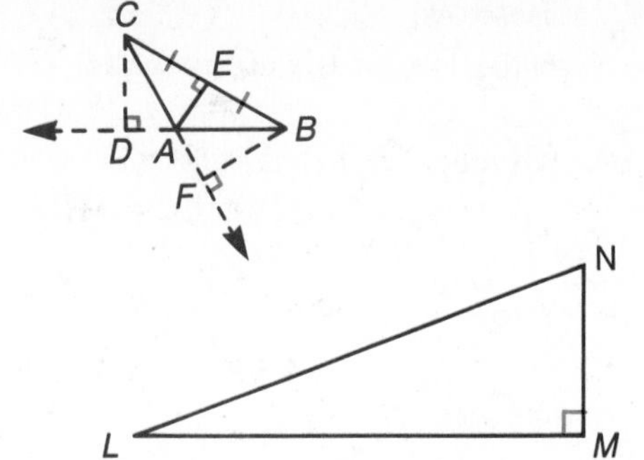

3. Name the point of concurrency of the three altitudes of right ΔLMN.

4. Is it possible for an altitude of a triangle to be a side of the triangle?

5. Is it possible for all three altitudes of a triangle to be congruent?

Oral Exercises

1. $\overline{AE}$, $\overline{BF}$, $\overline{CD}$
2. $\overline{AE}$
3. M
4. yes, in a right triangle
5. yes, in an equilateral triangle

6. no 7. acute

8. one

9. Theorem 5.3

Written Exercises

1-2. Drawings will vary.

3. any right triangle

4. any equilateral triangle

5. No; the perpendicular is the shortest distance from a point to a line.

6. Will be true for all but equilateral or isosceles triangles, where vertex A is between ≅ sides. In these cases the altitude is the median.

7. no 8. yes
9. no 10. no

11. The altitude to the base of an isosceles triangle forms two right triangles that are congruent by HL. Then the legs that form the larger base are congruent by CPCTC.

12. See *Selected Answers*, p. 631

13. See *Teacher's Manual*, p. T60

14. See *Selected Answers*, p. 631

15. Each altitude is the leg of a right triangle with a side as the hypotenuse. The hypotenuse is greater than a leg in the case of all three altitudes.

6. Could all three altitudes of a triangle fall outside the triangle?

7. In what kind of triangle would all three altitudes be in the interior of the triangle?

8. If a triangle is obtuse, how many of its altitudes lie in the interior of the triangle?

9. How can you be sure that only one altitude can be drawn from each vertex of a triangle?

WRITTEN EXERCISES

A. **1.** Draw an acute triangle and its three altitudes.

2. Draw an obtuse triangle and its three altitudes.

3. Draw a triangle in which two of the altitudes are also sides of the triangle.

4. Draw a triangle in which the altitides and medians are the same segments.

B. **5.** Can you draw a ΔABC in which the altitude from vertex A is longer than the median from vertex A? If not, why not?

6. Draw a ΔABC in which the altitude from vertex A is shorter than the median from vertex A.

Are the following lines concurrent?

7. x, y, z **8.** x, w, y

9. w, y, z **10.** x, w, z

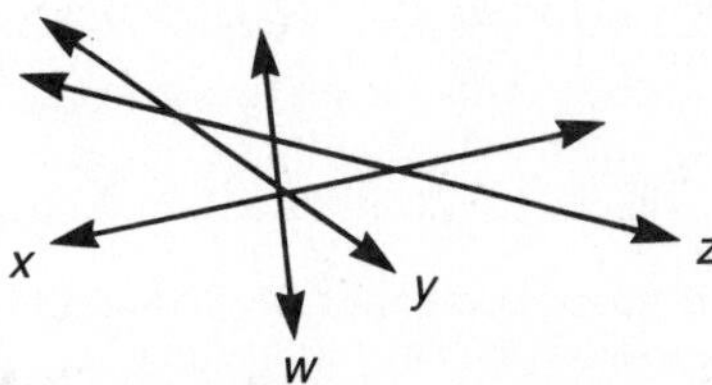

11. Prove that the altitude to the base of an isosceles triangle is also the median.

12. Prove that the altitudes of an equilateral triangle are congruent.

13. Prove that the altitudes drawn to two sides of a triangle are congruent if and only if the triangle is isosceles.
HINT: Two proofs are required.

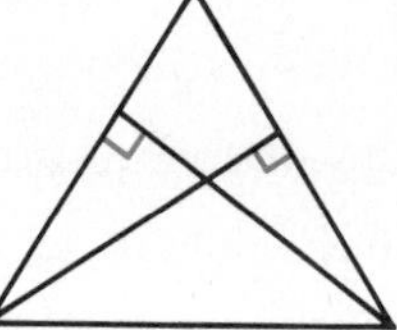

14. **Given:** ΔJKL, ΔPQR
$JK = PQ$, $JL = PR$,
$RS = LM$

Prove: $\Delta JKL \cong \Delta PQR$
State your conclusion as a biconditional.

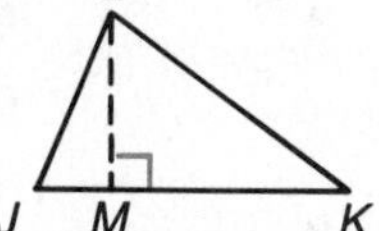

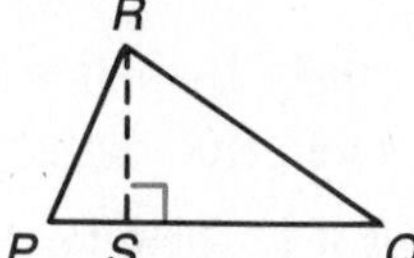

15. Prove that the perimeter of a triangle is greater than the sum of the three altitudes of a triangle.

SKILLS MAINTENANCE

Simplify.

1. $(2x + 5) + (7x + 3)$
2. $(3y - 2) + (8y + 4)$
3. $(9n - 3) + (2n - 4)$
4. $(2a^2 + 4a + 1) + (3a^2 + 7a - 2)$
5. $(x^2 - 2) + (3x^2 + 2)$
6. $(c^2 - 2c + 3) + (c - 5)$
7. $(5n + 2) - (2n + 5)$
8. $(4a - 6) - (3a - 2)$
9. $(3y^2 - 5) - (y^2 - 5)$
10. $(6x^2 + 7x - 3) - (2x^2 - 4x + 5)$
11. $(6v^2 + 4) - (3v + 2)$
12. $(5t^2 - 2t + 3) - (t - 3)$
13. $(7x^2 - 3y^2) + (7x^2 + 3y^2)$
14. $(3m^2 - 9n^2) + (-3m^2 - 9n^2)$
15. $(5m - 4) + (6m^2 - 11)$
16. $(6s^2 - 4s) + (3s + 6)$

EXPLORATION/The Fibonacci Sequence

A pair of rabbits one month old are too young to produce offspring. In their second month and every month thereafter, they produce a new pair. If each new pair of rabbits does the same, and none of the rabbits die, how many pairs of rabbits will there be at the end of each month?

The answers to this problem form a series of numbers called the *Fibonacci sequence:*

1 1 2 3 5 8 13 . . .

Each term of this sequence is derived from the sum of the preceding two.

1. Write the first 20 terms of the Fibonacci sequence. (You may want to use a calculator.) The 15th term is 610.

2. Find the sum of the first 5 terms. Notice the relationship between this sum and the seventh term.

3. Find the sum of the first 10 terms. What is its relationship to the 12th term? Are you ready to make a prediction? How will you test it?

Skills Maintenance

1. $9x + 8$
2. $11y + 2$
3. $11n - 7$
4. $5a^2 + 11a - 1$
5. $4x^2$
6. $c^2 - c - 2$
7. $3n - 3$
8. $a - 4$
9. $2y^2$
10. $4x^2 + 11x - 8$
11. $6v^2 - 3v + 2$
12. $5t^2 - 3t + 6$
13. $14x^2$
14. $-18n^2$
15. $6m^2 + 5m - 15$
16. $6s^2 - s + 6$

Exploration

1. 1, 1, 2, 3, 5, 8, 13, 21, 34, 55, 89, 144, 233, 377, 610, 987, 1597, 2584, 4181, 6765
2. 12 and 13
3. 143 and 144. It seems that the sum of terms 1 through $n - 2$ equals the nth term minus 1.

CAREER

Game Designer

A pinball machine designer needs a working knowledge of geometry to make a game fun for the players and worthwhile for a manufacturer to develop and produce. It may cost $250,000 to develop a new machine, so the designer has to plan ball movements that will keep the game exciting and make the machine profitable for the company. The ball must travel accurately from chutes to bumpers to targets to "slingshot kickers" without "chatter" or "clank," two terms designers use to describe awkward motions or loss of ball action. The ball also must come near drop-lanes that will end the play. To determine where parts of the playfield will be placed, the designer must plot the likely paths the ball will take when it ricochets. A ball will deflect away at the same angle as its approach.

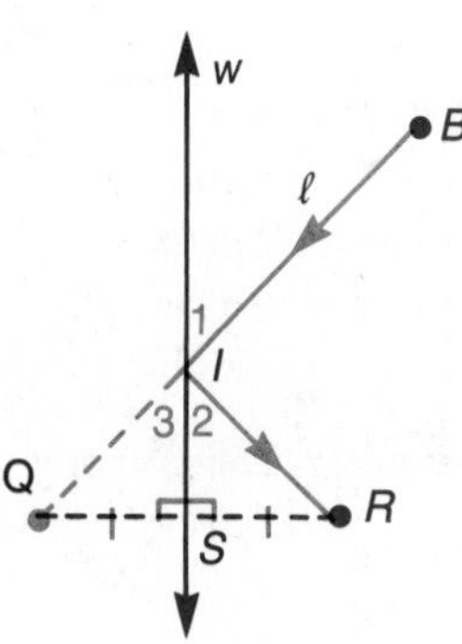

Line l at the left shows the original path of a pinball, B. If there was nothing in the path of B along l, it would continue straight on to some point Q. However, if the ball bounces off the side wall of the playfield (line w) at point I, it will change direction toward some point R, which lies the same distance from w as Q along a perpendicular from Q to w. $\overline{IS}$ is common to ΔISQ and ΔISR; $\overline{QS} \cong \overline{RS}$; and rt. $\angle ISQ \cong$ rt. $\angle ISR$, so the two triangles are congruent by SAS. By corresponding parts, $\angle 2 \cong \angle 3$. $\angle 1$ and $\angle 3$ are congruent vertical angles, so by substitution, $\angle 2 \cong \angle 1$.

Using this knowledge of angles, the designer places the next obstacle or bumper in the ball's path. By arranging the playfield so several ball paths have a point of concurrence, as shown at the right, the designer can plan features that will be encountered however the ball enters.

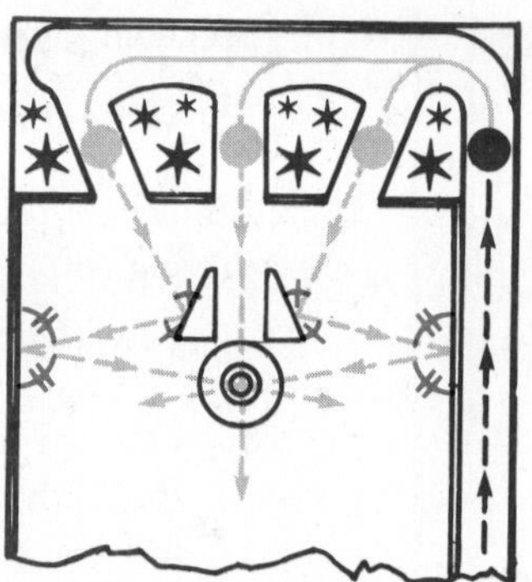

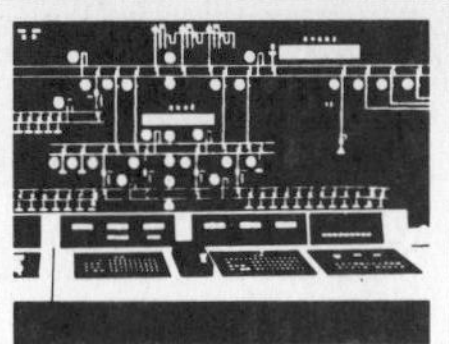

COMPUTER

The conditional branching feature of a computer is a powerful tool for classifying information. Even when the classification is simple enough to perform manually, the computer provides valuable speed and accuracy. Consider the following problem: *Given different sets of three numbers, determine which sets can represent the sides of a triangle.*

```
5   REM TRIANGLE INEQUALITY
10  READ X, Y, Z
20  IF X + Y < = Z THEN 70
30  IF X + Z < = Y THEN 70
40  IF Y + Z < = X THEN 70
50  PRINT X" ";Y" ";Z" ";" CAN FORM A TRIANGLE."
60  GO TO 10
70  PRINT; X" ";Y" ";Z" ";" CANNOT FORM A TRIANGLE."
80  GO TO 10
90  DATA 7,10,12,4,4,8,22,7,25,6,8,12
100 END
```

1. Run the program using your own sets of three numbers. Try your height (in cm), your weight, and the last two digits of your birth year. Then try your last three grades in math.

2. Another way to give the computer data is to use an INPUT statement. Rewrite and run the triangle inequality program using an INPUT statement.

3. FOR-NEXT loops can also be used to input data. Rewrite and run the triangle inequality program using these three nexted FOR-NEXT loops:

```
FOR X = 1 to 10
FOR Y = 1 to 15
FOR Z = 1 to 20 STEP 2
```

4. Although the computer quickly tests each pair of sides in the triangle inequality program, it really isn't necessary to have three test cases. Why? Write a flowchart of the procedure to test the triangle inequality by finding the largest side.

TEACHER'S RESOURCE MASTERS

Computer Master 6

Computer

1. Answers will vary

2.
```
5   REM TRIANGLE
    INEQUALITY
10  INPUT X,Y,Z
20  IF X + Y < = Z THEN
    70
30  IF X + Z < = Y THEN
    70
40  IF Y + Z < = X THEN
    70
50  PRINT X;Y;Z;"CAN
    FORM A TRIANGLE"
60  GO TO 100
70  PRINT X;Y;Z;"CANNOT
    FORM A TRIANGLE"
100 END
```

3.
```
5   REM TRIANGLE
    INEQUALITY
10  FOR X = 1 TO 10
20  FOR Y = 1 TO 15
30  FOR Z = 1 TO 20
    STEP 2
40  IF X + Y < = Z THEN
    90
50  IF X + Z < = Y THEN
    90
60  IF Y + Z < = X THEN
    90
70  PRINT X;Y;Z;"CAN
    FORM A TRIANGLE"
80  GO TO 100
90  PRINT X;Y;Z;"CANNOT
    FORM A TRIANGLE"
100 NEXT Z
110 NEXT Y
120 NEXT X
130 END
```

4. The largest side plus either of the other two will always be larger than the remaining side. The flowchart should reflect the following possibilities: If $x < y$, then 1. $x < y < x$, 2. $x < z < y$, or 3. $z < x < y$, or if $y < x$, then 4. $y < x < z$, 5. $z < y < x$, or 6. $y < z < x$.

1. chance discovery, intuition
2. reason, conjecture
3. $x \geq \frac{-5}{2}$, addition, subtraction, division properties
4. $x > 36$, addition, multiplication, division properties
5. $x \geq -12$
6. $x \geq 2$
7. $\angle 4, \angle 5, \angle 7, \angle 8$
8. $\angle 1, \angle 2, \angle 3$
9. $\angle 1, \angle 3$
10. If $\angle C$ is the right angle, then the external angle adjacent to $\angle C$ is also a right angle. By Theorem 6.1, this external angle is greater than either remote interior angle, so $\angle A$ and $\angle B$ are each acute.
11. $m\angle P < 90$
12. 

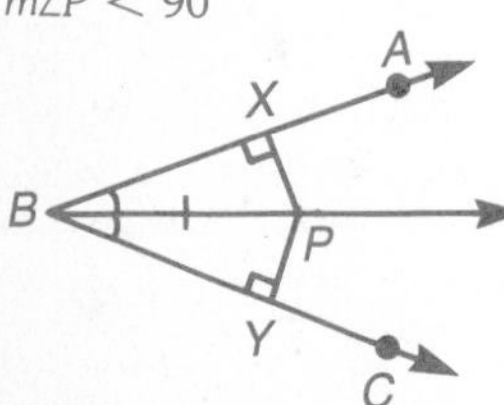

$\triangle BPX \cong \triangle BPY$ by SAA. Thus, $\overline{PX} \cong \overline{PY}$ by CPCTC, and $PX = PY$.

13. Right $\triangle WXZ \cong$ right $\triangle YZX$ by HL. Thus, $\overline{WZ} \cong \overline{YX}$ by CPCTC, and $WZ = YX$.
14. Draw the diagonal $\overline{AC}$. Given that $\overline{CD}$ is the shortest side, $AD > CD$ and therefore $m\angle 1 > m\angle 4$ by Theorem 6.4. Given $\overline{AB}$ is the longest side, $AB > BC$ and therefore $m\angle 2 > m\angle 3$ by Theorem 6.4. By addition, $m\angle C > m\angle A$.

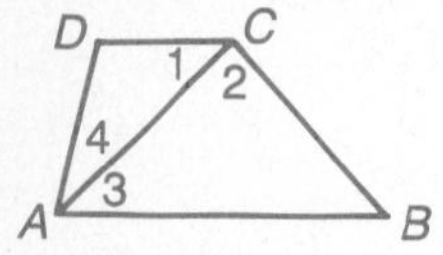

CHAPTER 6 REVIEW

VOCABULARY

$a > b$, $a < b$ (6.2)
altitude of a triangle (6.7)
chance discovery (6.1)
concurrent lines (6.7)
counterexample (6.1)
distance between a line and a point (6.5)
exterior angle of a triangle (6.3)
interior angle of a triangle (6.3)
intuition (6.1)
lemma (6.4)
negative number (6.2)
point of concurrency (6.7)
positive number (6.2)
remote interior angles (6.3)
rule for order reversal (6.2)

REVIEW EXERCISES

6.1

1. In what two ways is a child most likely to acquire knowledge?

2. What two ways of acquiring knowledge are likely to be demonstrated as a person matures?

6.2 **Solve each inequality and name the properties you use to reach a solution.**

3. $5 - 2x \leq 10$

4. $\frac{1}{3}x - 16 > 32 - x$

Solve each inequality for x, using the order reversal rule if needed.

5. $-3x \leq 36$

6. $-2 \geq -x$

6.3

7. List all the exterior angles numbered in the figure for $\triangle ABC$.

8. List all the interior angles numbered in the figure.

9. List all the remote interior angles with respect to $\angle 5$.

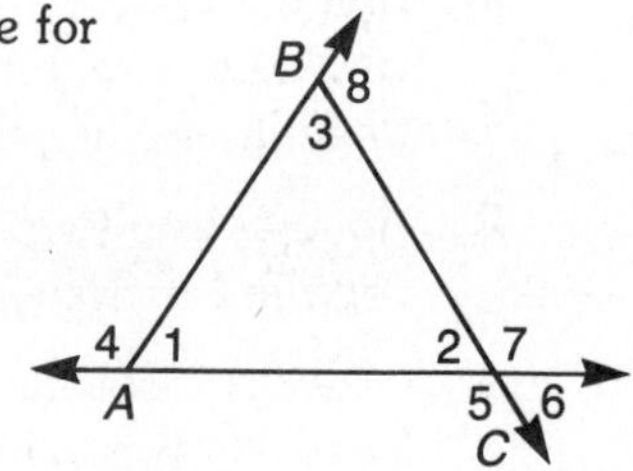

10. Use the Exterior Angle Theorem to prove that a triangle can have at most one right angle.

11. In $\triangle PQR$, $m\angle Q = 90$. Write an inequality that reflects $m\angle P$.

6.4

12. Prove that any point on the bisector of an angle is equidistant from the sides of the angle.

13. **Given:** Quadrilateral $WXYZ$, as marked

Prove: $WZ = XY$

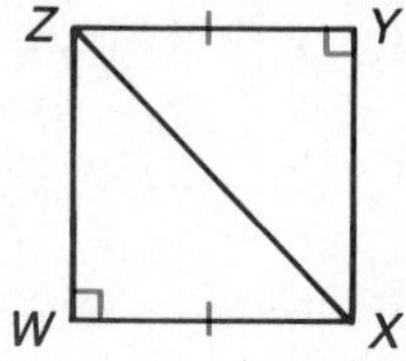

6.5 **14.** In the plane figure $ABCD$, $\overline{CD}$ is the shortest side, and $\overline{AB}$ is the longest side. Use an auxiliary figure to prove that $m\angle C > m\angle A$.

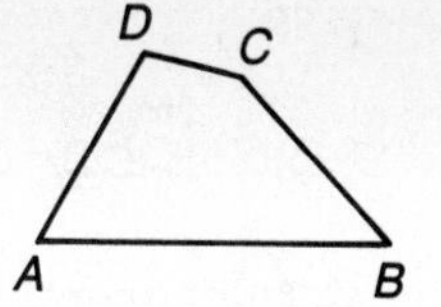

15. If this figure were drawn correctly, which segment would be the shortest? Explain your reasoning.

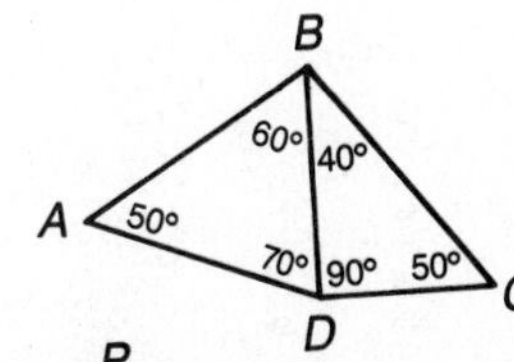

16. Referring to the figure, what is the distance between point P and $\overleftrightarrow{RV}$? between R and $\overleftrightarrow{UV}$?

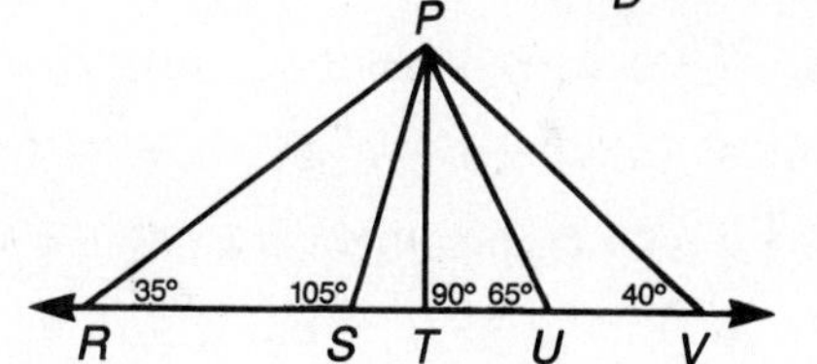

17. Prove that the sum of the distance from a point within a triangle to the ends of one side is less than the sum of the lengths of the other two sides. Restated, prove that $c + d < a + b$.

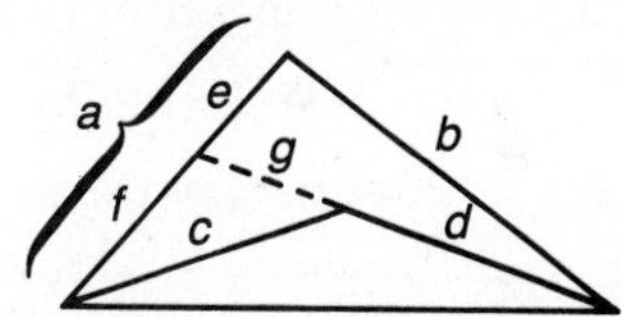

18. Restate Theorem 6.8 in terms of two doors of equal size and their openings.

19. Restate Theorem 6.9 in terms of two doors of equal size and their openings.

6.6 **Refer to the figure of $\triangle ABC$ with segment lengths as marked. Complete each statement with the correct symbol of inequality**

20. If $m\angle ADC < m\angle BDC$, then AC ● BC.

21. If $EC > AD$, then $m\angle EDC$ ● $m\angle ACD$.

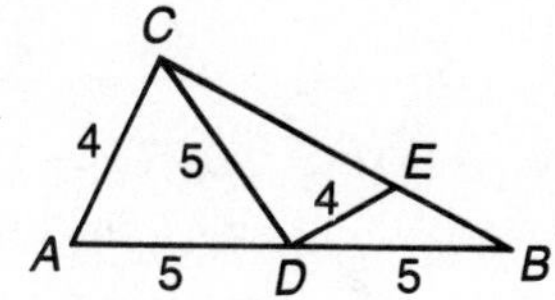

6.7 **Choose the correct word or phrase to complete each statement.**

22. The altitude of a triangle can mean a line, a segment, or _____.

a. a base **b.** the hypotenuse **c.** the length

23. The three altitudes of a triangle are always concurrent _____.

a. inside the triangle **b.** at a point **c.** outside the triangle

24. Two of the altitudes of a(n) _____ triangle are sides.

a. right **b.** acute **c.** obtuse

25. Where the three altitudes of a triangle intersect is the _____.

a. hypotenuse **b.** lemma **c.** point of concurrency

15. In $\triangle ABD$, $\overline{BD}$ is shortest; in $\triangle CBD$, $\overline{DC}$ is shorter than $\overline{BD}$ and is therefore the shortest segment in the figure.

16. PT; 0

17. By Theorem 6.7, $f + g > c$ and $b + e > g + d$. By addition, $f + g + b + e > c + g + d$, and $f + e + b + g > c + g + d$. But $f + e = a$, so substitution yields $a + b + g > c + g + d$. Subtract g from both sides to obtain $a + b > c + d$, or $c + d < a + b$.

18. If two doors of equal size are propped open so that the angle formed by one door is larger than the angle formed by the other door, then the distance from the outer edge of the first door to its door frame is greater than the distance from the outer edge of the second door to its door frame.

19. If two doors of equal size are propped open so that the distance from the outer edge of one door to its door frame is greater than the distance from the outer edge of the second door to its door frame, then the angle formed by the first door is greater than the angle formed by the second door.

20. $<$ 21. $>$ 22. c

23. b 24. a 25. c

ENRICHMENT

See Activities 11–12, p. T46–T47

Chapter 6 Test

1. b
2. d
3. a
4. b
5. c
6. a
7. b
8. a
9. d
10. c
11. d
12. b
13. a
14. c

TEACHER'S RESOURCE MASTERS

Chapter 6 Test
Multiple Choice Test—Chapter 6

CHAPTER 6 TEST

Choose the correct word or phrase to complete each sentence.

1. Conjecture is ____ based on limited evidence.

a. doubt **b.** a guess **c.** proof **d.** reason

2. A counterexample shows that a proposed theorem is ____.

a. true **b.** probable **c.** uncertain **d.** false

3. If $-x > 3$, then ____.

a. $x < -3$ **b.** $x = -3$ **c.** $x > -3$ **d.** $x = 4$

4. If $a > b$, then there is a positive number c such that ____.

a. $a < b + c$ **b.** $a - b = c$ **c.** $a + c = b$ **d.** $a + b = c$

5. If $a > 3$, and $3 > b$, then ____.

a. $a = b$ **b.** $a < b$ **c.** $a > b$ **d.** $a \leq -b$

6. If Q lies between P and S, then ____ is an exterior angle of ΔPQR.

a. $\angle RQS$ **b.** $\angle RPQ$ **c.** $\angle SRQ$ **d.** $\angle PQR$

7. If exterior $\angle ABD$ measures 90, then remote interior $\angle C$ is ____.

a. obtuse **b.** acute **c.** congruent **d.** unequal

8. The SAA Theorem is a ____ for the Hypotenuse-Leg Theorem.

a. lemma **b.** corollary **c.** postulate **d.** conjecture

9. In ΔABC, if $m\angle A > m\angle C$, then ____.

a. $AB > BC$ **b.** $BC > AC$ **c.** $BC < AB$ **d.** $BC > AB$

10. In ΔFGH, if $FG > FH$ and $FG < GH$, then

a. $m\angle F < m\angle H < m\angle G$ **b.** $m\angle F > m\angle G > m\angle H$
c. $m\angle G < m\angle H < m\angle F$ **d.** $m\angle G > m\angle H > m\angle F$

11. The set ____ could not represent the measures of the sides of a triangle.

a. {5, 12, 13} **b.** {5, 10, 11} **c.** {2, 3, 4} **d.** {3, 5, 8}

12. In ΔABC and ΔDEF, if $AB = DE$, $BC = EF$, and $m\angle B > m\angle E$, then ____.

a. $AC = DF$ **b.** $AC > DF$ **c.** $AC < DF$ **d.** none of these

13. In ΔFGH and ΔJKL, if $FG = JK$, $GH = KL$, and $FH < JL$, then

a. $m\angle K > m\angle G$ **b.** $m\angle F = m\angle J$ **c.** $m\angle F < m\angle J$ **d.** none of these

14. Two altitudes of a triangle are congruent in a(n) ____ triangle.

a. right **b.** obtuse **c.** isosceles **d.** scalene

CHAPTER 7

Perpendicular Relationships

OBJECTIVE

Identify perpendicular relationships between lines and planes.

TEACHER'S NOTES

See p. T30

MIXED REVIEW

1. Which segment is used to measure distance from a point to a line? perpendicular
2. If $RS = TS$, which point is equidistant from the two points? S
3. Multiply $(4x - 3)(2x + 5)$. $8x^2 + 14x - 15$
4. Solve $\frac{6}{x-3} = \frac{2}{2x-1}$. $x = 0$
5. Simplify: $\frac{48x^5y^3}{32xy^5}$. $\frac{3x^4}{2y^2}$

TEACHER'S RESOURCE MASTERS

Practice Master 19, Part 1

7.1 Basic Concepts and Definitions

Three-dimensional geometry, or space geometry, is more complex than plane geometry. Suppose a surveyor is looking through the telescope of a transit at an assistant, who is holding an upright range pole (as shown at the right). From the surveyor's line of sight, it appears that the pole is perpendicular to the ground. Indeed, it might be. But what if the assistant is actually leaning the pole slightly forward, as shown below?

Viewing the scene from the side, it is apparent that the pole is *not* perpendicular to the plane of the ground. This illustrates the need to exercise caution when defining the perpendicularity of a line to a plane.

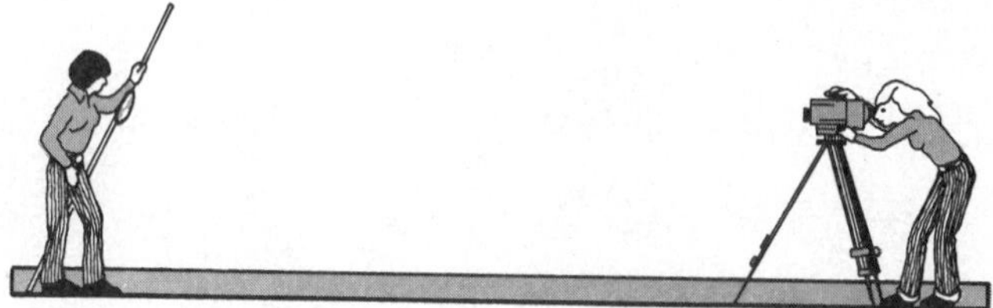

DEFINITION: perpendicular line and plane
A line and a plane are **perpendicular** if and only if they intersect, and if every line lying in the plane that passes through the point of intersection is perpendicular to the given line.

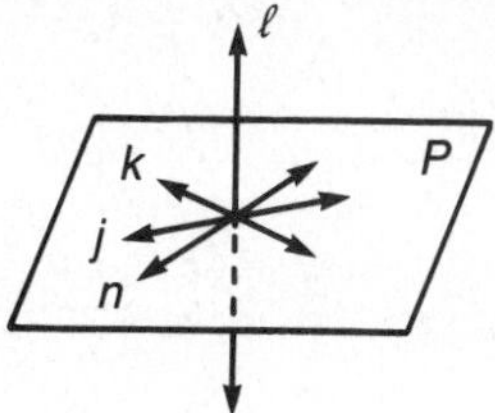

In the figure at the left, line l is perpendicular to lines k, j, and n, which lie in plane P. Any other line in plane P that intersects line l where line l intersects P would also be perpendicular to l.

Before proving the basic theorem on perpendicularity in space, a *lemma* must be established.

THEOREM 7.1
If each of two points of a line is equidistant from two given points, then every point of the line is equidistant from the given points.

Given: P and Q are points on line l.
$PA = PB$, $QA = QB$

Prove: For any other point R on line l,
$RA = RB$

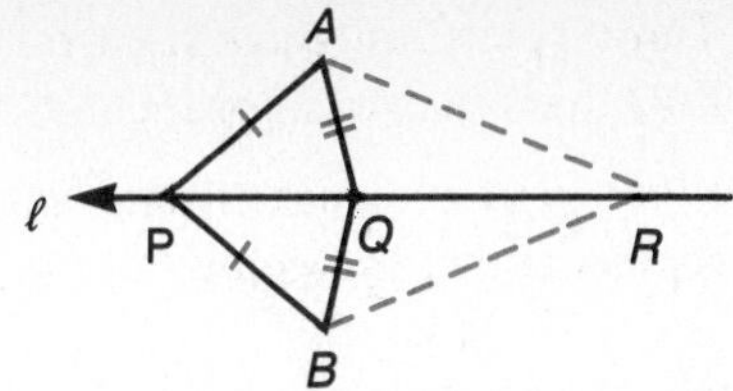

Proof: $\Delta APQ \cong \Delta BPQ$ by SSS (Theorem 4.5). Thus $\angle APQ$ and $\angle BPQ$ are congruent as corresponding parts. Therefore, ΔAPR and ΔBPR are congruent by SAS (Post. 15), making $\overline{RA} \cong \overline{RB}$ by correspondence. Therefore, $RA = RB$ by the definition of congruent.

ORAL EXERCISES

1. Can a line, not in a plane, form a right angle with a line in the plane and *not* be perpendicular to the plane? Explain your answer.

2. Did the proof of Theorem 7.1 deal with points in a plane or in space?

3. Could one line be perpendicular to each of two different planes? Explain your answer.

4. Can a line be perpendicular to just one line at a point in a plane? Explain your answer.

5. Which of the following determine a unique plane?

a. a line **b.** a ray **c.** a line and an external point

d. an angle **e.** a segment **f.** two intersecting lines

WRITTEN EXERCISES

A. 1. In the figure, $\overleftrightarrow{AB} \perp \overleftrightarrow{BC}$. Can you conclude that $\overleftrightarrow{AB}$ is perpendicular to plane P? Explain your answer.

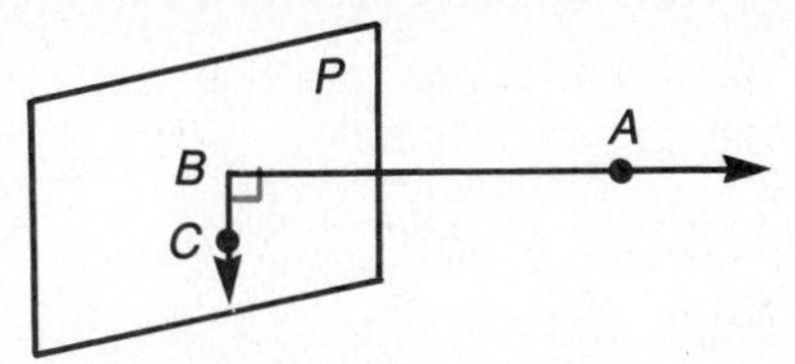

2. Can a triangle that lies in one plane also lie in a second plane? Explain your answer.

B. 3. Sketch a figure that satisfies the following description. Line l, not in plane X, intersects X at point A. Line l is perpendicular to $\overleftrightarrow{AB}$ and $\overleftrightarrow{AD}$, both of which lie in plane X. Based on what you already know, is your figure sufficient to show that $l \perp X$? Explain your answer.

4. If a point is equidistant from each of two other points, are the points necessarily coplanar? Explain your answer.

ASSIGNMENT GUIDE

Minimum 1-10
Regular 1-16
Maximum 1-18

Oral Exercises

1. Yes; to be perpendicular to a plane, a line must be perpendicular to every line of the plane that passes through the point of intersection.
2. in a plane
3. Yes; a line is perpendicular to an infinite number of planes.
4. Yes; if both lines are in the same plane, by Thm. 5.1; if the lines are in different planes, intuitively.
5. c, d, f

Written Exercises

1. No; by the definition, it must be shown that $\overleftrightarrow{AB}$ is perpendicular to every line in P that intersects B.
2. No; by Post. 7, three noncollinear points (the vertices) lie in exactly one plane.
3. No; you would have to show all lines through A in X are $\perp$ to l.

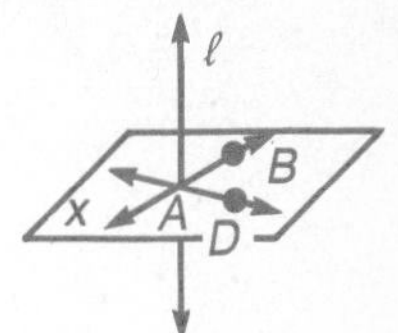

4. Yes; Post. 7 states that any three points determine *at least* one plane.

5. By Post. 7, they must be noncollinear, so no other condition is necessary.

6. an equilateral triangle

7. Theorem 7.1

8. Congruence of segments is transitive.

9. Congruence of segments is reflexive.

10. SSS

11. Theorem 3.8

12. Definition of right Δ

13. Congruence of segments is reflexive.

14. HL (Theorem 6.3)

15. Corres. parts of $\cong$ Δs are $\cong$.

16. Steps *1*, *6*, and Cor. 5.2.1

17.

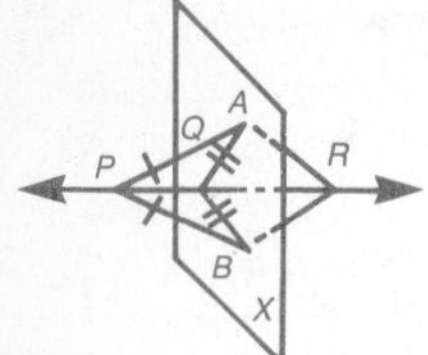

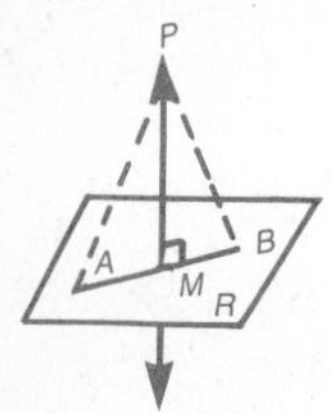

18. ΔPMB and ΔPMA are congruent by LL; $\overline{PA} \cong \overline{PB}$ by CPCTC

5. Three points are equidistant from each other. What condition is necessary to prove they determine a *unique* plane?

6. What type of figure is determined by the points described in Exercise 5 and the segments that they form?

Supply the missing reasons for the following proofs.

Given: $\overline{AC} \cong \overline{AD} \cong \overline{BC} \cong \overline{BD}$
$\overline{CF} \cong \overline{DE}$

Prove: $\Delta CFD \cong \Delta CED$

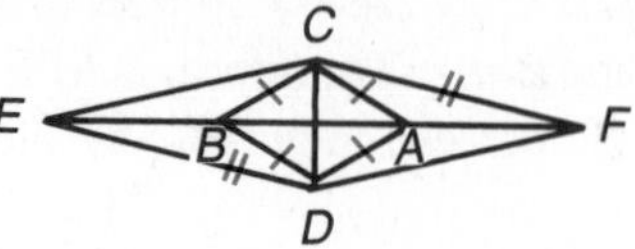

Proof:

STATEMENTS	REASONS
1. $\overline{AC} \cong \overline{AD} \cong \overline{BC} \cong \overline{BD}$, $\overline{CF} \cong \overline{DE}$	1. Given
2. $\overline{CF} \cong \overline{DF}$, $\overline{CE} \cong \overline{DE}$	2. **7.**
3. $\overline{CE} \cong \overline{DF}$	3. **8.**
4. $\overline{CD} \cong \overline{CD}$	4. **9.**
5. $\Delta CFD \cong \Delta CED$	5. **10.**

Given: $\overline{PC} \cong \overline{QC}$
$\angle ABP$ is a rt. $\angle$.

Prove: $\overleftrightarrow{AC}$ is the $\perp$ bisector of $\overline{PQ}$.

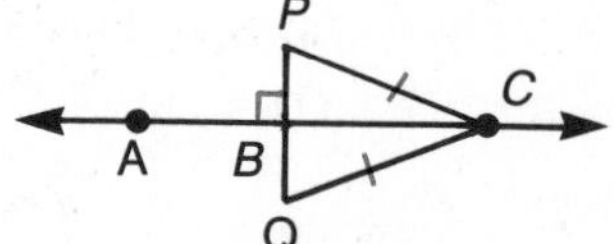

Proof:

STATEMENTS	REASONS
1. $\overline{PC} \cong \overline{QC}$, $\angle ABP$ is a rt. $\angle$.	1. Given
2. $\angle PBC$ and $\angle QBC$ are right $\angle$s.	2. **11.**
3. ΔPBC and ΔQBC are right Δs.	3. **12.**
4. $\overline{BC} \cong \overline{BC}$	4. **13.**
5. $\Delta PBC \cong \Delta QBC$	5. **14.**
6. $\overline{PB} \cong \overline{QB}$	6. **15.**
7. $\overleftrightarrow{AC}$ is the $\perp$ bisector of $\overline{PQ}$.	7. **16.**

C. 17. The points in the figure demonstrating the proof of Theorem 7.1 all lie in the same plane. Draw a figure that shows how the theorem could also apply to points in space.

18. Draw a figure based on the following information. $\overline{AB}$ lies in plane R, and M is the midpoint of $\overline{AB}$. An external line, $\overleftrightarrow{PM}$, intersects R at M and is perpendicular to R. Given these conditions, prove that $\overline{PA}$ and $\overline{PB}$ are congruent segments.

7.2 The Basic Perpendicular Theorem

Two fundamental theorems, or lemmas, must be established in order to prove the basic theorem on perpendicularity in space. Theorem 7.1 was the first. Now you are ready for the second.

THEOREM 7.2
If each of three noncollinear points of a plane is equidistant from two points not in that plane, then every point of the plane is equidistant from these two points.

Given: Points A, B, and C in plane E; points P and Q not in E
$AP = AQ$, $BP = BQ$, $CP = CQ$

Prove: For any other point X in E, $XP = XQ$.

Proof: From Theorem 7.1, you know that every point on $\overleftrightarrow{CB}$ or $\overleftrightarrow{AB}$ is equidistant from points P and Q (figure at the right). Choose any other point X in plane E. If X lies on $\overleftrightarrow{CB}$ or $\overleftrightarrow{AB}$, then its equidistance from P and Q is established by Theorem 7.1. Otherwise, X lies on one side of $\overleftrightarrow{CB}$ (figure below).

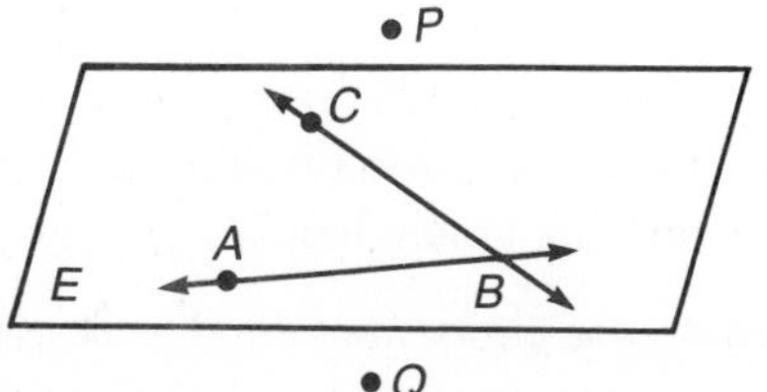

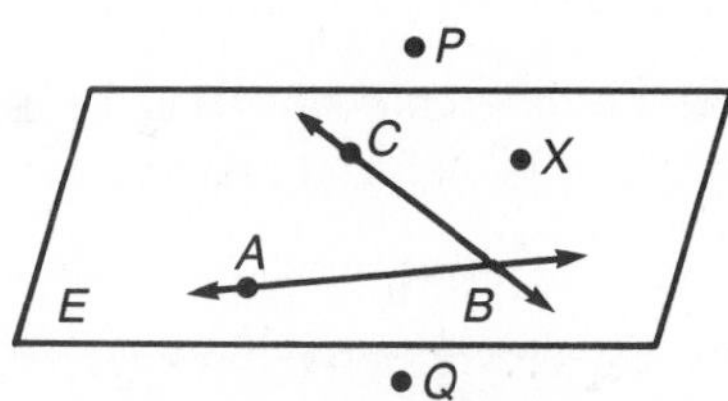

Now select a point Y on $\overleftrightarrow{AB}$ and on the other side of $\overleftrightarrow{BC}$ from X. The Plane Separation Postulate tells you that $\overleftrightarrow{YX}$ intersects $\overleftrightarrow{CB}$ in some point, Z (bottom figure). Since Z is on $\overleftrightarrow{CB}$, it is equidistant from P and Q. Y is on $\overleftrightarrow{AB}$, so it too is equidistant from P and Q. Therefore, by Theorem 7.1, every point on $\overleftrightarrow{YZ}$ is equidistant from P and Q.

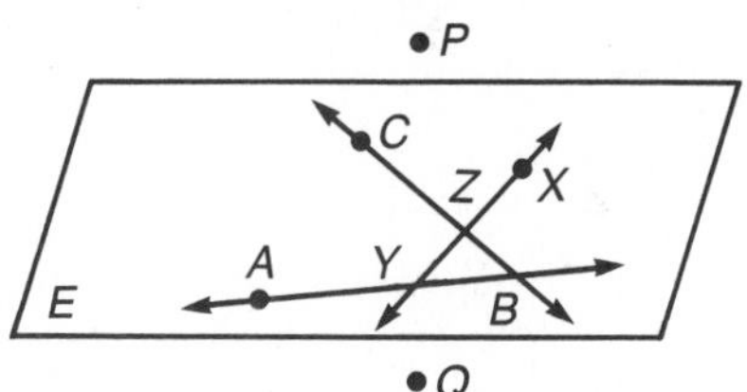

Since X lies on $\overleftrightarrow{YZ}$, Theorem 7.2 is proven.

OBJECTIVE

Use Theorems 7.2 and 7.3 in proofs.

TEACHER'S NOTES

See p. T30

MIXED REVIEW

1. Solve $7x - (2x - 3) = 41$. $x = 7\frac{3}{5}$
2. Find the supplement of $2x - 10$. $190 - 2x$
3. Simplify $\sqrt{48} + \sqrt{12}$. $6\sqrt{3}$
4. Find the decimal equivalents of $\frac{1}{7}$, $\frac{2}{7}$ and $\frac{3}{7}$. $0.\overline{142857}$ $0.\overline{285714}$ $0.\overline{428571}$
5. Solve $x + 2y = 4$, $3x - y = -9$. $(-2, 3)$

TEACHER'S RESOURCE MASTERS

Practice Master 19, Part 2
Quiz 13

To further your understanding of perpendicularity in space, consider the corner of a room, empty except for a broom lying on the floor, as pictured below.

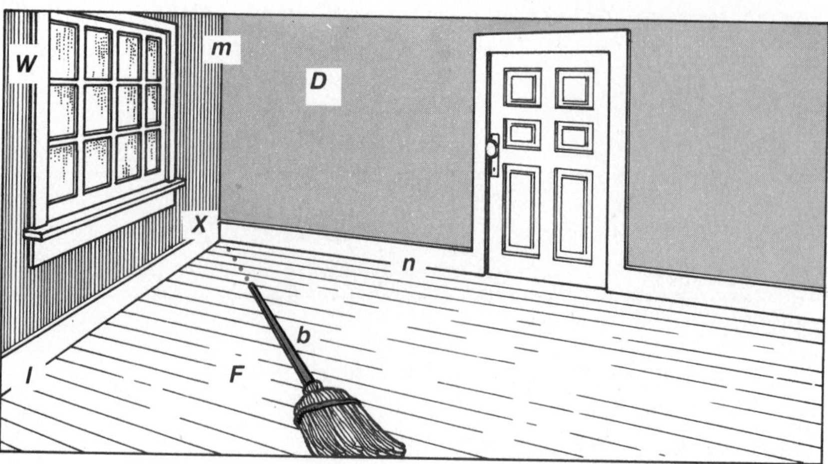

You can see three planes: F (floor), W (window), and D (door). The planes are separated by lines l, m, and n. (Recall Postulate 8, which states that the intersection of two planes is a line.) The line of the broom handle, b, intersects the corner point, X.

Based on this information, and using conjecture, answer *yes* or *no* to each of the following.

yes	yes	no
no	no	yes
yes	no	yes
yes	no	no

Is $l \perp m$?	Is $l \perp n$?	Is $l \perp b$?
Is $b \perp l$?	Is $b \perp n$?	Is $b \perp m$?
Is $l \perp D$?	Is $l \perp F$?	Is $m \perp F$?
Is $n \perp W$?	Is $b \perp D$?	Is $b \perp W$?

In answering these questions you are, in effect, expressing the difference between the perpendicularity of two lines and the perpendicularity of a line to a plane. You are now ready for the basic theorem on perpendicularity in space.

THEOREM 7.3
If a line is perpendicular to each of two intersecting lines at their point of intersection, then it is perpendicular to the plane of these lines.

Study the figure at the right carefully. You must see not only the plane shown, plane E, but also the planes formed by l and l_1, by l and l_2, and by l and l_3. Line l lies in the three planes just named, but not in E.

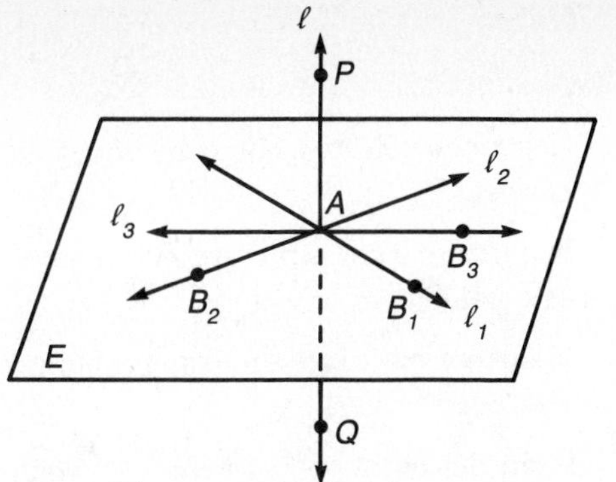

Given: l is $\perp$ to l_1 and l_2.

Prove: l is $\perp$ to plane E.
(Plan: Show $l \perp$ any line l_3 in plane E containing A.)

Proof:

STATEMENTS	REASONS
1. Let P be a point on l, B_1 a point on l_1, and B_2 a point on l_2, none coinciding with A.	*1.* Ruler Postulate
2. Let Q be a point on the ray opposite $\overleftrightarrow{AP}$ such that $AQ = AP$.	*2.* Point Plotting Theorem
3. A is a midpoint of $\overline{PQ}$.	*3.* Definition of midpoint
4. In the plane determined by l and l_1, l_1 is the perpendicular bisector of $\overline{PQ}$.	*4.* Definition of $\perp$ bisector
5. B_1 is equidistant from P and Q.	*5.* Theorem 5.2
6. In the plane determined by l and l_2, B_2 is equidistant from P and Q.	*6.* Similar to Steps *4* and *5*
7. B_3 is equidistant from P and Q.	*7.* Theorem 7.2, supported by Steps *2, 5,* and *6*
8. In the plane determined by l and l_3, l_3 is the perpendicular bisector of $\overline{PQ}$.	*8.* Steps *2, 7,* and Corollary 5.2.1
9. $l \perp l_3$	*9.* Definition of $\perp$ bisector
10. $l \perp$ plane E	*10.* Definition of perpendicularity of line and plane, since l_3 is *any* line in E through A other than l_1 and l_2

ORAL EXERCISES

1. Can three collinear points be equidistant from each other? What definition supports your answer?
2. In a plane, what is the maximum number of lines that can be perpendicular to each other at a point?
3. In space, what is the maximum number of lines that can be perpendicular to each other at a point?
4. From the proof of Theorem 7.2, what can you deduce about plane E in relation to $\overline{PQ}$? Support your answer.
5. Which theorem or corollary regarding points in a plane is similar to Theorem 7.2 regarding points in space?

WRITTEN EXERCISES

A. **1.** In the corner of a room, shown below, points A, B, and C lie in three different planes. Does this contradict Postulate 7, which states that 3 noncollinear points determine a unique plane? Explain your answer.

In the drawing at the right, how many lines other than *l* or *n* can be drawn on the floor that are

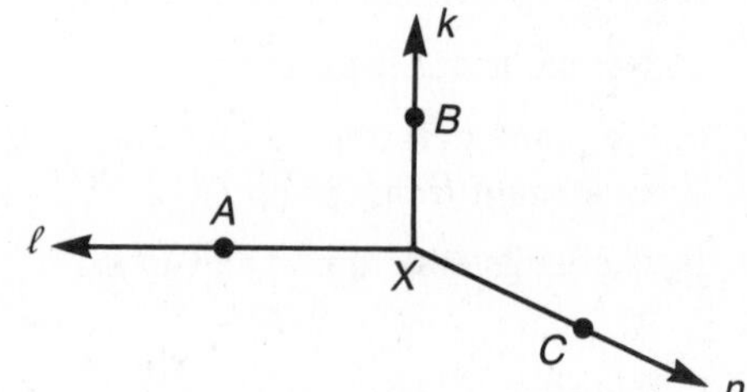

2. perpendicular to l at X?

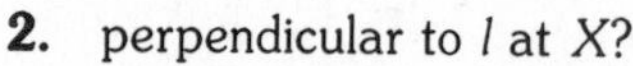

3. perpendicular to k at X?

4. perpendicular to n at X?

B. **5.** Points A, B, and C are noncollinear, and point D does not lie in the plane ABC. How many planes are determined by the four points? Name them, and draw a figure to support your answer.

6. **Given:** A, B, and C lie in plane P.
$AC = BC$
$\overline{XC} \perp$ plane P

Prove: $\Delta ACX \cong \Delta BCX$ and complete the statement $m\angle XBA = m\angle$ ______.

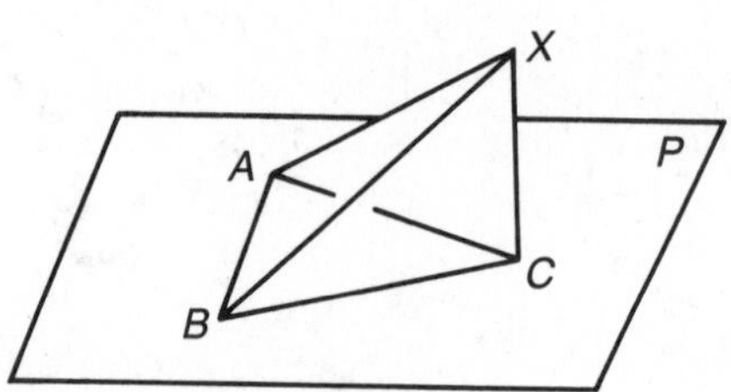

ASSIGNMENT GUIDE

Minimum 1-16
Regular 1-17
Maximum 1-18

Oral Exercises

1. no; definition of between
2. two
3. three
4. It is the bisector of $\overline{PQ}$. By Theorem 7.2, the intersection of $\overline{PQ}$ and E is equidistant from P and Q and is thus the midpoint of $\overline{PQ}$. Apply definition of bisector.
5. Corollary 5.2.1

Written Exercises

1. *All three* points lie in only one plane, which is not represented by the planes of the floor or the walls.
2. none
3. infinitely many
4. none
5. Four; ABD, ACD, BCD, and ABC

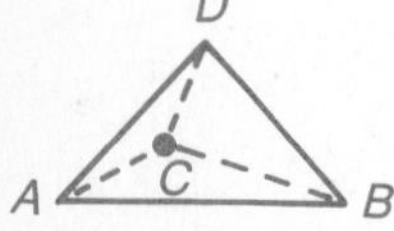

Read the following problem and determine the givens. Then fill in the missing statements and reasons in the proof.

A tent pole ($\overline{PO}$, below right) is secured to the ground by three wires, $\overline{AP}$, $\overline{BP}$, and $\overline{CP}$. The wires are the same length, and each is secured to the ground at exactly the same distance from O, the base of the pole. $\angle AOP$ is a right angle. Show that the pole is perpendicular to the ground, plane ABC.

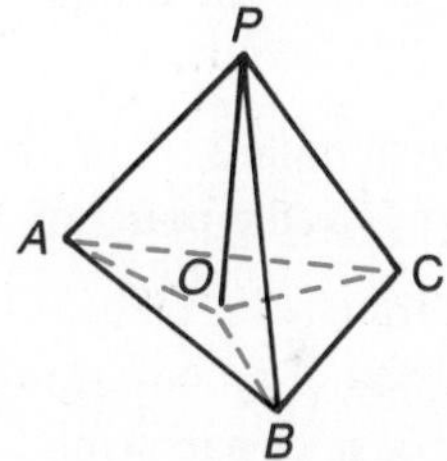

Given: $\overline{PO}$ intersects plane ABC at O.
7. ____
8. ____
9. ____

Prove: $\overline{PO} \perp$ plane ABC

Proof:

STATEMENTS	REASONS
1. **10.** ____ ____ ____ ____	1. Given
2. $\overline{PO} \cong \overline{PO}$	2. **11.** ____
3. $\triangle AOP \cong \triangle BOP \cong \triangle COP$	3. **12.** ____
4. $\angle AOP \cong \angle BOP \cong \angle COP$	4. **13.** ____
5. $\angle BOP$ and $\angle COP$ are right $\angle$s.	5. **14.** ____
6. $\overline{PO} \perp \overleftrightarrow{AO}$ $\overline{PO} \perp \overleftrightarrow{BO}$ $\overline{PO} \perp \overleftrightarrow{CO}$	6. **15.** ____
7. $\overline{PO} \perp$ plane ABC	7. **16.** ____

C. 17. In Step 6 of the previous problem, was it necessary to show that all three lines, $\overleftrightarrow{AO}$, $\overleftrightarrow{BO}$, and $\overleftrightarrow{CO}$ are perpendicular to $\overline{PO}$? Explain your answer.

18. Given the cube shown at the right, with $BP = BQ$, prove that $HP = HQ$. (HINT: It is given that the edges of a cube are all congruent, and any two intersecting edges of a cube are perpendicular.)

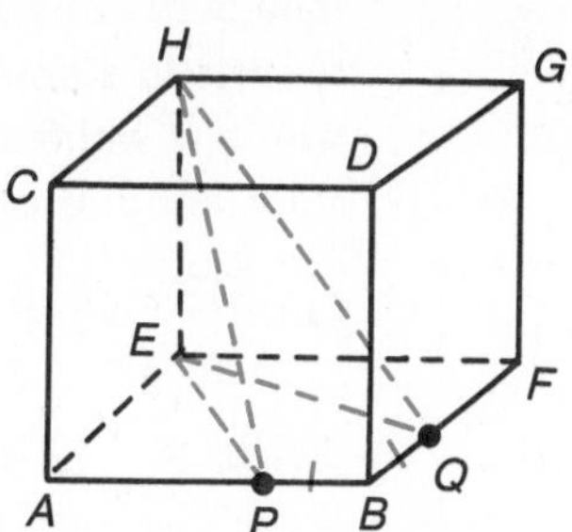

6. Since $\overline{XC} \perp$ plane P, $\overline{XC}$ is also $\perp$ $\overline{AC}$ and $\overline{BC}$ by the definition of a line perpendicular to a plane. Given that $AC = BC$, and $XC = XC$ by reflexive, $\triangle ACX \cong \triangle BCX$ by SAS (Postulate 15). So, $AX = BX$ by CPCTC, and $m\angle XBA = m\angle XAB$ by Theorem 4.3.
7. $AP = BP = CP$
8. $AO = BO = CO$
9. right $\angle AOP$
10. $\overline{PO}$ intersects plane ABC at O. $AP = BP = CP$ $AO = BO = CO$ right $\angle AOP$
11. Congruence of segments is reflexive.
12. SSS
13. Corres. parts of $\cong$ $\triangle$s are $\cong$.
14. Steps 1 and 4
15. Steps 1, 5, and definition of $\perp$
16. Theorem 7.3
17. No; to satisfy Theorem 7.3, only two lines are needed.
18. Given that $AB = FB$ and $BP = BQ$; $AP = FQ$ by subtraction; $\triangle AEP \cong \triangle FEQ$ by SAS; $EP = EQ$ by CPCTC; $\overline{HE} \perp \overline{EA}$ and $\overline{HE} \perp \overline{EF}$ by Given; $HE \perp$ plane $ABFE$ by Theorem 7.3; $\overline{HE} \perp \overline{EP}$ and $\overline{HE} \perp \overline{EQ}$ by def. of $\perp$ line and plane; $\angle HEP$ and $\angle HEQ$ are rt. $\angle$s by def. of $\perp$; $\triangle HEP$ and $\triangle HEQ$ are rt. $\triangle$s by def. of rt. $\triangle$s; $\triangle HEP \cong \triangle HEQ$ by LL; therefore, $\overline{HP} \cong \overline{HQ}$ by CPCTC, and $HP = HQ$ by def. of $\cong$ segments.

SELF-QUIZ

Self-Quiz

1. F 2. T
3. T 4. T
5. T 6. F
7. T 8. T

Identify each statement in Exercises 1–8 as *true* or *false*.

1. Line a is in plane J. Line b intersects a at X. If $a \perp b$, then $b \perp$ plane J.

2. If K and L are equidistant from G and H, all points on $\overleftrightarrow{KL}$ are equidistant from G and H.

3. Noncollinear points X, Y, and Z are each equidistant from points S and T. All of the other points in the plane of X, Y, and Z are equidistant from S and T.

4. Three corners of a billboard are equidistant from the base of a maple tree on one side and the base of an oak tree on the other side. The surface of the billboard is equidistant from the base of each tree.

Refer to the figure for Exercises 5–8.

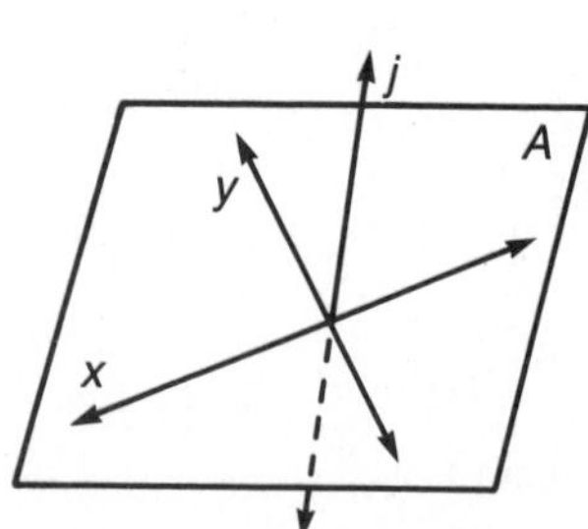

5. If $j \perp y$ and $j \perp x$, $j \perp$ plane A.

6. If $j \perp y$ and $y \perp x$, $j \perp$ plane A.

7. If $j \perp y$ and $y \perp x$, $y \perp$ the plane containing lines x and j.

8. If $j \perp x$ and $y \perp x$, $x \perp$ the plane containing lines j and y.

CALCULATOR

When a number n is expressed as a power of another number b, you can say that the power to which b is raised is the **logarithm** of n. Symbolically, if $n = b^x$, then $\log_b n = x$ (the log of n with base b is x).

If 10 is the base, the logarithm is called the *common log*. Since $100 = 10^2$, the common log of 100 is 2. What is the common log of 1000? To verify your answer, enter 1000 on your calculator and press [LOG]. Now predict the range of possible values for $\log_{10}240$. Verify your prediction.

One of the advantages of working with logarithms is that they behave as exponents. To multiply, you add exponents; to raise to a power, you multiply. Try the following problems with and without logs. After calculating with logs, your final steps are to press [INV] and [LOG]. Why?

1. $243 \cdot 3456$
   $\log 243 + \log 3456$
2. $3457 \div 0.000345$
   $\log 3457 - \log 0.000345$
3. $45.87^3 \cdot 1749^2$ ($\log 45.87 \cdot 3 + \log 1749 \cdot 2$)

Calculator

$\log_{10}1000 = 3$

Since $100 < 240 < 1000$, $2 < \log_{10}240 < 3$. Using the calculator, $\log_{10}240 \approx 2.3802$.

You must invert the log function to find a number given its log.

1. 839,808
2. 10,020,289
3. 2.95233×10^{11}

7.3 Perpendicular Planes and Lines

Before this chapter, your experience with perpendicular relationships concerned only lines in a plane. Now that you know about planes perpendicular to planes and planes perpendicular to lines, you can prove four important theorems about perpendicular relationships in space.

THEOREM 7.4
Through a given point on a given line there passes a plane perpendicular to the line.

Given: P, a point on line l

Prove: There is a plane, E, perpendicular to l at P.

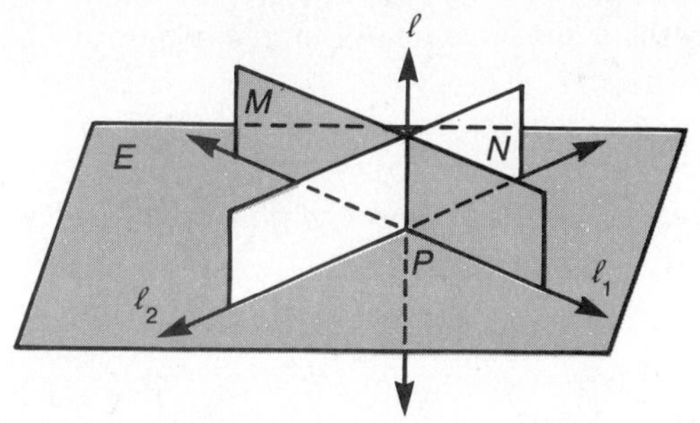

Proof: Let M and N be two different planes containing l. Since l is in both M and N, there is a line in each plane perpendicular to l at P by Theorem 5.1. Name these lines l_1 and l_2. By Theorem 7.3, plane E determined by l_1 and l_2 is perpendicular to l at P.

By definition, every line in plane E through point P is perpendicular to l. The next theorem shows that there cannot be lines outside of plane E that are also perpendicular to l at P.

THEOREM 7.5
If a line and a plane are perpendicular, then the plane contains every line perpendicular to the given line at its point of intersection with the given plane.

Given: Line $l \perp$ plane E at point P

Prove: Plane E contains every line perpendicular to l at P.

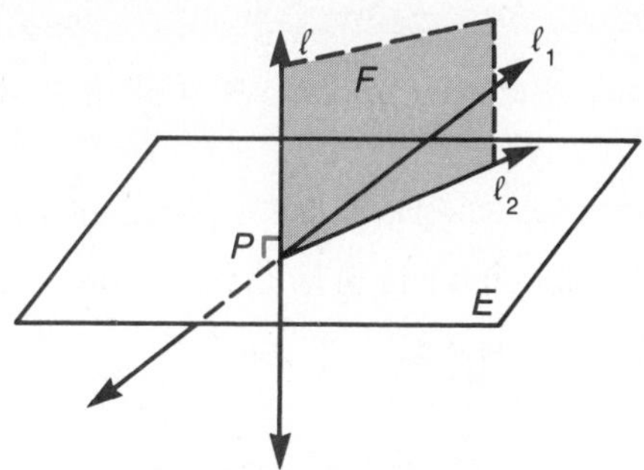

OBJECTIVE

Use Theorems 7.4–7.7 to answer questions regarding perpendicular lines and planes.

TEACHER'S NOTES

See p. T30

MIXED REVIEW

1. Find the greatest common factor of 80 and 48. 16
2. Simplify $\frac{x+2}{x^2-x-6}$ $\frac{1}{x-3}$
3. Multiply $\frac{x^2+2x+1}{x-3} \cdot \frac{x^2-x-6}{x+1}$. $(x+1)(x+2)$
4. Solve $8 - (2x + 3) > 12$. $x < -3\frac{1}{2}$
5. What is the least common multiple of 15 and 9? 45

TEACHER'S RESOURCE MASTERS

Practice Master 20, Part 1

Proof: Assume that l_1 is perpendicular to l at P, and that l_1 *does not* lie in plane E. Since l_1 and l are intersecting lines, they determine a plane F. Let l_2 be the intersection of planes F and E. By the definition of a perpendicular line and plane, l_2 is perpendicular to l at P. Having two lines in F perpendicular to l at P contradicts Theorem 5.1. Therefore, the assumption is incorrect, and Theorem 7.5 is established indirectly.

THEOREM 7.6
Through a given point on a given line, there is at most one plane perpendicular to the line.

Again, an indirect proof will be useful in establishing the uniqueness of the plane in this theorem.

Given: Line l and point P on l

Prove: There is at most one plane perpendicular to l at P.

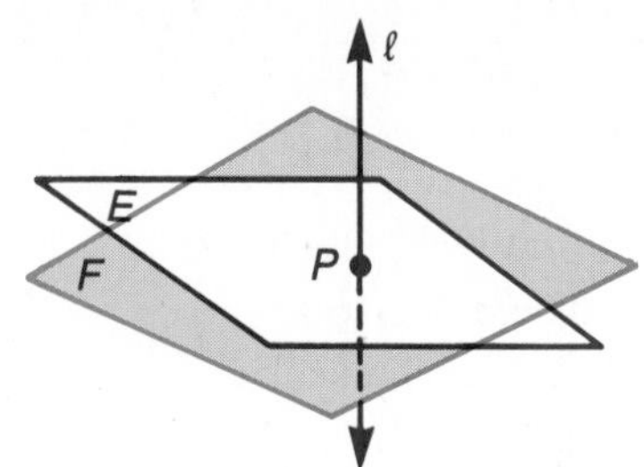

Proof: Assume that two planes, A and B, are both perpendicular to l at P. Then, by Theorem 7.5, both A and B contain every line perpendicular to l at P. But this is impossible, since two planes intersect at most in one line. Indirectly, then, Theorem 7.6 is established.

ASSIGNMENT GUIDE

Minimum 1-10
Regular 1-10
Maximum 1-13 odd, 14

THEOREM 7.7
The perpendicular bisecting plane of a segment is the set of all points equidistant from the endpoints of the segment.

The proof of this theorem is left as an exercise.

Oral Exercises

1. It is ⊥ to l.
2. It is perpendicular to every line in the plane that passes through the intersection.
3. one
4. no
5. Theorem 7.6

ORAL EXERCISES

1. If line l is perpendicular to plane K at point P, what is true of every line in K that passes through P?
2. What determines whether a line is perpendicular to a plane?
3. Through a point on a line, how many planes are perpendicular to the line?
4. If plane A is perpendicular to line l at point P, is there a line not in A perpendicular to l at P?
5. Which theorem in this lesson asserts uniqueness?

6. In a plane, how many lines are perpendicular to a given line at a given point on the line?

7. In space, how many lines are perpendicular to a given line at a given point on the line?

6. one

7. infinitely many

WRITTEN EXERCISES

A. **1.** Assume that two planes intersect in a line. Could either plane be perpendicular to the line of intersection? Explain.

2. How many planes can intersect a line segment at its midpoint?

3. How many planes can be perpendicular to a line segment at its midpoint? Explain.

4. In the figure, line $k \perp \overleftrightarrow{AB}$, which lies in plane E. Can you conclude that $k \perp E$? Explain.

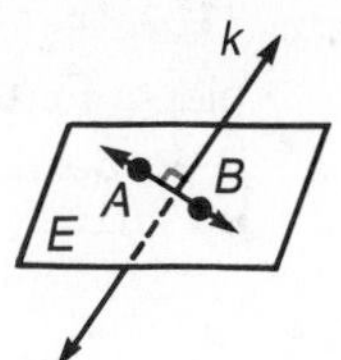

5. Does Theorem 7.4 guarantee that through a given point on a given line, there is *exactly* one plane perpendicular to the line?

B. **In the figure below, $\overleftrightarrow{QP} \perp$ plane E at point P.**

6. What guarantees that $\overleftrightarrow{QP} \perp \overleftrightarrow{PA}$ and $\overleftrightarrow{QP} \perp \overleftrightarrow{PB}$?

7. If $\overleftrightarrow{PR} \perp \overleftrightarrow{PQ}$, what guarantees that $\overleftrightarrow{PR}$ lies in E?

8. From the given information can you conclude that $\overleftrightarrow{PA} \perp \overleftrightarrow{PB}$?

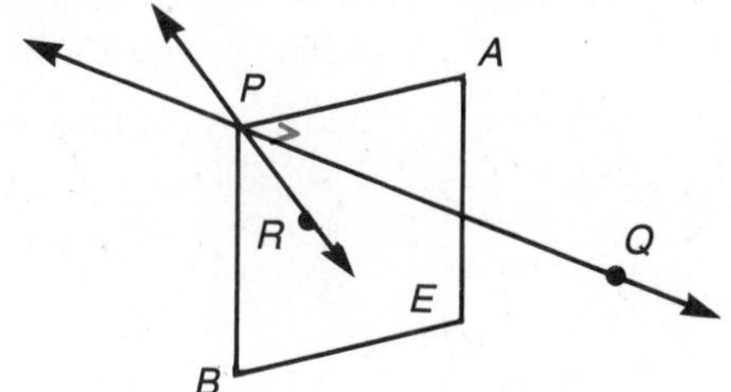

In the figure below, plane E is the perpendicular bisecting plane of $\overline{AB}$.

9. Name all the pairs of congruent segments that you can, and give the justification for your answer.

10. Name all the pairs of congruent triangles that you can, and give the justification for your answer.

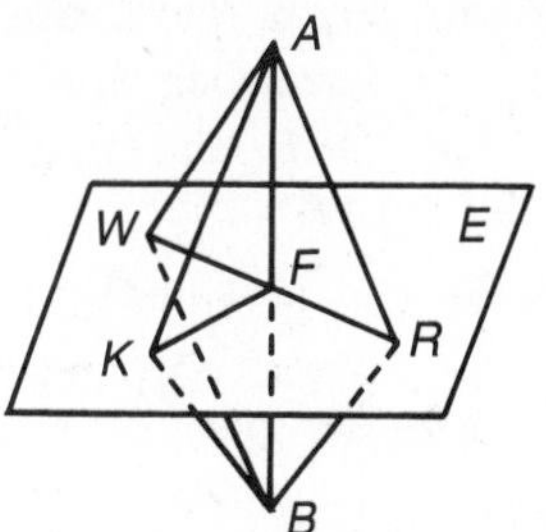

Written Exercises

1. No. The line of intersection lies entirely in each plane and cannot be perpendicular to itself.
2. infinitely many
3. exactly one, by Theorem 7.6
4. No. k must be $\perp$ to at least one other line in E that passes through the intersection by Theorem 7.3.
5. no
6. definition of perpendicular line and plane
7. Theorem 7.5
8. no
9. $\overline{AW} \cong \overline{WB}$, $\overline{AK} \cong \overline{KB}$, $\overline{AR} \cong \overline{RB}$, $\overline{AF} \cong \overline{FB}$, all by Theorem 7.7
10. $\triangle AFW \cong \triangle BFW$, $\triangle AFK \cong \triangle BFK$, $\triangle AFR \cong \triangle BFR$, all by SSS
11. *1.* Plane E, point K not in E (Given); *2.* Through K at T on l, there is a plane $E \perp l$ (Theorem 7.4); *3.* Assume another line m through $K \perp$ to plane E at R (Indirect assumption); *4.* K, T, R determine $\triangle KTR$ (Def. of $\triangle$); *5.* In $\triangle KTR$, $\angle KTR$ and $\angle KRT$ are rt. $\angle$s (Def. of $\perp$); *6.* Contradiction: At most one $\angle$ of a $\triangle$ can be a rt. $\angle$. (Corollary 5.3.1); Thus, the assumption is false, and there is at most one line through $K \perp$ to E.

12. *1.* Line l and point X not on l (Given); *2.* Assume there are 2 planes R and S each $\perp$ to l and each containing X (Indirect assumption); *3.* $\overleftrightarrow{XY} \perp l$, $\overleftrightarrow{XZ} \perp l$ (Def. of $\perp$ line and plane); *4.* Contradiction: There is only one line $\perp$ to a given line through a given external point. (Theorem 5.3.); Thus, the assumption is false, and there is at most one plane containing X and $\perp$ to l.

13. **(1)** *1.* Since P is in E, $\overleftrightarrow{PX} \perp \overleftrightarrow{AB}$ (Def. of $\perp$ line and plane); *2.* $AX = BX$ (Given); *3.* $m\angle AXP = m\angle BXP$ (Def. of $\perp$; All right angles are $\cong$.); *4.* $\triangle AXP \cong \triangle BXP$ (SAS); *5.* $\overline{AP} \cong \overline{BP}$ (CPCTC). **(2)** *1.* If $PA = PB$, then $\triangle APX \cong \triangle BPX$ (SSS); *2.* $\angle AXP \cong \angle BXP$ (CPCTC); *3.* $\angle AXP$ and $\angle BXP$ are rt. $\angle$s (Theorem 3.4); *4.* $\overleftrightarrow{PX} \perp \overleftrightarrow{AB}$ (Def. of $\perp$); *5.* $\overleftrightarrow{PX}$ lies in E (Theorem 7.5)

14. *1.* A, B, and C are noncollinear points; $AB = CB$, D the midpoint of $\overline{AC}$ (Given); *2.* $AD = CD$ (Def. of midpoint); *3.* B and D are equidistant from A and C (Def. of equidistant); *4.* $\overleftrightarrow{BD}$ is the $\perp$ bisector of $\overline{AC}$ (Cor. 5.2.1); *5.* Assume $\overline{BD}$ is not in the plane $\perp$ to $\overline{AC}$ at D (plane N) (Indirect assumption); *6.* Contadiction: By definition $\overline{AC}$ and N are $\perp$ if every line in plane N through the point of intersection, D, is $\perp$ to $\overline{AC}$. *7.* Therefore, $\overleftrightarrow{BD}$ (and thus B) lies in N.

11. Given: Plane E and point K not in E

Prove: There is at most one line containing K that is perpendicular to E.

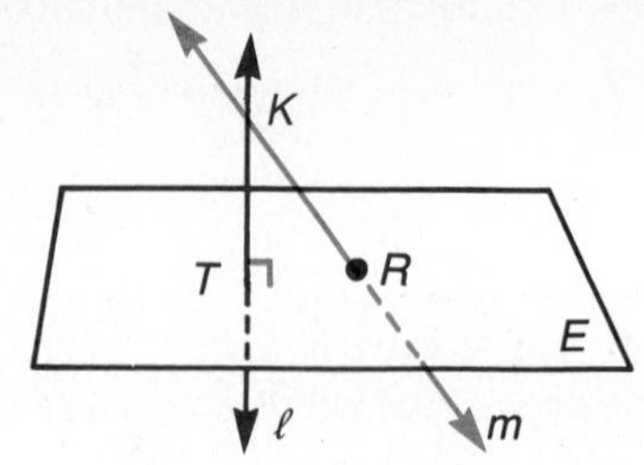

12. Given: Line l and point X not on l

Prove: There is at most one plane containing X that is perpendicular to l.

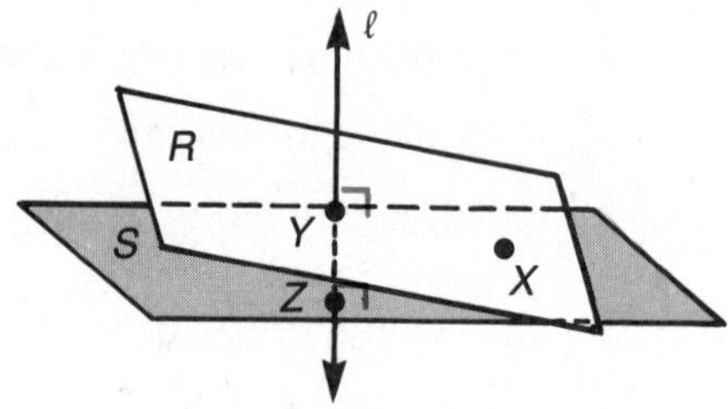

C. 13. Theorem 7.7 must be proved in two parts. You must prove that (1) if a point is in the plane, then it is equidistant, *and* (2) if a point is equidistant, then it is in the plane. Use the figure below to give a narrative proof of both (1) and (2).

Given: E is the perpendicular bisecting plane of $\overline{AB}$.

Prove:
1. If P is in E, then $AP = BP$.
2. If $AP = BP$, then P is in E.

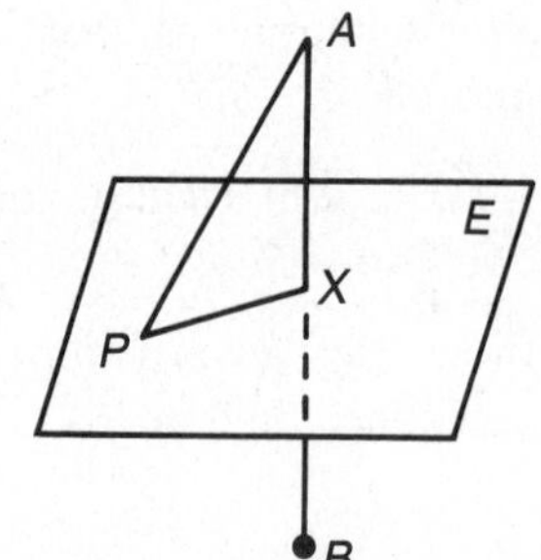

14. Given: A, B, and C are noncollinear points, $AB = CB$, D is the midpoint of $\overline{AC}$.

Prove: B is contained in the plane perpendicular to $\overline{AC}$ at D.

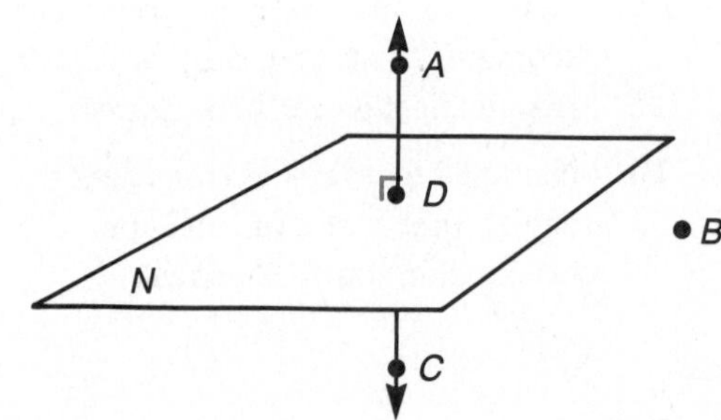

7.4 Existence and Uniqueness

In Chapter 5, you learned the difference between *existence* and *uniqueness* in geometry, and you used indirect methods to prove theorems about the existence and uniqueness of perpendicular lines in a plane. This lesson recalls the concepts and methods of Chapter 5 and extends them to the relationships between perpendicular lines and planes in space.

In the figure at the right, lines l_1 and l_2 are both perpendicular to plane E, intersecting E at points A and B. Does it appear to you that l_1 and l_2 determine a plane? This is what you will prove for the next theorem.

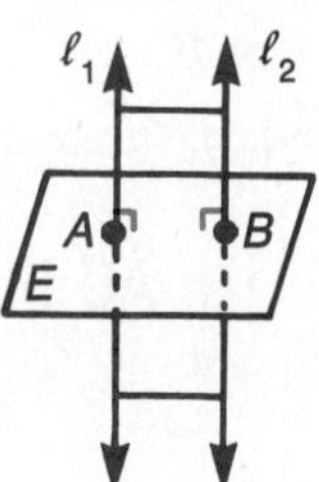

THEOREM 7.8
Two lines perpendicular to the same plane are coplanar.

Look at the figure on the right, which focuses on points A and B. Form $\overline{AB}$ and locate M, the midpoint of $\overline{AB}$. Then draw $\overline{PQ}$ in plane E perpendicular to $\overline{AB}$ such that M is also the midpoint of $\overline{PQ}$.

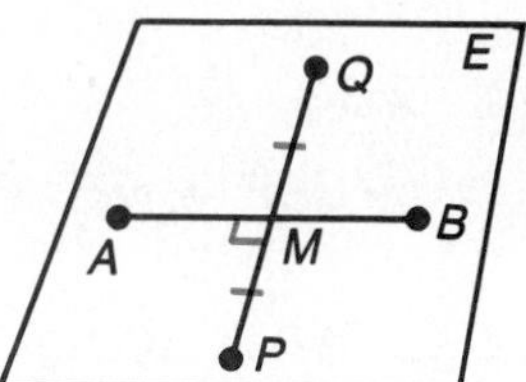

Theorem 7.6 tells you that there is *only one* perpendicular plane bisecting $\overline{PQ}$. Call this plane D. If you can prove that both l_1 and l_2 lie in D, then Theorem 7.8 is established. Start by proving that l_1 lies in plane D. To do this, expand the original figure as shown below.

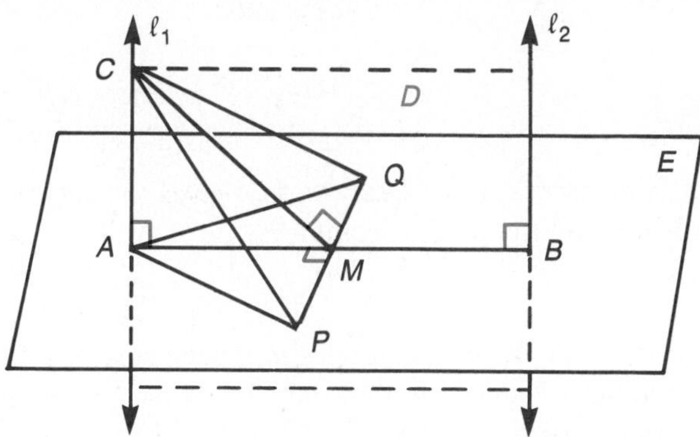

OBJECTIVE

Use Theorems 7.8–7.11 to answer questions regarding perpendicular lines and planes and use these theorems in proofs.

TEACHER'S NOTES

See p. T31

MIXED REVIEW

1. Multiply $\sqrt{6} \cdot \sqrt{24}$. 12
2. Simplify $\sqrt{1444}$. 38
3. Solve $x^2 - 2 = 0$. $\sqrt{2}, -\sqrt{2}$
4. What is the name of a segment that connects a vertex of a triangle to the midpoint of the opposite side? median
5. Solve $3x - 4(x + 2) < 5$. $x > -13$

TEACHER'S RESOURCE MASTERS

Practice Master 20, Part 2
Quiz 14

Given: $l_1 \perp$ plane E at A, $l_2 \perp$ plane E at B

Prove: l_1 and l_2 are coplanar.

Proof:

STATEMENTS	REASONS
1. $l_1 \perp$ plane E at A $l_2 \perp$ plane E at B	1. Given
2. Draw $\overline{AB}$ and M, the midpoint of $\overline{AB}$.	2. Every segment has exactly one midpoint (Theorem 1.5).
3. In E, draw $\overline{PQ} \perp \overline{AB}$ at M, such that M is the midpoint of $\overline{PQ}$.	3. Theorems 1.4 (The Point Plotting Theorem) and 1.5
4. $\overline{MP} \cong \overline{MQ}$	4. Definition of midpoint
5. $\overline{AM} \cong \overline{AM}$	5. Congruence of segments is reflexive.
6. $\angle AMP$ and $\angle AMQ$ are right $\angle$s.	6. Definition of $\perp$
7. $\Delta AMP \cong \Delta AMQ$	7. Steps *4, 5, 6,* and LL
8. $\overline{AP} \cong \overline{AQ}$	8. Corres. parts of $\cong$ Δs are $\cong$.
9. Draw C, a point on l_1.	9. A line is made up of an endless number of points.
10. $\overline{AC} \cong \overline{AC}$	10. Congruence of segments is reflexive.
11. $m\angle CAP = m\angle CAQ$	11. Definition of line $\perp$ to plane and Theorem 3.3.
12. $\Delta CAP \cong \Delta CAQ$	12. Steps *8, 10, 11,* and LL
13. $\overline{CP} \cong \overline{CQ}$	13. Corres. parts of $\cong$ Δs are $\cong$.
14. C and A (l_1) are equidistant from P and Q.	14. Steps *8* and *13*
15. l_1 lies in the $\perp$ bisecting plane of $\overline{PQ}$, plane D.	15. Theorem 7.7

By placing point C on l_2, an identical proof can be fashioned showing that l_2 also lies in D. Thus, l_1 and l_2 are coplanar, and the proof is complete.

Before continuing on to the next theorems, recall the significance of a "one and only one" theorem, discussed in Chapter 5. Remember that such theorems require *two* proofs: the proof of "one" is the proof of *existence;* the proof of "only one" is the proof of *uniqueness.*

THEOREM 7.9
Through a given point there passes one and only one plane perpendicular to a given line.

The "one and only one" form of this theorem calls for two proofs. Another condition requires two more proofs; the point could lie on the line or outside the line.

1. Through a given point on a line, there exists a plane perpendicular to the line.
2. At most one plane is perpendicular to a line through a given point on the line.
3. Through a given point outside a line, there exists a plane perpendicular to the line.
4. At most one plane is perpendicular to a line through a given point outside the line.

The first two statements were proved in Theorems 7.4 and 7.6. The last two are left as exercises.

THEOREM 7.10
Through a given point there passes one and only one line perpendicular to a given plane.

Theorem 7.10 requires four proofs for the same reasons; you must prove both existence and uniqueness for a point on or off the line.

DEFINITION: distance to a plane from an external point
The **distance to a plane from an external point** is the length of the perpendicular segment from the point to the plane.

From a point external to a plane, could there be a segment shorter than the perpendicular segment? The answer lies in the next theorem.

THEOREM 7.11
The shortest segment to a plane from an external point is the perpendicular segment.

The proof of this theorem is similar to that of Theorem 6.6 and is left as an exercise using the indirect method.

ORAL EXERCISES

Identify each of the following as true or false.

1. Two lines are perpendicular to each other if and only if they are coplanar.
2. Through a point there passes one and only one plane perpendicular to a given line.
3. A segment is perpendicular to a plane if and only if it represents the shortest distance from the point to the plane.
4. Through a point there passes one and only one line perpendicular to a given plane.
5. Two lines can each be perpendicular to a third line if and only if all three lines are coplanar.
6. Through a given line there passes one and only one plane perpendicular to the line.

WRITTEN EXERCISES

A.

1. On what line is the distance between two points measured?
2. On what line is the distance from a point to a line measured?
3. On what line is the distance from a point to a plane measured?

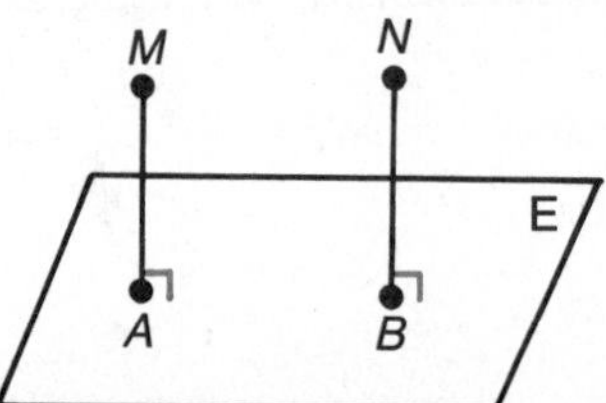

In the figure at the left, $\overline{MA}$ and $\overline{NB}$ are both perpendicular to plane E.

4. Are the segments always congruent?
5. Are they coplanar?
6. Do they determine a plane?

In the figure at the right, R lies outside plane E, and $\overline{RB} \perp E$. Points A and B lie in plane E.

7. Compare the lengths of RA and RB.
8. Compare the measures of $\angle A$ and $\angle B$.

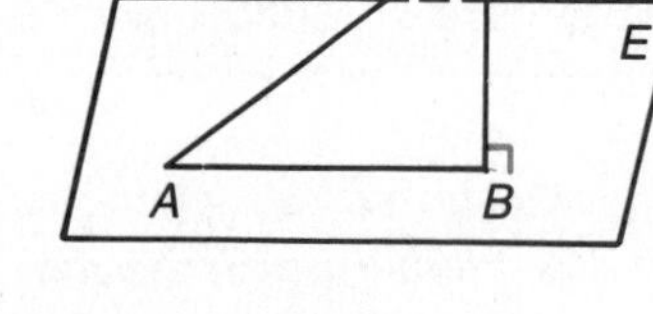

B.

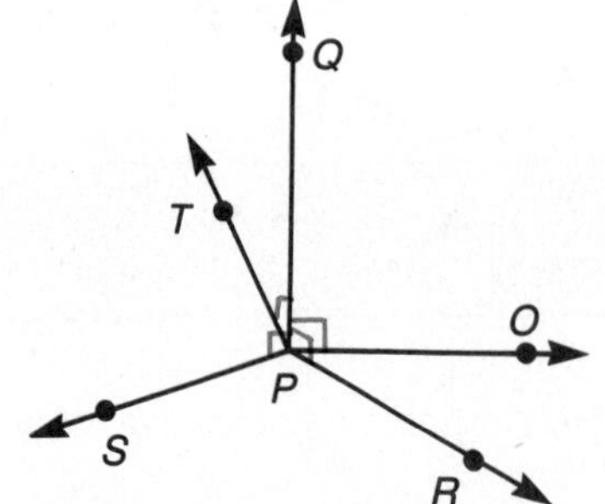

In the figure at the left, $\overrightarrow{PQ} \perp \overrightarrow{PO}, \overrightarrow{PR}, \overrightarrow{PS}$, and $\overrightarrow{PT}$.

9. What is the fewest number of planes that the intersecting rays might determine, given what you know?
10. If no three of the points shown are collinear, how many planes do the intersecting rays determine?

ASSIGNMENT GUIDE

Minimum 1-10
Regular 1-12
Maximum 1-13 odd, 14-17

Oral Exercises

1. F 2. T
3. T 4. T
5. F 6. F

Written Exercises

1. on the line containing those points
2. on the perpendicular through the point to the line
3. on the perpendicular through the point to the plane
4. no
5. yes
6. yes
7. $RA > RB$
8. $m\angle B > m\angle A$
9. three
10. five
11. Proof reads the same as text proof for Theorem 7.8, substituting B for A and l_2 for l_1 throughout.

11. Complete the proof of Theorem 7.8 by placing C on l_2 and showing that l_2 also lies in D, the perpendicular bisecting plane of $\overline{PQ}$.

12. What are the four statements that need to be proved to establish Theorem 7.10?

13. Prove that through a given point outside a line, there exists a plane perpendicular to the line.

14. Prove that at most one plane is perpendicular to a line through a given point outside the line.

15. **Given:** Points A and B are on opposite sides of plane M and are each equidistant from M. The perpendiculars from A and B to M intersect M at C and D, respectively. $\overline{AB}$ intersects $\overline{DC}$ at E.

Prove: E is the midpoint of $\overline{DC}$.

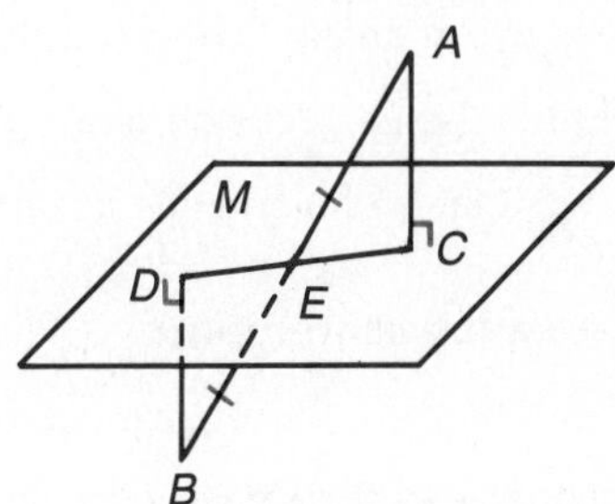

16. **Given:** Points A, B, C, and P in plane E; $PA = PB = PC$; $l \perp E$ at P

Prove: Every point X in l is equidistant from A, B, and C.

C. 17. **Given:** $\overline{AB} \perp$ plane E, F and H points of E such that $BF > BH$

Prove: $AF > AH$

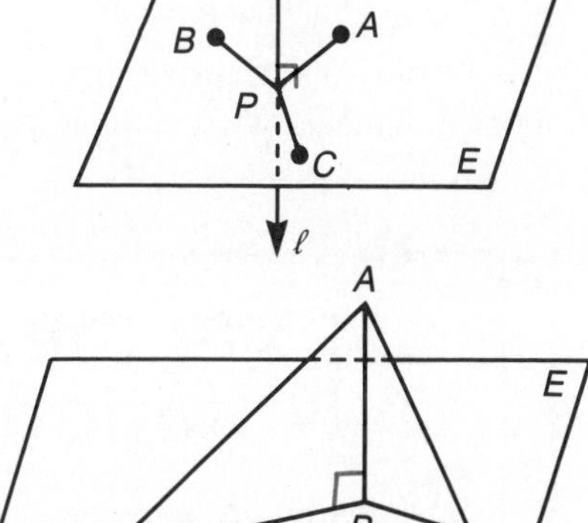

CHALLENGE

Draw a figure and write a narrative proof of Theorem 7.11.

12. Statements should read the same as text statements for Theorem 7.9, substituting line for plane throughout.

13. **Given:** Line l and an external point P
Prove: There is a plane $\perp$ to l through P.
Proof: Through P, there is a line $\perp$ to l by Theorem 5.3. Let Q be the point of intersection by Theorem 2.1. There is a plane $M \perp$ to l through Q by Thm. 7.4. By Theorem 7.5, M contains $\overleftrightarrow{PQ}$, so M is $\perp$ to l through P.

14. See *Selected Answers*, p. 632

15. $\overline{AC} \perp \overline{DC}$, $\overline{BD} \perp \overline{DC}$ (def. of line $\perp$ to a plane); $\angle BDE$ and $\angle ACE$ right $\angle$s (def. of $\perp$); ΔBDE and ΔACE right Δs (def. of right Δ); $\overline{AE} \cong \overline{BE}$, $\overline{AC} \cong \overline{BD}$ (given that A and B equidistant from M); $\Delta BDE \cong \Delta ACE$ (HL); $\overline{DE} \cong \overline{CE}$ (CPCTC); E is midpoint of $\overline{DC}$ (def. of midpoint).

16. See *Selected Answers*, p. 633

17. Select point P on $\overline{FB}$ such that $\overline{PB} \cong \overline{HB}$. Then $\Delta ABP \cong \Delta ABH$ (SAS) and $\overline{AP} \cong \overline{AH}$ (CPCTC). In ΔAPF, $AF > AP$ because $\overline{AF}$ is opposite the larger angle ($\angle P$ must be obtuse). By substitution, $AF > AH$.

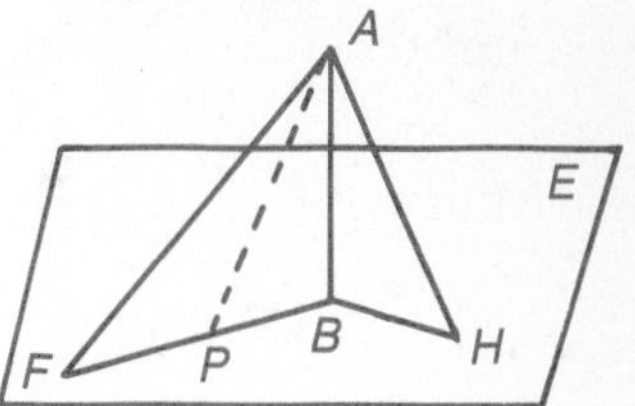

Challenge

See *Teachers Manual*, p. T60

Skills Maintenance

1. point, line, plane
2. Theorems are proven; postulates are accepted as true without proof.
3. All living things are humans.
4. the perpendicular bisector of the segment joining them
5. yes, no
6. the hypotenuse
7. yes
8. 0, 180
9. acute, right, obtuse
10. contradiction
11. sides, angles, medians, altitudes, angle bisectors
12. $2(180 - x) = 24 + 5(90 - x)$; $x = 38$.

Exploration

1. 8.65×10^{21} atoms
2. 5.88×10^{12} miles
3. 0.003 inches

SKILLS MAINTENANCE

1. What are the undefined terms in geometry?

2. What is the difference between theorems and postulates?

3. What is the converse of the statement "All humans are living things"?

4. In a plane, what is the set of points equidistant from two given points?

5. Does every angle have a supplement? a complement?

6. What is the longest side of a right triangle called?

7. If two angles of a triangle are congruent, are the sides opposite them congruent?

Complete each statement:

8. To every angle there corresponds a real number between ____ and ____.

9. According to their measures, angles may be classified as either ____, ____, or ____.

10. In an indirect proof, you reason until you reach a ____.

11. Every triangle has exactly three ____, ____, ____, ____, and ____.

12. Twice the measure of the supplement of an angle is 24 more than five times the measure of its complement. What is the measure of the angle?

EXPLORATION/Scientific Notation

Scientific notation consists of writing a numeral as the product of a number between one and ten and some power of ten. As an example, you could express the distance from Earth to the sun as 93 million, 93,000,000, or 9.3×10^7 miles. Similarly, 0.0009 means 9 ten thousandths or $9 \times \frac{1}{10{,}000}$, or 9×10^{-4}.

1. An ounce of gold contains 8,650,000,000,000,000,000,000 atoms. Write this in scientific notation.

2. A light year is $\approx$ 5,880,000,000,000 miles. Write this in scientific notation.

3. A sheet of paper is about 3×10^{-3} inches thick. Write this in decimal notation.

IN OTHER FIELDS/Joinery

The profession called *joinery* was first practiced in Italy. It was known in England by the 13th century and established in America by the 18th century. Like carpentry, joinery involves cutting, shaping, and joining timber into structures. While the carpenter is responsible for the skeleton of a building, and is therefore most concerned with its stability, the joiner applies the finishes. By crafting and installing paneling, doors, windows, and cupboards, the joiner completes a structure's appearance. Another craftsman whose skills and scope relate to carpentry and joinery is the cabinetmaker. Cabinetmaking involves working with better quality furniture and refining woodwork.

All three professions require an understanding of geometric relationships. For example, constructing the semicircular window you see above the front door of many houses requires a working knowledge of circles and angles. The joiner must be able to compute the area of a circle, determine the appropriate proportion between the diameter of the window and the width of the door below it, and calculate angle measurements so that the window panes (whose edges are radii) fit correctly.

A joiner might also be faced with the following problem. Suppose you want to put a 2-inch molding around the frame of a door that measures 8 ft by 3 ft (or 96 in. by 36 in.). In order to purchase the correct amount of material, you need to know the total area to be covered by the molding. The illustration should help you visualize the problem. Using your knowledge of computing area, how much molding would you, the joiner, require?

In Other Fields
464 sq. in.

TEACHER'S RESOURCE MASTERS

Computer Master 7

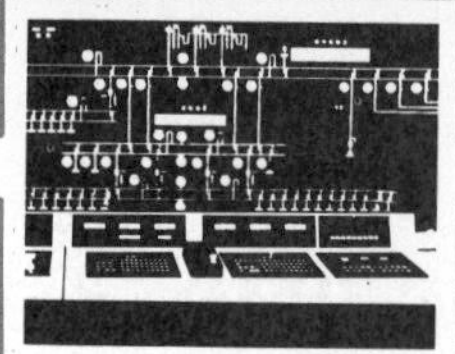

COMPUTER

Computer graphics is a rapidly expanding field with applications for highway planning, producing maps from satellite photos, architecture, textile design, automobile and aircraft design, simulations, and of course, video games.

Small personal computers display information on screens that can show about 1000 characters at a time. Many have graphics characters, such as shaded blocks, bars, and diagonals, that combine to create figures like those shown at the right.

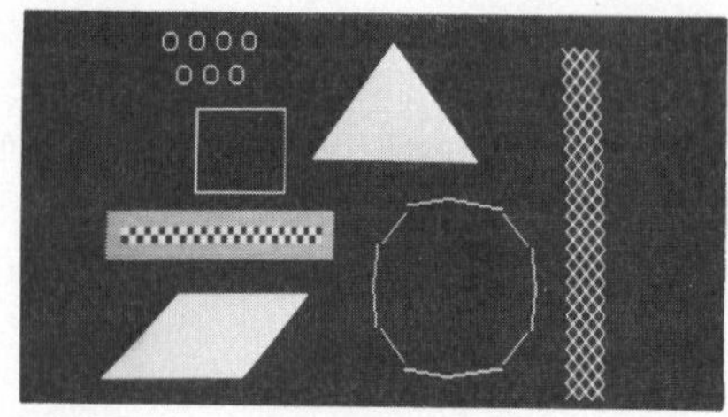

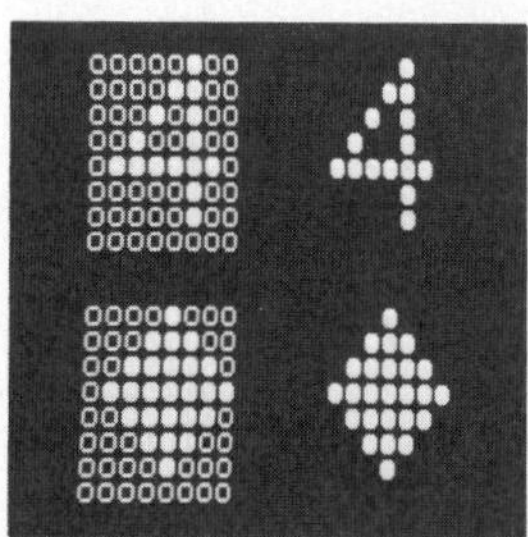

A special circuit in the computer groups each screen dot, or **pixel**, into an 8 × 8 block. Pixel is short for "picture element." Data stored in the computer tells how a block needs to be lit to make a specific character. As shown at the left, it takes 15 of the 64 block pixels to make the character for "4" and 25 to make a diamond-shaped character. A picture built with character blocks is like a mosaic, with all the pieces the same size but having jagged lines or rough edges. Some programmers call this uneven look "the jaggies."

The smoothness of a figure's lines is called its **resolution.** In a low-resolution display, character blocks are used. In a high-resolution display, each of the roughly 64,000 screen pixels can be programmed to light individually.

Printers which produce pictures using dots just like those on the screen often do not have enough resolution to produce a quality picture. To avoid the "jaggies," a plotter is usually used to output high-resolution graphics on paper. As shown at the right, a plotter feeds paper back and forth beneath a drawing pen which itself moves along a track or rod perpendicular to the paper path. The combined perpendicular motions of the paper and pen allow the pen to make diagonal movements.

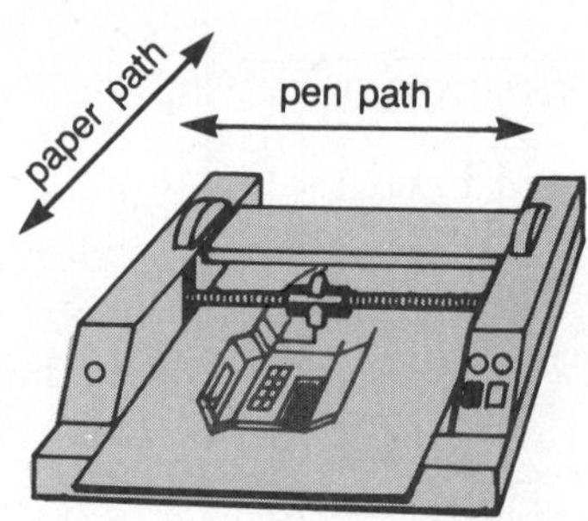

CHAPTER 7 REVIEW

VOCABULARY

distance to a plane from an external point (7.4)

perpendicular line and plane (7.1)

REVIEW EXERCISES

7.1

1. Is the following statement *true* or *false?*
If a line intersects a plane in only one point, then there is at least one line in the plane perpendicular to the given line.

2. If points A and B on line j are each equidistant from points X and Y, is point C, between A and B, equidistant from X and Y? Justify your answer.

3. Prove the following:

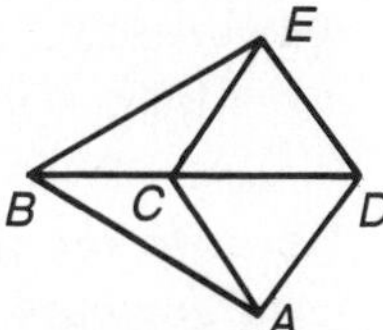

Given: C and D are equidistant from A and E.

Prove: $\triangle ABC \cong \triangle EBC$

7.2

4. If three noncollinear points X, Y, and Z of plane E are each equidistant from points P and Q not in E, then what can we say about the other points in E?

For Exercises 5–7, lines x, y, and z intersect at point R in space.
Lines x and y lie in plane A. Lines x and z lie in plane B.
Lines y and z lie in plane C.

5. If $x \perp y$ and $y \perp z$, $y \perp$ plane ____.

6. If $y \perp x$ and $x \perp z$, $x \perp$ plane ____.

7. If $x \perp z$ and $z \perp y$, $z \perp$ plane ____.

Write two-column proofs for Exercises 8 and 9.

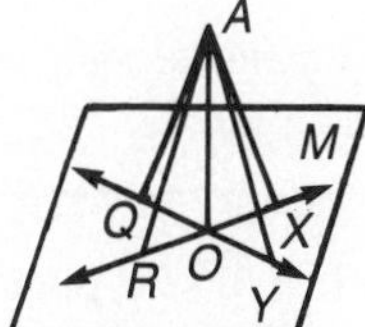

8. Given: $\overline{OX} \cong \overline{OY} \cong \overline{OR} \cong \overline{OQ}$
$\overline{AX} \cong \overline{AY} \cong \overline{AR} \cong \overline{AQ}$

Prove: $\overline{AO} \perp$ plane M

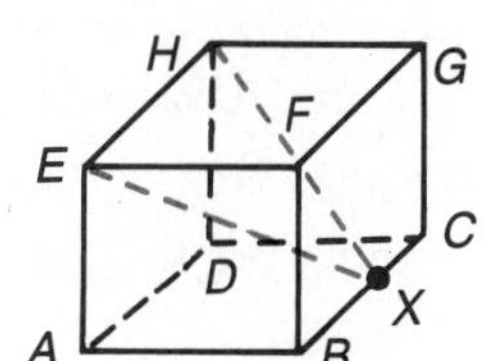

9. Given: In the cube at the right, X is the midpoint of $\overline{BC}$.

Prove: $\overline{EX} \cong \overline{HX}$

ENRICHMENT

See Activities 13-14, p. T47

Chapter 7 Review

1. T

2. yes, Thm. 7.1

3. $\overline{AC} \cong \overline{EC}$ (Def. of equidistant); $\overline{AB} \cong \overline{EB}$ (Thm. 7.1); $\overline{BC} \cong \overline{BC}$ (Congruence of segments is reflexive.); $\triangle ABC \cong \triangle EBC$ (SSS).

4. They are equidistant from P and Q.

5. B

6. C

7. A

8. Sides $\cong$ (Given); $\overline{AO} \cong \overline{AO}$ (Reflexive); triangles $\cong$ (SSS); $\angle QOA \cong \angle YOA \cong \angle ROA \cong \angle XOA$ (CPCTC); above angles are right (Theorem 4.4); $\overline{AO} \perp \overline{QY}$, $\overline{AO} \perp \overline{RX}$ (Def. of $\perp$); $\overline{AO} \perp$ plane E (Thm. 7.3).

9. $\overline{BX} \cong \overline{CX}$ (Def. of midpoint); $\angle XBA \cong \angle XCD$ ($\angle$s of cube are right angles.); $\overline{AB} \cong \overline{CD}$ (Edges of a cube are $\cong$.); $\triangle ABX = \triangle DCX$ (SAS); $\overline{AX} \cong \overline{DX}$ (CPCTC); $\overline{EA} \cong \overline{HD}$ (Edges of a cube are $\cong$.); $\angle EAX \cong \angle HDX$ (Thm. 7.5); $\triangle EAX \cong \triangle HDX$ (SAS); $\overline{EX} \cong \overline{HX}$ (CPCTC).

7.3 **Justify the following statements:**

10. At X on line $\overleftrightarrow{AB}$, plane E intersects $\overleftrightarrow{AB}$ and is $\perp$ AB.

11. On line $\overleftrightarrow{AB}$, plane E intersects $\overleftrightarrow{AB}$ at X and plane F intersects $\overleftrightarrow{AB}$ at Y. Both planes are $\perp$ AB. X and Y must be different points.

12. Line k is $\perp$ plane E and intersects E at X. Line $\overleftrightarrow{XZ}$ in plane E is perpendicular to k.

13. Prove the following:

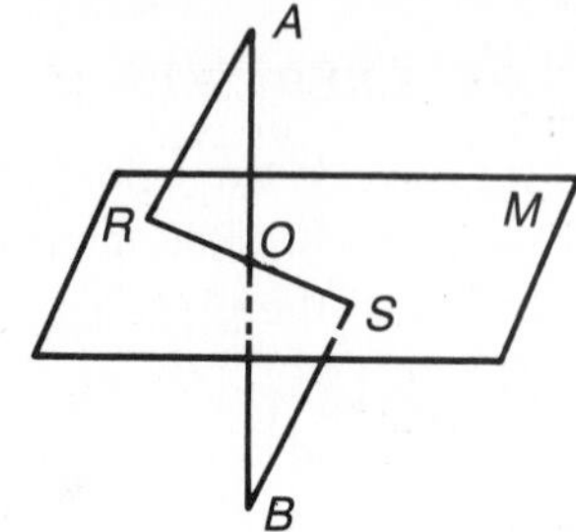

Given: Plane M is the perpendicular bisector of $\overline{AB}$ at O.
O is the midpoint of $\overline{RS}$.

Prove: $\Delta BOS \cong \Delta AOR$

7.4 **14.** $\overleftrightarrow{AB}$ is $\perp$ to plane M and intersects the plane at C. What is the shortest segment from A to plane M?

Refer to the figure at the right to answer the following questions. Justify your answers. $\overline{CA}$ $\perp$ plane E at A. $\overline{DB}$ $\perp$ plane E at B.

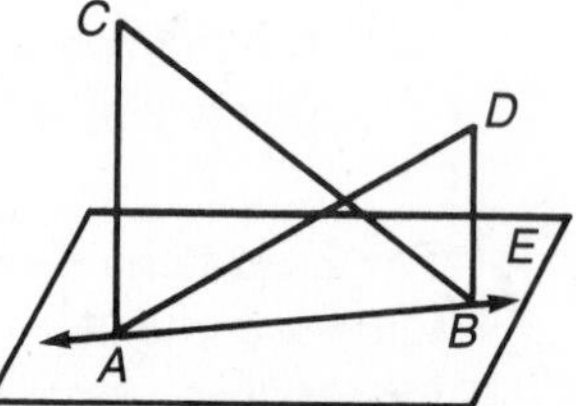

15. What do we know about $\overline{CA}$ and $\overline{DB}$?

16. Plane F is $\perp$ $\overline{CB}$ at B. Can plane F be the same plane as E?

17. Can $\overline{CB}$ $\perp$ plane E at B?

18. Can $\overline{DA}$ $\perp$ plane E at A?

19. Using the information above, prove $m\angle CAB > m\angle CBA$.

Supply the reasons in the following proof.

Given: $\overline{AB}$ $\perp$ plane E

Prove: $AC > AB$

Proof:

STATEMENTS	REASONS
1. $\overline{AB}$ $\perp$ plane E	1. **20.**
2. $\angle ABC$ is a right angle.	2. **21.**
3. $m\angle ABC = 90$ $m\angle ABD = 90$	3. **22.**
4. $m\angle ACB < 90$	4. **23.**
5. $m\angle ACB < m\angle ABC$	5. **24.**
6. $AB < AC$	6. **25.**

10. Theorem 7.4
11. Theorem 7.6
12. Theorem 7.5
13. $\overline{AO} \cong \overline{BO}$ (Def. of $\perp$ bisector); $\angle AOR \cong \angle BOS$ (Vertical $\angle$s are $\cong$.); $\overline{RO} \cong \overline{SO}$ (Def. of midpoint); $\Delta BOS \cong \Delta AOR$ (SAS).
14. $\overline{AC}$
15. They are coplanar (Thm. 7.8).
16. no (Thm. 7.9)
17. no (Thm. 7.10)
18. no (Thm. 7.10)
19. $CA < CB$ (Thm. 7.11); $m\angle CBA < m\angle CAB$ (Thm. 6.4)
20. Given
21. Def. of $\perp$
22. Def. of right $\angle$
23. Thm 6.1
24. Substitution
25. Thm 6.5

CHAPTER 7 TEST

Complete each sentence with the correct word or phrase.

1. Line l intersects plane M at X. Every line that passes through X is perpendicular to l. Line l is _____ to plane M.

2. If points A and C are each _____ two points P and Q, then every point of $\overleftrightarrow{AC}$ is equidistant from P and Q.

3. If each of three _____ points of a plane is equidistant from points K and L, then every point of the plane is equidistant from K and L.

4. Lines u and v intersect at point T. If another line x is perpendicular to both u and v at _____, then x is perpendicular to the plane determined by u and v.

5. If line x and plane M are perpendicular at point C, x will be perpendicular to _____ line in M that passes through C.

6. In space, the set of all points equidistant from the endpoints of a segment is called the _____ of the segment.

7. Prove the following:

Given: $\overleftrightarrow{CE}$, $\overleftrightarrow{FG}$ and H are in plane M.
$\overleftrightarrow{AD} \perp \overleftrightarrow{CE}$, $\overleftrightarrow{AD} \perp \overleftrightarrow{FG}$ at D

Prove: $m\angle ADH = 90$

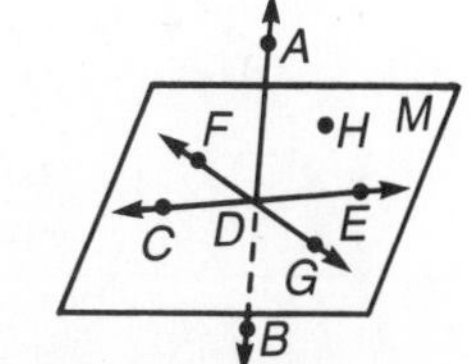

8. Prove the following:

Given: Plane M is the perpendicular bisecting plane of $\overline{AC}$.

Prove: $\triangle ADE \cong \triangle CDE$

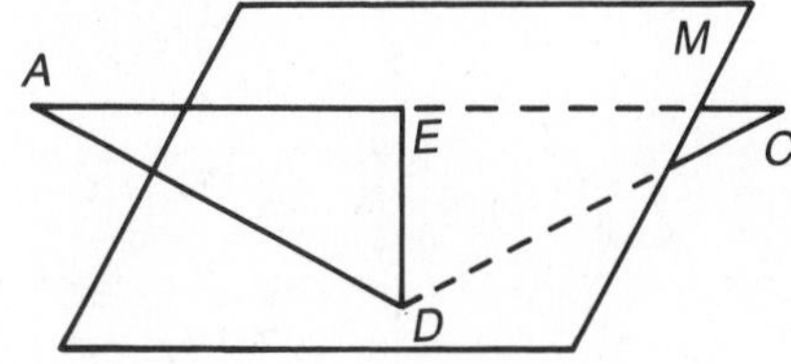

9. Two lines perpendicular to the same _____ are coplanar.

10. Through a given point there passes one and only one plane _____ a given line.

11. Through _____ there passes one and only one line perpendicular to a given plane.

12. The _____ a plane from an external point is the length of the perpendicular segment from the point to the plane.

13. Prove the following:

Given: $\overline{AC} \perp$ plane M at C

Prove: $m\angle ABC < m\angle ACB$

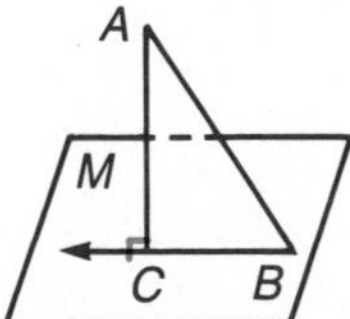

TEACHER'S RESOURCE MASTERS

Chapter 7 Test
Multiple Choice Test—Chapter 7

Chapter 7 Test

1. perpendicular
2. equidistant from
3. noncollinear
4. T
5. every
6. perpendicular bisecting plane
7. $\overleftrightarrow{AD} \perp \overleftrightarrow{CE}$, $\overleftrightarrow{AD} \perp \overleftrightarrow{FG}$ (Given); so $\overleftrightarrow{AD} \perp$ plane M (Theorem 7.3); $\overleftrightarrow{AD} \perp \overleftrightarrow{DH}$ (Theorem 7.5); $\angle ADH$ is a right angle (Def. of $\perp$); $m\angle ADH = 90$ (Def. of rt. $\angle$).
8. $\overline{AD} \cong \overline{CD}$, $\overline{AE} \cong \overline{CE}$ (Thm. 7.7); $\overline{ED} \cong \overline{ED}$ (Congruence of segments is reflexive); $\triangle ADE \cong \triangle CDE$ (SSS).
9. plane
10. perpendicular to
11. a given point
12. distance to
13. $AC < AB$ (Thm 7.11); $m\angle ABC < m\angle ACB$, Thm 6.4

CHAPTER 8

Parallels

8.1 The Necessary Conditions for Parallelism

So far, you have studied relationships among intersecting lines and planes. This chapter concerns sets that do *not* intersect.

In the figure at the right, lines a, b, and c lie in plane E. Lines b and c intersect as shown; a and b do not intersect and are therefore **parallel.** Line d is **skew** to a, b, and c because it does not lie in E and does not intersect those lines.

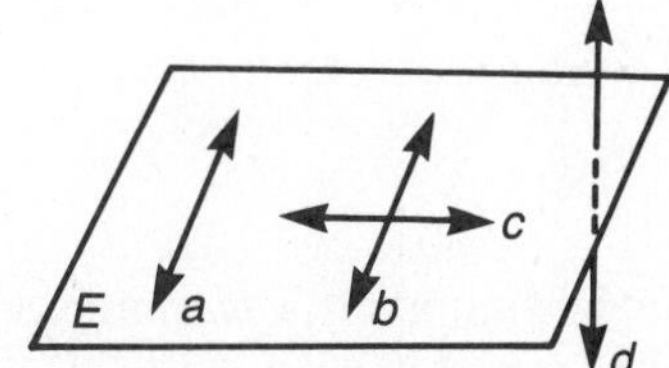

DEFINITIONS: parallel, skew
Two lines are **parallel** if and only if they are coplanar and do not intersect. Two lines are **skew** if and only if they are not coplanar.

The symbol used to indicate that two lines are parallel is $\parallel$. $\overleftrightarrow{AB} \parallel \overleftrightarrow{CD}$ indicates that $\overleftrightarrow{AB}$ is parallel to $\overleftrightarrow{CD}$. The symbol for not parallel is $\nparallel$. If $\overleftrightarrow{AB}$ and $\overleftrightarrow{CD}$ intersect, then $\overleftrightarrow{AB} \nparallel \overleftrightarrow{CD}$.

THEOREM 8.1
If two lines are parallel, then they lie in exactly one plane.

Given: $l \parallel k$

Prove: Exactly one plane contains l and k.

Proof: If l and k are parallel, then the definition of parallel lines guarantees that there is *at least* one plane containing the lines.

To prove that *at most* one plane contains the two lines, consider l and any point P on k. By Theorem 2.3, l and P determine exactly one plane. Because any plane containing both l and k would also contain P, the unique plane containing l and P is also unique to l and k.

Rays and segments are parallel to each other and to the lines that contain them if those lines are parallel. In the figure, if $l \parallel k$, then $\overline{AB} \parallel \overline{CD}$, $\overrightarrow{BA} \parallel \overrightarrow{CD}$, $\overrightarrow{CD} \parallel l$, and so on.

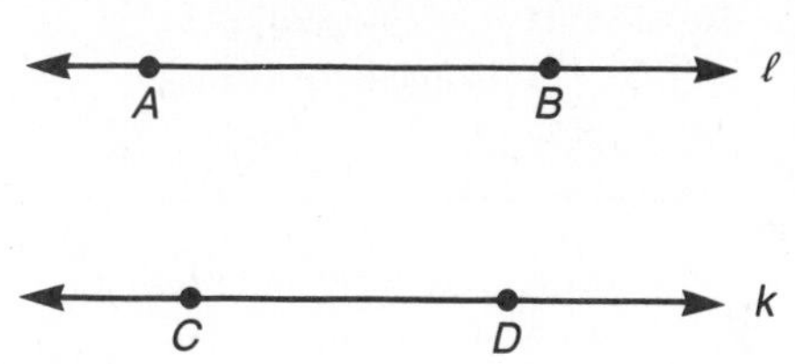

OBJECTIVE

Use Theorems 8.1–8.5 in proofs and use alternate interior angles of parallel lines to find the measure of an angle.

TEACHER'S NOTES

See p. T31

MIXED REVIEW

1. If $ax^2 + bx + c = 0$, then $x = \frac{-b \pm \sqrt{b^2 - 4ac}}{2a}$. Find x if $x^2 - x - 1 = 0$. $x = \frac{1 \pm \sqrt{5}}{2}$
2. When is a median also an altitude? When it connects the vertex to the base of an isosceles △
3. Divide $\frac{16}{25} \div \frac{4}{5}$. $\frac{4}{5}$
4. Divide $\frac{x+2}{x^2 - 4x + 4} \div \frac{x+2}{(x-2)}$. $\frac{1}{x-2}$
5. Solve $12 > 3x + 3 > 18$. $3 > x > 5$

TEACHER'S RESOURCE MASTERS

Practice Master 21

THEOREM 8.2
If two coplanar lines are both perpendicular to the same line, then they are parallel.

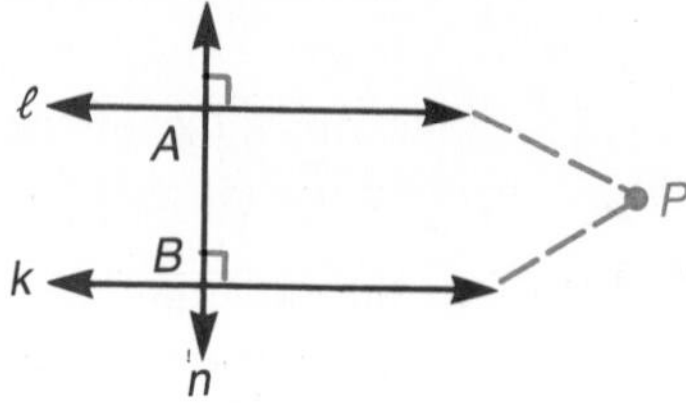

Given: $l \perp n$, $k \perp n$
l and k are coplanar.

Prove: $l \parallel k$

Proof: Using an indirect proof, suppose that l and k intersect at some point P.

This assumption contradicts Theorem 5.3 (Given a line and an external point, there is one and only one line perpendicular to the given line.), because both $\overleftrightarrow{AP}$ and $\overleftrightarrow{BP}$ would be perpendicular to n. Therefore, l and k cannot intersect and are, by definition, parallel.

Now you can prove an existence theorem for parallel lines.

THEOREM 8.3
If k is a line, and P is a point not on k, then there is at least one line through P that is parallel to k.

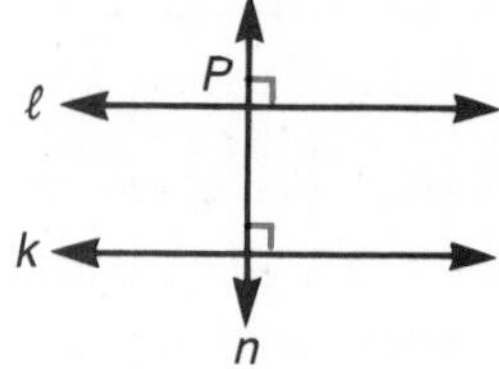

Given: Line k, point P not on k

Prove: There is a line l through P such that $l \parallel k$.

Proof: By Theorem 5.3, let n be the line through P that is perpendicular to k. By Theorem 5.1, let l be the line, coplanar with k and n, that is perpendicular to n at P. Then, by Theorem 8.2, l is parallel to k.

In the figure, n, which crosses both l and k, is called a **transversal.**

DEFINITION: transversal
A line is a **transversal** of two coplanar lines if and only if it intersects the lines at two different points.

When a transversal intersects two lines, four interior angles are formed. Nonadjacent interior angles formed on opposite sides of a transversal are **alternate interior angles.**

DEFINITION: alternate interior angles
Let line x be a transversal of lines y and z, intersecting them at points P and Q. Let A be a point on y, and let B be a point on z, such that A and B are on opposite sides of x. Then $\angle PQB$ and $\angle QPA$ are **alternate interior angles** formed by the transversal to y and z.

Applying the definition to the figure, you can see that $\angle 1$ and $\angle 4$ are alternate interior angles and that $\angle 2$ and $\angle 3$ are also alternate interior angles.

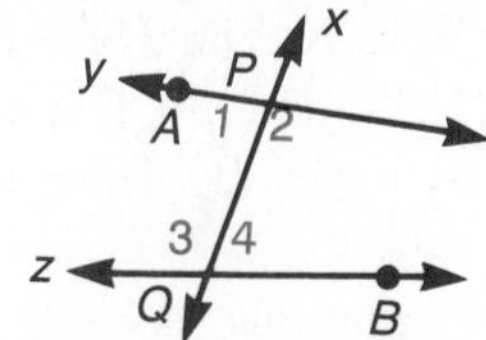

THEOREM 8.4
If two lines are cut by a transversal, and if one pair of alternate interior angles are congruent, then the other pair of alternate interior angles are also congruent.

This theorem can be proved using the Supplement Postulate.

Given: Lines r and s, transversal t, $\angle 1 \cong \angle 4$
Prove: $\angle 2 \cong \angle 3$

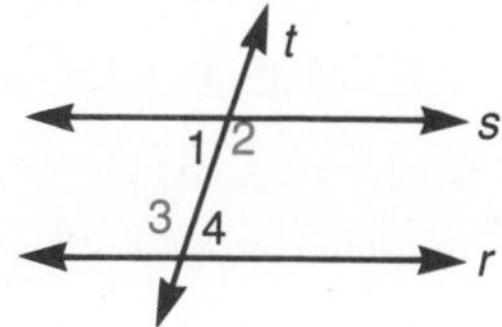

Proof:

STATEMENTS	REASONS
1. $\angle 1 \cong \angle 4$	1. Given
2. $\angle 1$ and $\angle 2$ form a linear pair. $\angle 3$ and $\angle 4$ form a linear pair.	2. Definition of linear pair
3. $\angle 2$ is the supplement of $\angle 1$. $\angle 3$ is the supplement of $\angle 4$.	3. If two $\angle$s form a linear pair, then they are supplementary (Postulate 14).
4. $\angle 2 \cong \angle 3$	4. Supplements of $\cong$ $\angle$s are $\cong$ (Theorem 3.5).

THEOREM 8.5
If two lines are cut by a transversal, and if a pair of alternate interior angles are congruent, then the lines are parallel.

Given: a is a transversal to lines b and c, forming a congruent pair of alternate interior angles.

Prove: $b \parallel c$

Proof: a intersects b and c at points P and Q to form one congruent pair of alternate interior angles. Let b and c intersect at some point R (indirect assumption).

Let S be a point on b on the opposite side of a from R. The $\angle SPQ$ is an exterior angle of $\triangle PQR$, and $\angle PQR$ is one of the remote interior angles. By Theorem 6.1 (Exterior Angle Theorem), $m\angle SPQ > m\angle PQR$. It is given that one pair of alternate interior angles are congruent, so by Theorem 8.4 both pairs of alternate interior angles are congruent. Therefore, $m\angle SPQ = m\angle PQR$. This is a contradiction, so $b \parallel c$.

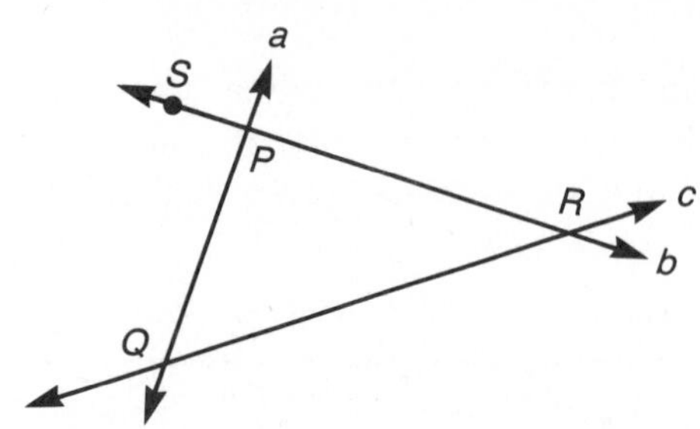

ASSIGNMENT GUIDE

Day 1
Minimum 1-11 odd
Regular 1-13 odd
Maximum 1-15 odd

Day 2
Minimum 2-12 even
Regular 2-14 even
Maximum 2-16 even

ORAL EXERCISES

1. What does the definition of parallel tell you about the distance between parallel lines?
2. Describe a case in which the alternate interior angles formed by a transversal across two lines are not congruent.
3. What symbol is used to show a parallel relationship?
4. How many planes can contain two parallel lines?

Refer to the figure at the right to answer questions 5-16. Points *P, Q, R,* and *S* are coplanar.

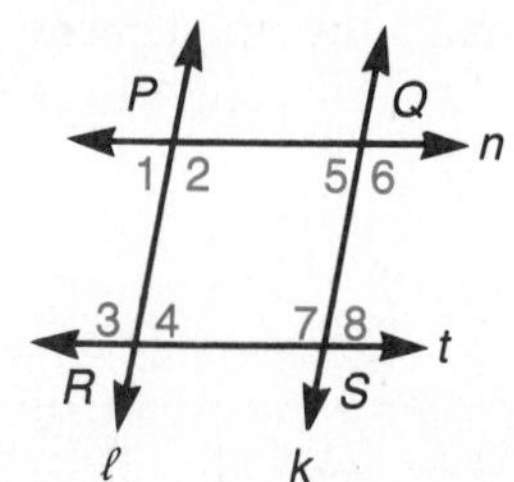

5. What do lines l, k, n, and t have in common?
6. If n and t never intersect, how are they related?
7. If $l \parallel k$, how does $\overline{RP}$ relate to $\overline{SQ}$?
8. If $n \parallel t$, $\overline{RS}$ is parallel to which ray(s), line(s), or segment(s)?
9. What term describes $\angle 5$, $\angle 6$, $\angle 7$, and $\angle 8$ formed by transversal k?
10. What is the relationship between $\angle 1$ and $\angle 4$?
11. What must be true about $\angle 1$ and $\angle 4$ to conclude that $n \parallel t$?
12. If $\angle 5 \cong \angle 8$, then $\angle 7$ is congruent to which angle?

Oral Exercises
1. It says nothing about distance.
2. when the two lines are not parallel
3. $\parallel$
4. one
5. They are coplanar.
6. They are parallel.
7. $\overline{RP} \parallel \overline{SQ}$
8. $\overline{PQ}$, $\overrightarrow{PQ}$, $\overrightarrow{QP}$, $\overleftrightarrow{PQ}$ or line n
9. interior $\angle$s
10. alternate interior $\angle$s
11. $\angle 1 \cong \angle 4$
12. $\angle 6$

13. If $m\angle 2 = m\angle 6 = 90$, which of the following can you deduce: $l \parallel k$ or $n \parallel t$?

14. If $m\angle 5 = 90$, what measure of $\angle 7$ would make $n \parallel t$?

15. If $n \parallel t$ and $m\angle 8 = 30$, what is $m\angle 6$?

16. If $n \parallel t$ and $m\angle 1 = 80$, what is $m\angle 3$?

WRITTEN EXERCISES

A. **1.** Is parallelism a transitive relationship? Is it reflexive?

2. Describe two lines in space that are neither parallel nor intersecting.

Refer to the numbered angles in the figure for Exercises 3–5.

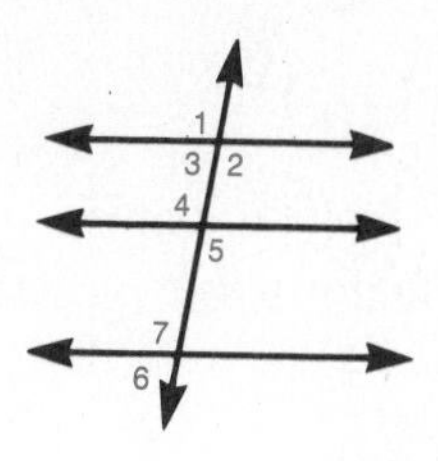

3. Name two pairs of alternate interior angles.

4. Name two pairs of vertical angles.

5. Name two linear pairs.

6. **Given:** $\overline{AB}$ and $\overline{MN}$ bisect each other at P.

Prove: $\overline{AM} \parallel \overline{NB}$

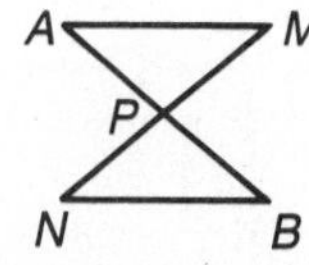

B. **For lines l, n, and t in the figure, determine if $l \parallel n$, given the following conditions.**

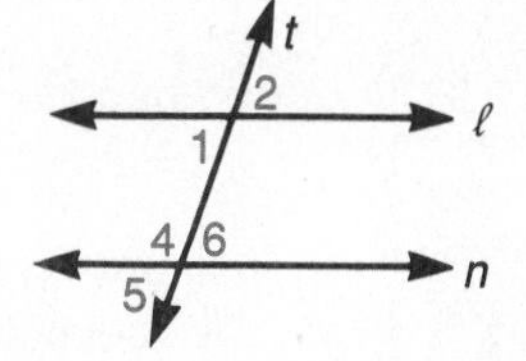

7. $m\angle 1 = 70$ and $m\angle 6 = 70$

8. $m\angle 2 = 60$ and $m\angle 4 = 120$

9. $m\angle 6 = 130$ and $m\angle 1 = 60$

10. $m\angle 2 = 70$ and $m\angle 4 = 70$

11. For lines l, n, and t above, if $\angle 2 \cong \angle 5$, prove $l \parallel n$.

12. **Given:** Quadrilateral PQRS right angles S and R $\overline{PS} \cong \overline{QR}$

Prove: $\angle P \cong \angle Q$
(HINT: Draw $\overline{PR}$ and $\overline{SQ}$.)

13. **Given:** $\angle 1 \cong \angle P$
$\overrightarrow{QS}$ bisects $\angle RQP$.

Prove: $\overrightarrow{QS} \parallel \overline{OP}$

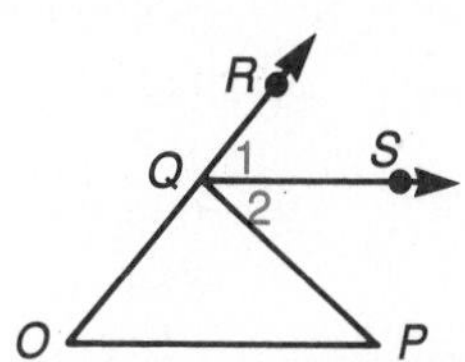

13. $l \parallel k$
14. 90
15.–16. TRAP: See *Teacher's Manual* Lesson Notes for Lesson 8.1.

Written Exercises

1. It is transitive but not reflexive.
2. Skew lines are neither parallel nor intersecting.
3. $\angle 2, \angle 4; \angle 5, \angle 7$
4. $\angle 1, \angle 2; \angle 4, \angle 5$
5. $\angle 1, \angle 3; \angle 6, \angle 7; \angle 2, \angle 3$
6. 1. $\overline{AP} \cong \overline{BP}$, $\overline{NP} \cong \overline{MP}$ (Def. of bisect); 2. $\angle APM \cong \angle BPN$ (Vert. ∠s are ≅.); 3. $\triangle APM \cong \triangle BPN$ (SAS Post.); 4. $\angle MAP \cong \angle NBP$ (CPCTC); 5. $\overline{AM} \parallel \overline{NB}$ (Theorem 8.5).
7. yes 8. yes
9. no 10. no
11. 1. $\angle 2 \cong \angle 5$ (Given); 2. $\angle 2 \cong \angle 1$, $\angle 5 \cong \angle 6$ (Vert. ∠s are ≅.); 3. $\angle 1 = \angle 6$ (Congruence of ∠s is trans.); 4. $l \parallel n$ (Theorem 8.5).
12. 1. $\angle S$ and $\angle R$ are rt. ∠s (Given); 2. $\overline{SR} \cong \overline{SR}$ (Congruence of segments is reflexive.); 3. $\overline{PS} \cong \overline{QR}$ (Given); 4. $\triangle PSR \cong \triangle QRS$ (SAS Postulate); 5. $\overline{SQ} \cong \overline{RP}$ (CPCTC); 6. $\overline{PQ} \cong \overline{PQ}$ (Congruence of segments is reflexive.); 7. $\triangle SPQ \cong \triangle RQP$ (SSS); 8. $\angle P \cong \angle Q$ (CPCTC).
13. 1. $\angle 1 \cong \angle P$ (Given); 2. $\angle 1 \cong \angle 2$ (Def. of bisector); 3. $\angle 2 \cong \angle P$ (Congruence of ∠s is trans.); 4. $\overrightarrow{QS} \parallel \overrightarrow{OP}$ (Theorem 8.5).

14. 1. $\triangle MJK \cong \triangle KLM$ (HL); 2. $\angle MKJ \cong \angle KML$ (CPCTC); 3. $\overline{JK} \parallel \overline{LM}$ (Theorem 8.5); 4. $\angle LKM \cong \angle JMK$ (CPCTC); 5. $\overline{JM} \parallel \overline{KL}$ (Theorem 8.5).

15. $x = 28$

16. $y = 39$

14. Given: Quadrilateral $JKLM$
right angles J and L
$\overline{JK} \cong \overline{LM}$

Prove: $\overline{JK} \parallel \overline{LM}$
$\overline{JM} \parallel \overline{KL}$

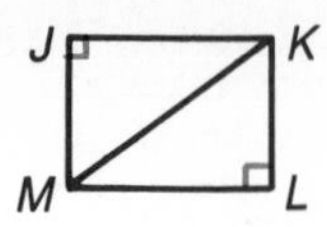

C. 15. For the figure at the right, find a value for x that will make $u \parallel v$.

16. For the figure at the right, find a value for y that will make $w \parallel z$.

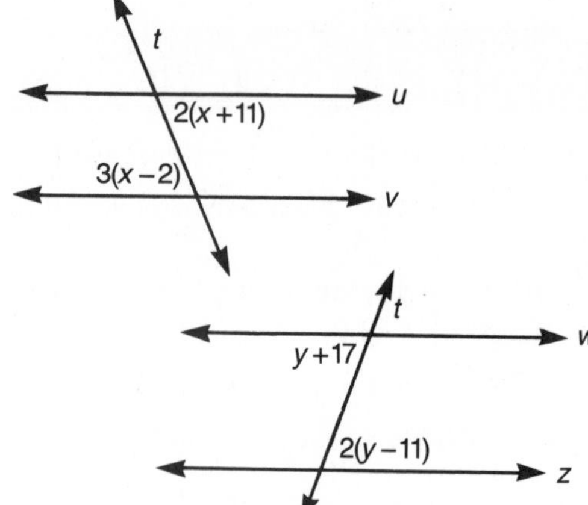

EXPLORATION
Parallel Lines

A popular optical illusion is that of two parallel lines placed on either side of the intersection of many transversals.

As you can see at the left below, the black lines appear to be radiating outward from a common center, and the red lines appear to be bowed away from the point of intersection.

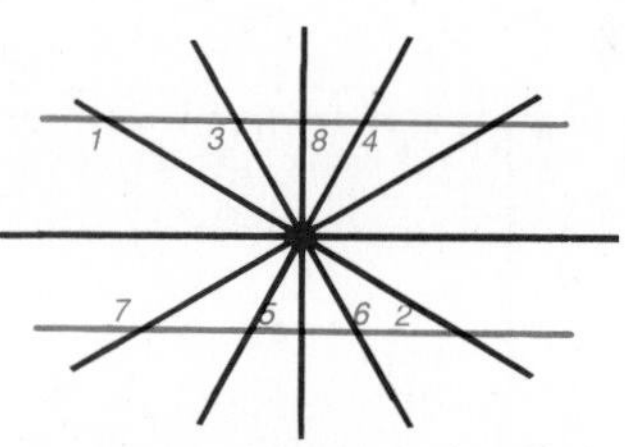

The figure at the right above is arranged the same way, but with fewer transverse lines. Which two numbered angles, if they are congruent, could be used to determine that the red lines are indeed parallel? Give the theorem that supports your choice.

Exploration
$\angle 3$ and $\angle 6$ are alternate interior angles, so if they are congruent, then the lines are parallel by Theorem 8.5.

8.2 Corresponding Angles

OBJECTIVE

Use Theorems 8.6 and 8.7 in proofs and use corresponding angles of parallel lines to find the measure of an angle.

TEACHER'S NOTES

See p. T31

MIXED REVIEW

1. Can a triangle have sides of 7, 11 and 3? no
2. Solve $2x^2 - x - 3 = 0$. $\{\frac{3}{2}, -1\}$
3. Add $\frac{4}{x-2} + \frac{3}{x-1}$. $\frac{7x-10}{(x-2)(x-1)}$
4. If two lines are not parallel, must they intersect? no; they can be skew
5. Average 18 and 37. 27.5

TEACHER'S RESOURCE MASTERS

Practice Master 22, Part 1

In the figure at the right, you know that the transversal l crossing lines k and n forms two pairs of alternate interior angles: $\angle 3$ and $\angle 6$, and $\angle 4$ and $\angle 5$. These angles have the special properties that if $\angle 3 \cong \angle 6$, then $\angle 4 \cong \angle 5$ and $k \parallel n$. The same can be deduced from $\angle 4 \cong \angle 5$.

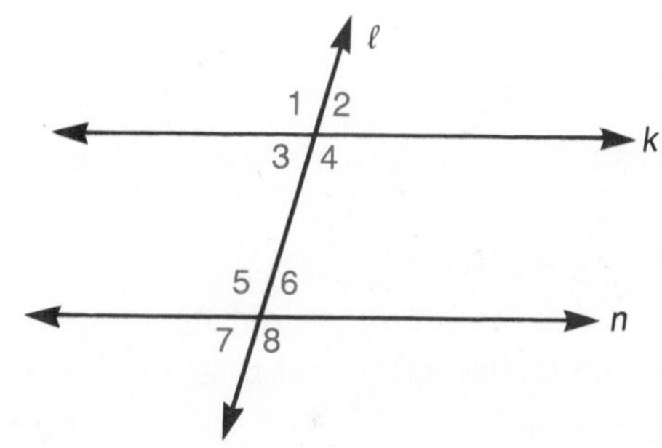

Other important angle relationships result when a transversal crosses two lines. In this lesson you will learn about **corresponding angles,** the nonadjacent interior and exterior angles on the same side of the transversal.

> **DEFINITION: corresponding angles**
> Let l be a transversal of k and n, intersecting them at points P and Q. Let A be a point on k, and let B be a point on n, such that A and B are on the same side of l. Let C be a point on l such that C and B are on opposite sides of k. Then $\angle CPA$ and $\angle PQB$ are **corresponding angles** formed by the transversal to the two lines.

In the figure at the right, $\angle 2$ and $\angle 6$ are corresponding angles. Name the other three pairs of corresponding angles.

1 and 5, 3 and 7, and 4 and 8

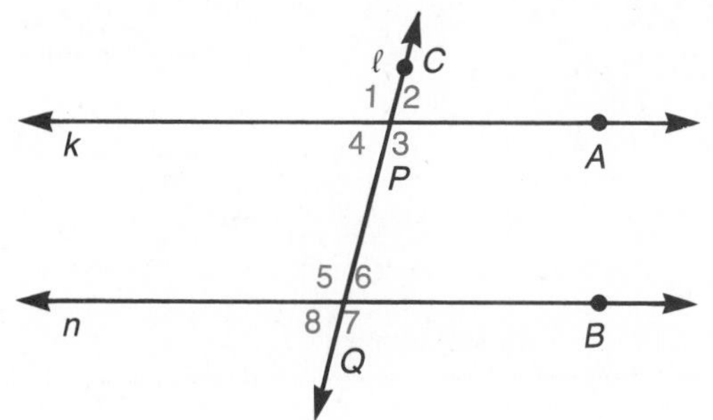

> **THEOREM 8.6**
> If two lines are cut by a transversal, and if one pair of corresponding angles are congruent, then the other three pairs of corresponding angles are congruent.

Given: $\angle 2 \cong \angle 6$

Prove: $\angle 4 \cong \angle 8$
$\angle 1 \cong \angle 5$
$\angle 3 \cong \angle 7$

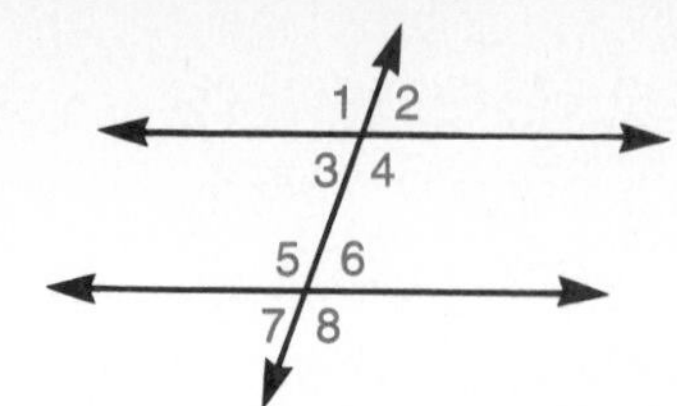

Proof:

STATEMENTS	REASONS
1. $\angle 2 \cong \angle 6$	1. Given
2. $\angle 4$ is the supplement of $\angle 2$. $\angle 8$ is the supplement of $\angle 6$.	2. The Supplement Postulate
3. $\angle 4 \cong \angle 8$	3. Supplements of $\cong$ $\angle$s are $\cong$ (Theorem 3.5).
4. $\angle 1$ is supplementary to $\angle 2$. $\angle 5$ is supplementary to $\angle 6$.	4. The Supplement Postulate
5. $\angle 1 \cong \angle 5$	5. Theorem 3.5
6. $\angle 3$ is the supplement of $\angle 1$. $\angle 7$ is the supplement of $\angle 5$.	6. The Supplement Postulate
7. $\angle 3 \cong \angle 7$	7. Theorem 3.5

THEOREM 8.7
If two lines are cut by a transversal, and if one pair of corresponding angles are congruent, then the lines are parallel.

Given: $\angle 2 \cong \angle 6$

Prove: $l \parallel k$

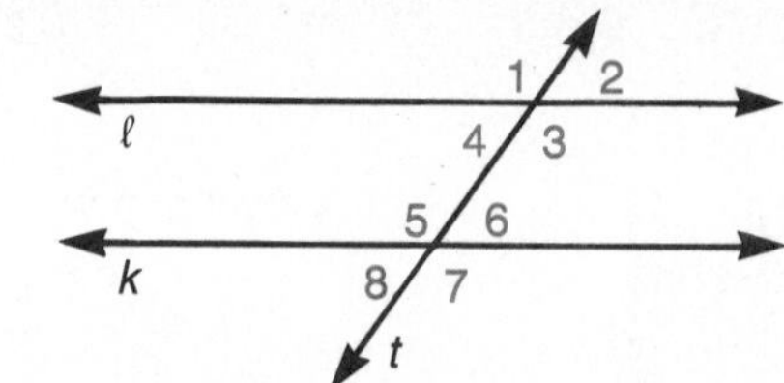

Proof:

STATEMENTS	REASONS
1. $\angle 2 \cong \angle 6$	1. Given
2. $\angle 2 \cong \angle 4$	2. Vertical $\angle$s are $\cong$ (Theorem 3.7).
3. $\angle 4 \cong \angle 6$	3. Congruence of $\angle$s is transitive.
4. $l \parallel k$	4. If two lines are cut by a transversal, and a pair of alternate interior $\angle$s are $\cong$, then the lines are $\parallel$ (Theorem 8.5).

ORAL EXERCISES

1. What is the contrapositive of Theorem 8.7? Is it true?

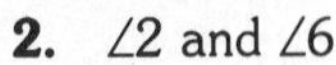

In Exercises 2–7, if t is a transversal to l and k, identify how each pair of angles are related.

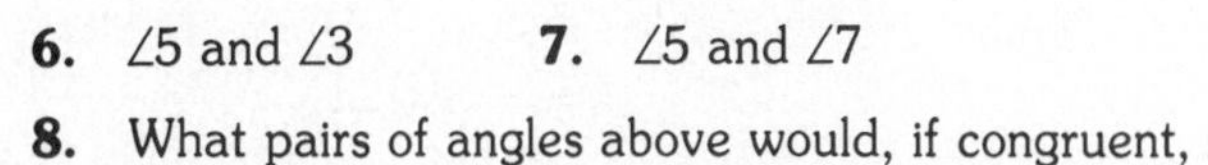

2. $\angle 2$ and $\angle 6$
3. $\angle 4$ and $\angle 6$
4. $\angle 2$ and $\angle 3$
5. $\angle 4$ and $\angle 8$
6. $\angle 5$ and $\angle 3$
7. $\angle 5$ and $\angle 7$
8. What pairs of angles above would, if congruent, make $l \parallel k$?
9. State the converse of Theorem 8.5.
10. State the converse of Theorem 8.7.

WRITTEN EXERCISES

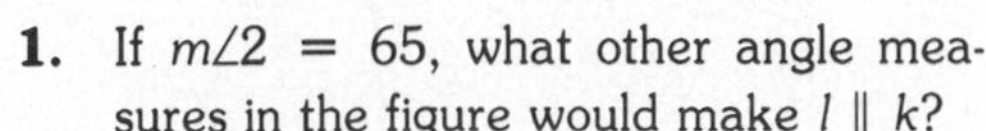

A. Refer to the figure at the right for Exercises 1–7.

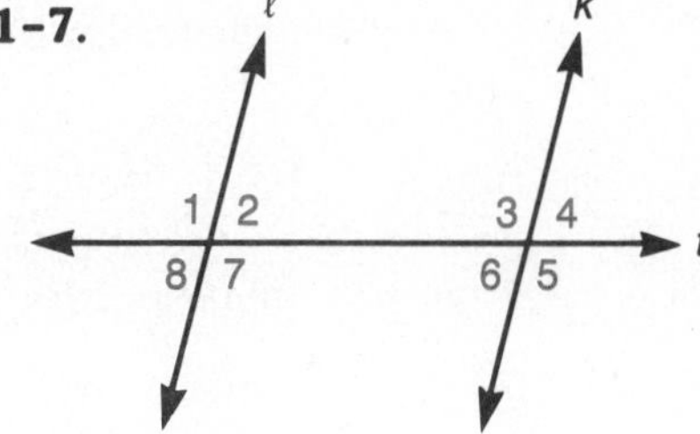

1. If $m\angle 2 = 65$, what other angle measures in the figure would make $l \parallel k$?

Given the following angles measures, find the value of x that will make $l \parallel k$ in Exercises 2–7.

2. $m\angle 1 = 2x + 6$, $m\angle 3 = 8x - 12$
3. $m\angle 7 = 6x - 3$, $m\angle 3 = 2x + 18$
4. $m\angle 7 = 8x + 25$, $m\angle 5 = 4x + 75$
5. $m\angle 2 = 2x + 5$, $m\angle 4 = x + 14$
6. $m\angle 2 = 5x - 6$, $m\angle 3 = 2x + 18$
7. $m\angle 8 = 3x + 9$, $m\angle 5 = 5x + 11$

B.

8. **Given:** $\angle 1 \cong \angle 3$
   $\angle 2 \cong \angle 4$
   Prove: $j \parallel n$

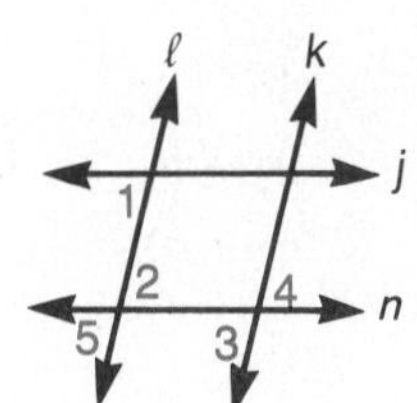

9. **Given:** $\angle 1 \cong \angle 3$
   $\angle 5 \cong \angle 4$
   Prove: $l \parallel k$

10. **Given:** $\overrightarrow{BE}$ bisects $\angle ABD$.
    $\angle 2 \cong \angle C$
    Prove: $\overleftrightarrow{BE} \parallel \overline{DC}$

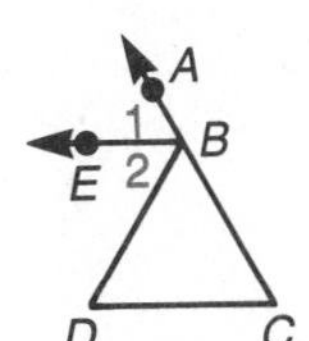

ASSIGNMENT GUIDE

Minimum 1–9
Regular 1–15 odd
Maximum 1–15 odd, 14, 16

Oral Exercises

1. If two lines are not parallel, then the corresponding angles formed by a transversal across the two lines are not congruent. Yes.
2. corres.
3. alt. int.
4. supp.
5. corres.
6. alt. int.
7. vertical
8. (1, 5), (2, 6), (4, 8), (3, 7), (4, 6), (3, 5), (1, 7), (2, 8)
9. Theorem 8.8
10. Theorem 8.9

Written Exercises

1. $m\angle 1 = 115$, $m\angle 3 = 115$, $m\angle 4 = 65$, $m\angle 5 = 115$, $m\angle 6 = 65$, $m\angle 7 = 115$, $m\angle 8 = 65$
2. $x = 3$
3. $x = \frac{21}{4}$
4. $x = \frac{25}{2}$
5. $x = 9$
6. $x = 24$
7. $x = 20$
8. *1.* $\angle 1 \cong \angle 3$, $\angle 2 \cong \angle 4$ (Given); *2.* $\angle 3 \cong \angle 4$ (Thm. 3.7); *3.* $\angle 1 \cong \angle 2$ (Congruence of $\angle$s is transitive.); *4.* $j \parallel n$ (Thm. 8.5)
9. *1.* $\angle 1 \cong \angle 3$, $\angle 5 \cong \angle 4$ (Given); *2.* $\angle 3 \cong \angle 4$ (Thm. 3.7) *3.* $\angle 1 \cong \angle 5$ (Congruence of $\angle$s is transitive.); *4.* $l \parallel k$ (Thm. 8.7)
10. *1.* $\overrightarrow{BE}$ bisects $\angle ABD$ (Given); *2.* $\angle 1 \cong \angle 2$ (Def. of bisect); *3.* $\angle 2 \cong \angle C$ (Given); *4.* $\angle 1 \cong \angle C$ (Congruence of $\angle$s is transitive.); *5.* $\overleftrightarrow{BE} \parallel \overline{DC}$ (Thm. 8.7)

11. 1. $\overline{AC} \cong \overline{BC}$ (Given); 2. $\angle A \cong \angle B$ (Thm. 4.3); 3. $\angle CRS \cong \angle B$ (Given); 4. $\angle CRS \cong \angle A$ (Congruence of $\angle$s is transitive); 5. $\overline{RS} \parallel \overline{AB}$ (Thm. 8.7)

12. 1. $\overline{AB} \cong \overline{BC}$ (Given); 2. $\angle A \cong \angle C$ (Thm. 4.3); 3. $\overline{DF} \cong \overline{DC}$ (Given); 4. $\angle DFC \cong \angle C$ (Thm. 4.3); 5. $\angle DFC \cong \angle A$ (Congruence of $\angle$s is transitive); 6. $\overline{DF} \parallel \overline{AB}$ (Thm. 8.7)

13. 1. $\angle 1$ and $\angle 2$ are supplementary (Given); 2. $\angle 1$ and $\angle 3$ are supplementary (The Supplement Post.); 3. $\angle 2 \cong \angle 3$ (Thm. 3.2 and Thm. 3.5); 4. $l \parallel n$ (Thm. 8.7)

14. 1. $\angle 4 \cong \angle 6$ (Given); 2. $\angle 4 \cong \angle 1$ (Theorem 3.7); 3. $\angle 6 \cong \angle 1$ (Congruence of $\angle$s is transitive.); 4. $l \parallel n$ (Theorem 8.7)

15. $x = -1$
The quadratic equation also produces an extraneous root ($x = -3$), which yields angles of negative measure.

16. $x = -4, \frac{1}{2}$

Challenge
1. $\angle 1 \cong \angle 2$, $\angle 9 \cong \angle 10$ (Given); 2. $\angle 2 \cong \angle 7$ (Theorem 8.6); 3. $\angle 1 \cong \angle 3$ (Theorem 3.7); 4. $\angle 3 \cong \angle 7$ (Substitution); 5. $\angle 9 \cong \angle ZYX$ (Theorem 3.7); 6. $m\angle ZYW = m\angle 5 + m\angle 6$ (Angle Addition Postulate); 7. $m\angle 9 = m\angle 5 + m\angle 6$ (Substitution and def. of congruence); 8. $m\angle 8 = m\angle 4 + m\angle 5$ (Given); 9. $m\angle 5 + m\angle 6 = m\angle 4 + m\angle 5$ (Substitution); 10. $m\angle 4 = m\angle 6$ (Subtraction prop. of equality); 11. $\triangle WXY \cong \triangle ZYX$ (SAA)

11. Given: Isosceles $\triangle ABC$ with $\overline{AC} \cong \overline{BC}$
$\angle CRS \cong \angle B$

Prove: $\overline{RS} \parallel \overline{AB}$

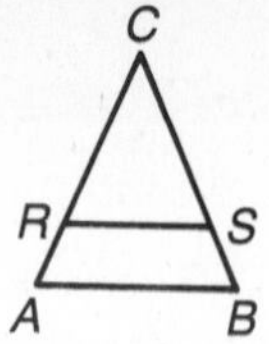

12. Given: Isosceles $\triangle ABC$ with $\overline{AB} \cong \overline{BC}$
$\overline{DF} \cong \overline{DC}$

Prove: $\overline{DF} \parallel \overline{AB}$

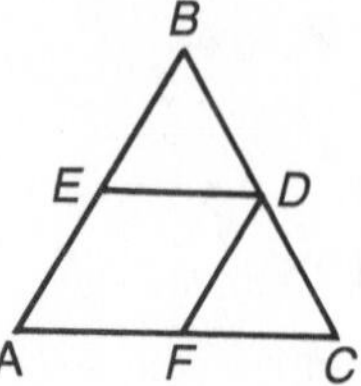

13. Given: $\angle 1$ is supplementary to $\angle 2$.

Prove: $l \parallel n$

14. Given: $\angle 4 \cong \angle 6$

Prove: $l \parallel n$

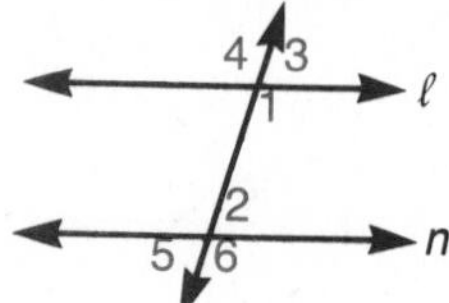

C. 15. If $m\angle 1 = x^2 + 6x + 7$ and $m\angle 3 = 2x + 4$, what value of x will make $l \parallel k$?

16. If $m\angle 2 = 3x^2 + 9x - 5$ and $m\angle 6 = x^2 + 2x - 1$, what value of x will make $l \parallel k$?

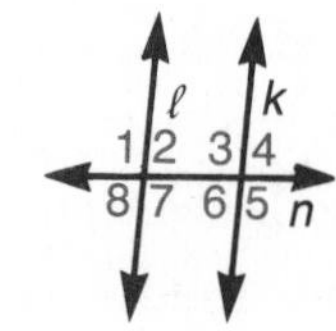

CHALLENGE

Given: $\angle 1 \cong \angle 2$
$\angle 9 \cong \angle 10$
$m\angle 8 = m\angle 4 + m\angle 5$

Prove: $\triangle WXY \cong \triangle ZYX$

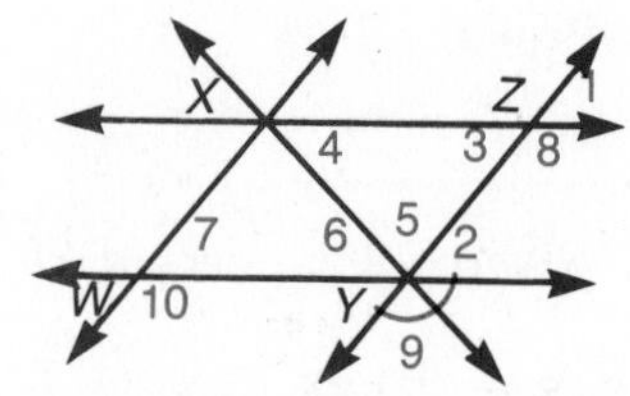

8.3 The Parallel Postulate

In the first two lessons of this chapter, you learned that parallelism follows from congruent alternate interior or corresponding angles. As you may have conjectured,the converse is also true, but you cannot prove it unless you assume that there is a unique line parallel to a given line through an external point. This assumption is established in the important Parallel Postulate.

POSTULATE 16 (The Parallel Postulate)
Through a given external point there is at most one line parallel to a given line.

THEOREM 8.8
If two parallel lines are cut by a transversal, then alternate interior angles are congruent.

Given: $k \parallel n$, cut by transversal l at points P and Q

Prove: $\angle 1 \cong \angle 2$

Proof: Assume that $\angle 1$ and $\angle 2$ are not congruent. Now let t be a transversal to k and n through P for which alternate interior angles *are* congruent, as provided by the Angle Construction Postulate. Thus, in the figure, $\angle 3 \cong \angle 2$.

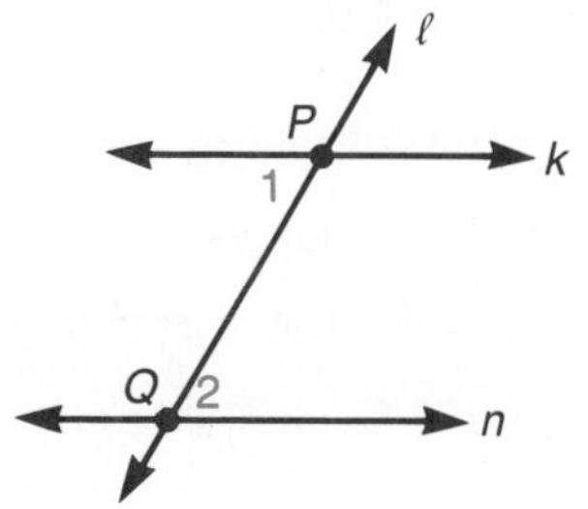

Because $\angle 1 \not\cong \angle 2$, you can deduce that $\angle 1 \not\cong \angle 3$, so that t and k are not the same line. It is given that $k \parallel n$. By Theorem 8.5, $t \parallel n$, so there are two distinct lines through P parallel to n. This contradicts the Parallel Postulate. Therefore, $\angle 1 \cong \angle 2$.

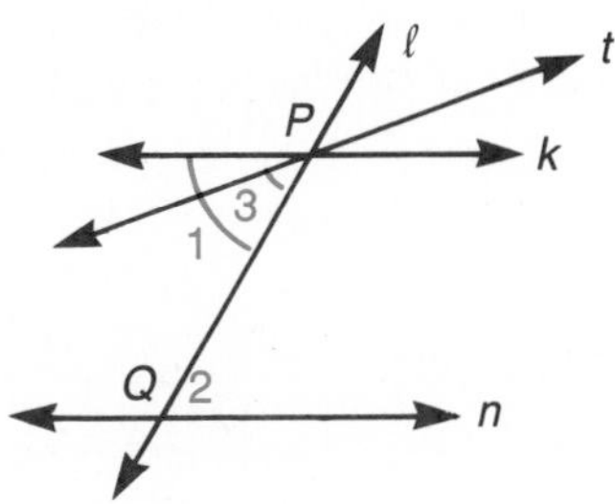

The next four theorems follow easily from Theorem 8.8 and the Parallel Postulate. Their proofs are left as exercises.

THEOREM 8.9
If two parallel lines are cut by a transversal, each pair of corresponding angles are congruent.

OBJECTIVE

Use the Parallel Postulate and Theorems 8.8–8.12 in proofs and to find angle measures.

TEACHER'S NOTES

See p. T31

MIXED REVIEW

1. Divide $\frac{x^2 - 2x - 15}{(x + 1)} \div \frac{x^2 - 6x + 5}{x^2 + 4x + 3}$. $\frac{(x + 3)^2}{(x - 1)}$
2. Are two parallel lines always coplanar? yes
3. Add $\sqrt{9} + \sqrt{16}$. 7
4. Simplify $\sqrt{9 + 16}$. 5
5. Simplify $\sqrt{128}$. $8\sqrt{2}$

TEACHER'S RESOURCE MASTERS

Practice Master 22, Part 2

THEOREM 8.10
If two parallel lines are cut by a transversal, interior angles on the same side of the transversal are supplementary.

THEOREM 8.11
In a plane, two lines parallel to the same line are parallel to each other.

THEOREM 8.12
In a plane, if a line is perpendicular to one of two parallel lines, then it is perpendicular to the other.

ORAL EXERCISES

Complete the following statements.

1. In plane, two lines parallel to the same line are ______ to each other.

2. In a plane, if a line is perpendicular to one of two parallel lines, it is ______ to the other.

3. In the figure at the right, how many lines can be drawn through point P parallel to $\overleftrightarrow{AB}$?

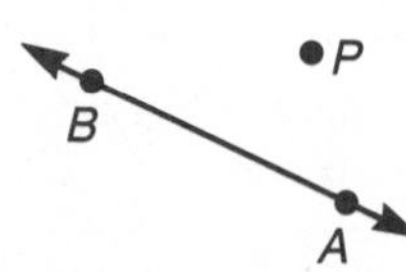

4. How many lines can be drawn through point P perpendicular to $\overleftrightarrow{AB}$?

WRITTEN EXERCISES

A. If $r \parallel s$, state the equation you would use to solve for x in Exercises 1-4.

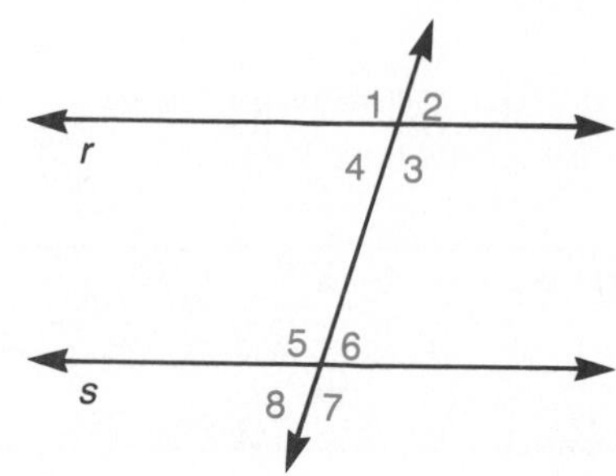

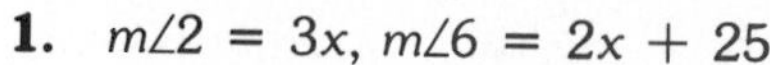

1. $m\angle 2 = 3x$, $m\angle 6 = 2x + 25$

2. $m\angle 3 = 5x$, $m\angle 6 = 7x - 20$

3. $m\angle 4 = x + 5$, $m\angle 6 = 9x - 18$

4. $m\angle 1 = 3x + 9$, $m\angle 7 = 7x - 30$

ASSIGNMENT GUIDE

Minimum 1-9
Regular 1-11 odd
Maximum 1-15 odd

Oral Exercises

1. parallel
2. perpendicular
3. one
4. one

Written Exercises

1. $2x + 25 = 3x$
2. $5x + 7x - 20 = 180$
3. $x + 5 = 9x - 18$
4. $3x + 9 = 7x - 30$
5. $x = 14$
6. $x = 32$
7. $x = 30$
8. $x = 35$
9. *1.* $RS = RT$ (Given); *2.* $\angle S \cong \angle T$ (Thm. 4.3); *3.* $\angle S \cong \angle PQT$ (Thm. 8.9); *4.* $\angle T \cong \angle PQT$ (Congruence of $\angle$s is transitive.); *5.* $\overline{PT} \cong \overline{PQ}$ (Thm. 4.4); *6.* $PT = PQ$ (Def. of $\cong$).
10. Let $\overrightarrow{BC}$ and $\overrightarrow{YX}$ intersect at point Q. Consider $\overrightarrow{BQ}$ to be a transversal crossing $\overleftrightarrow{BA}$ and $\overleftrightarrow{YX}$. By Thm. 8.8, the alternate interior angles

B. If $k \parallel n$, solve for x in Exercises 5–8.

5. $m\angle 6 = 2x + 4$, $m\angle 1 = 3x - 10$

6. $m\angle 5 = 3x - 6$, $m\angle 1 = 2x + 26$

7. $m\angle 8 = 5x - 10$, $m\angle 1 = 3x + 50$

8. $m\angle 7 = 2x + 5$, $m\angle 1 = 3x$

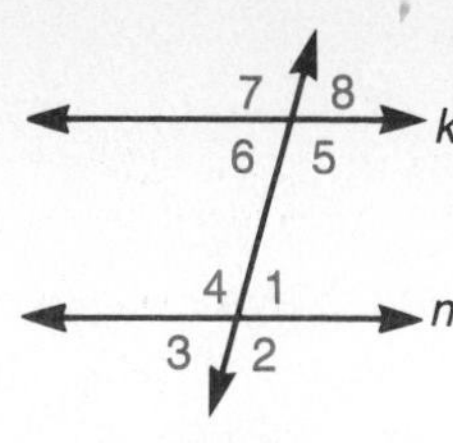

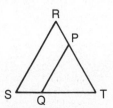

9. Given: $RT = RS$
$\overline{PQ} \parallel \overline{RS}$

Prove: $PT = PQ$

10. Prove that two angles in a plane are congruent if their corresponding sides are parallel and extend in the same direction.

Given: $\overrightarrow{BA} \parallel \overrightarrow{YX}$, $\overrightarrow{BC} \parallel \overrightarrow{YZ}$

Prove: $\angle ABC \cong \angle XYZ$

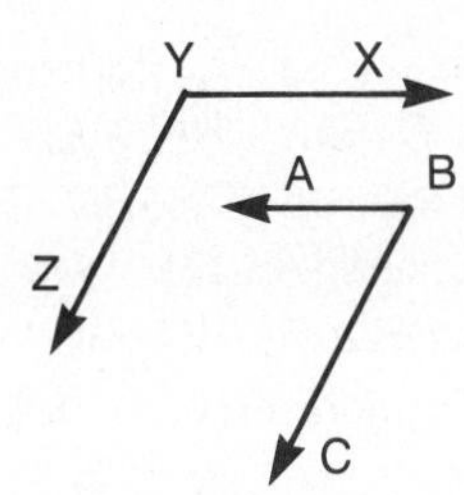

11. Prove that two angles in a plane are supplementary if their corresponding sides are parallel, but only one pair extend in the same direction.

Given: $\overrightarrow{BA} \parallel \overrightarrow{YX}$, $\overrightarrow{BC} \parallel \overrightarrow{YZ}$

Prove: $m\angle ABC + m\angle XYZ = 180$

C. Refer to the following figures for Exercises 12–15.

12. Prove Theorem 8.9.

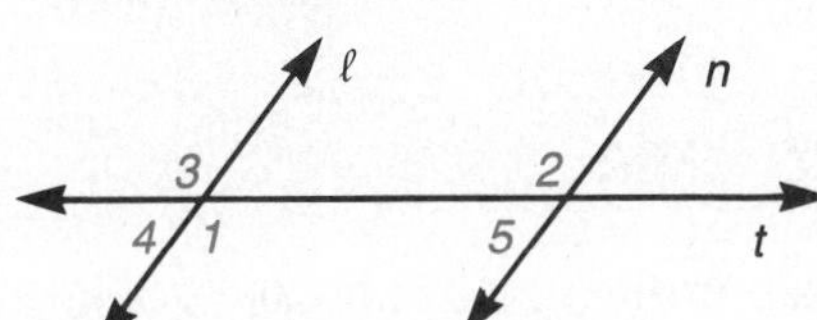

13. Prove Theorem 8.10.

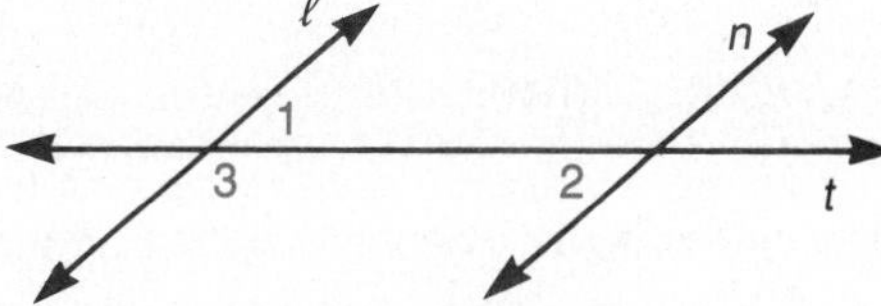

14. Prove Theorem 8.11

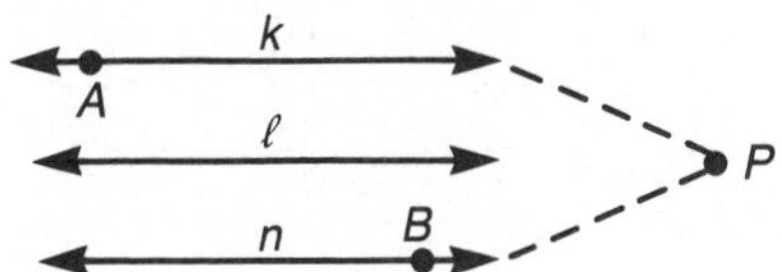

15. Prove Theorem 8.12.

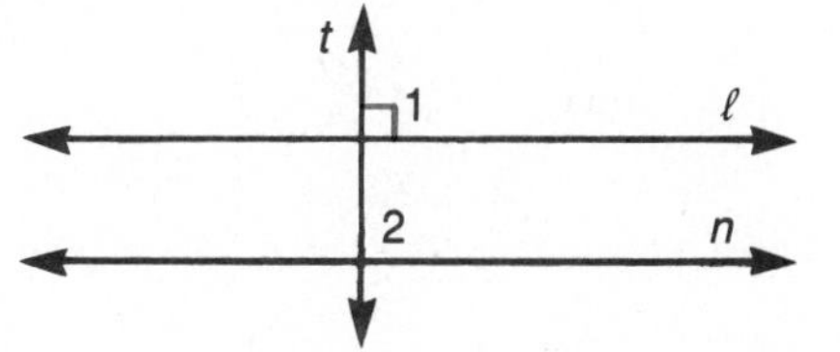

are congruent, so $\angle ABC \cong \angle BQY$. Now consider $\overrightarrow{YQ}$ as a transversal crossing $\overleftrightarrow{BC}$ and $\overleftrightarrow{YZ}$. By Thm. 8.8, $\angle BQY \cong \angle XYZ$. Since congruence of $\angle$s is transitive, $\angle ABC \cong \angle XYZ$.

11. Let $\overrightarrow{YX}$ intersect $\overleftrightarrow{BC}$ at Q, and place P on $\overrightarrow{YX}$ on the opposite side of $\overleftrightarrow{BC}$ from Y. Consider $\overleftrightarrow{YQ}$ a transversal across $\overleftrightarrow{YZ}$ and $\overleftrightarrow{BC}$. By Thm. 8.9, $\angle PQB \cong \angle XYZ$. Now consider $\overleftrightarrow{QC}$ a transversal across $\overleftrightarrow{YX}$ and $\overleftrightarrow{AB}$. By Thm. 8.8, $\angle PQB \cong \angle QBA$. Since congruence of $\angle$s is transitive, $\angle XYZ \cong \angle QBA$, and $m\angle QBA + m\angle ABC = 180$ (Suppl. Post.). Substitute, and $m\angle ABC +$ $m\angle XYZ = 180$.

12. See *Selected Answers*, p. 633

13. Given: $l \parallel n$, transversal t
Prove: $\angle 2$ and $\angle 3$ are supplementary.
Proof: *1.* $\angle 1 \cong \angle 2$ (alt. int. $\angle$s, Thm. 8.8); *2.* $m\angle 1 + m\angle 3 = 180$ (Supplement Postulate); *3.* $m\angle 2 + m\angle 3 = 180$ (Substitution); *4.* $\angle 2$ and $\angle 3$ are supplementary (Def. of supplementary).

14. See *Selected Answers*, p. 634

15. Given: $l \parallel n$, $t \perp l$
Prove: $t \perp n$
Proof: Consider t a transversal across l and n. By Thm. 8.9, corresponding angles are congruent, so $\angle 1 \cong \angle 2$. By the definition of perpendicular, $m\angle 1 = 90$, so $m\angle 2 = 90$. Thus, $\angle 2$ is a right angle, and $t \perp n$ by definition of $\perp$.

OBJECTIVE

Use Theorem 8.13 and its corollaries to find the measure of an angle of a triangle.

TEACHER'S NOTES

See p. T31

MIXED REVIEW

1. What are the four ways to prove that any triangles are congruent? SAS, ASA, SSS, and SAA
2. Supplementary and congruent angles are ________. right angles
3. Multiply $\sqrt{15} \cdot \sqrt{12}$. $6\sqrt{5}$
4. Solve $2x^2 + x - 2 = 0$. $x = \frac{-1 \pm \sqrt{17}}{4}$
5. Solve $\frac{x}{x+3} = \frac{7}{8}$. $x = 21$

TEACHER'S RESOURCE MASTERS

Practice Master 23, Part 1
Quiz 15

8.4 Parallels and Triangles

In previous mathematics courses, you may have learned that the angles of a triangle have a combined measure of 180. This is a concept you have probably accepted on the basis of intuition or experimentation, because its proof requires knowledge of the Parallel Postulate. Now you are ready to prove this fundamental concept as a theorem.

THEOREM 8.13
The sum of the measures of the angles of a triangle is 180.

Given: $\triangle ABC$, with $\angle 2$, $\angle 4$, and $\angle 5$ as shown
Prove: $m\angle 4 + m\angle 2 + m\angle 5 = 180$

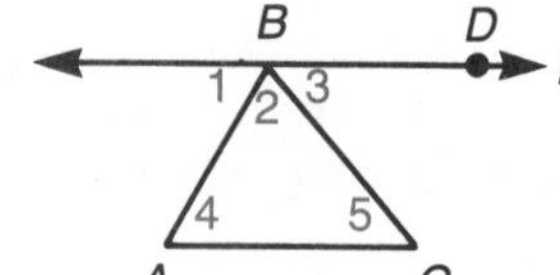

Proof: Using Postulate 16, let k be the line through B parallel to $\overline{AC}$, forming $\angle 1$ and $\angle 2$ as shown. Let D be a point of k on the same side of $\overleftrightarrow{AB}$ as C. Since $\overline{AC} \parallel \overleftrightarrow{BD}$, A is on the same side of $\overleftrightarrow{BD}$ as C. Therefore, by definition, C is in the interior of $\angle ABD$. By the Angle Addition Postulate, $m\angle ABD = m\angle 2 + m\angle 3$. By the Supplement Postulate, $m\angle 1 + m\angle ABD = 180$. Therefore $m\angle 1 + m\angle 2 + m\angle 3 = 180$. By Theorem 8.8, $m\angle 1 = m\angle 4$ and $m\angle 3 = m\angle 5$, because they are alternate interior angles. By substitution, $m\angle 4 + m\angle 2 + m\angle 5 = 180$.

Theorem 8.13 has three corollaries, whose proofs are left as exercises.

COROLLARY 8.13.1
Given a correspondence between two triangles, if two pairs of corresponding angles are congruent, then the third pair of corresponding angles are congruent.

Thus, in the figure below, if $\angle A \cong \angle A'$ and $\angle B \cong \angle B'$, then $\angle C \cong \angle C'$. As the figure suggests, the corollary applies to noncongruent as well as congruent triangles.

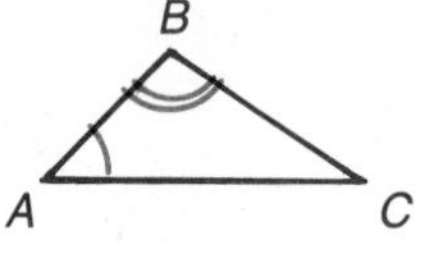

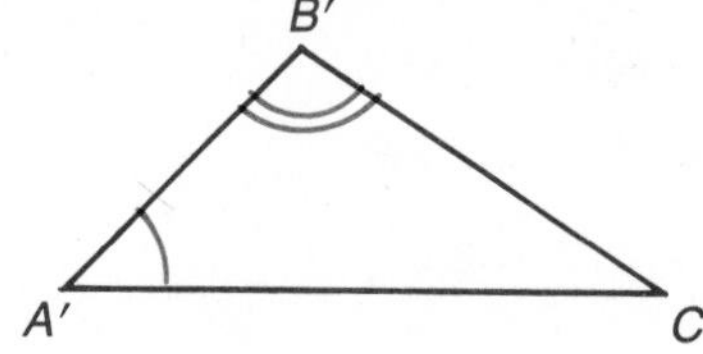

COROLLARY 8.13.2
The acute angles of a right triangle are complementary.

COROLLARY 8.13.3
For any triangle, the measures of an exterior angle is the sum of the measures of the two remote interior angles.

In the figure at the right, $m\angle 1 = m\angle 3 + m\angle 4$, and $m\angle 5 = m\angle 2 + m\angle 3$. If an exterior angle of a triangle is acute, what do you know about the remote interior angles?

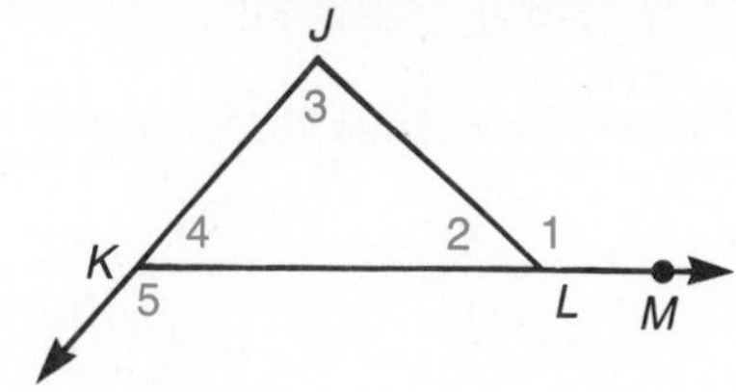

They must be acute.

ASSIGNMENT GUIDE

Minimum 1-12
Regular 1-17 odd
Maximum 1-13 odd, 14-18

ORAL EXERCISES

Complete the following statements.

1. In $\triangle ABC$, $m\angle A + m\angle B + m\angle C =$ _____.
2. In $\triangle DEF$, if $\angle D$ is a right angle, then $m\angle E + m\angle F =$ _____.
3. In $\triangle KLM$ and $\triangle PQR$, if $m\angle K = m\angle P = 45$ and $m\angle L = m\angle Q = 35$, then $m\angle M = m\angle R =$ _____.
4. In $\triangle WXY$, the measure of the exterior angle at W equals $m\angle X +$ _____.

Answer true or false, referring to the figure.

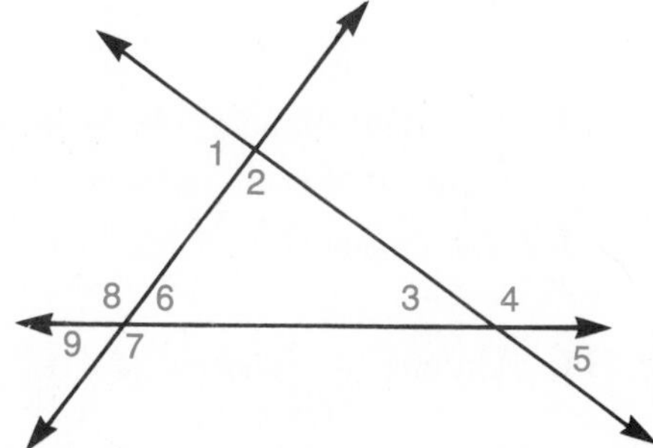

5. $\angle 5$ is an exterior angle.
6. $\angle 7$ is an exterior angle.
7. $\angle 6 \cong \angle 9$
8. $m\angle 2 + m\angle 6 = 90$
9. $m\angle 2 + m\angle 6 + m\angle 5 = 180$
10. $m\angle 8 = m\angle 2 + m\angle 3$
11. $m\angle 4 = m\angle 2 + m\angle 9$
12. $m\angle 1 = m\angle 2 + m\angle 3$

Complete the following statements, referring to the figure.

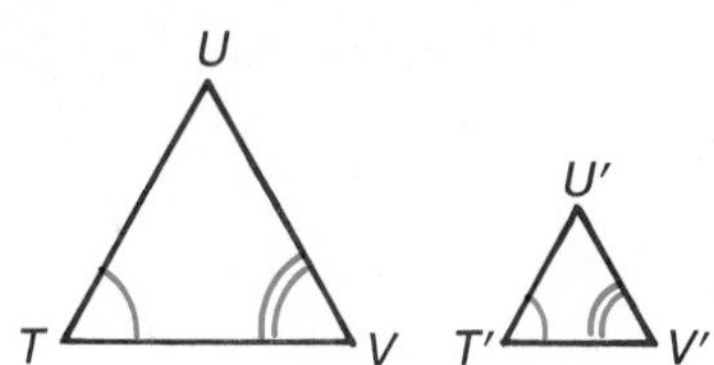

13. If $m\angle T' = 60$, then $m\angle T =$ _____.
14. If $m\angle U = 40$, then $m\angle T + m\angle V =$ _____.
15. If $m\angle T = 50$ and $m\angle U' = 60$, then $m\angle V' =$ _____.

Oral Exercises

1. 180
2. 90
3. 100
4. $m\angle Y$
5. F
6. T
7. T
8. F
9. T
10. T
11. T
12. F
13. 60
14. 140
15. 70

Written Exercises

1. 97 2. 2
3. $180 - 3x$ 4. $180 - a - b$
5. 90 6. $90 - \frac{1}{2}d$
7. $x = 100, y = 80$
8. $x = 30, y = 30$
9. $x = 80, y = 40$
10. $x = 70, y = 120$
11. $x = 50, y = 35$
12. 15, 75 13. 80
14. *1.* $\angle 1 \cong \angle 2$ (Def. of bisect); *2.* $\angle 2 \cong \angle B$ (Thm. 8.8); *3.* $\angle 1 \cong \angle A$ (Thm. 8.9); *4.* $\angle A \cong \angle B$ (Congruence of $\angle$s is transitive.); *5.* $\overline{AC} \cong \overline{BC}$ (Thm. 4.4) If the bisector of an exterior angle of a triangle is parallel to the opposite side, then the triangle is isosceles.
15. Converse of #14: If a triangle is isosceles, then the bisector of the exterior angle at the vertex is parallel with the base.
Given: $\triangle ABC$, $AC = BC$, $\overrightarrow{CE}$ bisects $\angle DCB$.
Prove: $\overline{CE} \parallel \overline{AB}$
Proof: *1.* $\angle 1 \cong \angle 2$ (Def. of bisect); *2.* $\angle A \cong \angle B$ (Thm. 4.3); *3.* $m\angle A + m\angle B + m\angle ACB = 180$ (Thm. 8.13); *4.* $m\angle DCB + m\angle ACB = 180$ (Supplement Post.); *5.* $m\angle A + m\angle B = 180 - m\angle ACB$, $m\angle DCB = 180 - m\angle ACB$ (Subtraction prop. of equality); *6.* $m\angle A + m\angle B = m\angle DCB$ (Transitive prop. of equality); *7.* $2 \cdot m\angle A = m\angle DCB$ (Substitution); *8.* $m\angle DCB = m\angle 1 + m\angle 2$ (Angle Add. Post.); *9.* $m\angle DCB = 2 \cdot m\angle 1$ (Substitution); *10.* $2 \cdot m\angle A = 2 \cdot m\angle 1$ (Transitive Prop. of equality); *11.* $m\angle A = m\angle 1$ (Division); *12.* $\overline{CE} \parallel \overline{AB}$ (Thm. 8.7)

WRITTEN EXERCISES

A. If the measures of two angles of a triangle are as follows, what is the measure of the third angle?

1. 27 and 56 **2.** 149 and 29

3. x and $2x$ **4.** a and b

5. $45 + y$ and $45 - y$ **6.** 90 and $\frac{1}{2}d$

B. Find the values for x and y.

7.

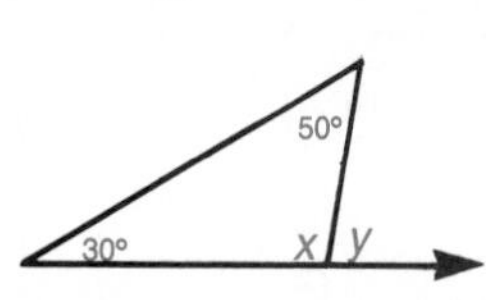

8.

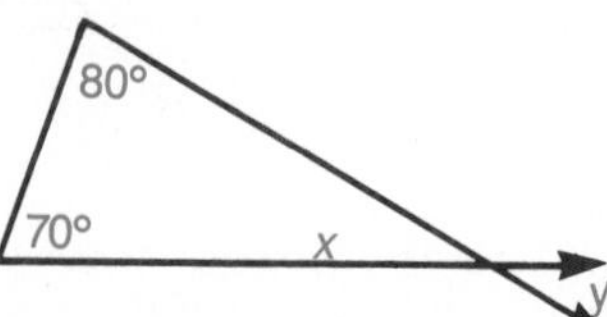

9.

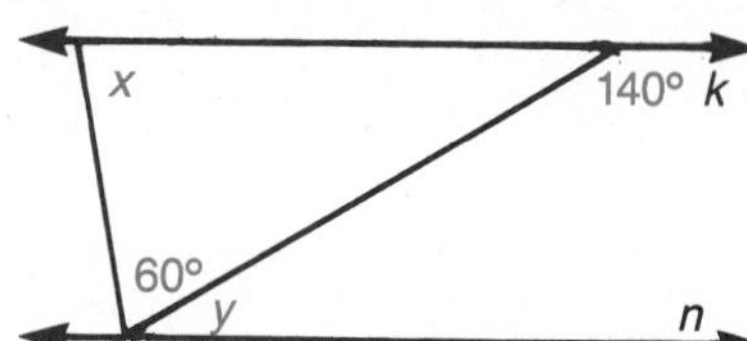

10.

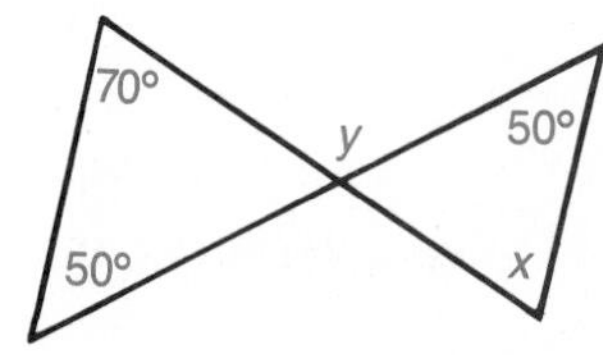

11.

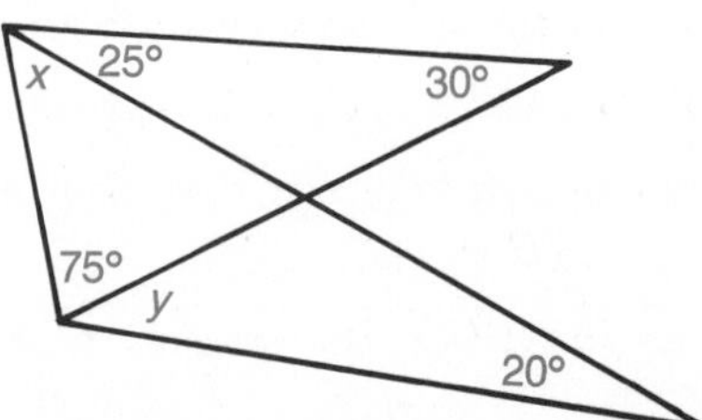

12. In a right triangle, one acute angle is 5 times as large as the other one. Find the measure of each acute angle.

13. The angles of a triangle are in the ratio of 2:3:4. Find the measure of the largest angle.

14. Given: $\overrightarrow{CE}$ bisects $\angle DCB$
$\overrightarrow{CE} \parallel \overline{AB}$

Prove: $\overline{AC} \cong \overline{BC}$
State your conclusion in if-then form.

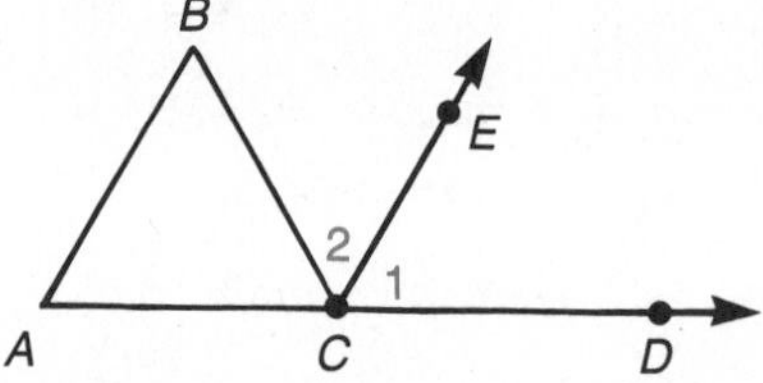

15. State and prove the converse of your conclusion in Exercise 14.

16. Prove Corollary 8.13.1.

C. 17. State Corollary 8.13.2 as a biconditional and prove both cases.

18. Prove Corollary 8.13.3.

SELF-QUIZ

Provide the correct word to complete the following sentence in Exercises 1–2: "If two parallel lines are cut by a tranversal, then the . . ."

1. . . . same-side interior angles are _____.

2. . . . corresponding angles are _____.

Refer to the figure at the right for Exercises 3–6.

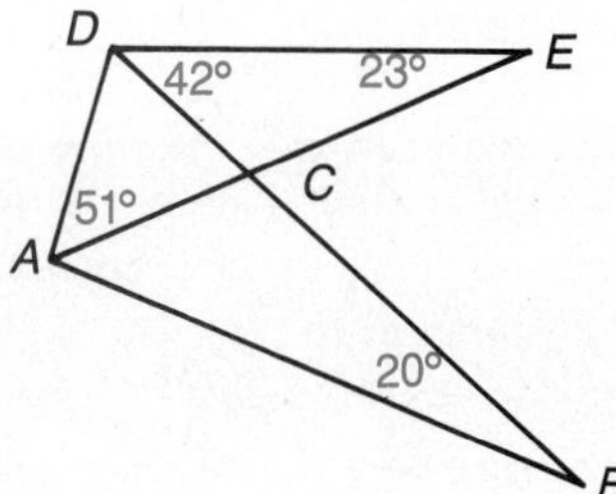

3. What is $m\angle DCA$?

4. What is $m\angle DAB$?

5. What is $m\angle ADC$?

6. What is $m\angle ADE$?

Given that $l \parallel k$, determine the following angle measures.

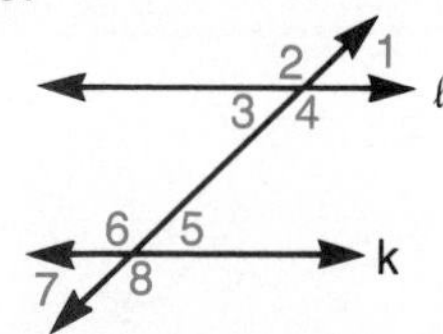

7. If $m\angle 6 = 54$, then $m\angle 1 =$ _____.

8. If $m\angle 8 = 120$, then $m\angle 2 =$ _____.

9. If $m\angle 3 = 44$, then $m\angle 5 =$ _____.

10. If $m\angle 1 = m\angle 4$, then $m\angle 6 =$ _____.

11. Given: E is the midpoint of $\overline{AC}$ and $\overline{BD}$.
Prove: $\overline{AB} \parallel \overline{DC}$

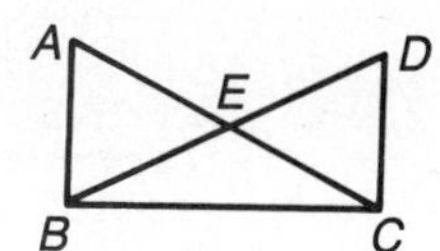

CHALLENGE

In the figure at the right, $\overline{AH} \cong \overline{HB} \cong \overline{BG} \cong \overline{GC} \cong \overline{CF} \cong \overline{FD} \cong \overline{DE}$, and $\overline{AE} \cong \overline{AD}$.
Find $m\angle DAE$.

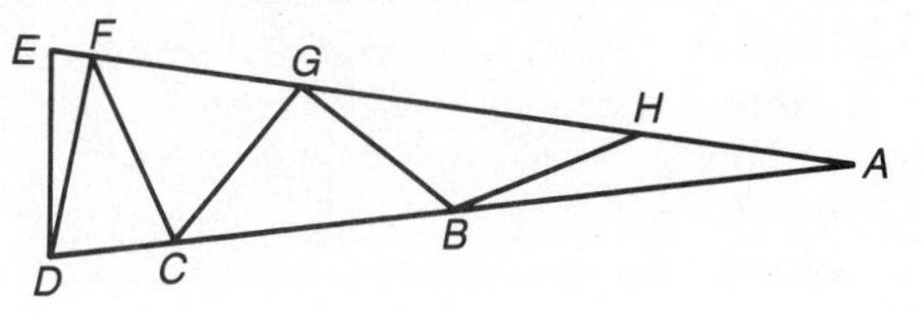

16. See *Selected Answers*, p. 634
17. See *Teacher's Manual*, p. T60
18. See *Selected Answers*, p. 634

Self-Quiz

1. supplementary
2. congruent
3. 65
4. 96
5. 64
6. 106
7. 126
8. 120
9. 44
10. 90
11. *1.* $AE = CE$, $BE = DE$ (Def. of midpoint); *2.* $\angle AEB \cong \angle CED$ (Vert. $\angle$s are $\cong$.); *3.* $\triangle AEB \cong \triangle CED$ (SAS); *4.* $\angle EAB \cong \angle ECD$ (CPCTC); *5.* $\overline{AB} \parallel \overline{DC}$ (Theorem 8.5).

Challenge

$13\frac{11}{13}$

OBJECTIVES

Identify opposite sides and vertices, consecutive sides and vertices, and diagonals of quadrilaterals and identify trapezoids and parallelograms.

Use Theorems 8.14–8.22 to answer questions regarding parallelograms.

TEACHER'S NOTES

See p. T32

MIXED REVIEW

1. Solve for y if $m = \frac{xy}{x + y}$ $y = \frac{mx}{x - m}$

2. For $\frac{y}{x - 3}$, x never equals ______. 3

3. Write a quadratic equation whose solutions are 2 and 3. $x^2 - 5x + 6 = 0$

4. Can a triangle have sides of 12, 13 and 27? no

5. Solve $\frac{3}{x - 7} = \frac{2}{2x + 1}$. $x = -4\frac{1}{4}$

TEACHER'S RESOURCE MASTERS

Practice Master 23, Part 2

8.5 Quadrilaterals in a Plane

As you will recall from the formal definition presented in Chapter 4, a *quadrilateral* is a plane figure having four sides that intersect only at their endpoints. Using what you have learned thus far about triangles and parallel lines, you can discover many interesting properties about quadrilaterals. For this purpose, it will be helpful to learn a few special terms that apply to quadrilaterals.

> **DEFINITIONS: opposite sides and angles, consecutive sides and angles, diagonal of a quadrilateral**
> **Opposite sides** of a quadrilateral are two sides that do not intersect; **opposite angles** are two angles that do not contain a common side. **Consecutive sides** of a quadrilateral are two sides having a common vertex; **consecutive angles** are two angles having a common side. A **diagonal of a quadrilateral** is a segment joining two nonconsecutive angles.

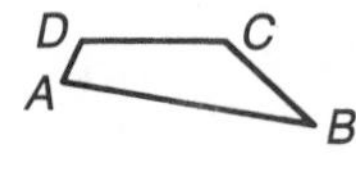

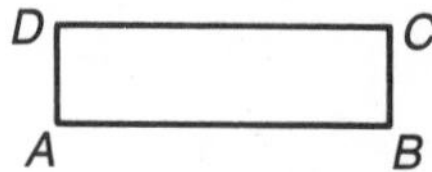

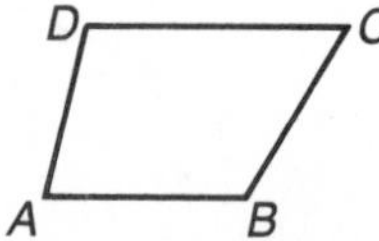

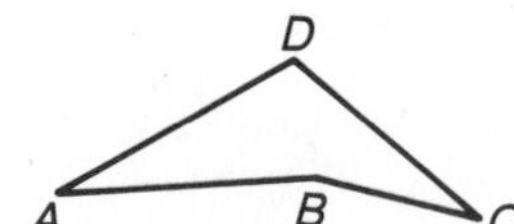

In each of the quadrilaterals $ABCD$ above, $\overline{AB}$ and $\overline{CD}$ are opposite sides, and $\overline{BC}$ and $\overline{AD}$ are opposite sides. Consecutive sides are $\overline{AB}$ and $\overline{BC}$, $\overline{BC}$ and $\overline{CD}$, $\overline{CD}$ and $\overline{DA}$, or $\overline{DA}$ and $\overline{AB}$. Opposite angles are $\angle A$ and $\angle C$ or $\angle B$ and $\angle D$, while consecutive angles are $\angle A$ and $\angle B$, $\angle B$ and $\angle C$, $\angle C$ and $\angle D$, or $\angle D$ and $\angle A$. The diagonals are $\overline{AC}$ and $\overline{BD}$.

Just as triangles may be classified according to their special features, quadrilaterals are distinguished by the relationships among their sides.

> **DEFINITIONS: trapezoid, bases of a trapezoid, parallelogram**
> A **trapezoid** is a quadrilateral in which two and only two opposite sides are parallel. The parallel sides of a trapezoid are called **bases.** A **parallelogram** is a quadrilateral in which both pairs of opposite sides are parallel.

Parallelogram can be written as "▱".

Notice the difference between the two figures above. The figure on the left, a *trapezoid,* has two parallel sides or *bases* and two nonparallel sides. The figure on the right, a *parallelogram,* has two pairs of parallel sides.

Parallelograms and trapezoids are both useful figures in geometry, but the following theorems specifically relate to parallelograms. You are asked to prove them in the written exercises.

THEOREM 8.14
Either diagonal separates a parallelogram into two congruent triangles.

THEOREM 8.15
Opposite sides of a parallelogram are congruent.

COROLLARY 8.15.1
If $l_1 \parallel l_2$ and if P and Q are any two points on l_1, then the distances of P and Q from l_2 are equal.

Corollary 8.15.1 is sometimes restated as "parallel lines are everywhere equidistant."

THEOREM 8.16
Opposite angles of a parallelogram are congruent.

THEOREM 8.17
Two consecutive angles of a parallelogram are supplementary.

THEOREM 8.18
The diagonals of a parallelogram bisect each other.

Applying Theorems 8.14–8.18 to the parallelogram at the right, you can conclude the following: $\triangle ABC \cong \triangle CDA$ and $\triangle ABD \cong \triangle CDB$; $\overline{AB} \cong \overline{DC}$ and $\overline{AD} \cong \overline{BC}$; $\angle ADC \cong \angle CBA$ and $\angle DAB \cong \angle DCB$; $\angle DAB$ and $\angle ABC$, $\angle ABC$ and $\angle BCD$, $\angle BCD$ and $\angle CDA$, and $\angle CDA$ and $\angle DAB$ are supplementary; and $AE = EC$ and $DE = EB$.

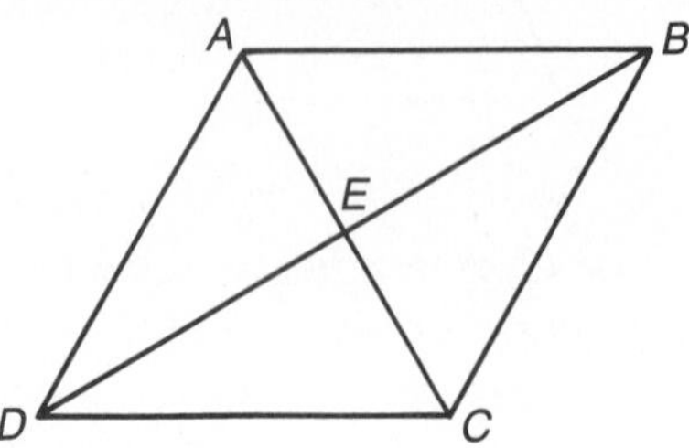

If a quadrilateral is a parallelogram, all of these relationships exist, but do these relationships alone determine a parallelogram? In other words, are any of the converses of Theorems 8.14–8.18 true? The following three theorems answer that question.

THEOREM 8.19
If both pairs of opposite sides of a quadrilateral are congruent, then the quadrilateral is a parallelogram.

THEOREM 8.20
If two sides of a quadrilateral are parallel and congruent, then the quadrilateral is a parallelogram.

THEOREM 8.21
If the diagonals of a quadrilateral bisect each other, then the quadrilateral is a parallelogram.

What you have learned about parallelograms in these theorems allows you to prove an interesting fact about all triangles. It is revealed in the next theorem and proof.

THEOREM 8.22
The segment joining the midpoints of two sides of a triangle is parallel to and half as long as the third side.

Given: $\triangle ABC$ with D and E the midpoints of $\overline{AB}$ and $\overline{BC}$, respectively

Prove: $\overline{DE} \parallel \overline{AC}$ and $DE = \frac{1}{2}AC$

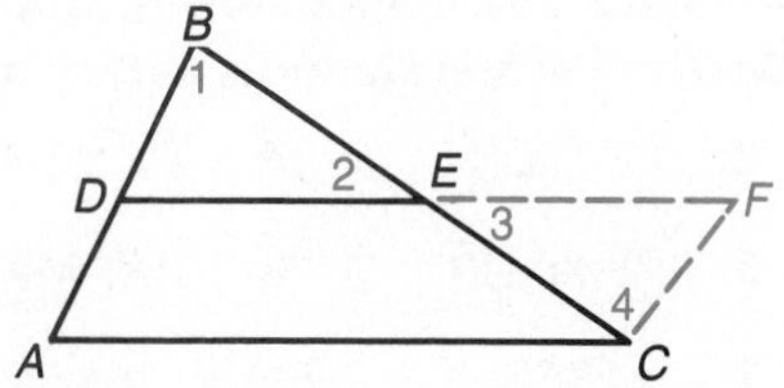

Proof:

STATEMENTS	REASONS
1. Let F be the point on the ray opposite $\overrightarrow{ED}$ such that $EF = ED$.	1. Point Plotting Theorem
2. $EB = EC$	2. Def. of midpoint
3. $\angle 2 = \angle 3$	3. Vertical $\angle$s are $\cong$ (Theorem 3.7).
4. $\triangle EFC \cong \triangle EDB$	4. SAS
5. $\angle 1 = \angle 4$	5. Corres. parts of $\cong$ $\triangle$s are $\cong$.
6. $\overleftrightarrow{AB} \parallel \overleftrightarrow{CF}$	6. If 2 lines are cut by a transversal and a pair of alt. int. $\angle$s are $\cong$, the lines are $\parallel$ (Theorem 8.5).
7. $AD = DB$	7. Def. of midpoint
8. $\overline{DB} \cong \overline{FC}$	8. Corres. parts of $\cong$ $\triangle$s are $\cong$.
9. $DB = FC$	9. Def. of $\cong$ segments
10. $AD = FC$	10. Transitive property of equality
11. $ADFC$ is a $\square$.	11. If two sides of a quadrilateral are $\parallel$ and $\cong$, then the quadrilateral is a $\square$ (Theorem 8.20).
12. $\overline{DE} \parallel \overline{AC}$	12. Definition of $\square$
13. $DE = \frac{1}{2}DF$	13. Step *1*
14. $DF = AC$	14. Opposite sides of a $\square$ are $\cong$ (Theorem 8.15).
15. $DE = \frac{1}{2}AC$	15. Substitution

ORAL EXERCISES

1. In ▱$ABCD$, $m\angle A = 50$. What are the measures of $\angle B$, $\angle C$, and $\angle D$?

2. In trapezoid $EFGH$, $\overline{FG}$ and $\overline{EH}$ are not parallel. $\overline{EF}$ and $\overline{GH}$ are called the _____.

▱PQRS has diagonals $\overline{PR}$ and $\overline{QS}$ intersecting at X. Justify each statement with a definition or theorem.

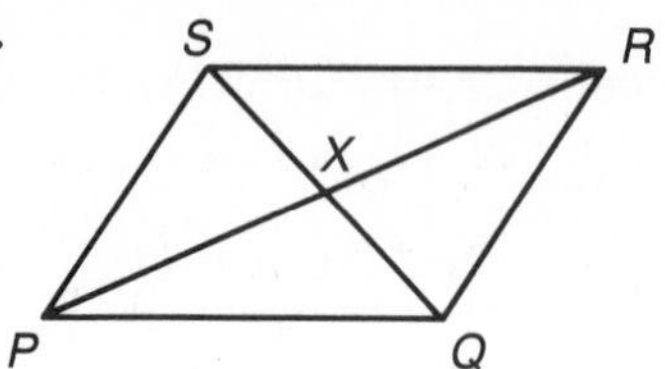

3. $\overline{PS} \parallel \overline{QR}$ **4.** $\overline{PX} \cong \overline{RX}$

5. $\overline{PS} \cong \overline{QR}$ **6.** $RX = \frac{1}{2}RP$

7. $m\angle RSP + m\angle SPQ = 180$

Given the following information, state the theorem or definition that allows you to conclude that *QUAD* is a parallelogram in each case.

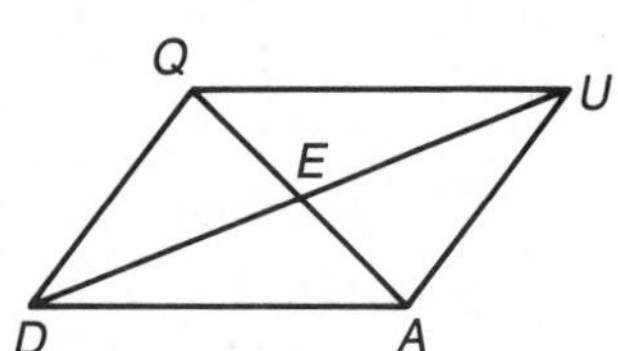

8. $\overline{QD} \cong \overline{UA}$, $\overline{QU} \cong \overline{DA}$ **9.** $\overline{QE} \cong \overline{EA}$, $\overline{DE} \cong \overline{EU}$

10. $\overline{QU} \parallel \overline{DA}$, $\overline{QD} \parallel \overline{UA}$ **11.** $\overline{QD} \cong \overline{UA}$, $\overline{QD} \parallel \overline{UA}$

12. $m\angle UQD = m\angle UAD$, $m\angle ADQ = m\angle QUA$

In the figure, B and C are midpoints of $\overline{AE}$ and $\overline{AD}$, respectively.

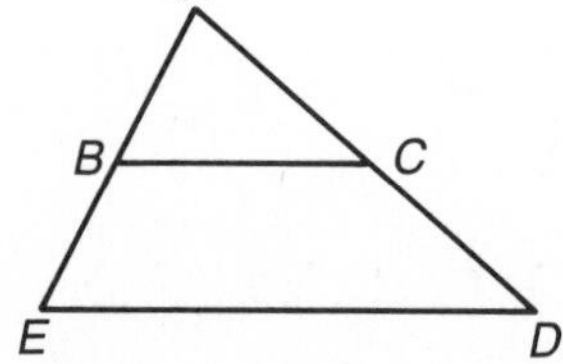

13. If $BC = 6$, then $ED =$ _____

14. If $ED = 20$, then $BC =$ _____

15. If $AE = 12$, then $AB =$ _____

16. If $BC = 3x$, then $ED =$ _____

WRITTEN EXERCISES

A. Refer to the figure for ▱KLMN to complete Exercises 1–5.

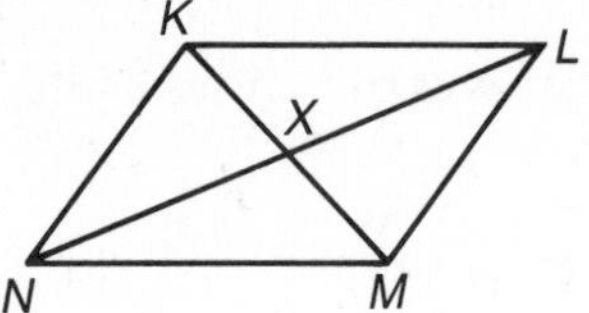

1. If $KN = 7$, then $LM =$ _____.

2. If $KX = 6$, then $MX =$ _____.

3. If $m\angle LKN = 120$, then $m\angle NML =$ _____.

4. If $m\angle LMN = 100$, then $m\angle MNK =$ _____.

5. $\overline{KL} \cong$ _____

ASSIGNMENT GUIDE

Day 1
Minimum 1-7
Regular 1-7
Maximum 1-7
Day 2
Minimum 8-11
Regular 8-14
Maximum 8-16

Oral Exercises

1. 130, 50, 130
2. bases
3. Def. of a parallelogram
4. Thm. 8.18
5. Thm. 8.15
6. Thm. 8.18
7. Thm. 8.17
8. Thm. 8.19
9. Thm. 8.21
10. Def. of a parallelogram
11. Thm. 8.20
12. Converse of Thm. 8.16
13. 12
14. 10
15. 6
16. $6x$

Written Exercises

1. 7
2. 6
3. 120
4. 80
5. $\overline{MN}$

B. 6. Given: $\overline{AB} \parallel \overline{DC}$ and $\overline{AD} \parallel \overline{BC}$

Prove: $\angle A \cong \angle C$

7. Given: Quadrilateral $ABCD$
$\angle 1 \cong \angle 2$, $\angle 3 \cong \angle 4$

Prove: Quadrilateral $ABCD$ is a ▱.

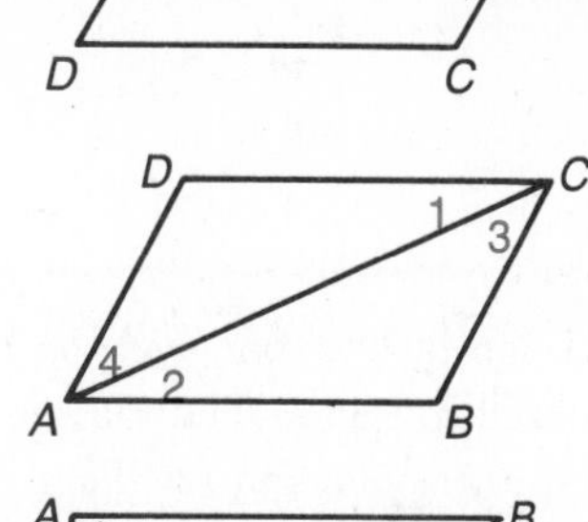

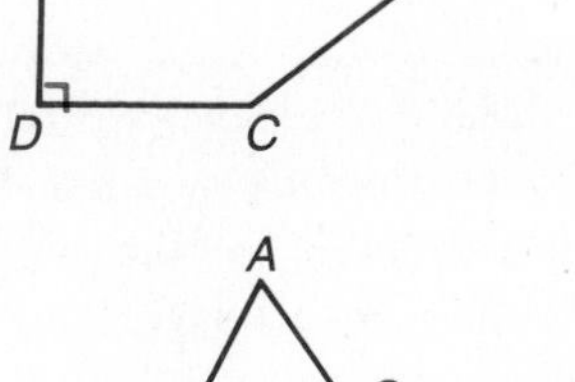

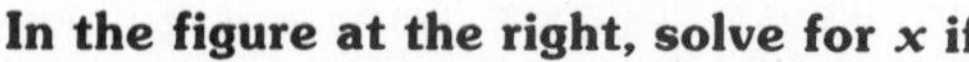

In the figure at the right, solve for *x* if

8. $m\angle B = x - 24$ and $m\angle C = x$.

9. $m\angle B = 3x + 7$ and $m\angle C = 13x - 1$.

10. $m\angle B = 3x - 9$ and $m\angle C = \frac{x}{2}$.

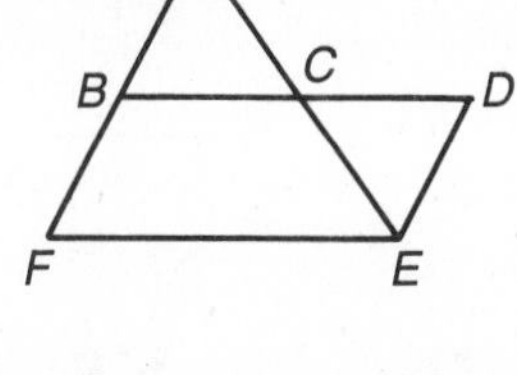

11. Given: $\triangle AFE$ with B the midpoint of $\overline{AF}$ and C the midpoint of $\overline{BD}$ and $\overline{AE}$

Prove: Quadrilateral $BDEF$ is a ▱.

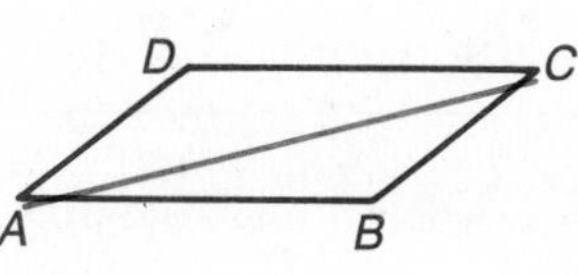

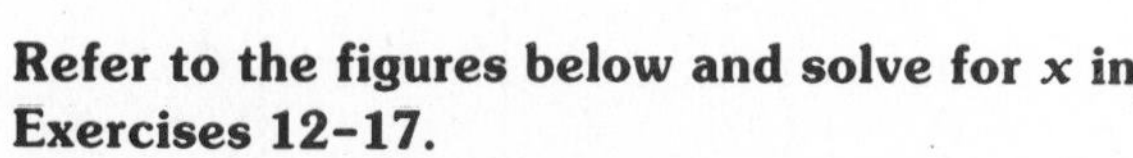

Refer to the figures below and solve for *x* in Exercises 12–17.

12. Given: ▱$ABCD$
diagonal $\overline{AC}$

Prove: $\triangle ABC \cong \triangle CDA$ (Theorem 8.14)
$\overline{AB} \cong \overline{DC}$ and $\overline{AD} \cong \overline{BC}$ (Theorem 8.15)
$\angle ADC \cong \angle CBA$ and $\angle DAB \cong \angle BCD$ (Theorem 8.16)

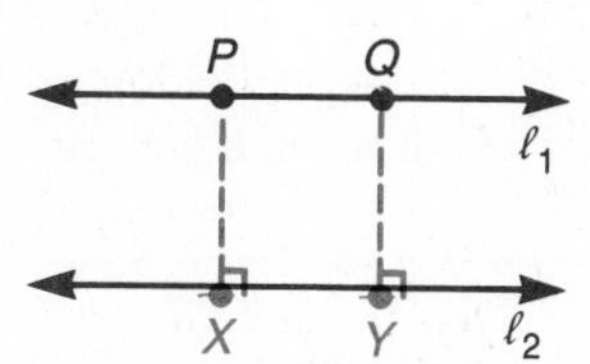

13. Given: $\ell_1 \parallel \ell_2$
P and Q lie on ℓ_1

Prove: P and Q are equidistant from ℓ_2 (Cor. 8.15.1)
HINT: Use the figure at the right.

14. The proof for Theorem 8.17 follows directly from what other theorem in this chapter?

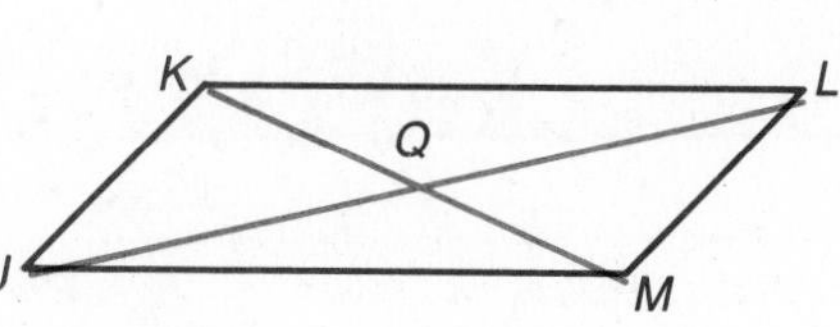

C. 15. Given: ▱$JKLM$
$\overline{JL}$ and $\overline{KM}$ intersect at Q

Prove: $\overline{KQ} \cong \overline{QM}$ and $\overline{JQ} \cong \overline{QL}$ (Theorem 8.18)

16. Given: Quadrilateral $ABCD$, $\overline{AF} \perp \overline{BF}$, $\overline{CG} \perp \overline{DG}$
$\overline{CG}$ bisects $\angle DCB$; $\overline{BF}$ bisects $\angle CBA$.
$\overline{AF}$ bisects $\angle BAD$; $\overline{DG}$ bisects $\angle ADC$.
$m\angle CGB \neq m\angle AFD \neq 90$

Prove: $ABCD$ is a trapezoid.

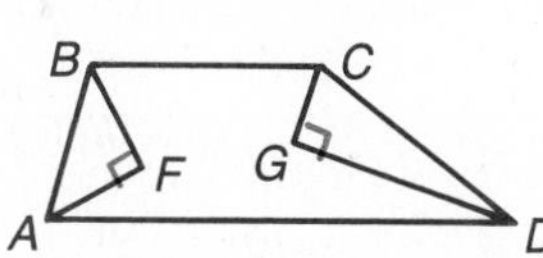

6. Quadrilateral $ABCD$ is a ▱ (Def. of ▱); $\angle A \cong \angle C$ (Thm. 8.16)
7. $\angle 1 \cong \angle 2$ (Given); $\overline{DC} \parallel \overline{AB}$ (Thm. 8.5); $\angle 3 \cong \angle 4$ (Given); $\overline{BC} \parallel \overline{AD}$ (Thm. 8.5); Quadrilateral $ABCD$ is a ▱ (Def. of ▱).
8. 102
9. 11
10. 54
11. $BC = CD$ (Def. of midpoint); $BC = \frac{1}{2}FE$ (Thm. 8.22); $2(BC) = FE$ (Mult. prop.); $BC + BC = FE$ (Def. of mult.); $BC + CD = FE$ (Substitution); $BC + CD = BD$ (Def. of between); $BD = FE$ (Trans. prop. of equal.); $\overline{BD} \cong \overline{FE}$ (Def. of $\cong$); $\overline{BC} \parallel \overline{FE}$ (Thm. 8.22); $\overline{BD} \parallel \overline{FE}$ (Def. of $\parallel$); $BDEF$ is a ▱ (Thm. 8.20).
12. $\overline{AB} \parallel \overline{DC}$ and $\overline{AD} \parallel \overline{BC}$ by def. of ▱; $\angle ACD \cong \angle CAB$ and $\angle DAC \cong \angle ACB$ by Thm. 8.8; $\overline{AC} \cong \overline{AC}$ by congruence of segments is reflex.; $\triangle ABC \cong \triangle CDA$ by ASA; $\overline{AB} \cong \overline{DC}$ and $\overline{AD} \cong \overline{BC}$ by CPCTC; $\angle ADC \cong \angle CBA$ and $\angle DAB \cong \angle BCD$ by CPCTC.
13. Draw $\overline{PX} \perp$ to ℓ_2 at X, and $\overline{QY} \perp$ to ℓ_2 at Y; $\overline{PX} \perp \ell_1$ and $\overline{PY} \perp \ell_1$ by Thm. 8.12; $\overline{PX} \parallel \overline{PY}$ by Thm. 8.2; ▱ $PXYQ$ by def. of ▱; $\overline{PX} \cong \overline{QY}$ by Thm. 8.15; $PX = QY$ or def. of $\cong$.
14. Theorem 8.10
15. $\overline{KL} \cong \overline{JM}$ by Thm. 8.15; $\overline{KL} \parallel \overline{JM}$ by def. of ▱; $\angle MKL \cong \angle KMJ$ and $\angle KLJ \cong \angle LJM$ by Thm. 8.8; $\triangle KQL \cong \triangle MQJ$ by ASA; $\overline{KQ} \cong \overline{QM}$ and $\overline{JQ} \cong \overline{QL}$ by CPCTC.
16. See *Selected Answers*, p. 634

OBJECTIVES

Identify rhombuses, rectangles, and squares.

Use Theorems 8.23–8.26 to find missing measures in figures and use these theorems in proofs.

TEACHER'S NOTES

See p. T32

MIXED REVIEW

1. Are alternate interior angles always congruent? no
2. What is the third angle in a triangle if two angles are 30 and 100? 50
3. Solve $4x + 5y = 13$
   $2x + 3y = 7$ (2, 1)
4. Solve $3x - 6 \leq x + 6$. $x \leq 6$
5. What is the coefficient of x in the expression $3x^5 - 2x^3 - 4x + 7$? -4

TEACHER'S RESOURCE MASTERS

Practice Master 24, Part 1

8.6 Special Parallelograms and Transversals to Many Lines in a Plane

In the last section, you learned about two special classes of quadrilaterals: trapezoids and parallelograms. The class of parallelograms can be subdivided into even more specialized types, depending on the relationship among their sides and angles. Three special types of parallelograms are defined and illustrated below.

DEFINITIONS: rhombus, rectangle, square
A **rhombus** is a parallelogram all of whose sides are congruent. A **rectangle** is a parallelogram all of whose angles are right angles. A **square** is a rectangle all of whose sides are congruent.

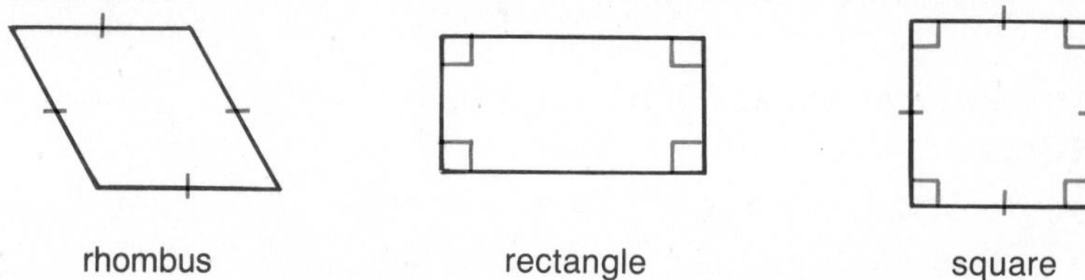

According to the definitions, a *rhombus may* be a rectangle, but it does not have to be. Likewise, a *rectangle may also* be a rhombus, but not necessarily. When a quadrilateral is *both* a rhombus and a rectangle, it is a *square*.

The next three theorems establish other particular features of rectangles and rhombuses. The proofs of these theorems are left as exercises.

THEOREM 8.23
If a parallelogram has one right angle, then it has four right angles, and the parallelogram is a rectangle.

THEOREM 8.24
The diagonals of a rhombus are perpendicular to one another.

THEOREM 8.25
If the diagonals of a quadrilateral bisect each other and are perpendicular, then the quadrilateral is a rhombus.

Mathematics Around You

Notice how pentagons are used repeatedly in the design of these buildings.

Mathematics in Nature

Below: A branch of geometry called transformation geometry deals with translations, rotations, and reflections. This striking photograph illustrates a reflection, with the horizon line being a line of reflection.

Upper right: Notice the geometric designs of these star mica and quartz crystals.

Lower right: The pinecone is one of many items in nature that are related to the sequence of numbers called the Fibonacci sequence. The sequence is 1, 1, 2, 3, 5, 8, 13, 21, 34, 55, ... In some pinecones, there are 5 spirals in one direction and 8 spirals in the other. These are adjoining numbers in the Fibonacci sequence.

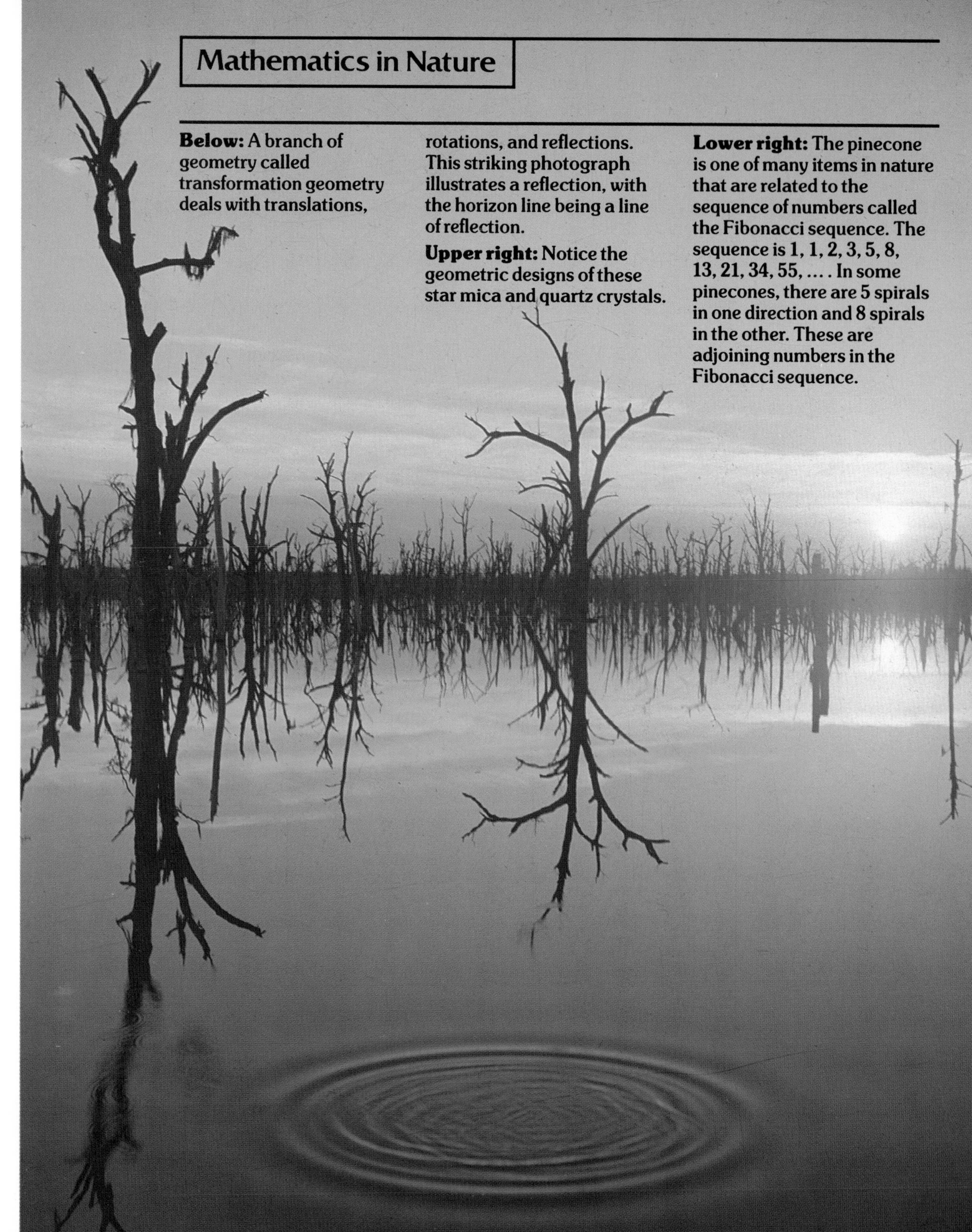

C

Below: Here is a greatly enlarged photograph of a peacock feather, another of nature's splendid designs.

Background, right: Butterflys display a beautiful application of transformation geometry. The body of the butterfly is a line of symmetry. Each wing is a reflection of the other wing.

Insert, right: This greatly enlarged photograph of a swallowtail butterfly shows its intricate design.

D

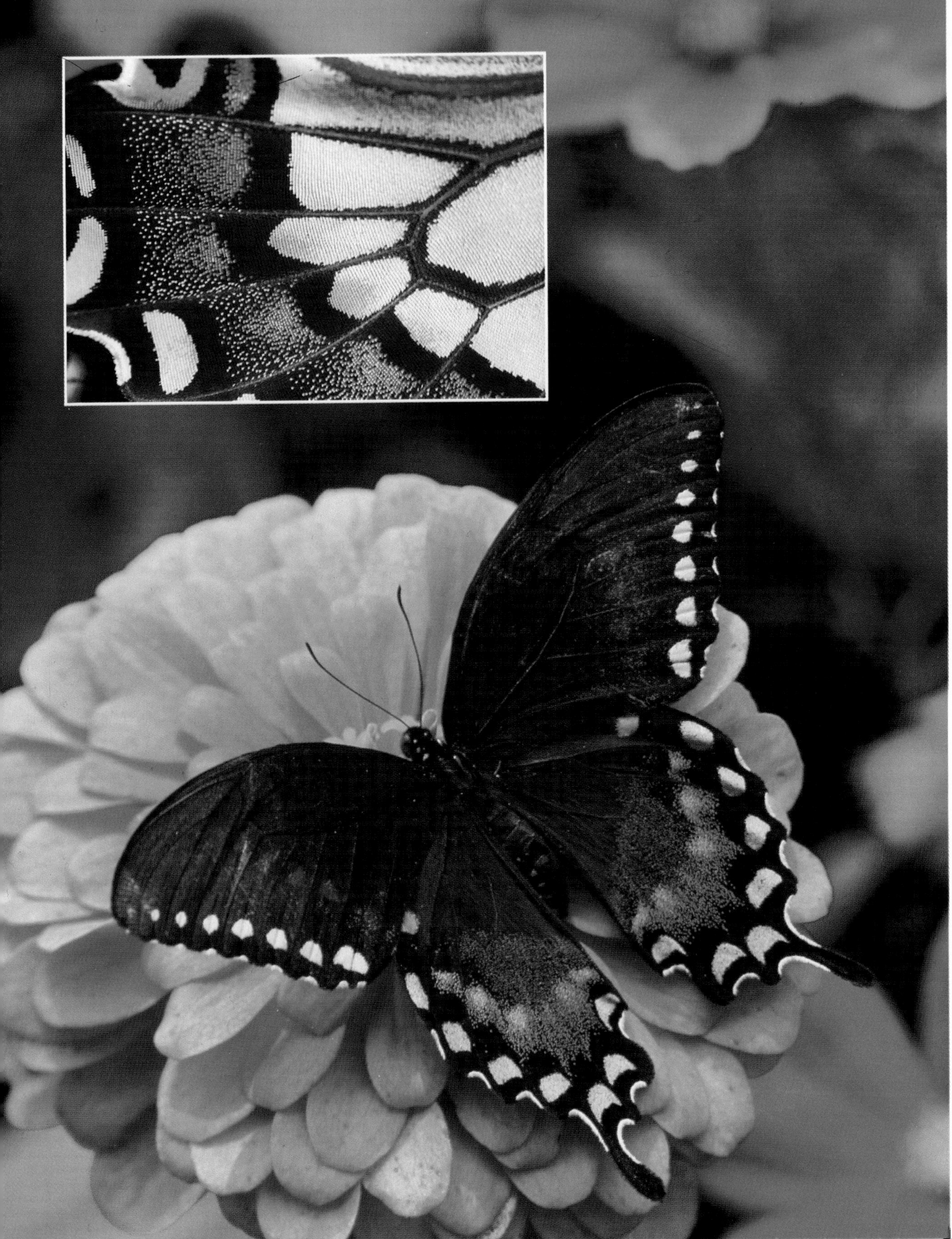

Mathematics in Architecture

Below: Notice how this modern building employs both circles and triangles in its unusual design. **Background, right:** The lobby of the Hyatt Regency Hotel in San Francisco illustrates a variety of geometric designs.

Insert, top right: These modern buildings in Indianapolis, Indiana, have sides in the shape of trapezoids. **Insert, bottom right:** The Mitchell Park Conservatory in Milwaukee, Wisconsin, is a geodesic dome made of interlocking triangles.

This photo shows Embarcadero Plaza in San Francisco. Notice how the parallel lines in the steel overhead structure seem to converge in the distance.

Mathematics in Ancient History

The Colosseum in Rome employs hundreds of arches in its graceful design. The overall shape of the Colosseum is roughly an ellipse.

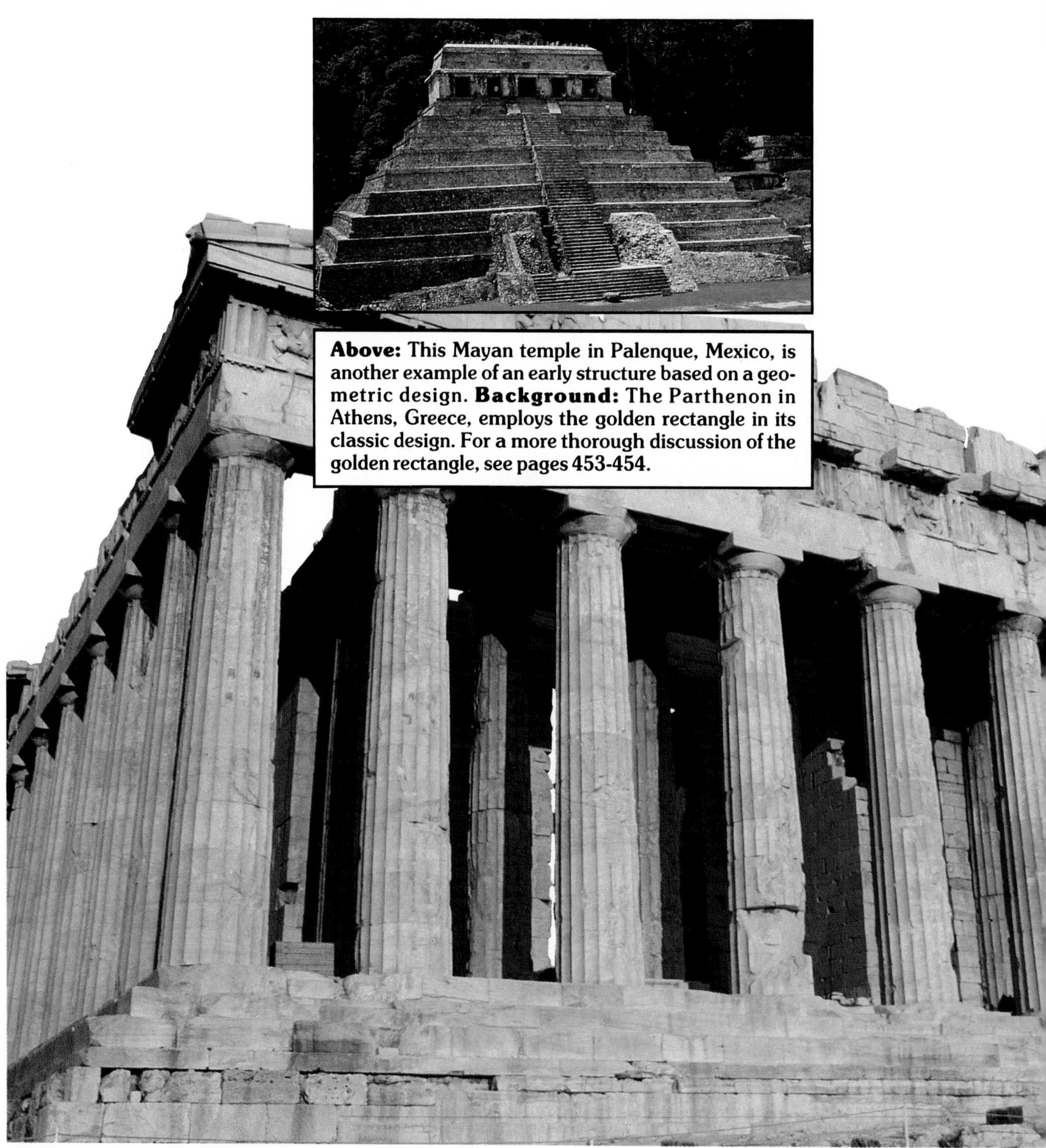

Above: This Mayan temple in Palenque, Mexico, is another example of an early structure based on a geometric design. **Background:** The Parthenon in Athens, Greece, employs the golden rectangle in its classic design. For a more thorough discussion of the golden rectangle, see pages 453-454.

J

Mathematics in Technology

This storage tank illustrates an unusual geometric shape. Although it is not spherical, it approximates a sphere in shape.

Left: Modern computers use extremely complicated circuitry. In this photo, a person is working with a greatly enlarged version of a computer circuit.

Below: Many oil storage tanks like the ones shown in this photograph are cylindrical in shape.

Mathematics in Art and Design

This modern sculpture employs dozens of metal cylinders in its design.

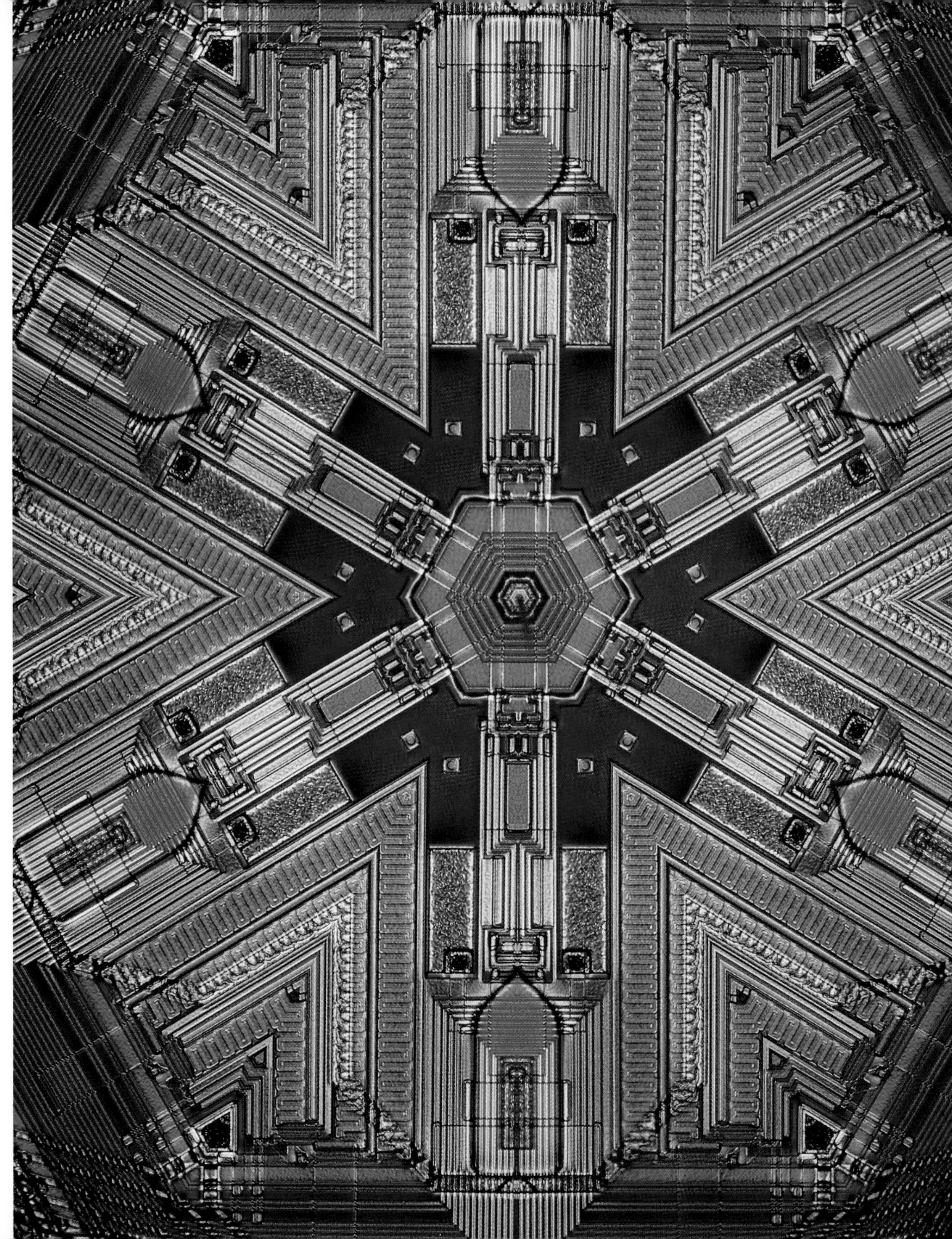

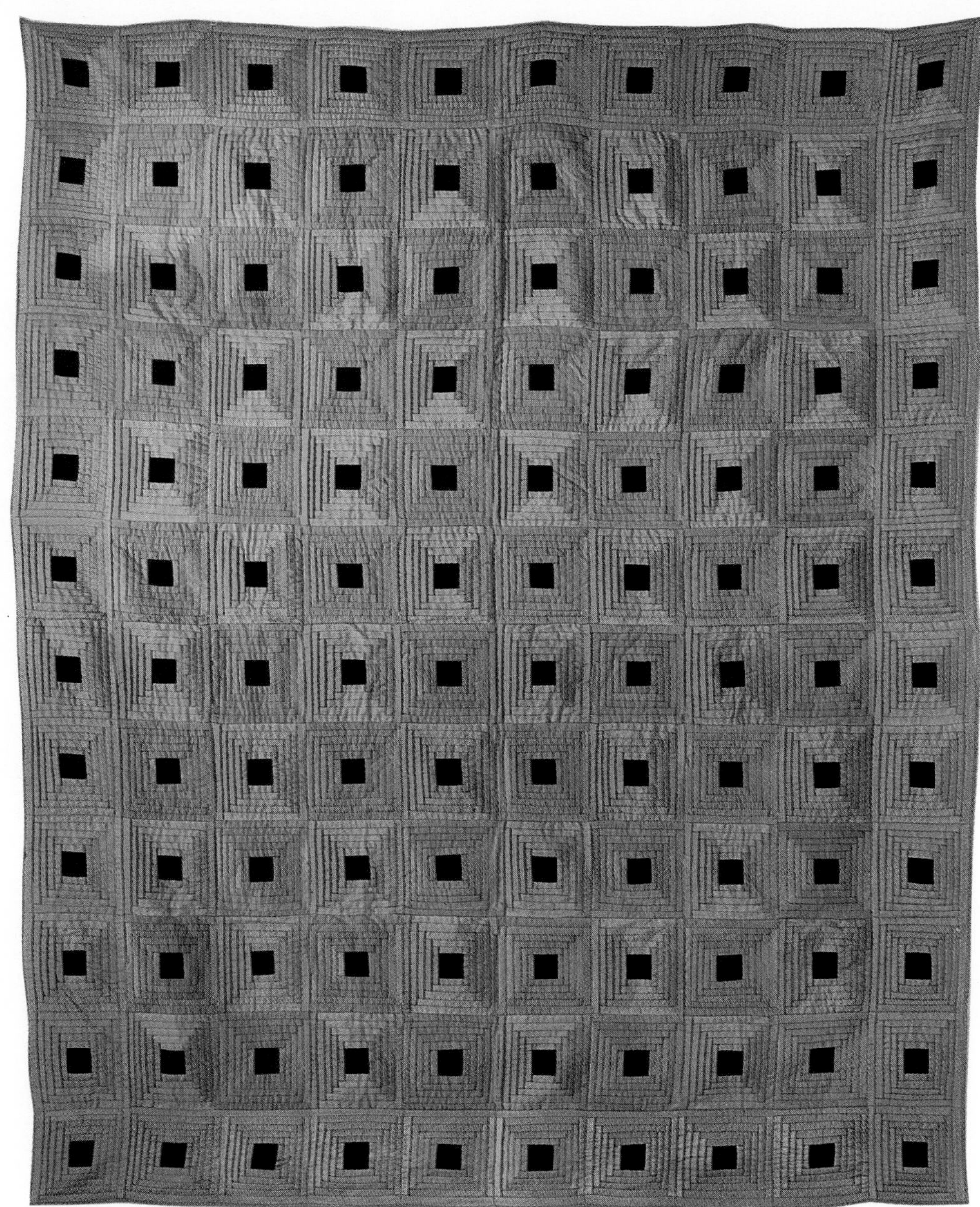

Left: Today's computers can produce intricate and beautiful designs, as shown in this photograph.

Above: This quilt employs tiny squares and rectangles of cloth to form a colorful geometric design.

Top: In this overhead photo of a crowd at a football game, you see how design can appear in unusual places. Thousands of squares of colored paper are used to create an overall mosaic effect. **Bottom, left:** This painting by Frank Stella is called "Hiraqla." It was painted in 1968. **Bottom, right:** Mosaics have always allowed for beautiful applications of geometry. This mosaic appears in a building in Isfahan, Iran.

Now, using what you know about parallelograms, you can prove an important theorem about transversals crossing three parallel lines. In Theorem 8.26, the term **intercept** is used to mean "determines the bounds of," as in "lines a and b intercept $\overline{XY}$ on transversal t," as shown at the right.

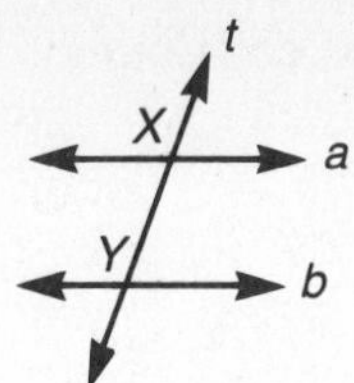

> **THEOREM 8.26**
> If three parallel lines intercept congruent segments on one transversal, then they intercept congruent segments on any other transversal.

Given: $l_1 \parallel l_2 \parallel l_3$ cut by transversals t_1 and t_2
$\overline{AB} \cong \overline{BC}$

Prove: $\overline{DE} \cong \overline{EF}$

Proof: Consider the general case in which t_1 and t_2 are not parallel and do not intersect l_1 at the same point. Using the Parallel Postulate, let t_3 be the line through A that is parallel to t_2, intersecting l_2 and l_3 at G and H. Let t_4 be the line through B parallel to t_2 and intersecting l_3 in I. Label ∠1, ∠2, ∠3, and ∠4 as shown in the figure below.

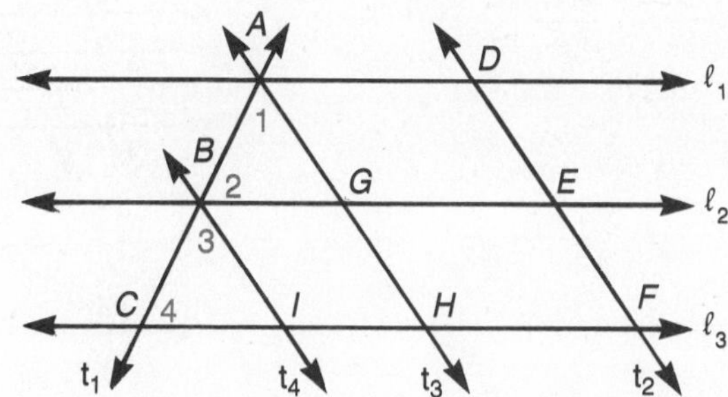

Proof:

STATEMENTS	REASONS
1. $l_2 \parallel l_3$	1. Given
2. $\angle 2 \cong \angle 4$	2. If 2 ∥ lines are cut by a transversal, each pair of corresponding ∠s are ≅ (Theorem 8.9).
3. $AB = BC$	3. Given
4. $t_3 \parallel t_4$	4. Two lines ∥ to the same line are ∥ to each other (Thm. 8.11).
5. $\angle 1 \cong \angle 3$	5. Theorem 8.9

Proof continued

ASSIGNMENT GUIDE

Day 1
Minimum 1-9
Regular 1-10
Maximum 1-10
Day 2
Minimum 11-15
Regular 11-16
Maximum 11-19

Proof continues:

STATEMENTS	REASONS
6. $\triangle ABG \cong \triangle BCI$	6. ASA
7. $\overline{AG} \cong \overline{BI}$	7. Corres. parts of $\cong$ $\triangle$s are $\cong$.
8. $l_1 \parallel l_2 \parallel l_3$ $t_2 \parallel t_3 \parallel t_4$	8. Given
9. Quadrilaterals *AGED* and *BIFE* are ▱s.	9. Definition of ▱
10. $\overline{AG} \cong \overline{DE}$, $\overline{BI} \cong \overline{EF}$	10. Opposite sides of a ▱ are $\cong$ (Theorem 8.15).
11. $\overline{DE} \cong \overline{EF}$	11. Congruence of segments is transitive.

COROLLARY 8.26.1
If three or more parallel lines intercept congruent segments on one transversal, then they intercept congruent segments on any other transversal.

Given that $\overline{A_1A_2} \cong \overline{A_2A_3} \cong \overline{A_3A_4} \cong \ldots$, it follows that $\overline{B_1B_2} \cong \overline{B_2B_3} \cong \overline{B_3B_4} \cong \ldots$, by repeated applications of Theorem 8.26.

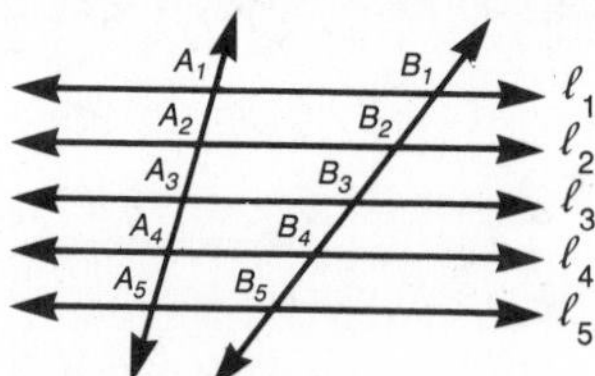

ORAL EXERCISES

Oral Exercises

1. 5 2. 20

3. ⊥ 4. 5

Given rhombus *ABCD*, complete Exercises 1-4.

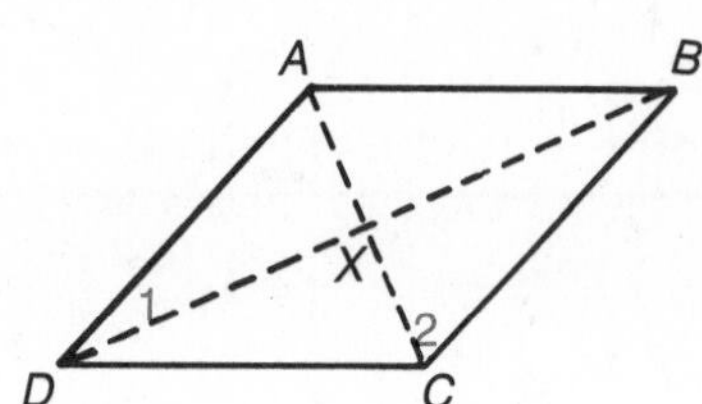

1. If $AD = 5$, then $DC =$ _____.

2. If $m\angle ADC = 20$, then $m\angle ABC =$ _____.

3. $\overline{DB}$ ● $\overline{AC}$

4. If $DB = 10$, then $DX =$ _____.

5. rhombus, square

6. all

7. all

8. rhombus, square

Which quadrilaterals (parallelogram, rhombus, rectangle, or square) have the properties described in Exercises 5-16?

5. The diagonals are always perpendicular.

6. The opposite angles are congruent.

7. The diagonals always bisect each other.

8. The diagonals are always perpendicular bisectors of each other.

9. The opposite sides are congruent.
10. The intersection of the diagonals forms four congruent angles.
11. The diagonals are always congruent.
12. Two angles may be acute.
13. Each diagonal bisects two angles.
14. Each pair of consecutive angles is supplementary.
15. The consecutive sides are congruent.
16. Two angles may be obtuse.

9. all 10. rhombus, square
11. rectangle, square
12. parallelogram, rhombus
13. rhombus, square
14. all
15. rhombus, square
16. rhombus, parallelogram

WRITTEN EXERCISES

A. Given that $l_1 \parallel l_2 \parallel l_3$ and $\overline{DE} \cong \overline{EF}$, complete Exercises 1–4.

1. If $AB = 10$, then $BC =$ ____.
2. If $AG = 2.4$, then $GH =$ ____.
3. If $AH = 32.5$, then $AG =$ ____.
4. If $BC = 14$, then $AC =$ ____.

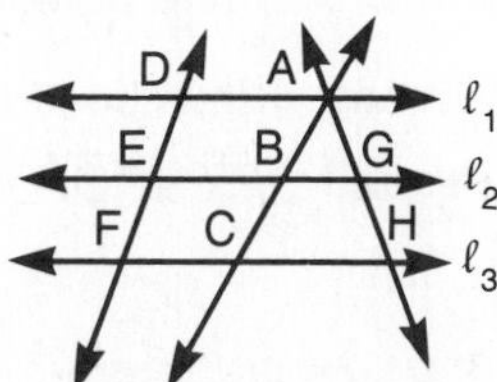

Given ▱$ABCD$, where $\angle B = x + 30$ and $\angle C = 2x - 60$, complete Exercises 5–8.

5. $m\angle A =$ ____.
6. $m\angle B =$ ____.
7. $m\angle D =$ ____.
8. $m\angle C =$ ____.

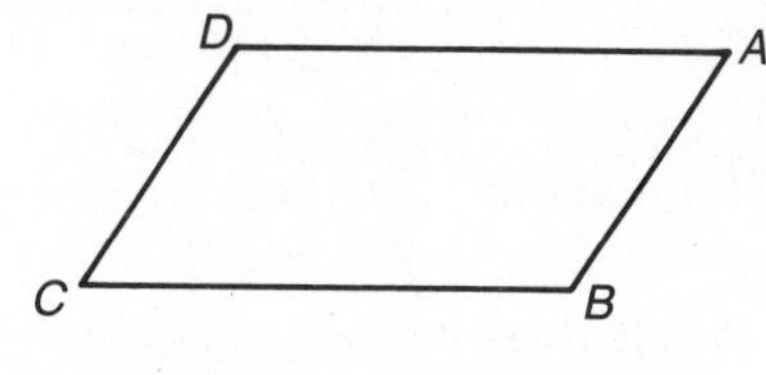

B. 9. **Given:** ▱$ABHQ$ and ▱$AFRM$
Prove: $\angle R \cong \angle H$

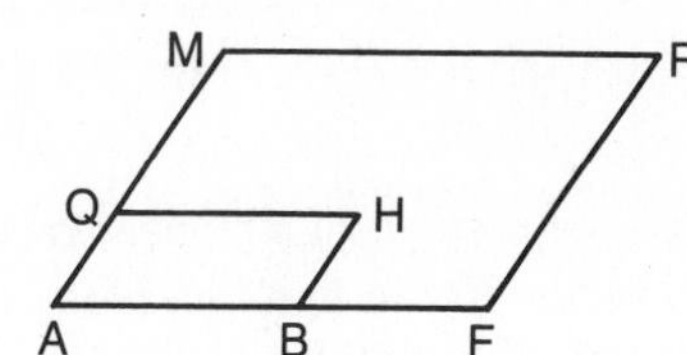

10. **Given:** Trapezoid $ABCF$
$\overline{BE}$ bisects $\overline{CF}$.
$\overline{BC} \parallel \overline{AE}$
Prove: $\overline{DB} \cong \overline{DF}$

B C D A F E

Written Exercises

1. 10
2. 2.4
3. 16.25
4. 28
5. 80 6. 100
7. 100 8. 80
9. By Theorem 8.16, $\angle A \cong \angle H$ in ▱$ABHQ$, and $\angle A \cong \angle R$ in ▱$AFRM$. Since congruence of angles is transitive, $\angle R \cong \angle H$.
10. $\overline{CD} \cong \overline{FD}$ by Def. of bisect and $\angle BDC \cong \angle EDF$ by Theorem 3.7. Because $\overline{BC} \parallel \overline{AE}$, alternate interior $\angle$s CBD and FED are $\cong$. So $\triangle CBD \cong \triangle FED$ by SAA and $\overline{DB} \cong \overline{DE}$ by CPCTC. (You can also prove the triangles $\cong$ by ASA.)

11. 6 12. 12
13. 20 14. 14
15. By the Def. of ▱, $\overline{AD} \parallel \overline{BC}$ and $\overline{AB} \parallel \overline{DC}$. So by Theorem 8.10, $\angle A$ and $\angle D$, $\angle A$ and $\angle B$, and $\angle B$ and $\angle C$ are supplementary. Thus, $m\angle A = m\angle B = m\angle C = m\angle D = 90$, and by definition, ▱$ABCD$ is a rectangle.
16. Let $\overline{PR}$ and $\overline{QS}$ intersect at T. By Theorem 8.18, $ST = QT$ and $PT = RT$. Because all four sides are $\cong$, $\triangle STP \cong \triangle PTQ \cong \triangle QTR \cong \triangle RTS$ by SSS. Then $\angle STP \cong \angle PTQ \cong \angle QTR \cong \angle RTS$ by CPCTC. Since all are $\cong$, adjacent $\angle$s, the measure of each is 90 by Theorem 3.4. By Def. of $\perp$, $\overline{PR} \perp \overline{QS}$.
17. By Def. of $\perp$, all the $\angle$s formed at G are rt. $\angle$s. Thus, $\triangle FGE \cong \triangle CGF \cong \triangle DGC \cong \triangle EGD$ by SAS. Then $FE = CF = DC = ED$ by CPCTC, which makes $CDEF$ both a ▱ and a rhombus.
18. Because $ABCD$ is a ▱, $\overline{AB} \parallel \overline{DC}$, $\overline{AD} \parallel \overline{BC}$, $\overline{AB} \cong \overline{DC}$, and $\overline{AD} \cong \overline{BC}$. $\angle DAP \cong \angle BCR$ (Thm. 8.8) and $AP = CR$ (Given). So $\triangle DAP \cong \triangle BCR$ by SAS, and $\overline{DP} \cong \overline{BR}$ by CPCTC. Similarly, $\angle RCD \cong \angle PAB$ by Thm. 8.8. So $\triangle RCD \cong \triangle PAB$ by SAS and $\overline{DR} \cong \overline{BP}$ by CPCTC. Thus, by Thm. 8.19, $DPBR$ is a ▱.
19. See *Teacher's Manual*, p. T60

Given $l_1 \parallel l_2 \parallel l_3$, B is the midpoint of $\overline{AC}$, and E is the midpoint of $\overline{DF}$, complete Exercises 11–14.

11. If $AB = 6$, $BC =$ ____.

12. If $DF = 24$, $DE =$ ____.

13. If $AB = 3x + 1$ and $BC = 6x - 8$, $AC =$ ____.

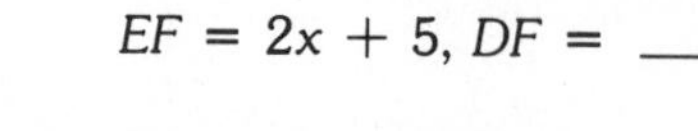

14. If $DE = x^2 + 9x - 3$ and $EF = 2x + 5$, $DF =$ ____.

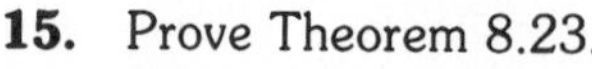

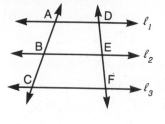

15. Prove Theorem 8.23.

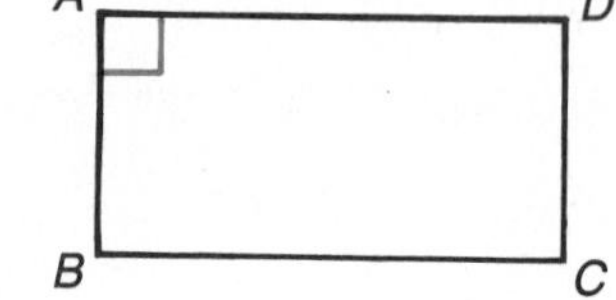

Given: ▱$ABCD$, rt. $\angle A$

Prove: $\angle B$, $\angle C$, $\angle D$ are rt. $\angle$s.
▱$ABCD$ is a rectangle.

16. Prove Theorem 8.24.

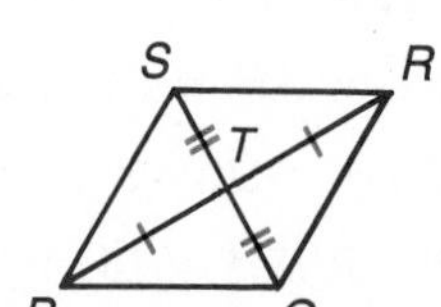

Given: Rhombus $PQRS$

Prove: $\overline{PR} \perp \overline{QS}$

17. Prove Theroem 8.25.

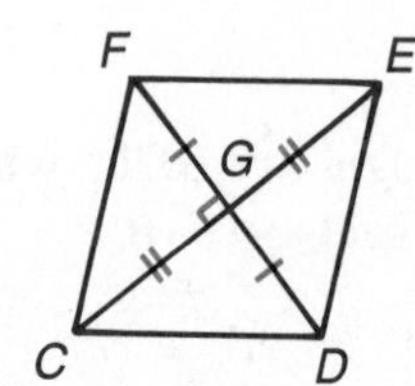

Given: In quadrilateral $CDEF$, $\overline{FD} \perp \overline{CE}$
$FG = DG$, $CG = EG$

Prove: Quadrilateral $CDEF$ is a rhombus.

C. 18. Given: ▱$ABCD$ with diagonal $\overline{AC}$
$AP = CR$

Prove: Quadrilateral $DPBR$ is a ▱.

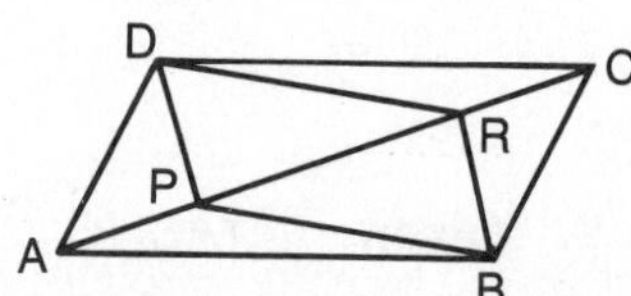

19. The *median of a trapezoid* is the segment joining the midpoints of the nonparallel sides. Prove that *the median of a trapezoid is parallel to the bases and equal in length to half the sum of the lengths of the bases.*

Given: Trapezoid $ABCD$ with $\overline{DC} \parallel \overline{AB}$, P the midpoint of $\overline{AD}$, and Q the midpoint of $\overline{BC}$.

Prove: $\overline{PQ} \parallel \overline{AB}$, $\overline{PQ} \parallel \overline{DC}$
$PQ = \frac{1}{2}(AB + DC)$

(HINT: Draw $\overline{DB}$ with midpoint K.)

8.7 Parallel Planes

This chapter began with the definition of parallel lines as "two lines in a plane that do not intersect." Until now, you have considered parallelism as a plane concept. Parallelism is also a *space concept.* Lines can be parallel to planes, and planes can be parallel to each other. The only condition for parallelism in space is stated in the following definition.

DEFINITION: parallel lines and planes in space
Two planes, or a plane and a line, are parallel if they do not intersect.

The notation for parallel planes A and B is $A \parallel B$, and the notation for line k parallel to plane C is $k \parallel C$ or $C \parallel k$.

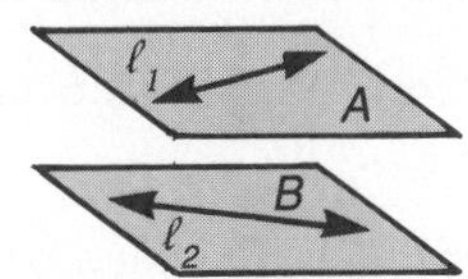

All parallel planes contain lines that are parallel to each other, but they also contain nonparallel lines. In the figure at the right, the parallel planes A and B contain lines l_1 and l_2, which are not parallel. Line k is parallel to plane C, and C is parallel to A and B, but k is not necessarily parallel to l_1 or l_2, nor is it parallel to l_3 in C.

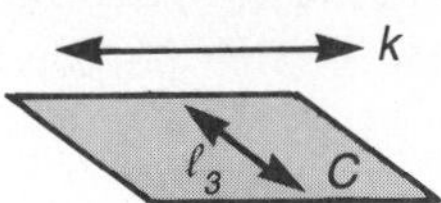

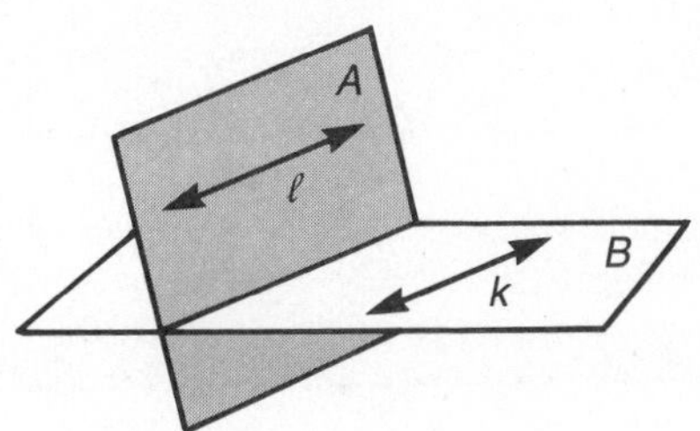

Two nonparallel planes can contain lines parallel to each other. In the figure at the left, planes A and B intersect, yet they contain the parallel lines l and k. The notation for not parallel is "$\nparallel$." In the figure, $A \nparallel B$.

THEOREM 8.27
If a plane intersects two parallel planes, then it intersects them in two parallel lines.

OBJECTIVE

Use Theorems 8.27–8.31 to answer questions regarding parallel lines and planes and use these theorems in proofs.

TEACHER'S NOTES

See p. T32

MIXED REVIEW

1. Simplify $x(x + c) - c(x - c)$. $x^2 + c^2$
2. Simplify $-2x + 5x - 9x$. $-6x$
3. What is the next largest even number after x if x is an even number? $x + 2$
4. Solve $\frac{x}{2x - 3} = \frac{5}{8}$. $x = 7\frac{1}{2}$
5. Give four conditions that would make a quadrilateral a parallelogram. Section 8.5

TEACHER'S RESOURCE MASTERS

Practice Master 24, Part 2

Given: Plane $E \parallel$ plane F
Plane G intersects E and F in lines l and k.

Prove: $l \parallel k$

Proof: Lines l and k lie in the same plane G. They have no point in common, because E and F have no point in common. Therefore, l and k are parallel by the definition of parallel lines.

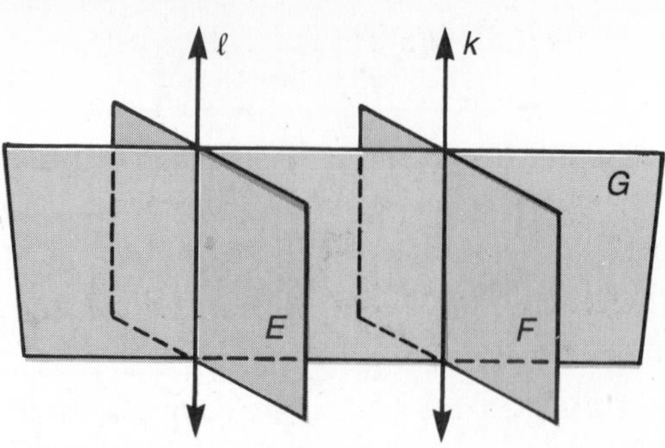

> **THEOREM 8.28**
> If a line is perpendicular to one of two parallel planes, then it is perpendicular to the other.

Given: Plane $E \parallel$ plane F, line $l \perp E$

Prove: $l \perp F$

Proof: In F, take a point A not on l, and by Theorem 2.3, let G be the plane determined by l and A. By Theorem 8.27, G intersects E and F in parallel lines j and k. Since $l \perp E$, then $l \perp j$, and so by Theorem 8.12, $l \perp k$. Now take a point B in F, not on l, and repeat the process. You thus obtain two lines in F each perpendicular to l at the point where l intersects F, and so $l \perp F$ by Theorem 7.3.

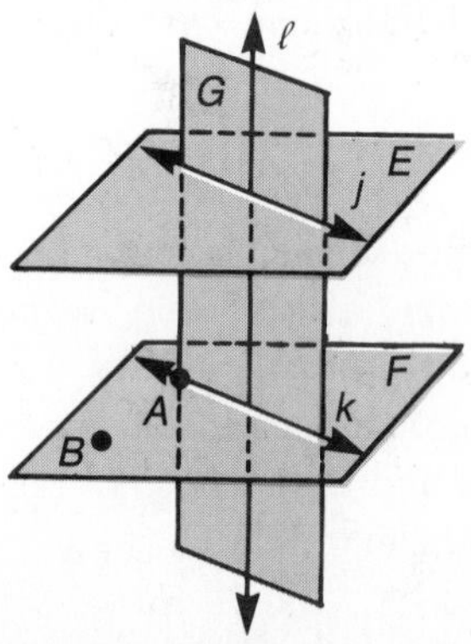

> **THEOREM 8.29**
> Two planes perpendicular to the same line are parallel.

> **COROLLARY 8.29.1 (Parallelism of Planes is Transitive)**
> If two planes are each parallel to a third plane, they are parallel to each other.

Given: Planes E_1, E_2, E_3
$E_1 \parallel E_3$, $E_2 \parallel E_3$

Prove: $E_1 \parallel E_2$

Proof: Let l be a line perpendicular to E_3. By Theorem 8.28, $l \perp E_1$, and $l \perp E_2$. Thus, $E_1 \parallel E_2$ by Theorem 8.29.

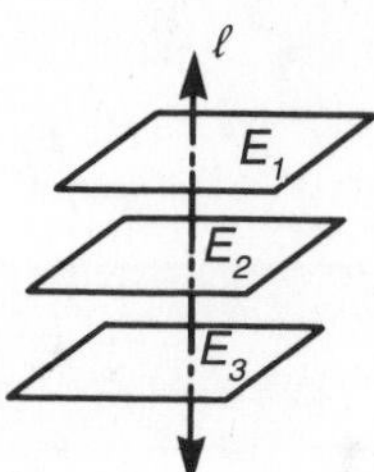

THEOREM 8.30
Two lines perpendicular to the same plane are parallel.

COROLLARY 8.30.1
A plane perpendicular to one of two parallel lines is perpendicular to the other.

COROLLARY 8.30.2 (Parallelism of Lines is Transitive)
If two lines are each parallel to a third line, they are parallel to each other.

THEOREM 8.31
Two parallel planes are everywhere equidistant.

Another way of stating this theorem is that *all segments perpendicular at their endpoints to two parallel planes have the same length.*

Many of these theorems have been left as exercises.

ASSIGNMENT GUIDE

Day 1
Minimum 1-8
Regular 1-10
Maximum 1-10
Day 2
Minimum 9-11
Regular 11-17 odd
Maximum 11-17 odd, 18-19

ORAL EXERCISES

State whether each statement is true or false. Support your answer with models from the classroom or with chalkboard sketches.

1. If a line is perpendicular to one of two parallel planes, it is perpendicular to the other.
2. Two lines parallel to the same plane may be perpendicular to each other.
3. Two planes perpendicular to the same line may intersect.
4. If two planes are both perpendicular to each of two parallel lines, the segments of the two lines intercepted between the planes are congruent.
5. If a plane intersects two intersecting planes, the lines of intersection may be parallel.
6. If a line lies in a plane, a perpendicular to the line is always perpendicular to the plane.
7. If two planes are parallel, any line in one of them is parallel to any line in the other.

Oral Exercises

1. T
2. T
3. F
4. T
5. T
6. F
7. F

8. T 9. T
10. F 11. T
12. F

Written Exercises

1. yes; Theorem 8.27
2. yes; Theorem 8.28
3. yes; Theorem 8.29
4. yes; Theorem 8.30
5. yes; Corollary 8.30.1
6. yes; Theorem 8.31
7. No; it is transitive and symmetric, but not reflexive.
8. No; it is transitive and symmetric, but not reflexive.
9. They are parallel.
10. $\overline{PQ} \cong \overline{SR}$ by Theorem 8.31; $\overline{PQ} \parallel \overline{SR}$ by Theorem 8.30; $PQRS$ is a ▱ by Theorem 8.20; $\overline{PS} \cong \overline{RQ}$ by Def. of ▱.
11. $\overline{AB} \perp S$ by Theorem 8.28; $\angle ACX \cong \angle ACY$ by Def. of $\perp$ and Thm. 3.3; $\overline{AC} \cong \overline{AC}$ by Congruence of segments is reflexive; $\triangle ACX \cong \triangle ACY$ by SAS; $\overline{AX} \cong \overline{AY}$ by CPCTC; $AX = AY$ by Def. of $\cong$ segments.
12. *1.* $M \parallel N$ (Theorem 8.29); *2.* $M \perp CD$ (Given); *3.* $N \perp CD$ (Theorem 8.28)

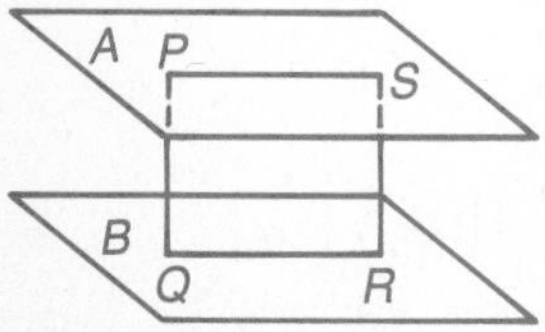

8. If two planes, perpendicular to the same line, are intersected by a third plane, the lines of intersection are parallel.

9. If a line lies in a plane, a perpendicular to the plane at some point of the line is perpendicular to the line.

10. If two lines are parallel, every line intersecting one of them intersects the other.

11. If two planes are parallel, any line in one of them is parallel to the other plane.

12. If a line is parallel to a plane, a second line perpendicular to the first line is also perpendicular to the plane.

WRITTEN EXERCISES

A. Refer to the figure at the right for Exercises 1–6. Explain your answers. l_1 and l_2 lie in plane X.

1. If $Y \parallel Z$, is $\overleftrightarrow{AB} \parallel \overleftrightarrow{CD}$?

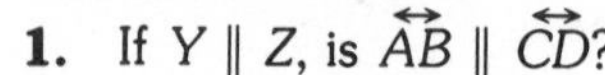

2. If $Y \parallel Z$, and $l_1 \perp Y$, is $l_1 \perp Z$?

3. If $Y \perp l_2$ and $Z \perp l_2$, is $Y \parallel Z$?

4. If $l_1 \perp Z$ and $l_2 \perp Z$, is $l_1 \parallel l_2$?

5. If $l_1 \parallel l_2$ and $X \perp l_1$, is $X \perp l_2$?

6. If $X \parallel Y$, $l_1 \perp Y$ and Z, and $l_2 \perp Y$ and Z, is $AC = BD$?

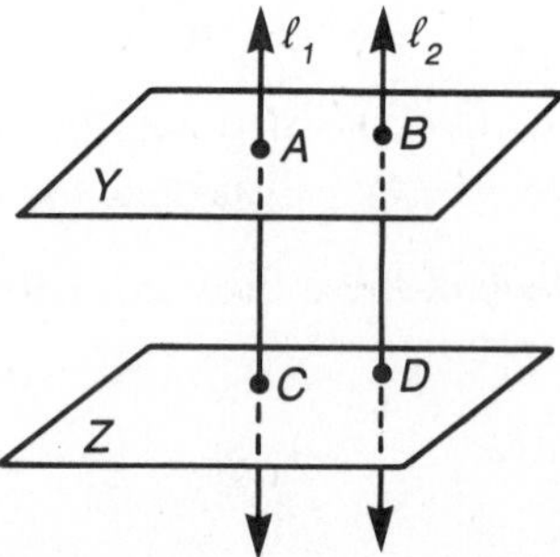

B. **7.** By Corollary 8.29.1, you know that parallelism of planes is transitive. Is parallelism of planes an equivalence relation? Explain your answer.

8. Is parallelism of lines an equivalence relation? Explain your answer.

9. If two congruent segments are both perpendicular at their endpoints to two planes, what can you deduce about the planes?

10. Illustrate and prove the following. Plane $A \parallel$ plane B; $\overline{PQ} \perp A$ at P; Q is in B, $\overline{RS} \perp A$ at S; and R is in B. Prove $\overline{PS} \cong \overline{QR}$.

11. Given: $S \parallel R$
$\overline{AB} \perp R$
$CX = CY$

Prove: $AX = AY$

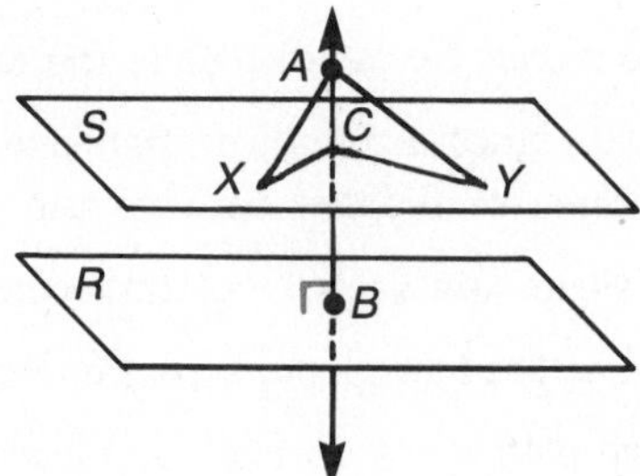

12. Given: $M \perp \overline{AB}$
$M \perp \overline{CD}$
$N \perp \overline{AB}$

Prove: $N \perp \overline{CD}$

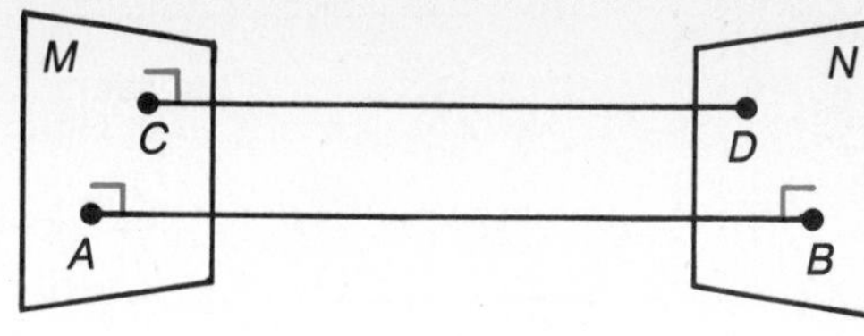

13. Prove Theorem 8.29 (Two planes perpendicular to the same line are parallel.) indirectly.

14. Prove Theorem 8.30 (Two lines perpendicular to the same plane are parallel.).

15. Prove Corollary 8.30.1 (A plane perpendicular to one of two parallel lines is perpendicular to the other.).

16. Prove Corollary 8.30.2 (If two lines are each parallel to a third line, they are parallel to each other.).

C. 17. Use the following illustration to prove Theorem 8.31 (Two parallel planes are everywhere equidistant.).

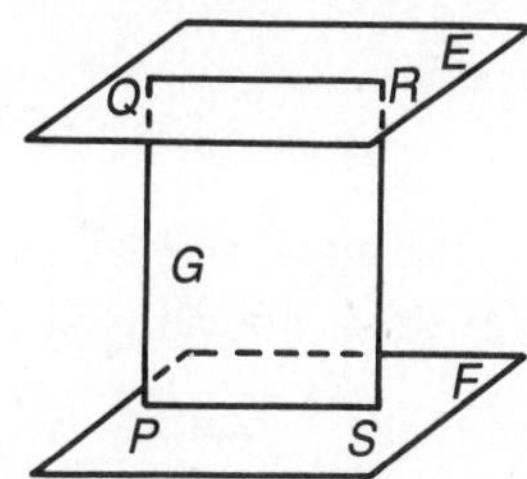

Given: Plane $E \parallel$ plane F
$\overline{PQ}$ and $\overline{RS} \parallel$ between E and F

Prove: $PQ = RS$

18. Given: $M \parallel N$
$\overline{AB} \perp N$
$\overline{CD} \perp N$

Prove: $AD = CB$

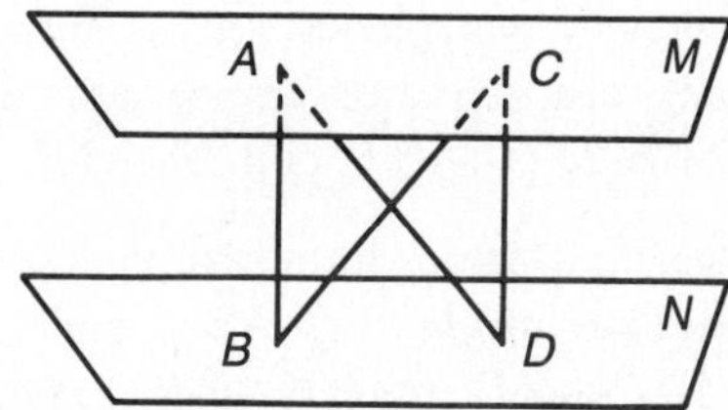

19. Given: Parallel planes X, Y, and Z
$\overline{CE}$ in Z
point A in X
$\overline{AC}$ intersects Y at B.
$\overline{AE}$ intersects Y at D.
$AB = BC$, $AC = CE$

Prove: $AB = BD$

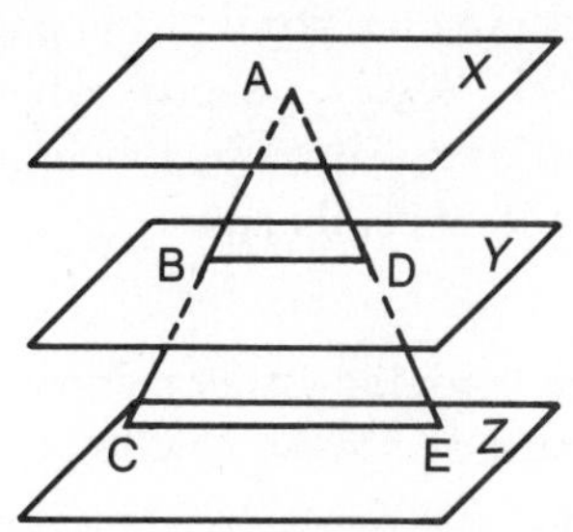

13.

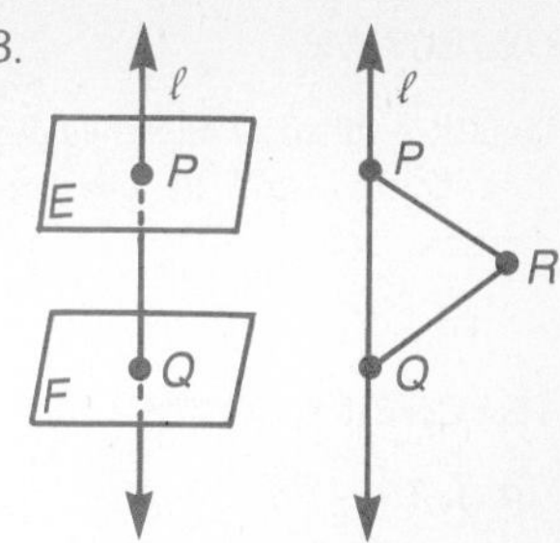

Given: Plane $E \perp$ line l at P plane $F \perp l$ at Q
Prove: $E \parallel F$
Proof: If E is not parallel to F, then their intersection includes some point R. You know that $l \perp \overleftrightarrow{PR}$ and $l \perp \overleftrightarrow{QR}$, because by Theorem 7.5, l is perpendicular to every line in E through P and every line in F through Q. This contradicts Theorem 5.3, so E must be parallel to F.

14, 16, 18. See *Selected Answers,* p. 635

15, 17. See *Teacher's Manual,* p. T60 and p. T61

19. Consider the plane determined by points A, B, and D. By Theorem 8.27, the plane of ABD intersects Y and Z in two parallel lines. Since it intersects Y in B and D, and Z in C and E, it intersects the planes in $\overleftrightarrow{BD}$ and $\overleftrightarrow{CE}$, and $\overleftrightarrow{BD} \parallel \overleftrightarrow{CD}$. By Theorem 8.3, there is a line through A parallel to $\overleftrightarrow{BD}$ (and also $\overleftrightarrow{CE}$). By Theorem 8.26, therefore, if $AB = BC$, $AD = DE$. Thus BD joins the midpoints of $\overline{AC}$ and $\overline{AE}$ in $\triangle ACE$, and $BD = \frac{1}{2}CE$ by Theorem 8.22. Given $AC = CE$, substitution yields $BD = \frac{1}{2}AC = AB$.

OBJECTIVE

Identify a dihedral angle, its parts in figures, and its characteristics.

TEACHER'S NOTES

See p. T32

MIXED REVIEW

1. Does the union of two half-planes make a plane? no
2. Which quadrilateral is both a rectangle and a rhombus? square
3. Which type of triangle has one angle bisector that is a median? isosceles
4. Divide $\frac{x^2 - x - 20}{x + 4} \div \frac{x - 5}{x + 1}$. $(x + 1)$
5. Add $\frac{2}{x - 3} + \frac{3}{x^2 - 5x + 6}$. $\frac{2x - 1}{x^2 - 5x + 6}$

TEACHER'S RESOURCE MASTERS

Practice Master 25, Part 1

8.8 Dihedral Angles and Perpendicular Planes

Another perpendicular relation in space remains to be considered, and that is perpendicularity between two planes.

When you open this book, you are forming a **dihedral angle** with an **edge** and two **faces** or **sides.**

> **DEFINITIONS: dihedral angle, edge, face, side**
> A **dihedral angle** is the union of a line and two noncoplanar half-planes having this line as their common edge. Thus, the line is called the **edge** of the dihedral angle. The union of the edge and either half-plane is called a **face,** or **side,** of the dihedral angle.

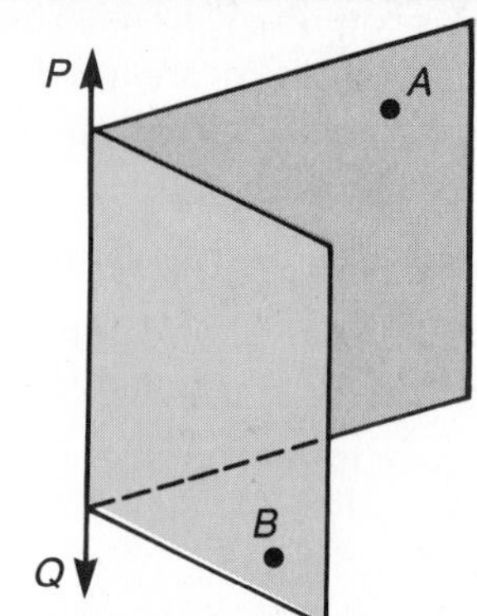

If $\overleftrightarrow{PQ}$ is the edge, and A and B are points on different sides, the dihedral angle is named

$$\angle A\text{-}\overleftrightarrow{PQ}\text{-}B$$
or
$$\angle B\text{-}\overleftrightarrow{PQ}\text{-}A$$

Four dihedral angles are formed by the intersection of two planes. In the figure at the right, the dihedral angles are $\angle E\text{-}\overleftrightarrow{AB}\text{-}D$, $\angle D\text{-}\overleftrightarrow{AB}\text{-}C$, $\angle C\text{-}\overleftrightarrow{AB}\text{-}F$, and $\angle F\text{-}\overleftrightarrow{AB}\text{-}E$.

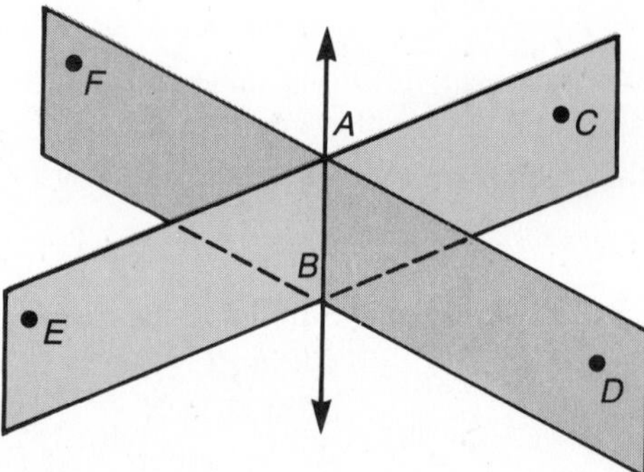

These four angles form two pairs of **vertical dihedral angles:** $\angle F\text{-}\overleftrightarrow{AB}\text{-}C$ and $\angle E\text{-}\overleftrightarrow{AB}\text{-}D$, and $\angle C\text{-}\overleftrightarrow{AB}\text{-}D$ and $\angle F\text{-}\overleftrightarrow{AB}\text{-}E$. Extending the comparison between angles in a plane and angles in space, you should be able to define and identify *interior* dihedral angles, *exterior* dihedral angles, *supplementary* dihedral angles, *complementary* dihedral angles, and *adjacent* dihedral angles.

Missing from the list for comparison is a *right* dihedral angle. To *define* a right dihedral angle, you must first know how to *measure* a dihedral angle. Consider the following definition and figure.

> **DEFINITION: plane angle**
> Through any point on the edge of a dihedral angle there passes a plane perpendicular to the edge, intersecting each of the sides in a ray. The angle formed by these rays is called a **plane angle** of the dihedral angle.

The sides of a plane angle are perpendicular to the edge of the dihedral angle. Thus, another way of defining a plane angle is the angle formed by two rays, one in each side of the dihedral angle, that are perpendicular to the edge of the dihedral angle at the same point.

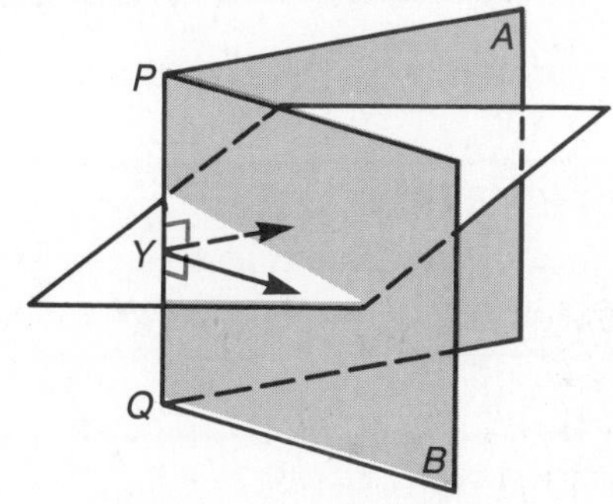

> **THEOREM 8.32**
> Any two plane angles of a given dihedral angle are congruent.

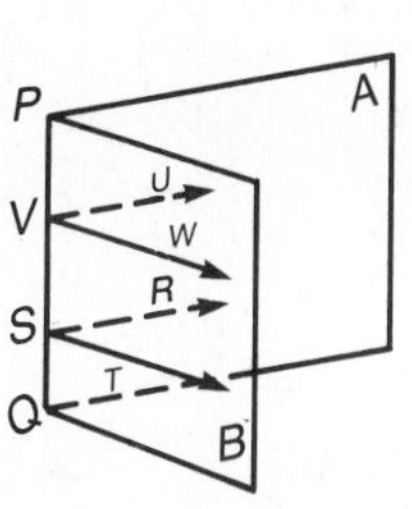

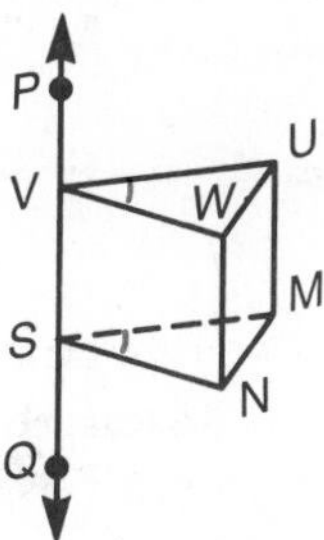

Given: Dihedral angle $\angle A\text{-}\overleftrightarrow{PQ}\text{-}B$, V and S are the vertices of plane $\angle UVW$ and $\angle RST$ in $\angle A\text{-}\overleftrightarrow{PQ}\text{-}B$.

Prove: $\angle UVW \cong \angle RST$

Proof: By the Point Plotting Theorem, points M and N can be chosen on the sides of $\angle RST$ such that $SM = VU$ and $SN = VW$. $\overline{VU}$ and $\overline{SM}$ are coplanar and perpendicular to $\overline{PQ}$; hence they are parallel by Theorem 8.2. By Theorem 8.20, quadrilateral $UVSM$ is a ▱, so that $UM = VS$ and $\overline{UM} \parallel \overline{VS}$. Similarly, $WN = VS$ and $\overline{WN} \parallel \overline{VS}$. Hence, $UM = WN$ and $\overline{UM} \parallel \overline{WN}$, following from Corollary 8.30.2. Therefore, quadrilateral $UMNW$ is a ▱, and $UW = MN$. It follows that $\triangle UVW = \triangle MSN$ by SSS (Theorem 4.5), and $\angle UVW \cong \angle RST$ (or $\angle MSN$) by correspondence.

Now you can define the **measure of a dihedral angle,** a **right dihedral angle,** and **perpendicular planes.**

DEFINITIONS: measure of a dihedral angle, right dihedral angle, and perpendicular planes
The **measure of a dihedral angle** is the real number that is the measure of any of its plane angles. A dihedral angle is a **right dihedral angle** if its plane angles are right angles. Two planes are **perpendicular** if they determine right dihedral angles.

Two corollaries are based on these definitions. The proofs are left as exercises.

COROLLARY 8.32.1
If a line is perpendicular to a plane, then any plane containing this line is perpendicular to the given plane.

COROLLARY 8.32.2
If two planes are perpendicular, then any line in one of them that is perpendicular to their line of intersection is perpendicular to the other plane.

ASSIGNMENT GUIDE

Minimum 1-13
Regular 1-22
Maximum 1-13 odd, 14-24

In the figure at the right, $\overleftrightarrow{AB}$ and plane F containing it are perpendicular to plane E. If E and F are perpendicular, then any line perpendicular to $\overleftrightarrow{PQ}$ in one plane is perpendicular to the other plane.

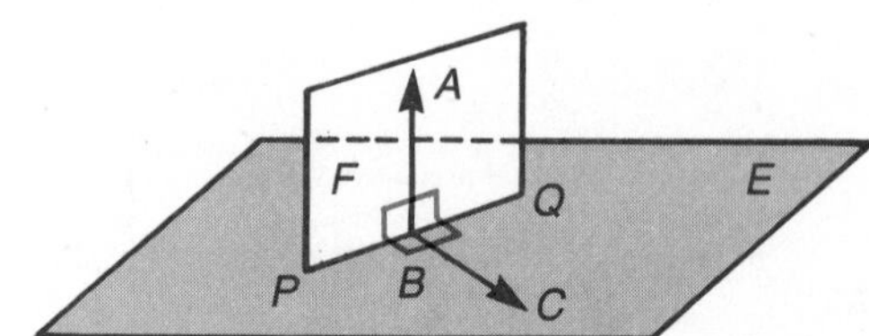

ORAL EXERCISES

1. A dihedral angle is named by two points on different sides and two points in _____.
2. How many dihedral angles are formed by the intersection of two planes? Three planes?
3. Name the four dihedral angles in the figure at the right.
4. Point W would be in a _____ of $\angle W\text{-}\overleftrightarrow{XY}\text{-}Z$.

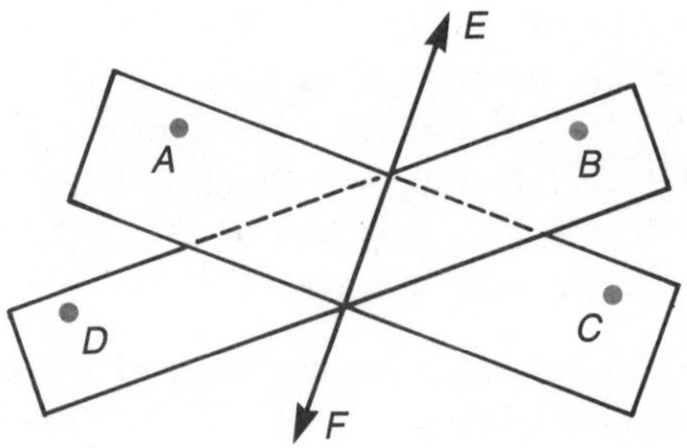

Oral Exercises

1. the edge
2. four; twelve
3. $\angle A\text{-}\overleftrightarrow{EF}\text{-}D$, $\angle A\text{-}\overleftrightarrow{EF}\text{-}B$, $\angle B\text{-}\overleftrightarrow{EF}\text{-}C$, $\angle C\text{-}\overleftrightarrow{EF}\text{-}D$
4. face or side

5. The edge of a dihedral angle is a ______.
6. The sum of the measures of two supplementary dihedral angles is ______.
7. The faces of a dihedral angle are ______ of intersecting planes.
8. If the measure of the plane angle of a dihedral angle is 50, the measure of the dihedral angle is ______.
9. The measure of the complement of a dihedral angle with measure of 65 is ______.
10. The measure of a right dihedral angle is ______.

5. line
6. 180
7. half-planes and edge
8. 50
9. 25
10. 90

WRITTEN EXERCISES

A. Identify the statements in Exercises 1–6 as <u>true</u> or <u>false</u>. Rewrite any false statements so they are true.

1. The sides of a plane angle of a dihedral angle are perpendicular to the edge of the dihedral angle.
2. A dihedral angle is obtuse if its angle is acute.
3. The edge of $\angle A\text{-}\overleftrightarrow{BC}\text{-}D$ is $\overleftrightarrow{AD}$.
4. A plane angle is found in a plane parallel to the edge of a dihedral angle.
5. Every dihedral angle has two edges.
6. Point P is contained in one face of $\angle P\text{-}\overleftrightarrow{QR}\text{-}S$.

B. In the figure at the right, $\overline{AP}$, $\overline{BP}$, and $\overline{CP}$ are each perpendicular to the others and $m\angle 1 = m\angle 2 = m\angle 3 = 45$.

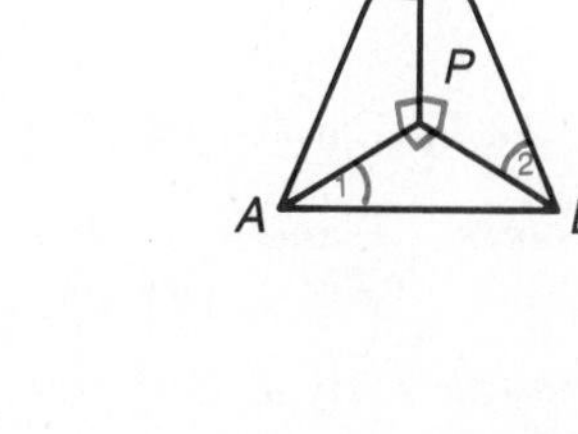

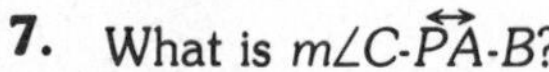
7. What is $m\angle C\text{-}\overleftrightarrow{PA}\text{-}B$?
8. What is $m\angle CAB$?

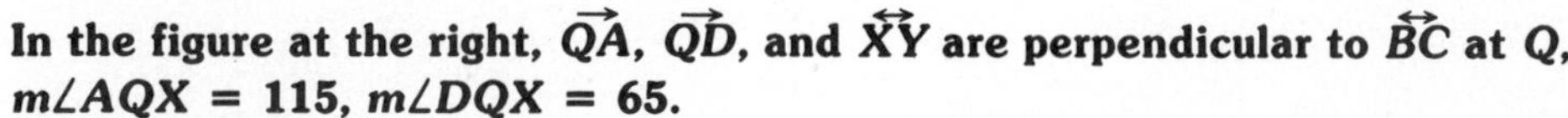
In the figure at the right, $\overrightarrow{QA}$, $\overrightarrow{QD}$, and $\overleftrightarrow{XY}$ are perpendicular to $\overleftrightarrow{BC}$ at Q, $m\angle AQX = 115$, $m\angle DQX = 65$.

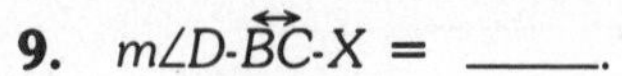
9. $m\angle D\text{-}\overleftrightarrow{BC}\text{-}X =$ ______.
10. $m\angle A\text{-}\overleftrightarrow{BC}\text{-}D =$ ______.
11. $m\angle A\text{-}\overleftrightarrow{BC}\text{-}Y =$ ______.
12. $m\angle Y\text{-}\overleftrightarrow{BC}\text{-}D =$ ______.
13. If $\overleftrightarrow{AC}$ is continued to some point R, such that C is a point on $\overleftrightarrow{AR}$, what will be $m\angle D\text{-}\overleftrightarrow{BC}\text{-}R$?

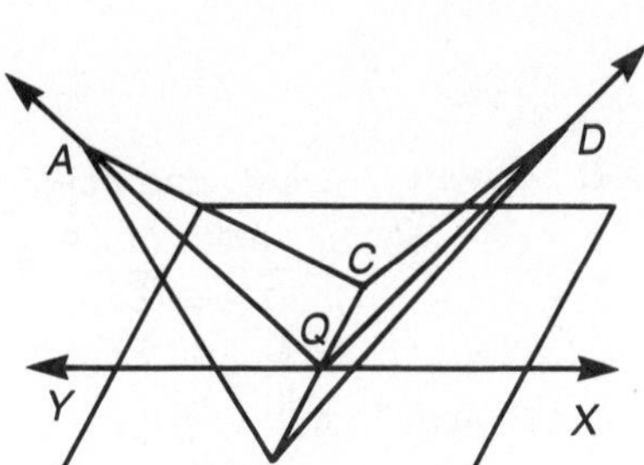
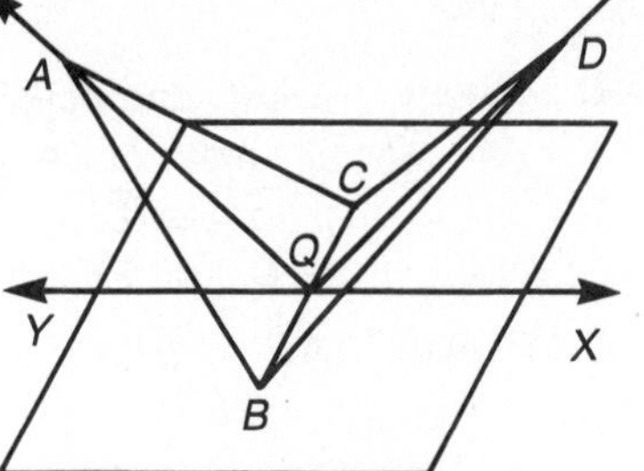

Written Exercises

1. T
2. F; is *acute* if
3. F; $\overleftrightarrow{BC}$
4. F; *perpendicular* to the edge
5. F; one edge, two sides or faces
6. T
7. 90
8. 60
9. 65
10. 50
11. 65
12. 115
13. 130

Refer to the figure at the right to complete the proofs for Corollaries 8.32.1 and 8.32.2.

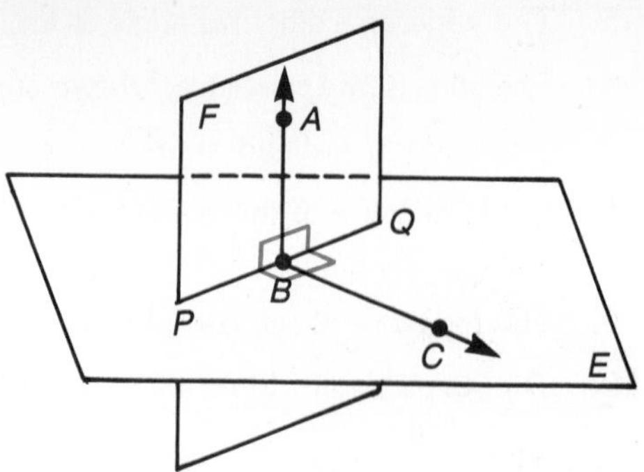

Proof for Corollary 8.32.1

Given: $\overleftrightarrow{AB} \perp$ plane E
Plane F contains $\overleftrightarrow{AB}$.

Prove: Plane $F \perp$ plane E

Proof:

STATEMENTS	REASONS
1. $\overleftrightarrow{AB} \perp E$; F contains $\overleftrightarrow{AB}$.	1. Given
2. Let $\overleftrightarrow{PQ}$ be the intersection of E and F.	2. 14.
3. $\overleftrightarrow{AB} \perp \overleftrightarrow{PQ}$	3. 15.
4. Take point C in E, such that $\overleftrightarrow{BC} \perp \overleftrightarrow{PQ}$.	4. 16.
5. $\overleftrightarrow{AB}$ and $\overleftrightarrow{BC}$ determine a plane $\perp$ to $\overleftrightarrow{PQ}$.	5. 17.
6. $\overleftrightarrow{AB} \perp$ plane E	6. 18.
7. $\overleftrightarrow{AB} \perp \overleftrightarrow{BC}$	7. 19.
8. $\angle ABC$ is a rt. plane $\angle$ of $\angle A\text{-}\overleftrightarrow{PQ}\text{-}C$.	8. Definition of $\perp$ and dihedral $\angle$
9. Every plane $\angle$ of $\angle A\text{-}\overleftrightarrow{PQ}\text{-}C$ is a rt. $\angle$.	9. 20.
10. $\angle A\text{-}\overleftrightarrow{PQ}\text{-}C$ is a rt. dihedral $\angle$.	10. 21.
11. $E \perp F$	11. 22.

14. Postulate 8
15. Def. of a line $\perp$ to a plane
16. Theorem 5.1
17. Theorem 7.3
18. Given
19. Def. of a line $\perp$ to a plane
20. Theorem 8.32
21. Def. of rt. dihedral $\angle$
22. Def. of $\perp$ planes

C. 23. Prove for Corollary 8.32.2.

Given: Plane $F \perp$ plane E, intersecting in $\overleftrightarrow{PQ}$
$\overleftrightarrow{AB} \perp \overleftrightarrow{PQ}$; $\overleftrightarrow{AB}$ lies in plane F.

Prove: $\overleftrightarrow{AB} \perp E$

23. $\overleftrightarrow{AB} \perp \overleftrightarrow{PQ}$, Given; take point C in E such that $\overleftrightarrow{BC} \perp \overleftrightarrow{PQ}$, Theorem 5.1; $\overleftrightarrow{AB} \perp E$ by last step and Theorem 7.3.

24. Given: $\angle ABC$ and $\angle DEF$ are plane angles of $\angle A\text{-}\overleftrightarrow{XY}\text{-}F$.
$\overline{AB} \cong \overline{DE}$
$\overline{BC} \cong \overline{EF}$

Prove: $\overline{AC} \cong \overline{DF}$

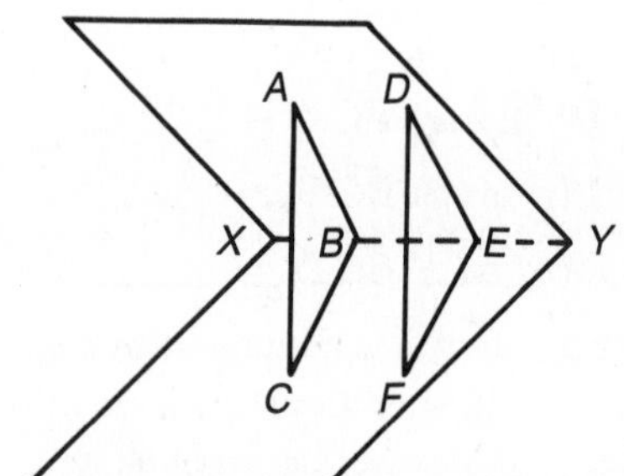

24. *1.* $\angle ABC \cong \angle DEF$ (Theorem 8.32); *2.* $\overline{AB} \cong \overline{DE}$ and $\overline{BC} \cong \overline{EF}$ (Given); *3.* $\triangle ABC \cong \triangle DEF$ (SAS); *4.* $\overline{AC} \cong \overline{DF}$ (CPCTC).

8.9 Projections

When you are outside on a sunny day, the sun's rays project an image of you in the form of a shadow. Depending on the position of the sun, the projection may be short or long. When the sun is directly overhead, your shadow is directly beneath your feet.

If you have taken a course in mechanical drawing, then you have worked with **projections** in the form of scale drawings or models. You know the importance of precise measurements and location of figures with respect to other figures.

In geometry, figures or parts of figures can also be projected.

DEFINITION: projection of a point
The **projection of a point** into a plane is the foot of the perpendicular from the point to the plane.

DEFINITION: projection of a line
The **projection of a line** into a plane is the set of points that are projections into the plane of the points of the line.

In the figure, A' is the projection of A, B' is the projection of B, and C' is the projection of C into E. It appears that the projection of $\overleftrightarrow{AC}$ is a line. In fact, it is, except when the line is perpendicular to the plane.

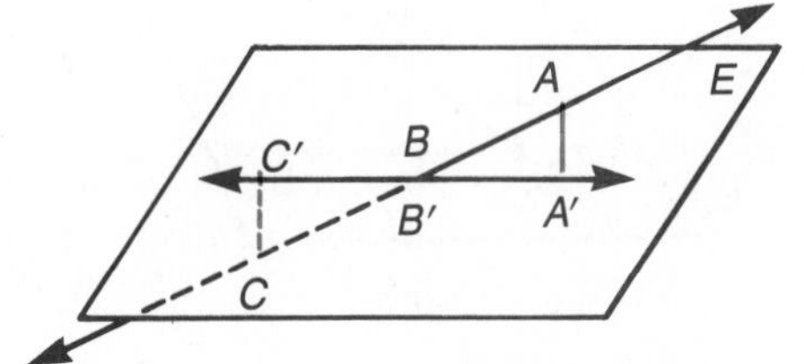

THEOREM 8.33
The projection of a line into a plane is a line, unless the line and the plane are perpendicular.

If l is the given line and E is the plane, then the proof of Theorem 8.33 must consider two possibilities: (1) l lies in E, and (2) l is external to E. In the first case, since each point of l already lies in the plane, l is its own projection in E.

OBJECTIVE

Identify projections onto a plane.

TEACHER'S NOTES

See p. T32

MIXED REVIEW

1. If a plane is perpendicular to two other planes, must the other planes be parallel? yes
2. What kind of parallelograms have congruent diagonals? rectangles
3. Can a quadrilateral have congruent and perpendicular diagonals and not be a square? yes; kite and trapezoid
4. Does every angle have a complement? no
5. Solve $x + y = 7$
   $3x + 7y = 13$
   (9, −2)

TEACHER'S RESOURCE MASTERS

Practice Master 25, Part 2
Quiz 16

The conclusions in Case 2 follow from proving that $\overleftrightarrow{RR'}$ and line k through S' (where $k \perp l'$) are both coplanar with $\overleftrightarrow{PP'}$.

The second case is somewhat more involved. By choosing any point P on l and finding its projection P' in E, you can determine a plane F that contains P, P', and l and that intersects plane E in a new line, l'. You must then prove that l' is the projection of l in E by showing: (a) the projection of any point R of l lies on l', and (b) for any point S' on l', S' is the projection of a point S of l.

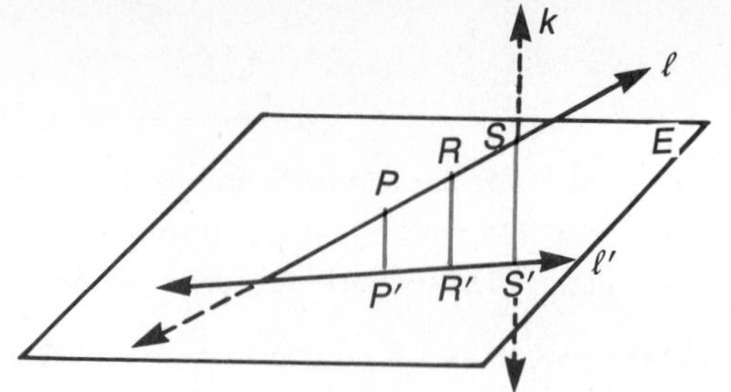

Having proven that the projection of a line is a line, you can now define *projection* more generally. For any set of points X, the projection of X into a plane E is the set of all points that are projections of points of X into E. As Theorem 8.33 suggests, a projection is not always congruent to the figure being projected. A sketch will convince you that the projection of a line is a single point if the line is perpendicular to the plane of projection. Likewise, as shown in the figure below, the projection of a triangle is usually a triangle. But if the triangle and plane are perpendicular, the projection will be a segment.

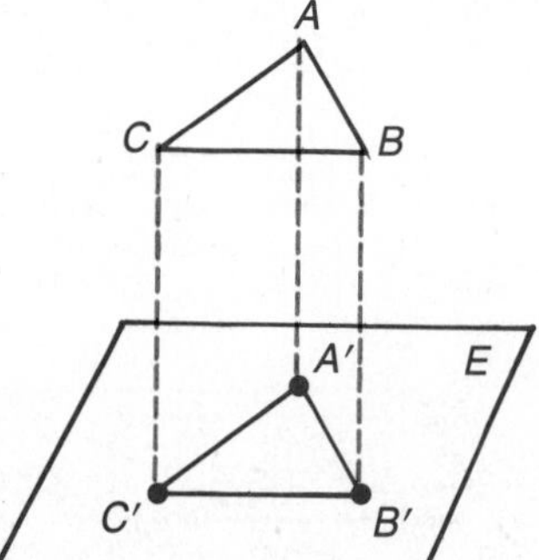

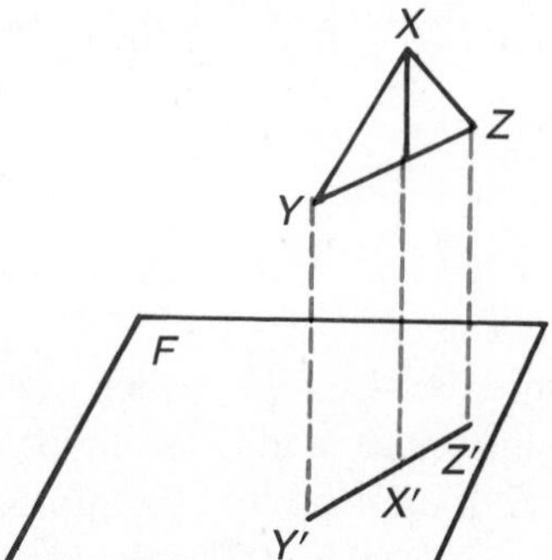

ASSIGNMENT GUIDE

Minimum 1-12
Regular 1-15
Maximum 1-16, 18-20

Oral Exercises

1. yes
2. no
3. no
4. yes, yes, yes
5. no
6. yes
7. no

ORAL EXERCISES

1. Is the projection of a point always a point?

2. Is the projection of a segment always a segment?

3. Can the projection of a segment be longer than the segment?

4. Can the projection of an angle be a ray? a line? an angle?

5. If two segments are congruent, will their projections always be congruent?

6. If two lines intersect, can their projections be a line?

7. If two lines intersect, can their projections be a single point?

WRITTEN EXERCISES

A. Tell whether a rectangle that measures 3 × 5 units can be positioned so that its projection is the figure named. A rectangular piece of cardboard held beneath a bright light may help you visualize all the possibilities.

1. a point **2.** a segment **3.** a line

4. a triangle **5.** a rhombus **6.** a circle

7. a 3 × 3 square **8.** a 4 × 4 square **9.** a 1 × 5 rectangle

10. a 3 × 6 rectangle **11.** a trapezoid **12.** a ray

B. 13. F', G', H', and I' are the projections of F, G, H, and I into plane E. If $FG = GH = HI$, what is the relationship between $\overline{F'G'}$, $\overline{G'H'}$, and $\overline{H'I'}$? Justify your answer.

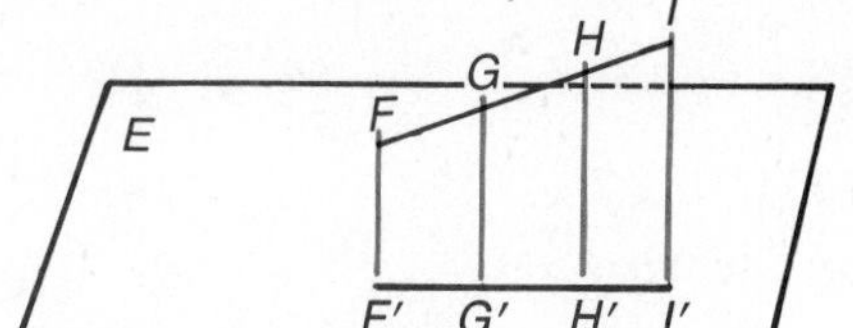

$\angle P\text{-}\overleftrightarrow{AB}\text{-}Q$ is an acute dihedral angle. Face AQB contains equilateral $\triangle ACB$.

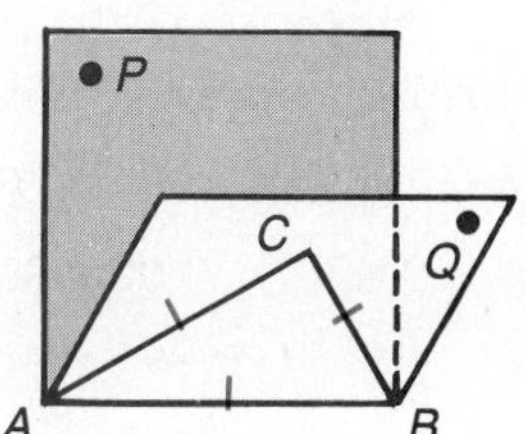

14. What type of figure is the projection of $\triangle ACB$ into face ABP?

15. What figure would result from the same projection if $\angle P\text{-}\overleftrightarrow{AB}\text{-}Q$ were a right dihedral angle?

16. Given parallel planes M and N, with ▱$ABCD$ in M, prove that the projection ▱$A'B'C'D'$ into N is congruent to ▱$ABCD$.

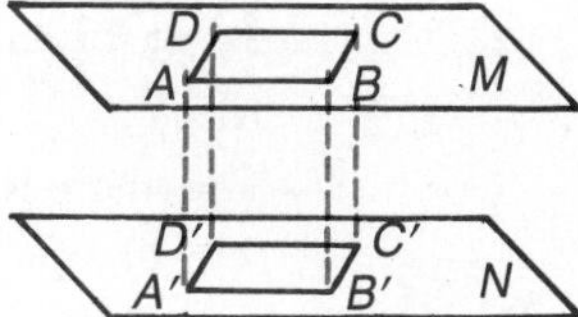

C. 17. Given: $\overrightarrow{AX}$ in plane P; $\angle XAZ$ is a right $\angle$; Y is the projection of Z into P.

Prove: $\angle XAY$ is a right $\angle$.
(HINT: Draw $\overrightarrow{AW} \perp P$ at A.)

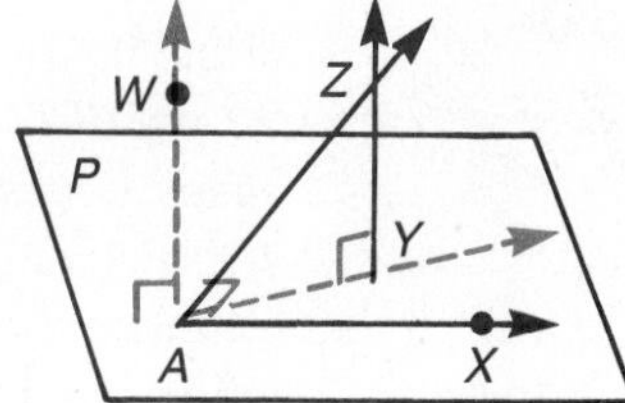

Describe all the possible projections in a plane of each figure named.

18. three points **19.** two parallel lines **20.** a right angle

Written Exercises

1. no 2. yes 3. no 4. no
5. yes 6. no 7. yes 8. no
9. yes 10. no 11. yes 12. no
13. The segments are congruent, by Theorem 8.26.
14. isosceles △
15. $\overline{AB}$
16. Prove that ▱ $BCC'B'$ is a rectangle. Then $B'C' = BC = AD$. Reapply to the other three rectangles formed by the perpendiculars from M and N. By transitivity, $A'D' = AD = BC = B'C'$ and $A'B' = AB = DC = D'C'$. Corresponding angles are congruent by Theorem 8.32.
17. Draw $\overrightarrow{AW} \perp P$ at A (Thm. 7.10), so $\overrightarrow{AX} \perp \overrightarrow{AW}$; $\overrightarrow{AX} \perp \overrightarrow{AZ}$ (Def. of rt. $\angle$); $\overrightarrow{AX} \perp$ the plane determined by A, W, and Z (Theorem 7.3); $\overrightarrow{AW}$ and $\overrightarrow{ZY}$ are coplanar (Theorem 7.8); the plane determined by A, W, Z, and Y is the plane $\perp$ to $\overrightarrow{AX}$ at A (Theorem 7.9); $\overrightarrow{AX} \perp \overrightarrow{AY}$ (Def. of line $\perp$ to a plane).
18. one, two, or three points
19. two points, two lines, one line
20. a ray, a line, a right angle, an acute angle, an obtuse angle

Skills Maintenance

1. a^{xy} 2. a^{x-y}
3. a^{xy} 4. $a^x b^x$
5. x^{-3} 6. x^6
7. x^{-2} 8. $-2x^8$
9. 2^{-5} 10. $(-3)^4$ or 81
11. $\frac{3^2}{5^2}$ or $\frac{9}{25}$ 12. 23
13. $\frac{1}{(-13)^3}$ 14. $\frac{9}{4}$
15. $-\frac{1}{81}$ 16. $\frac{1}{81}$
17. $\frac{x^3}{7^3}$ or $(\frac{x}{7})^3$ 18. $\frac{5^4}{x^9y^4}$
19. $\frac{2^2x}{y^3}$ 20. $\frac{x^3}{7^3}$
21. $\frac{12s^{13}}{x^3}$ 22. $\frac{k^2}{n^2p^2}$
23. $\frac{xy^3}{3^5}$ 24. $\frac{x^3}{y^5}$
25. $\frac{b^2d}{a^2c^5}$
26. 1.24×10^{14}
27. 1.23×10^{-10}
28. 6.3×10^{-10}
29. 1.61×10^{17}

Exploration

65°

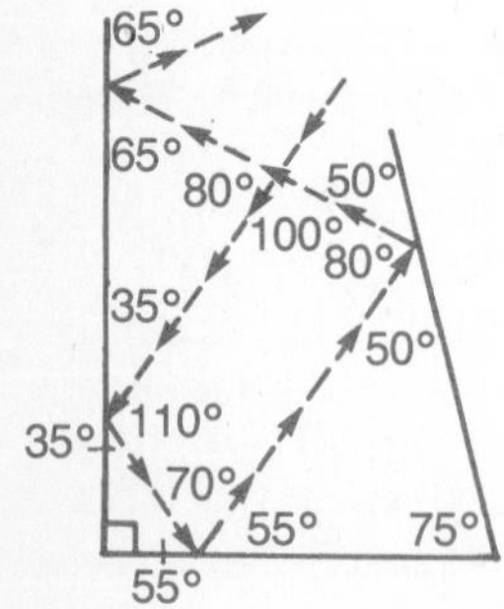

SKILLS MAINTENANCE

Write the following expressions in simplest exponential form.

1. $a^x \cdot a^y$ **2.** $\frac{a^x}{a^y}$ **3.** $(a^x)^y$ **4.** $(ab)^x$

5. $\frac{x^2}{x^5}$ **6.** $(x^2)^3$ **7.** $x^3 \cdot x^{-5}$ **8.** $-2(x^2)^4$

9. $\frac{1}{2^5}$ **10.** $\frac{1}{(-3)^{-4}}$ **11.** $\frac{1}{(\frac{-3}{5})^{-2}}$ **12.** $\frac{23}{(\frac{17}{3})^0}$

Write the simplest fractional expression without using negative exponents.

13. $(-13)^{-3}$ **14.** $(\frac{-2}{3})^{-2}$ **15.** -9^{-2} **16.** $(-9)^{-2}$

17. $7^{-9}x^6 7^6 x^{-3}$ **18.** $5^{-3}x^{-7}y^{-12}5^7x^{-2}y^8$ **19.** $(2^3x^2y) \div (2xy^4)$

20. $7^{-9}x^6 7^6 x^{-3}$ **21.** $12s^7x^{-5}x^2s^6$ **22.** $(k^{-3}n^{-4}p^{-5}) \div (k^{-5}p^{-3}n^{-2})$

23. $\frac{(x^2y^3)}{(3^5x)}$ **24.** $\frac{(x^5y^4)}{(x^2y^9)}$ **25.** $\frac{(a^{-4}b^{-2}c^{-1})}{(a^{-2}b^{-4}c^4d^{-1})}$

Write in scientific notation.

26. 124,000,000,000,000 **27.** 0.000000000123

28. 0.0007 · 0.0000009 **29.** 23,000,000,000 · 7,000,000

EXPLORATION/Angles of Reflection

The angle formed by the surface of the mirror and the incoming rays of light is always congruent to the angle formed by the mirror and the reflected rays. That is, *the angle of incidence is equal to the angle of reflection.*

In the figure at the right, $m\angle ABC = 90$, $m\angle BCD = 75$, and the incoming beam of light makes an angle of 35° with $\overrightarrow{RA}$. Copy the figure and complete the beam's path as it reflects from $\overline{AB}$, from $\overline{BC}$, from $\overline{DC}$, and from $\overline{AB}$ again. At what angle does the beam reflect from $\overline{AB}$ the second time?

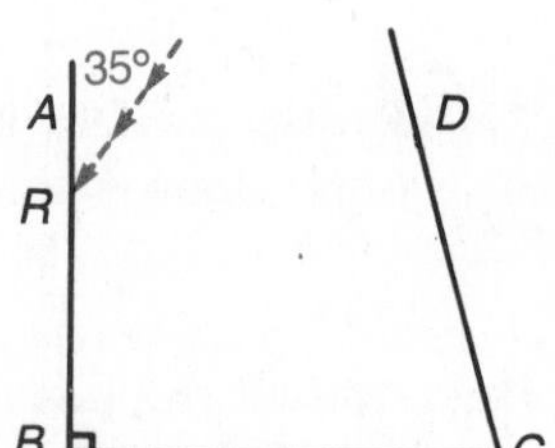

MATH HERITAGE/Non-Euclidian Geometry

Over 150 years ago in Russia, Nikolai Lobachevsky published his revolutionary discovery of non-Euclidean geometry. It is remarkable that when the time for a new idea is ripe, it sometimes occurs to several people simultaneously. So it was when Janos Bolyai of Hungary published his discovery of non-Euclidean geometry at the same time as Lobachevsky.

Nikolai Lobachevsky

Karl Gauss, often considered the founder of modern mathematics, had developed similar theories in Germany but did not publicize his discoveries because he felt they might be ridiculed. Until that time, no one had challenged Euclid's Parallel Postulate. *(Through a point P not on line l, there is exactly one line parallel to l.)* Lobachevsky, Boylai, and Guass recognized, however, that this postulate cannot be proved from Euclid's other postulates.

They proposed, therefore, to replace the Parallel Postulate with another postulate: *For any line l and any point P not on l, there is more than one line that contains P and is parallel to l.* Remembering that the terms *point, line,* and *plane* are undefined in geometry and that *parallel* means nonintersecting, you can use any model that satisfies the conditions of the postulate. The figure at the right illustrates one possibility.

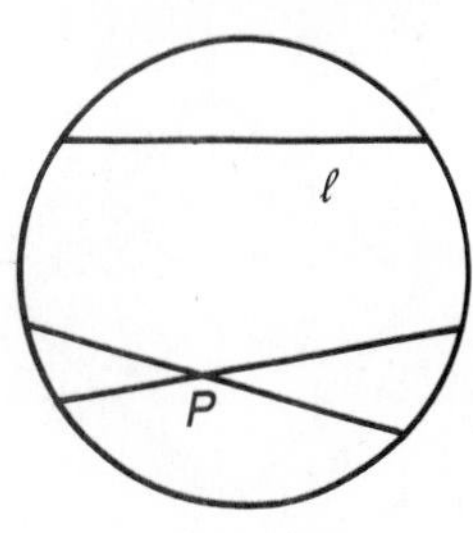

Not many years later, Bernhard Riemann of Germany formulated a non-Euclidean geometry using another version of the Parallel Postulate: *For any line l and any point P not on l, there is no line that contains P and is parallel to l.* A model frequently used to described Riemannian geometry is the globe, with the equator being the line *l*. (In this case a line means a great circle around the globe.) The point *P* is the north pole, so there is no "line" through the north pole that does not intersect the equator. Riemann's discoveries were important not only for mathematics but for astronomy and navigation as well. The non-Euclidean geometries would later, in the twentieth century, provide a foundation for Einstein's theory of relativity.

TEACHER'S RESOURCE MASTERS

Computer Master 8

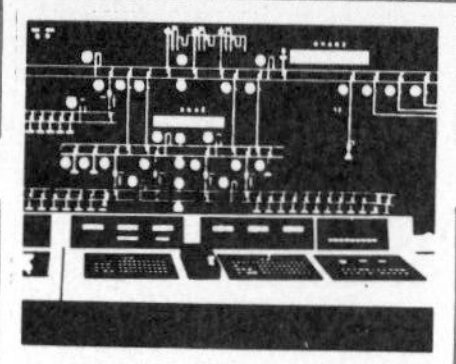

COMPUTER

A computer program for three-dimensional graphics assembles a picture from planes, clusters, and objects. Clusters are groups of planes that the program can draw at the same time and that always appear together. Objects are made up of two or more clusters. For example, only three planes of an object like a solid cube can be seen from one viewpoint as shown at the right. The three planes *A*, *B*, and *C*, which can be seen, form cluster 1. Planes *D*, *E*, and *F* form cluster 2, which lies behind cluster 1.

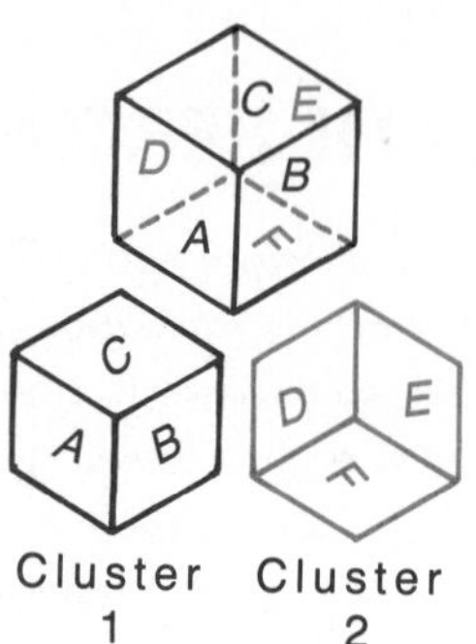

A graphics program first determines if each plane is visible, using perpendicular and parallel lines.

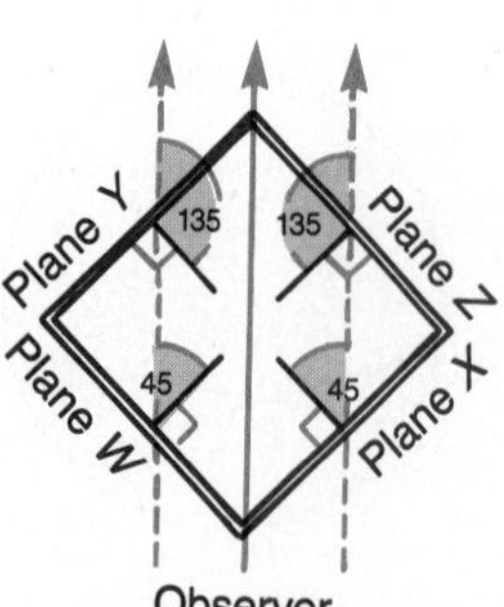

Example: At the left is a four-sided box, formed by planes *W*, *X*, *Y*, and *Z*. The computer finds the angle between a line parallel with your line of sight and a perpendicular to the line of the plane by viewing the plane "on edge." The angles formed on the planes you can see are acute. If a plane is not visible, the angles are obtuse. Next, the computer determines which elements seem to overlap from the observers viewpoint and then prints each one in sequence.

Example: The two cubes at the right both have two clusters of three planes each. Planes *A*, *B*, and *C* are cluster 1; *D*, *E*, and *F* are cluster 2; *T*, *U*, and *V* are cluster 3; and *W*, *X*, and *Y* are cluster 4. Covering cluster 4 with 3, adding 2, and covering it with 1 makes cube *ABCDEF* appear to be above and behind cube *TUVWXY*.

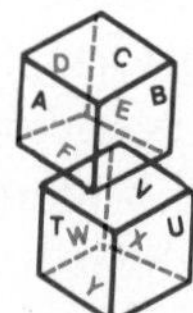

CHAPTER 8 REVIEW

VOCABULARY

adjacent dihedral angles (8.8)
alternate interior angles (8.1)
bases of a trapezoid (8.5)
complementary dihedral angles (8.8)
consecutive sides and angles of a quadrilateral (8.5)
corresponding angles (8.2)
diagonal of a quadrilateral (8.5)
dihedral angle (8.8)
edge of a dihedral angle (8.8)
exterior of a dihedral angle (8.8)
face of a dihedral angle (8.8)
intercept (8.6)
interior of a dihedral angle (8.8)
measure of a dihedral angle (8.8)
opposite sides and angles of a quadrilateral (8.5)
parallel lines (8.1, 8.7)
parallelogram (8.5)
parallel planes in space (8.7)
perpendicular planes (8.8)
plane angle (8.8)
projection of a line (8.9)
projection of a point (8.9)
rectangle (8.6)
rhombus (8.6)
right dihedral angle (8.8)
skew lines (8.1)
square (8.6)
supplementary dihedral angles (8.8)
transversal (8.1)
trapezoid (8.5)
vertical dihedral angles (8.8)

REVIEW EXERCISES

8.1 **1. Given:** $\overline{AB}$ and $\overline{CD}$ bisect each other at O.
Prove: $\overline{AC} \parallel \overline{BD}$

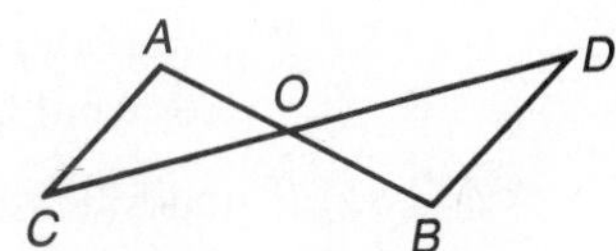

8.2 **Find the angle measure that makes $l \parallel n$.**

2. $m\angle 1 = 46$, $m\angle 5 =$ _____

3. $m\angle 2 = 120$, $m\angle 6 =$ _____

4. $m\angle 3 = 145$, $m\angle 8 =$ _____

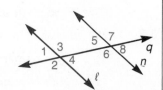

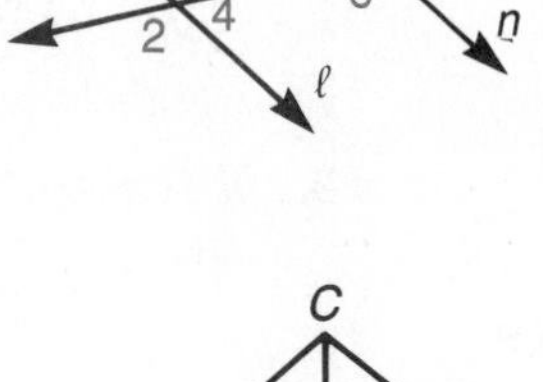

8.3 **5. Given:** $\overline{AD} \cong \overline{BD}$, $\overline{CE} \perp \overline{AB}$, $\overline{EB} \parallel \overline{AC}$
Prove: $\overline{CD} \cong \overline{ED}$

TEACHER'S RESOURCE MASTERS

Enrichment Master 5

ENRICHMENT

See activities 15–16, p. T48

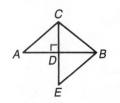

Chapter 8 Review

1. $\triangle AOC \cong \triangle BOD$ by SAS; $\angle ACO \cong \angle BDO$ by CPCTC; $\overline{AC} \parallel \overline{BD}$ by Theorem 8.5.
2. 46
3. 120
4. 35
5. *1.* $\angle CDA$ is a rt. $\angle$ (Def. of $\perp$); *2.* $\angle EDB$ is also a rt. $\angle$ (Thm. 3.8); *3.* $\angle CDA \cong \angle EDB$ (All rt. $\angle$s are $\cong$.); *4.* $\angle CAD \cong \angle EBD$ (Thm. 8.8); *5.* $\triangle CDA \cong \triangle EDB$ (ASA); *6.* $\overline{CD} \cong \overline{ED}$ (CPCTC).

6. $x = 38$
7. 64
8. $\overline{BC}$
9. $\overline{DC}$
10. $\overline{DP}$
11. 8
12. 40
13. 60
14. 90
15. two
16. perpendicular
17. transitive, reflexive
18. parallel
19. plane
20. 90
21. point
22. perpendicular

6. In the figure, $\overleftrightarrow{AB} \parallel \overleftrightarrow{EF}$, $m\angle BCD = 2x + 10$, and $m\angle FDC = 3x - 20$. Find the value of x.

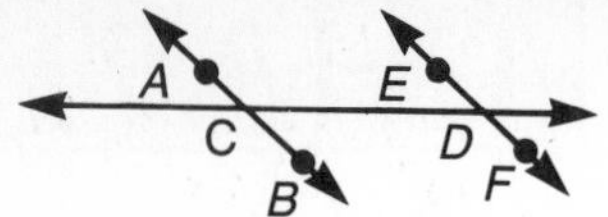

8.4 **7.** In the figure, $\overleftrightarrow{AB} \parallel \overleftrightarrow{CD}$, $\overline{AE} \perp \overline{CB}$, and $m\angle BCD = 26$. Find $m\angle BAE$.

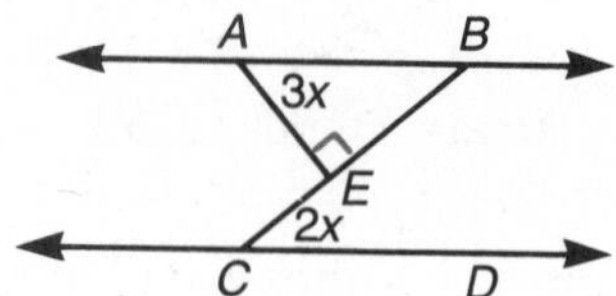

8.5 **Given ▱$ABCD$ with diagonals $\overline{AC}$ and $\overline{BD}$, complete each statement.**

8. $\overline{AB} \parallel \overline{DC}$ and $\overline{AD} \parallel$ _____.

9. $\overline{AB} \cong$ _____ and $\overline{AC} \cong \overline{BC}$.

10. _____ $\cong \overline{BP}$ and $\overline{AP} \cong \overline{CP}$.

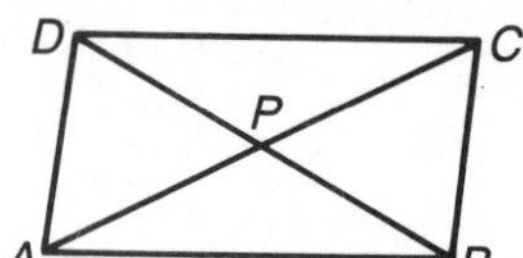

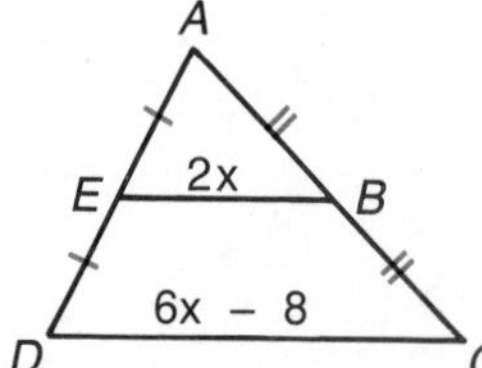

11. Given $\triangle ADC$ as marked in the figure, find EB.

8.6 **12.** If quadrilateral $MKWR$ is a parallelogram, $m\angle 1 = 30$, and $m\angle WKM = 110$, what is $m\angle 4$?

13. If quadrilateral $MKWR$ is a rectangle with $m\angle 1 = 30$, what is $m\angle 3$?

14. If quadrilateral $MKWR$ is a rhombus with $m\angle 1 = 30$, what is $m\angle 2$?

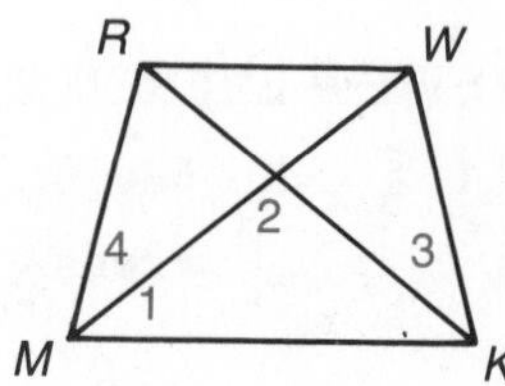

Complete each statement with the correct word or number.

8.7 **15.** A plane intersects two parallel planes in _____ parallel lines.

16. A line perpendicular to one of two parallel planes is _____ to the other.

17. Parallelism among planes is symmetric and _____, but not _____.

18. If two lines are perpendicular to the same plane, they are _____ to each other.

8.8 **19.** All _____ angles of a given dihedral angle are congruent.

20. The measure of a right dihedral angle is _____.

8.9 **21.** The projection of a point into a plane is a(n) _____.

22. The projection of a line into a plane is a line unless the two are _____.

CHAPTER 8 TEST

Refer to the top figure for Exercises 1–2.

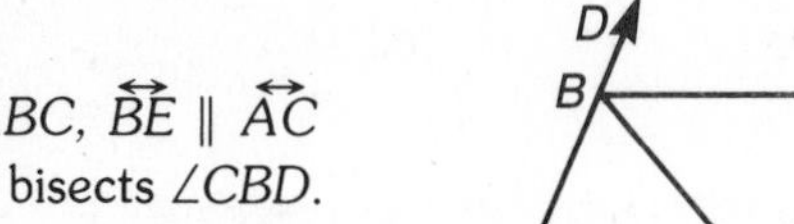

1. Given: $m\angle 1 = m\angle 3$
$m\angle 2 = m\angle 4$

Prove: $l_1 \parallel l_2$

2. Given: $m\angle 4 = 60$
$m\angle 5 = 120$

Prove: $l_1 \parallel l_2$

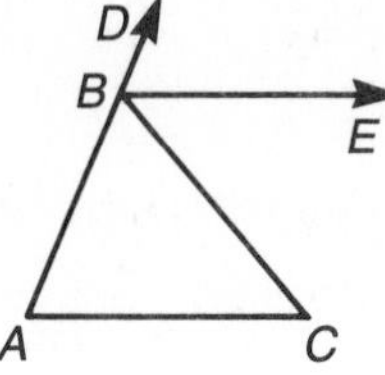

3. Given: $\triangle ABC$, $\overleftrightarrow{BE} \parallel \overleftrightarrow{AC}$
$\overrightarrow{BE}$ bisects $\angle CBD$.

Prove: $\triangle ABC$ is isosceles.

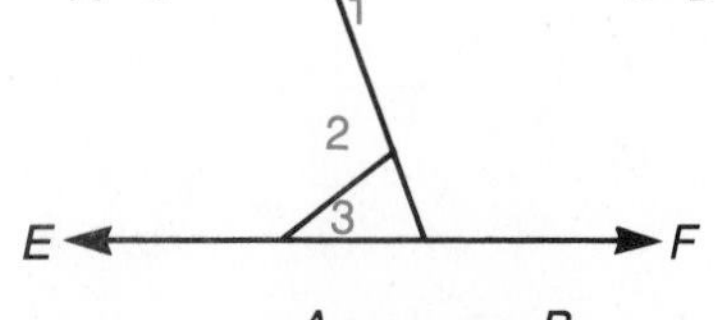

4. $\overleftrightarrow{AB} \parallel \overleftrightarrow{EF}$, $m\angle 1 = 70$, and $m\angle 2 = 105$. Find $m\angle 3$.

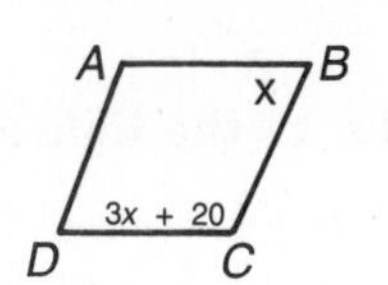

5. Given $\square ABCD$ with $m\angle B = x$ and $m\angle C = 3x + 20$, find $m\angle D$.

Indicate whether each statement is <u>true</u> or <u>false</u>. ("True" means true in every case.)

6. A rhombus is a square.

7. A quadrilateral with two right angles is a rectangle.

8. The diagonals of a rhombus are perpendicular.

9. Two planes perpendicular to the same line are parallel.

10. In space, two parallel lines are perpendicular to the same planes.

11. A dihedral angle is named by its edge and a face.

12. Any two plane angles of a dihedral angle are congruent.

13. Alternate interior dihedral angles formed by the intersection of three planes are congruent.

14. The projection of a square may be a point.

15. The projection of a line into a plane is a line.

Chapter 8 Test

1. $m\angle 3 = m\angle 4$ (Vert. $\angle$s are $\cong$); $m\angle 1 = m\angle 2$ (Substitution); $\angle 1 \cong \angle 2$ (Def. of $\cong$ $\angle$s); $l_1 \parallel l_2$ (Theorem 8.5).

2. If $m\angle 5 = 120$, then $m\angle 6 = 60$ (Def. of supp. $\angle$s); then $\angle 4 \cong \angle 6$ (Def. of $\cong$ $\angle$s); $l_1 \parallel l_2$ (Theorem 8.7)

3. If $\overline{BE} \parallel \overline{AC}$, then $\angle DBE \cong \angle BAC$ (Theorem 8.9) and $\angle EBC \cong \angle ACB$ (Theorem 8.8). But $\angle DBE \cong \angle EBC$ (Def. of bisect), so $\angle BAC \cong \angle ACB$. By Theorem 4.4, $\triangle ABC$ is isosceles.

4. $m\angle 3 = 35$
5. $m\angle D = 40$
6. F
7. F
8. T
9. T
10. T
11. F
12. T
13. F
14. F
15. F

TEACHER'S RESOURCE MASTERS

Chapter 8 Test
Multiple Choice Test—Chapter 8

TEACHER'S RESOURCE MASTERS

Cumulative Test—Chapters 1-8 Form A or B

Cumulative Review Chapters 1-8

1. a
2. b
3. c
4. b
5. a
6. d
7. c
8. d
9. b
10. c

CUMULATIVE REVIEW: CHAPTERS 1–8

1. Which sentence is true about the figure?

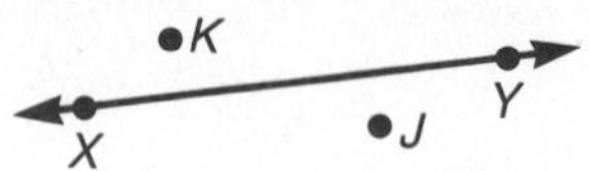

a. $\overline{KJ}$ intersects $\overline{XY}$. **b.** K lies on $\overline{XY}$.
c. $\overline{KY}$ contains J. **d.** Y lies on $\overline{XJ}$.

2. Which property of real numbers states that $(9x + 12) - 7 = 9x + (12 - 7)$?
a. commutative **b.** associative **c.** distributive **d.** subtraction

3. Supply the missing symbols: If $x < 9$, then $x + 5$ ● 14.
a. $>$ **b.** $=$ **c.** $<$ **d.** $\leq$

Use the coordinate system at the right for Exercises 4–5.

4. The distance from B to E in the coordinate system at the right is _____.

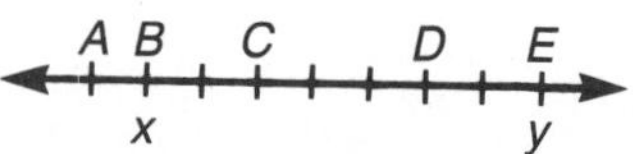

a. $|y + x|$ **b.** $|y - x|$
c. $|y| + |x|$ **d.** $|y| - |x|$

5. Which of the following are congruent segments?
a. $\overline{AC}$ and $\overline{CD}$ **b.** $\overline{BC}$ and $\overline{CD}$ **c.** $\overline{AC}$ and $\overline{DE}$ **d.** $\overline{AD}$ and $\overline{AE}$

Refer to the figure at the right for Exercises 6–7.

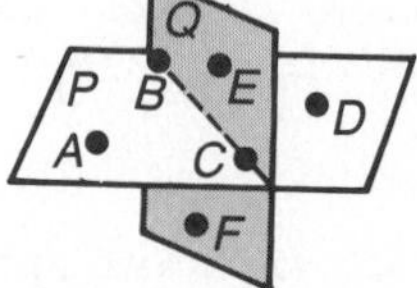

6. The intersection of $\overleftrightarrow{EF}$ and plane P is a point _____.
a. coplanar with $\overleftrightarrow{BC}$ **b.** coplanar with $\overleftrightarrow{AD}$
c. coplanar with $\overleftrightarrow{AB}$ **d.** all of these

7. Which points are on opposite sides of plane Q?
a. A, B **b.** A, C **c.** A, D **d.** B, C

8. If $\angle F \cong \angle G$, $m\angle F = 29 - 4x$, and $m\angle G = 17x - 34$, then $x =$ _____.
a. 6 **b.** $\frac{5}{13}$ **c.** $4\frac{11}{13}$ **d.** 3

Refer to the figure at the right for Exercises 9–10.

9. Two supplementary angles are ___.
a. $\angle AGB, \angle BGC$ **b.** $\angle AGC, \angle CGD$
c. $\angle BGD, \angle AGF$ **d.** $\angle AGF, \angle FGE$

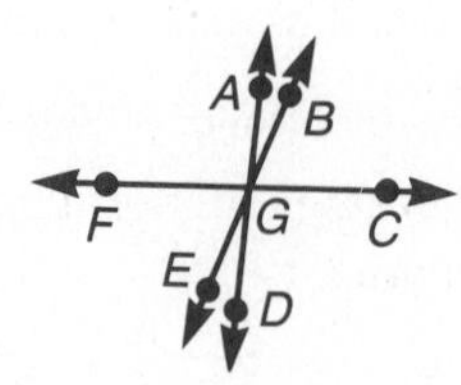

10. If $\overleftrightarrow{AD} \perp \overleftrightarrow{FC}$, and $\angle AGB \cong \angle DGE$, then _____.
a. $\angle BGC \cong \angle FGE$ **b.** $\angle CGD \cong \angle BGA$
c. $\angle FGE \cong \angle CGD$ **d.** $\angle BGC \cong \angle FGD$

11. If the triangles at the right are congruent, which correspondences are true? 11. a

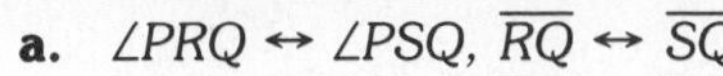

a. $\angle PRQ \leftrightarrow \angle PSQ$, $\overline{RQ} \leftrightarrow \overline{SQ}$
b. $\angle RQP \leftrightarrow \angle QSP$, $\overline{PR} \leftrightarrow \overline{PS}$
c. $\angle RPQ \leftrightarrow \angle PSQ$, $\overline{PQ} \leftrightarrow \overline{PQ}$
d. $\angle RQP \leftrightarrow \angle SQP$, $\overline{RQ} \leftrightarrow \overline{PS}$

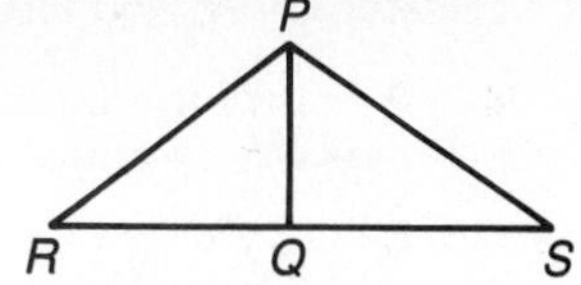

12. Which of the following is true in the figure above? 12. d

a. $\angle PQR \cong \angle PQS$
b. $\angle PQR$ and $\angle PQS$ form a linear pair.
c. $\angle PQR$ and $\angle PQS$ are supplementary.
d. all of the above

Refer to the figure at the right for Exercises 13–15.

13. If $\triangle ABC \cong \triangle EBG$ and D and H are midpoints of $\overline{AC}$ and $\overline{EG}$, then ____. 13. b

a. $\angle ABD \cong \angle DBC$
b. $\overline{BD} \cong \overline{BH}$
c. $\overline{DC} \cong \overline{BH}$
d. $\overline{BD} \cong \overline{BG}$

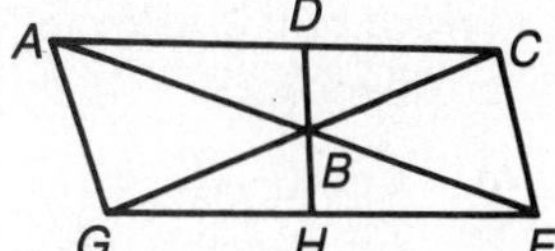

14. How would you prove $\triangle ABD \cong \triangle EBH$ given B is the midpoint of $\overline{AE}$ and $\overline{DH}$? 14. b

a. ASA b. SAS c. SSS d. LL

15. How would you prove $\triangle AGE \cong \triangle ECA$ given $\angle EAG \cong \angle AEC$ and $\angle GEA \cong \angle CAE$? 15. a

a. ASA b. SAS c. SSS d. LL

16. In $\triangle FGH$, $\overline{FG} \cong \overline{FH}$. Which of the following is true? 16. d

a. $\angle G \cong \angle F$ b. $\overline{FG} \cong \overline{GH}$ c. $\angle H \cong \angle F$ d. $\angle G \cong \angle H$

17. In the figure at the right, how would you prove that the two triangles are congruent? 17. c

a. ASA
b. SAS
c. SSS
d. LL

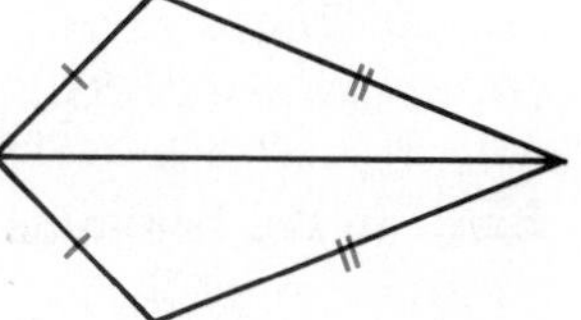

18. Using the congruences shown, what can you prove about quadrilateral $ABCD$? 18. d

a. $\angle A \cong \angle C$
b. All four sides are congruent.
c. All four vertex angles are congruent.
d. all of the above

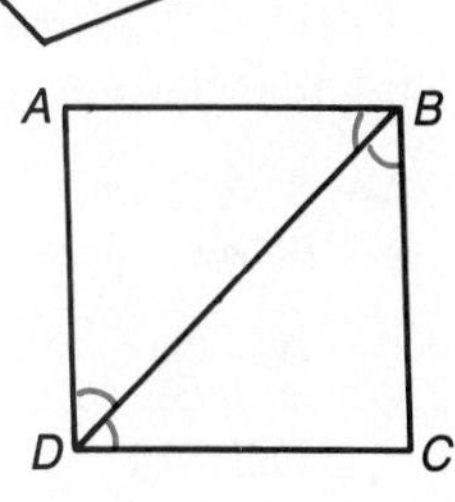

19. State the inverse of "If it is a weekday, then I go to school." 19. c

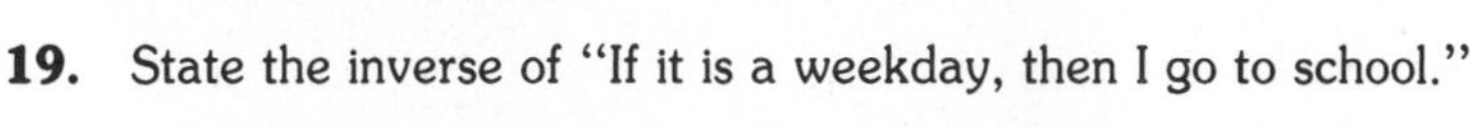

a. If I go to school, then it is a weekday.
b. If it is not a weekday, then I go to school.
c. If it is not a weekday, then I do not go to school.
d. If I do not go to school, then it is not a weekday.

20. a **20.** In the figure at the right, to prove $\overleftrightarrow{LP}$ is the $\perp$ bisector of $\overline{JK}$, you would show that _____.

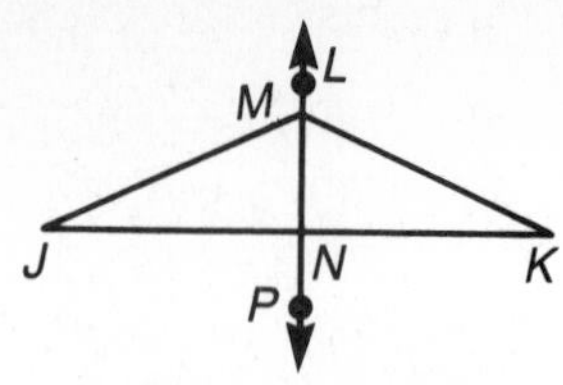

a. N and M are equidistant from J and K
b. $\angle JMN \cong \angle KMN$
c. $\overline{LP} \perp \overline{JK}$
d. $\overline{JP} \cong \overline{MK}$

21. b **21.** To prove Exercise 20 indirectly, you would assume _____.

a. $JM \ncong KM$ and $\angle JLN \ncong \angle KMN$ **b.** $\overleftrightarrow{LP}$ is not the $\perp$ bisector of $\overline{JK}$.
c. $\overline{JK}$ is not the $\perp$ bisector of $\overleftrightarrow{LP}$ **d.** $\overline{JK}$ is the $\perp$ bisector of $\overleftrightarrow{LP}$.

22. d **22.** Which of the following is an acceptable auxiliary set?

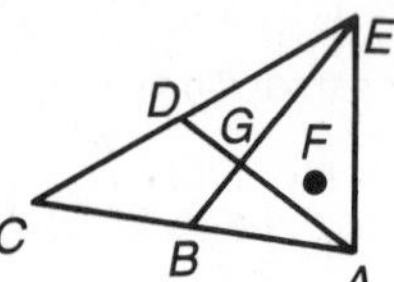

a. $\overleftrightarrow{CF} \perp \overline{AE}$ **c.** $\overleftrightarrow{CF}$ intersects $\overleftrightarrow{BE}$ at G.
b. $\overleftrightarrow{EF}$ bisects $\angle AEG$. **d.** $\overleftrightarrow{CF}$ intersects $\overleftrightarrow{BE}$ at J.

23. b **23.** Which expression best illustrates the relationship between $>$ and $<$?

a. If $a > b$, and $b > c$, then $a > c$ **b.** If $a < b$, then $b > a$
c. $a < b$, $a = b$, or $a > b$ **d.** $a + c > b + c$

24. d **24.** Which of the following are exterior angles of $\triangle HJE$?

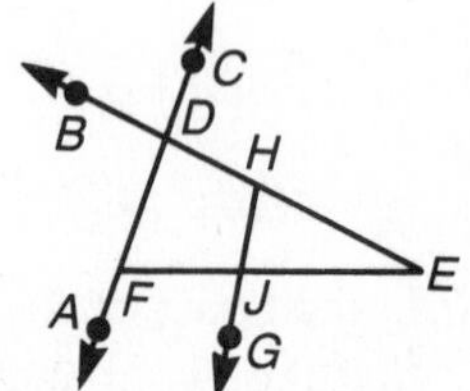

a. $\angle BDF$ and $\angle BDC$

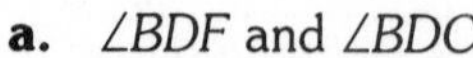

b. $\angle BDF$ and $\angle DHG$
c. $\angle DHJ$ and $\angle JFA$
d. $\angle HJF$ and $\angle EJG$

Refer to the triangles at the right for Exercises 25–27.

25. c **25.** If $\angle F \cong \angle J$, $\angle L \cong \angle H$, and $\overline{JK} \cong \overline{FG}$, then the triangles are congruent by _____.

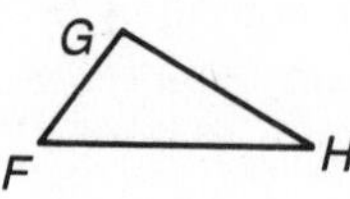

a. ASA **b.** SAS
c. SAA **d.** HL

26. a **26.** Which of the following could not be the sides of $\triangle FGH$?

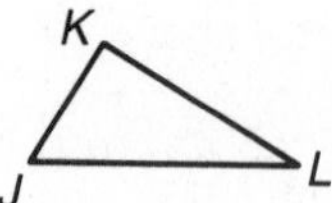

a. 6, 7, 13 **b.** 3, 4, 5
c. 8, 12, 18 **d.** 3, 8, 10

27. d **27.** If $\overline{FG} \cong \overline{JK}$, $\overline{FH} \cong \overline{JL}$, and $GH > KL$, then _____.

a. $m\angle G > m\angle K$ **b.** $m\angle H < m\angle L$ **c.** $m\angle J > m\angle F$ **d.** $m\angle J < m\angle F$

28. If points X and Y are equidistant from points P and Q, then _____. 28. a

a. point R on $\overline{PQ}$ is equidistant from X and Y
b. point Z on $\overline{XY}$ is equidistant from P and Q
c. $\overline{PQ} \parallel \overline{XY}$ **d.** $\overline{PQ} \cong \overline{XY}$

29. Lines a and b lie in plane N. If $c \perp a$ and $c \perp b$, then _____. 29. a

a. $c \perp N$ **b.** $c \parallel N$ **c.** $c \parallel a$ **d.** $c \parallel b$

30. If $\overleftrightarrow{AB} \perp$ plane E at B, then _____. 30. c

a. $\overleftrightarrow{CD} \perp \overleftrightarrow{AB}$ **b.** if $\overleftrightarrow{CD}$ lies in E, $\overleftrightarrow{CD} \perp \overleftrightarrow{AB}$
c. if $\overleftrightarrow{BC}$ lies in E, $\overleftrightarrow{BC} \perp \overleftrightarrow{AB}$ **d.** no conclusion can be drawn

31. $\overleftrightarrow{AB} \perp$ plane G at B. The distance from C, a point on $\overleftrightarrow{AB}$, to G is _____. 31. a

a. BC **b.** BG **c.** AB **d.** AC

32. In quadrilateral $ABCD$, $\triangle ABC \cong \triangle CDA$. To prove $\overline{AB} \parallel \overline{CD}$ you could state that _____. 32. c

a. $\angle DAC \cong \angle BCA$ **b.** $\angle ADC \cong \angle CBA$
c. $\angle BAC \cong \angle DCA$ **d.** $\overline{AB} \cong \overline{CD}$

Refer to the figure at the right for Exercises 33–34.

33. Solve for x to make $a \parallel b$ if $m\angle 1 = 3x + 5$ and $m\angle 5 = 5x - 65$. 33. b

a. 30 **b.** 35 **c.** 40 **d.** 45

34. Given that $a \parallel b$, find x if $m\angle 3 = 4x$ and $m\angle 6 = 5x + 9$. 34. d

a. 10 **b.** 16 **c.** 17 **d.** 19

35. In $\triangle ABC$ at the right, find $m\angle DBA$. 35. c

a. 14 **b.** 89
c. 101 **d.** 93

36. Planes E and F intersect to form dihedral $\angle E\text{-}\overleftrightarrow{AB}\text{-}F$. Points C and D lie in E and points G and H lie in F. Which of the following conclusions can you make? 36. d

a. $\angle CAG \cong \angle DBH$ **b.** $\angle CBH \cong \angle DAG$
c. $\angle CBH \cong \angle DBF$ **d.** No conclusion can be drawn.

37. The projection of a point into a plane is a _____. 37. c

a. plane **b.** line **c.** point **d.** ray

Preparing for College Entrance Exams

1. b

2. a

3. a

4. c

5. b

6. e

7. d

PREPARING FOR COLLEGE ENTRANCE EXAMS

Choose the letter for the correct answer in each exercise.

1. In the figure at the right, $\overline{AD} \cong \overline{CD}$, $\overline{AC} \cong \overline{BC}$, and $m\angle ADC = 120$. Find $m\angle CAB$.

a. 10 **b.** 15 **c.** 20

d. 25 **e.** 30

2. In $\triangle PQR$, $\overline{QS}$ and $\overline{RS}$ bisect $\angle Q$ and $\angle R$, respectively. If $m\angle P = x$. express $m\angle S$ in terms of x.

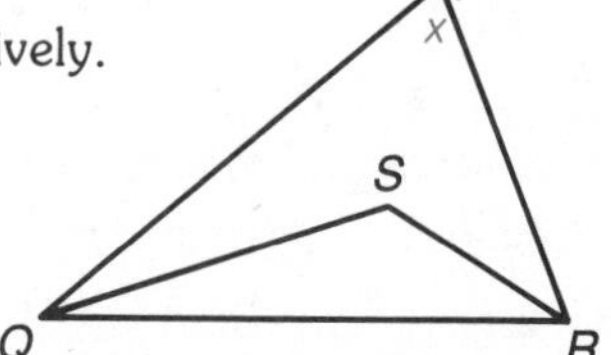

a.  $90 + \frac{x}{2}$ **b.**  $90 - \frac{x}{2}$ **c.** x

d.  $2x$ **e.** $180 - x$

Exercises 3–5 each consist of two quantities, shown in the figure below, which are given in Column A and Column B. Compare the two quantities and choose: *a*, if the quantity in Column A is greater; *b*, if the quantity in column B is greater; *c*, if the two quantities are equal; or *d*, if the relationship cannot be determined. NOTE: The figure is *not necessarily* drawn to scale and *may not* agree with the measures given. $\overline{JK} \cong \overline{KM} \cong \overline{JM}$ and $\overline{JK} \perp \overline{KL}$.

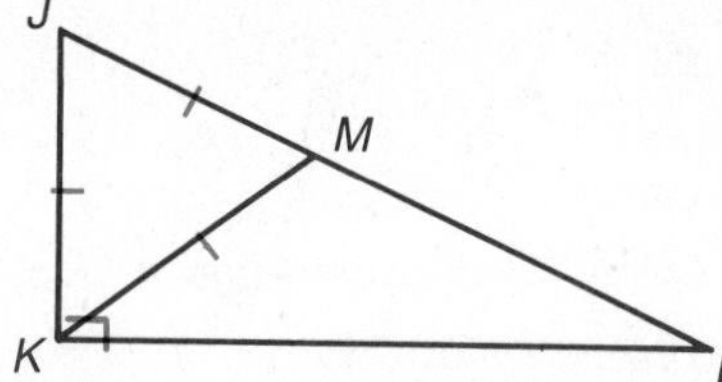

	Column A	Column B
3.	$\overline{KL}$	$\overline{KM}$
4.	$\overline{KM}$	$\overline{ML}$
5.	$\overline{ML}$	$\overline{KL}$

6. In $\square QRST$, $m\angle PSR = m\angle PST = 60$. $m\angle QTP = m\angle PTS$. Find $m\angle SPT$.

a. 100 **b.** 60 **c.** 45

d. 120 **e.** 90

7. $\overline{BC} \parallel \overline{ED}$, $m\angle A = 81$, $m\angle B = 30$. What is $m\angle AED$?

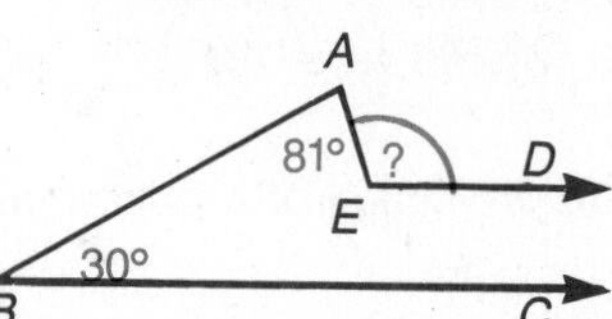

a. 81 **b.** 130 **c.** 60

d. 111 **e.** 99

CHAPTER 9

Area and the Pythagorean Theorem

OBJECTIVE

Use Postulate 18 to determine the area of a polygonal region.

TEACHER'S NOTES

See p. T32

MIXED REVIEW

1. If the base angles of an isosceles triangle have measures of $3x - 40$ and $2x - 10$, find x. $x = 30$
2. Solve $12x - 3(6 + x) = 42$. $x = 6\frac{2}{3}$
3. Solve $2x - y = 12$
   $x + 2y = 16$ (8, 4)
4. Factor $3x^3 - 9x^2 + 6x$. $3x(x - 2)(x - 1)$
5. Add $\frac{x}{y} + \frac{2}{5}$. $\frac{5x + 2y}{5y}$

TEACHER'S RESOURCE MASTERS

Practice Master 26, Part 1

9.1 Polygonal Regions

A **polygon** is a closed, plane figure having three or more angles and sides. Examples of polygons you have studied so far are triangles and quadrilaterals.

This section will introduce some of the special characteristics of a **polygonal region,** which is the union of a polygon and its interior.

> **DEFINITION: triangular region**
> A **triangular region** is the union of a triangle and its interior.

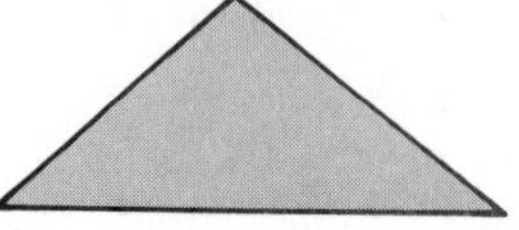

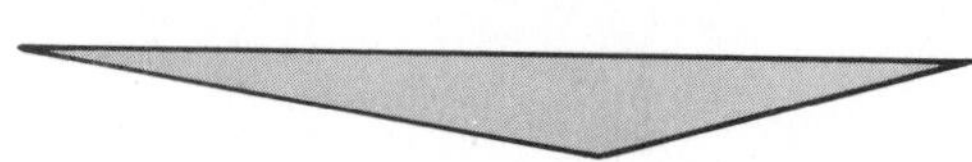

The figure above shows two triangular regions. If a limited, or *finite,* number of triangular regions are joined, as shown below, a polygonal region may be formed.

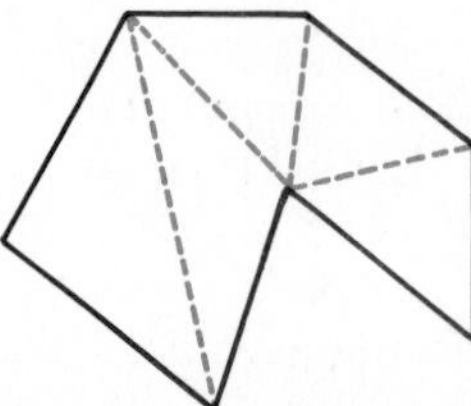

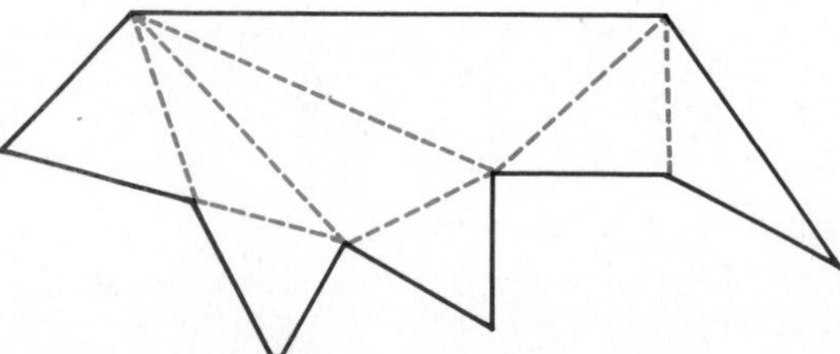

> **DEFINITION: polygonal region**
> A region is a **polygonal region** if and only if it is the union of a finite number of triangular regions, in a plane, such that the intersection of any two is either a point or a segment.

Three new postulates, similar to the postulates used in measuring distance and angle, provide the basis for measuring the area of a polygonal region.

POSTULATE 17 (The Area Postulate)
To every polygonal region there corresponds a unique positive number.

DEFINITION: area of a polygonal region
The **area of a polygonal region** is the number assigned to it by Postulate 17.

Throughout the remainder of this text, "area of the polygon" will mean "area of the polygonal region." Likewise, the area of $\triangle ABC$ means the area of the triangular region ABC.

POSTULATE 18
If two triangles are congruent, then the triangular regions have the same area.

The polygons shown below have each been divided into two polygonal regions.

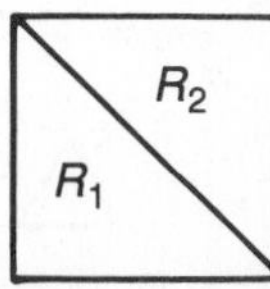

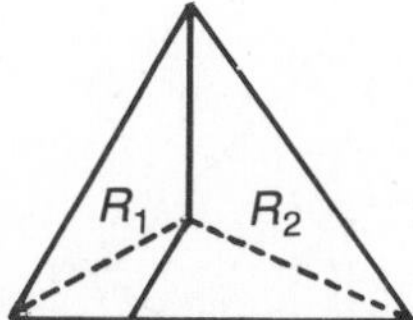

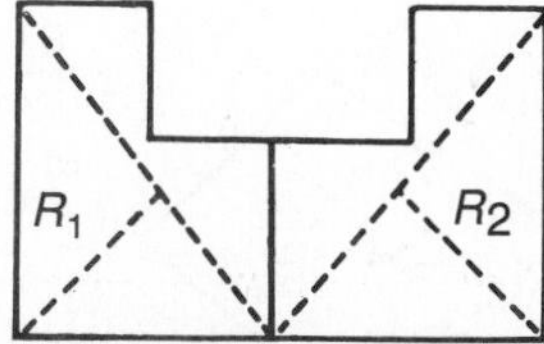

POSTULATE 19
Suppose that the region R is the union of two regions R_1 and R_2. Suppose that R_1 and R_2 intersect at most in a finite number of segments and points. Then the area of polygon R is the sum of the areas of R_1 and R_2.

ASSIGNMENT GUIDE

Minimum 1-12
Regular 1-13 odd
Maximum 1-13 odd, 14-16

ORAL EXERCISES

Indicate whether each statement is true or false. Give a reason for your answer.

1. To every polygonal region there corresponds a unique, positive real number.
2. To every positive number there corresponds a unique polygonal region.
3. A quadrilateral is a polygonal region.

Oral Exercises

1. T; Postulate 17
2. F; converse of Postulate 17 not necessarily true
3. F; definition of polygonal region

4. F; definition of polygonal region
5. T; Postulate 17
6. T; Postulate 18
7. F; converse of Postulate 18 not necessarily true
8. F; regions may overlap
9. F; definition of polygonal region
10. F; the two not necessarily the same, by definition

Written Exercises

1-6. Answers will vary. Examples are given.

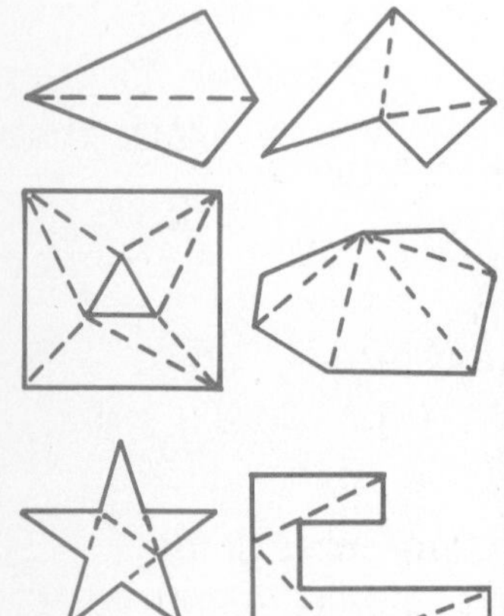

7. No; Postulate 19
8. No; Postulate 19
9. Answers will vary. One example is given.

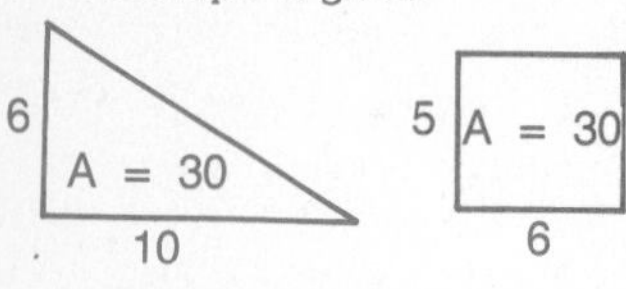

4. The interior of a rhombus is a polygonal region.

5. Every polygonal region has a unique area.

6. If two triangles are congruent, their areas are equal.

7. If two triangles have equal areas, they are congruent.

8. The union of two polygonal regions has an area equal to the sum of the areas of each region.

9. According to the definition, a polygonal region could be the union of triangular regions having no points in common.

10. A polygonal region is a convex set.

WRITTEN EXERCISES

A. Copy each figure below and divide it into triangles according to the definition of a polygonal region. Use the smallest possible number of triangles.

1.

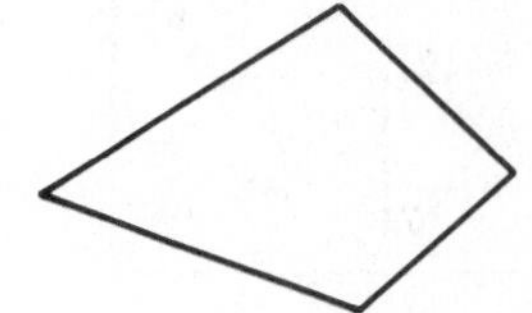

2.

3.

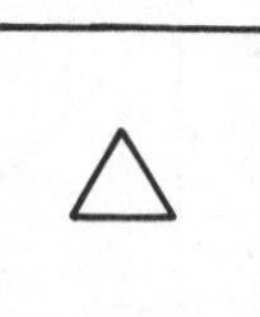

4.

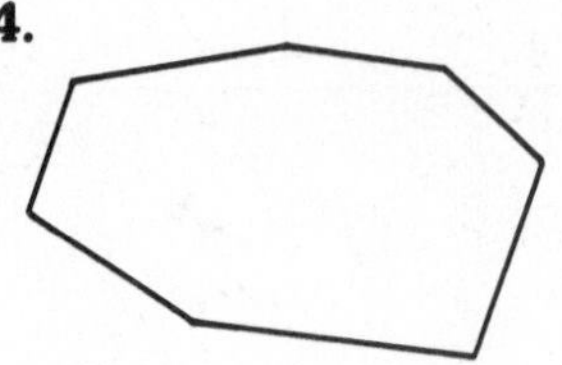

5.

6.

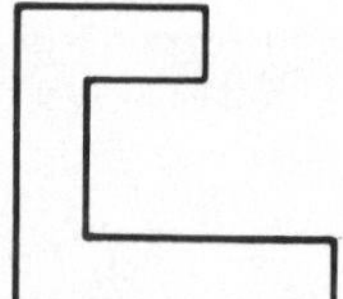

B. 7. In the figure at the right, the area of $R_1 = 80$, the area of $R_2 = 35$, and R is the union of R_1 and R_2. Is the area of $R = 75$? What postulate supports your answer?

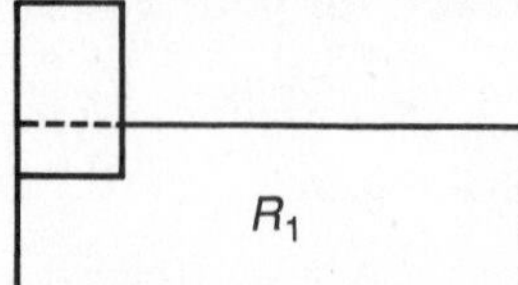

8. In the figure at the left, R_1 and R_2 overlap. The area of $R_1 = 50$, the area of $R_2 = 25$, and R is the union of R_1 and R_2. Is the area of $R = 75$? What postulate supports your answer?

9. Draw a counterexample to this statement: If two polygonal regions have the same area, then they have the same number of sides.

10. In the figure at the right, is the union of the convex hexagon and its interior a polygonal region? What is the least number of triangular regions in this union?

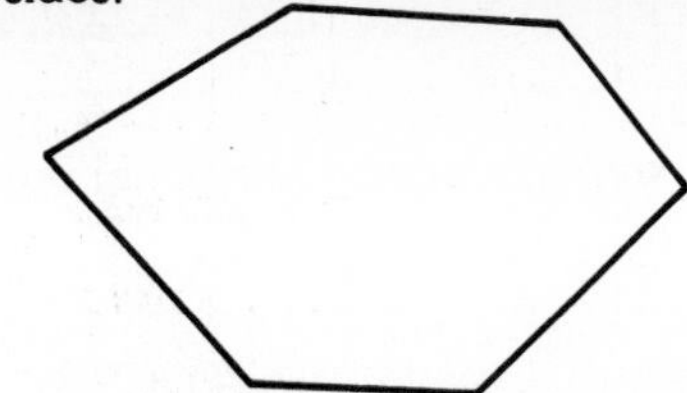

11. Based on the results of Exercises 1-6 and Exercise 10, what is the least number of triangular regions into which a polygonal region of n sides may be subdivided?

12. In the figure, $\overline{AB}$ and $\overline{CD}$ bisect each other at E. Prove that the area of $\triangle AEC$ = the area of $\triangle BED$.

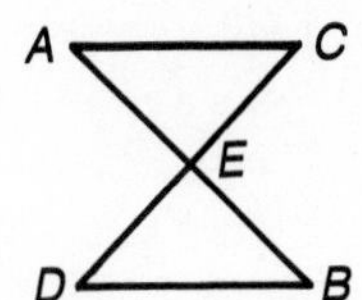

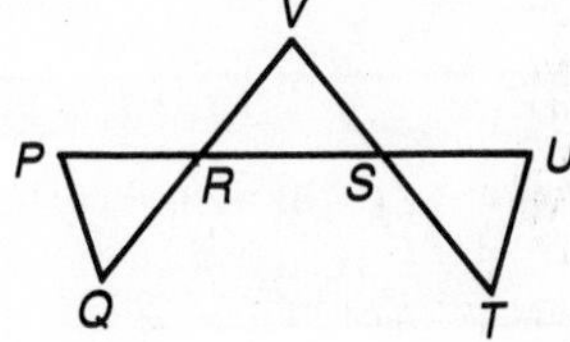

13. In the figure, $\overline{PS}$ and $\overline{QV}$ bisect each other at R, and $\overline{RU}$ and $\overline{VT}$ bisect each other at S. Also, $\overline{VR} \cong \overline{VS}$. Prove that the area of $\triangle PQR$ = the area of $\triangle UTS$.

C. 14. In the figure at the right, quadrilateral $MTRP$ is a rectangle, and quadrilateral $MRQP$ is a parallelogram. Prove that the area of $\triangle MTR$ = the area of $\triangle PRQ$.

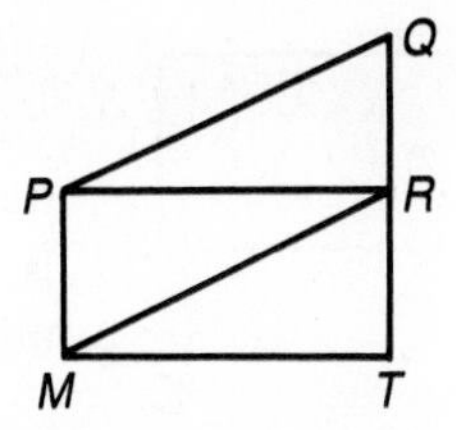

15. In the figure at the right, quadrilateral $LXWK$ is a rectangle, and $\overline{JW}$ and $\overline{KV}$ bisect each other at M. Prove that the area of quadrilateral $LXWJ$ = the area of quadrilateral $LXVK$.

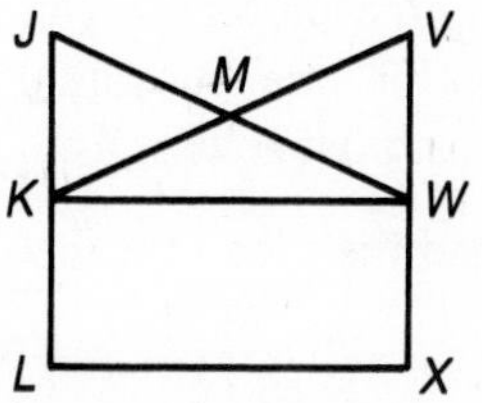

16. The triangular regions ABC and DEF overlap as shown in the figure to form hexagonal region $ABFE$. As drawn, the union of the two triangular regions does not satisfy the definition of a polygonal region. Why? Redraw the hexagonal region $ABFE$ with the smallest number of divisions possible to show that it is a polygonal region.

10. Yes; 4 11. $n - 2$

12. $\triangle AEC \cong \triangle BED$ by SAS; area of $\triangle AEC$ = area of $\triangle BED$ by Postulate 18.

13. $\triangle PQR \cong \triangle VRS$ by SAS; $\triangle VRS \cong \triangle UTS$ by SAS; $\triangle PQR \cong \triangle UTS$ by transitivity; area of $\triangle PQR$ = area of $\triangle UTS$ by Postulate 18.

14. *1.* $\overline{MT} \cong \overline{PR}$, $\overline{PM} \cong \overline{RT}$ (Definition of rectangle); *2.* $\overline{PM} \cong \overline{QR}$ (Theorem 8.15). *3.* $\overline{RT} \cong \overline{QR}$ (Congruence of segments is transitive.); *4.* $\overline{MR} \cong \overline{PQ}$ (Theorem 8.15); *5.* $\triangle MTR \cong \triangle PRQ$ (SSS); *6.* Area of $\triangle MTR$ = area of $\triangle PRQ$ (Postulate 18).

15. *1.* $\overline{KM} \cong \overline{VM}$, $\overline{JM} \cong \overline{WM}$ (Definition of bisect); *2.* $\angle JMK \cong \angle WMV$ (Vert. $\angle$s are $\cong$.); *3.* $\triangle JKM \cong \triangle WMV$ (SAS) *4.* $\overline{JK} \cong \overline{VW}$ (CPCTC); *5.* $\overline{KW} \cong \overline{KW}$ (Congruence of segments is reflexive.); *6.* $\angle JKW$ and $\angle VWK$ are rt. $\angle$s (Definition of rectangle and def. of $\perp$ lines); *7.* $\angle JKW \cong \angle VWK$ (All rt. $\angle$s are $\cong$.); *8.* $\triangle JKW \cong \triangle VWK$ (SAS); *9.* area of $\triangle JKW$ = area of $\triangle VWK$ (Postulate 18); *10.* area of quad. $LXWJ$ = area of quad. $LXWK$ + area of $\triangle JKW$ (Postulate 19); *11.* area of quad. $LXVK$ = area of quad. $LXWK$ + area of $\triangle VWK$ (Postulate 19); *12.* area of quad. $LXWJ$ = area of quad. $LXVK$ (Substitution).

16. See *Selected Answers*, p. 636

OBJECTIVE

Use Postulate 20 to determine the area of a rectangle.

TEACHER'S NOTES

See p. T33

MIXED REVIEW

1. If the sides of a triangle are 7, 11 and x, find the possible size of x. $4 < x < 18$
2. If one angle of a parallelogram is 40, find the other angles. 40, 140, 140
3. Factor $3x^2 - 13x - 10$. $(3x + 2)(x - 5)$
4. Do non-coplanar lines intersect? no
5. The sum of the measures of two complementary angles is ______. 90

TEACHER'S RESOURCE MASTERS

Practice Master 26, Part 2

9.2 Area of Rectangles

The next step in studying polygonal regions is learning how to measure *area.*

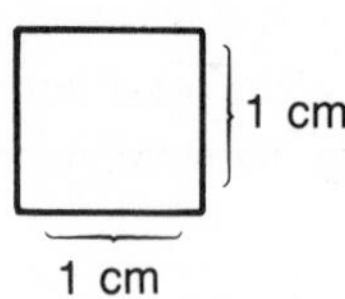

The square at the left has an area of one square centimeter; each side measures one cm. The rectangle at the right has an area of six square centimeters.

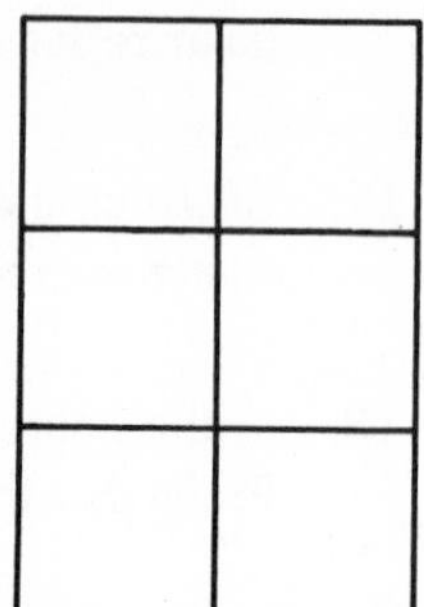

POSTULATE 20
The area of a rectangle is the product of the length of its base and the length of its altitude. That is, $A = bh$.

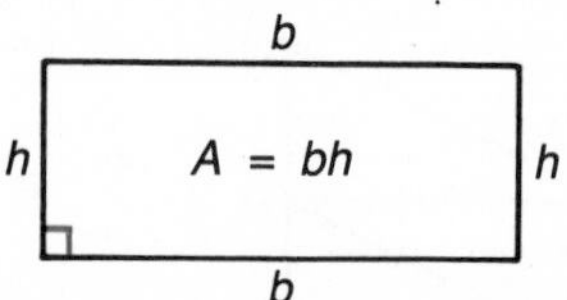

From this point on in the text, "the length of the base" and "the length of the altitude" will be shortened to "base" and "altitude." The context will tell you if the meaning is a real number, which measures distance, or a line segment. Altitude is sometimes called **height,** and in a rectangle the base and altitude may be called the **length** and **width.**

When solving area problems, you may find it helpful to draw a figure and label it, write the basic equation for area, substitute given information for unknowns in the equation, and solve for the remaining unknowns, as in the following examples.

Example: Find the area of a rectangle whose base is 16 cm and whose altitude is 12 cm.

$$\begin{aligned} A &= bh \\ &= 16 \cdot 12 \\ &= 192 \end{aligned}$$

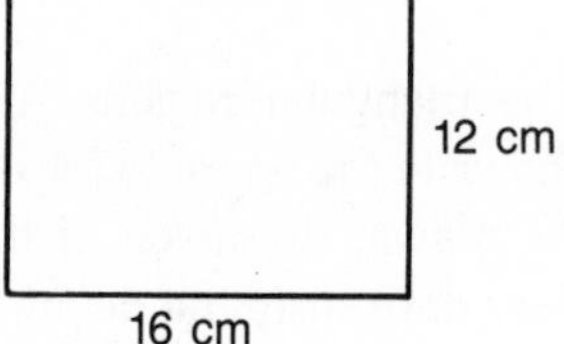

The area is 192 cm^2
Note that the unit for area in the example is cm^2 or "square centimeters."

It is customary to associate the unit of area with the unit of distance from which it is calculated. Thus, if the length of a side is measured in inches, the area of the corresponding region is measured in square inches. If the length is in miles, the area is stated in square miles. Like the notation for "square centimeters," these units are abbreviated as in.^{2} and mi^2.

The area of a rectangle is 144 square inches. The base is 18 inches. What is the altitude?

$$A = b \cdot h$$
$$144 = 18 \cdot h$$
$$\frac{144}{18} = h$$
$$8 = h$$

A = 144

h

18

The height is 8 inches.

Because a square is a special rectangle, a special formula may be derived for its area.

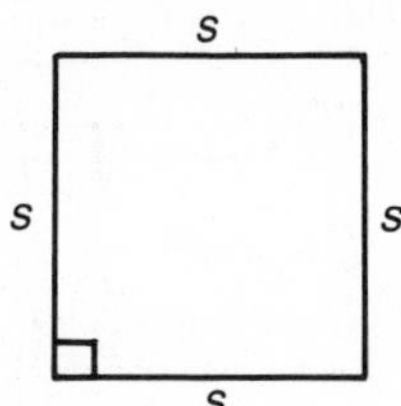

$$A = bh$$
$$= s \cdot s$$
$$= s^2$$

In other words, the area of a square is equal to length of its side squared.

Example: Find the area of a square whose side is 11 mm.

$$A = s^2$$
$$= 11^2$$
$$= 121$$

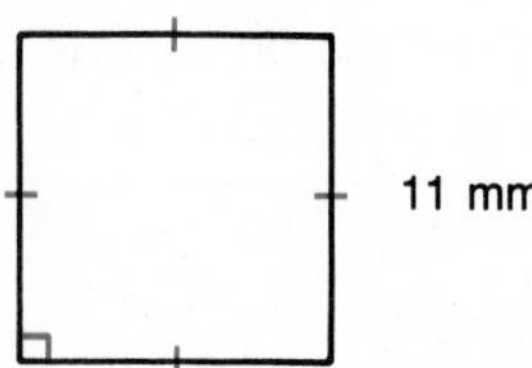

The area is 121 mm^2

Example: Find the area of a square whose side is $\frac{1}{2}$ in.

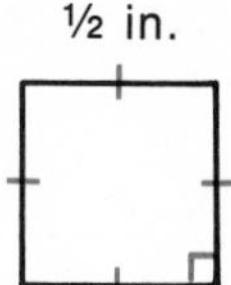

$$A = s^2$$
$$= (\tfrac{1}{2})^2$$
$$= \tfrac{1}{4}$$

The area is $\frac{1}{4}$ in.^{2}

ASSIGNMENT GUIDE

Minimum 1–13
Regular 1–15
Maximum 1–15 odd, 18–19

Oral Exercises

1. It doubles.
2. It doubles.
3. It is quadrupled.
4. It is sextupled.
5. Yes, for any case in which $b \cdot h = s^2$
6. 144
7. 10,000
8. 360 ft^2
9. 49 mi^2
10. 1 $in.^2$

Written Exercises

1. 240 $in.^2$
2. 80 cm^2
3. 27 m
4. 15 yd
5. $7x$ yd^2
6. n ft
7. $2x$ in.
8. 21 ab^2c mm^2
9. 484 cm^2

ORAL EXERCISES

1. If the length of the base of a rectangle is doubled, what happens to the area?
2. If the length of the altitude of a rectangle is doubled, what happens to the area?
3. If both the base and the altitude of a rectangle are doubled, what happens to the area?
4. If the altitude is doubled, and the base is tripled, what happens to the area of the rectangle?
5. Can a square and a rectangle have the same area? Why? Give two examples.
6. How many square inches are in a square foot?
7. How many square centimeters are in a square meter?

Find the area of the following figures.

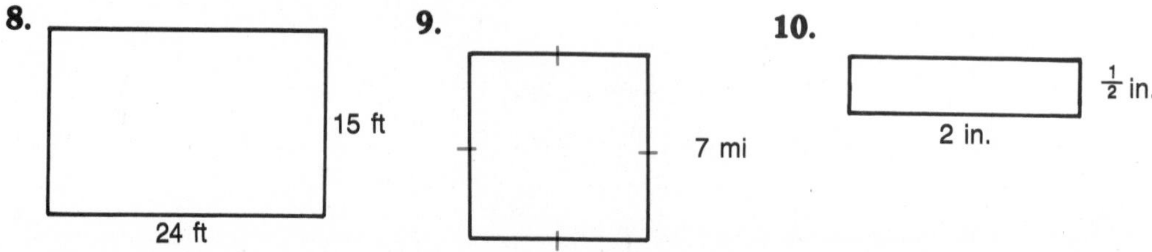

WRITTEN EXERCISES

A. In each of the following, *A* is the area of a rectangle with altitude *h* and base *b*. Find the missing measure.

	b	*h*	*A*
1.	16 in.	15 in.	____
2.	4 cm	20 cm	____
3.	8 m	____	216 m^2
4.	____	6 yd	90 yd^2
5.	7 yd	x yd	____
6.	$3n$ ft	____	$3n^2$ ft^2
7.	____	$4y$ in.	$8xy$ $in.^2$
8.	$3ab$ mm	$7bc$ mm	____

B. **9.** What is the area of a square whose edge is 22 cm?

10. Does a rectangle exist whose area is $5\sqrt{3}$ and whose base is a rational number? Explain.

10. Yes, $b = 5$, $h = \sqrt{3}$

11. Find the area of the figure on the right. (All angles are right.)

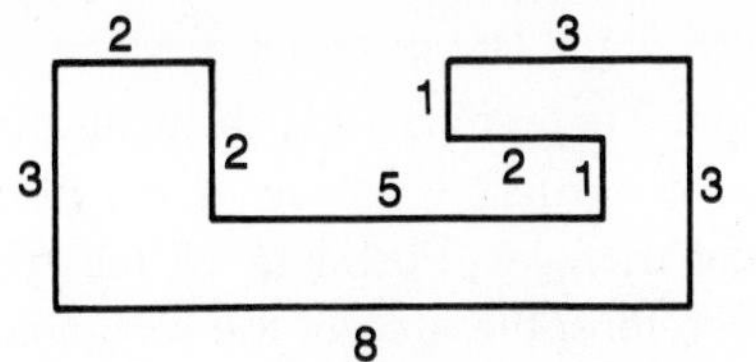

11. 16

12. 144

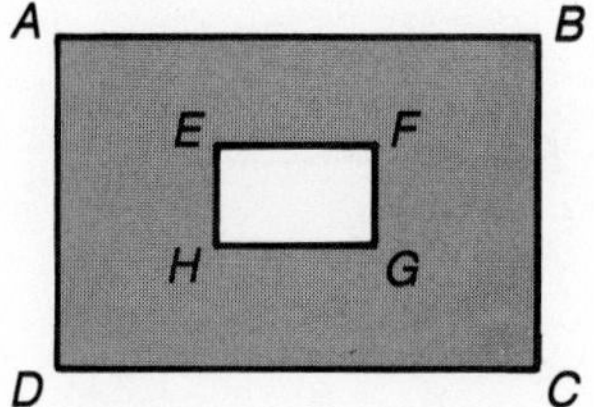

12. Find the area of the shaded region. (All angles are right.) $AB = 16$, $BC = 12$, $EH = 6$, $HG = 8$.

13. Prove that if two rectangles have the same base, the ratio of their areas equals the ratio of their altitudes.

13. $\frac{\text{the area of rectangle}_1}{\text{the area of rectangle}_2} = \frac{bh_1}{bh_2} = \frac{h_1}{h_2}$

C. A room that is 12 feet long, 10 feet wide, 8 feet high needs to be painted.

14. What is the area that needs to be painted? (Paint the ceiling, but don't paint the floor.)

14. 472 ft^2

15. A 1-gal can of paint will cover 300 square feet. How many cans must be purchased to paint the room?

15. two cans

16. The room has a door that is 7 feet by $2\frac{1}{2}$ feet and a large window 4 feet by 3 feet that do not need to be painted. Recalculate 15 and 16 with this added information.

16. 442.5 ft^2, 2 gal

17. Carpet for this room is $17.25 per square yard. How much will it cost to carpet the room?

17. $230

18. Attic insulation is sold in rolls 15 inches wide and covers an area of 39 square feet. How long is the roll?

18. 31.2 ft

19. A path surrounds a plot of grass 45 feet wide and 35 feet long. If the path is 6 feet wide, find its area.

19. 1104 ft^2

20. Geometrically prove the algebraic identity $(x + y)^2 = x^2 + 2xy + y^2$.

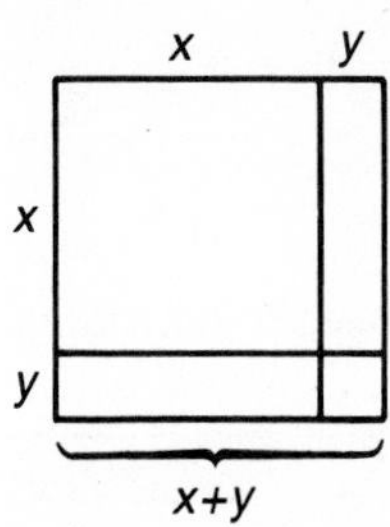

20. *1.* The area of the large square $= (x + y)^2$ (Postulate 20); *2.* The area of the large square = the sum of the areas of the four parts. (Postulate 19); *3.* $(x + y)^2 = x^2 + yx + xy + y^2$ (Substitution); *4.* $(x + y)^2 = x^2 + 2xy + y^2$ (Distributive property).

OBJECTIVE

Use Theorems 9.1 and 9.2 to determine the area of a triangle.

TEACHER'S NOTES

See p. T33

MIXED REVIEW

1. If two lines are cut by a transversal they must be ______. coplanar
2. Multiply $(x - 2)(x + 1)(x + 3)$. $x^3 + 2x^2 - 5x - 6$
3. Solve $\frac{x}{12} = \frac{7}{3}$. $x = 28$
4. Solve $4x - 5y = -2$
   $2x + 2y = -10$
   $(-3, -2)$
5. Can two angles of a triangle by supplementary? no

TEACHER'S RESOURCE MASTERS

Practice Master 27, Part 1

9.3 Area of Triangles

From Theorem 8.14, you know that the diagonal of a parallelogram divides the figure into two congruent triangles. If the parallelogram is a rectangle, then the triangles created are right triangles. Postulate 18 tells you that the areas of these congruent triangles are equal. Therefore, the area of the rectangle is equal to twice the area of one right triangle.

In the figure at the right, 2 times the area of $\triangle DAB$ = the area of rectangle $ABCD$. Thus, 2 times the area of $\triangle DAB = bh$ and the area $\triangle DAB = \frac{1}{2}bh$. You have just proved the first *area theorem.*

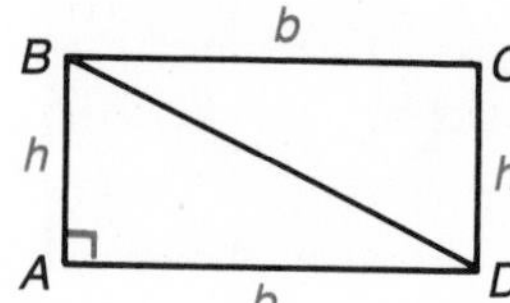

THEOREM 9.1
The area of a right triangle is half the product of the length of its legs.

Theorem 9.1 is important because it is used to derive a general formula for the area of any triangle.

Example: In rectangle $QRST$, $\overline{RT}$ divides the rectangle into two congruent right triangles. The area of rt. $\triangle TQR = \frac{1}{2} \cdot 6 \cdot 8 = 24$, and the area of rt. $\triangle RST = \frac{1}{2} \cdot 6 \cdot 8 = 24$. The area of the two triangles together comprise the area of rectangle $QRST$. That is, $24 + 24 = 6 \cdot 8 = 48$.

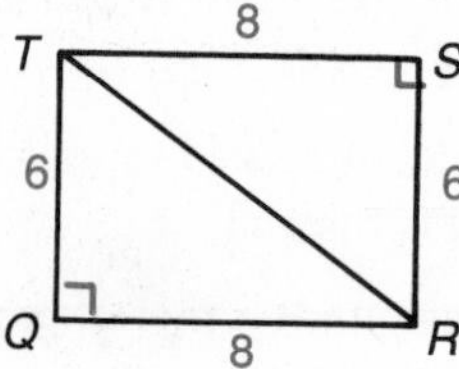

Theorem 9.2 applies to all triangles, including the special case addressed in Theorem 9.1.

THEOREM 9.2
The area of a triangle is half the product of any base and the altitude to that base.

Given: A triangle with base b and altitude h, where A represents the area of the triangle.

Prove: $A = \frac{1}{2}bh$

Proof: The proof must consider three cases, depending upon the location of the altitude.

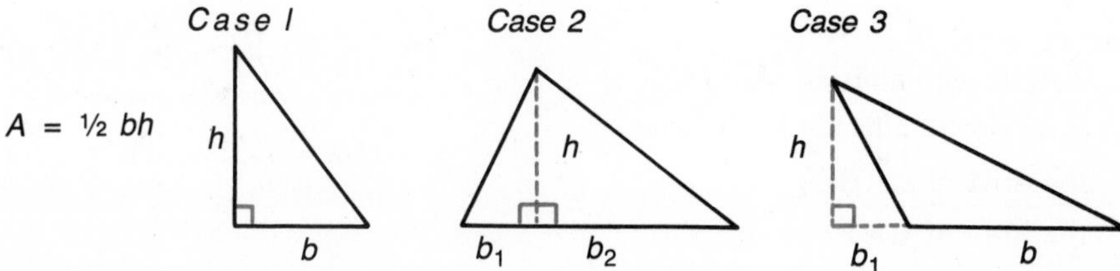

Case 1: The foot of the altitude is an endpoint of the base. Since this is a right triangle, Theorem 9.1 proves $A = \frac{1}{2}bh$.

Case 2: The foot of the altitude lies between the endpoints of the base. This divides the triangle into two right triangles whose areas are $\frac{1}{2}b_1h$ and $\frac{1}{2}b_2h$. By Postulate 19,

$$A = \tfrac{1}{2}b_1h + \tfrac{1}{2}b_2h$$

$$\text{or } A = \tfrac{1}{2}h(b_1 + b_2) \text{ (Distributive Property)}$$

$$\text{Because} \quad b_1 + b_2 = b,$$

$$A = \tfrac{1}{2}hb = \tfrac{1}{2}bh.$$

Case 3: The foot of the altitude falls outside the triangle. This case produces two right triangles, one with base equal to b_1 and the other with base equal to $b_1 + b$. By Theorem 9.1,

$$\tfrac{1}{2}b_1h + A = \tfrac{1}{2}h(b_1 + b),$$

$$\tfrac{1}{2}hb_1 + A = \tfrac{1}{2}hb_1 + \tfrac{1}{2}hb,$$

$$\text{and} \quad A = \tfrac{1}{2}hb = \tfrac{1}{2}bh.$$

Example: $\triangle TUR$ lies within rectangle $QRST$ as shown at the right. To find the area, A, of $\triangle TUR$, first find the area of rt. $\triangle TQR$ and subtract the area of rt. $\triangle TQU$.

$$\tfrac{1}{2}(3 \cdot 4) + A = \tfrac{1}{2} \cdot 4(3 + 6)$$

$$6 + A = \tfrac{1}{2} \cdot 36$$

$$6 + A = 18$$

$$A = 12$$

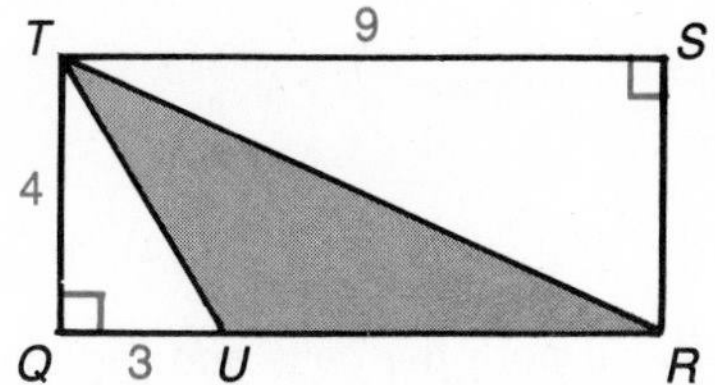

Two useful theorems follow directly from Theorem 9.2.

THEOREM 9.3
If two triangles have the same altitude, then the ratio of their areas is equal to the ratio of their bases.

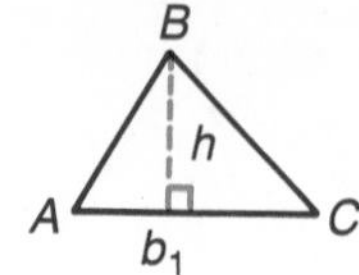

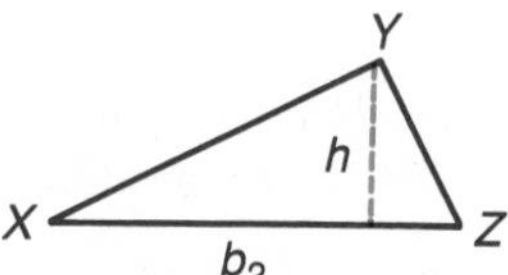

Given: $\triangle ABC$ with altitude h and base b_1
$\triangle XYZ$ with altitude h and base b_2

Prove: $\dfrac{\text{the area of } \triangle ABC}{\text{the area of } \triangle XYZ} = \dfrac{b_1}{b_2}$

Proof: $\dfrac{\text{the area of } \triangle ABC}{\text{the area of } \triangle XYZ} = \dfrac{\frac{1}{2}b_1h}{\frac{1}{2}b_2h} = \frac{b_1}{b_2}$

THEOREM 9.4
If two triangles have equal altitudes and equal bases, then they have equal areas.

From Theorem 9.4, you can deduce the following fact about triangles whose endpoints lie on two parallel lines. Take $\overline{AB}$ and a line l parallel to $\overline{AB}$. Let C be any point on l. No matter where C is located, the area of $\triangle ABC$ will be the same.

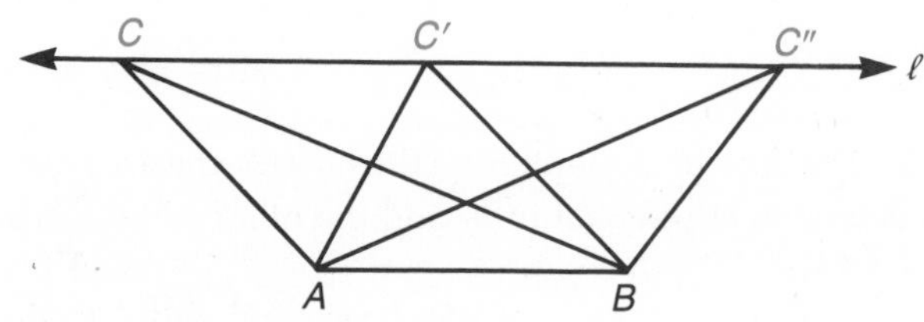

The proofs of this statement and Theorem 9.4 are left as exercises.

ASSIGNMENT GUIDE

Minimum 1-15
Regular 1-19
Maximum 1-19 odd, 21-23

ORAL EXERCISES

1. If the base of a triangle is doubled, what happens to the area?
2. If both the base and the altitude of a triangle are tripled, what happens to the area?
3. If a triangle and a rectangle have equal areas and equal bases, how do their altitudes compare?

Oral Exercises
1. It doubles.
2. It is multiplied by 9.
3. The altitude of the triangle is twice the altitude of the square.

4. Given: $\triangle PQR$ and $\triangle STW$ as shown. If the area of $\triangle PQR$ = the area of $\triangle STW$, what is WT?

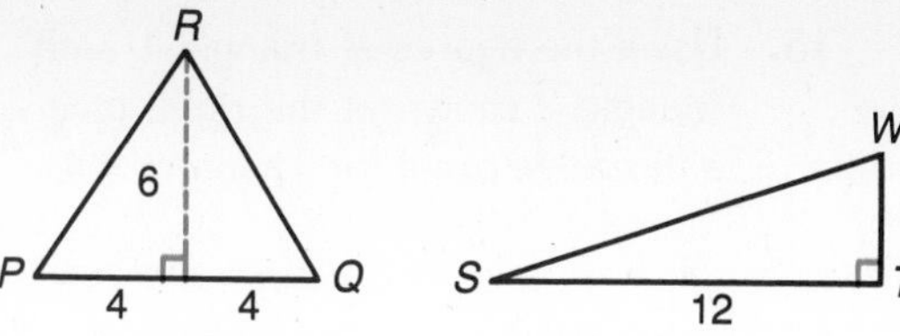

For $\triangle ABC$ at the right, name the altitude to the sides given in Exercises 5–7.

5. $\overline{AB}$

6. $\overline{AC}$

7. $\overline{CB}$

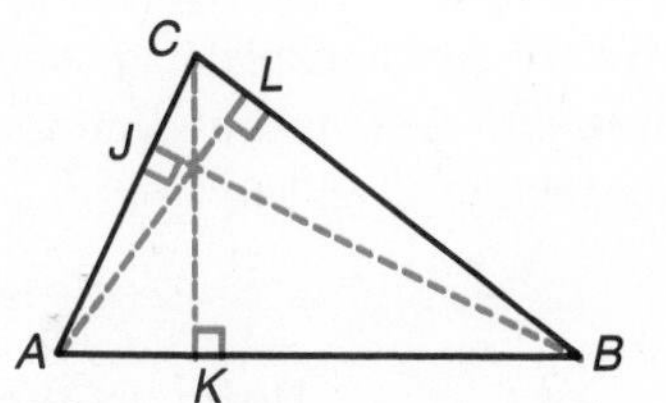

Complete the area formulas for $\triangle RST$, as shown, in Exercises 8–10.

8. area $\triangle RST = \frac{1}{2}b_1 \cdot$ ____

9. area $\triangle RST = \frac{1}{2}b_2 \cdot$ ____

10. area $\triangle RST = \frac{1}{2}b_3 \cdot$ ____

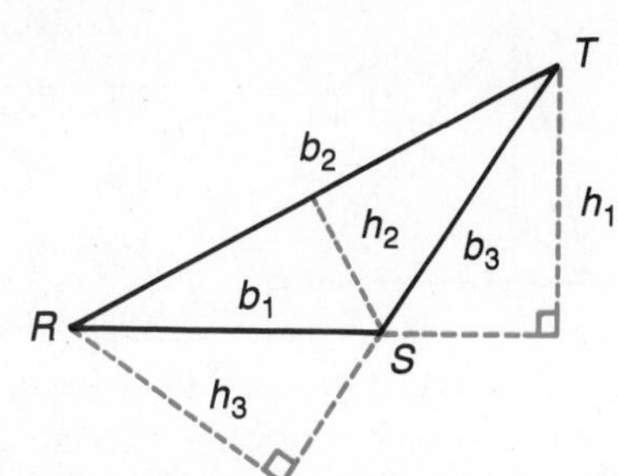

4. 4
5. $\overline{CK}$
6. $\overline{BJ}$
7. $\overline{AL}$
8. h_1
9. h_2
10. h_3

WRITTEN EXERCISES

A. In each of the following, *A* is the area of a triangle with base *b* and altitude *h*. Find the missing measure in the terms given.

1. $b = 8$ mm, $h = 9$ mm, $A =$ ____
2. $b = 15$ in., $h = 10$ in., $A =$ ____
3. $b = 22$ m, $h =$ ____, $A = 88$ m^2
4. $b =$ ____, $h = 7$ cm, $A = 84$cm^2
5. $b = \frac{2}{3}$ ft, $h = \frac{2}{5}$ ft, $A =$ ____
6. $b = 6\frac{2}{5}$ m, $h =$ ____, $A = 4$ m^2

B.

7. $b = 5$ cm, $h = 4$ mm, $A =$ ____
8. $b = 2\sqrt{3}$ in., $h = 4\sqrt{3}$ in., $A =$ ____
9. $b = 3x$, $h = 8x$, $A =$ ____
10. $b =$ ____, $h = 7x$, $A = \frac{21}{2}(x^2)$
11. A right triangle has legs of 16 cm and 9 cm. What is its area?

In $\triangle ABC$, $\angle A$ is a right angle, $BC = 25$, $AC = 15$, and $AB = 20$.

12. What is the area of $\triangle ABC$?
13. What is the altitude to the hypotenuse?
14. The hypotenuse of a right triangle measures 40 in. The area of the triangle is 240 in.^{2}. What is the length of the altitude to the hypotenuse?

Written Exercises
1. 36 mm^2
2. 75 in.^{2}
3. 8 m
4. 24 cm
5. $\frac{2}{15}$ ft^2
6. $1\frac{1}{4}$ m
7. 100 mm^2
8. 12 in.^{2}
9. $12x^2$
10. $3x$
11. 72 cm^2
12. 150
13. 12
14. 12 in.

15. Given that $b_1 = b_2$ and $h_1 = h_2$. The area of triangle $1 = \frac{1}{2}b_1h_1$, and the area of triangle $2 = \frac{1}{2}b_2h_2$, then by substitution, the area of triangle 1 = the area of triangle 2.

16. $\overline{AB}$ determines the base for all the triangles. Because parallel lines are everywhere equidistant, any perpendicular (altitude) from l to $\overleftrightarrow{AB}$ is the same length. So, $\frac{1}{2}bh$ will be constant for any point on l.

17. 18

18. 10.8

19. $7\frac{8}{13}$

20. $\frac{bh}{a}$

21. 288 ft^2

22. 72 $in.^2$

23. The area of each envelope is 91.5 $in.^2$. 91.5 × 16,000 = 1.464 million $in.^2$. 1,464,000 ÷ 24,000 = 61; 61 gal of ink are required.

15. Using the figures of triangle 1 and triangle 2 shown at the right, give a narrative proof for Theorem 9.4.

16. Given the figure at the right, write a narrative proof explaining why the area of $\triangle ABC$ is the same for any location of C on line l.

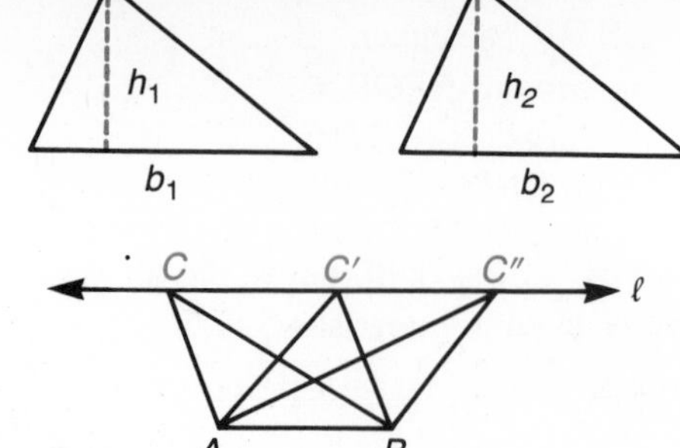

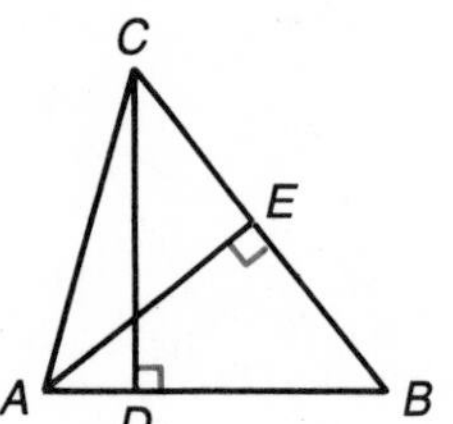

Refer to the figure of △ABC at the left for Exercises 17–20.

17. If $AB = 12$, $CD = 15$, and $AE = 10$, find BC.

18. If $AE = 6$, $CD = 10$, and $BC = 18$, find AB.

19. If $AB = 9$, $CD = 11$, and $BC = 13$, find AE.

20. If $AB = b$, $CD = h$, and $BC = a$, find AE.

C. 21. As shown at the right, what is the area of the gable end of a house that is 24 ft wide, 8 ft high at the eaves, and 16 ft high at the peak?

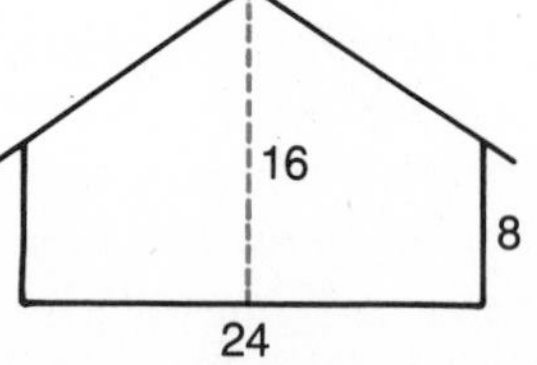

22. A rectangular front-door stoop has been constructed, using half and whole five-sided flagstones, as shown at the right. Given the measurements shown, what is the total area left to be fitted with half and whole triangular stones?

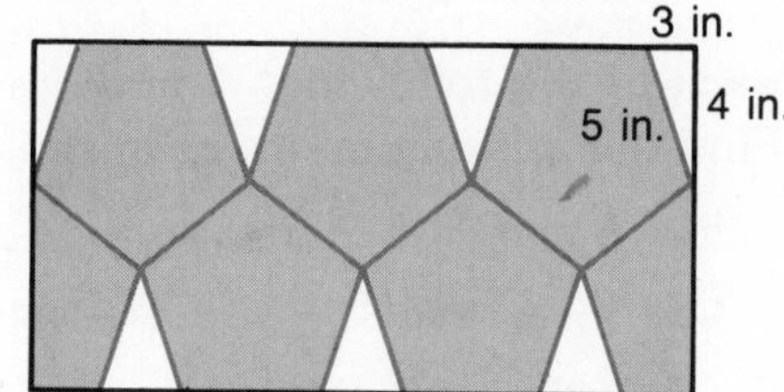

23. A stationery manufacturer must figure the amount of ink needed to print an order of 16,000 business envelopes on one side. What is the total area of one side of an unfolded envelope as shown? What is the total area needing ink to fill the order? If 1 gal of ink will print 24,000 $in.^2$, how many gallons are required for the order? (HINT: One flap needs to be divided up into triangles.)

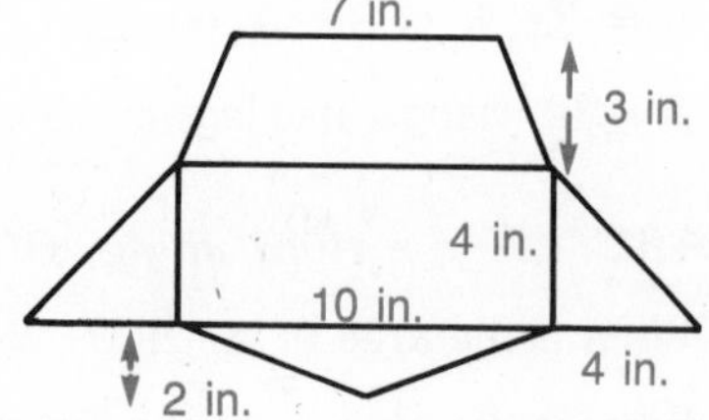

9.4 Areas of Other Quadrilaterals

If you can divide a region into triangles and total the triangular areas, you can find the area of any polygon. This can be used to prove theorems for finding the areas of certain quadrilaterals. For this purpose, you need to know how to find the altitudes of these quadrilaterals.

DEFINITION: altitude of a parallelogram
The **altitude of a parallelogram** is the distance between a pair of parallel sides.

Because a parallelogram has two pairs of parallel sides, the definition means that every parallelogram has two altitudes.

THEOREM 9.5
The area of a parallelogram is the product of any base and the corresponding altitude.

Given: Parallelogram with base b, corresponding altitude h, and area A

Prove: $A = bh$

Proof: Either diagonal divides the region into two congruent triangles (Theorem 8.14), each with area $= \frac{1}{2}bh$.
Therefore, $A = 2(\frac{1}{2}bh) = bh$.

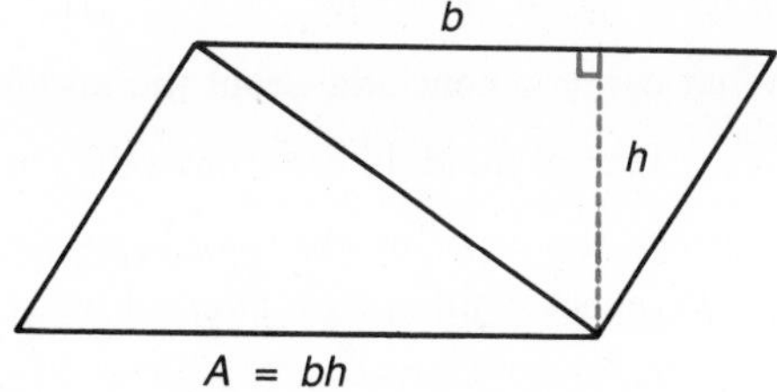

$A = bh$

Recall that a trapezoid is a quadrilateral with only one pair of parallel sides, called bases.

DEFINITION: altitude of a trapezoid
The **altitude of a trapezoid** is the distance between the lines containing the parallel sides.

THEOREM 9.6
The area of a trapezoid is half the product of its altitude and the sum of its bases.

OBJECTIVE

Use Theorem 9.5 to determine the area of a parallelogram and Theorem 9.6 to determine the area of a trapezoid.

TEACHER'S NOTES

See p. T33

MIXED REVIEW

1. What is the supplement of $90 - x$? $90 + x$
2. Solve $x + 3(x - 4) = 5(x + 7)$. $x = -47$
3. Factor $6x^2 + 11x - 7$. $(2x - 1)(3x + 7)$
4. Solve $\frac{x+6}{x} = \frac{9}{2}$. $x = 1\frac{5}{7}$
5. Find $|-9 - 3| - |7 - (-2)|$. 3

TEACHER'S RESOURCE MASTERS

Practice Master 27, Part 2
Quiz 17

Given: Trapezoid with altitude h, bases b_1 and b_2, and area A

Prove: $A = \frac{1}{2}h(b_1 + b_2)$

Proof: Either diagonal divides the region into two triangles with areas $\frac{1}{2}hb_1$ and $\frac{1}{2}hb_2$. This makes $A = \frac{1}{2}hb_1 + \frac{1}{2}hb_2 = \frac{1}{2}h(b_1 + b_2)$.

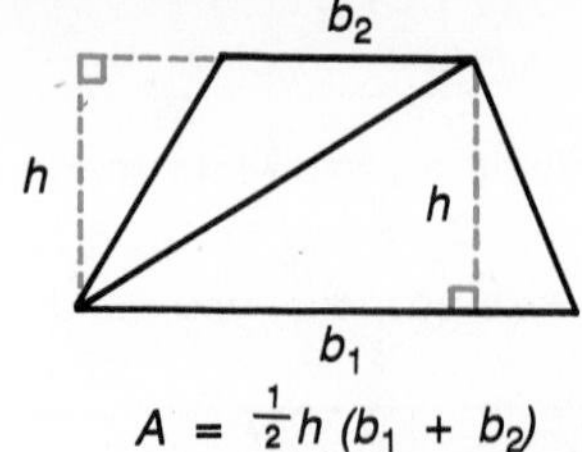

ORAL EXERCISES

In quadrilateral *ABCD*, $\overline{AC}$ and $\overline{BD}$ are diagonals, and $\overline{AC} \perp \overline{BD}$.

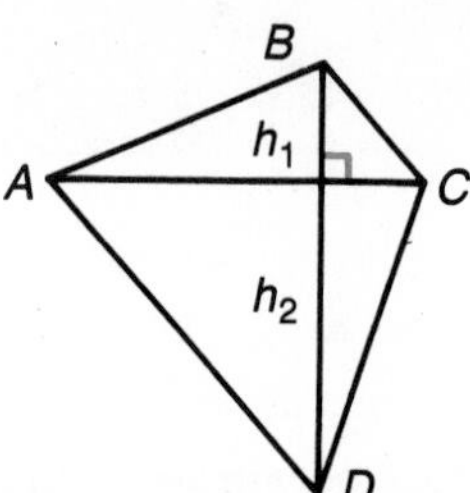

1. What is the area of $\triangle ABC$?
2. What is the area of $\triangle ADC$?
3. What is $h_1 + h_2$?
4. What is the area of quadrilateral *ABCD* in terms of *AC* and *BD*?
5. What can you conclude about the area of a quadrilateral with perpendicular diagonals?
6. What special quadrilaterals have diagonals that are perpendicular to each other?
7. Express the area of the parallelogram shown at the right in two different ways.

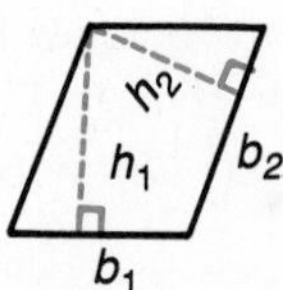

WRITTEN EXERCISES

A. Find the area of each figure.

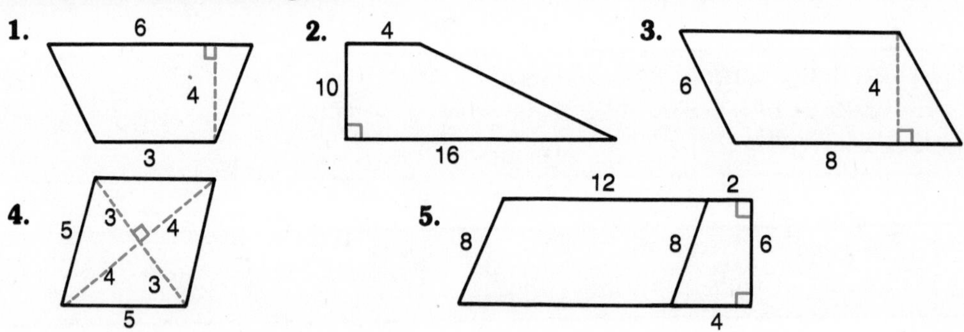

ASSIGNMENT GUIDE

Minimum 1-15
Regular 1-16
Maximum 1-15 odd, 16-22

Oral Exercises

1. $\frac{1}{2}h_1(AC)$
2. $\frac{1}{2}h_2(AC)$
3. *BD*
4. $\frac{1}{2}(AC)(BD)$
5. The area is $\frac{1}{2}$ the product of the lengths of the diagonals.
6. square, rhombus, kite
7. $A = b_1h_1$ or $A = b_2h_2$

Written Exercises

1. 18
2. 100
3. 32
4. 24
5. 90

B. In $\square ABCD$, $\overline{BE} \perp \overline{AD}$, and $\overline{BF} \perp \overline{CD}$.

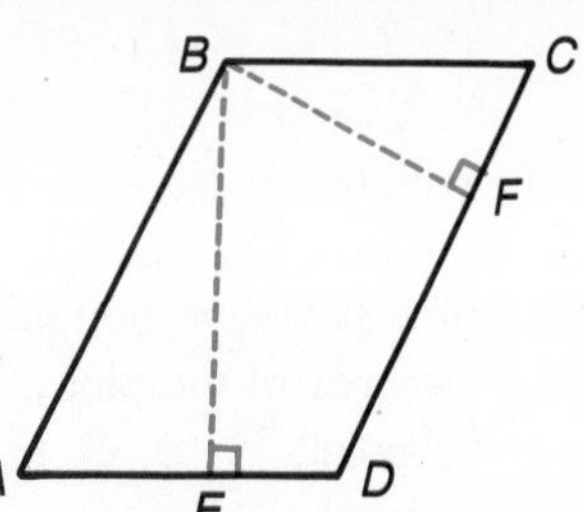

6. If $AD = 9$, and $BE = 8$, what is the area of $\square ABCD$?

7. If $CD = 16$, and $BF = 14$, what is the area of $\square ABCD$?

8. If the area of $\square ABCD = 75$, and $BE = 12$, what is BC?

9. If $AD = 15$, $BE = 8$, and $BF = 6$, what is AB?

10. If $BE = 6\frac{1}{2}$, $BF = 10$, and $BC = 8$, what is CD?

11. If the area of $\square ABCD = 360$, $AD = 12$, and $AB = 48$, what are BE and BF?

Quadrilateral *ABDC* is a trapezoid with $\overline{AB} \parallel \overline{CD}$.

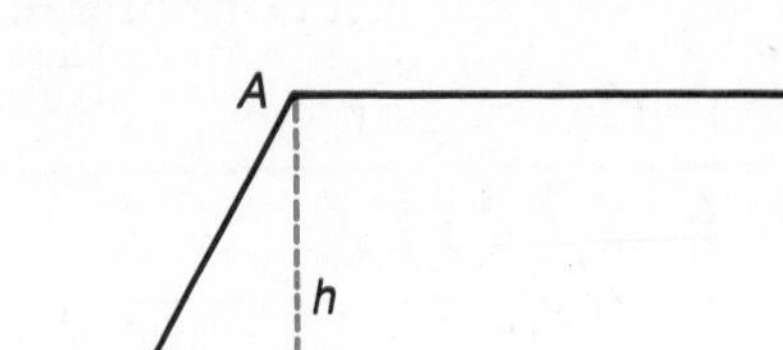

12. If $AB = 4$, $CD = 8$, and $h = 5$, what is the area of quadrilateral $ABDC$?

13. If $CD = 6$, $AB = 10$, and the area of quadrilateral $ABDC = 56$, what is h?

14. If the area of quadrilateral $ABDC = 63$, $h = 9$, and $AB = 3$, what is CD?

15. If the area of quadrilateral $ABDC = 96$, $h = 8$, and $CD = 16$, what is AB?

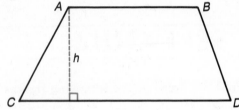

16. Find the area of the end of the barn with measurements as indicated in the figure shown at the right.

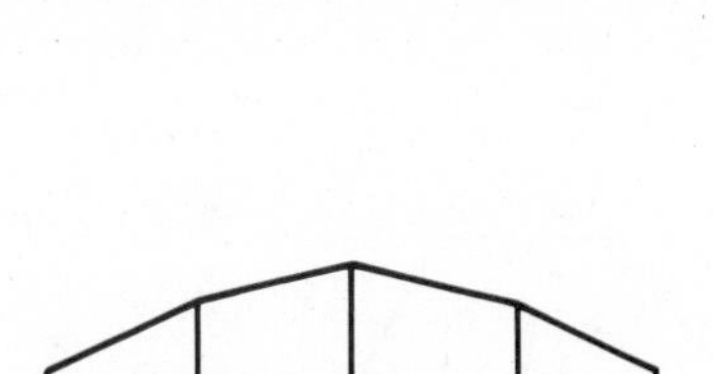

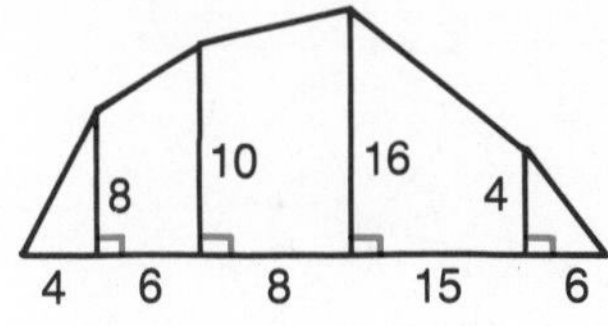

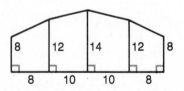

17. Find the area of the figure shown at the left.

18. The diagonals of a rhombus are 16 and 10. What is the area?

C. 19. Prove that the area of a rhombus is equal to half the product of the lengths of its diagonals.

20. A square with edge 8 in. and a right triangle with one leg 6 in. have the same area. What is the length of the other leg?

6. 72

7. 224

8. $6\frac{1}{4}$

9. 20

10. $5\frac{1}{5}$

11. 30, $7\frac{1}{2}$

12. 30

13. 7

14. 11

15. 8

16. 420

17. 336

18. 80

19.

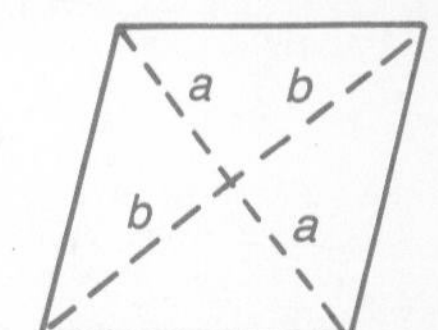

By Theorem 8.25, the diagonals of a rhombus bisect each other and are perpendicular. Thus, for the rhombus shown, $A = 4 \cdot \frac{1}{2}(ab)$, or 4 times the area of a right triangle with legs a and b. So, $A = 2ab$. This is also half the product of the two diagonals.

20. $21\frac{1}{3}$ in.

21. 144

22. 451 sq ft, $\approx$ 50 sq yd

21. In the figure at the right, $\overline{AB} \parallel \overline{FC} \parallel \overline{ED}$, $\overline{AE} \perp \overline{ED}$, $AB = ED = 9$, $FC = 15$, $AE = 12$. What is the area of polygonal region $ABCDEF$?

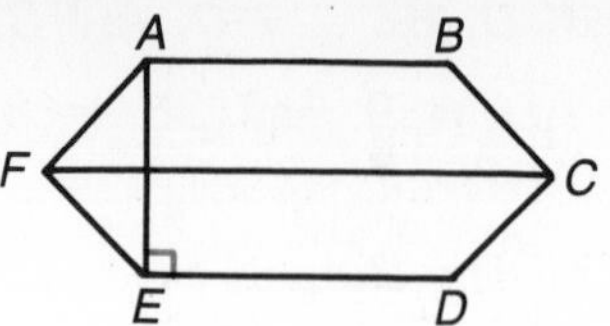

22. As a surveyor, you must determine the area of the plot of land defined by points A, B, C, D, and E. You make the following measurements:
$DF = 12$ ft, $CG = 30$ ft,
$BH = 25$ ft, $AO = 20$ ft,
$FG = 6$ ft, $GE = 4$ ft,
$EH = 10$ ft, $HO = 8$ ft.
Find the area of the plot to the nearest square yard.

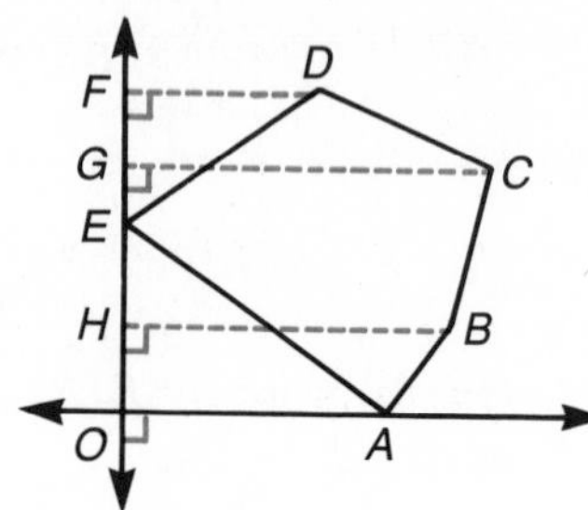

SELF-QUIZ

Self-Quiz

1. 65
2. 126
3. 60
4. 60
5. 96
6. 27
7. 78
8. 8

Find the areas of the following figures.

1.

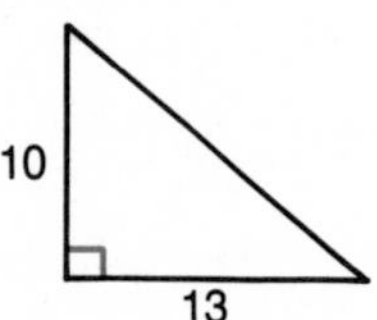

2.

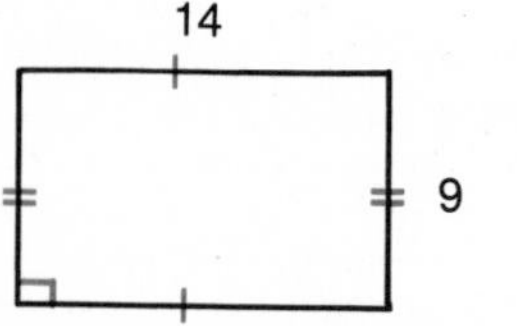

3.

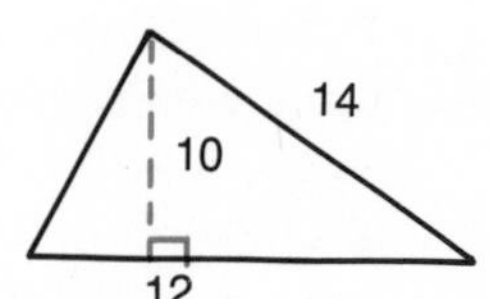

4.

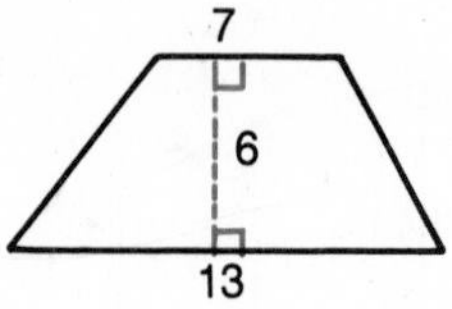

7
6
13

5.

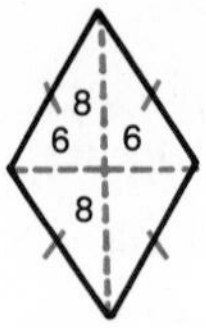

8
6
6
8

6.

12
6
9

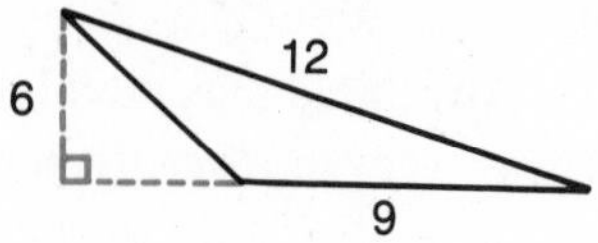

7. The area of region R_1 is 13. What is the area of the entire polygonal region if all the triangular regions shown are congruent?

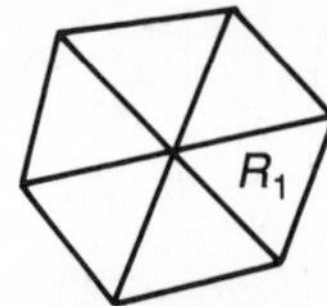

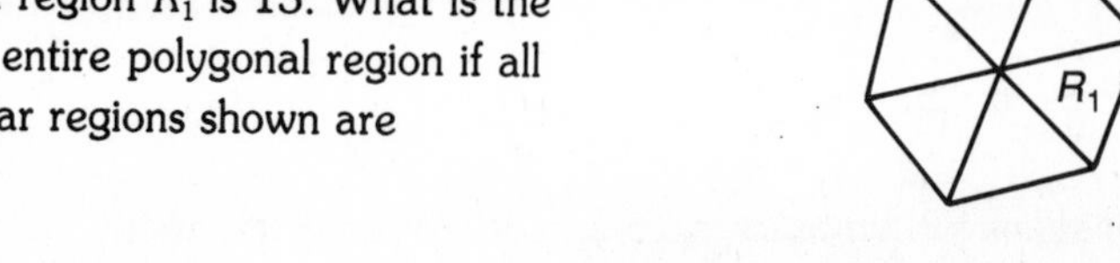

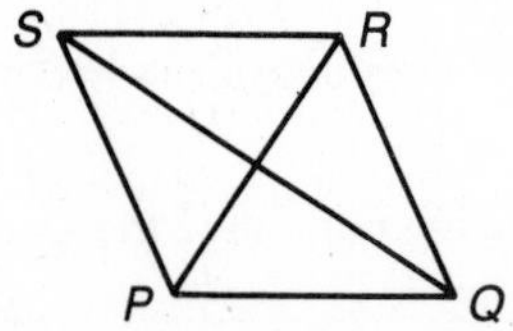

S
R
P
Q

8. The area of rhombus $PQRS$ is 28. PR is 7. What is QS?

9.5 The Pythagorean Theorem

Your understanding of areas enables you to prove one of the most useful theorems in all of geometry.

THEOREM 9.7 (The Pythagorean Theorem)
In a right triangle, the square of the length of the hypotenuse is equal to the sum of the squares of the lengths of the legs.

Given: Right triangle with legs of lengths a and b and hypotenuse of length c

Prove: $c^2 = a^2 + b^2$

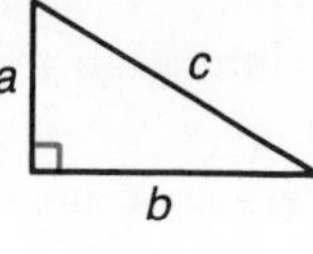

$a^2 + b^2 = c^2$

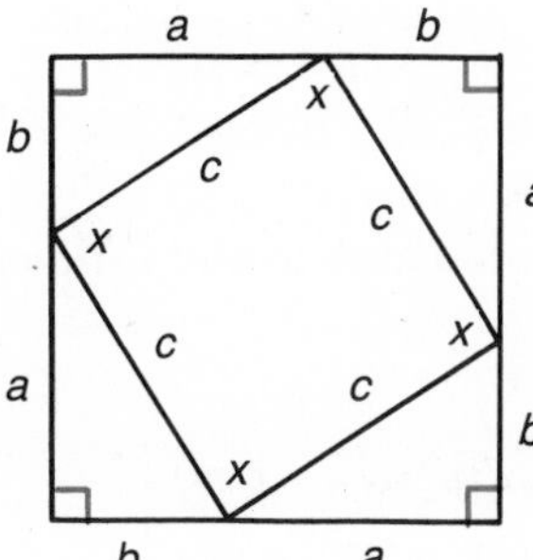

Proof: Construct a square whose sides equal $a + b$. This produces four right triangles congruent by LL. Because their hypotenuses are corresponding parts, they are congruent and may be labeled c.

Since the acute angles of a right triangle are complementary (Corollary 8.13.2), each $m\angle x = 90$, making the quadrilateral formed by the hypotenuses a square. The area of the large square is equal to the sum of the area of the small square and the area of the four right triangles, or

$$(a + b)^2 = c^2 + 4(\tfrac{1}{2}ab).$$

$$\text{Therefore, } a^2 + 2ab + b^2 = c^2 + 2ab$$

$$\text{and } a^2 + b^2 = c^2.$$

The converse of Theorem 9.7 is also true.

THEOREM 9.8 (Converse of the Pythagorean Theorem)
If the square of one side of a triangle is equal to the sum of the squares of the other two sides, then the triangle is a right triangle.

OBJECTIVE

Use the Pythagorean Theorem to solve problems regarding right triangles.

TEACHER'S NOTES

See p. T33

MIXED REVIEW

1. Find all of the factors of 48. 1, 2, 3, 4, 6, 8, 12, 16, 24, 48
2. Is the converse of Theorem 9.4 true or false? false
3. What square has an area number equal to its perimeter? square with sides of 4 units
4. Factor $7x^2 + 19x - 6$. $(7x - 2)(x + 3)$
5. Multiply $(a + b)^3$. $a^3 + 3a^2b + 3ab^2 + b^3$

TEACHER'S RESOURCE MASTERS

Practice Master 28, Part 1

Pythagoras, a Greek mathematician and philosopher who lived in the sixth century B.C., is believed to have established the Pythagorean Society. The members of this secret mathematical organization studied mathematical problems and tried to develop proofs for existing theorems. The society gave Pythagoras credit for one of the first of several hundred proofs of the Pythagorean Theorem.

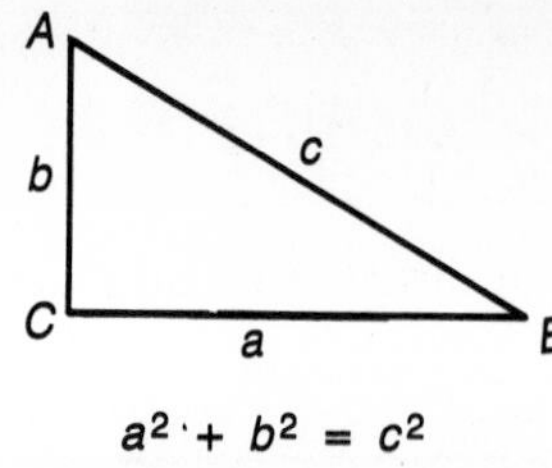

$a^2 + b^2 = c^2$

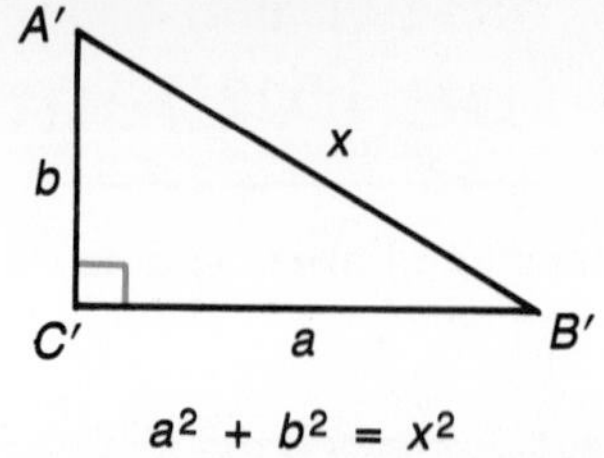

$a^2 + b^2 = x^2$

Given: $\triangle ABC$, with legs of lengths a and b and hypotenuse of length c such that $a^2 + b^2 = c^2$

Prove: $\triangle ABC$ is a right triangle.

Proof: Introduce right $\triangle A'B'C'$ with legs a, b, and hypotenuse x. By the Pythagorean Theorem, $a^2 + b^2 = x^2$, and since $a^2 + b^2 = c^2$, then $x^2 = c^2$, and $x = c$. Therefore, the triangles are congruent by SSS. Since $\triangle A'B'C'$ is a right triangle, then $\triangle ABC$ must also be a right triangle.

ASSIGNMENT GUIDE

Minimum 1-18 odd
Regular 1-21 odd
Maximum 1-21 odd, 22-24

ORAL EXERCISES

Supply the reasons in the following proof:

Given: $\triangle ABC$ and $\triangle RTS$
$\angle C$ is a right angle.
$\angle T$ is an obtuse angle.

Prove: $t^2 > a^2 + b^2$

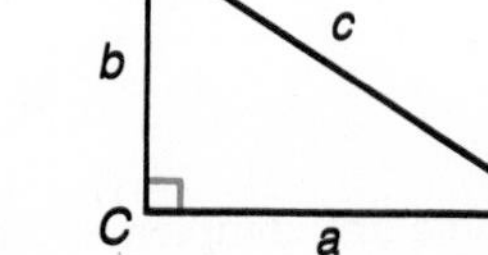

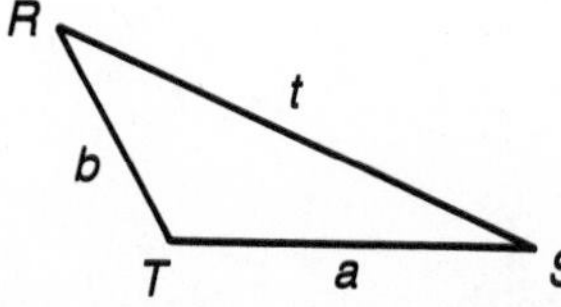

Proof:

STATEMENTS	REASONS
1. $AC = RT$ $BC = ST$	1. **1.** ____
2. $m\angle T > m\angle C$	2. **2.** ____
3. $t > c$	3. **3.** ____
4. $t^2 > c^2$	4. **4.** ____
5. $c^2 = a^2 + b^2$	5. **5.** ____
6. $t^2 > a^2 + b^2$	6. **6.** ____

7. What generalization can you make from the proof in Exercises 1-6?

8. State the converse of your conclusion in Exercises 1-6.

Oral Exercises

1. Given
2. Def. of obtuse
3. Theorem 6.8
4. Multiplication prop. of inequality
5. Pythagorean Theorem
6. Substitution
7. If a triangle is obtuse, then $a^2 + b^2 < c^2$.
8. If $a^2 + b^2 < c^2$, then the triangle is obtuse. If $a^2 + b^2 > c^2$, then it is acute.

What type of triangle (right, acute, or obtuse) would have sides with the following lengths:

9. 6, 8, 10 **10.** 5, 12, 13 **11.** 4, 9, 12

12. 12, 16, 20 **13.** 4, 5, 6 **14.** 7, 11, 14

9. right 10. right

11. obtuse 12. right

13. acute 14. obtuse

WRITTEN EXERCISES

A. Given that a and b are the lengths of legs of a right triangle, and c is the length of the hypotenuse, find the missing length in each of the following:

	a	b	c
1.	6	8	____
2.	5	12	____
3.	7	____	25
4.	____	15	17
5.	11	____	61
6.	10	____	26
7.	7	8	____
8.	4	____	8
9.	9	9	____
10.	1	1	____
11.	1	$\sqrt{2}$	____
12.	____	$5\sqrt{3}$	10

B. 13. The hypotenuse of a right triangle is 26 and one side is 24. What is the area of the triangle?

In $\triangle ABC$, $\angle C$ is a right angle, $AC = 12$, and $BC = 16$. Determine the following measurements.

14. AB

15. the area of $\triangle ABC$

16. the altitude to $\overline{AB}$

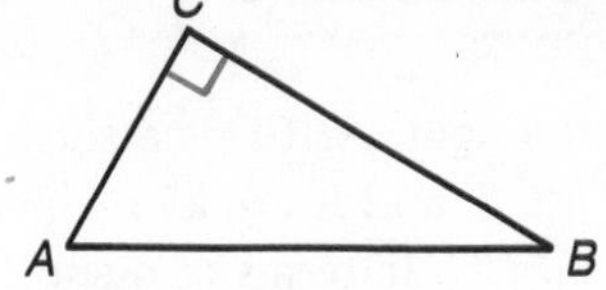

Each side of a rhombus is 25 and one diagonal is 14.

17. What is the other diagonal?

18. What is the area of the rhombus?

Written Exercises

1. 10
2. 13
3. 24
4. 8
5. 60
6. 24
7. $\sqrt{113}$
8. $4\sqrt{3}$
9. $9\sqrt{2}$
10. $\sqrt{2}$
11. $\sqrt{3}$
12. 5
13. 120
14. 20
15. 96
16. $9\frac{3}{5}$
17. 48
18. 336

19. 48
20. 18 in.
21. 24 ft^2
22. 84
23. *1.* $\triangle EDB \cong \triangle ACB$ (SAS); *2.* $m\angle DEB + m\angle DBE = 90 = m\angle CBA + m\angle CAB$ (Cor. 8.13.2); *3.* $\angle DEB \cong \angle CBA$, $\angle DBE \cong \angle CAB$ (CPCTC); *4.* $m\angle DBE + m\angle CBA = 90$ (Substitution); *5.* $m\angle EBA = 90$ (Supplement Postulate); *6.* the area of $\triangle EBA = \frac{1}{2}c^2$ (Def. of area of a $\triangle$); *7.* the area of $AEDC = \frac{1}{2}(a + b)(a + b)$ (Def. of area of a trapezoid); *8.* $= \frac{1}{2}(a^2 + 2ab + b^2)$ (Distributive property); *9.* the area of $\triangle EDB$ = the area of $\triangle ACB = \frac{1}{2}(ab)$ (Def. of area of a $\triangle$); *10.* the area of $\triangle EBA = \frac{1}{2}c^2$ = the area of $AEDC$ − (the area of $\triangle EDB$ + the area of $\triangle ACB$) (Postulate 17); *11.* $= \frac{1}{2}(a^2 + 2ab + b^2) - (ab)$ (Substitution); *12.* $= \frac{1}{2}a^2 + ab + \frac{1}{2}b^2 - ab$ (Distributive property); *13.* $= \frac{1}{2}a^2 + \frac{1}{2}b^2$ (Subtraction prop. of equality); *14.* $c^2 = a^2 + b^2$ (Multiplication prop. of equality).
24. $\approx$8 miles

Challenge

Let AB, BC, CD, and $DA = c$. Then the area of $ABCD = c^2$. Let BQ, CR, DS, and $AP = a$. Let AQ, BR, CS, and $DP = b$. Then the areas of $\triangle AQB$, $\triangle BRC$, $\triangle CSD$, and $\triangle DPA = \frac{1}{2}ab$. So, the area of $PQRS = c^2 - 4(\frac{1}{2}ab)$, or $c^2 - 2ab$. But, $c^2 = a^2 + b^2$, so the area of $PQRS = a^2 - 2ab + b^2 = (a - b)^2$. This makes the ratio

$$\frac{(a - b)^2}{a^2 + b^2}.$$

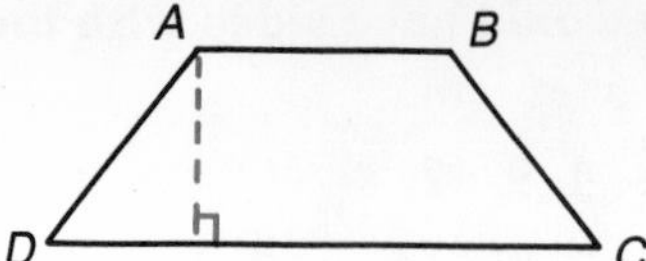

19. Isosceles trapezoid $ABCD$ has bases of 12 and 20. $AD = BC = 5$. What is the area of the trapezoid?

20. The diagonal measure of a television screen is 25 in. If the screen is a square, what is the length of a side to the nearest inch?

21. A tent with a rectangular floor has a diagonal measure of 7 feet and is 5 feet across the front. What is its floor area to the nearest square foot?

C. 22. In $\triangle ABC$, $\overline{BE}$ is an altitude, and D is the midpoint of $\overline{AC}$. If $AB = 13$, $BC = 15$, and $BE = 12$, what is the area of $\triangle ABC$?

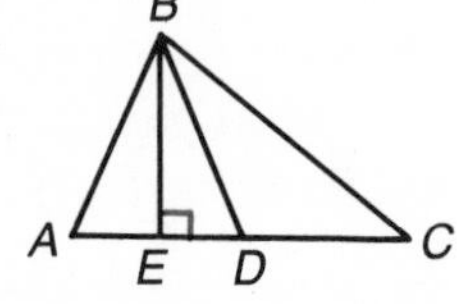

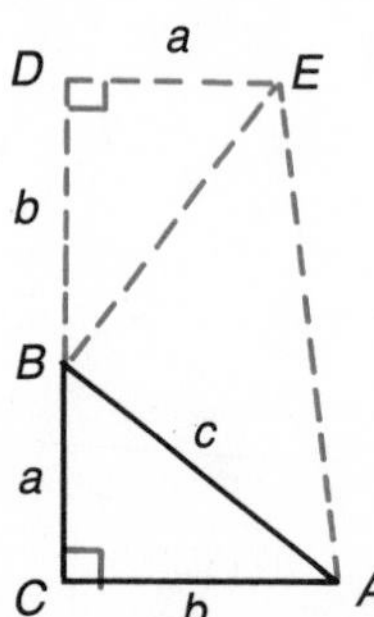

23. General James A. Garfield, later a President of the United States, discovered another proof of the Pythagorean Theorem in about 1875. Using the figure on the left, prove that $a^2 + b^2 = c^2$ by showing that the area of the trapezoid equals the sum of the areas of the three triangles. (You must also prove $\angle EBA$ is a right angle).

24. A man travels 5 miles due north, then 4 miles due east, and then 2 more miles north. How far is he from his starting point (to the nearest mile)?

CHALLENGE

In the figure at the right, $ABCD$ is a square, $PQRS$ is a square, and H, I, J, and K are all midpoints of the sides of square $ABCD$. In terms of a and b, find the ratio of

$$\frac{\text{the area of } PQRS}{\text{the area of } ABCD}.$$

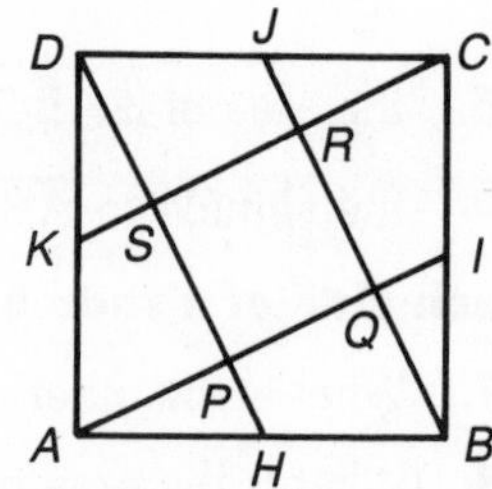

9.6 Special Right Triangles

When the Pythagorean Theorem is applied to special types of triangles, two important theorems result.

THEOREM 9.9 (The 30–60 Right Triangle Theorem)
The length of the hypotenuse of a right triangle is twice as long as the length of the shorter leg if and only if the measures of the acute angles are 30 and 60.

Applying what you know about congruent triangles to the equilateral triangle shown at the right, you can prove both parts of Theorem 9.9. This proof is left as an exercise.

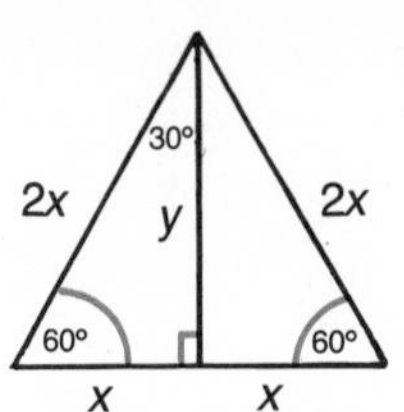

Next, using the Pythagorean Theorem, you can find the length of the side opposite the 60° angle:

$$\begin{aligned} x^2 + y^2 &= (2x)^2, \\ x^2 + y^2 &= 4x^2, \\ y^2 &= 3x^2, \\ y &= x\sqrt{3}. \end{aligned}$$

Therefore, in a 30–60 right triangle, if the side opposite the 30° angle is 7, then the hypotenuse is 14 and the other leg is $7\sqrt{3}$. These relationships are summarized in the following chart.

30–60 Right Triangle		
side opposite 30° angle	side opposite 60° angle	hypotenuse
x	$x\sqrt{3}$	$2x$
$\frac{x}{\sqrt{3}}$	x	$\frac{2x}{\sqrt{3}}$
$\frac{x}{2}$	$\frac{x\sqrt{3}}{2}$	x

OBJECTIVE

Use Theorems 9.9 and 9.10 to determine the lengths of sides of special right triangles.

TEACHER'S NOTES

See p. T34

MIXED REVIEW

1. Solve $\frac{2x - 3}{x} = \frac{8}{7}$ $x = 3\frac{1}{2}$
2. Factor $a^3 + 3a^2b + 3ab^2 + b^3$. $(a + b)^3$
3. If a triangle and a rectangle have the same base and same area, what is the ratio of their altitudes? 2:1
4. Find three ordered pairs that satisfy $3x + 2y = 7$. possible answers: $(-1, 5)$, $(1, 2)$, $(3, -1)$
5. In a right triangle with legs 0.75 and 1, find the hypotenuse. 1.25

TEACHER'S RESOURCE MASTERS

Practice Master 28, Part 2
Quiz 18

THEOREM 9.10 (The Isosceles Right Triangle Theorem)
A right triangle is isosceles if and only if the length of the hypotenuse is $\sqrt{2}$ times the length of a leg.

The relationships defined by Theorem 9.10 are summarized in the following chart. Again, the proof is left as an exercise.

45-45 (Isosceles) Right Triangle		
leg	leg	hypotenuse
x	x	$x\sqrt{2}$
$\frac{x\sqrt{2}}{2}$	$\frac{x\sqrt{2}}{2}$	x

ASSIGNMENT GUIDE

Day 1
Minimum 1-15
Regular 1-24
Maximum 1-30
Day 2
Minimum 19-31 odd
Regular 25-35 odd
Maximum 31-41 odd

These special triangle relationships are used extensively in trigonometry.

ORAL EXERCISES

Oral Exercises

1. 30-60
2. isosceles, or 45-45
3. 2 in., $2\sqrt{3}$ in.
4. $6\sqrt{3}$ in., 12 in.
5. $3\sqrt{3}$ in., $6\sqrt{3}$ in.
6. $2\sqrt{2}$ cm, $2\sqrt{2}$ cm
7. 6 cm, $6\sqrt{2}$ cm

1. In what type of right triangle is the hypotenuse twice as long as the shorter leg?
2. In what type of right triangle is the hypotenuse $\sqrt{2}$ times as long as either leg?

Complete the following statements for a 30-60-90 triangle.

3. If the hypotenuse measures 4 in., the two legs measure ______ and ______.
4. If the shorter leg measures 6 in., the longer leg measures ______ and the hypotenuse measures ______.
5. If the longer leg measures 9 in., the shorter leg measures ______ and the hypotenuse measures ______.

Complete the following statements for a 45-45-90 triangle.

6. If the hypotenuse measures 4 cm, the two legs measure ______ and ______.
7. If a leg measures 6 cm, the other leg measures ______ and the hypotenuse measures ______.

Identify the following as the lengths of the sides of a 30-60-90 or 45-45-90 triangle.

8. $1, \sqrt{3}, 2$ **9.** $\sqrt{2}, \sqrt{2}, 2$ **10.** $4, 8, 4\sqrt{3}$

11. $\sqrt{3}, 3, 2\sqrt{3}$ **12.** $1, \sqrt{2}, 1$

WRITTEN EXERCISES

A. Refer to the figure below to supply the missing information in each case.

	AB	*AC*	*BC*
1.	6	____	____
2.	3	____	____
3.	____	____	18
4.	____	____	9
5.	____	$5\sqrt{3}$	____
6.	____	$2\sqrt{3}$	____
7.	____	9	____
8.	$3\sqrt{3}$	____	____
9.	____	____	$12\sqrt{3}$
10.	____	8	____

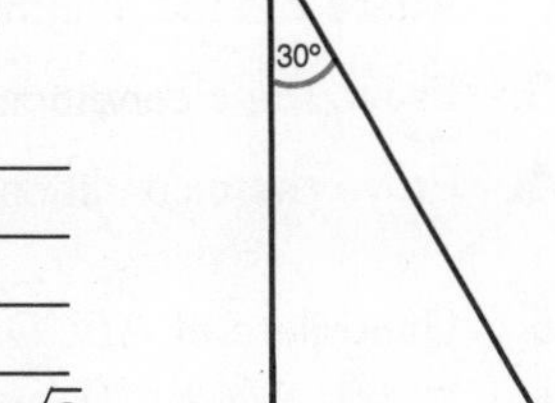

Refer to the figure below to supply the missing information in each case.

	RS	*RT*	*ST*
11.	8	____	____
12.	____	12	____
13.	____	____	16
14.	$2\sqrt{3}$	____	____
15.	____	____	15
16.	____	____	$9\sqrt{2}$
17.	____	$5\sqrt{6}$	____
18.	____	____	$2\sqrt{6}$

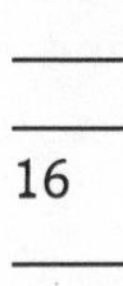
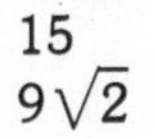

S
45°
45°
T
R

8. 30-60-90
9. 45-45-90
10. 30-60-90
11. 30-60-90
12. 45-45-90

Written Exercises

1. $6\sqrt{3}, 12$
2. $3\sqrt{3}, 6$
3. $9, 9\sqrt{3}$
4. $\frac{9}{2}, \frac{9\sqrt{3}}{2}$
5. 5, 10
6. 2, 4
7. $3\sqrt{3}, 6\sqrt{3}$
8. $9, 6\sqrt{3}$
9. $6\sqrt{3}, 18$
10. $\frac{8\sqrt{3}}{3}, \frac{16\sqrt{3}}{3}$
11. $8, 8\sqrt{2}$
12. $12, 12\sqrt{2}$
13. $8\sqrt{2}, 8\sqrt{2}$
14. $2\sqrt{3}, 2\sqrt{6}$
15. $\frac{15\sqrt{2}}{2}, \frac{15\sqrt{2}}{2}$
16. 9, 9
17. $5\sqrt{6}, 10\sqrt{3}$
18. $2\sqrt{3}, 2\sqrt{3}$

19. 6 20. $6\sqrt{2}$
21. 12 22. $6\sqrt{3}$
23. $18 + 6\sqrt{2} + 6\sqrt{3}$
24. $18 + 18\sqrt{3}$
25. $6\sqrt{2}$ 26. $12\sqrt{2}$
27. $3\sqrt{2}$ 28. 2 29. $\sqrt{6}$
30. 6 31. $6\sqrt{3}$, $36\sqrt{3}$
32. $A = \frac{s^2\sqrt{3}}{4}$
33. (1) *If the hypotenuse of a rt. △ is twice as long as the shorter leg, the acute ∠s measure 30 and 60.* Given rt. △ABC as shown below left, draw $\overline{CD}$ such that *m∠DCB* = *m∠ACB* (Postulate 12) and *CD* = *CA* (Point Plotting Theorem). Then △ABC ≅ △DBC by SAS. So *AC* = *DC* = *AD* = 2*x*, and △ACD is equilateral. Thus *m∠A* = *m∠D* = *m∠ACD* = 60, and *m∠ACB* = *m∠DCB* = 30. △ABC is therefore a 30–60 rt. △. (2) *If the acute ∠s of a rt. △ measure 30 and 60, then the hypotenuse is twice as long as the shorter leg.* In rt. △ABC as shown above right, draw $\overline{CD}$ so that *m∠DCB* = *m∠ACB* and *CA* = *CD*. Then △ABC ≅ △DBC by SAS, and $\overline{AB} \cong \overline{DB}$ by CPCTC. So *AD* = 2*x*. But △ADC is equiangular, so *AC* = *DC* = *AD* = 2*x*, and in △ABC, *AC* = 2*AB*.

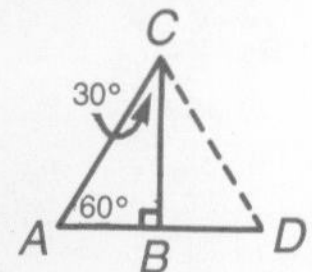

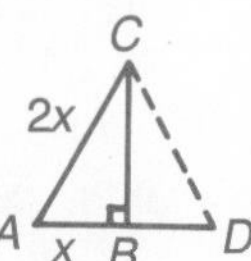

34. See *Selected Answers*, p. 636
35. $120\sqrt{3}$
36. $34 + 6\sqrt{2} + 6\sqrt{3}$
37. $66 + 18\sqrt{3}$
38. $6\sqrt{3}$ 39. $8\sqrt{3}$
40. $9\sqrt{3}$ 41. $s\sqrt{3}$

B. In △*ABC*, as marked, *BD* = 6. Find the following:

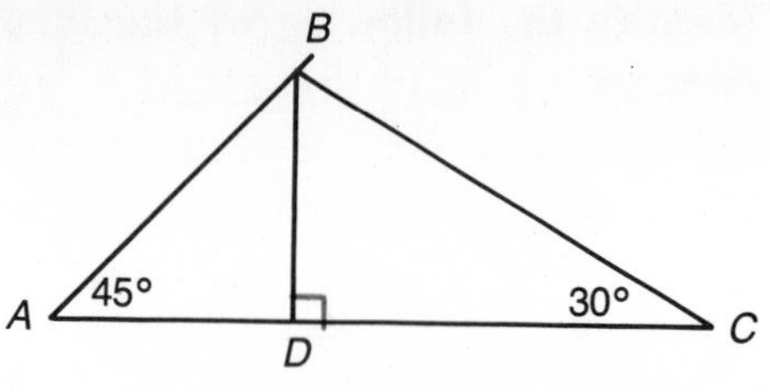

19. *AD*

20. *AB*

21. *BC*

22. *DC*

23. the perimeter of △*ABC*

24. the area of △*ABC*

Determine the length of the diagonal of each square given the length of one side as follows.

25. 6 **26.** 12 **27.** 3

28. $\sqrt{2}$ **29.** $\sqrt{3}$ **30.** $3\sqrt{2}$

31. Find the altitude of an equilateral triangle if the length of one side is 12. Find the area.

32. Using the figure at the right, derive a formula for the area of an equilateral triangle in terms of *s*, where *s* is the length of a side.

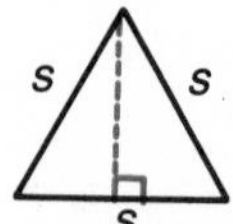

33. Prove the biconditional stated in Theorem 9.9.

34. Prove the biconditional stated in Theorem 9.10.

C. 35. Quadrilateral *ABCD* is a parallelogram. *m∠A* = 60, *AD* = 10, and *AB* = 24. What is the area of ▱*ABCD*?

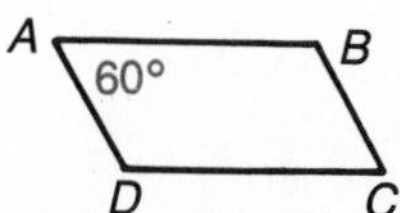

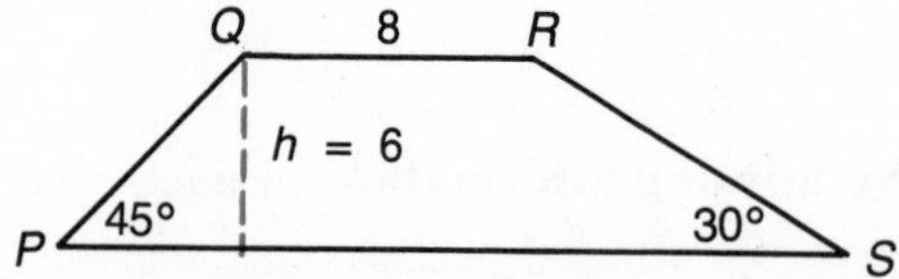

36. Find the perimeter of trapezoid *PQRS*.

37. Find the area of trapezoid *PQRS*.

In a cube with the length of a side given, find the length of $\overline{AH}$. (HINT: Find *AC* first.)

38. *AB* = 6

40. *AB* = 9

39. *AB* = 8

41. *AB* = *s*

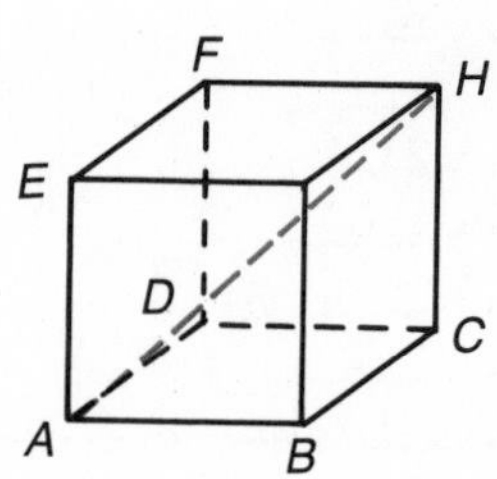

SKILLS MAINTENANCE

Factor by removing a common factor.

1. $5x - 5y$ **2.** $0.3k + 0.15n$

3. $12xy + 6x$ **4.** $3x^2 + 9xy$

Factor completely.

5. $x^2 - y^2$ **6.** $s^2 - 9$

7. $a^2 + 2ab + b^2$ **8.** $100x^2 - 20xy + y^2$

9. $36x^2 + 12x + 1$ **10.** $0.09a^2 - 0.25b^2$

11. $3x^2 - 13x + 14$ **12.** $2x^2 + 17x + 21$

13. $5w^2 + 13w + 6$ **14.** $5p^2 + 3p - 2$

15. $5x^2 - 35x + 30$ **16.** $\frac{1}{2}x^2 + 2x + 2$

17. $\frac{1}{2}a^2 - a + \frac{1}{2}$ **18.** $0.5x^2 + 5x + 12.5$

19. $k^4 + \frac{2}{3}k^2 + \frac{1}{9}$ **20.** $\frac{1}{16}r^4 - 1$

Factor by grouping.

21. $x^3 + 3x^2 - x - 3$ **22.** $t^3 + t^2 - t - 1$

Determine b so that the expression is a trinomial square.

23. $x^2 + 16x + b$ **24.** $x^2 + bx + 81$

CALCULATOR

In the figure below, all surfaces are rectangular. The projections at either end are identical, and the dimensions are as shown. If one quart of paint will cover 130 square feet, how many quarts should you buy to paint the entire surface?

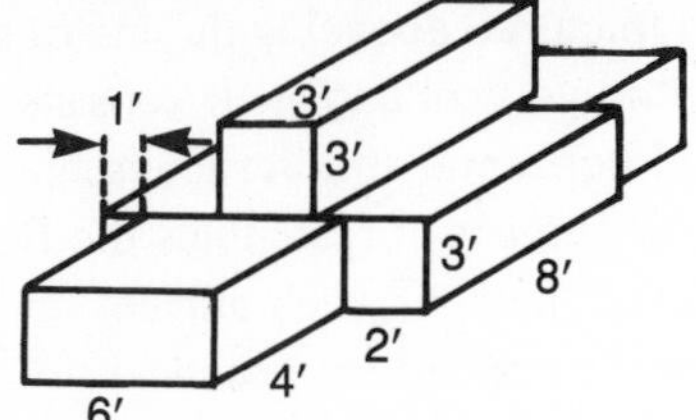

Skills Maintenance

1. $5(x - y)$
2. $0.15(2k + n)$
3. $6x(2y + 1)$
4. $3x(x + 3y)$
5. $(x + y)(x - y)$
6. $(s + 3)(s - 3)$
7. $(a + b)^2$
8. $(10x - y)^2$
9. $(6x + 1)^2$
10. $(0.3a + 0.5b)(0.3a - 0.5b)$
11. $(3x - 7)(x - 2)$
12. $(2x + 3)(x + 7)$
13. $(5w + 3)(w + 2)$
14. $(5p - 2)(p + 1)$
15. $5(x - 6)(x - 1)$
16. $\frac{1}{2}(x + 2)^2$
17. $\frac{1}{2}(a - 1)^2$
18. $0.5(x + 5)^2$
19. $(k^2 + \frac{1}{3})^2$
20. $\frac{1}{16}(r^2 + 4)(r + 2)(r - 2)$
21. $(x + 3)(x + 1)(x - 1)$
22. $(t + 1)^2(t - 1)$
23. $b = 64$
24. $b = 18$

Calculator

3 quarts

CAREER/Surveyor

Since 2700 B.C., when the first measurements of land and water areas and boundaries were made, geometry has been used in surveying. Through mathematics, new instruments and methods have been developed that allow the modern surveyor to measure distance, depth, altitude, slope, volume, direction, and angle—all with a high degree of accuracy.

Many of today's methods, however, employ principles developed thousands of years ago. For example, the chain and the steel tape, both used for measuring distance, resemble the simpler device used in Thebes in 1400 B.C. To measure a grainfield, workers would stretch a rope, knotted or marked at uniform intervals, across the field. The Roman architect and engineer Vitruvius invented another instrument for measuring distance in 15 B.C. He mounted a large wheel of a known circumference in a small frame, much like the wheel of a wheelbarrow. As he pushed it along the ground by hand, it automatically dropped a pebble into a container at each revolution, thus measuring the distance traveled. Today's odometer operates on the same principle.

An invention that made possible construction of the Romans' great road system was the plane table, the first device capable of measuring angles. It consisted of a drawing board on a stable support and a straightedge, along which lines were drawn. With it, the Roman builders were able to construct 90° and 180° planes.

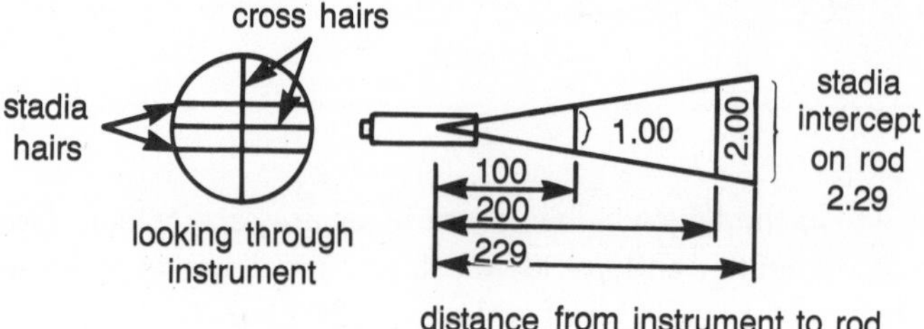

Today, a *theodolite* (pictured above) is the instrument commonly used to measure horizontal and vertical angles. It consists of a sighting tube in the form of a telescope and of horizontal and vertical scales. Although the theodolite is a more sophisticated instrument, it resembles the Roman plane table in principle. Surveying is yet another field in which ancient and unchanging mathematical principles continue to be applied for practical purposes.

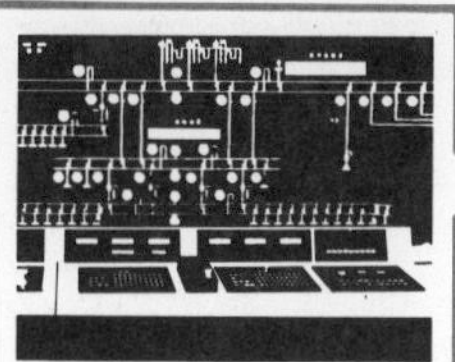

COMPUTER

Hero's Formula is used to find the area of any triangle given the lengths of all three sides. The formula is usually written as follows:

$$\text{Area} = \sqrt{s(s - a)\ (s - b)\ (s - c)}.$$

The lengths of the sides are *a*, *b*, and *c*, and *s* is a constant value equal to $\frac{a + b + c}{2}$.

It is easy to use Hero's formula to compute the area of a single triangle with a calculator, but a computer can determine and compare the areas of *many* triangles in minimal time. To use Hero's formula, the values must be for a real triangle. That is, the sum of any two of the values must be greater than the third value. The program follows:

```
 5 REM HERO'S FORMULA
10 PRINT "ENTER LENGTHS OF SIDES OF TRIANGLE"
20 PRINT "TO STOP THE PROGRAM INPUT 0,0,0"
30 INPUT A,B,C
40 IF A = 0 THEN 90
50 LET S = (A + B + C)*0.5
60 LET R = SQR(S*(S-A)*(S-B)*(S-C))
70 PRINT "AREA OF TRIANGLE WITH SIDES";TAB(5);
   A;TAB(5);B;TAB(5);C.;"IS";R
80 GOTO 10
90 END
```

Use the program to find the area of triangles whose sides are as follows:

1. $a = 5$, $b = 12$, $c = 13$

2. $a = 7.5$, $b = 7.5$, $c = 12$

3. $a = 44$, $b = 55$, $c = 66$

4. Run the program keeping two sides of the triangle the same while varying the third side. What is the relationship between the resulting areas and the changes in the third side?

TEACHER'S RESOURCE MASTERS

Computer Master 9

Computer

1. 30.
2. 27
3. 1200.5
4. Area decreases when the length of the third side increases to $1\frac{1}{2}$ times the length of the other two sides.

TEACHER'S RESOURCE MASTERS

Enrichment Master 6

ENRICHMENT

See Activities 17–18, p. T49

Chapter 9 Review

1. Area
2. congruent
3. triangular
4. 10
5. 72
6. 3, 9
7. 141
8. $4x$
9. 72 in.^{2}
10. 6

CHAPTER 9 REVIEW

VOCABULARY

altitude of a parallelogram (9.4)
altitude of a trapezoid (9.4)
area of a polygonal region (9.1)
height (9.2)
length (9.2)
polygon (9.1)
polygonal region (9.1)
triangular region (9.1)
width (9.2)

REVIEW EXERCISES

9.1 **Complete the following statements, referring to the figure.**

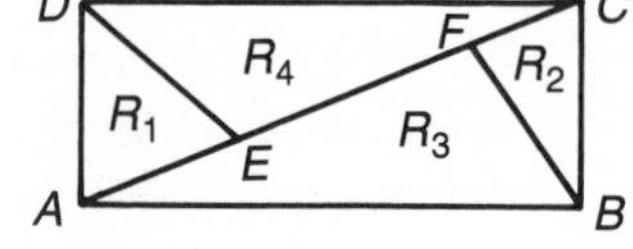

1. Postulate 17 is called the _____ Postulate because it assigns a unique positive number to every polygonal region.
2. Postulate 18 states that if $\triangle AED$ and $\triangle BFC$ are _____, R_1 and R_2 have the same area.
3. Quadrilateral *ABCD* defines a region because it is comprised of _____ regions intersecting in segments.
4. If the area of quadrilateral $ABCD = 110$, $R_4 = 45$, $R_3 = R_4$, and $R_1 = R_2$, what is the area of R_2?
5. If the area of $R_1 = 11$, $R_3 = 25$, $R_1 = R_2$, and $R_3 = R_4$, what is the area of *ABCD?*

9.2

6. A rectangle has an area of 27 square inches. The length is one third as long as the width. Find the length and width of the rectangle.

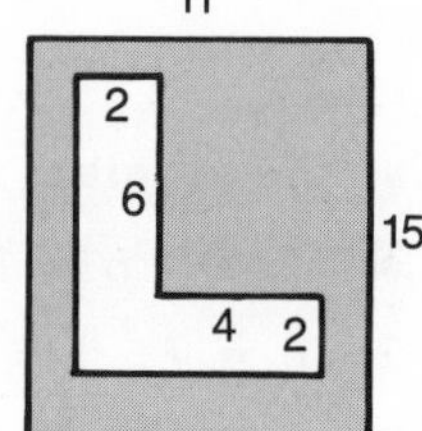

7. Find the area of the shaded region in the figure at the right.

8. The area of a square is $16x^2$. Find the length of each side of the square.
9. In the checkerboard at the right, the side of each square is $1\frac{1}{2}$ inches. What is the total area of the dark squares?

9.3

10. In right $\triangle ABC$, if $AB = 3$, $BC = 4$, and $m\angle B = 90$, what is the area of $\triangle ABC$?

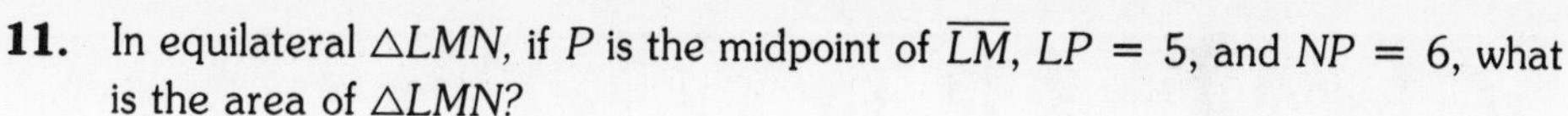

11. In equilateral $\triangle LMN$, if P is the midpoint of $\overline{LM}$, $LP = 5$, and $NP = 6$, what is the area of $\triangle LMN$?

12. Find the area of the triangle at the right. $BD = 3$, $AC = 8$.

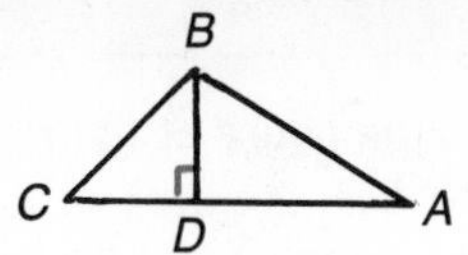

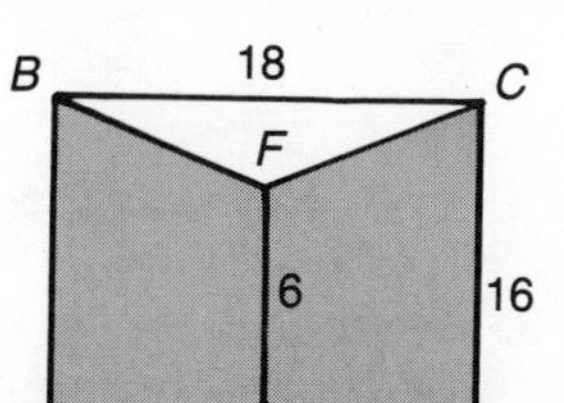

13. Find the area of the shaded region in the figure at the left. $\triangle AED \cong \triangle BFC$.

For each of the following figures, find x.

9.4 **14.**

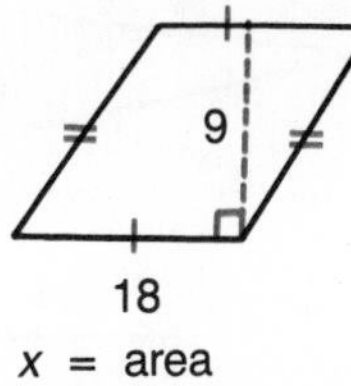

15.

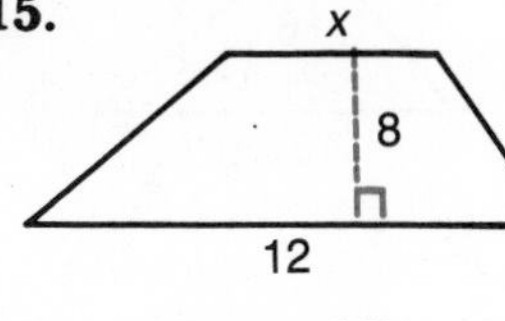

16.

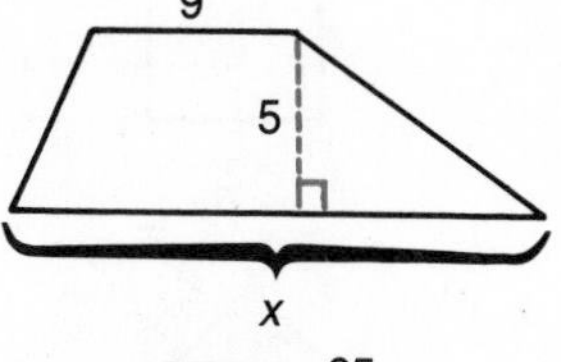

9.5 **17.**

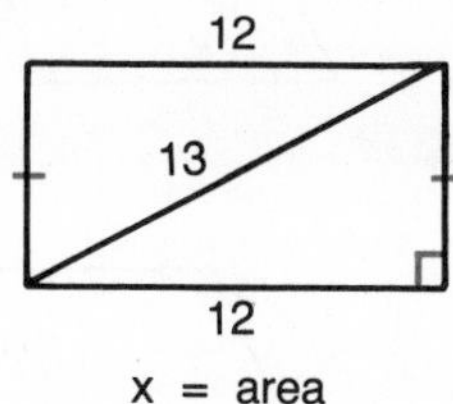

18.

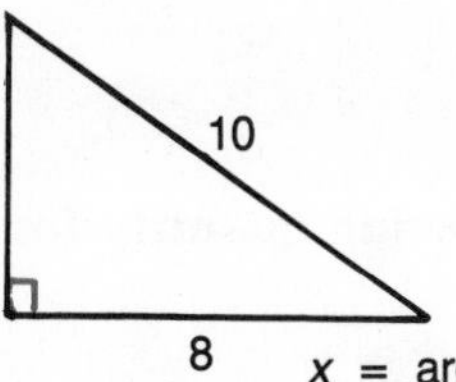

19.

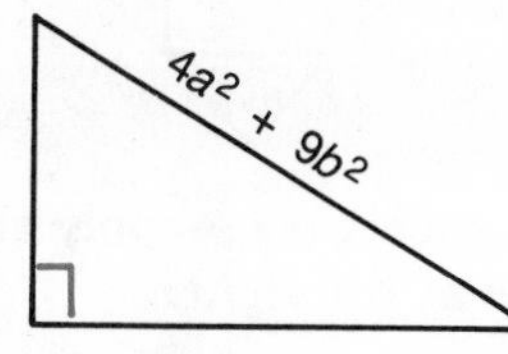

9.6 **20.**

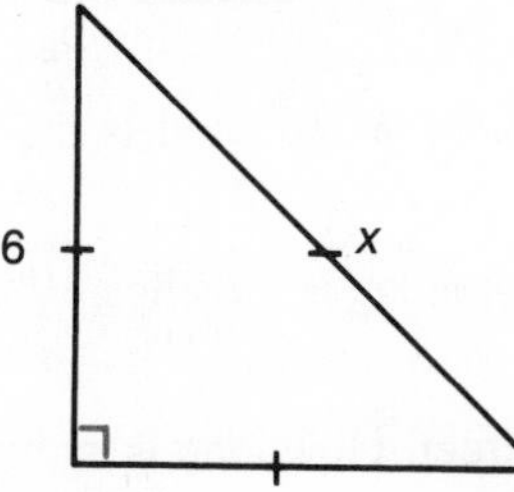

21.

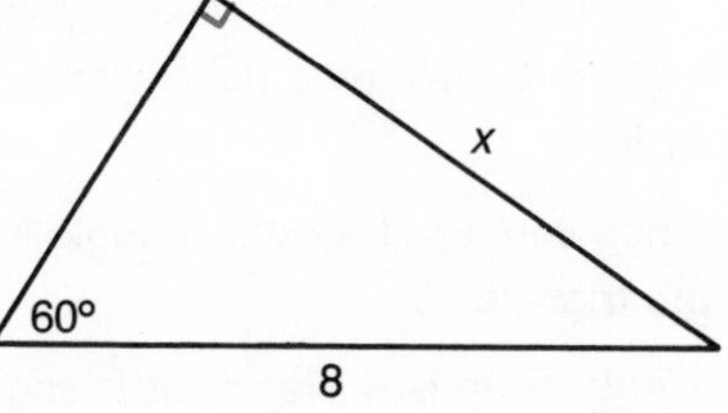

22.

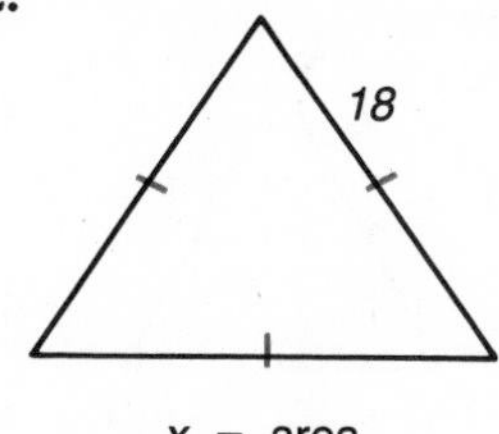

23.

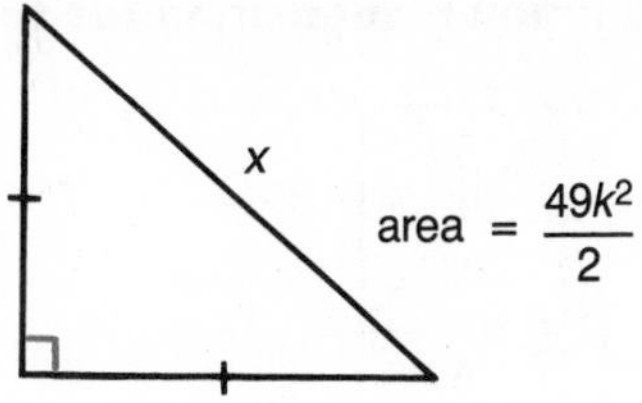

11. 30
12. 12
13. 198
14. 162
15. 6
16. 17
17. 60
18. 24
19. $6ab$
20. $6\sqrt{2}$
21. $4\sqrt{3}$
22. $81\sqrt{3}$
23. $7k\sqrt{2}$

TEACHER'S RESOURCE MASTERS

Chapter 9 Test
Multiple Choice Test—Chapter 9
Chapter 9 Test

1. 23
2. 54
3. 144
4. 30
5. 9
6. 32
7. 108
8. 96
9. 30
10. 15
11. 12
12. 84 in.^{2}
13. 10
14. 8
15. $8\sqrt{2}$
16. 8

CHAPTER 9 TEST

1. In the figure at the right, $\triangle ABD \cong \triangle CDB$, the area of $\triangle AFD = 17$, and the area of $\triangle AFB = 6$. What is the area of $\triangle CDB$?

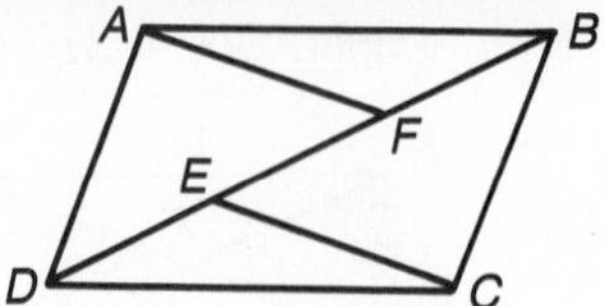

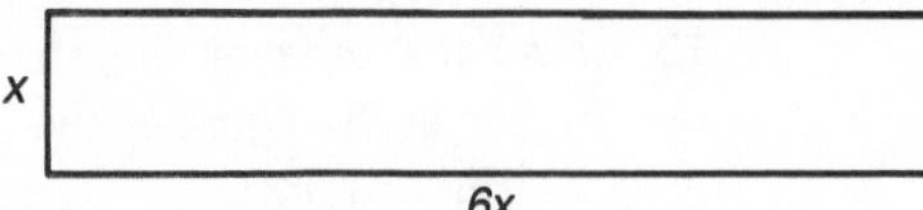

2. In the rectangle at the left, if $x = 3$, what is the area of the rectangle?

Find the area of each polygonal region.

3.

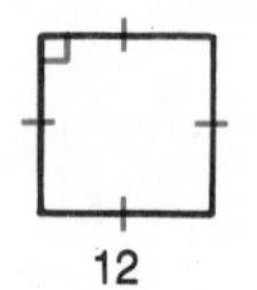

4.

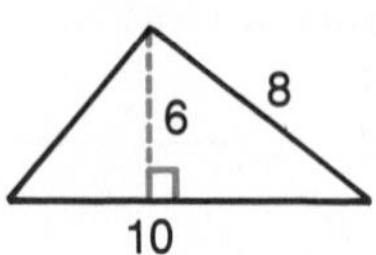

5.

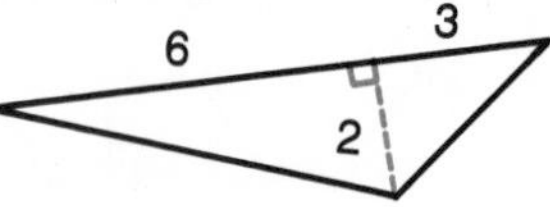

6.

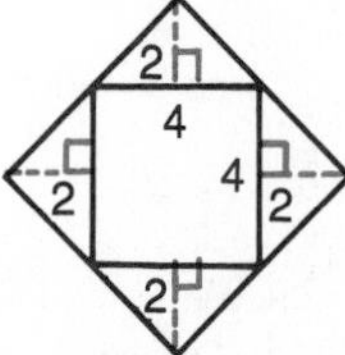

7.

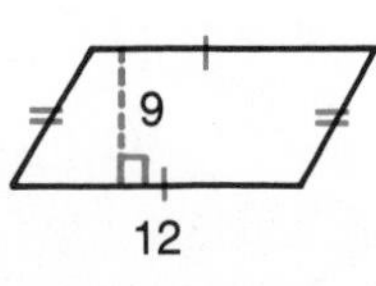

8.

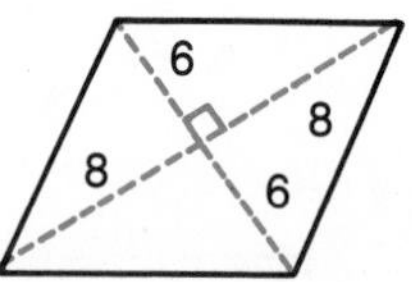

In each case, supply the missing quantity for the figure at the right.

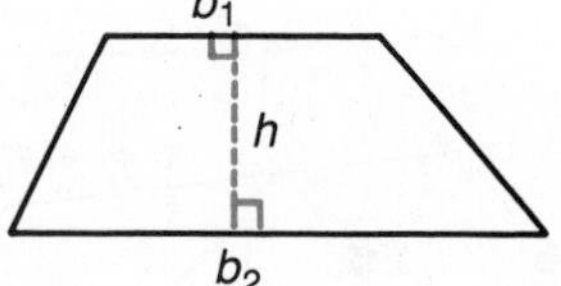

9. $b_1 = 4$, $b_2 = 6$, $h = 6$, area = _____

10. $b_1 = 13$, $b_2 =$ _____, $h = 6$, area = 84

11. If the hypotenuse of a right triangle is 20 and one leg is 16, what is the length of the other leg?

12. The hypotenuse of a right triangle is 25 inches and one leg is 7 inches. What is the area of the triangle?

13. The area of an isosceles right triangle is 25 square feet. How long is its hypotenuse?

Find the unknown quantities for the following figures.

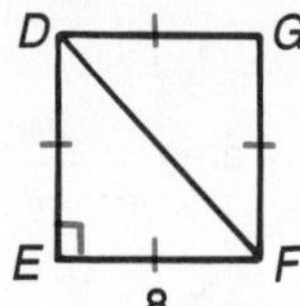

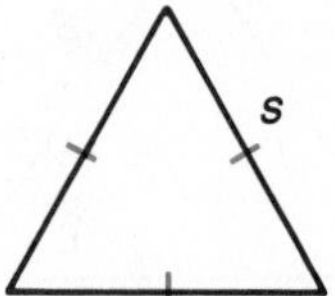

14. $DE =$ _____ **15.** $DF =$ _____ **16.** Area $= 16\sqrt{3}$, $s =$ _____

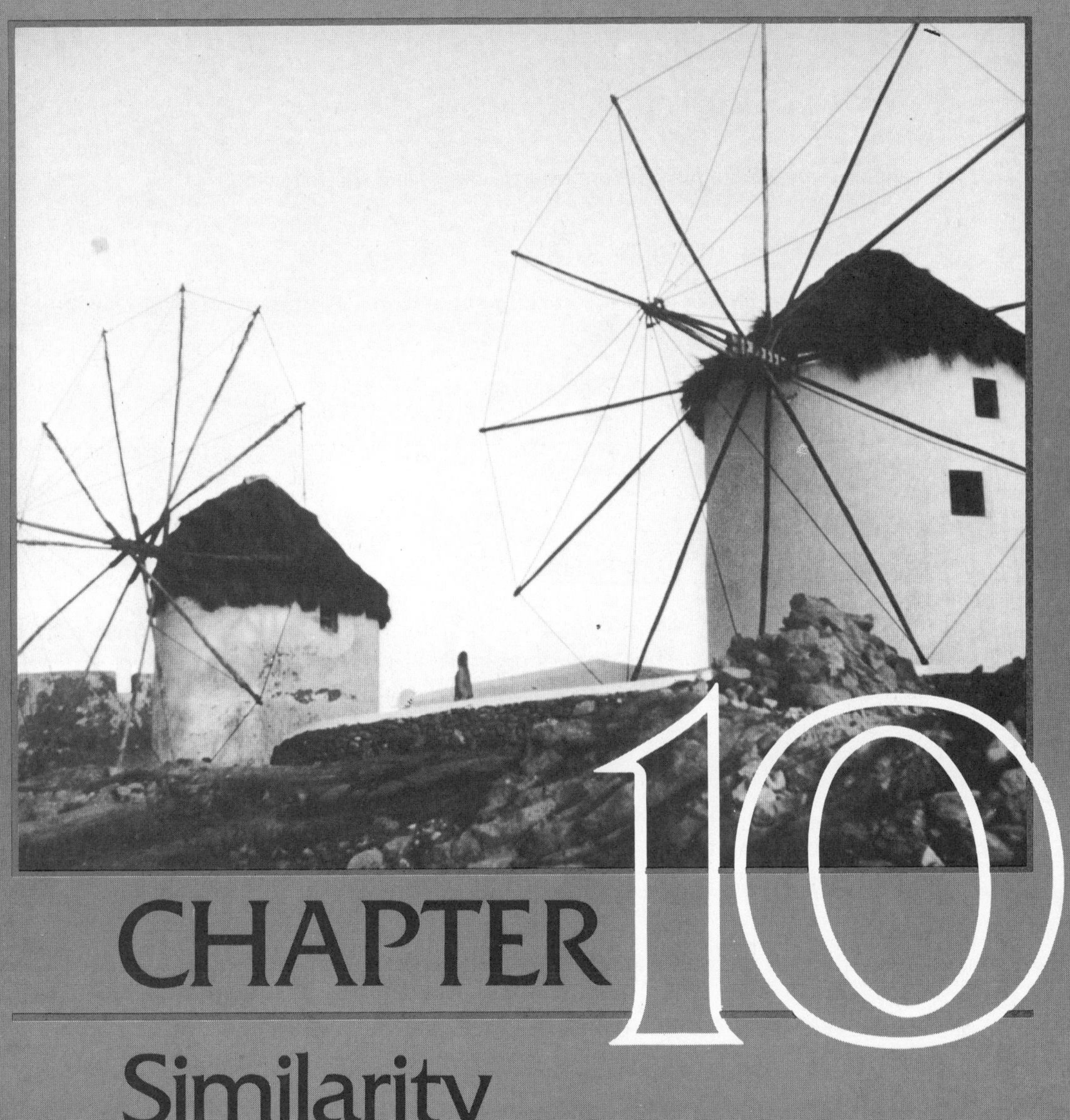

CHAPTER 10

Similarity

OBJECTIVE

Write ratios and proportions, solve proportions, and identify the properties of proportions.

TEACHER'S NOTES

See p. T34

MIXED REVIEW

1. Give four ways to prove any triangles are similar. AAA, AA, SAS, SSS
2. Add $\frac{3x}{x+2} + \frac{x}{x-2}$. $\frac{4x^2 - 4x}{(x+2)(x-2)}$
3. Multiply $\frac{x+2}{x^2 - x - 12} \cdot \frac{(x-4)}{x^2 + 3x + 2}$. $\frac{1}{(x+3)(x+1)}$
4. Simplify $\sqrt{(-1-6)^2 + (-12-12)^2}$. 25
5. What is the slope of a line with the equation $2x - 4y = 3$? $\frac{1}{2}$

TEACHER'S RESOURCE MASTERS

Practice Master 29, Part 1

10.1 Concepts of Similarity and Proportion

In algebra, you may have encountered problems like the following:

$$\frac{5}{12} = \frac{x}{10} \quad \frac{a}{b} = \frac{x}{y} \quad \frac{2}{x+4} = \frac{3}{2y-7}$$

Equations written in this form are called **proportions.** A proportion is an equality of ratios. For example, in the proportion $\frac{a}{b} = \frac{x}{y}$, the ratios $\frac{a}{b}$ and $\frac{x}{y}$ have the same numerical value. This concept will now be extended to geometry.

DEFINITION: proportional

Given two sequences $a, b, c \ldots$ and $p, q, r \ldots$ of positive numbers, if $\frac{a}{p} = \frac{b}{q} = \frac{c}{r} = \ldots$, then the sequences $a, b, c \ldots$ and $p, q, r \ldots$ are called **proportional.**

When you are working with proportions, you may find it necessary to express a given proportion in another form. The special properties of proportions that allow you to do this are stated below. It is assumed that none of the variables may be zero.

1. $\frac{a}{b} = \frac{c}{d}$ and $ad = bc$ are equivalent.

   a and *d* are called the extremes, while *b* and *c* are called the means. The product of the means is equal to the product of the extremes. This is sometimes called **cross-multiplication.**

2. $\frac{a}{b} = \frac{c}{d}, \frac{a}{c} = \frac{b}{d}, \frac{b}{a} = \frac{d}{c}, \frac{c}{a} = \frac{d}{b}$ are equivalent.

   Each proportion is formed by transforming the equation $ad = bc$.

3. $\frac{a}{b} = \frac{c}{d}$ is equivalent to $\frac{a+b}{b} = \frac{c+d}{d}$.

   Adding 1 to the proportion $\frac{a}{b} = \frac{c}{d}$ results in $\frac{a}{b} + 1 = \frac{c}{d} + 1$.

   Replacing 1 with $\frac{b}{b}$ and $\frac{d}{d}$ yields $\frac{a}{b} + \frac{b}{b} = \frac{c}{d} + \frac{d}{d}$ and $\frac{a+b}{b} = \frac{c+d}{d}$.

4. $\frac{a}{b} = \frac{c}{d}$ is equivalent to $\frac{a-b}{b} = \frac{c-d}{d}$.

   The original equation is transformed as in #3 using subtraction instead of addition.

5. If $\frac{a}{b} = \frac{c}{d} = \frac{e}{f} = \ldots$, then $\frac{a+c+e+\cdots}{b+d+f+\cdots} = \frac{a}{b} = \frac{c}{d} = \ldots$.

Let n be the number that represents each ratio. This means

$\frac{a}{b} = n, \frac{c}{d} = n, \frac{e}{f} = n, \ldots$ and $a = bn, c = dn, e = fn \ldots.$

Therefore, $\frac{a + c + e + \cdots}{b + d + f + \cdots} = \frac{bn + dn + fn + \cdots}{b + d + f + \cdots} = \frac{(b + d + f + \cdots)n}{b + d + f + \cdots} = n$, which in turn equals $\frac{a}{b}, \frac{c}{d}, \frac{e}{f} \ldots.$

> **DEFINITION: geometric mean**
>
> If a, b, and c are positive numbers, and $\frac{a}{b} = \frac{b}{c}$, then b is called the **geometric mean** of a and c.

Applying cross-multiplication to the equation $\frac{a}{b} = \frac{b}{c}$, you find that $b^2 = ac$, or $b = \sqrt{ac}$.

Study the following examples, where the above properties are used.

Example: Supply the missing numbers: $\frac{1}{3} = \frac{7}{?} = \frac{?}{15} = \frac{14}{?} = \frac{?}{81}$

Solution: Solve each unknown separately, using the known proportion and cross multiplication.

$\frac{1}{3} = \frac{7}{d}$	$\frac{1}{3} = \frac{c}{15}$	$\frac{1}{3} = \frac{14}{d}$	$\frac{1}{3} = \frac{c}{81}$
$1 \cdot d = 3 \cdot 7$	$3 \cdot c = 1 \cdot 15$	$1 \cdot d = 3 \cdot 14$	$3 \cdot c = 1 \cdot 81$
$d = 21$	$c = 5$	$d = 42$	$c = 27$

Therefore, $\frac{1}{3} = \frac{7}{21} = \frac{5}{15} = \frac{14}{42} = \frac{27}{81}$

Example: Express as a ratio: 14 inches to 3 feet

Solution: Convert the measures into the same units: 3 feet = 36 inches. The resulting ratio is $\frac{14}{36}$, or $\frac{7}{18}$.

Example: Find the value of x.

$$\frac{7}{x} = \frac{21}{54}$$

Solution:

$$(21)(x) = (7)(54)$$
$$21x = 378$$
$$x = 18$$

Example: Find the geometric mean of 4 and 49.

Solution: Use the equation $\frac{a}{b} = \frac{b}{c}$ and solve for b.

$$\frac{4}{b} = \frac{b}{49}$$
$$b^2 = 196$$
$$b = 14$$

The geometric mean of 4 and 49 is 14.

ASSIGNMENT GUIDE

Day 1
Minimum 1-15
Regular 1-35 odd
Maximum 1-41 odd
Day 2
Minimum 19-33 odd
Regular 10-36 even
Maximum 10-40 even

Oral Exercises

1. $\frac{14}{3}$
2. A *ratio* is a comparison of numbers by division. A *proportion* is a true statement that ratios are equal.
3. $\frac{a}{b} = \frac{c}{d}$ is equivalent to $ad = bc$.
4. geometric mean
5. 3, 18, 4, 6
6. 44, 54, 18
7. 91, 66, 176
8. $5b$, $9b$, $10a$
9. $16x$, $30y$, $66y$, $20x$, $\frac{3y}{2}$

10.	T	11.	F
12.	T	13.	F
14.	T	15.	F
16.	F	17.	T
18.	F	19.	T
20.	T	21.	T
22.	$\frac{7}{4}$	23.	$\frac{-3}{8}$
24.	$\frac{r+s}{s}$	25.	$\frac{m-n}{n}$

Written Exercises

1.	$\frac{160}{11}$	2.	$\frac{4}{9}$
3.	$\frac{14}{9}$	4.	$\frac{7}{30}$
5.	$\frac{17}{6}$	6.	$\frac{47}{300}$
7.	$\frac{247}{300}$	8.	$\frac{17}{26}$

ORAL EXERCISES

1. What is the ratio of 2 weeks to 3 days?
2. Explain the difference between a ratio and a proportion.
3. State the cross-multiplication property of a proportion.
4. If $\frac{a}{x} = \frac{x}{b}$, then x is called the _____ of a and b.

Supply the missing numbers.

5. $\frac{1}{2} = \frac{?}{6} = \frac{9}{?} = \frac{2}{?} = \frac{?}{12}$
6. $\frac{3}{4} = \frac{33}{?} = \frac{?}{72} = \frac{?}{24}$
7. $\frac{7}{11} = \frac{?}{143} = \frac{42}{?} = \frac{112}{?}$
8. $\frac{a}{b} = \frac{5a}{?} = \frac{9a}{?} = \frac{?}{10b}$
9. $\frac{8x}{6y} = \frac{?}{12y} = \frac{40x}{?} = \frac{88x}{?} = \frac{?}{15y} = \frac{2x}{?}$

If $\frac{r}{s} = \frac{t}{u}$, then state whether each of the following is true or false.

10. $r \cdot u = s \cdot t$
11. $\frac{r}{u} = \frac{s}{t}$
12. $\frac{s}{r} = \frac{u}{t}$
13. $r \cdot s = t \cdot u$
14. $\frac{r}{t} = \frac{s}{u}$
15. $r \cdot t = s \cdot u$

If $c \cdot d = e \cdot f$, then state whether each of the following is true or false.

16. $\frac{c}{d} = \frac{e}{f}$
17. $\frac{e}{d} = \frac{c}{f}$
18. $c \cdot e = d \cdot f$
19. $\frac{d}{e} = \frac{f}{c}$
20. $\frac{c}{e} = \frac{f}{d}$
21. $\frac{d}{f} = \frac{e}{c}$
22. If $\frac{a}{b} = \frac{3}{4}$, what is $\frac{a+b}{b}$?
23. If $\frac{x}{y} = \frac{5}{8}$, what is $\frac{x-y}{y}$?
24. If $\frac{r}{s} = \frac{2}{11}$, what is $\frac{13}{11}$ in terms of r and s?
25. If $\frac{m}{n} = \frac{19}{13}$, what is $\frac{6}{13}$ in terms of m and n?

WRITTEN EXERCISES

A. Express the following as ratios.

1. 10 lb to 11 oz
2. 4 ft to 3 yd
3. 2 weeks to 9 days
4. 14 min to 1 hr
5. 17 in. to 0.5 ft
6. 47 cm to 3 m
7. 247 ml to 0.3L
8. 17 weeks to 0.5 years

Given $ax = by$, complete the following proportions.

9. $\frac{a}{y} =$ _____ **10.** $\frac{y}{x} =$ _____ **11.** _____ $= \frac{x}{b}$

12. $\frac{b}{x} =$ _____ **13.** _____ $= \frac{a}{b}$

B. Find the value of x.

14. $\frac{3}{14} = \frac{9}{x}$ **15.** $\frac{17}{8} = \frac{x}{64}$ **16.** $\frac{x}{13} = \frac{24}{39}$ **17.** $\frac{5}{x} = \frac{60}{84}$

18. $\frac{5}{x} = \frac{2}{9}$ **19.** $\frac{3}{7} = \frac{x}{10}$ **20.** $\frac{x}{8} = \frac{9}{2}$ **21.** $\frac{5}{11} = \frac{12}{x}$

Find the geometric mean of the following pairs of numbers.

22. 4 and 9 **23.** 16 and 4 **24.** 5 and 3 **25.** 9 and 7

Supply the missing number.

26. 8 is the geometric mean of 2 and _____.

27. 7 is the geometric mean of 10 and _____.

28. 21 is the geometric mean of 7 and _____.

29. 25 is the geometric mean of 6 and _____.

Find the value of x.

30. $\frac{x}{8} = \frac{11}{x}$ **31.** $\frac{(x + 3)}{8} = \frac{(5x + 1)}{12}$

32. $\frac{6}{(2x + 3)} = \frac{10}{(7x - 6)}$ **33.** $\frac{2}{x} = \frac{3x}{24}$

C. 34. $\frac{x}{15} = \frac{10}{6x}$

35. Find x if $\frac{1}{x}$ is the geometric mean of 16 and 4.

36. Find x if $\frac{4}{(x + 3)} = \frac{(x + 9)}{18}$.

37. Find x if 6 is the geometric mean of $x - 1$ and $x + 4$.

38. Find y if $\frac{(y + 2)}{21} = \frac{3}{(2y - 7)}$. **39.** Find y if $\frac{(y - 3)}{y} = \frac{(2y + 2)}{(7y - 5)}$.

40. An architect must design an apartment building 110 feet wide, 90 feet long, and 140 feet high. His drafting paper is 24 × 30 inches. If he makes each drawing as large as possible (he can turn his paper vertically or horizontally), what will be the scale of feet per inch for each drawing of the front, side, and top of the building?

41. If he builds a model of the building on a board 4 × 4 ft, what will be the scale of feet per inch?

9. $\frac{b}{x}$ 10. $\frac{a}{b}$
11. $\frac{y}{a}$ 12. $\frac{a}{y}$
13. $\frac{y}{x}$ 14. 42
15. 136 16. 8
17. 7 18. $22\frac{1}{2}$
19. $4\frac{2}{7}$ 20. 36
21. $26\frac{2}{5}$ 22. 6
23. 8 24. $\sqrt{15}$
25. $3\sqrt{7}$ 26. 32
27. $4\frac{9}{10}$ 28. 63
29. $104\frac{1}{6}$ 30. $2\sqrt{22}$
31. 1 32. 3
33. 4 34. 5
35. $\frac{1}{8}$ 36. 3
37. 5 38. 7 39. 5 or $\frac{3}{5}$
40. NOTE: Assume that the edge of the paper can be used for the outside lines of the drawings.
Front: (110′ × 140′)
Drawing = 23.6″ × 30″
Scale: 1 in. = $4\frac{2}{3}$ ft

Side: (90′ × 140′)
Drawing = 19.3″ × 30″
Scale: 1 in. = $4\frac{2}{3}$ ft

Top: (90′ × 110′)
Drawing = 24″ × $29\frac{1}{3}$″
Scale: 1 in. = 3.75 ft
41. Model base (90′ × 110′) = 39.3 × 48 in. Scale: 1 in. = 2.29 ft

OBJECTIVE

Use the Basic Proportionality Theorem to find the length of a side of a triangle.

TEACHER'S NOTES

See p. T34

MIXED REVIEW

1. Find the perimeter and area of a right triangle with legs of 10 and 24. P = 60 A = 120
2. Find the coordinates of the midpoint between (−2, 7) and (12, −5). (5, 1)
3. Are corresponding angles always congruent? no
4. What is the diagonal of a square with sides of 7? $7\sqrt{2}$
5. Find the altitude to the hypotenuse of a right triangle with legs of 6 and 8. h = 4.8

TEACHER'S RESOURCE MASTERS

Practice Master 29, Part 2

10.2 Conditions for Similar Polygons

Two geometric figures are said to be **similar** if they have the same shape but not necessarily the same size. Each pair of figures shown below (circles, squares, triangles, pentagons) are considered similar because they have the same shape.

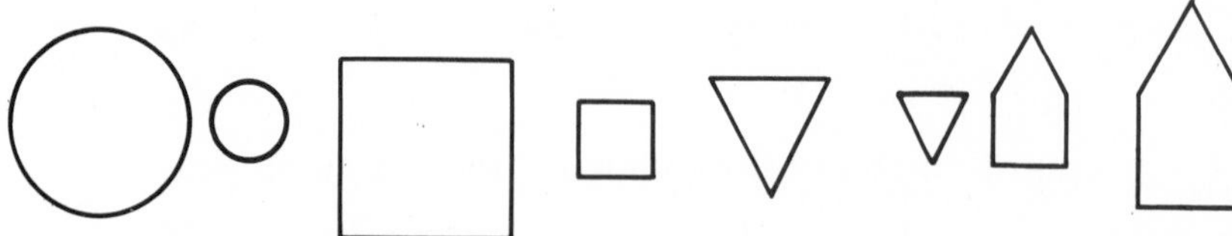

If two figures are congruent, they are also similar. The converse is not true, however, because similarity does not relate to size. Thus, one of two similar figures may be enlarged or made smaller without altering their similarity, as long as the shape is not altered. In the figure below, $\triangle ABC$ and $\triangle DEF$ are similar because each side of $\triangle ABC$ is three times as long as each side of $\triangle DEF$.

The symbol $\sim$ is used when referring to polygons to mean "is similar to." For example, $\triangle ABC \sim \triangle DFE$ means that $\triangle ABC$ and $\triangle DFE$ are similar.

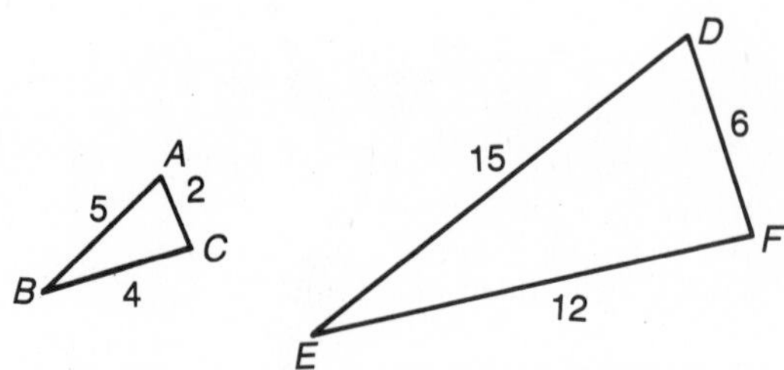

Because geometric similarity depends on shape rather than size, similar figures have congruent angles and *proportional,* rather than congruent, sides. This connection between similarity and proportion is established in the next definition.

> **DEFINITION: similarity**
> Given a correspondence between two polygons, if corresponding angles are congruent, and corresponding sides are proportional, then the correspondence is called a **similarity,** and the polygons are said to be similar.

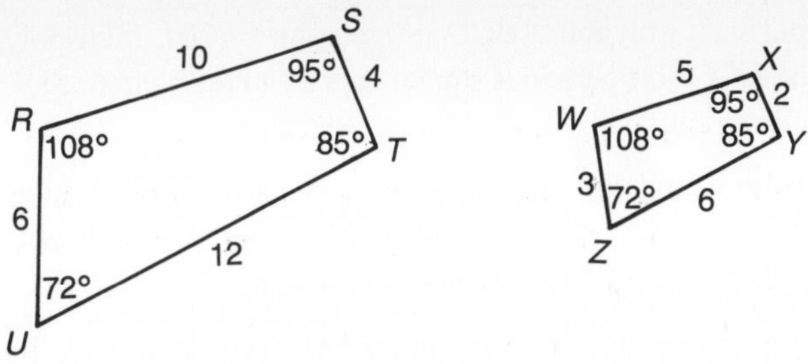

The two figures shown above have congruent corresponding angles:

$$\angle R \cong \angle W \qquad \angle S \cong \angle X \qquad \angle T \cong \angle Y \qquad \angle U \cong \angle Z$$

and proportional corresponding sides: $\frac{RS}{WX} = \frac{ST}{XY} = \frac{TU}{YZ} = \frac{UR}{ZW} = \frac{2}{1}$.

The requirements for similarity are therefore met, and quadrilateral $RSTU \sim$ quadrilateral $WXYZ$.

Only figures that satisfy both requirements of the definition are similar. For example, two figures may have congruent corresponding angles, but if their sides are not proportional, the figures are not similar. In the figure below, square $ABCD$ and rectangle $EFGH$ have congruent corresponding angles, but they are not similar.

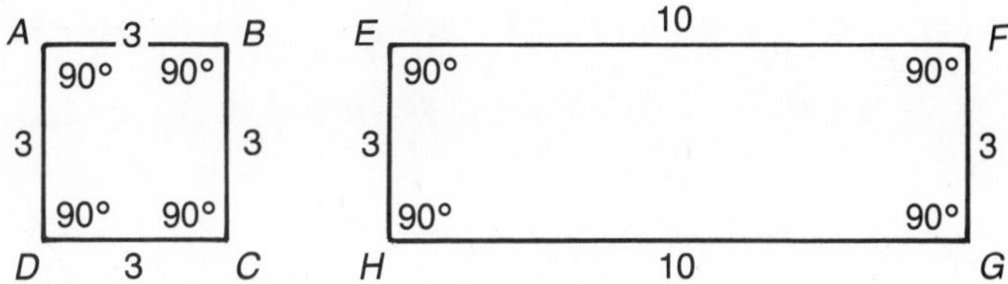

Likewise, two figures may have proportional corresponding sides, but if their corresponding angles are not congruent, the figures are not similar. Although the sides of rectangle $IJKL$ are proportional to the sides of ▱$MNOP$, their corresponding angles are not congruent, so rectangle $IJKL \nsim$ ▱$MNOP$.

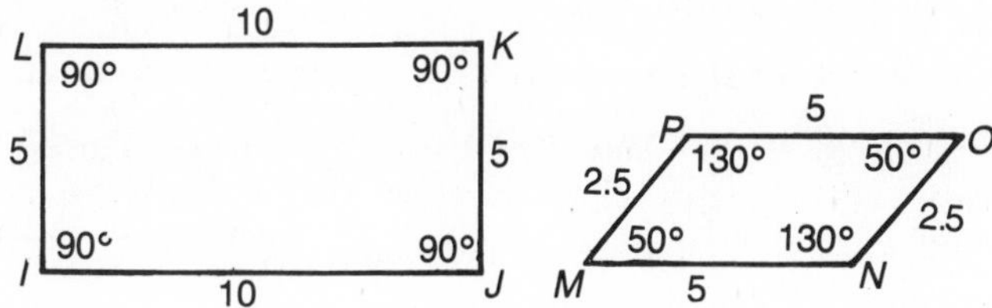

Because the following properties are true, similarity between polygons is an equivalence relation.

1. Reflexive property: polygon $ABCD \sim$ polygon $ABCD$. That is, every polygon is similar to itself.

2. Symmetric property: If polygon $ABCD \sim$ polygon $EFGH$, then polygon $EFGH \sim$ polygon $ABCD$. That is, if one polygon is similar to a second polygon, then the second polygon is similar to the first polygon.

3. Transitive property: If polygon $ABCD \sim$ polygon $EFGH$, and polygon $EFGH \sim$ polygon $IJKL$, then polygon $ABCD \sim$ polygon $IJKL$. That is, if two polygons are each similar to a third polygon, then they are similar to each other.

The first two theorems of this chapter can be used to prove a new property of triangles that will be useful in exploring similarity.

THEOREM 10.1 (The Basic Proportionality Theorem)
If a line parallel to one side of a triangle intersects the other sides in distinct points, then it intercepts segments that are proportional to these sides.

Given: $\overline{XY} \parallel \overline{BC}$

Prove: $\frac{AX}{AB} = \frac{AY}{AC}$

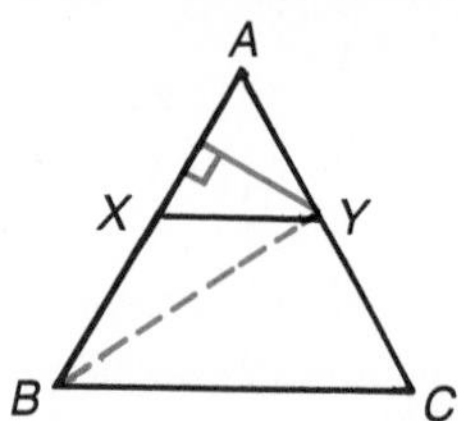

Proof: In $\triangle AXY$ (with $\overline{AX}$ as base) and $\triangle XBY$ (with $\overline{XB}$ as base), the altitudes drawn from Y are the same. So, (1) $\frac{\text{the area of } \triangle XBY}{\text{the area of } \triangle AXY} = \frac{XB}{AX}$ by Theorem 9.3.

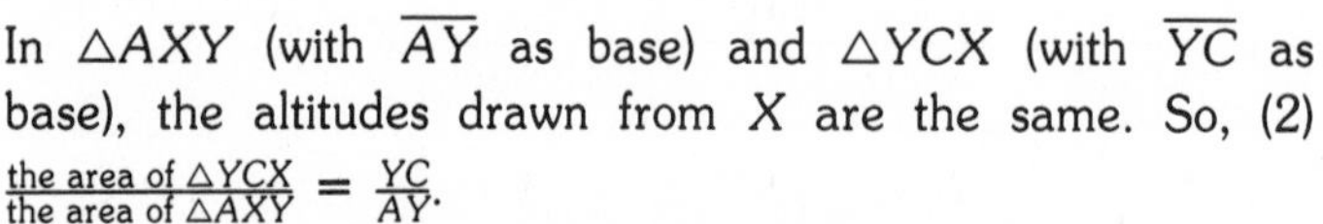

In $\triangle AXY$ (with $\overline{AY}$ as base) and $\triangle YCX$ (with $\overline{YC}$ as base), the altitudes drawn from X are the same. So, (2) $\frac{\text{the area of } \triangle YCX}{\text{the area of } \triangle AXY} = \frac{YC}{AY}$.

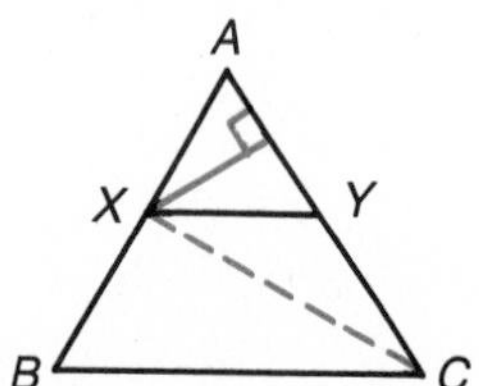

Because $\overline{XY} \parallel \overline{BC}$, $\triangle XBY$ and $\triangle YCX$ have the same altitude to their common base $\overline{XY}$, as shown in red. Therefore, (3) the area of $\triangle XBY$ = the area of $\triangle YCX$ by Theorem 9.4. Combining equations (1), (2), and (3) yields

$\frac{XB}{AX} = \frac{\text{the area of } \triangle XBY}{\text{the area of } \triangle AXY} = \frac{\text{the area of } \triangle YCX}{\text{the area of } \triangle AXY} = \frac{YC}{AY}$,

or (4) $\frac{XB}{AX} = \frac{YC}{AY}$. Adding 1 to each side results in $\frac{AX + XB}{AX} = \frac{AY + YC}{AY}$, or $\frac{AB}{AX} = \frac{AC}{AY}$. This is equivalent to $\frac{AX}{AB} = \frac{AY}{AC}$.

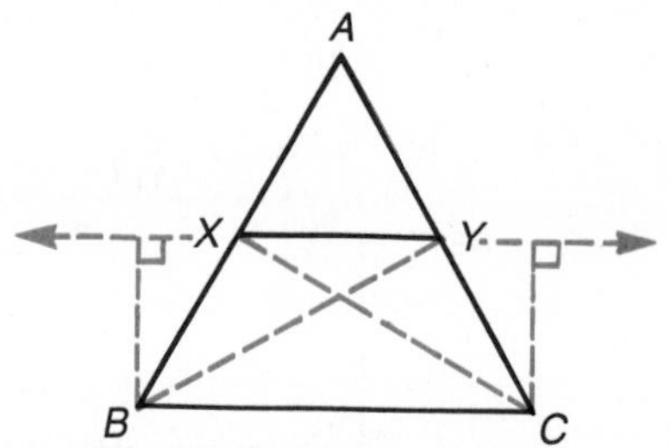

The converse of Theorem 10.1 can also be proved.

THEOREM 10.2
If a line intersects two sides of a triangle and intercepts segments proportional to these sides, then it is parallel to the third side.

Given: $\frac{AX}{AB} = \frac{AY}{AC}$

Prove: $\overline{XY} \parallel \overline{BC}$

Proof: Suppose $\overline{XY}$ and $\overline{BC}$ are not parallel. Then there is a segment through B parallel to $\overline{XY}$, intersecting $\overleftrightarrow{AY}$ at some point C' different from C. Then by Theorem 10.1, $\frac{AX}{AB} = \frac{AY}{AC'}$. Comparing this proportion with the given suggests that $AC = AC'$, or C and C' are the same point. Therefore, by indirect proof, the supposition is false, and $\overline{XY}$ and $\overline{BC}$ must be parallel.

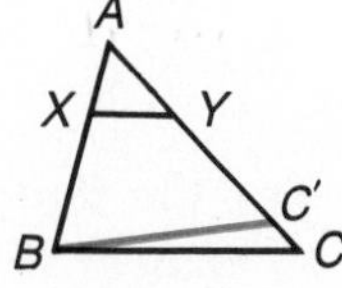

ASSIGNMENT GUIDE

Minimum 1-15 odd
Regular 1-21 odd
Maximum 1-17 odd, 18-22

ORAL EXERCISES

Complete the following statements with sometimes, always, or never.

1. Two equilateral triangles are _____ similar.
2. Two isosceles triangles are _____ similar.
3. An isosceles triangle is _____ similar to a scalene triangle.
4. Two scalene triangles with the same area are _____ similar.
5. Similar polygons _____ have the same shape.
6. Two squares are _____ similar.

Refer to the figure to complete the following proportions, given $\overline{AB} \parallel \overline{XY}$.

7. $\frac{ZA}{AX} = \frac{?}{?}$ 8. $\frac{XZ}{AZ} = \frac{?}{?}$ 9. $\frac{XZ}{XA} = \frac{?}{?}$

10. $\frac{BY}{YZ} = \frac{?}{?}$ 11. $\frac{BZ}{ZY} = \frac{?}{?}$ 12. $\frac{BZ}{BY} = \frac{?}{?}$

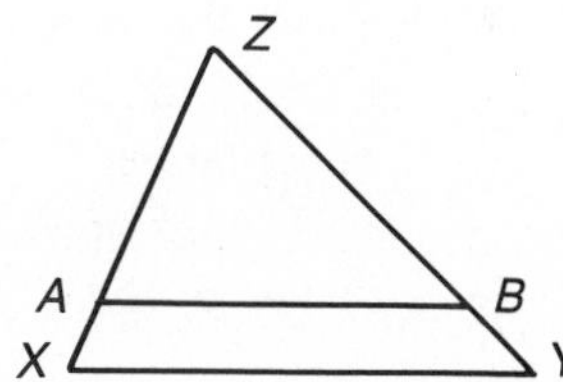

Oral Exercises

1. always
2. sometimes
3. never
4. sometimes
5. always
6. always
7. $\frac{ZB}{BY}$ 8. $\frac{YZ}{YB}$
9. $\frac{AZ}{ZX}$ 10. $\frac{YZ}{BZ}$
11. $\frac{AX}{XZ}$ 12. $\frac{AZ}{AX}$

WRITTEN EXERCISES

A. Use the figure at the right, in which $\overline{AB} \parallel \overline{RS}$, to answer the following.

1. If $AT = 6$, $BT = 5$, and $RT = 12$, find ST.
2. If $AT = 8$, $TR = 20$, and $ST = 15$, find BT.
3. If $AT = 6$, $AR = 9$, and $BT = 5$, find BS.
4. If $BT = 4$, $BS = 8$, and $AT = 5$, find TR.
5. If $BT = 7$, $BS = 14$, and $RT = 36$, find AR.

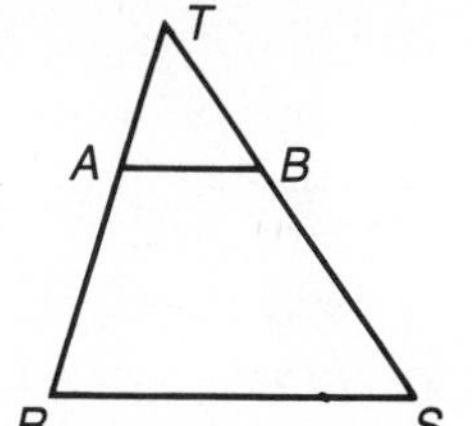

Written Exercises

1. 10 2. 6
3. $7\frac{1}{2}$ 4. 15
5. 24

6. yes
7. no
8. yes
9. $\frac{12}{5}$
10. $\frac{18}{11}$
11. 8
12. $\frac{30}{7}$
13. $\frac{7}{8}$
14. $\frac{14}{3}$
15. 10.5 sec
16. $11\frac{1}{5}$ in.
17. $x = \frac{18}{5}$, $y = \frac{10}{3}$, $z = \frac{20}{3}$
18. 1
19. 20
20. 4
21. 10, 5, 12, 6
22. Proof: By Thm. 10.1, $\frac{AF}{AE} = \frac{AB}{AC}$ and $\frac{ED}{EC} = \frac{AB}{AC}$. Thus, by transitivity, $\frac{AF}{AE} = \frac{ED}{EC}$, or $\frac{AE}{AF} = \frac{EC}{ED}$. Subtract 1 from each side: $\frac{AE - AF}{AF} = \frac{EC - ED}{ED}$, leaving $\frac{FE}{AF} = \frac{DC}{ED}$, or $\frac{AF}{FE} = \frac{ED}{DC}$.

In the figure at the right, which sets of lengths will result in $\overline{AB}$ being parallel to $\overline{RS}$?

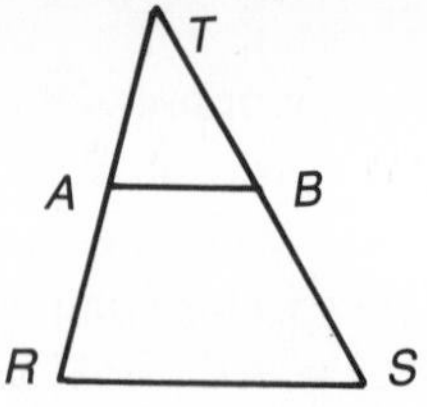

6. $AT = 6$; $AR = 9$; $BT = 4$; $BS = 6$

7. $RT = 14$; $AT = 4$; $ST = 12$; $BT = 2$

8. $RT = 24$; $AT = 8$; $ST = 21$; $SB = 14$

B. Use the figure at the right, in which $\overline{EB} \parallel \overline{DC}$, to answer the following.

9. If $AB = 8$, $BC = 2$, and $AD = 12$, find ED.

10. If $AC = 14$, $BC = 3$, and $AE = 6$, find ED.

11. If $AE = x$, $ED = 4$, $AB = x + 1$, and $BC = 4.5$, find x.

12. If $AD = 2x$, $AE = 6$, $AB = 7$, and $BC = 3$, find x.

13. If $AB = 3x$, $BC = x + 1$, $AD = 12$, and $ED = 5$, find x.

14. If $AD = 2x$, $ED = x - 2$, $AB = 5$, and $BC = 2$, find x.

15. A football player can run 40 yards in 4.2 seconds. At that rate how long would it take to run 100 yards?

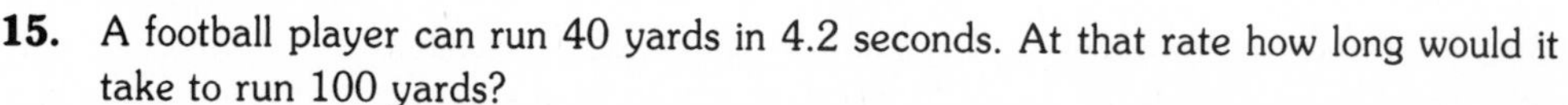

16. A photograph measures 7 inches by 5 inches. If it is enlarged so that the shorter dimension is 8 inches, what will be the larger dimension?

C. 17. Given that quadrilateral $ABCD$ and quadrilateral $RSTU$ are similar, find x, y, and z.

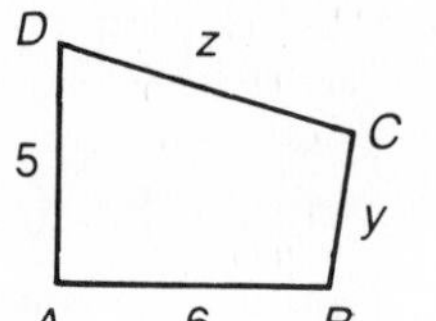

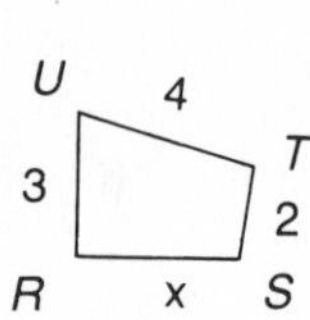

Use the figure at the right, in which $\overline{RS} \parallel \overline{XZ}$, to answer the following.

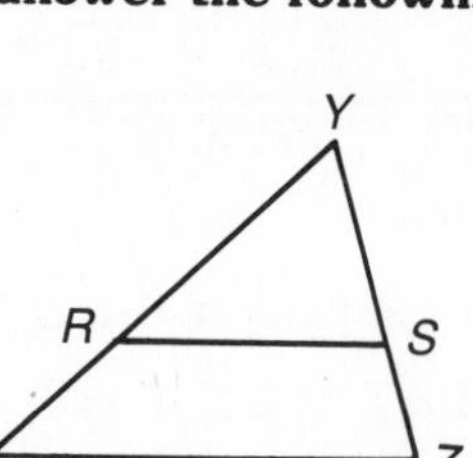

18. If $YR = x + 5$, $RX = x + 2$, $YS = x + 7$, and $SZ = x + 3$, find x.

19. If $YR = 3x$, $RX = x + 3$, $YS = 2x + 6$, and $SZ = x + 5$, find YZ.

20. If $YR = 2x$, $RX = YS = x + 4$, and $SZ = 4x + 1$, find YR.

21. If $YR = 3x + 1$, $RX = 2x - 1$, $YS = 2x + 6$, and $SZ = 3x - 3$, find the lengths of all four segments.

22. Given $\overline{FB} \parallel \overline{EC}$ and $\overline{BD} \parallel \overline{AE}$, prove that $\frac{AF}{FE} = \frac{ED}{DC}$.

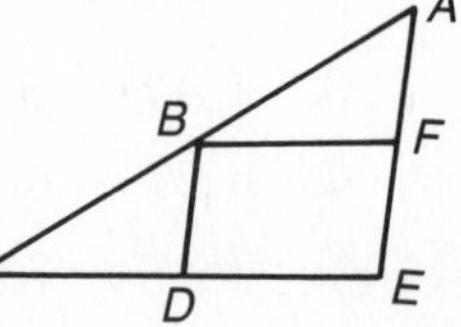

10.3 AAA and AA Similarities in Triangles

In Chapter 3 you learned that two triangles are congruent if the three angles and three sides of one triangle are congruent to the corresponding parts of the other triangle. Theorems were then introduced that allowed you to prove triangles congruent if only some of the corresponding parts are congruent (by SAS, ASA, SSS, LL, HL, or SAA).

This same process can be applied to proving similarity between triangles.

THEOREM 10.3 (The Angle-Angle-Angle [AAA] Similarity Theorem)
Given a correspondence between two triangles, if corresponding angles are congruent, then the correspondence is a similarity.

Given: $\triangle ABC \leftrightarrow \triangle XYZ$
$\angle A \cong \angle X$, $\angle B \cong \angle Y$
$\angle C \cong \angle Z$

Prove: $\triangle ABC \sim \triangle XYZ$

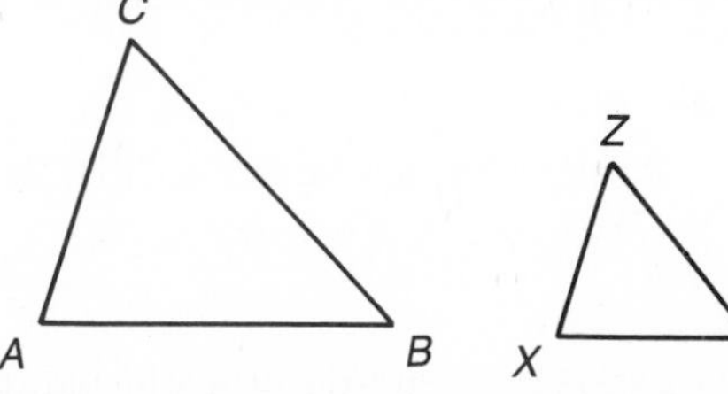

Proof: For $\triangle ABC \sim \triangle XYZ$, the corresponding angles must be congruent and the corresponding sides proportional.

You are given that the corresponding angles are congruent, so it is necessary only to prove that the corresponding sides are in proportion, or that $\frac{AC}{XZ} = \frac{AB}{XY} = \frac{BC}{YZ}$.

If $\triangle ABC \cong \triangle XYZ$, then $\frac{AC}{XZ} = \frac{AB}{XY} = \frac{BC}{YZ} = 1$. Therefore, suppose $\triangle ABC$ and $\triangle XYZ$ are not congruent. Then, because $\angle C \cong \angle Z$, the figure can be redrawn as shown below.

Because $\angle A \cong \angle CXY$, $\overline{AB} \parallel \overline{XY}$ by Theorem 8.7. Therefore, by Theorem 10.1, $\frac{XZ}{AC}$ $\frac{YZ}{BC}$ $\frac{AC}{XZ} = \frac{BC}{YZ}$. By the same reasoning, it is possible to show that $\frac{BC}{YZ} = \frac{AB}{XY}$. Applying the transitive property, you conclude that $\frac{AC}{XZ} = \frac{AB}{XY} = \frac{BC}{YZ}$, and $\triangle ABC \sim \triangle XYZ$ by definition.

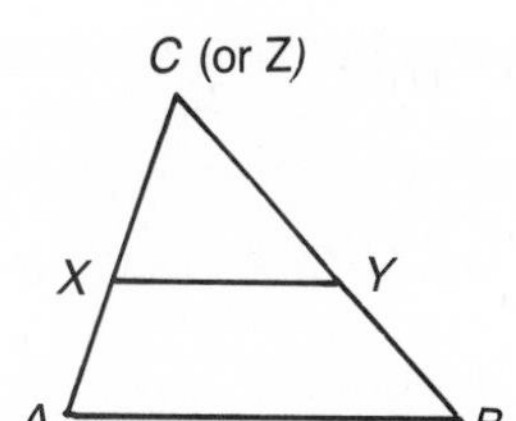

Theorem 10.3 suggests the next two corollaries.

COROLLARY 10.3.1 (The Angle-Angle [AA] Corollary)
Given a correspondence between two triangles, if two pairs of corresponding angles are congruent, then the correspondence is a similarity.

OBJECTIVE

Use AAA, AA, and ASA in proofs.

TEACHER'S NOTES

See p. T35

MIXED REVIEW

1. If $\triangle ABC \sim \triangle RST$, make four conclusions. $\angle A \cong \angle R$, $\angle B \cong \angle S$, $\angle C \cong \angle T$, $\frac{AB}{RS} = \frac{BC}{ST} = \frac{AC}{RT}$
2. If $\frac{a}{b} = \frac{c}{d}$, then $\frac{a+b}{b} =$ ______. $\frac{c+d}{d}$
3. If $\triangle ABC \cong \triangle POM$, what is the ratio of their areas? 1:1
4. If the sides of two squares are 3 and 5, what is the ratio of their areas? $\frac{9}{25}$
5. In an isosceles right triangle with a leg of x, the hypotenuse is ______. $x\sqrt{2}$

TEACHER'S RESOURCE MASTERS

Practice Master 30, Part 1

This corollary is based on Corollary 8.13.1. That is, if two pairs of corresponding angles are congruent in two triangles, then the third pair must also be congruent. This results in all three angles in one triangle being congruent to all three angles in the other triangle. Therefore, in the figure below, if $\angle A \cong \angle X$ and $\angle B \cong \angle Y$, then $\angle C$ must be congruent to $\angle Z$.

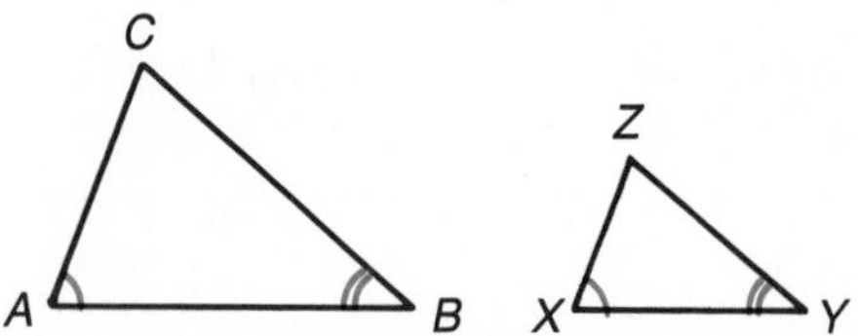

COROLLARY 10.3.2
If a line parallel to one side of a triangle intersects the other two sides in distinct points, then it intercepts a triangle similar to the given triangle.

Given: $\overline{XY} \parallel \overline{AB}$

Prove: $\triangle ABC \sim \triangle XYC$

Proof: Because $\overline{XY} \parallel \overline{AB}$, the two pairs of corresponding angles formed are congruent, so $\angle A \cong \angle CXY$ and $\angle B \cong \angle CYX$. Therefore, the two triangles are similar by Corollary 10.3.1.

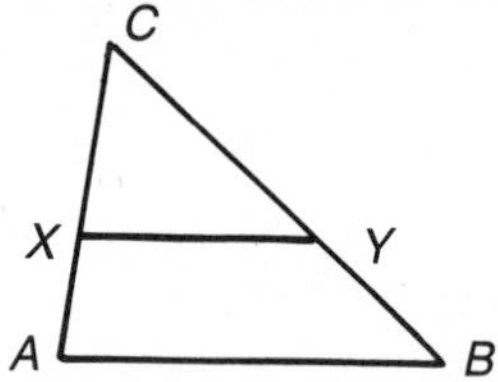

A line parallel to one side of a triangle does not necessarily have to intersect the other two sides of the triangle. When this situation occurs, Corollary 10.3.2 still applies. Thus, in both cases shown below, $\overline{XY} \parallel \overline{BC}$ and $\triangle AXY \sim \triangle ABC$.

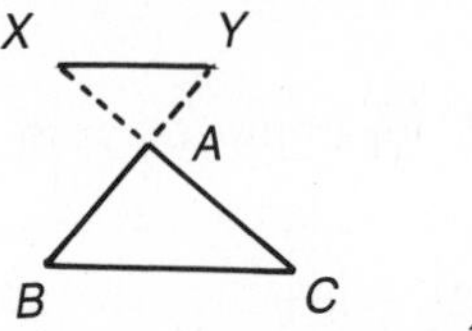

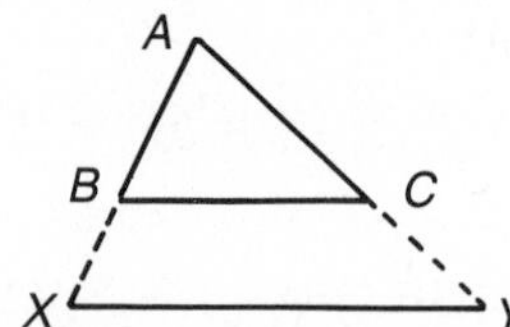

ASSIGNMENT GUIDE

Minimum 1-11
Regular 1-17 odd
Maximum 1-17 odd, 18-21

Oral Exercises

1. *XY, ZY, XZ*
2. *DE, ST, RT*
3. See text, Theorem 10.3.
4. See text, Corollary 10.3.1.
5. It intercepts a triangle similar to the given triangle.

ORAL EXERCISES

1. If $\triangle ABC \sim \triangle XYZ$, complete the extended proportion: $\frac{AB}{?} = \frac{CB}{?} = \frac{AC}{?}$.
2. If $\triangle RST \sim \triangle DEF$, complete the extended proportion: $\frac{RS}{?} = \frac{?}{EF} = \frac{?}{DF}$.
3. Give the full statement on similarity abbreviated as AAA.
4. Give the full statement on similarity abbreviated as AA.
5. Complete this statement: If a line parallel to one side of a triangle intersects the other two sides in distinct points, then ______.

6. If $\overline{EC} \parallel \overline{AB}$ in the figure at the right, complete the extended proportion $\frac{AD}{?} = \frac{AB}{?} = \frac{DB}{?}$.

7. If $\overline{SV} \parallel \overline{TU}$ in the figure at the right, complete the extended proportion $\frac{?}{VS} = \frac{RU}{?} = \frac{?}{RS}$.

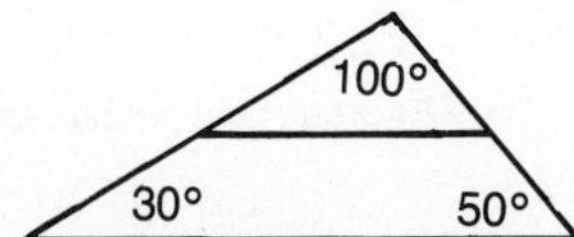

8. Are the two triangles shown in the figure at the left similar? What theorem supports your answer?

WRITTEN EXERCISES

A. Given $\overline{XY} \parallel \overline{AB}$ in $\triangle ABC$, complete each statement.

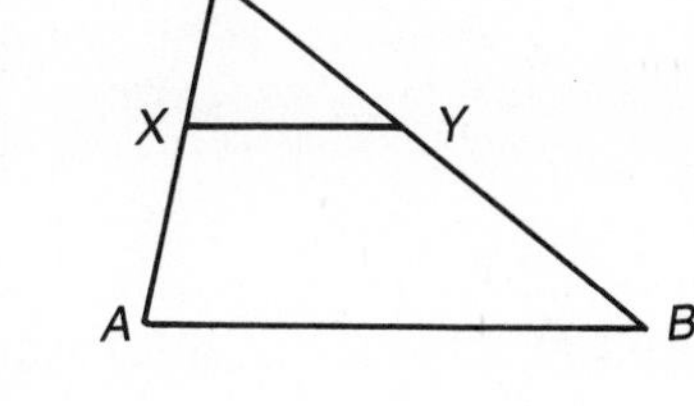

1. $\frac{XY}{?} = \frac{?}{CA} = \frac{?}{CB}$.

2. If $CX = 5$, $CA = 10$, and $XY = 6$, then $AB =$ _____.

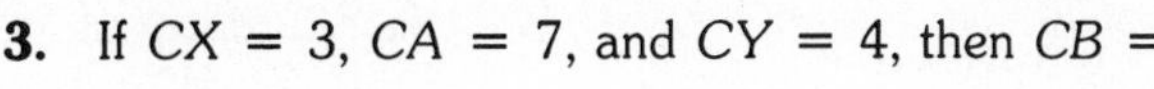

3. If $CX = 3$, $CA = 7$, and $CY = 4$, then $CB =$ _____.

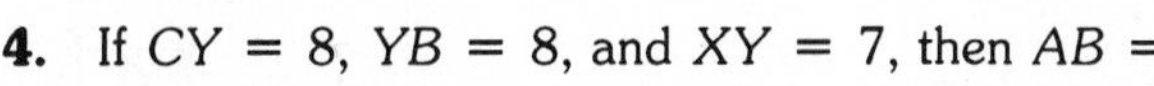

4. If $CY = 8$, $YB = 8$, and $XY = 7$, then $AB =$ _____.

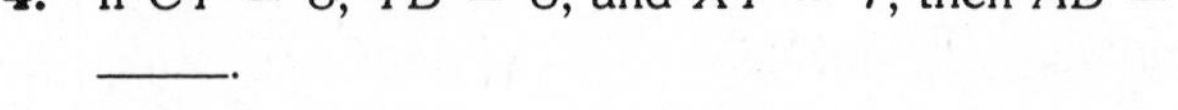

5. If $XY = 9$, $AB = 12$, and $CX = 6$, then $CA =$ _____.

6. If $AB = 15$, $XY = 9$, and $CB = 10$, then $YB =$ _____.

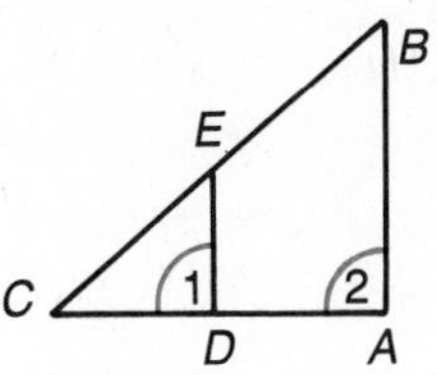

7. Given: $\angle 1 \cong \angle 2$

Prove: $\triangle ABC \sim \triangle DEC$

8. Given: $\angle B \cong \angle DEC$

Prove: $\frac{DE}{AB} = \frac{CD}{CA}$

B. 9. Given: $\angle 1 \cong \angle 4$

Prove: $\triangle ABC \sim \triangle EDC$

10. Given: $\angle B \cong \angle D$

Prove: $AB \cdot DC = ED \cdot BC$

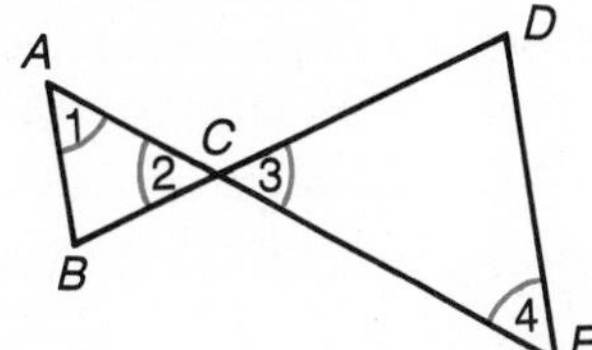

6. *ED, EC, DC*

7. *UT, RV, RT*

8. The triangles are similar by AAA, because their angles measure 30, 50, and 100.

Written Exercises

1. *AB, CX, CY* 2. 12

3. $\frac{28}{3}$ 4. 14

5. 8 6. 4

7. *1.* $\angle 1 \cong \angle 2$ (Given); *2.* $\overline{DE} \parallel \overline{AB}$ (Theorem 8.7); *3.* $\triangle ABC \sim \triangle DEC$ (Corollary 10.3.2).

8. *1.* $\angle B \sim \angle DEC$ (Given); *2.* $\angle C \cong \angle C$ (Congruence of $\angle$s is reflexive.); *3.* $\triangle ABC \sim \triangle DEC$ (Corollary 10.3.1); *4.* $\frac{DE}{AB} = \frac{CD}{CA}$ (CSSTP).

9. *1.* $\angle 1 \cong \angle 4$ (Given); *2.* $\angle 2 \cong \angle 3$ (Vert. $\angle$s are $\cong$.); *3.* $\triangle ABC \sim \triangle EDC$ (Corollary 10.3.1).

10. *1.* $\angle B \cong \angle D$ (Given); *2.* $\angle 2 \cong \angle 3$ (Vert. $\angle$s are $\cong$.); *3.* $\triangle ABC \sim \triangle EDC$ (Corollary 10.3.1); *4.* $\frac{AB}{ED} = \frac{BC}{DC}$ (CSSTP); *5.* $AB \cdot DC = ED \cdot BC$ (Cross-multiplication).

11. 1. $\overline{BD} \parallel \overline{AE}$ (Theorem 8.2); 2. $\triangle BCD \sim \triangle ACE$ (Corollary 10.3.2); 3. $\frac{CB}{CA} = \frac{CD}{CE}$ (CSSTP).

12. 1. $\angle E \cong \angle BDC$ (Def. of $\cong$ $\angle$s); 2. $\angle C \cong \angle C$ (Congruence of $\angle$s is reflexive.); 3. $\triangle BCD \sim \triangle ACE$ (Corollary 10.3.1); 4. $\frac{BD}{AE} = \frac{CB}{CA}$ (CSSTP); 5. $BD \cdot CA = AE \cdot CB$ (Cross-multiplication).

13. 1. $\angle 1 \cong \angle W$ (Given); 2. $\angle Y \cong \angle Y$ (Congruence of $\angle$s is reflexive.); 3. $\triangle YZX \cong \triangle YWV$ (Corollary 10.3.1).

14. 1. $\angle YXZ \cong \angle YVW$ (Given); 2. $\angle Y \cong \angle Y$ (Congruence of $\angle$s is reflexive.); 3. $\triangle YZX \sim \triangle YWV$ (Corollary 10.3.1); 4. $\frac{YZ}{YW} = \frac{ZX}{WV}$ (CSSTP); 5. $YZ \cdot WV = YW \cdot ZX$ (Cross-multiplication).

15. 3 16. 12 17. 1

18. 1. $\triangle ABD \sim \triangle DBC$ (Given); 2. $\frac{AB}{DB} = \frac{DB}{BC}$ (CSSTP); 3. DB is the geometric mean between AB and BC (Definition of geometric mean).

19. 1. $\overline{CE} \perp \overline{AD}$, $\overline{DB} \perp \overline{AC}$ (Definition of altitude); 2. $\angle DEC$ and $\angle DBC$ are rt. $\angle$s (Definition of $\perp$); 3. $\angle DEC \cong \angle DBC$ (All rt. $\angle$s are $\cong$.); 4. $\angle DXE \cong \angle CXB$ (Vert. $\angle$s are $=$.); 5. $\triangle DXE \sim \triangle CXB$ (Corollary 10.3.1).

20. See *Selected Answers,* p. 637

21. By the result of Exercise 20, $\triangle AEC$ is isosceles when either $\overline{AC}$ or $\overline{EC}$ is considered the base. So, $AE = CE$ and $AE = AC$. By transitivity $AE = AC = CE$, and $\triangle AEC$ is equilateral.

11. Given: $\overline{AE} \perp \overline{AC}$, $\overline{BD} \perp \overline{AC}$

Prove: $\frac{CB}{CA} = \frac{CD}{CE}$

12. Given: $m\angle E = n$, $m\angle BDC = n$

Prove: $BD \cdot CA = AE \cdot CB$

13. Given: $\angle 1 \cong \angle W$

Prove: $\triangle YZX \sim \triangle YWV$

14. Given: $\angle YXZ \cong \angle YVW$

Prove: $YZ \cdot WV = YW \cdot ZX$

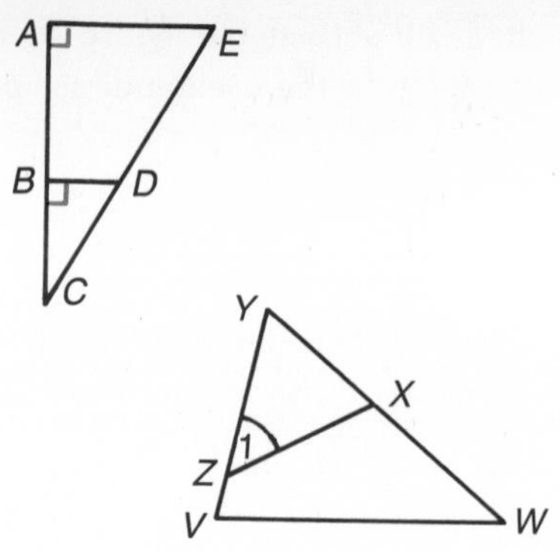

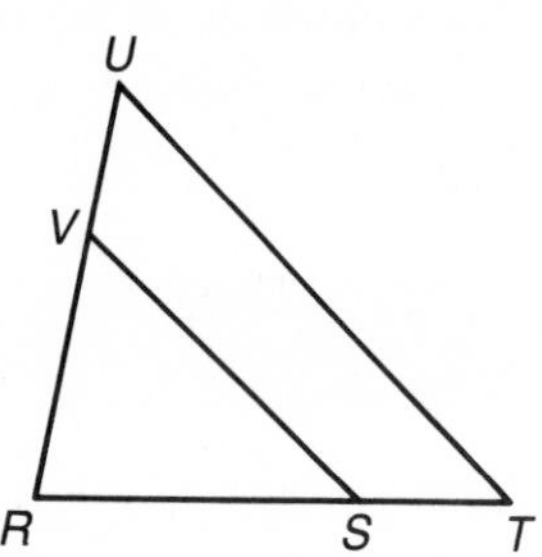

Given $\overline{SV} \parallel \overline{TU}$ in the figure on the left, complete each statement.

15. If $SV = x + 3$, $TU = 10$, $RS = x$, and $RT = 5$, $x =$ _____.

16. If $RS = 9$, $RT = x$, $SV = x$, and $TU = x + 4$, $RT =$ _____.

17. If $SV = x + 2$, $TU = x + 4$, $RV = x - 2$, and $RU = x - 1$, $VU =$ _____.

18. Given: $\triangle ABD \sim \triangle DBC$

Prove: DB is the geometric mean between AB and BC.

D
A B C

19. Given: $\triangle ACD$ with altitudes $\overline{CE}$ and $\overline{DB}$

Prove: $\triangle DXE \sim \triangle CXB$

C. 20. Use the figure of $\triangle ABC$ at the right to prove the following statement: If the median from a vertex of a triangle is the same as the angle bisector from that vertex, then the triangle is isosceles.
(HINT: Draw an auxiliary line from vertex C parallel to the median and use similarity.)

21. Given: D and B are midpoints of $\overline{EC}$ and AC, respectively; $\overline{EB}$ bisects $\angle AEC$, and $\overline{AD}$ bisects $\angle EAC$.

Prove: $\triangle ACE$ is equilateral.

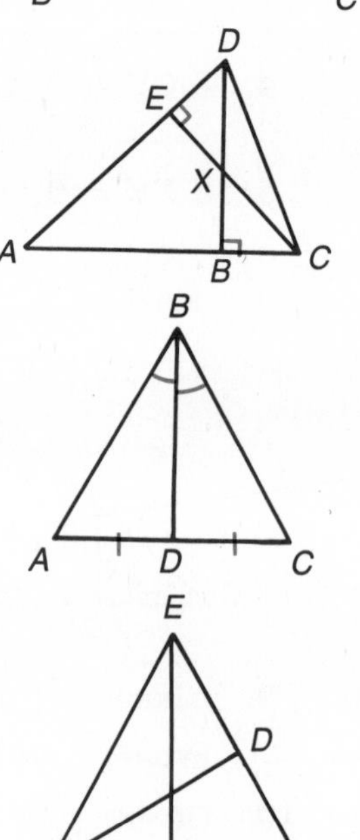

10.4 SAS and SSS Similarities in Triangles

THEOREM 10.4 (The Side-Angle-Side [SAS] Similarity Theorem)
Given a correspondence between two triangles, if two pairs of corresponding sides are proportional, and the included angles are congruent, then the correspondence is a similarity.

Given: $\triangle ABC$, $\triangle XYZ$
$\angle C \cong \angle Z$
$\frac{XZ}{AC} = \frac{YZ}{BC}$

Prove: $\triangle ABC \sim \triangle XYZ$

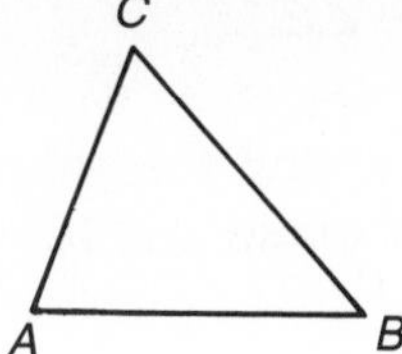

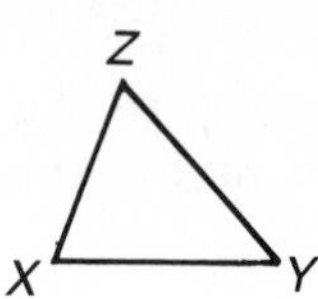

Proof: If the triangles are congruent, then they are similar. Suppose the triangles are not congruent. Then they could be positioned as shown at the right. By Theorem 10.2, $\overline{XY} \parallel \overline{AB}$, and $\triangle ABC \sim \triangle XYZ$ by Corollary 10.3.2.

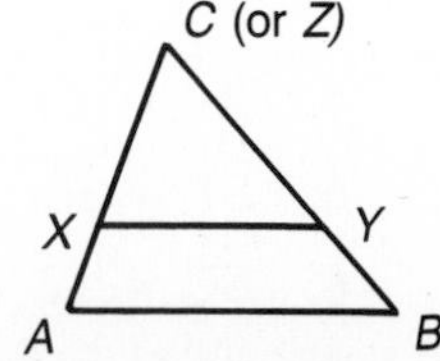

THEOREM 10.5 (The Side-Side-Side [SSS] Similarity Theorem)
Given a correspondence between two triangles, if corresponding sides are proportional, then the correspondence is a similarity.

The proof of Theorem 10.5 is left as an exercise.

ORAL EXERCISES

1. Give the full statement on similarity abbreviated as SAS.
2. Give the full statement on similarity abbreviated as SSS.

Tell whether each of the following statements is true or false.

3. Congruent triangles are similar.
4. Similar triangles are congruent.
5. Similar triangles have the same area.

OBJECTIVE

Use SAS and SSS in proofs and to find a measure of a triangle.

TEACHER'S NOTES

See p. T35

MIXED REVIEW

1. In a right triangle with a hypotenuse of 12 and a 30° angle, find the legs. $6, 6\sqrt{3}$
2. Find the altitude of an equilateral triangle with a side of 8. $4\sqrt{3}$
3. What is the ratio of 11 days to 4 years? $\frac{11}{1461}$
4. Factor $12x^2 + 17x - 5$. $(4x - 1)(3x + 5)$
5. Solve $2x^2 + 13x - 7 = 0$. $\{7, \frac{1}{2}\}$

TEACHER'S RESOURCE MASTERS

Practice Master 30, Part 2
Quiz 19

ASSIGNMENT GUIDE

Minimum 1-7 odd, 9-22
Regular 1-7 odd, 9-23
Maximum 1-7 odd, 9-26

Oral Exercises

1. Theorem 10.4
2. Theorem 10.5
3. T
4. F
5. F

6. T

7. F

8. Theorem 10.5

Written Exercises

1. *1.* $\overline{AC}$ and $\overline{BC}$ proportional to $\overline{EC}$ and $\overline{DC}$ (Given); *2.* $\angle ACB \cong \angle ECD$ (Vert. $\angle$s are $\cong$.); *3.* $\triangle ABC \sim \triangle EDC$ (Theorem 10.4).

2. *1.* $\overline{AB} \parallel \overline{ED}$ (Given); *2.* $\angle BAC \cong \angle DEC$, $\angle ABC \cong \angle EDC$ (Theorem 8.8); *3.* $\angle ACB \cong \angle ECD$ (Vert. $\angle$s are $\cong$.); *4.* $\triangle ABC \sim \triangle EDC$ (Theorem 10.3).

3. $x = 25$, $y = 24$

4. $x = 15$, $y = \frac{20}{3}$

5. $x = 6$, $y = \frac{95}{3}$

6. $x = \frac{77}{25}$, $y = \frac{-26}{3}$

7. $x = \frac{-33}{2}$, $y = \frac{225}{26}$

8. $x = \pm 8$, $y = 222$

9. Given

10. Substitution

11. Theorem 10.2

6. Any two equilateral polygons with the same number of sides are similar.

7. Any two equiangular polygons with the same number of sides are similar.

8. Explain how you would prove that all equilateral triangles are similar.

WRITTEN EXERCISES

A. 1. Given: $\frac{AC}{EC} = \frac{BC}{DC}$

Prove: $\triangle ABC \sim \triangle EDC$

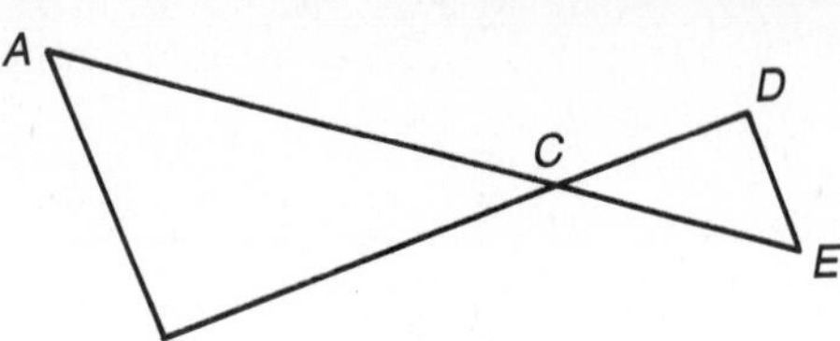

2. Given: $\overline{AB} \parallel \overline{ED}$

Prove: $\triangle ABC \sim \triangle EDC$

Referring to the figure, find the values for x and y that will make $\triangle ABC \sim \triangle TRS$.

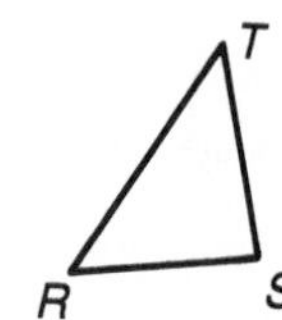

3. $m\angle A = 40$, $m\angle R = 60$, $m\angle T = x + 15$, $m\angle B = 2y + 12$

4. $AB = 24$, $RT = 18$, $AC = 20$, $RS = 15$, $TS = x$, $BC = 3y$

5. $ST = 10$, $CA = 15$, $m\angle S = 85$, $BC = 12$, $RS = x + 2$, $m\angle C = 3y - 10$

6. $BC = 12$, $RS = 10$, $CA = 14$, $RT = 12$, $BA = 5x - 1$, $ST = 3 - y$

7. $m\angle A = 44$, $AC = 16$, $ST = 13$, $RT = 10$, $m\angle T = 11 - 2x$, $BA = 2y - 5$

8. $m\angle B = 57$, $m\angle S = 84$, $m\angle R = x^2 - 7$, $m\angle C = \frac{1}{3}y + 10$

B. Supply the reasons in the following proof of Theorem 10.5 (SSS).

Given: $ABC \leftrightarrow XYZ$

$\frac{AB}{XY} = \frac{CB}{ZY} = \frac{CA}{ZX}$

Prove: $\triangle ABC \sim \triangle XYZ$

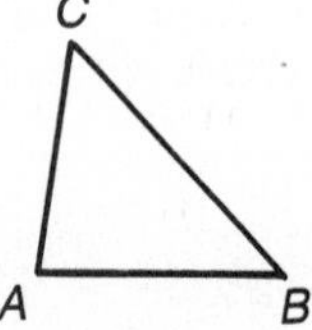

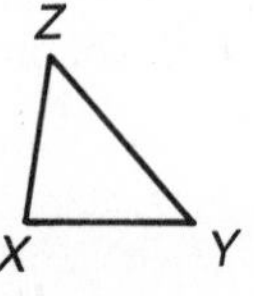

Let X' and Y' be points on $\overline{CA}$ and $\overline{CB}$ such that $CX' = ZX$ and $CY' = ZY$. Then show that $\triangle XYZ \cong \triangle X'Y'C'$ and that $\triangle X'Y'C' \sim \triangle ABC$.

Proof:

STATEMENTS	REASONS
1. $\frac{CA}{XZ} = \frac{CB}{ZY}$	*1.* **9.** ____
2. $\frac{CA}{CX'} = \frac{CB}{CY'}$	*2.* **10.** ____
3. $\overline{X'Y'} \parallel \overline{AB}$	*3.* **11.** ____

4. $\triangle ABC \sim \triangle X'Y'C$ | 4. **12.**
5. $\frac{AB}{X'Y'} = \frac{CA}{CX'}$ | 5. **13.**
6. $\frac{AB}{X'Y'} = \frac{CA}{ZX}$ | 6. **14.**
7. $\frac{AB}{X'Y'} = \frac{AB}{XY}$ | 7. **15.**
8. $X'Y' \cdot AB = AB \cdot XY$ | 8. **16.**
9. $X'Y' = XY$ | 9. **17.**
10. $\overline{X'Y'} \cong \overline{XY}$ | 10. **18.**
11. $\overline{CX'} \cong \overline{ZX}, \overline{CY'} \cong \overline{ZY}$ | 11. **19.**
12. $\triangle X'Y'C \cong \triangle XYZ$ | 12. **20.**
13. $\triangle X'Y'C \sim \triangle XYZ$ | 13. **21.**
14. $\triangle ABC \sim \triangle XYZ$ | 14. **22.**

Use the figure below in Exercises 23–25 to prove that corresponding altitudes, medians, and angle bisectors in similar triangles have the same ratio as any pair of corresponding sides.

23. Given: $\triangle ABC \sim \triangle WXY$ with altitudes $\overline{CD}$ and $\overline{YZ}$

Prove: $\frac{CD}{YZ} = \frac{CA}{YW}$

C. **24. Given:** $\triangle ABC \sim \triangle WXY$ with medians $\overline{CD}$ and $\overline{YZ}$

Prove: $\frac{CD}{YZ} = \frac{CA}{YW}$

25. Given: $\triangle ABC \sim \triangle WXY$ with $\angle$ bisectors $\overline{CD}$ and $\overline{YZ}$

Prove: $\frac{CD}{YZ} = \frac{CA}{YW}$

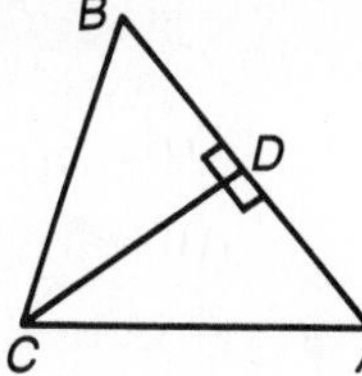

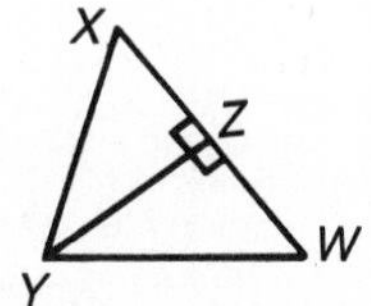

26. Given: ▱$ABCE$

Prove: $FE \cdot FB = FA \cdot FD$

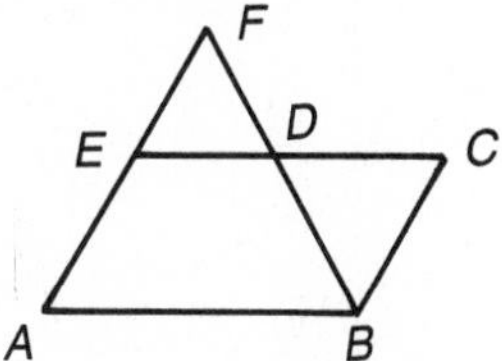

12. Corollary 10.3.2
13. CSSTP
14. Substitution
15. Substitution
16. Cross-multiplication
17. Division prop. of equality
18. Definition of $\cong$ segments
19. Given
20. SSS, Theorem 4.5
21. $\cong$ $\triangle$s are similar.
22. Similarity is transitive.
23. *1.* $\overline{CD} \perp \overline{AB}$, $\overline{YZ} \perp \overline{WX}$ (Definition of altitude); *2.* $\angle CDA$ and $\angle YZW$ are rt. $\angle$s (Definition of $\perp$); *3.* $\angle CDA \cong \angle YZW$ (All rt. $\angle$s are $\cong$.); *4.* $\triangle ABC \sim \triangle WXY$ (Given); *5.* $\angle A \cong \angle W$ (Definition of similar $\triangle$s); *6.* $\triangle ADC \sim \triangle WZY$ (AA, Cor. 10.3.1); *7.* $\frac{CD}{YZ} = \frac{CA}{YW}$ (CSSTP).
24. See *Selected Answers,* p. 637
25. *1.* $\angle A \cong \angle W$, $\angle C \cong \angle Y$ (Definition of similar $\triangle$s); *2.* $m\angle DCA = \frac{1}{2} m\angle C$, $m\angle ZYW = \frac{1}{2} m\angle Y$ (Definition of $\angle$ bisector); *3.* $\angle DCA \cong \angle ZYW$ (Substitution); *4.* $\triangle CAD \sim \triangle YWZ$ (AA, Cor. 10.3.1); *5.* $\frac{CD}{YZ} = \frac{CA}{YW}$ (CSSTP).
26. *1.* $\overline{ED} \parallel \overline{AB}$ (Definition of ▱); *2.* $\triangle FED \sim \triangle FAB$ (Cor. 10.3.2); *3.* $\frac{FE}{FA} = \frac{FD}{FB}$ (CSSTP); *4.* $FE \cdot FB = FA \cdot FD$ (Cross-multiplication).

SELF QUIZ

1. Find the ratio of 5 ft to 11 in.

2. Find x if $\frac{3}{4} = \frac{x}{10}$.

3. Find the geometric mean of 9 and 5.

4. Find the geometric mean of 2 and 8.

5. Explain the difference between similar and congruent polygons.

Given the figure at the right, with $\overline{BE} \parallel \overline{CD}$, answer the following.

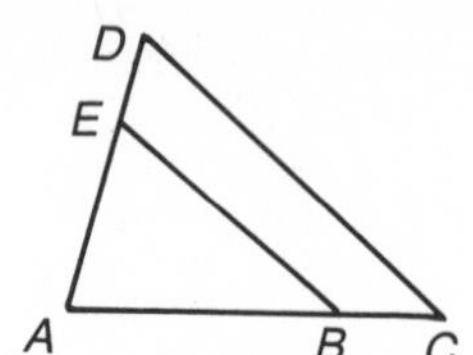

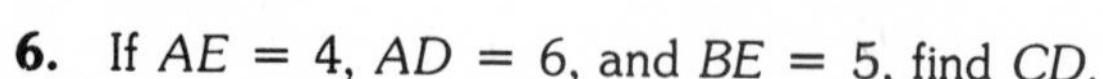

6. If $AE = 4$, $AD = 6$, and $BE = 5$, find CD.

7. If $AE = 6$, $ED = 3$, $EB = 8$, find CD.

For Exercises 8–10, refer to the figure at the right where $\triangle XYZ \sim \triangle RML$.

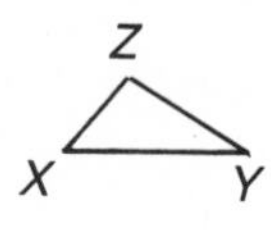

8. Complete the extended proportion $\frac{XY}{?} = \frac{?}{RL} = \frac{YZ}{?}$

If $ZY = 4$, $XY = 6$, $RL = 5$, and $LM = 6$,

9. find ZX.

10. find RM.

11. Draw two equiangular polygons with the same number of sides such that the polygons are not similar.

CALCULATOR

In each of the problems below, substitute the known quantities in the given formula, rewrite the equation in the form $ax^2 + bx + c = 0$, and then find x using the quadratic formula:

$$x = \frac{-b \pm \sqrt{b^2 - 4ac}}{2a}.$$

1. The distance required to stop a car is related to speed and road friction by the formula $s^2 + 3.3fs - 30fd = 0$, where s is the speed in mph, f is the coefficient of friction for the road surface, and d is the stopping distance in feet. If a car stops in 100 feet on a dry oiled-gravel road ($f = 0.5$), at what speed was the car traveling?

2. If an object is thrown upward, the height h it will reach in a given time depends upon the initial velocity v, the time t, and acceleration due to gravity. The formula relating these four values is $h = vt - 16t^2$. If a ball is thrown upward at 72 feet per second, in how many seconds will it reach 81 feet?

Self-Quiz

1. $\frac{60}{11}$
2. $\frac{15}{2}$
3. $3\sqrt{5}$
4. 4
5. Similar polygons have the same shape; that is, all corresponding angles are congruent and corresponding sides are proportional. Congruent polygons have the same size *and* shape; that is, all corresponding parts are congruent.
6. $7\frac{1}{2}$
7. 12
8. *RM, XZ, ML*
9. $\frac{10}{3}$
10. 9
11. Answers may vary; possible answers are a square and a rectangle.

Calculator

1. $s^2 + 3.3(0.5)s - 30(0.5)(100) = 0$

   $s^2 + 1.65s - 1500 = 0$

   $s = \frac{-1.65 \pm \sqrt{(1.65)^2 - 4(-1500)}}{2}$

   $= \frac{-1.65 + \sqrt{6002.7225}}{2}$

   $= 38$ mph

2. $81 = 72t - 16t^2$

   $16t^2 - 72t + 81 = 0$

   $t = \frac{72 \pm \sqrt{(-72)^2 - 4(16)(81)}}{2(16)} = \frac{72 \pm \sqrt{0}}{32} = 2.25$ sec

10.5 Special Similarities in Right Triangles

Two of the altitudes of a right triangle are also legs of the triangle. The third altitude, drawn from the right angle to the hypotenuse, has special properties.

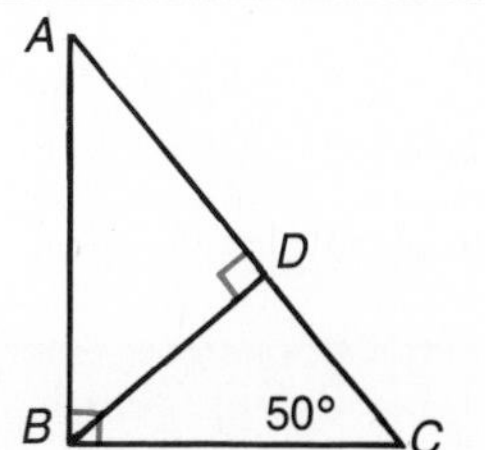

Consider right $\triangle ABC$, shown in the figure. If $\angle B$ is a right angle, $\overline{BD}$ is the altitude to $\overline{AC}$, and $m\angle C = 50$.

Since $m\angle A + m\angle B + m\angle C = 180$, you can substitute the known angle measurements and determine that $m\angle A = 40$. The same process applied to $\triangle DBC$ results in $m\angle DBC = 40$. If $m\angle ABC = 90$, and $m\angle DBC = 40$, then $m\angle DBA = 50$. This means that the three triangles have congruent angle measurements, so $\triangle ABC \sim \triangle ADB \sim \triangle BDC$, which suggests the next theorem.

THEOREM 10.6
In any right triangle, the altitude to the hypotenuse separates the triangle into two triangles that are similar both to each other and to the original triangle.

Given: Right $\triangle ABD$ with altitude $\overline{AC}$

Prove: $\triangle ABC \sim \triangle DAC \sim \triangle DBA$

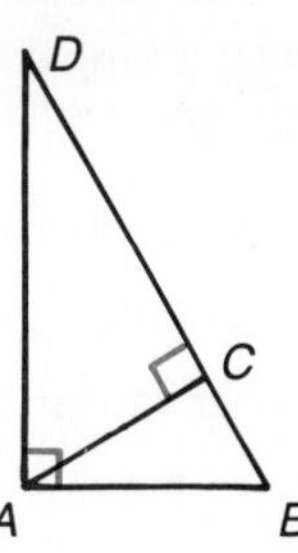

Proof: Because $\overline{AC}$ is an altitude, all three triangles are right triangles. $\triangle DAC$ and $\triangle DBA$ each contain $\angle D$ and thus are similar by AA (Corollary 10.3.1). $\triangle DBA$ and $\triangle ABC$ each contain $\angle B$ and so are also similar by AA. Thus, both $\triangle DAC$ and $\triangle ABC$ are similar to $\triangle DBA$. Because similarity is an equivalence relation, all three triangles are similar to each other.

Theorem 10.6 can be used to show an interesting feature of the altitude to the hypotenuse of a right triangle.

Example: $\triangle EFG$ is a right triangle with right $\angle EFG$. $\overline{FH}$ is the altitude to $\overline{EG}$, $EH = 16$, and $HG = 9$. What is FH?

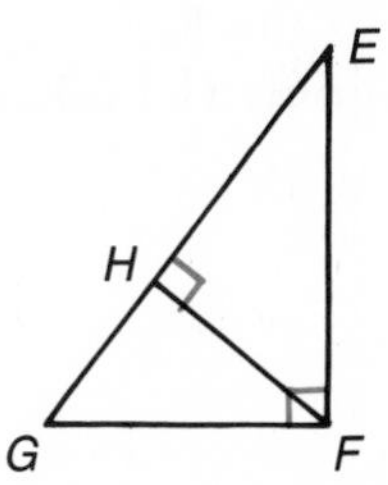

Solution: By Theorem 10.6, $\triangle EHF \sim \triangle FHG$, so $\frac{EH}{FH} = \frac{FH}{HG}$. Substituting the known values produces $\frac{16}{FH} = \frac{FH}{9}$, or $(FH)^2 = 144$. Thus, $FH = 12$ and is the geometric mean between EH and HG.

OBJECTIVE

Use Theorem 10.6 and its corollary to find a measure of a triangle.

TEACHER'S NOTES

See p. T35

MIXED REVIEW

1. What is the set of all points that are r units from P in a plane? a circle of radius r
2. What is the contrapositive of $A \to B$? $\sim B \to \sim A$
3. Divide $16 \div \frac{1}{2}$. 32
4. Solve $ax^2 + bx + c = 0$. $x = \frac{-b \pm \sqrt{b^2 - 4ac}}{2a}$
5. $(a + b)^4 = ?$ $a^4 + 4a^3b + 6a^2b^2 + 4ab^3 + b^4$

TEACHER'S RESOURCE MASTERS

Practice Master 31, Part 1

Example: $\triangle JKL$ is a right triangle with right angle at J. $\overline{JM}$ is the altitude to $\overline{KL}$, $KJ = 10$, and $KL = 15$. What is KM?

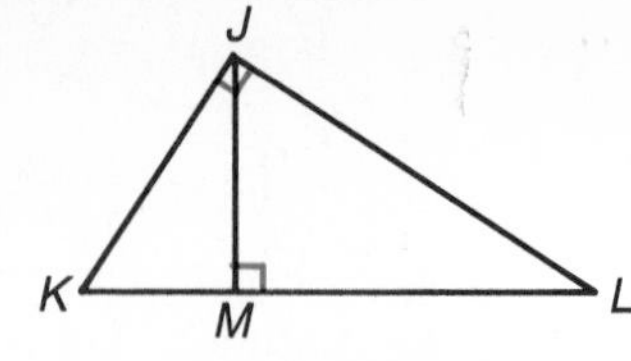

Solution: Again, by Theorem 10.6, $\triangle JMK \sim \triangle LJK$, so $\frac{KM}{KJ} = \frac{KJ}{KL.}$ Substituting for KJ and KL yields $\frac{KM}{10} = \frac{10}{15}$, or $KM = 6\frac{2}{3}$. In this case, KJ is the geometric mean between KM and KL.

These examples illustrate the corollary to Theorem 10.6.

COROLLARY 10.6.1
Given a right triangle and the altitude to the hypotenuse,
(1) the altitude is the geometric mean of the segments into which it separates the hypotenuse; and
(2) either leg is the geometric mean of the hypotenuse and the segment of the hypotenuse adjacent to the leg.

Given: Right $\triangle ABD$ with altitude $\overline{AC}$

Prove: (1) $\frac{CD}{AC} = \frac{AC}{CB}$

(2) $\frac{DB}{AB} = \frac{AB}{CB}$ and $\frac{DB}{AD} = \frac{AD}{CD}$

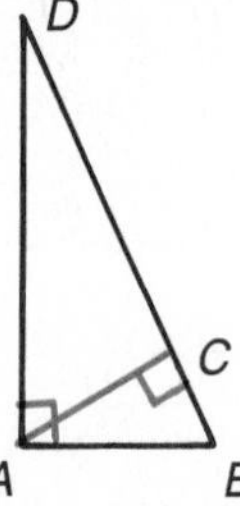

Proof: This corollary follows directly from the existence of three similar triangles and the proportionality of segments in similar triangles.

(1) Consider similar triangles CBA and CAD. The ratio of the two longer legs must be the same as the ratio of the two shorter legs, so $\frac{CD}{AC} = \frac{AC}{CB}$.

(2) Consider similar triangles ABD and CBA. The ratio of the two hypotenuses must be the same as the ratio of the two shorter or two longer legs, so $\frac{DB}{AB} = \frac{AB}{CB}$. Likewise, in $\triangle ABD$ and $\triangle CAD$, $\frac{DB}{AD} = \frac{AD}{CD}$.

ASSIGNMENT GUIDE

Minimum 1-20
Regular 1-27 odd
Maximum 1-33 odd

ORAL EXERCISES

Refer to the figure of right $\triangle WXY$, with altitude $\overline{XZ}$, to complete the following.

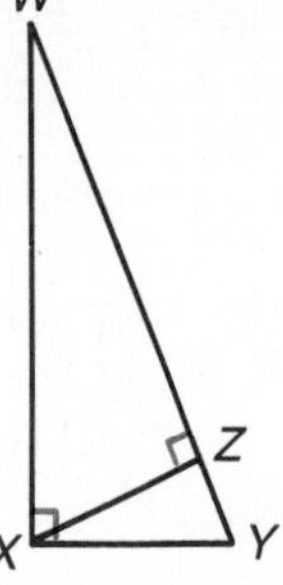

1. $\triangle WXY \sim$ ____ $\sim$ ____

2. $\frac{WZ}{XZ} = \frac{XZ}{?}$

3. $\frac{WY}{WX} = \frac{WX}{?}$

4. $\frac{ZY}{XY} = \frac{XY}{?}$

5. $\frac{WY}{XY} = \frac{?}{?} = \frac{?}{?}$

6. $\frac{XZ}{XW} = \frac{YZ}{?}$

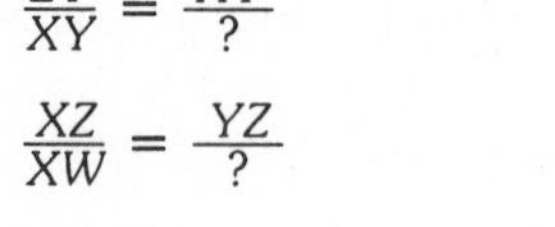

Oral Exercises

1. $\triangle WZX$, $\triangle XZY$ 2. YZ
3. WZ 4. WY
5. $\frac{XY}{ZY}$, $\frac{WX}{ZX}$ 6. YX

Find x in each of the following.

7. $\frac{3}{4} = \frac{18}{x}$ **8.** $\frac{1}{2} = \frac{11}{x}$ **9.** $\frac{2}{x} = \frac{8}{20}$ **10.** $\frac{x}{5} = \frac{20}{25}$

Find r in each of the following.

11. $\frac{5}{r} = \frac{r}{20}$ **12.** $\frac{3}{r} = \frac{r}{12}$ **13.** $\frac{2}{r} = \frac{r}{4}$ **14.** $\frac{3}{r} = \frac{r}{27}$

15. What is the geometric mean of 4 and 9?

16. 10 is the geometric mean of 2 and what number?

WRITTEN EXERCISES

A. Refer to the figure of right $\triangle RSU$.

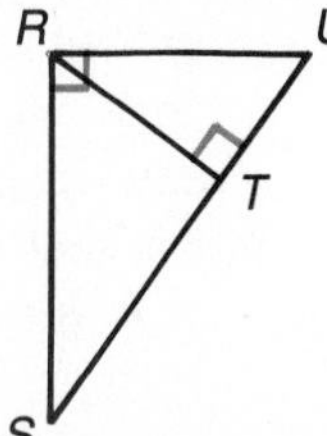

1. $\triangle TRU \sim$ ____ $\sim$ ____

2. $\frac{SU}{SR} = \frac{?}{ST}$

3. $\frac{ST}{RT} = \frac{RT}{?}$

4. $\frac{?}{RU} = \frac{RU}{SU}$

5. $\frac{RU}{TU} = \frac{SU}{?}$

6. $\frac{US}{RS} = \frac{?}{?} = \frac{?}{?}$

Find y in each of the following.

7. $\frac{4}{y} = \frac{9}{3}$ **8.** $\frac{y}{2} = \frac{7}{8}$ **9.** $\frac{9}{11} = \frac{y}{2}$ **10.** $\frac{2}{3} = \frac{4}{y}$

Find the geometric mean between the following pairs.

11. 2 and 3 **12.** $4a$ and b **13.** 9 and 10 **14.** $\frac{1}{2}$ and $\frac{1}{8}$

Complete for each of the following: 8 is the geometric mean of

15. 2 and ____. **16.** 10 and ____. **17.** $4r$ and ____. **18.** $\frac{1}{3}$ and ____.

B. Refer to the figure of right $\triangle ADB$, with $\overline{AC} \perp \overline{BD}$, to complete the following.

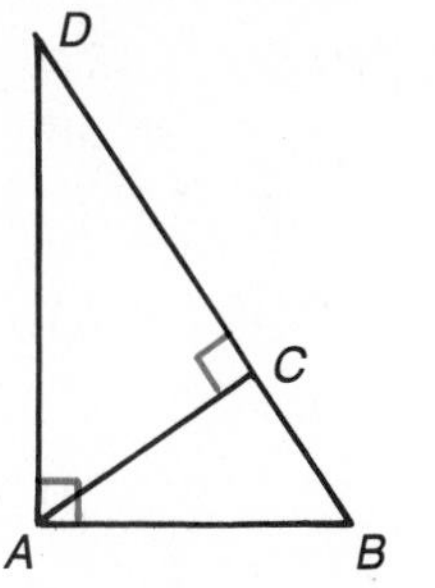

19. If $BC = 4$ and $CD = 9$, $AC =$ ____.

20. If $AC = 10$ and $BC = 4$, $DC =$ ____.

21. If $AB = 8$ and $BC = 4$, $BD =$ ____.

22. If $DC = 10$ and $DB = 12$, $AD =$ ____.

23. If $BC = 5$ and $CD = 7$, $AB =$ ____.

24. If $BC = 3$ and $AC = 6$, $BD =$ ____.

7. 24 8. 22

9. 5 10. 4

11. 10 12. 6

13. $2\sqrt{2}$ 14. 9

15. 6 16. 50

Written Exercises

1. $\triangle TSR$, $\triangle RSU$

2. SR

3. UT

4. UT

5. RU

6. $\frac{RS}{TS}$, $\frac{UR}{TR}$

7. $\frac{4}{3}$ 8. $\frac{7}{4}$

9. $\frac{18}{11}$ 10. 6

11. $\sqrt{6}$ 12. $2\sqrt{ab}$

13. $3\sqrt{10}$ 14. $\frac{1}{4}$

15. 32 16. 6.4

17. $\frac{16}{r}$ 18. 192

19. 6 20. 25

21. 16 22. $2\sqrt{30}$

23. $2\sqrt{15}$ 24. 15

25. Since $\overline{BD}$ is the altitude to the hypotenuse in rt. $\triangle ADC$, by Cor. 10.6.1, $\frac{AB}{BD} = \frac{BD}{BC}$. By cross-multiplication, $AB \cdot BD = (BD)^2$.

26. Since $\overline{BD}$ is the altitude to the hypotenuse in rt. $\triangle ADC$, by Cor. 10.6.1, $\frac{AB}{AD} = \frac{AD}{AC}$. By cross-multiplication, $(AD)^2 = AB \cdot AC$.

27. $\sqrt{xy}$ 28. $\sqrt{rs}$

29. $\sqrt{x(x + y)}$

30. $\sqrt{r(s - r)}$ 31. $\frac{x^2}{y}$

32. $\frac{s^2 + r^2}{r}$

33. $\frac{c}{a} = \frac{a}{s}$ means $a = \sqrt{cs}$, $\frac{c}{b} = \frac{b}{r}$ means $b = \sqrt{cr}$. $a^2 + b^2 = (\sqrt{cs})^2 + (\sqrt{cr})^2 = cs + cr = c(s + r)$. But $s + r = c$, so $a^2 + b^2 = c(c) = c^2$.

Error Search

1. $\frac{BC}{BF} = \frac{AC}{AG}$

2. $\frac{CD}{BD} = \frac{CE}{AE}$

3. $\frac{CD}{DE} = \frac{CF}{FG}$

4. $\frac{CE}{CD} = \frac{AC}{BC}$

5. $(CG)^2 = (AG)(GE)$

6. $(BC)^2 = (BD)(BF)$, or $(CD)^2 = (BD)(FD)$

Refer to the figure of right $\triangle ADC$, with $\overline{DB} \perp \overline{AC}$, for the following.

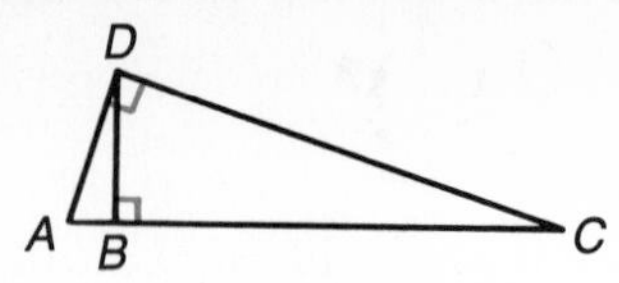

25. Prove that $AB \cdot BC = (BD)^2$.

26. Prove that $(AD)^2 = AB \cdot AC$.

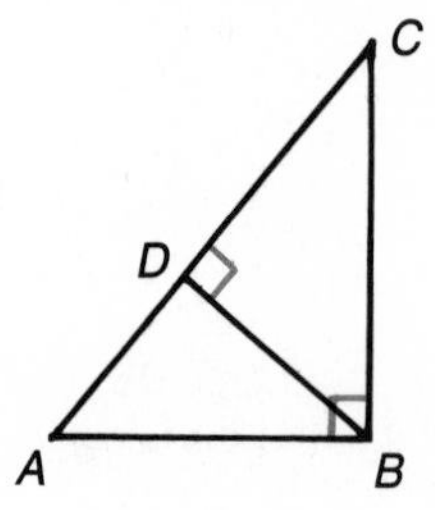

Refer to the figure of right $\triangle ABC$, with $\overline{BD} \perp \overline{AC}$, to complete the following.

27. If $AD = x$ and $DC = y$, $BD =$ _____.

28. If $AC = r$ and $AD = s$, $AB =$ _____.

29. If $AD = x$ and $DC = y$, $AB =$ _____.

30. If $AD = r$ and $AC = s$, $DB =$ _____.

31. If $BD = x$ and $DC = y$, $AD =$ _____.

32. If $DB = s$ and $AD = r$, $AC =$ _____.

C. 33. In Chapter 9, the Pythagorean Theorem was proved using area formulas. Corollary 10.6.1 suggests another proof. In $\triangle ABC$, $\angle C$ is a right angle and $\overline{CD}$ is the altitude to $\overline{AB}$. Corollary 10.6.1 tells you that $\frac{c}{a} = \frac{a}{s}$ and $\frac{c}{b} = \frac{b}{r}$. From this, prove that $c^2 = a^2 + b^2$.

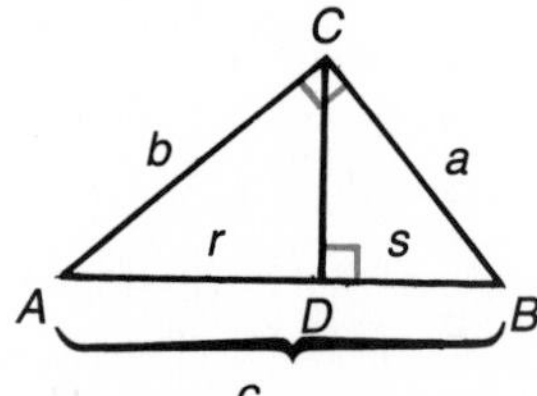

ERROR SEARCH

Correct the error in each of the following, given that $BD \parallel AE$, $AC \perp CE$, and $CG \perp AE$.

1. $\frac{BC}{BF} = \frac{AC}{AE}$ 2. $\frac{CD}{BC} = \frac{CG}{AE}$

3. $\frac{CD}{DE} = \frac{CF}{CG}$ 4. $\frac{CE}{CD} = \frac{AB}{BC}$

5. $(CG)^2 = (AG)(FD)$ 6. $(BC)^2 = (BD)(FD)$

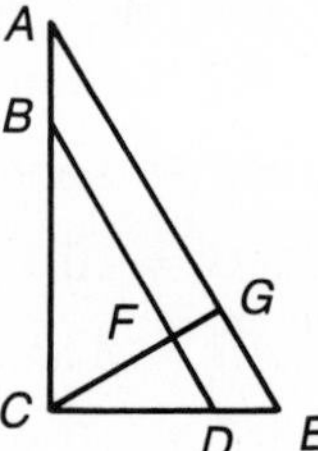

10.6 Area Ratios in Similar Triangles

Postulate 18 states that areas of congruent triangles are always equal. Because similar triangles may or may not be congruent, it follows that their areas may or may not be equal. In this lesson you will compare the areas of similar triangles. A special mathematical relationship for determining the areas of similar triangles is expressed formally in the following theorem.

THEOREM 10.7
The ratio of the areas of two similar triangles is the square of the ratio of any two corresponding sides.

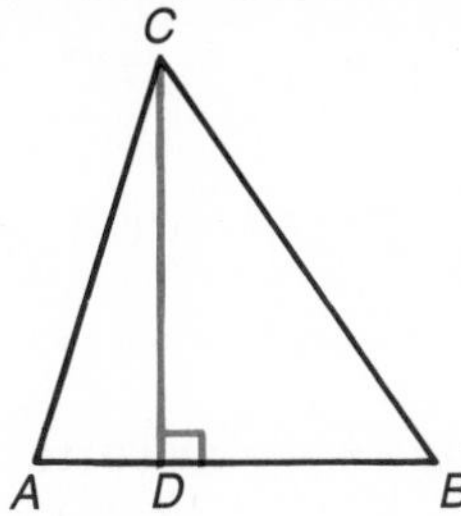

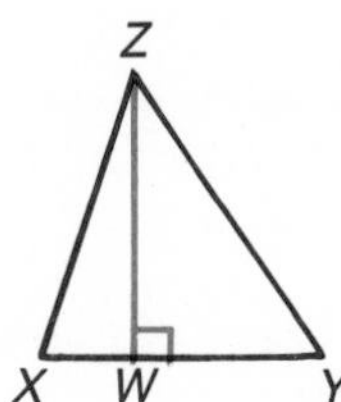

Given: $\triangle ABC \sim \triangle XYZ$

Prove: $\dfrac{\text{the area of } \triangle ABC}{\text{the area of } \triangle XYZ} = \left(\dfrac{AB}{XY}\right)^2$

Proof: Let $\overline{CD}$ and $\overline{ZW}$ be the altitudes of $\triangle ABC$ and $\triangle XYZ$. Then the area of $\triangle ABC = \frac{1}{2}(AB \cdot CD)$ and the area of $\triangle XYZ = \frac{1}{2}(XY \cdot ZW)$. The ratio of these two areas can then be expressed:

$$\frac{\text{the area of } \triangle ABC}{\text{the area of } \triangle XYZ} = \frac{\frac{1}{2}(AB \cdot CD)}{\frac{1}{2}(XY \cdot ZW)} = \frac{AB}{XY} \cdot \frac{CD}{ZW}.$$

In Lesson 10.4, you proved that the ratio of a pair of corresponding altitudes has the same ratio as a pair of corresponding sides. Therefore,

$$\frac{AB}{XY} = \frac{CD}{ZW}.$$

Substitution yields:

$$\frac{\text{the area of } \triangle ABC}{\text{the area of } \triangle XYZ} = \frac{AB}{XY} \cdot \frac{AB}{XY} = \left(\frac{AB}{XY}\right)^2.$$

Thus, the ratio of the areas of two similar triangles is equal to the square of the ratio of two corresponding sides.

OBJECTIVE

Use Theorem 10.7 to find a measure of a triangle.

TEACHER'S NOTES

See p. T36

MIXED REVIEW

1. What is the converse of the Isosceles Triangle Theorem? If 2 ∠s ≅, then sides opp. are ≅
2. If the altitude of an equilateral triangle is $5\sqrt{3}$, what is the perimeter? 30
3. Add $\frac{2x+3}{x} + \frac{4x-1}{3}$. $\frac{4x^2+5x+9}{3x}$
4. Find the complement of $23\frac{1}{4}$. $66\frac{3}{4}$
5. Can a triangle have sides of 8, 15, and 22? yes

TEACHER'S RESOURCE MASTERS

Practice Master 31, Part 2
Quiz 20

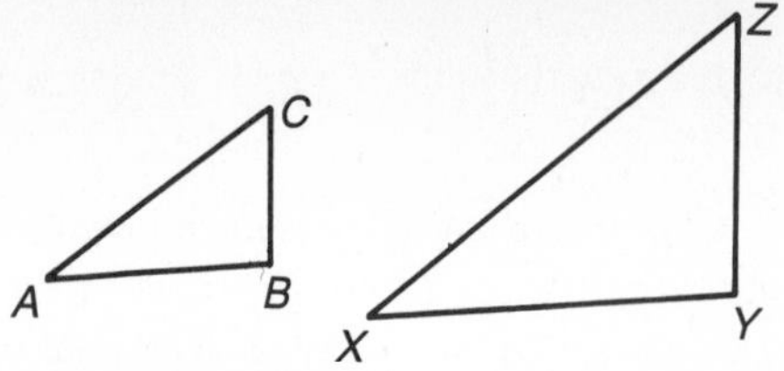

Observe in the following examples how Theorem 10.7 may be applied.

Example: If $AC = 5$, $XZ = 10$, and the area of $\triangle ABC = 6$, find the area of $\triangle XYZ$. The ratio of a pair of corresponding sides is $\frac{5}{10}$ (or $\frac{1}{2}$). Therefore, the ratio of the areas is $\frac{1}{4}$ or $\frac{\triangle ABC}{\triangle XYZ} = \frac{1}{4} = \frac{6}{\triangle XYZ}$. Solving the equation, you find that $\triangle XYZ = 24$.

Example: If $\triangle ABC = 4$, $\triangle XYZ = 9$, and $YZ = 5$, find BC. Since the ratio of the areas is $\frac{4}{9}$, the ratio of corresponding sides is $\frac{2}{3}$. Thus, $\frac{2}{3} = \frac{BC}{YZ} = \frac{BC}{5}$, and $BC = \frac{10}{3}$.

ASSIGNMENT GUIDE

Minimum 1-20
Regular 1-33 odd
Maximum 1-33 odd, 35-40

ORAL EXERCISES

Find the ratio of the areas of two similar triangles whose corresponding sides have the following measures.

1. 4 and 5 **2.** 3 and 6 **3.** r and s

4. What is the ratio between corresponding angles of similar triangles?

Identify each statement as true or false.

5. Two triangles with the same area are congruent.

6. Congruent triangles are also similar.

7. If the ratio of the areas of two triangles is $\frac{4}{9}$, then the triangles are similar with sides in the ratio of $\frac{2}{3}$.

8. All squares are similar.

9. Similar polygons have the same area.

10. The perimeters of two similar polygons are in the same ratio as any pair of corresponding sides.

11. If the sides of a triangle are doubled, what effect does this have on the area?

12. You can double the area of a triangle if you multiply each side by what number?

Given the following areas of two similar triangles, find the ratio of their corresponding sides.

13. 16 and 25 **14.** 169 and 81 **15.** 10 and 1 **16.** 7 and 9

Oral Exercises

1. $\frac{16}{25}$ 2. $\frac{1}{4}$
3. $\frac{r^2}{s^2}$ 4. $\frac{1}{1}$
5. F 6. T
7. F 8. T
9. F 10. T
11. increases by 4 times
12. $\sqrt{2}$
13. $\frac{4}{5}$ 14. $\frac{13}{9}$
15. $\frac{\sqrt{10}}{1}$ 16. $\frac{\sqrt{7}}{3}$

WRITTEN EXERCISES

A. If two similar triangles have a pair of corresponding sides with the given measurements, find the ratio of their areas.

1. 6 cm and 3 cm **2.** 3 ft and 2 ft

3. 1 yd and 8 yd **4.** 2 cm and 5 cm

If the areas of two similar triangles have the given measure, find the ratio of a pair of corresponding sides.

5. 64 and 25 **6.** 100 and 1 **7.** 36 and 49 **8.** 16 and 9

If two similar triangles have a pair of corresponding sides in the given ratio, find the ratio of their areas.

9. $\frac{3}{5}$ **10.** $\frac{6}{4}$ **11.** $\frac{2}{6}$ **12.** $\frac{10}{30}$

B. If two similar triangles have corresponding sides in the ratio of $\frac{2}{7}$, find the ratio of the following.

13. corresponding angles **14.** perimeters

15. the areas **16.** corresponding altitudes

17. corresponding angle bisectors **18.** corresponding medians

In the figure, $\triangle ABC \sim \triangle WXY$, with altitudes $\overline{BD}$ and $\overline{XZ}$.

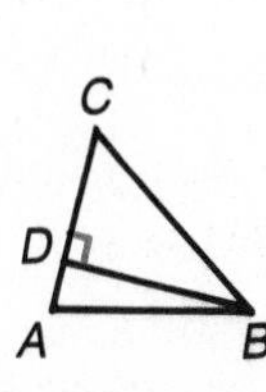

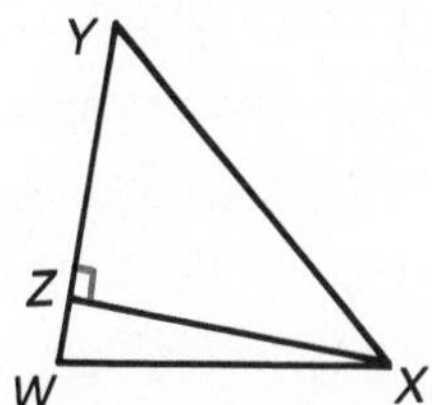

19. If $AC = 4$ and $WY = 5$, find the ratio of the area of $\triangle ABC$ to the area of $\triangle WXY$.

20. If $AB = 6$ and $WX = 8$, find $\frac{ZX}{DB}$.

21. If the ratio of the area of $\triangle WXY$ to the area of $\triangle ABC = \frac{49}{36}$, find $\frac{XY}{BC}$.

22. If $WX = \sqrt{5}$ and $AB = \sqrt{3}$, find the ratio of the area of $\triangle ABC$ to the area of $\triangle WXY$.

23. If $\frac{DB}{ZX} = \frac{6}{7}$, find $\frac{ZY}{DC}$. **24.** If $\frac{CB}{YX} = \frac{8}{11}$, find $\frac{m\angle A}{m\angle W}$.

Written Exercises

1. $\frac{4}{1}$ 2. $\frac{9}{4}$
3. $\frac{1}{64}$ 4. $\frac{4}{25}$
5. $\frac{8}{5}$ 6. $\frac{10}{1}$
7. $\frac{6}{7}$ 8. $\frac{4}{3}$
9. $\frac{9}{25}$ 10. $\frac{36}{16}$ or $\frac{9}{4}$
11. $\frac{4}{36}$ or $\frac{1}{9}$ 12. $\frac{100}{900}$ or $\frac{1}{9}$
13. $\frac{1}{1}$ 14. $\frac{2}{7}$
15. $\frac{4}{49}$ 16. $\frac{2}{7}$
17. $\frac{2}{7}$ 18. $\frac{2}{7}$
19. $\frac{16}{25}$ 20. $\frac{4}{3}$
21. $\frac{7}{6}$ 22. $\frac{3}{5}$
23. $\frac{7}{6}$ 24. $\frac{1}{1}$

25. A right triangle has sides of length 3, 4, and 5. A similar triangle has sides four times as long. Find the area of the larger triangle.

26. A right triangle has sides of length 5, 12, 13. A similar triangle has an area of 120. Find the lengths of the sides of the larger triangle.

In the figure, $\triangle RSU \sim \triangle ABD$ with altitudes $\overline{RT}$ and $\overline{AC}$.

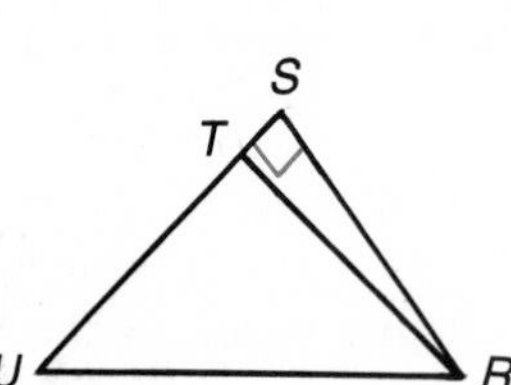

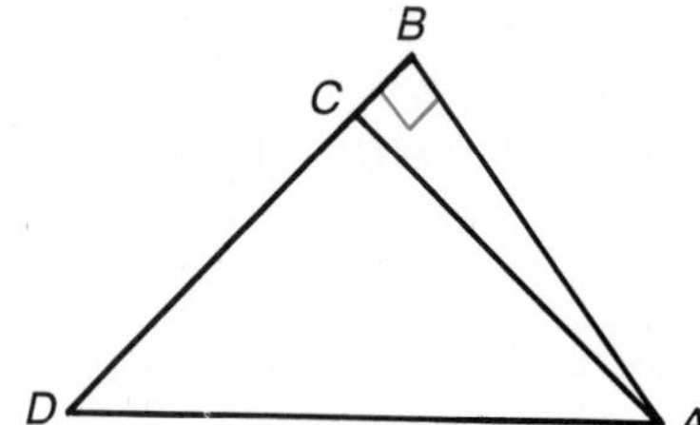

27. If $RS = 4$, $AB = 8$, and the area of $\triangle RSU = 11$, find the area of $\triangle ABD$.

28. If the area of $\triangle RSU = 16$, the area of $\triangle ABD = 25$, and $RT = 8$, find AC.

29. If the area of $\triangle ABD = 8$, the area of $\triangle RSU = 4$ and $RT = 3$, find AC.

30. If $RU = 9$, $AD = 10$, and the area of $\triangle RSU = 20$, find the area of $\triangle ABD$.

31. What is the effect on the area of a triangle if the length of each side is tripled?

32. Two similar triangles have areas of 25 and 36. If the shortest side in the smaller triangle is 3, find the shortest side in the larger triangle.

33. In two similar triangles, the ratio of a pair of corresponding sides is $\frac{2}{5}$. If the area of the smaller triangle is 10, find the area of the larger.

34. $\triangle ABC$ and $\triangle DEF$ are similar. If the area of $\triangle ABC$ is four times the area of $\triangle DEF$, what is the ratio of any two corresponding sides?

35. The area of $\triangle RST$ is 12 square inches with side $\overline{RS}$ being 5 inches long. In similar $\triangle XYZ$, the side corresponding to $\overline{RS}$ is 15 inches long. What is the area of $\triangle XYZ$?

36. The areas of two similar triangles are 48 and 432 square meters respectively. If the length of a side in the first triangle is 10 meters, find the length of the corresponding side in the second triangle.

C. 37. A pair of corresponding sides of two similar triangles have lengths of $\sqrt{2}$ and $3\sqrt{2}$, respectively. What is the ratio of their areas?

38. The lengths of a pair of corresponding sides of two similar triangles are 10 and $5\sqrt{2}$, respectively. Find the ratio of the perimeters of the triangles.

39. The perimeters of two similar triangles are 100 and 225, respectively. Find the ratio of a pair of corresponding sides.

40. The areas of two similar triangles, $\triangle ABC$ and $\triangle GHJ$, are 25 and 9, respectively. Find the perimeter of $\triangle GHJ$ if the perimeter of $\triangle ABC$ is 10 cm.

25. 96
26. 10, 24, 26
27. 44
28. 10
29. $3\sqrt{2}$
30. $\frac{2000}{81}$
31. increases by 9 times
32. $\frac{18}{5}$
33. $62\frac{1}{2}$
34. $\frac{2}{1}$
35. 108 in.^{2}
36. 30 m
37. $\frac{1}{9}$
38. $\frac{2}{\sqrt{2}}$
39. $\frac{4}{9}$
40. 6

SKILLS MAINTENANCE

Solve by using the zero product property.

1. $(x - 3)(x + 3) = 0$ **2.** $(3x + 2)(3x - 2) = 0$ **3.** $x^2 - 81 = 0$

4. $11x^2 - 44x = 0$ **5.** $y^2 - 10y + 25 = 0$ **6.** $x^2 = x + 12$

Solve by using the square root property of equality. Complete the square if necessary.

7. $y^2 + 4y + 4 = 25$ **8.** $16 - x^2 = 0$ **9.** $5 + n^2 = 9$

10. $(x - 3)^2 - 9 = 0$ **11.** $x^2 + 6x + 8 = 0$ **12.** $y^2 = y + 12$

13. $k^2 + 10k + 7 = 0$ **14.** $n^2 - 6 = 5n$ **15.** $x^2 + 6 = 5x$

Solve by using the quadratic formula: $x = \dfrac{-b \pm \sqrt{b^2 - 4ac}}{2a}$

16. $x^2 + 2x = 1$ **17.** $5n^2 = 7n$ **18.** $0 = y^2 - 3y - 2$

19. $3x^2 + 6x + 1 = 0$ **20.** $3y^3 - y = 2$ **21.** $3x^2 + 1 = 5x$

1. 3, −3 2. $\frac{2}{3}, \frac{-2}{3}$
3. 9, −9 4. 0, 4
5. 5, 5 6. 4, −3
7. −7, 3 8. 4, −4
9. 2, −2 10. 0, 6
11. −4, −2 12. 4, −3
13. $-5 \pm 3\sqrt{2}$ 14. 6, −1
15. 3, 2 16. $-1 \pm \sqrt{2}$
17. $0, \frac{7}{5}$ 18. $\frac{3 \pm \sqrt{17}}{2}$
19. $-1 \pm \frac{\sqrt{6}}{3}$ 20. $1, \frac{-2}{3}$
21. $\frac{5 \pm \sqrt{13}}{6}$

CHALLENGE

1. In the figure at the left, ladder A and ladder B are both 20 ft long. Suppose that ladder B is resting at a point on the wall 16 feet above the ground and ladder A at a point 12 feet above the ground. What is the length of the perpendicular from their point of intersection to the ground?

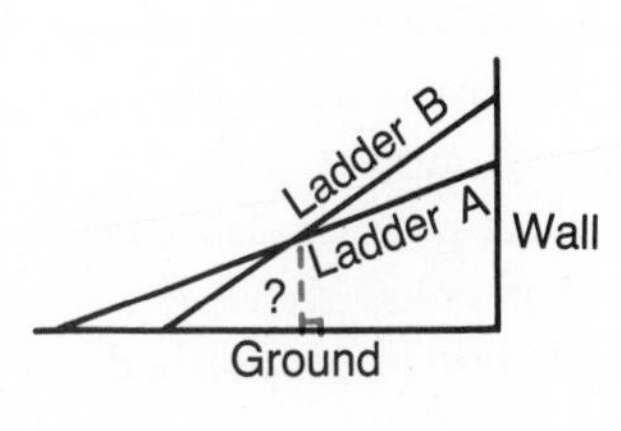

2. Given that l_1 and l_2 are parallel and the area of $\triangle ABC$ is 365, what is the area of $\triangle ACD$?

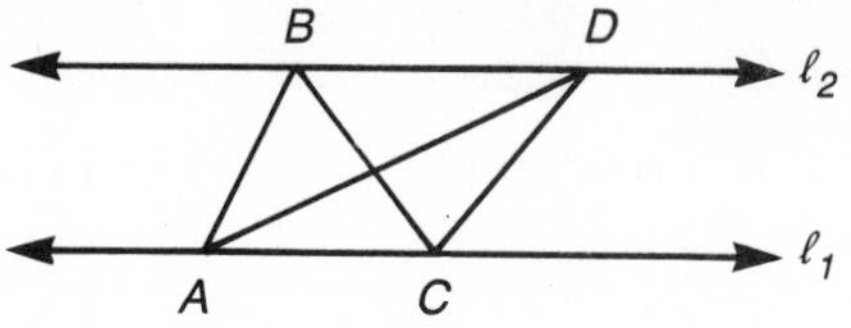

Challenge

1. $6\frac{6}{7}$ ft

2. 365

CAREER/Diamond Cutter

Geometric shapes and patterns can be seen everywhere in the world around us, from buildings and automobiles to fabrics and fashions. Through the centuries, artists and designers have used geometry to give ordinary objects interest and appeal. This has been especially true in the art of jewelry making. Using geometry, a skilled craftsman can transform a dull lump of diamond rock into one of the beautiful gems pictured at the right.

Originated in India and perfected in Italy, diamond cutting is a highly paid craft that requires great skill. Diamond cutters must have a thorough knowledge of both geometry and the properties of diamonds. The diamond draws great amounts of light into its center. When cut in *facets,* or faces, it reflects pinpoints of light from all these surfaces, giving the gem its sparkle. Because the diamond is harder than any other mineral, it can be cut only with diamond.

The natural diamond crystal ranges in color from clear or white to brown or black and is usually in the shape of an octahedron. Less common are the dodecahedron, or 12-faced, crystal and the cube.

Formed from carbon, the diamond has an atomic structure that affects the way it breaks. The diamond will split perfectly in any of the four directions parallel to the faces of the octahedron. Using this knowledge, diamond cutters can create an endless variety of shapes and sizes. One of the most popular shapes is the *diamond brilliant cut,* which has 58 facets. The illustration below shows the steps that transform a diamond from its natural, octahedral state into a finished brilliant cut.

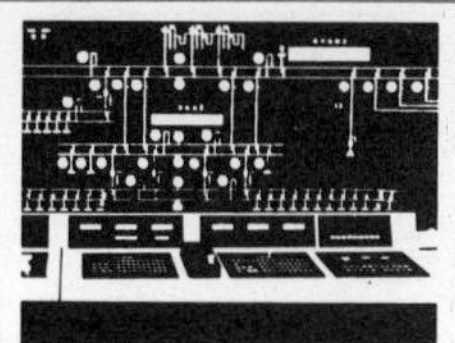

COMPUTER

This program determines if two triangles are similar. The lengths of the three sides of each triangle must be entered in corresponding order.

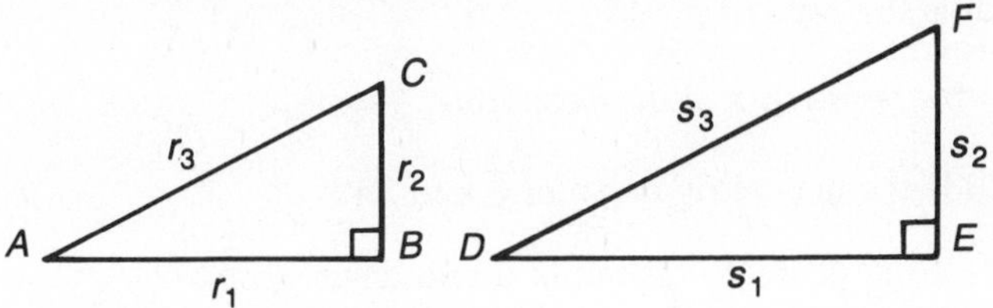


```
10 PRINT "WHAT IS THE LENGTH OF THE FIRST SIDE OF TRIANGLE ABC?": INPUT
   R1
20 PRINT "WHAT IS THE LENGTH OF THE SECOND SIDE OF TRIANGLE ABC?":
   INPUT R2
30 PRINT "WHAT IS THE LENGTH OF THE THIRD SIDE OF TRIANGLE ABC?":
   INPUT R3
40 PRINT "WHAT IS THE LENGTH OF THE FIRST SIDE OF TRIANGLE DEF?": INPUT
   S1
50 PRINT "WHAT IS THE LENGTH OF THE SECOND SIDE OF TRIANGLE DEF?":
   INPUT S2
60 PRINT "WHAT IS THE LENGTH OF THE THIRD SIDE OF TRIANGLE DEF?": INPUT
   S3
70 IF R1 <= 0 OR R2 <= 0 OR R3 <= 0 OR S1 <= 0 OR S2 <= 0 OR S3 <=
   0 THEN 90
80 IF R1/S1 = R2/S2 AND R1/S1 = R3/S3 AND R2/S2 = R3/S3 THEN 110
85 GO TO 130
90 PRINT "SORRY, INVALID NUMBER. PLEASE TRY AGAIN."
100 GO TO 10
110 PRINT "THE TRIANGLES ARE SIMILAR."
120 GO TO 140
130 PRINT "THE TRIANGLES ARE NOT SIMILAR."
140 END
```

1. How else could step 80 have been written to achieve the same results?

2. Write and run a program to determine if two right triangles are similar without comparing all three sides.

TEACHER'S RESOURCE MASTERS

Computer Master 10

COMPUTER SOFTWARE

Angles, Arcs, and Transformations

Computer

1. Could compare $\frac{R1}{R2} = \frac{S1}{S2}$ and $\frac{R1}{R3} = \frac{S1}{S3}$ or $\frac{R2}{R3} = \frac{S2}{S3}$.

2. To show similarity in right triangles, only 2 sides need to be compared; LL or HL. The program would be the same as the one in the text, only with one less comparison.

TEACHER'S RESOURCE MASTERS

Enrichment Master 7

ENRICHMENT

See Activities 19–20, p. T49–T50

Chapter 10 Review

1. $\frac{3}{1}$
2. $x = 4$
3. 12
4. 2.5
5. Similar polygons have the same shape. Congruent polygons have the same size and shape.
6. T
7. F
8. F
9. T
10. F
11. rectangle
12. sides
13. Yes; by Theorem 10.2
14. $BY = 6$
15. 1. $\angle B \cong \angle D$, $\angle A \cong \angle E$ (Thm. 8.8); 2. $\angle BCA \cong \angle DCE$ (Thm. 3.7); 3. $\triangle ABC \sim \triangle EDC$ (AAA Similarity).
16. 1. $\angle EAC \cong \angle DBC$ (Def. of rt. $\angle$; All rt. $\angle$s are $\cong$.); 2. $\angle C \cong \angle C$ (Reflexive); 3. $\triangle ACD \sim \triangle BCD$ (AA Similarity), so $\frac{AE}{BD} = \frac{AC}{BC}$, or $AE \cdot BC = BD \cdot AC$.

CHAPTER 10 REVIEW

VOCABULARY

cross-multiplication (10.1)	proportion (10.1)	similar (10.2)
geometric mean (10.1)	proportional (10.1)	similarity (10.2)

REVIEW EXERCISES

10.1

1. What is the ratio of 10 yd to 10 ft?

2. Find the value of x in the proportion $\frac{x}{6} = \frac{14}{21}$.

3. What is the geometric mean of 6 and 24?

4. $\sqrt{10}$ is the geometric mean of 4 and what number?

5. Explain the difference between similar polygons and congruent polygons.

According to the properties of proportions, if $\frac{a}{30} = \frac{5}{b}$, are the following statements true or false?

6. $ab = 150$ **7.** $\frac{a}{b} = \frac{5}{30}$ **8.** $\frac{a}{5} = \frac{b}{30}$

9. $\frac{a + 30}{30} = \frac{5 + b}{b}$ **10.** $\frac{a + 5}{30 + b} = \frac{a}{30} = \frac{5}{b}$

10.2 **Complete each statement.**

11. Two quadrilaterals that have congruent corresponding angles but are not similar are a square and a ______.

12. If two polygons are similar, they have congruent corresponding angles and proportional corresponding ______.

13. In the figure, if $AX = 2$, $ZX = 6$, $BY = 3$, and $ZY = 9$, is $\overline{AB} \parallel \overline{XY}$? Give your reason.

14. What value for BY would make $\overline{AB} \parallel \overline{XY}$ if $AX = 3$, $AZ = 4$, and $ZY = 14$?

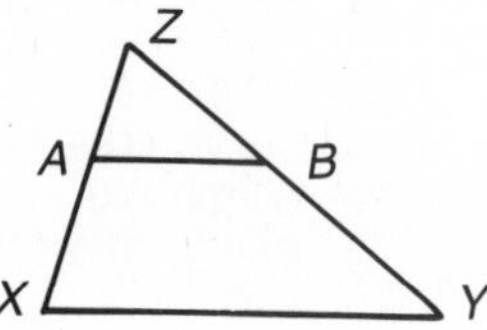

10.3

15. Given: $\overline{AB} \parallel \overline{DE}$
Prove: $\triangle ABC \sim \triangle ECD$

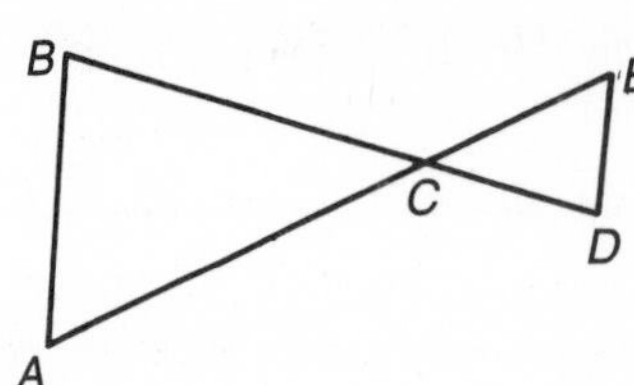

16. Given: $\overline{EA} \perp \overline{AC}$, $\overline{DB} \perp \overline{AC}$
Prove: $AE \cdot BC = BD \cdot AC$

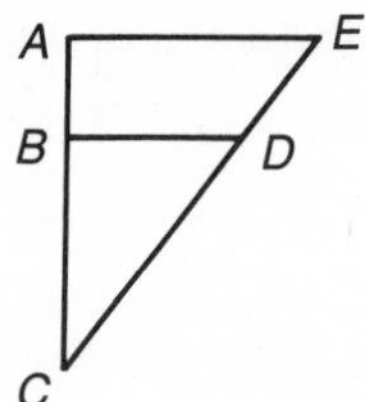

17. If $\overline{RS} \parallel \overline{BC}$, $AR = 6$, $RB = 4$, and $RS = 6$, find BC.

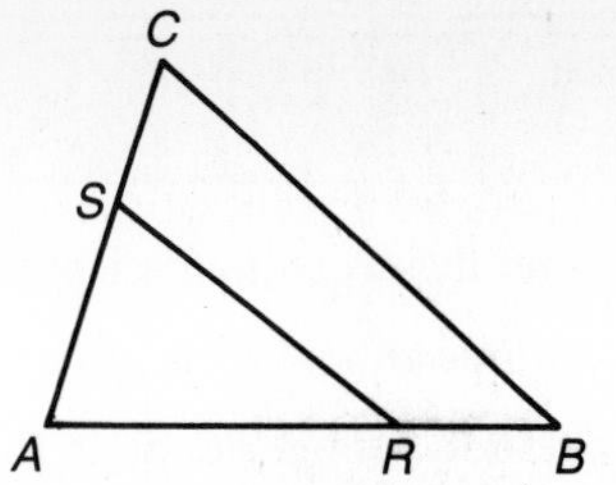
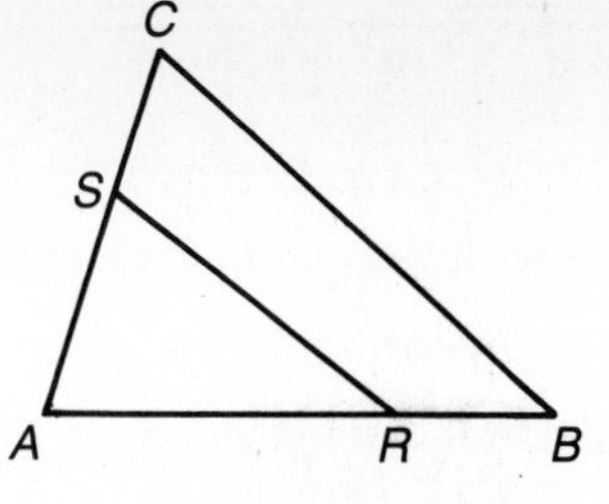

10.4 **Find the values for x and y that will make $\triangle ABC \sim \triangle DEF$.**

18. $AC = 12$, $DF = 6$, $m\angle C = 25$, $m\angle F = 3x - 5$, $BC = 10$, $FE = 3y - 4$

19. $AB = 8$, $DE = 6$, $BC = 10$, $EF = x$, $AC = 12$, $DF = 2y + 1$

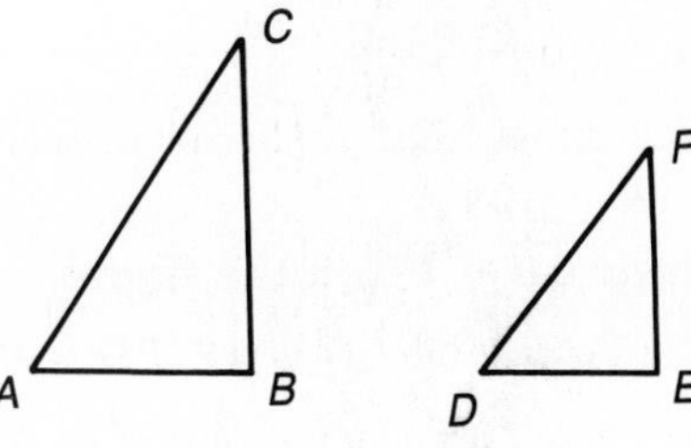

Given $\triangle ABC \sim \triangle DEF$, is it true or false that $\frac{ES}{BT} = \frac{EF}{BC} = \frac{DF}{AC}$ if

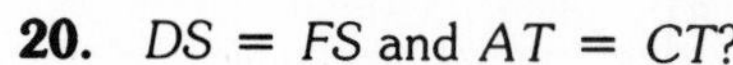

20. $DS = FS$ and $AT = CT$?

21. $\overline{ES} \perp \overline{DF}$ and $\overline{BT} \perp \overline{AC}$?

22. $\overline{FE} \perp \overline{DE}$ and $\overline{CB} \perp \overline{AB}$?

23. $\angle DES \cong \angle FES$ and $\angle ABT \cong \angle CBT$?

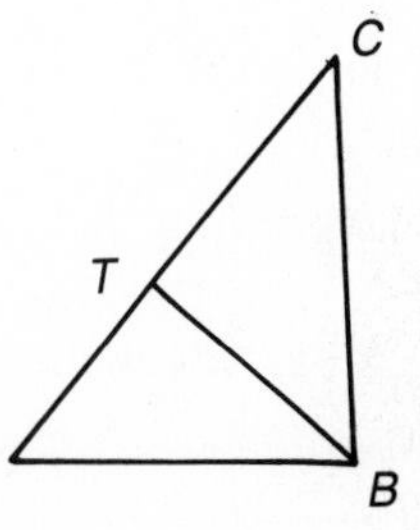

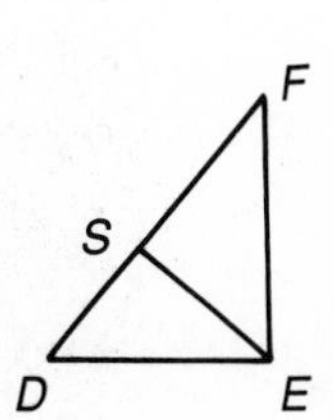

10.5 **Given right $\triangle ADC$ with altitude $\overline{DB}$.**

24. Find DB if $AB = 6$ and $BC = 10$.

25. Find DB if $AB = 5$ and $AC = 16$.

26. Find AD if $AB = 3$ and $AC = 10$.

27. Find BC if $DC = 9$ and $AC = 10$.

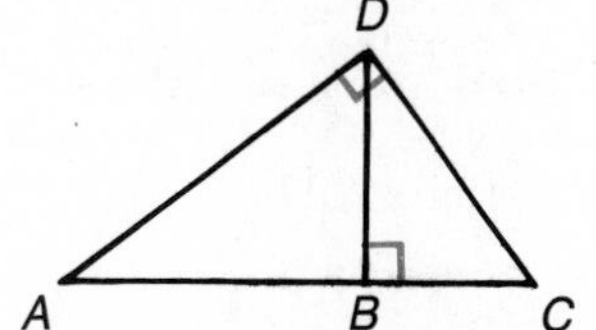

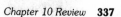

10.6 28. What effect does it have on the area of a triangle if each side is multiplied by 5?

29. Two similar triangles have areas of 81 and 49. If the longest side in the larger triangle is 6, find the longest side in the smaller triangle.

30. $\triangle ABC \sim \triangle XYZ$, and the area of $\triangle ABC = 16 \cdot$ the area of $\triangle XYZ$. In numerical terms, what is the ratio of any two corresponding sides?

31. In two similar triangles, the ratio of two corresponding altitudes is $\frac{\sqrt{3}}{1}$. If the area of the larger triangle is 24, what is the area of the smaller triangle?

17. 10

18. $x = 10$, $y = 3$

19. $x = \frac{15}{2}$, $y = 4$

20. T　21. T

22. F　23. T

24. $2\sqrt{15}$

25. $\sqrt{55}$

26. $\sqrt{30}$

27. $\frac{81}{10}$

28. The area increases times 25.

29. $\frac{14}{3}$

30. $\frac{4}{1}$

31. 8

TEACHER'S RESOURCE MASTERS

Chapter 10 Test
Multiple Choice Test—Chapter 10

Chapter 10 Test

1. If $\frac{a}{b} = \frac{c}{d}$, then $ad = bc$
2. $\frac{48}{7}$ 3. $\sqrt{42}$
4. 72 5. $\frac{RS}{AB} = \frac{AB}{ST}$
6. Similar triangles have congruent angles and proportional sides; congruent triangles have congruent angles and sides.
7. $AB = 12$
8. $DB = 16$
9. EC, DB, ED
10. $XY = 9\frac{3}{5}$, $ST = 10$
11. 1. $\angle 1 \cong \angle 2$ (Given); 2. $\angle D \cong \angle D$ (Reflexive); 3. $\triangle ABD \sim \triangle ECD$ (AA Similarity).
12. 1. $\angle EBA \cong \angle DBC$ (Thm. 3.7); 2. $\triangle ABE \sim \triangle CBD$ (SAS Similarity).
13. DC, BC 14. BD, BC
15. $AC = 6$ 16. $DB = 20$
17. $\frac{9}{16}$
18. $\frac{9}{11}$

CHAPTER 10 TEST

1. State the cross-multiplication property of a proportion.
2. Find the ratio of 6 lbs to 14 oz.
3. Find the geometric mean of 6 and 7.
4. 12 is the geometric mean of 2 and what number?
5. Write a proportion for which it is true that $(AB)^2 = RS \cdot ST$.
6. Explain the distinction between congruent and similar triangles.

Given $\overline{AB} \parallel \overline{EC}$ in the figure.

7. Find AB if $AD = 12$, $ED = 9$, and $EC = 9$.
8. Find DB if $DC = 8$, $EC = 9$, and $AB = 18$.
9. If $\triangle ABD \sim \triangle ECD$, complete the extended proportion $\frac{AB}{?} = \frac{?}{DC} = \frac{AD}{?}$.
10. If $\triangle XYZ \sim \triangle RST$, find XY and ST.

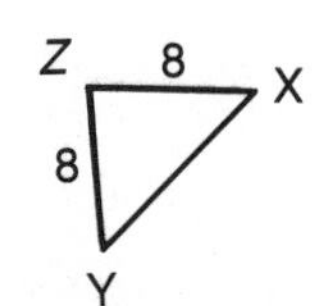

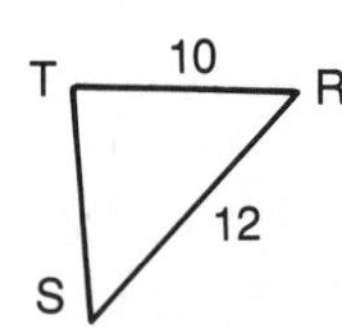

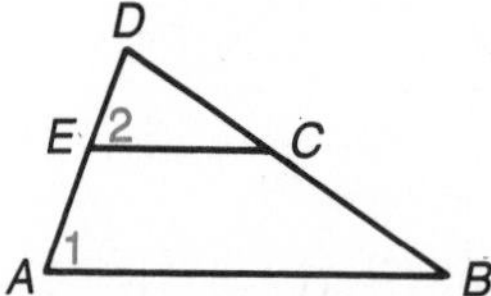

11. **Given:** $\angle 1 \cong \angle 2$
Prove: $\triangle ABD \sim \triangle ECD$

12. **Given:** $\frac{EB}{DB} = \frac{AB}{CB}$
Prove: $\triangle ABE \sim \triangle CBD$

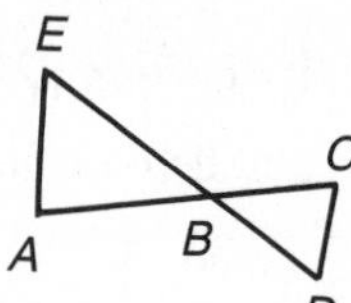

Refer to the figure at the right, in which $\overline{AC}$ is an altitude of right $\triangle ABD$, to complete the following.

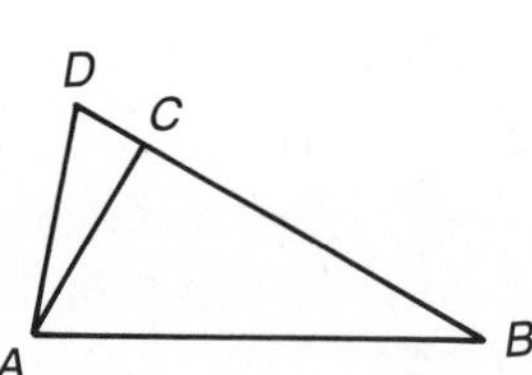

13. $\frac{?}{AC} = \frac{AC}{?}$
14. $\frac{?}{AB} = \frac{AB}{?}$
15. If $DC = 3$, and $BC = 12$, find AC.
16. If $AD = 10$, and $DC = 5$, find DB.

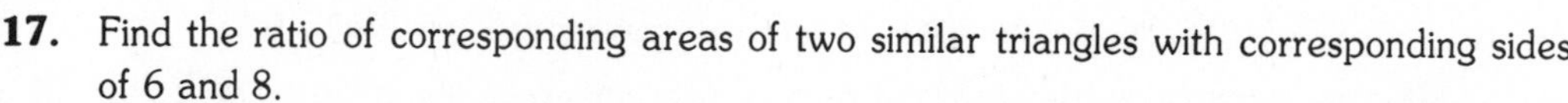

17. Find the ratio of corresponding areas of two similar triangles with corresponding sides of 6 and 8.
18. Find the ratio of corresponding sides in similar triangles with areas of 81 and 121.

CHAPTER 11

Coordinate Geometry of the Plane

OBJECTIVE

Graph and locate points in the coordinate plane.

TEACHER'S NOTES

See p. T36

MIXED REVIEW

1. The segment joining the midpoints of sides of a triangle is ________. parallel to and half the length of the third side
2. What is the reciprocal of $-\frac{2}{3}$? $-\frac{3}{2}$
3. What is the additive inverse of $-\frac{4}{7}$? $\frac{4}{7}$
4. Can three lines be perpendicular to each other at the same point? yes
5. If $\triangle ABC \sim \triangle RST$, then $\angle B \cong$. $\angle S$

TEACHER'S RESOURCE MASTERS

Practice Master 32, Part 1

11.1 Establishing the Coordinate Plane

You have already learned how to set up a coordinate system on a *line:*

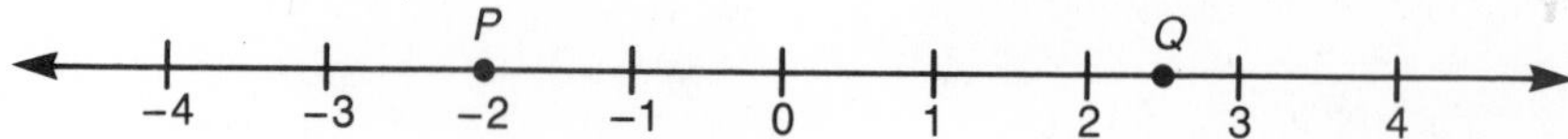

Recall that every number describes a unique point and that every point represents a unique number. In the system shown above, -2 is the **coordinate** of P, and $2\frac{1}{2}$ is the *coordinate* of Q. Point P is the **graph** of -2, and Q is the *graph* of $2\frac{1}{2}$. The distance from 0 to 1 establishes the length of one **unit,** and this length is the basis of plotting all other points on the number line.

In a *plane,* two perpendicular lines form a **rectangular coordinate system.** The plane these lines determine is sometimes called the **Cartesian plane.** Every point in the plane relates to *two* numbers—one on the horizontal line, or ***x*-axis,** and one on the vertical line, or ***y*-axis.** The plural of axis is *axes.*

In this figure, the x-value of P is found by dropping a perpendicular from P to the x-axis. The foot of the x-projection of P is -2. Similarly, the projection of P on the y-axis has a y-value of 1. Thus, the coordinates of point P are $(-2, 1)$. The x-coordinate is always given first and the y-coordinate second.

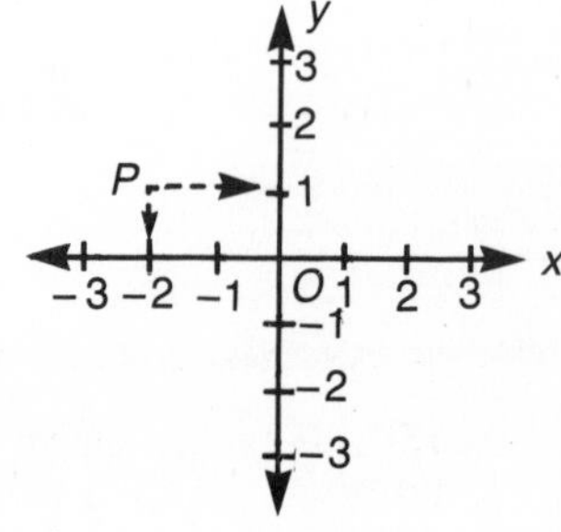

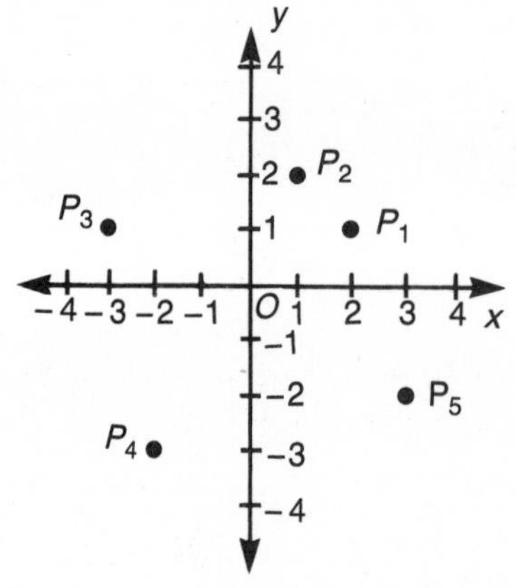

The coordinates of the five points in the rectangular coordinate system shown on the left are:

$P_1(2, 1)$ $P_2(1, 2)$

$P_3(-3, 1)$ $P_4(-2, -3)$

$P_5(3, -2)$

P_1 and P_2 illustrate why Cartesian coordinates are called **ordered pairs.** The graph of (2, 1) is a point *entirely different* from the graph of (1, 2).

Whereas a line divides a plane into two half-planes, the rectangular axes divide the plane into four **quadrants.** They are identified by Roman numerals, as shown at the right.

Every point in the plane lies either in one of the quadrants or on one of the axes.

The point where the two axes intersect has coordinates (0, 0) and is called the **origin.** On the graph it is identified by the capital letter O.

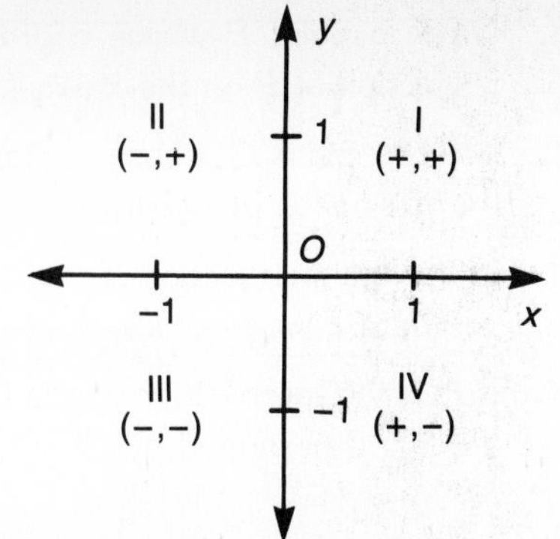

ASSIGNMENT GUIDE

Minimum 1-22
Regular 1-29 odd
Maximum 1-29 odd, 30-33

ORAL EXERCISES

In which quadrant does each of the following points lie?

1. (4, −2) **2.** (−1, −5) **3.** (3, 1) **4.** (−2, 2)

5. Name the point that is the projection of (2, −6) on the y-axis.

6. What will be the x-coordinate of every point on the y-axis?

7. What will be the y-coordinate of every point on the x-axis?

8. What can be said about the coordinates of a point that does not lie in any quadrant?

Oral Exercises

1. IV 2. III
3. I 4. II
5. (0, −6) 6. $x = 0$
7. $y = 0$ 8. $x = 0$ or $y = 0$

WRITTEN EXERCISES

A. Refer to the system at the right for Exercises 1-16.

Write the coordinates of each of the named points.

1. A **2.** B **3.** C **4.** O
5. E **6.** F **7.** G **8.** H

Name the quadrant, if any, in which each of the points falls.

9. A **10.** B **11.** C **12.** D
13. E **14.** F **15.** G **16.** H

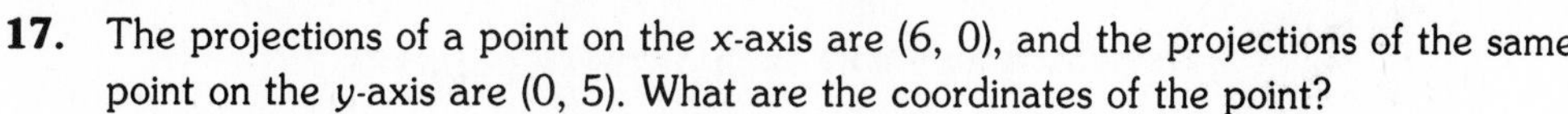

17. The projections of a point on the x-axis are (6, 0), and the projections of the same point on the y-axis are (0, 5). What are the coordinates of the point?

B. Graph the following ordered pairs of numbers.

18. $A(-1, 4)$ **19.** $B(4, -1)$ **20.** $C(3, 2)$ **21.** $D(0, -3)$
22. $E(-3, -4)$ **23.** $F(-3, 0)$ **24.** $G(-3, 2)$ **25.** $H(0, 2)$

Written Exercises

1. (1, 4) 2. (4, 2)
3. (3, 0) 4. (0, 0)
5. (0, −4) 6. (−3, −2)
7. (−4, 0) 8. (−3, 4)
9. I 10. I
11. none 12. IV
13. none 14. III
15. none 16. II
17. (6, 5)

18.-25.

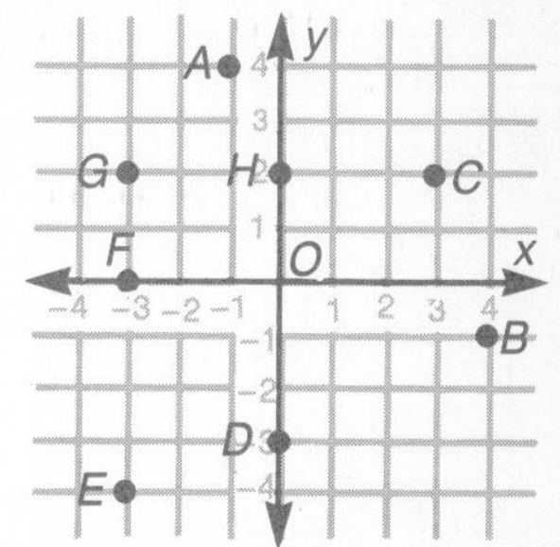

26. x-axis (9, 0), y-axis (0, 3)

27. x-axis (−3, 0), y-axis (0, −4)

28. T(3, 5)

29. H(−1, 4)

30. A right triangle: the axes are perpendicular at (0, 0).

31. 5

32. $A = 28$

33. $A = 15$

Exploration

1. eight 2. y-axis

3. x-axis 4. z-axis

5. 3; 2; 5

26. Given a point P whose coordinates are $P(9, 3)$, what are the coordinates of the projection of P on the x-axis? on the y-axis?

27. Given a point Q whose coordinates are $Q(-3, -4)$, what are the coordinates of the projection of Q on the x-axis? on the y-axis?

C. 28. If T is the intersection of the line determined by $R(6, 5)$ and its y-projection and the line determined by $S(3, 9)$ and its x-projection, what are the coordinates of T?

29. If H is the intersection of the line determined by $F(-1, 8)$ and its x-projection and the line determined by $G(-4, 4)$ and its y-projection, what are the coordinates of H?

30. Given $A(0, 0)$, $B(-3, 0)$, and $C(0, 4)$, what type of triangle do A, B, and C determine? What relation between the x-axis and y-axis tells you this?

31. Given the triangle in Exercise 30 above, what is the measure of $\overline{BC}$?

32. What is the area of a quadrilateral whose vertices are $P(4, 2)$, $Q(-3, 2)$, $R(-3, -2)$, and $S(4, -2)$?

33. What is the area of a triangle whose vertices are $A(4, 1)$, $B(-1, 1)$, and $C(-2, 7)$?

EXPLORATION/Space Coordinates

You can form a *three-dimensional coordinate system* by considering three mutually perpendicular axes, as shown.

Note that the z-axis, although drawn on this page, actually represents a line perpendicular to the plane of this page. Now, every point in space has three coordinates, (x, y, z). The x-coordinate is its projection on the x-axis. The y-coordinate is its projection on the y-axis. The z-coordinate is its projection on the z-axis.

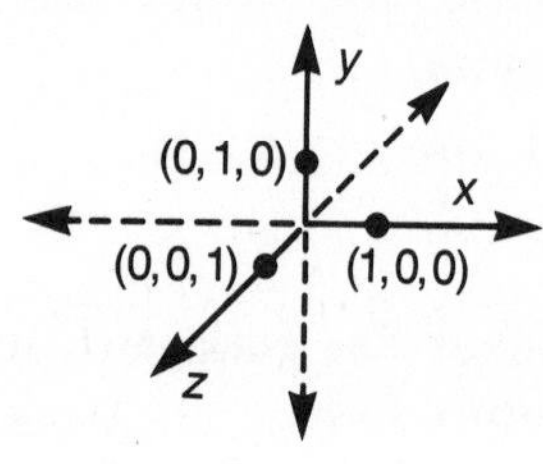

1. Into how many regions is space divided by the three axes?

On which axis will each of these points lie?

2. (0, 3, 0) **3.** (−2, 0, 0) **4.** (0, 0, 5)

5. What is the distance of the point (5, −2, 3) from the xy-plane? from the xz-plane? from the yz-plane?

11.2 Slope

OBJECTIVE

Find the slope of a line.

TEACHER'S NOTES

See p. T36

MIXED REVIEW

1. What is the product of $-\frac{a}{b} \cdot \frac{b}{a}$? -1
2. What is the average of -14 and 20? 3
3. Solve $2x - y = 8$
   $x + 3y = 11$ (5, 2)
4. Solve for P if $A = \pi P - \pi r$. $P = \frac{A + \pi r}{\pi}$
5. In a rhombus, the diagonals are ______. $\perp$ bisectors of each other

TEACHER'S RESOURCE MASTERS

Practice Master 32, Part 2

To show that the slope of the ski run on the right is greater than that of the ski run on the left, place the runs in the framework of a rectangular coordinate *system.* Assume the top of the first run is point A, and the bottom is point B. Likewise, let the top of the run on the right be point C, and let the bottom be point D.

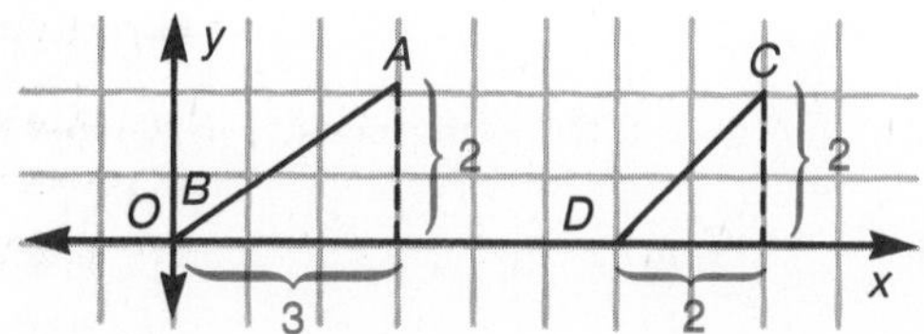

From the "top" to the "bottom" of segment AB, the drop, or *change in y*, is 2 units. This is true also of segment CD. The *decrease in x* is 3 units on segment AB, whereas it is only 2 units on segment CD.

For segment AB, the ratio of the change in y to the change in x is $\frac{-2}{-3}$, or $\frac{2}{3}$. For segment CD, the ratio is $\frac{-2}{-2}$, or 1. Since 1 is greater than $\frac{2}{3}$, the slope of the line containing segment CD is greater than the slope of the line containing segment AB.

Each endpoint of a segment that is placed in a coordinate system has two coordinates, so that for endpoints P_1 and P_2 you would write $P_1(x_1, y_1)$ and $P_2(x_2, y_2)$. The change in y can be written as $y_2 - y_1$, and the change in x can be written as $x_2 - x_1$.

DEFINITION: slope

The **slope** of $\overline{P_1P_2}$ is the number $m = \frac{y_2 - y_1}{x_2 - x_1}$.

P_1 and P_2 are the endpoints of $\overline{P_1P_2}$.

Notice that the slope of a line is designated by the lowercase italic letter *m*.

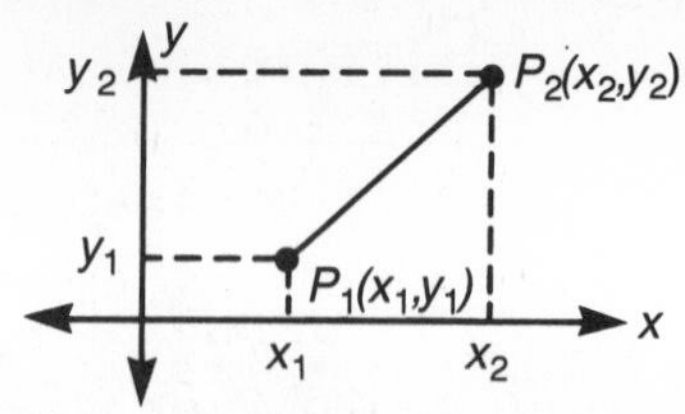

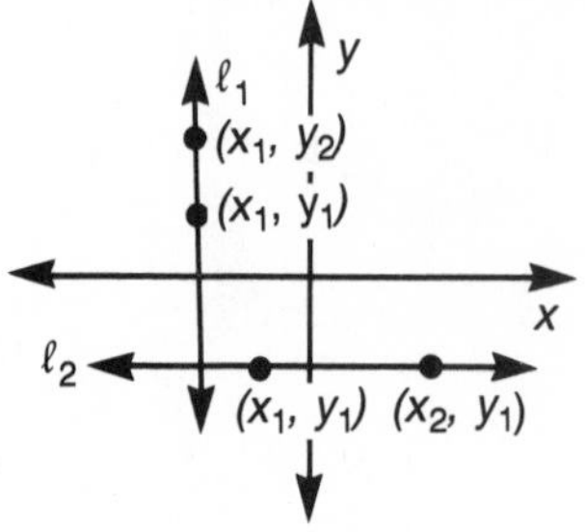

The segments considered so far have been **oblique,** that is, *neither vertical nor horizontal.*

Recall that on a vertical line, the *x*-value of every point is the same. Thus, the slope of l_1 is $\frac{y_2 - y_1}{0}$. Since division by zero is undefined, you can conclude that *a vertical line has no slope.*

On a horizontal line, the *y*-value of every point is the same, so the slope of l_2 is $\frac{0}{x_2 - x_1}$. Since zero divided by any number (other than 0) equals 0, you can conclude that *the slope of a horizontal line is 0.*

Example: Find the slope of a segment with endpoints (−3, 1) and (5, 3).

Solution: In the formula, substitute $x_1 = -3$, $y_1 = 1$, $x_2 = 5$, and $y_2 = 3$. Thus $m = \frac{y_2 - y_1}{x_2 - x_1} = \frac{3 - 1}{5 - (-3)} = \frac{2}{8} = \frac{1}{4}$.

Example: Find the slope of a segment with endpoints (1, 4) and (6, 1).

Solution: In the formula, substitute $x_1 = 1$, $y_1 = 4$, $x_2 = 6$, and $y_2 = 1$. Thus $m = \frac{y_2 - y_1}{x_2 - x_1} = \frac{1 - 4}{6 - 1} = \frac{-3}{5}$.

Slope can also be a negative number. If you now look at the segment just considered, you can see that it slopes "downward" from the left, rather than "upward" from the left, as in the example of the hills.

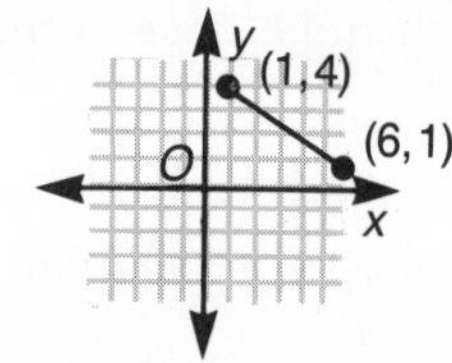

The slope of a segment is the same as the slope of the line to which the segment belongs. But a line contains an infinite number of segments. Can you be certain that the slope of a line can be determined by considering any one of these segments? The following theorem assures you that it can.

THEOREM 11.1
On a nonvertical line, all segments have the same slope.

Proof: There are three cases that must be considered.

Case 1. If the line is horizontal, all segments on it have a slope of 0.

Case 2. Line p has a positive slope. It includes two segments, $\overline{P_1P_2}$ and $\overline{P_1'P_2'}$. Assume two points, R and R_1 such that $\triangle P_1P_2R$ and $\triangle P_1'P_2'R'$ are right triangles. Sides $\overline{P_1P_2}$ and $\overline{P_1R}$ have an included angle A. Sides $\overline{P_1'P_2'}$ and $\overline{P_1'R'}$ have an included angle A'.

Case 3. Same as Case 2, but p has a negative slope.

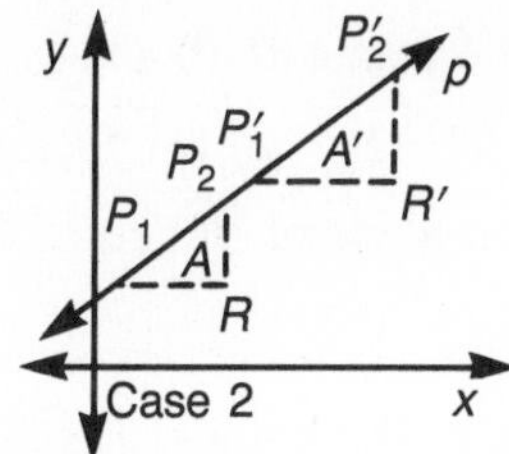

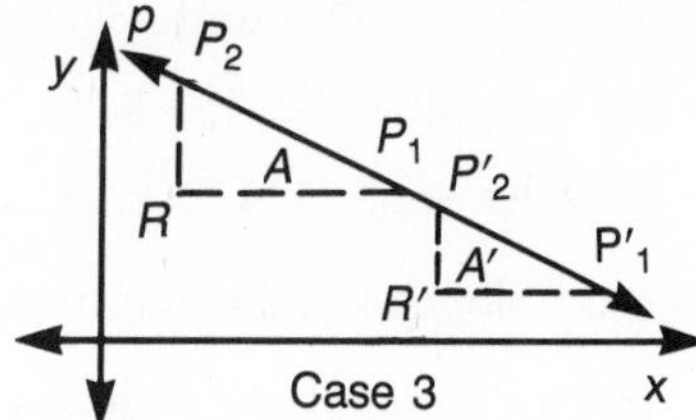

In either Case 2 or Case 3, $m\angle A = m\angle A'$, and since the triangles are right triangles, $\triangle P_1P_2R \sim \triangle P_1'P_2'R'$.

Therefore in either case, $\frac{RP_2}{P_1R} = \frac{R'P_2'}{P_1'R'}$.

In Case 2 these ratios are the slopes of $\overline{P_1P_2}$ and $\overline{P_1'P_2'}$, and therefore the segments have the same slope. In Case 3, the slopes are equal ratios, and are therefore equal.

Thus, Theorem 11.1 is established.

ASSIGNMENT GUIDE

Minimum 1-14
Regular 1-23 odd
Maximum 1-23 odd, 25-29

ORAL EXERCISES

1. If the slope of $\overline{AB}$ does not equal the slope of $\overline{BC}$, are points A, B, and C collinear?
2. If the slope of $\overline{MN}$ equals the slope of $\overline{PQ}$, does it follow that M, N, P, and Q are collinear?
3. According to the definition, is the slope of a line an angle or a number?
4. Consider line l, which has a *negative* slope. If l contains a point that lies in Quadrant I, is it possible that l also contains a point that lies in Quadrant III?
5. What is the slope of the x-axis? of the y-axis?

Oral Exercises

1. no
2. no
3. a number
4. no
5. 0, no slope

6. no slope 7. 0

8. positive 9. negative

Written Exercises

1. $\frac{1}{2}$ 2. -2 3. $\frac{11}{5}$ 4. $\frac{6}{5}$

5. no slope 6. 0 7. $\frac{-1}{3}$

8. $\frac{-2}{3}$

9. $\frac{4}{3}$

10. 1 11. $\frac{11}{3}$

12. yes 13. yes

14. 6 15. -2

16. 3 17. -4

18. 0 and no slope

19. $\frac{-4}{3}$ 20. no

21. 3 22. 2

23. 4 24. 7

25. $\frac{-20}{9}$ 26. $\frac{-64}{33}$

27. $\frac{-160}{189}$

28.

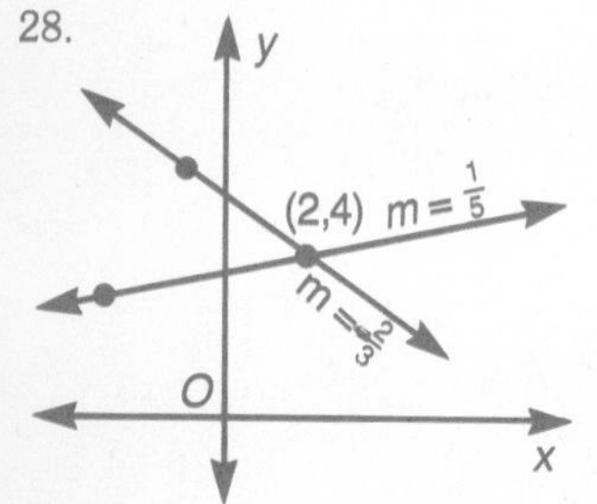

29. yes

6. What is the slope of a vertical line? **7.** What is the slope of a horizontal line?

8. What is the slope of an oblique line that slopes upward to the right?

9. What is the slope of an oblique line that slopes upward to the left?

WRITTEN EXERCISES

A. Find the slope of the segments with the following pairs of endpoints.

1. (0, −3), (6, 0) **2.** (0, 6), (3, 0) **3.** (7, 3), (2, −8)

4. (−2, −1), (3, 5) **5.** (13, 7), (13, 4) **6.** (7, −9), (−3, −9)

7. (4, −5), (−5, −2) **8.** (−6, 4), (−3, 2)

9. What is the slope of the line that contains the points (0, 0) and (3, 4)?

B. Use the coordinates $A(-3, 4)$, $B(2, 9)$, and $C(-1, -2)$ for Exercises 10–13.

10. Find the slope of $\overline{AB}$. **11.** Find the slope of $\overline{BC}$.

12. Is the slope of $\overline{AC}$ equal to the slope of $\overline{CA}$?

13. Will the slope of any segment $\overline{P_1P_2}$ be equal to the slope of $\overline{P_2P_1}$?

Supply the missing value that will make the line passing through the two points vertical.

14. (n, −5) and (6, 1) **15.** (−2, 5) and (n, −2)

16. (3, 4) and (n, −3) **17.** (n, 1) and (−4, −5)

18. A square has vertices (−5, 0), (0, 5), (5, 0), and (0, −5). What are the slopes of its two diagonals?

19. Consider a right triangle with vertices $A(0, 4)$, $B(0, 0)$, and $C(3, 0)$. What is the slope of the hypotenuse?

20. Line M passes through the origin of a rectangular coordinate system, and it has a slope of 2. Does the line pass through the point (8, 4)?

Supply the missing value that will make the line through the two points have the slope given.

21. (6, 7), (4, n), $m = 2$ **22.** (n, −2), (−2, −6), $m = 1$

23. (−2, 4), (n, −1), $m = \frac{-5}{6}$ **24.** (4, −3), (8, n), $m = \frac{5}{2}$

Find the slope of the segments with the following pairs of endpoints.

25. $(\frac{1}{4}, \frac{1}{3}), (\frac{3}{4}, \frac{-7}{9})$ **26.** $(\frac{7}{16}, \frac{-3}{5}), (\frac{-1}{4}, \frac{11}{15})$ **27.** $(\frac{-1}{2}, \frac{1}{3}), (\frac{2}{5}, \frac{-3}{7})$

C. 28. Draw a coordinate system and plot the point (2, 4). Through this point, draw a line that has a slope $-\frac{2}{3}$, and a line that has a slope $\frac{1}{5}$.

29. Is the point $B(2, 0)$ on the line joining $A(-3, -5)$ to $C(8, 6)$?

11.3 Parallel and Perpendicular Lines

So far, you have defined parallel lines as coplanar lines that do not intersect or that have no point in common. In the next theorem, coordinate geometry provides another definition of parallelism.

THEOREM 11.2
Two nonvertical lines are parallel *if and only if* they have the same slope.

Since this theorem is a biconditional, its proof must be given in two parts.

Proof
Part 1: If two nonvertical lines are parallel, then they have the same slope.

Assume that R is the intersection of perpendiculars drawn from P_1 and P_2 and that R' is the intersection of perpendiculars drawn from P_1' and P_2'. Given what you already know about parallel lines cut by transversals, it can be established that $\angle P_2P_1R \cong \angle P_2'P_1'R'$. Since $\triangle P_1RP_2 \sim \triangle P_1'R'P_2'$, it follows that their corresponding sides are proportional, or $\frac{P_2R}{P_1R} = \frac{P_2'R'}{P_1'R'}$. Since the change in x and the change in y for the two parallel lines will also be proportional, both lines will have the same slope, or $m = m'$.

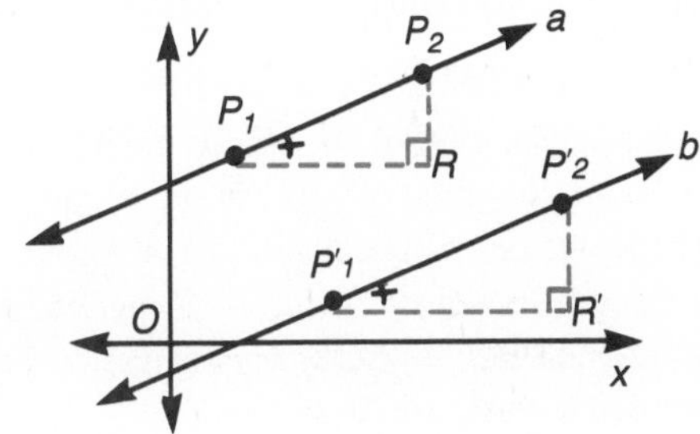

Part 2: If two different lines have the same slope, then they are parallel. (This is proved by contradiction, or indirect proof).

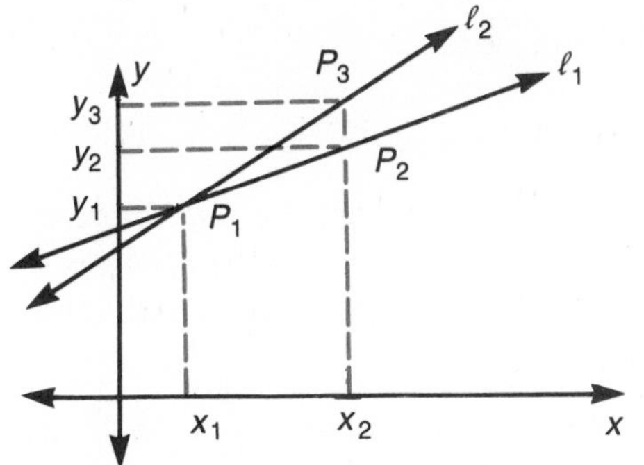

Assume that lines l_1 and l_2 have the same slope but are *not* parallel. Thus, they must intersect at some point $P(x_1, y_1)$.

Now select P_2 on l_1 and P_3 on l_2 such that they have the same x-coordinate, x_2, and y_2 and y_3 as their respective y-coordinates.

$$\text{The slope of } l_1 = \frac{y_2 - y_1}{x_2 - x_1}.$$

$$\text{The slope of } l_2 = \frac{y_3 - y_1}{x_2 - x_1}.$$

OBJECTIVE

Use slopes to determine whether two lines are parallel, perpendicular, or neither.

TEACHER'S NOTES

See p. T36

MIXED REVIEW

1. Simplify $\sqrt{(10 - 2)^2 + [1 - (-14)]^2}$. 17
2. Are all vertical lines parallel? yes
3. Find the area of a square whose diagonal is $5\sqrt{2}$. 25
4. The average of -12 and 7 is ______. $-2\frac{1}{2}$
5. Find $\sqrt{(\frac{a-b}{2})^2}$. $\left|\frac{a-b}{2}\right|$

TEACHER'S RESOURCE MASTERS

Practice Master 33, Part 1

Since y_3 does not equal y_2, these slopes are *not* equal. But this contradicts the given fact that their slopes *are* equal. Hence, the assumption that l_1 and l_2 are *not* parallel must be rejected.

THEOREM 11.3
Two nonvertical lines are perpendicular *if and only if* their slopes are the negative reciprocals of each other.

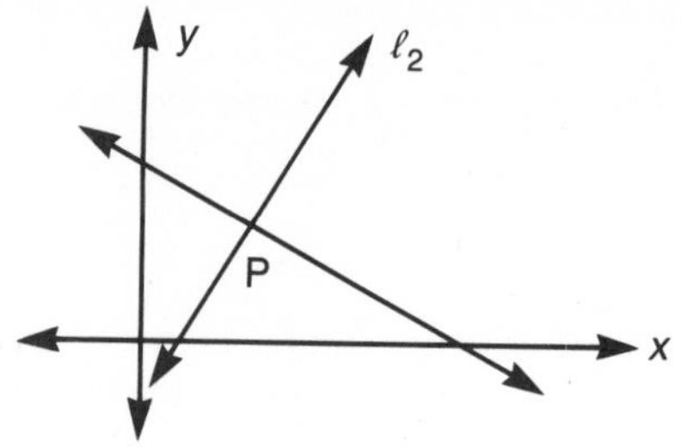

The strategy of this proof is to *assume that the lines are perpendicular* and then to investigate the relationship between their slopes.

Select points Q and Q' on l_2 and l_1, respectively, so that both lie above P and so that $PQ = PQ'$. Next, complete right triangles PQR and $Q'PR'$, as shown in the bottom figure.

$\angle PRQ \cong \angle Q'R'P$ because both are right angles. Also, $\angle PQR \cong \angle RPS$, because they are complements of the same angle, and $\angle Q'PR' \cong \angle RPS$, because vertical angles are congruent. So $\angle PQR \cong \angle Q'PR'$ by transitivity, and $\triangle PRQ \cong \triangle Q'R'P$ because of Theorem 6.2 (SAA).

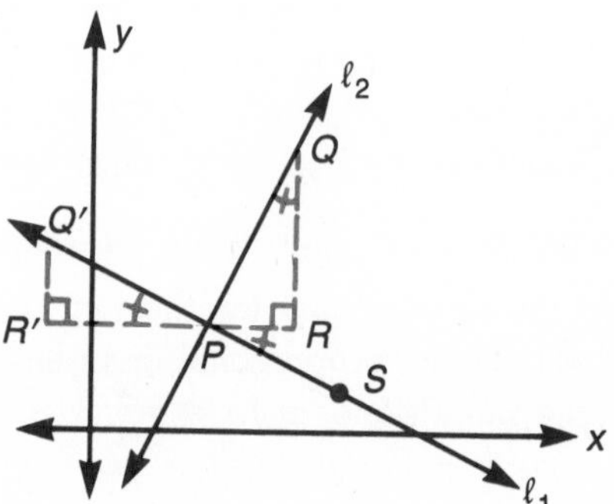

Therefore, $\frac{RQ}{PR} = \frac{R'P}{Q'R'}$.

$\frac{RQ}{PR}$, call it m_2, is the slope of l_2. The slope of l_1, call it m_1, is $-\frac{Q'R'}{R'P}$.

By substituting corresponding parts of congruent triangles, $-\frac{Q'R'}{R'P}$ can be rewritten as $-\frac{PR}{RQ}$. This expression of m_1 is the negative reciprocal of the expression for m_2.

$$m_1 = -\frac{PR}{RQ} \qquad m_2 = \frac{RQ}{PR}$$

This proves that if two lines are perpendicular, the slopes of the lines are the negative reciprocals of each other. Before accepting Theorem 11.3, you must also prove the converse of this statement, namely that if the slopes of two lines are the negative reciprocals of each other, the lines are perpendicular. This is left as an exercise.

Notice that the last two theorems exclude vertical lines, which have no slope. Note also that since the number 0 has no reciprocal, the slope of a horizontal line has no negative reciprocal.

ORAL EXERCISES

1. Are two lines with the same slope always parallel?
2. Are two segments with the same slope necessarily parallel?
3. If two lines are perpendicular, what is the product of their slopes?

Refer to the figure to answer Exercises 4–8.

4. In terms of segment ratios, what are the slopes of lines p and q?
5. If $p \perp q$, $ED = 3$, and $CD = 4$, what is the slope of p? the slope of q?
6. Given the coordinates $A(2, 8)$, $B(2, 6)$, and $C(6, 6)$, what is the slope of q? If $p \perp q$, what is the slope of p?
7. If p is parallel to the x-axis, what is its slope?
8. If q is parallel to the y-axis, what is its slope?

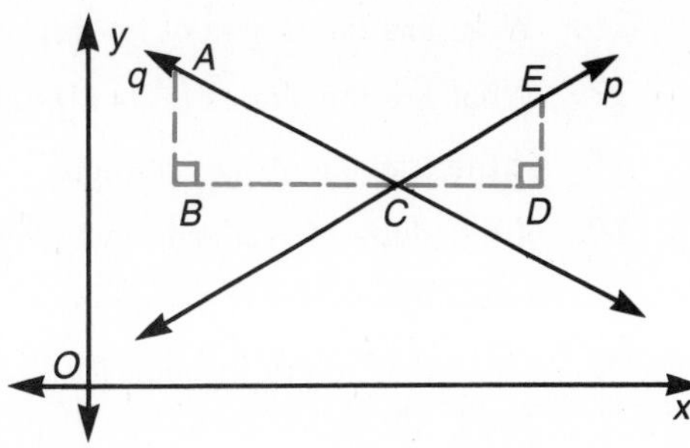

WRITTEN EXERCISES

A. Find the slope of each line in Exercises 1–5.

1. $\overleftrightarrow{AB}$, given $A(2, 1)$ and $B(3, 2)$
2. $\overleftrightarrow{GH}$, given $G(1, 2)$ and $H(3, 0)$
3. $\overleftrightarrow{KL}$, given $K(4, 5)$ and $L(0, 5)$
4. $\overleftrightarrow{PR}$, given $P(-1, 0)$ and $R(2, -3)$
5. $\overleftrightarrow{XY}$, given $X(7, 0)$ and $Y(7, 8)$
6. Which lines in Exercises 1–5 are parallel to each other?
7. Which line in Exercises 1–5 is parallel to the x-axis?
8. Which line in Exercises 1–5 is parallel to the y-axis?
9. Which lines in Exercises 1–5 are perpendicular to each other?
10. B and what other point named above determine a line parallel to $\overleftrightarrow{XY}$?

ASSIGNMENT GUIDE

Minimum 1–16
Regular 1–18
Maximum 1–18, 22–24

Oral Exercises

1. yes
2. No; they may be collinear.
3. -1
4. slope of $p = \frac{ED}{CD}$, slope of $q = \frac{-AB}{BC}$
5. $\frac{3}{4}$, $\frac{-4}{3}$
6. $\frac{-1}{2}$, 2
7. 0
8. It has no slope.

Written Exercises

1. 1
2. -1
3. 0
4. -1
5. no slope
6. $\overleftrightarrow{GH} \parallel \overleftrightarrow{PR}$
7. $\overleftrightarrow{KL}$
8. $\overleftrightarrow{XY}$
9. $\overleftrightarrow{KL} \perp \overleftrightarrow{XY}$, $\overleftrightarrow{AB} \perp \overleftrightarrow{GH}$, $\overleftrightarrow{AB} \perp \overleftrightarrow{PR}$
10. H

11. $\parallel$ 12. $\perp$
13. $\perp$ 14. neither
15. $\parallel$ 16. $2, \frac{-4}{3}, \frac{-2}{9}$
17. $\frac{-1}{2}, \frac{3}{4}, \frac{9}{2}$ 18. no
19. $x = 6$
20. $m_1 = \frac{b}{a}$, $m_2 = \frac{a}{-b}$, so m_1 and m_2 are negative reciprocals, and the lines are $\perp$.

21. $m_1 = -\frac{n}{3n} = -\frac{1}{3}$ and $m_2 = -\frac{2n}{6n} = -\frac{1}{3}$, so the lines are parallel.

22. The slope of $\overleftrightarrow{AB} = \frac{-4}{4} = -1$, and the slope of $\overleftrightarrow{DC} = \frac{2}{-2} = -1$, so $\overleftrightarrow{AB} \parallel \overleftrightarrow{DC}$. The slope of $\overleftrightarrow{AD} = \frac{2}{4} = \frac{1}{2}$, and the slope of $\overleftrightarrow{BC} = \frac{4}{2} = 2$, so $\overline{AD} \nparallel \overline{BC}$. The slope of diagonal $\overleftrightarrow{BD} = \frac{6}{0}$, so $\overleftrightarrow{BD}$ has no slope and is a vertical line. The slope of diagonal $\overleftrightarrow{AC} = \frac{0}{6} = 0$, so $\overleftrightarrow{AC}$ is horizontal and $\perp$ to $\overleftrightarrow{BD}$.
23. $b = -16$
24. Given that $m_1 = \frac{-1}{m_2}$, rt. $\triangle Q'R'P \sim$ rt. $\triangle QRP$ because their sides are proportional. $\angle 1 \cong \angle 2$ because corres. $\angle$s of $\sim$ $\triangle$s are $\cong$ by definition. $\angle 2 \cong \angle 3$ by $\cong$ vertical $\angle$s (Theorem 3.7). $\angle 1 \cong \angle 3$ by transitivity. $m\angle 1 + m\angle 4 = 90$ by Corollary 8.13.2. $m\angle 3 + m\angle 4 = 90$ by substitution. Therefore, $\angle Q'PS$ is a right angle, and lines l_1 and l_2 are $\perp$.

B. In Exercises 11–15, determine the slopes of $\overline{PQ}$ and $\overline{RS}$. Then tell whether $\overleftrightarrow{PQ} \parallel \overleftrightarrow{RS}$, $\overleftrightarrow{PQ} \perp \overleftrightarrow{RS}$, or neither.

11. $P(4, 3)$, $Q(2, 1)$, $R(0, 5)$, $S(-2, 3)$

12. $P(6, 0)$, $Q(-1, 0)$, $R(2, 8)$, $S(2, 5)$

13. $P(5, 4)$, $Q(7, 2)$, $R(1, 3)$, $S(-1, 1)$

14. $P(8, 13)$, $Q(3, 10)$, $R(11, 5)$, $S(6, 3)$

15. $P(26, 18)$, $Q(10, 6)$, $R(-17, 22)$, $S(-13, 25)$

The vertices of a triangle are $A(1, 1)$, $B(4, 7)$, and $C(10, -1)$.

16. What are the slopes of its sides?

17. What are the slopes of its altitudes?

18. Is the triangle a right triangle?

19. If the slope of $\overleftrightarrow{AB}$ is $\frac{2}{3}$, and $\overleftrightarrow{CD} \parallel \overleftrightarrow{AB}$, what is the value of x if the coordinates of C are $(0, -3)$ and the coordinates of D are $(x, 1)$?

20. Show that a line through $(0, 0)$ and (a, b) is perpendicular to a line through $(0, 0)$ and $(-b, a)$.

21. Show that a line through $(3n, 0)$ and $(0, n)$ is parallel to a line through $(6n, 0)$ and $(0, 2n)$.

22. Show that the quadrilateral joining $A(-2, 2)$, $B(2, -2)$, $C(4, 2)$, and $D(2, 4)$ is a trapezoid with perpendicular diagonals.

C. 23. Given the points $P(1, 3)$, $Q(4, -1)$, and $R(b, b)$, find the value of b so that $\angle PQR$ is a right angle.

24. Prove the second part of Theorem 11.3: If the slopes of two lines are the negative reciprocals of each other, then the lines are perpendicular. (HINT: Keep in mind that two lines are perpendicular if they intersect to form a right angle.)

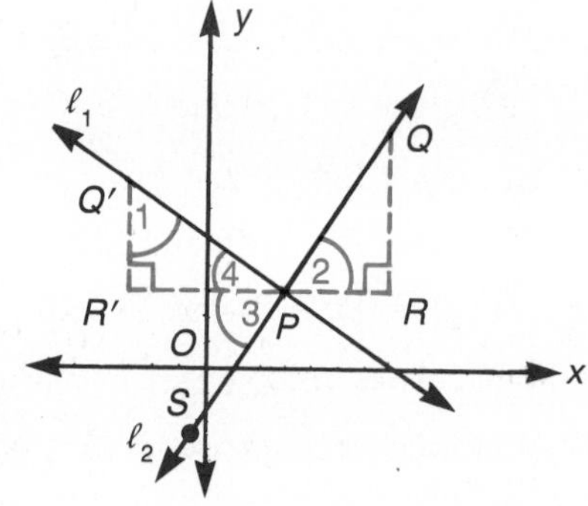

11.4 The Distance Formula

In this section you will learn the **distance formula.**

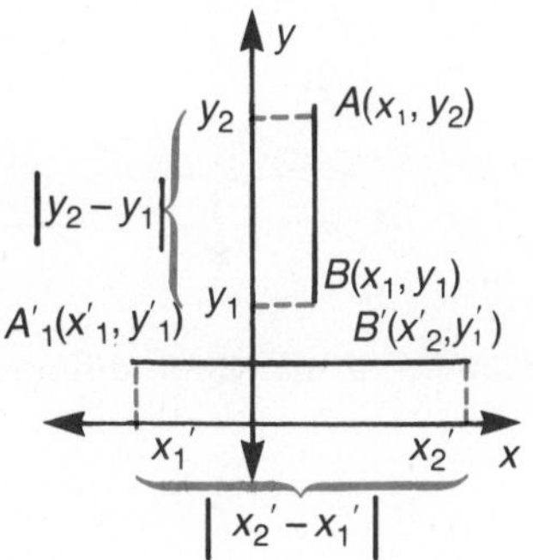

In the figure at the left, vertical segment $\overline{AB}$ has the same measure as the length of its projection on the y-axis, $|y_2 - y_1|$. (The absolute value symbol is used because distance cannot be negative.)

Similarly, the length of horizontal segment $\overline{A'B'}$ is $|x_2' - x_1'|$.

If you assign values to the coordinates, the distances will be as follows:

The distance (d) between $A(2, 10)$ and $B(2, 4) = |4 - 10| = |-6| = 6$.

The distance (d) between $A'(-4, 2)$ and $B'(7, 2) = |7 - (-4)| = |7 + 4| = 11$.

Note that the *length* of a segment or the *distance* between its endpoints mean the same.

The next step is to determine, in terms of x_1, y_1, x_2, and y_2, the length of a segment that is parallel to neither of the axes.

Given the oblique segment $\overline{P_1P_2}$, let x_1 and y_1, and x_2 and y_2, be the projections of P_1 and P_2, and call the point at (x_2, y_1) R. By the Pythagorean Theorem, $(P_1P_2)^2 = (P_1R)^2 + (RP_2)^2$. Also, because the legs of the right triangle are parallel to the axes, $P_1R = |x_2 - x_1|$, and $RP_2 = |y_2 - y_1|$, as explained above.

Therefore, $(P_1P_2)^2 = |x_2 - x_1|^2 + |y_2 - y_1|^2$.

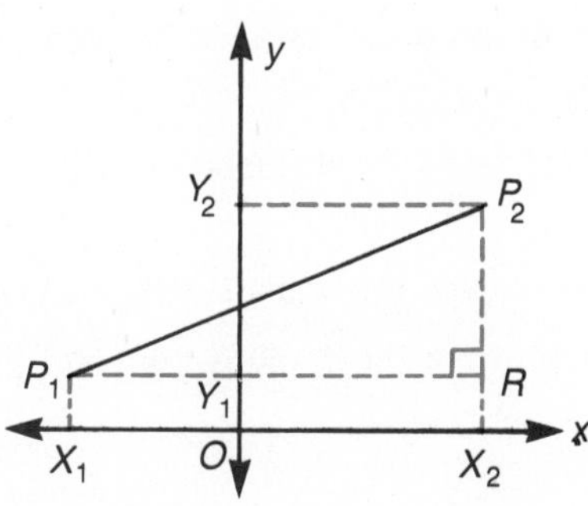

Since the square of the absolute value of a number is equal to the square of the number itself, this can be written as follows:

$$(P_1P_2)^2 = (x_2 - x_1)^2 + (y_2 - y_1)^2$$

$P_1P_2 \geq 0$, so the result is the distance formula.

OBJECTIVE

Use the distance formula to determine the distance between two points, given their coordinates.

TEACHER'S NOTES

See p. T37

MIXED REVIEW

1. Simplify $\sqrt{7^2 + 24^2}$. 25
2. Solve $x - 4(3 - x) = 12$. $4\frac{4}{5}$
3. Factor $6x^2 - 29x - 5$. $(6x + 1)(x - 5)$
4. Solve for y if $3x + 2y = 8$. $y = -\frac{3}{2}x + 4$
5. What type of line contains the points (7, 3) and (−12, 3)? horizontal

TEACHER'S RESOURCE MASTERS

Practice Master 33, Part 2
Quiz 21

THEOREM 11.4 (The Distance Formula)
The distance between the points (x_1, y_1) and (x_2, y_2) is equal to $\sqrt{(x_2 - x_1)^2 + (y_2 - y_1)^2}$.

Example: Given $P_1(-6, 2)$ and $P_2(9, 8)$, find the distance between P_1 and P_2.

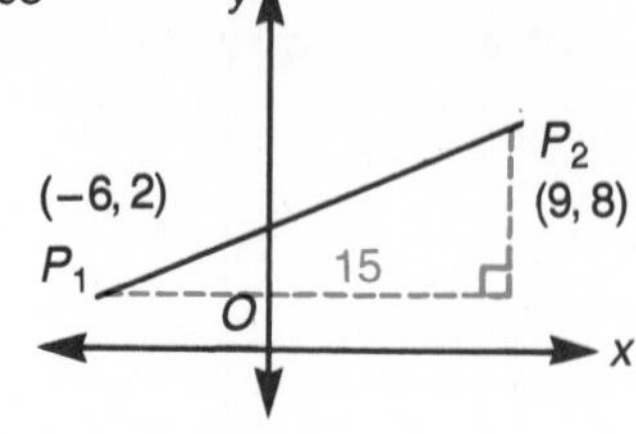

Solution:
$$\begin{aligned} P_1P_2 &= \sqrt{(9 - (-6))^2 + (8 - 2)^2} \\ &= \sqrt{225 + 36} \\ &= \sqrt{261} \\ &= 3\sqrt{29} \end{aligned}$$

As was the case when calculating the slope of a line segment, it makes no difference which points you call (x_1, y_1) and (x_2, y_2).

ASSIGNMENT GUIDE

Minimum 1-8
Regular 1-17 odd
Maximum 1-25 odd, 26

ORAL EXERCISES

1. What do you know about a segment whose endpoints are (x_1, k) and (x_2, k)?

2. Substitute the coordinates in Exercise 1 for x_1, y_1, x_2, and y_2 in the distance formula. What simpler formula do you derive?

3. What do you know about a segment whose endpoints are (k, y_1) and (k, y_2)?

4. Substitute the coordinates in Exercise 3 for x_1, y_1, x_2, and y_2 in the distance formula. What simpler formula do you derive?

5. Without using the distance formula or a graph, state the distance between (5, −3) and (5, 8).

6. Without using the distance formula or a graph, state the distance between (6, 2) and (9, 2).

7. How far from the origin is the point (0, 8)?

8. How far from the origin is the point (3, 4)?

Oral Exercises

1. It lies on a horizontal line.
2. $d = |x_2 - x_1|$
3. It lies on a vertical line.
4. $d = |y_2 - y_1|$
5. 11
6. 3
7. 8
8. 5

WRITTEN EXERCISES

A. Use the distance formula to find the distance between each pair of points.

1. (0, 0) and (3, 5)
2. (0, 0) and (−3, −5)
3. (2, 0) and (6, 4)
4. (0, 2) and (6, 4)
5. (1, 2) and (6, 14)
6. (−6, 3) and (4, −2)

Written Exercises

1. $\sqrt{34}$ 2. $\sqrt{34}$
3. $4\sqrt{2}$ 4. $2\sqrt{10}$
5. 13 6. $5\sqrt{5}$

B. **Each of the following sets of coordinates are the vertices of a triangle. Find the perimeter of each triangle.**

7. A(1, 3), B(5, 5), C(9, 3)

8. A(−1, −2), B(9, 5), C(4, 6)

9. J(4, 4), K(9, 5), C(4, 6)

10. X(7, −11), Y(10, −2), Z(4, −5)

Tell whether each of the following sets of coordinates make up an <u>isosceles</u>, <u>scalene</u>, or <u>equilateral</u> triangle.

11. X(4, 0), Y(6, 7), Z(2, 7)

12. P(4, 1), Q(2, 8), R(−3, 3)

13. A(4, 0), B(9, 5), C(4, 6)

14. X(−5, −5), Y(−9, −9), Z(−1, −9)

Are the triangles with the following vertices right triangles?

15. D(−2, 1), E(4, 6), F(2, −3)

16. X(−5, −5), Y(−9, −9), Z(−1, −9)

The vertices of a quadrilateral are P(0, 2), Q(3, 0), R(7, 4), and S(4, 6). Without drawing the figure, determine the following.

17. the length of each side

18. the lengths of diagonals $\overline{PR}$ and $\overline{SQ}$

19. What type of quadrilateral is described?

20. Using the converse of the Pythagorean Theorem, show that the triangle joining $D(2, 2)$, $E(4, 1)$, and $F(5, 8)$ is a right triangle with a right angle at D.

21. Given the points $A(-1, 3)$, $B(2, 4)$, and $C(5, 5)$, prove without plotting the points that B is between A and C.

C. **22.** Use the distance formula and a hand calculator to find the distance between $P(-0.5, 1.3)$ and $Q(2.1, -0.1)$. Give your answer to two decimal places.

Visualize a rectangular solid 2 units by 3 units by 8 units placed in the "corner" of a 3-dimensional coordinate system, as shown. (Recall the Exploration on page 342.)

23. Give the coordinates of the following points: A, B, C, D, O, E, F, and G.

24. Determine the distance from C to O.

25. Write a simplified formula for the distance between (0, 0, 0) and (x, y, z).

26. Write a formula for the distance between $P_1(x_1, y_1, z_1)$ and $P_2(x_2, y_2, z_2)$. Use this formula to check your answer to Exercise 24.

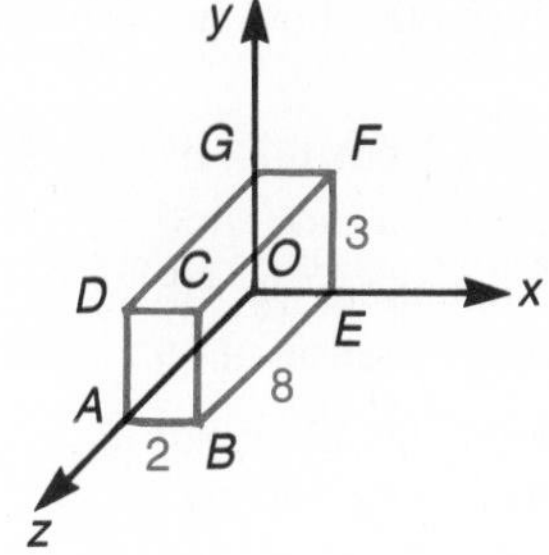

7. $8 + 4\sqrt{5}$

8. $\sqrt{149} + \sqrt{26} + \sqrt{89}$

9. $2 + 2\sqrt{26}$

10. $6\sqrt{5} + 3\sqrt{10}$

11. isosceles 12. isosceles

13. scalene 14. isosceles

15. no 16. yes

17. $PQ = \sqrt{13}$, $QR = 4\sqrt{2}$, $RS = \sqrt{13}$, $SP = 4\sqrt{2}$

18. $PR = \sqrt{53}$, $SQ = \sqrt{37}$

19. parallelogram

20. $DE = \sqrt{5}$, $DF = 3\sqrt{5}$, $EF = 5\sqrt{2}$; $(\sqrt{5})^2 + (3\sqrt{5})^2 = 5 + 45 = 50 = (5\sqrt{2})^2$; so $(DE)^2 + (DF)^2 = (EF)^2$, and DE and DF are the legs of rt. $\triangle DEF$.

21. $AB = \sqrt{10}$, $BC = \sqrt{10}$, $AC = 2\sqrt{10}$; so $AB + BC = AC$, and B is between A and C by the def. of between.

22. 2.95

23. $A(0, 0, 8)$, $B(2, 0, 8)$, $C(2, 3, 8)$, $D(0, 3, 8)$, $O(0, 0, 0)$, $E(2, 0, 0)$, $F(2, 3, 0)$, $G(0, 3, 0)$

24. $(OC)^2 = (OF)^2 + (CF)^2$
$OC = \sqrt{77}$

25. $d = \sqrt{x^2 + y^2 + z^2}$

26. $d = \sqrt{(x_2 - x_1)^2 + (y_2 - y_1)^2 + (z_2 - z_1)^2}$

SELF-QUIZ

Give the coordinates for the points in the rectangular coordinate system at the right.

1. X **2.** Y **3.** Z

4. What is the slope of $\overline{TZ}$?

5. What is the slope of $\overline{TX}$?

6. What is the slope of $\overline{TY}$?

7. In $\square PQRS$, if the slope of $\overline{PQ}$ is $\frac{2}{5}$, find the slope of $\overline{RS}$.

8. In rhombus $EFGH$, if the slope of diagonal $\overline{EG}$ is $\frac{1}{4}$, find the slope of $\overline{HF}$.

9. Given $A(5, 8)$ and $B(6, 3)$, find AB.

10. Given $H(-3, -1)$ and $J(9, 4)$, find HJ.

11. Given $I(4, 3)$ and $T(-3, -4)$, find IT.

12. Given $U(-2, 5)$ and $G(3, -6)$, find UG.

CHALLENGE

An ant (A) is on the *outside* of a jar, 6 cm from the rim. Diametrically opposite the ant, and 10 cm from the bottom of the jar, there is a sugar crystal (S_1) stuck to the *inside* of the jar. The ant crawls to the crystal by the shortest path. Directly below, at the jar's bottom, is another crystal. The ant crawls to the second crystal (S_2) in a spiral path, which takes it once around the jar at a uniform slope. From its starting point, how far does the ant crawl to get both sugar crystals?

The jar is 13 cm tall, 24 cm in circumference, and has no thickness worth considering. (HINT: The ant's journey can be measured using only subtraction and the Pythagorean Theorem.)

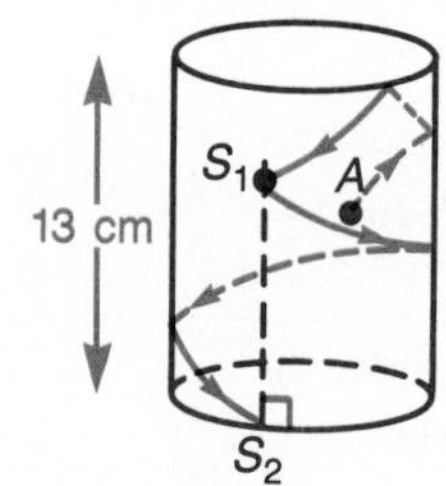

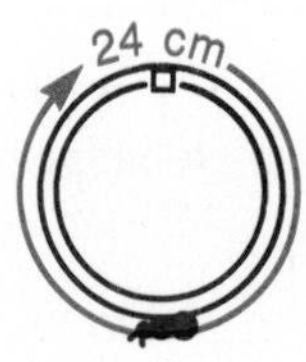

Self-Quiz

1. $(-4, -4)$ 2. $(-1, 2)$

3. $(-5, -1)$ 4. 0

5. no slope 6. 1

7. $\frac{2}{5}$ 8. -4

9. $\sqrt{26}$ 10. 13

11. $7\sqrt{2}$ 12. $\sqrt{146}$

Challenge

Consider the cylinder when unrolled into a rectangle:

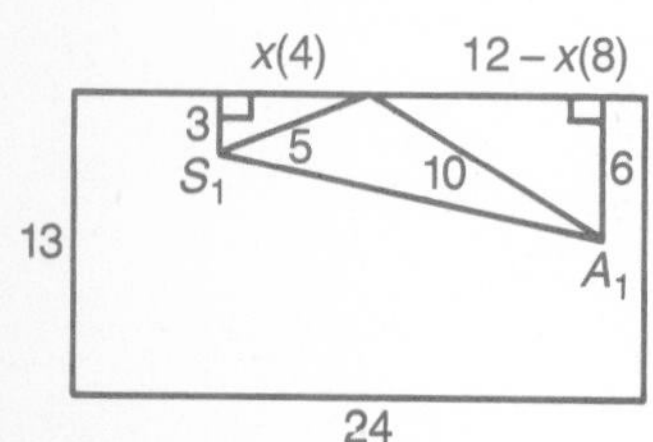

$\frac{3}{6} = \frac{x}{12 - x}$

$36 - 3x = 6x$

$36 = 9x$

$4 = x$

$16 + 9 = 25$

$64 + 36 = 100$

$A \to S_1 = \sqrt{25} + \sqrt{100}$

$= 15$ cm

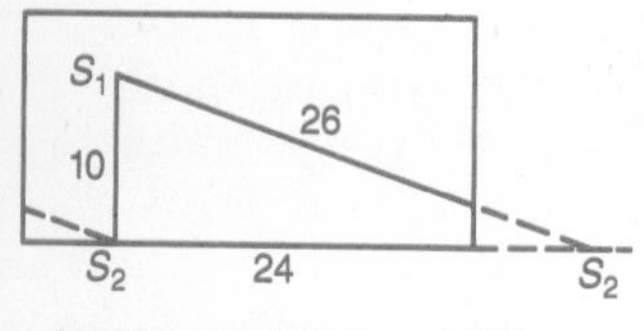

$\sqrt{100} + \sqrt{576} = \sqrt{676} = 26$

$S_1 \to S_2 = 26$ cm

Total distance = 15 + 26 = 41 cm.

11.5 The Midpoint Formula

In addition to the distance formula, you will find the **midpoint formula** useful in proving theorems by means of coordinate geometry. Given the coordinates of the endpoints of a segment, you are able to find the coordinates of the midpoint.

First, take the case of a segment on the x-axis.

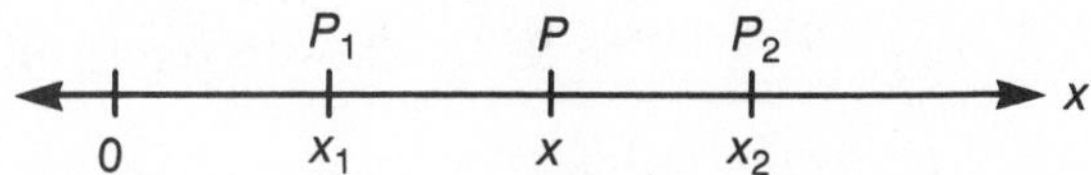

x_1 and x_2 represent the coordinates of the endpoints of $\overline{P_1P_2}$, and x represents the coordinate of the midpoint. Thus,

$$x - x_1 = x_2 - x$$
$$2x = x_1 + x_2$$
$$x = \frac{x_1 + x_2}{2}$$

Similarly, the midpoint of a segment on the y-axis is $y = \frac{y_1 + y_2}{2}$.

Now you can extend this system to segments that are neither horizontal nor vertical.

Since P is the midpoint of $\overline{P_1P_2}$, it follows by similar triangles that R is the midpoint of $\overline{P_1S}$. Because opposite sides of a rectangle are congruent, U is the midpoint of $\overline{TV}$. Therefore,

$$x = \frac{x_1 + x_2}{2}.$$

In the same way, by projecting onto the y-axis, you can show that

$$y = \frac{y_1 + y_2}{2}.$$

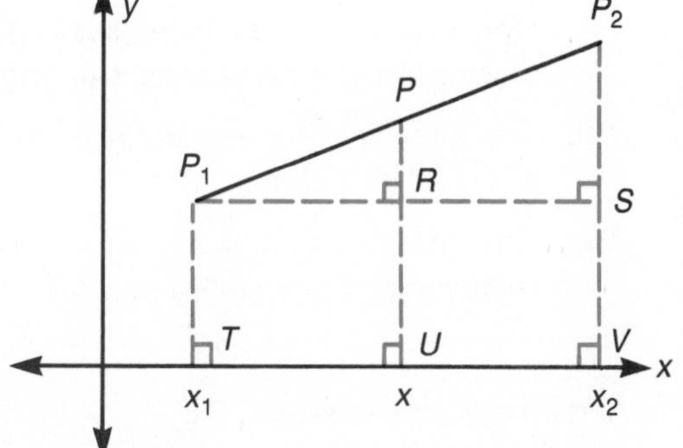

Thus, you have proved the next theorem.

THEOREM 11.5 (The Midpoint Formula)
Let $P_1 = (x_1, y_1)$ and let $P_2 = (x_2, y_2)$. Then the midpoint of $\overline{P_1P_2}$ is the point

$$P = \left(\frac{x_1 + x_2}{2}, \frac{y_1 + y_2}{2}\right).$$

OBJECTIVE

Use the midpoint formula to determine the coordinates of the midpoint of a segment, given the coordinates of its endpoints.

TEACHER'S NOTES

See p. T37

MIXED REVIEW

1. Solve for y if $5x - 3y = 9$. $y = \frac{5}{3}x - 3$
2. Simplify $\sqrt{(15 - 3)^2 + (-2 - 3)^2}$. 13
3. If $\triangle PQR \sim \triangle ABC$, give the ratios of the sides. $\frac{PQ}{AB} = \frac{QR}{BC} = \frac{PR}{AC}$
4. $(a - b)^3 =$ ______? $a^3 - 3a^2b + 3ab^2 - b^3$
5. Simplify $\sqrt{(7 - 4)^2 + [2 - (-2)]^2 + (14 - 2)^2}$. 13

TEACHER'S RESOURCE MASTERS

Practice Master 34, Part 1

ASSIGNMENT GUIDE

Day 1
Minimum 1-10
Regular 1-15
Maximum 1-18
Day 2
Minimum 20-24
Regular 20-26
Maximum 25-30

ORAL EXERCISES

Visualize the points whose coordinates are listed below and compute mentally the coordinates of the midpoint of the segment joining each pair.

1. (0, 0) and (0, 8)
2. (5, 4) and (5, 2)
3. (6, 0) and (0, 0)
4. (1, 1) and (1, −1)
5. (0, 1) and (0, 5)
6. (−7, 4) and (−7, −4)
7. (3, 5) and (7, 15)
8. (−3, −3) and (1, 9)

Oral Exercises

1. (0, 4) 2. (5, 3)
3. (3, 0) 4. (1, 0)
5. (0, 3) 6. (−7, 0)
7. (5, 10) 8. (−1, 3)

WRITTEN EXERCISES

A. Use the midpoint formula to compute the coordinates of the midpoint of the segments joining each pair of points.

1. (13, 8) and (11, 20)
2. (−5, 5) and (−9, −7)
3. $(\frac{1}{2}, 1\frac{1}{5})$ and $(\frac{1}{3}, \frac{4}{5})$
4. (4.2, −1.4) and (1.4, 3.2)
5. $(a + b, -c)$ and $(a - b, c + 2d)$
6. (−5, −7) and (4, −6)

B. **7.** One endpoint of a segment is (8, 0). The midpoint is (4, 0). Visualize the location of these points and state, without using formulas, the coordinates of the other endpoint.

8. One endpoint of a segment is (16, 20). The midpoint is (11, 14). Compute the coordinates of the other endpoint by using the appropriate formula.

9. One endpoint of a segment is (−4, 8). The midpoint is (0, 2). Find the coordinates of the other endpoint.

10. One endpoint of a segment is (−10, −6). The midpoint is (−1, −2). Find the coordinates of the other endpoint.

A triangle has vertices *A*(−1, −2), *B*(11, 8), and *C*(5, 10). *D* is the midpoint of $\overline{AC}$, *E* is the midpoint of $\overline{AB}$, and *F* is the midpoint of $\overline{BC}$.

11. Find the perimeter of △DEF.
12. Is $\overline{DE} \parallel \overline{BC}$?
13. Is $\overline{EF} \parallel \overline{AC}$?
14. Is $\overline{DF} \parallel \overline{AB}$?
15. Is $\triangle DEF \sim \triangle ABC$?

Written Exercises

1. (12, 14) 2. (−7, −1)
3. $(\frac{5}{12}, 1)$ 4. (2.8, 0.9)
5. (a, d) 6. $(\frac{-1}{2}, \frac{-13}{2})$
7. (0, 0)
8. (6, 8)
9. (4, −4)
10. (8, 2)
11. $\sqrt{10} + 3\sqrt{5} + \sqrt{61}$
12. yes
13. yes
14. yes
15. yes

Quadrilateral *ABCD* has vertices *A*(1, 2), *B*(6, −1), *C*(5, −5), and *D*(0, −2).

16. Determine whether the diagonals bisect each other.

17. Determine whether the lengths of the diagonals are equal.

18. Using the results of Exercises 9 and 10, what can be said about the quadrilateral?

Given a quadrilateral with vertices *A*(1, 3), *B*(3, 5), *C*(5, 3),and *D*(3, 1), show each of the following by use of appropriate formulas.

19. Opposite sides are congruent.

20. All four sides are congruent.

21. The diagonals are congruent.

22. The diagonals bisect each other.

23. The diagonals are perpendicular to each other.

24. The vertices of a triangle are $A(-4, 1)$, $B(2, 7)$, and $C(4, -1)$. Find the lengths of the three medians.

25. Given the quadrilateral joining the points $A(-3, 2)$, $B(1, 6)$, $C(5, 2)$, and $D(3, -3)$. Show that the quadrilateral formed by joining its midpoints P, Q, R, and S in order is a parallelogram.

26. Prove that two of the medians of $\triangle ABC$ are perpendicular to each other, given $A(-3, 0)$, $B(3, 0)$, and $C(0, 9)$.

C. With the midpoint formula, you can find the coordinates of the point that is the bisector of a segment, given the coordinates of the segment's endpoints. Consider the possibility of finding the two points that trisect a segment.

27. In the figure, let P be $\frac{1}{3}$ of the way from P_1 to P_2. Now, find the value of x in terms of x_1 and x_2.

P_1 — P — P_2; x_1, x, x_2; $x_2 > x_1$

28. By comparing this result with the development of the midpoint formula, what would you expect the x- and y-coordinates of P to be?

29. Now let P' be $\frac{2}{3}$ of the way from P_1 to P_2. Follow the same steps as in Exercises 27 and 28 to find the coordinates of P' in this location.

P_1 — P' — P_2; x_1, x_2; $x_2 > x_1$

30. If your work is correct, you now have a formula for finding the coordinates of the two trisecting points of a segment. Using this formula, find the coordinates of the two points that trisect the segment joining $P_1(1, 2)$ and $P_2(5, 12)$. Check your answer by using the distance formula to find the length of each of the three segments determined.

16. Yes; their common midpoint is $P(3, \frac{-3}{2})$.

17. No; $AC = \sqrt{65}$ and $DB = \sqrt{37}$.

18. It is a parallelogram but not a rectangle.

19–20. $AB = CD = BC = AD = 2\sqrt{2}$

21. $AC = BD = 4$

22. The midpoint $P(3, 3)$ is the same for $\overline{AC}$ and $\overline{BD}$. Also, $AP = CP = BP = DP = 2$, so the diagonals bisect each other.

23. The slope of $\overline{AC} = 0$; $\overline{BD}$ has no slope. So $\overline{AC} \perp \overline{BD}$.

24. $\sqrt{53}$ from vertices A and B; $5\sqrt{2}$ from vertex C.

25. $PQ = SR = 4$, and $PS = QR = \sqrt{21.25}$, so opposite sides are of equal length. Also, the slope of $\overline{PQ}$ = the slope of $\overline{SR}$ = 0, and the slope of $\overline{PS}$ = the slope of $\overline{QR} = \frac{-9}{2}$, so opposite sides are also parallel. $PQRS$ is a ▱ by Theorem 8.20.

26. For the median from B, $m = -1$. For the median from A, $m = 1$. So the medians to $\overline{AC}$ and $\overline{BC}$ are $\perp$ by Theorem 11.3.

27. $\frac{2x_1 + x_2}{3}$

28. $P(\frac{2x_1 + x_2}{3}, \frac{2y_1 + y_2}{3})$

29. $P'(\frac{x_1 + 2x_2}{3}, \frac{y_1 + 2y_2}{3})$

30. $P(2\frac{1}{3}, 5\frac{1}{3})$; $P'(3\frac{2}{3}, 8\frac{2}{3})$

OBJECTIVE

Use the coordinate plane, the distance formula, and slope to prove theorems involving figures in a plane.

TEACHER'S NOTES

See p. T37

MIXED REVIEW

1. What is the altitude of an equilateral triangle with side 6? $3\sqrt{3}$
2. What is the diagonal of a square with side 7? $7\sqrt{2}$
3. Solve for y if $-2x + 3y = 7$. $y = \frac{2}{3}x + \frac{7}{3}$
4. Factor $a^3 - 3a^2b + 3ab^2 - b^3$. $(a - b)^3$
5. Find the area of an equilateral triangle with side 8. $16\sqrt{3}$

TEACHER'S RESOURCE MASTERS

Practice Master 34, Part 2

11.6 Proofs Using Coordinate Geometry

The theorems and methods of coordinate geometry make it easier to prove some theorems.

Consider Theorem 8.22, which states that the segment joining the midpoints of each of two sides of a triangle is parallel to and half as long as the third side.

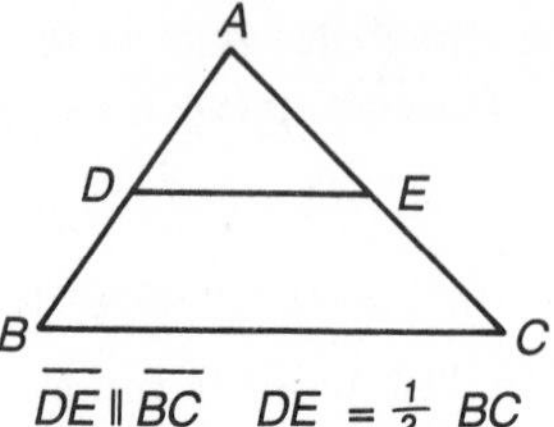

You will recall that the proof of this theorem was rather complex. By contrast, you will see that in the framework of a coordinate system, the proof is simpler.

The first step in this proof is to draw a triangle in the coordinate plane and indicate the coordinates of each vertex so that the figure represents *any* triangle.

Consider these three possibilities:

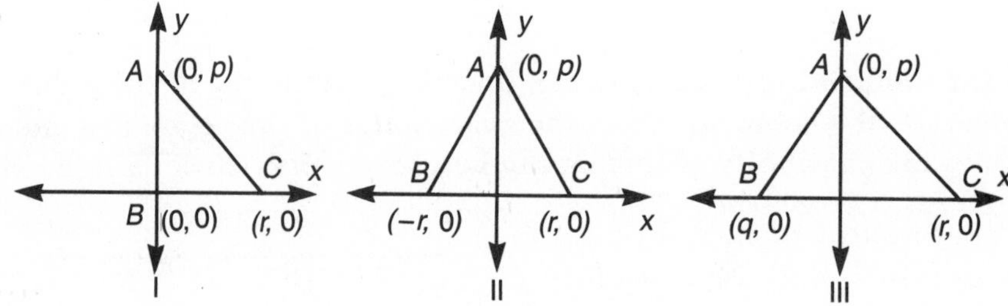

I would not be a good choice, because the triangle is a right triangle, and this theorem must be true for any triangle.

II is also unsatisfactory, because the proof would be limited to isosceles triangles.

III is a good placement (although not the only possible one). Do you see that any triangle can be placed in the plane so that one side lies on the x-axis, and the opposite vertex lies on the y-axis? The algebra involved will be simplified since three of the six coordinates are zeros.

Next decide which formulas to use. To prove that two segments are parallel, you would use the slope formula. To prove that one segment is half the length of another, you would use the distance formula.

With the coordinates of A, B, and C given in the figure at the right, you would use the midpoint formula to determine that the coordinates of D are $(\frac{q}{2}, \frac{p}{2})$ and those of E are $(\frac{r}{2}, \frac{p}{2})$.

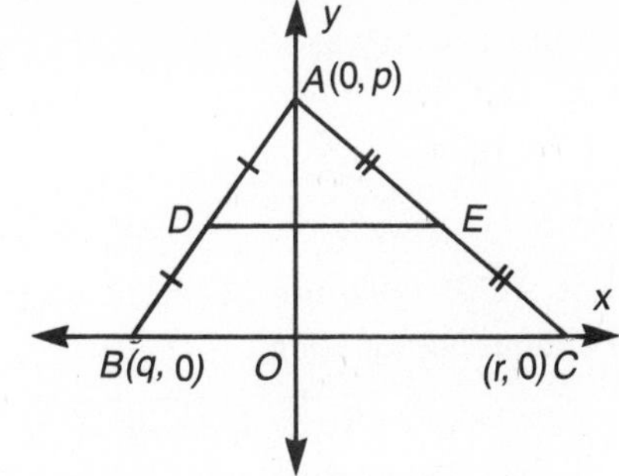

Therefore, the slope of $\overline{DE}$ is

$$\frac{\frac{p}{2} - \frac{p}{2}}{\frac{r}{2} - \frac{q}{2}} = \frac{0}{\frac{r - q}{2}} = 0.$$

The slope of $\overline{BC}$ is $\frac{0 - 0}{r - q} = 0$.

Since the slopes of the two segments are equal, $\overline{DE} \parallel \overline{BC}$, which is the first part of the proof.

By the distance formula, $DE = \sqrt{(\frac{r}{2} - \frac{q}{2})^2 + (\frac{p}{2} - \frac{p}{2})^2} = \frac{r - q}{2}$, and $BC = \sqrt{(r - q)^2 + (0 - 0)^2} = r - q$, showing that $DE = \frac{1}{2}BC$, which is the second part of the proof.

If you let $A = (0, 2p)$, $B = (2q, 0)$, and $C = (2r, 0)$, no fractions will arise when you divide by 2 in applying the midpoint formula, and the algebra in the proofs will be simplified.

The next theorem to be proved by the methods of coordinate geometry involves a *parallelogram.* First draw a figure that represents *any* parallelogram.

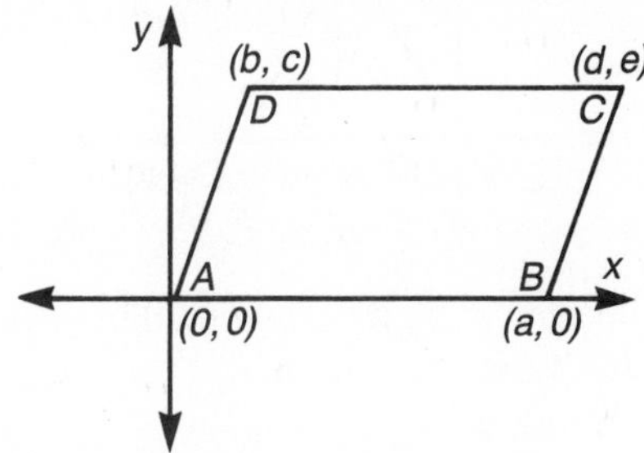

The upper figure represents any *quadrilateral.* Since you know that $\overline{DC} \parallel \overline{AB}$, the slope of $\overline{DC}$ must be 0. Thus $c = e$, and the coordinates of C are (d, c).

You can also establish that $d = a + b$. This makes the coordinates of $C(a + b, c)$.

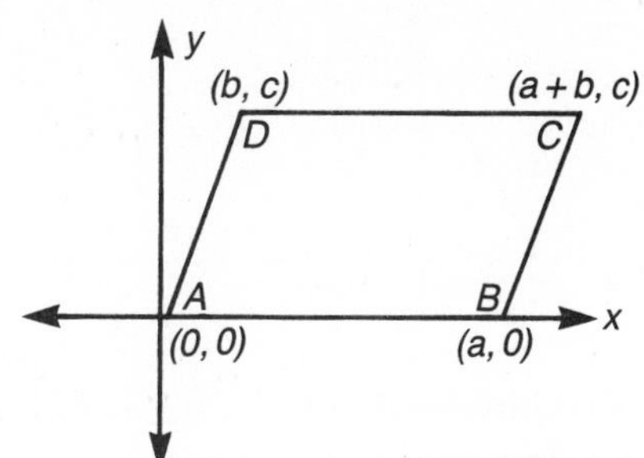

Prove: If the diagonals of a parallelogram are congruent, then the parallelogram is a rectangle.

Proof: From what was said above, the parallelogram can be drawn and labeled as shown at the right.

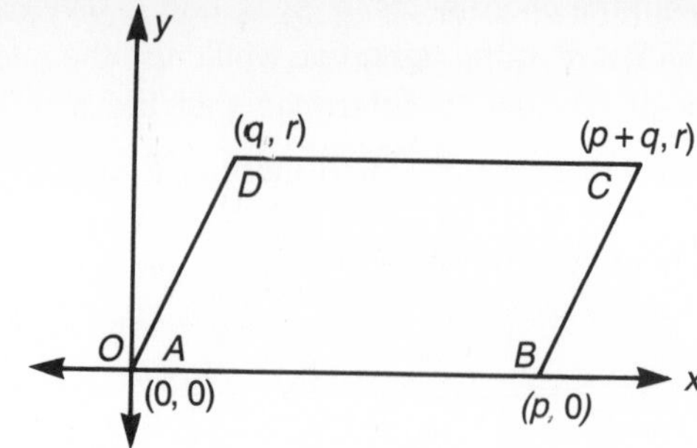

Given that $\overline{AC} \cong \overline{BD}$, use the distance formula to obtain the equation,

$$\begin{aligned} \sqrt{(p+q-0)^2+(r-0)^2} &= \sqrt{(q-p)^2+(r-0)^2}. \\ \text{Square both sides. } (p+q)^2+r^2 &= (q-p)^2+r^2 \\ p^2+2pq+q^2+r^2 &= q^2-2pq+p^2+r^2 \\ 4pq &= 0 \end{aligned}$$

Since $4 \neq 0$ and $p \neq 0$, it follows that $q = 0$, and thus D lies on the y-axis. Therefore, $\angle BAD$ is a right angle and $\square ABCD$ is a rectangle.

ASSIGNMENT GUIDE

Day 1
Minimum 1-2
Regular 1-3
Maximum 1-4
Day 2
Minimum 3, 6, 9
Regular 6-9
Maximum 5-9 odd, 10-11

ORAL EXERCISES

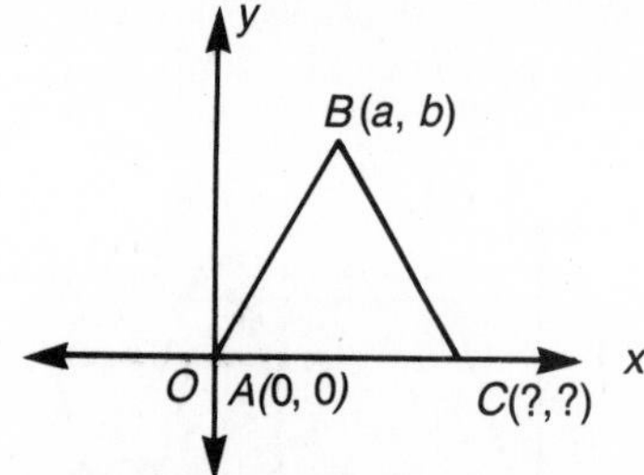

1. If the figure at the left is intended to represent any isosceles triangle, how should you represent the coordinates of C in terms of a and/or b?

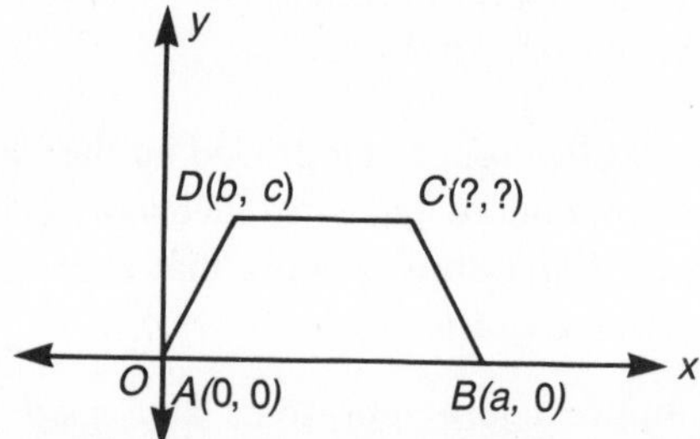

2. If the next figure is intended to represent any isosceles trapezoid, how should you represent the coordinates of C in terms of a, b, and c?

3. Do the coordinates of the vertices of the triangle shown here satisfactorily represent those of an equilateral triangle?

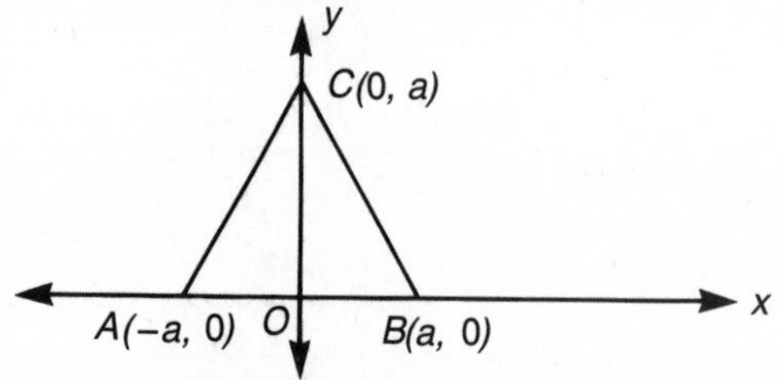

4. If quadrilateral $PQRS$ is a rectangle, supply the missing coordinates.

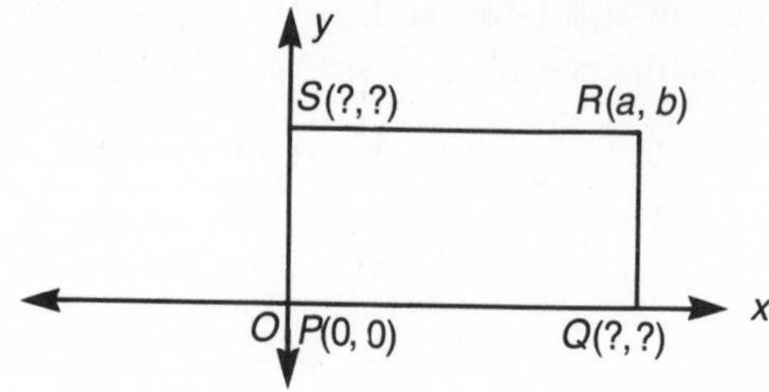

Oral Exercises

1. $(2a, 0)$

2. $(a - b, c)$

3. no

4. $Q(a, 0)$, $S(0, b)$

5. If quadrilateral $FGHI$ is a square, supply the missing coordinates.

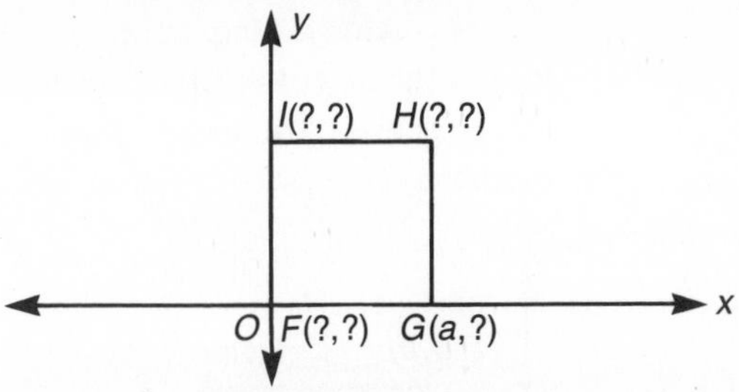

6. If quadrilateral $JKLM$ is a rhombus, supply the missing coordinates.

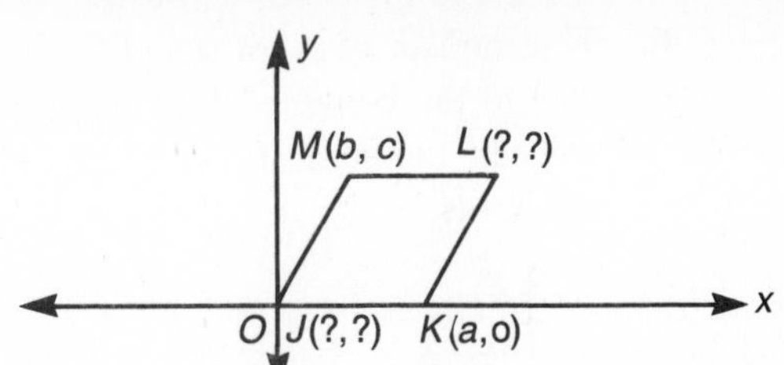
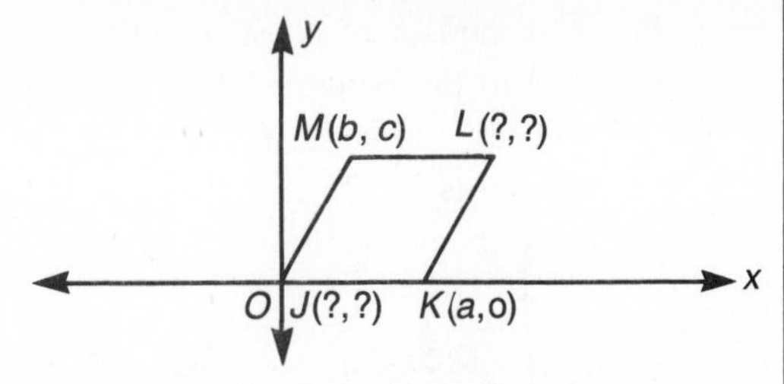

5. $F(0, 0)$, $G(a, 0)$, $H(a, a)$, $I(0, a)$

6. $J(0, 0)$, $L(a + b, c)$

WRITTEN EXERCISES

A. Prove the following by the methods of coordinate geometry.

1. The diagonals of a rectangle are congruent.

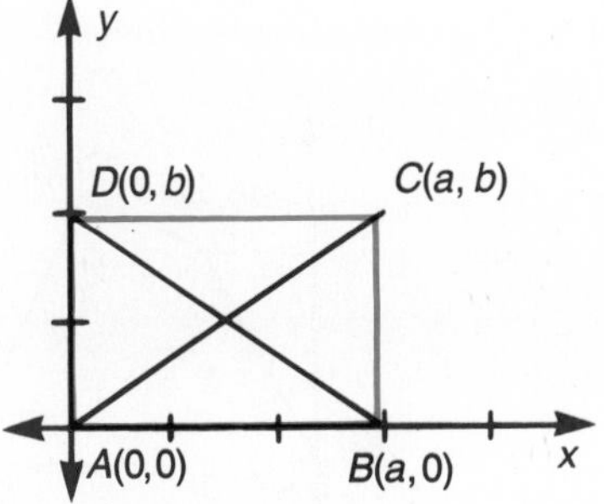

2. The midpoint of the hypotenuse of a right triangle is equidistant from its three vertices.

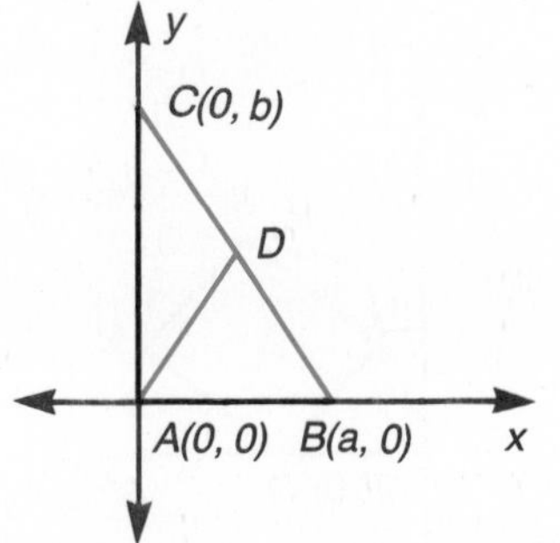

B. 3. The diagonals of a parallelogram bisect each other.

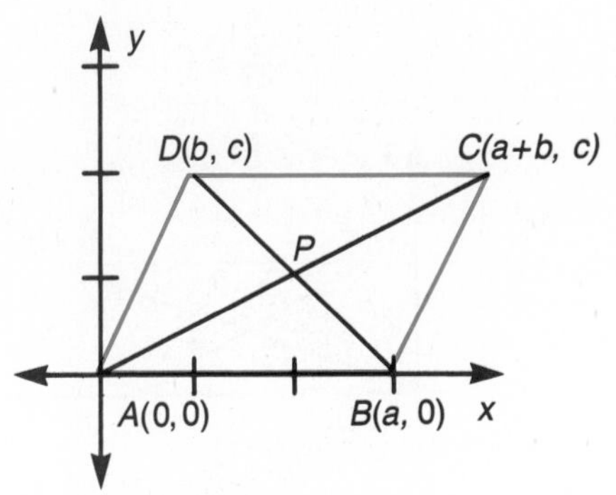

4. The diagonals of a rhombus are perpendicular to each other. (Show that the product of the slopes = −1.)

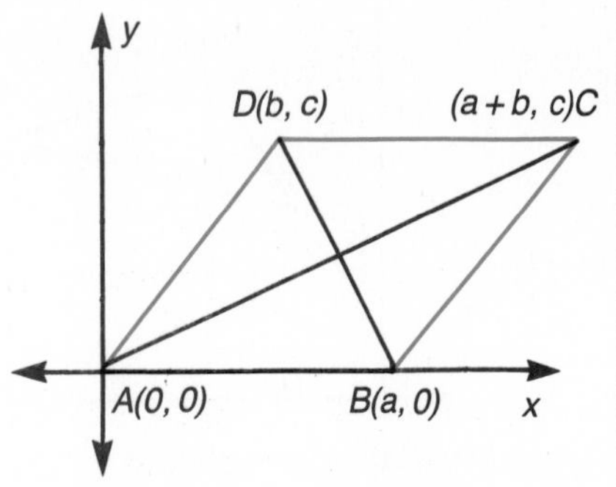

Written Exercises

1. $AC = BD = \sqrt{a^2 + b^2}$. Since $AC = BD$, $\overline{AC} \cong \overline{BD}$.

2. $D(\frac{a}{2}, \frac{b}{2})$ by midpoint formula; $AD = BD = CD = \sqrt{(\frac{a}{2})^2 + (\frac{b}{2})^2}$, so D is equidistant from A, B, and C.

3. The midpoint of both $\overline{AC}$ and $\overline{BD}$ is $(\frac{a + b}{2}, \frac{c}{2})$.

4. m_1 of $\overline{AC} = \frac{c}{a + b}$; m_2 of $\overline{BD} = \frac{c}{b - a}$; $m_1 \cdot m_2 = \frac{c^2}{b^2 - a^2}$. $AB = AD$ (Def. of rhombus), so $(AB)^2 = (AD)^2$, or $a^2 = b^2 + c^2$. By substitution, $m_1 \cdot m_2 = \frac{c^2}{-c^2} = -1$, and the diagonals are $\perp$.

5. Given $m_1 \cdot m_2 = \frac{c^2}{b^2 - a^2} = -1$. So $c^2 = a^2 - b^2$, or $a^2 = b^2 + c^2$. $AD = \sqrt{b^2 + c^2}$, so $(AD)^2 = b^2 + c^2 = a^2$. $AB = \sqrt{a^2} = a$, so $(AB)^2 = a^2$. Thus, $(AD)^2 = (AB)^2$; $AD = AB$, $\overline{AD} \cong \overline{AB}$. $\overline{AD} \cong \overline{BC}$ and $\overline{AB} \cong \overline{CD}$ (Def. of ▱), so ▱$ABCD$ is a rhombus by Def. of rhombus.

6. By the midpoint formula, $P(b, c)$ and $Q(a + d, c)$. m of $\overline{PQ}$ = m of $\overline{AB}$ = m of $\overline{DC}$ = 0. By the distance formula, $PQ = a + d - b$, $AB = 2a$, $DC = 2d - 2b$. $a + d - b = \frac{1}{2}(2a + 2d - 2b)$, so $PQ = \frac{1}{2}(AB + DC)$.

7. Use the midpoint formula to find P, Q, R, and S. Use the slope formula to show $\overline{PQ} \parallel \overline{RS}$. Use the distance formula to show $\overline{PQ} \cong \overline{QR} \cong \overline{RS} \cong \overline{SP}$.

8. Use the midpoint formula to find P, Q, R, and S. Use the slope formula to show $\overline{PQ} \parallel \overline{RS}$. Use the distance formula to show $\overline{PQ} \cong \overline{RS}$.

9. By the midpoint formula, the midpoints are $S(2b, 2c)$, $T(2a, 0)$, $U(2a + 2d, 2e)$, and $V(2b + 2d, 2c + 2e)$. The common midpoint of $\overline{SU}$ and $\overline{VT}$ is at $(a + b + d, c + e)$.

10. The area of $\triangle ABC$ = the area of quad. $ABKJ$ + the area of quad. $BCLK$ − the area of quad. $ACLJ$.

11. $a^2 + (b^2 + c^2) + a^2 + (b^2 + c^2) = (a + b)^2 + c^2 + (b - a)^2 + c^2$

5. If the diagonals of a parallelogram are perpendicular, the parallelogram is a rhombus. (HINT: Let the vertices be the same as in Exercise 4.)

6. The median of a trapezoid is parallel to the bases, and its length is one-half the sum of the lengths of the bases.

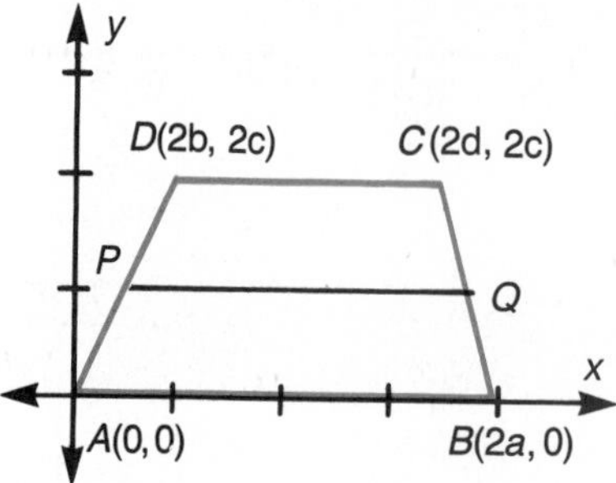

7. The segments joining, in order, the midpoints of consecutive sides of an isosceles trapezoid form a rhombus.

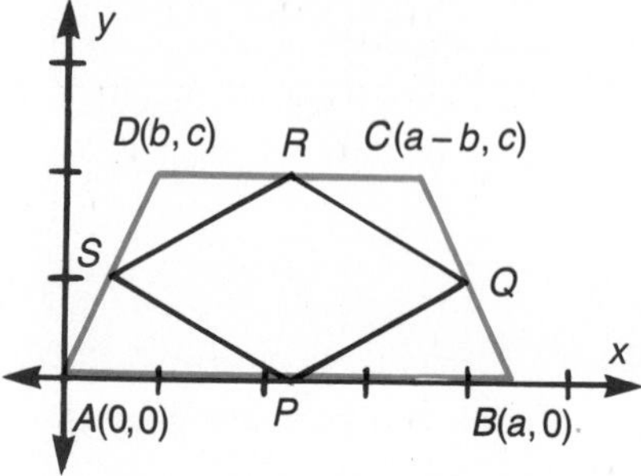

8. The segments joining, in order, the midpoints of the consecutive sides of any quadrilateral form a parallelogram.

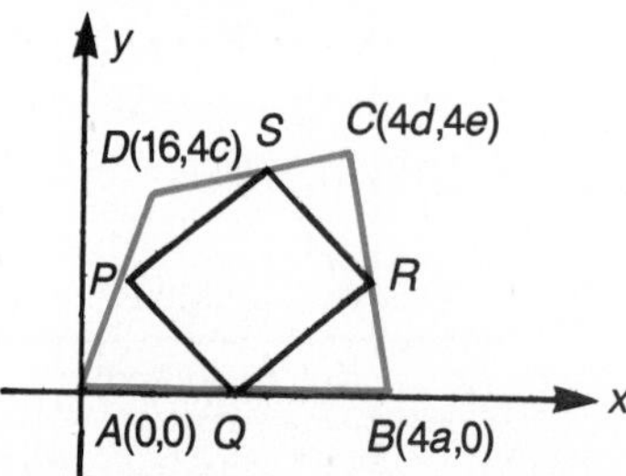

9. The segments joining midpoints of opposite sides of any quadrilateral bisect each other.

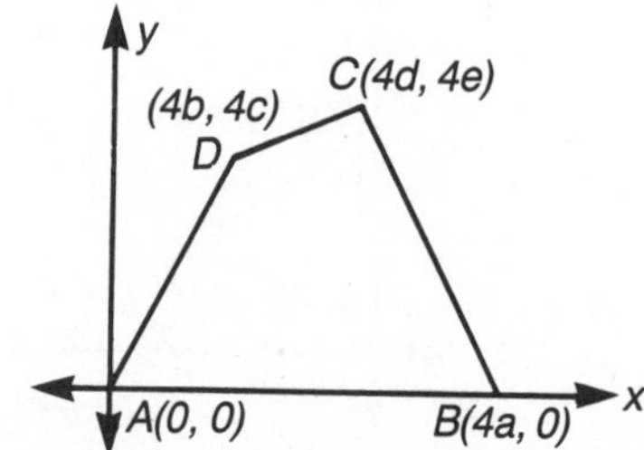

C. 10. The area of $\triangle ABC$ is $\frac{a(t - s) + b(r - t) + c(s - r)}{2}$, where $A = (a, r)$, $B = (b, s)$, and $C = (c, t)$. (HINT: Find three trapezoids in the figure)

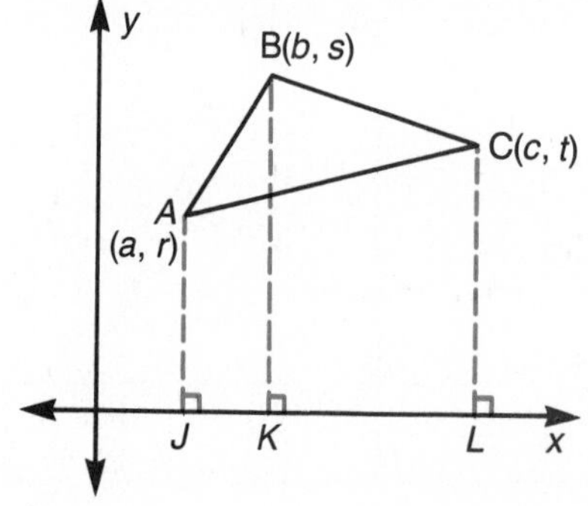

11. The sum of the squares of the sides of a parallelogram is equal to the sum of the squares of the diagonals.

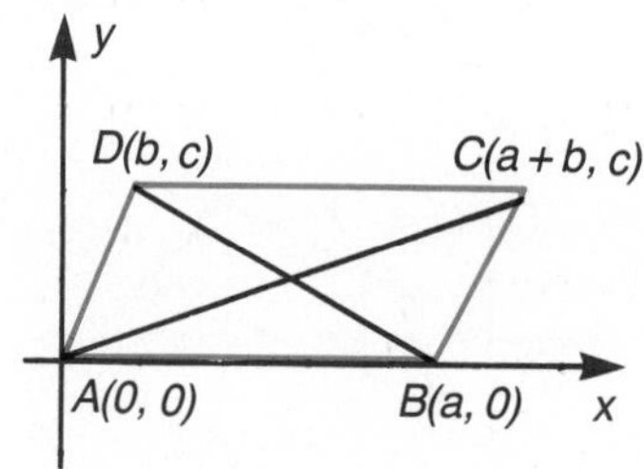

EXPLORATION
Seeing Isn't Believing

You have often been reminded in this course that figures are approximations, or representations, of geometric relations. That is, seeing is not necessarily believing. Some obviously apparent relations in a figure crumble when tested.

Square *QUWR*, as shown at the right, measures 16×16 cm. It has been divided into four regions—two right triangles, regions I and II, and two trapezoids, regions III and IV. The combined area of all four regions is the area of the square: 256 cm^2.

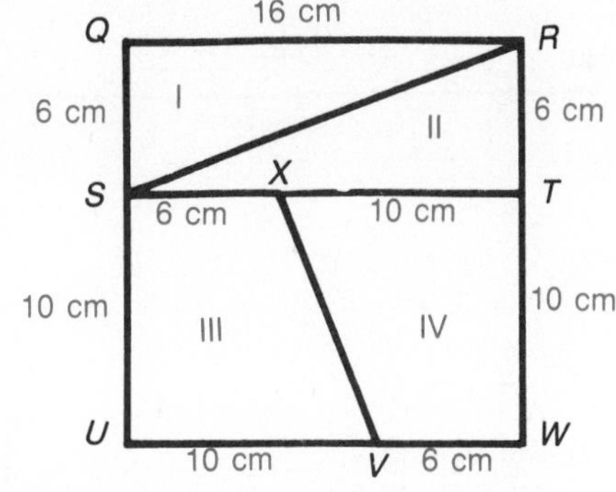

If the four regions were cut apart and refitted, as shown in the second figure, they would seem to form a 26×10 cm rectangle. However, the area of the rectangle would have to be 260 cm^2.

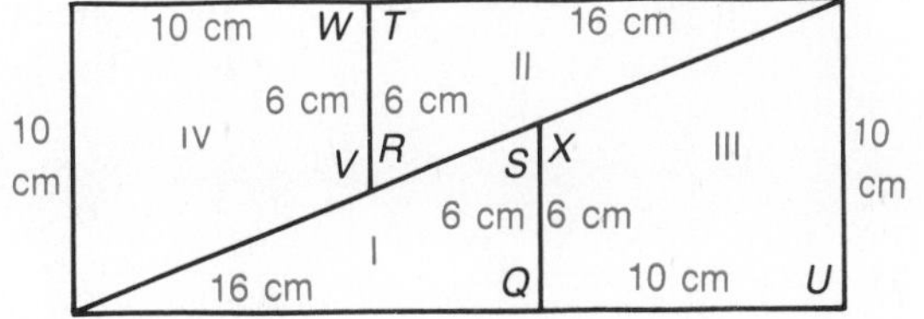

Is it possible to rearrange a figure and *gain* 4 cm^2? From the figures, the answer seems to be obviously "Yes." The length of all the sides in the rectangle match perfectly. However, this is an optical and mental illusion. Place regions I and III in a coordinate system as shown below, and apply what you know about the slope of line segments. Explain why the rectangle is not a true figure.

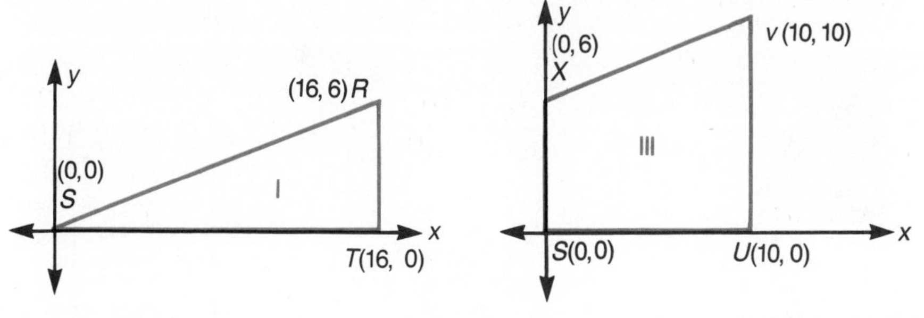

Exploration

By applying the slope formula to $\overline{SR}$ in the bottom left figure, you find that its slope is $\frac{6-0}{16-0}$ = 0.375. The slope of $\overline{XV}$ in the bottom right figure is $\frac{10-6}{10-0}$ = 0.4.

Although $\overline{TR}$ and $\overline{XS}$ have the same length, 6 cm, the slopes of $\overline{SR}$ and $\overline{XV}$ are different, and there can be no line that contains points *S*, *R*, *X*, and *V*. The same case applies to the fit of regions II and IV. Since the regions do not fit together exactly, there is no true rectangle with an area of 260 cm^2.

OBJECTIVE

Graph algebraic equations and inequalities in the coordinate plane.

TEACHER'S NOTES

See p. T37

MIXED REVIEW

1. What is the slope of a horizontal line? 0
2. Solve $\frac{1}{2}(3x - 2) = 2x + 7$. $x = -16$
3. What is the area of a right triangle with a leg of 8 and hypotenuse of 17. 60
4. Solve for y if $-4x + 2y = 18$. $y = 2x + 9$
5. Find the area of a rectangle with diagonal of 25 and side of 24. 168

TEACHER'S RESOURCE MASTERS

Practice Master 35, Part 1

11.7 Graphing Algebraic Statements

In the last lesson you saw how algebra comes to the aid of geometry in helping to prove geometric theorems. Coordinate geometry, however, is not a one-way street. By use of geometry, algebra can be clarified. This is accomplished by the graphing of algebraic statements.

A graph is simply a figure drawn in the plane. Every point that makes up the figure has coordinates that satisfy some condition or conditions. These conditions are usually expressed algebraically.

Examples:

CONDITION	GRAPH
1. $x = 3$	1. the vertical line 3 units to the right of the origin
2. $y = 0$	2. the x-axis
3. $x = 0$	3. the y-axis
4. $x > 0$ and $y > 0$	4. the first quadrant
5. $x > 0$ and $y < 0$	5. the fourth quadrant
6. $0 < x < 3$	6. the infinite vertical strip lying between the lines described in Conditions 1 and 3

1.

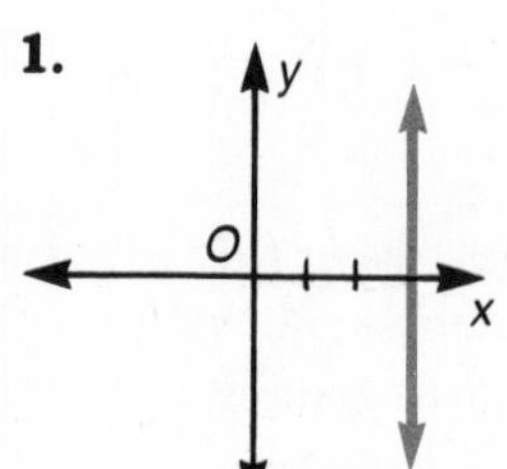

2.

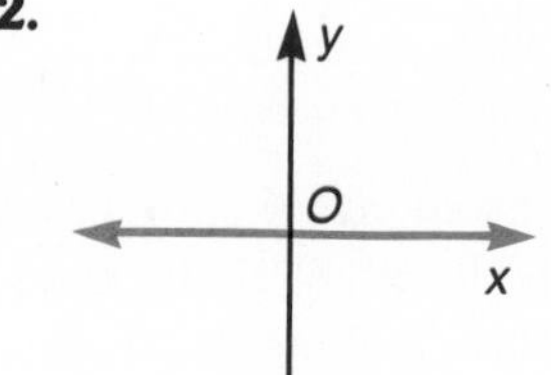

3.

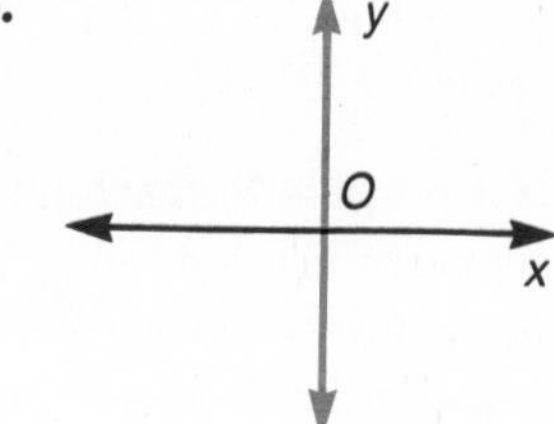

4. **5.**

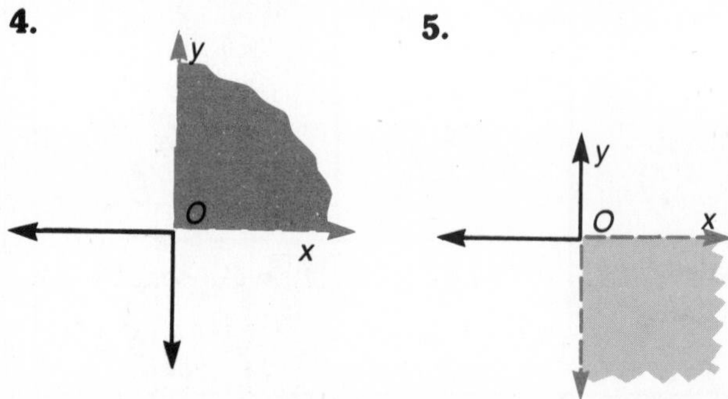

6.

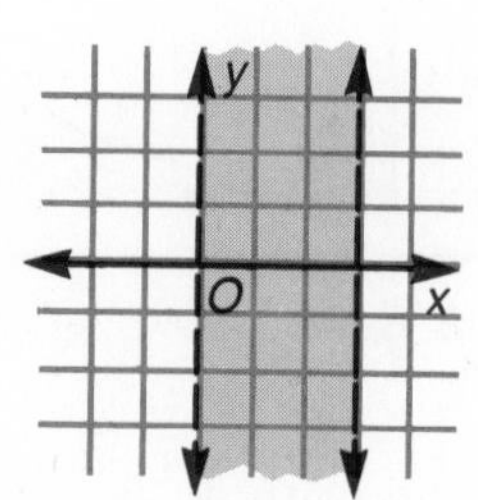

A graph can be a single point, a finite number of points, a segment, a ray, a line, an area, or any variety of geometric figures.

Note from the drawings that shading or color is used to designate areas that satisfy a condition. When an area is bordered by a solid line, the points on the line are included in the graph. If the line is dashed, the points on the line are not included in the graph.

Consider the graph $x = 3$. The line divides the plane into three sets of points, the line itself, the half-plane to the left of the line, and the half-plane to the right of the line.

Each point in the left half-plane has coordinates such that $x < 3$. Each point in the right half-plane has coordinates such that $x > 3$. All points for which $x = 3$ are on the line.

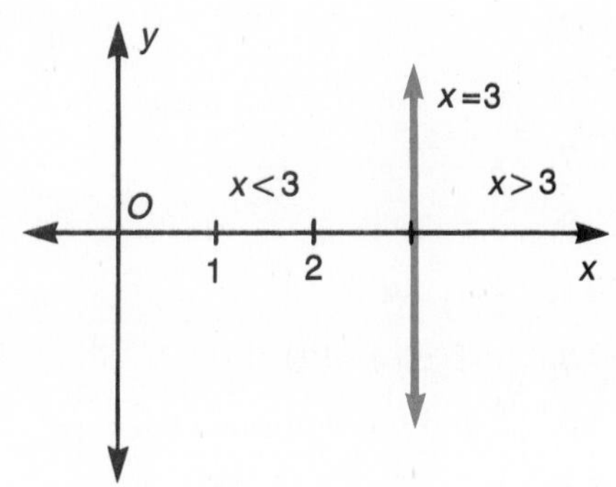

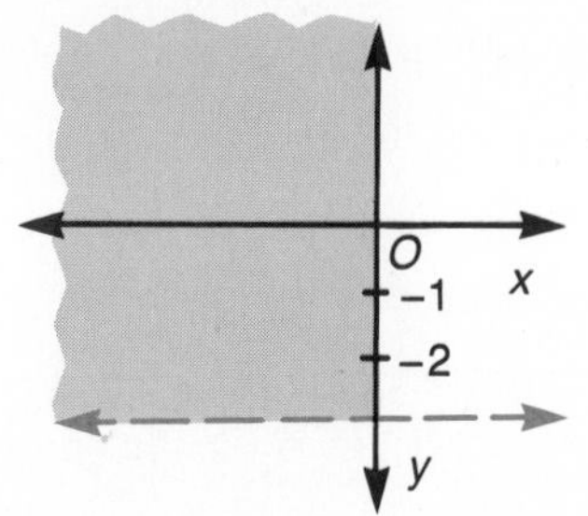

The graph on the left satisfies two conditions.

$$x \leq 0$$
$$y > -3$$

The interior region of the square is the intersection of four conditions.

$$x \geq 0$$
$$x \leq 2$$
$$y \geq 0$$
$$y \leq 2$$

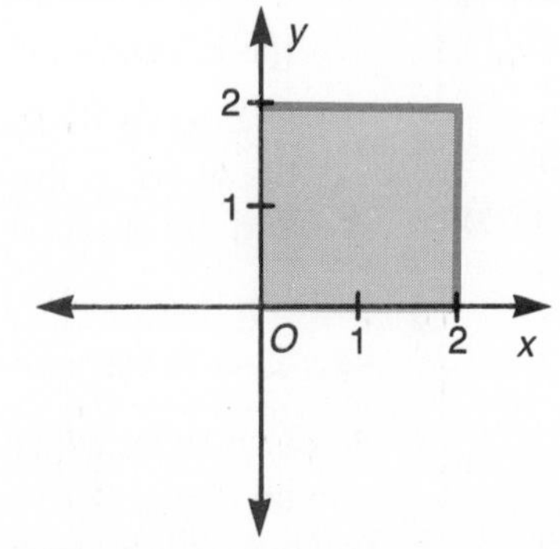

ASSIGNMENT GUIDE

Minimum 1-6
Regular 1-13 odd
Maximum 1-9 odd, 13-19

Oral Exercises

1.

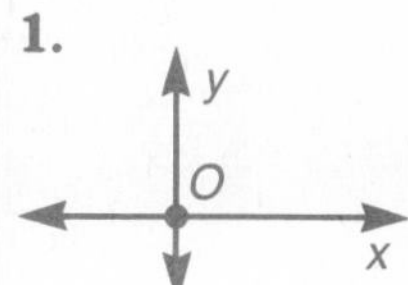

2.

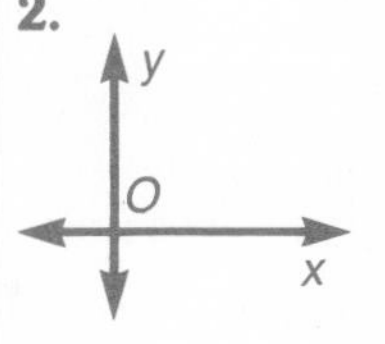

3.

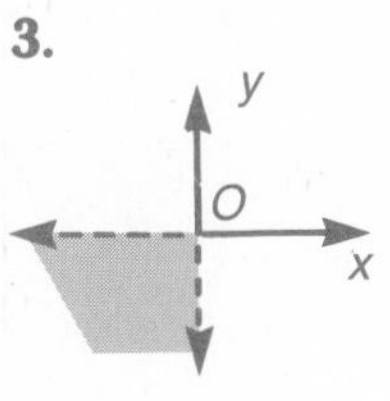

4.

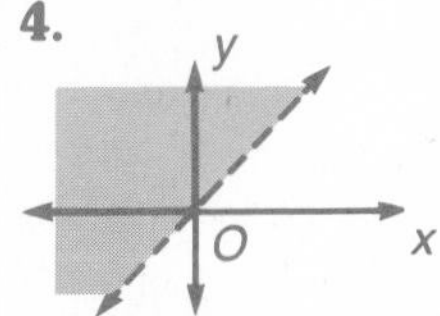

ORAL EXERCISES

Without drawing the graph, describe the graph of each of the following conditions.

1. $x = 0$ and $y = 0$

2. $x = 0$ or $y = 0$

3. $x < 0$ and $y < 0$

4. $y > x$

Written Exercises

1-19. odd *See Teacher's Manual*, p. T60

2-18. even See *Selected Answers*, p. 639

WRITTEN EXERCISES

Sketch and describe the graph of each condition described below.

A. **1.** $y = -2$ **2.** $-1 < y < 1$

3. $1 \leq x < 4$ **4.** $x = 2$ or $y = -1$

B. **5.** $y = 0$ and x is a positive integer. **6.** $y \leq 0$ and $x = 3$

7. $x > 0$ and $y = 2$ **8.** $|x| = 3$

9. $y = |x|$ **10.** $x > 0$, $y > 0$, and $y > x$

11. $|x| > 0$ **12.** $xy > 0$

13. $-2 \leq y < 0$ **14.** $x < 2$ and $y > 0$

15. x and y are positive integers. **16.** $1 \leq x \leq 3$ and $1 \leq y \leq 5$

C. **17.** $xy < 0$ **18.** $|y| = |x|$ **19.** $|x| + |y| = 1$

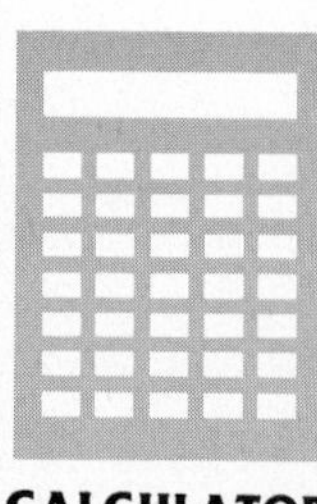

CALCULATOR

1. From the bridge of a ship at sea the approximate distance to the horizon can be calculated by using the formula $d = \frac{5}{4}\sqrt{h}$ where h is the height of the observer above the surface of the water. If the bridge of a ship is 88 ft above the water and the observer is 6 ft tall, how far is it to the horizon?

Did you use your $\boxed{\sqrt{x}}$ key? Try the same problem using the $\boxed{y^x}$ key. Use 94 for y and 0.5 for x. Do you get the same results?

A root may be expressed as a fractional power. Thus $\sqrt[3]{27}$ can also be written $27^{1/3}$. Try entering 27, $\boxed{y^x}$, $\boxed{(}$1, $\boxed{\div}$, 3 $\boxed{)}$. Do you get 3? Is 3 the cube root of 27? Whenever you wish to test an operation on your calculator, first try it with numbers for which you know the correct answer. Now try:

2. $\sqrt[3]{125}$ **3.** $\sqrt[5]{32}$ **4.** $\sqrt[4]{16}$

Calculator

1. 12.12 mi

yes

2. 5 3. 2 4. 2

11.8 Algebraic Descriptions of Linear Graphs

Equations that describe graphs of lines are called **linear equations.**

Consider line l with slope m. Let $P(x_1, y_1)$ be a point with known coordinates on l and $Q(x, y)$ represent *any* point other than P on l. (Note that x_1 and y_1 are known coordinates, while x and y are variables.)

By the definition of slope, you know that $\frac{y - y_1}{x - x_1} = m.$

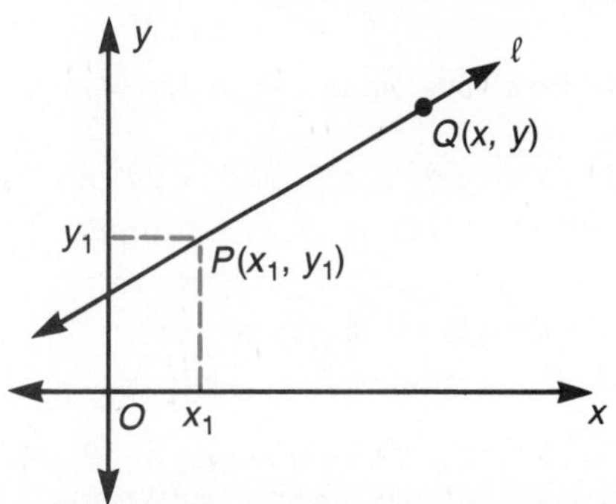

Since P and Q are distinct points, $x \neq x_1$, so the denominator does not equal zero and you can multiply both sides of the equation by $x - x_1$. This produces $y - y_1 = m(x - x_1)$.

This, then, is an equation that describes line l.

> **THEOREM 11.6**
> Let l be a nonvertical line with slope m, and let P be a point of l with coordinates (x_1, y_1). For every point $Q = (x, y)$ of l, the equation $y - y_1 = m(x - x_1)$ is satisfied.

You have already shown that (1) every point of l satisfies the equation. Now you must prove that (2) any point not on l fails to satisfy the equation.

Here it is given that $Q(x, y)$ is not on l. This being so, there is a point $Q'(x, y')$ on l such that $y' \neq y$. The slope of $\overline{PQ'}$ is

$$\frac{y' - y_1}{x - x_1} = m.$$

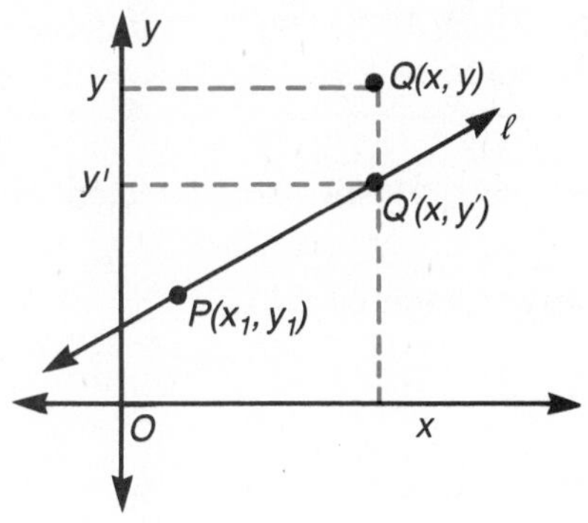

Hence, $y' = y_1 + m(x - x_1)$.
Since $y' \neq y$, $y' \neq y_1 + m(x - x_1)$.
Therefore, $y - y_1 \neq m(x - x_1)$.

This proves (2), that any point not on l fails to satisfy the equation, and leads to the following important theorem.

OBJECTIVE

Write and graph equations in point-slope form, y-intercept form, or standard form.

TEACHER'S NOTES

See p. T37

MIXED REVIEW

1. In rhombus $ABCD$, $m\angle A = 60$. Find the other angles. 120, 60, 120
2. If the side of rhombus $ABCD$ in question 1 is 10, find the diagonals. 10 and $10\sqrt{3}$
3. Find the area of rhombus ABCD in question 2. $50\sqrt{3}$
4. Simplify $\sqrt{2 + (x - \frac{1}{2x})^2}$. $x + \frac{1}{2x}$
5. At what points does the graph of $y = |x| - 2$ cross the x-axis? 2 and -2

TEACHER'S RESOURCE MASTERS

Practice Master 35, Part 2
Quiz 22

THEOREM 11.7
The graph of the equation $y - y_1 = m(x - x_1)$ is the line that passes through the point (x_1, y_1) and has slope m.

The equation given in Theorem 11.7 is called the **point-slope form** of the equation of a line (linear equation). With it you can find the equation of any line provided you know the coordinates of one point of the line and the slope of the line.

Example 1: Find the equation of the line that passes through $P(1, 2)$ and $Q(2, 4)$.

Solution: The slope of the line is $m = \frac{4-2}{2-1} = 2$.

The coordinates of either P or Q can be used as x_1 and y_1. Using $P(1, 2)$ as the fixed point, and knowing that $m = 2$, substitution provides the equation $y - 2 = 2(x - 1)$.

Every nonvertical line must cross the y-axis at some point. This point is called the **y-intercept.** The y-intercept is designated b.

If you know the slope of a line, m, and the y-intercept, b, then you know the slope and a point P on the line, namely $P(x_1, y_1)$, where $x_1 = 0$ and $y_1 = b$. You can use these values in the point-slope form, obtaining

$$\begin{aligned} y - b &= m(x - 0) \\ y - b &= mx \\ y &= mx + b. \end{aligned}$$

The equation $y = mx + b$ is called the **slope-intercept form** of a linear equation. When the equation of a line is written in this form, it is easy to determine its slope and y-intercept by inspection.

THEOREM 11.8
The graph of the equation $y = mx + b$ is the line with the slope m and y-intercept b.

If you know the slope and y-intercept of a line, you can draw its graph.

Example: Graph $y = 2x - 3$.

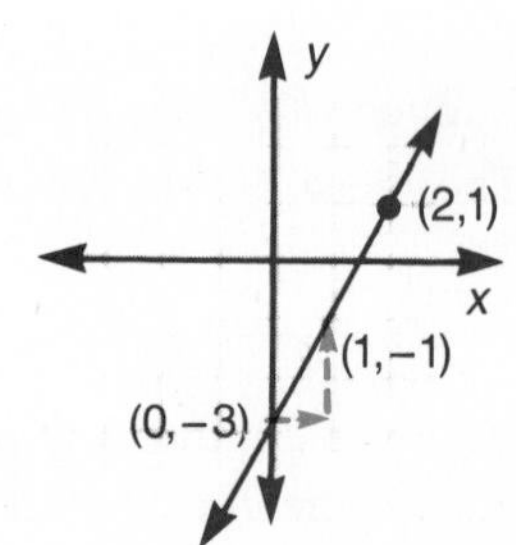

Solution: You can see that $b = -3$. Therefore, the y-intercept is -3. The slope, m, is 2. Starting at $(0, -3)$, move two units up and one unit to the right. To check that the resulting line is correct, you can select another point on the line, such as $(2, 1)$, and see if it satisfies the equation $y = 2x - 3$.

Consider the definition of a linear equation.

> **DEFINITION: linear equation**
> A **linear equation** in x and y is an equation in the form $Ax + By + C = 0$ where A and B are not both zero.

This definition provides you with a third form, the **standard form,** of the linear equation.

To write an equation in standard form:

1. let A be positive;
2. let A, B, and C be integers;
3. let A, B, and C have no common factor.

Example: Write each equation in standard form.

a. $y - x = 3$ **b.** $y = 3x + 2$ **c.** $\frac{1}{2}x + \frac{1}{4}y - 5 = 0$

Solution:

a. $y - x = 3$
$-x + y - 3 = 0$
$x - y + 3 = 0$

b. $y = 3x + 2$
$-3x + y - 2 = 0$
$3x - y + 2 = 0$

c. $\frac{1}{2}x + \frac{1}{4}y - 5 = 0$
$2x + y - 20 = 0$

To convert the standard form to the slope-intercept form, do as follows:

$Ax + By + C = 0$ $By = -Ax - C$ $y = \frac{-A}{B}x - \frac{C}{B}, B \neq 0$

You can see that the slope of the line is $-\frac{A}{B}$ and that the y-intercept is $-\frac{C}{B}$.

Example: Give the slope and the y-intercept for $2x - 3y + 1 = 0$.

Solution: $A = 2$, $B = -3$, and $C = 1$. The slope $m = -\frac{2}{-3} = \frac{2}{3}$, and the y-intercept $= -\frac{1}{-3} = \frac{1}{3}$.

Linear equations provide the basis for the following two theorems describing the relationship between geometry and algebra. Their proofs are left as exercises.

> **THEOREM 11.9**
> Every line in the plane is the graph of a linear equation in x and y.

> **THEOREM 11.10**
> The graph of a linear equation in x and y is always a line.

Example: Consider the equations of two lines.

$$l_1 : 2x - y - 3 = 0$$
$$l_2 : 2x + y - 5 = 0$$

Since $m_1 = 2$ and $m_2 = -2$, the lines are not parallel, so they intersect at some point (x, y). Determine the coordinates of the point of intersection.

Solution: The geometric problem of finding the x- and y-coordinates of this point is algebraically equivalent to *solving a system of equations in two unknowns.* One way of finding the solution is to graph both lines, as shown below.

The intersection of the two lines is the point (2, 1). Since this point lies on both lines, it satisfies both equations. This can be checked easily.

$$2(2) - (1) - 3 = 0$$
$$2(2) + (1) - 5 = 0$$

If the graphs of two equations are parallel lines, there is no intersection, and hence the system has no solution. Such a system is called *inconsistent.* If the graphs of two equations are the same line, the equations are *dependent.*

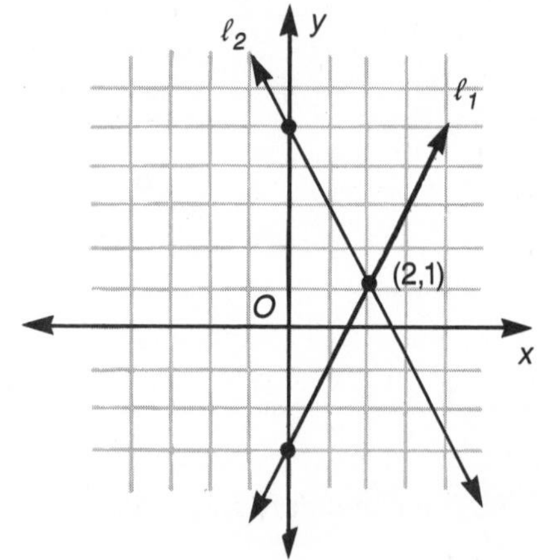

ASSIGNMENT GUIDE

Minimum 1-19 odd
Regular 1-23 odd
Maximum 1-23 odd, 25-26

Oral Exercises

1. $m = \frac{2}{3}$, $P(3, -1)$, (many other points are possible)
2. $m = -1$, $P(-1, -4)$
3. $m = 1$, $P(1, 0)$
4. $m = \frac{-3}{4}$, $P(5, 6)$
5. 6
6. 0
7. 5
8. 2
9. $m = -2$
10. $\frac{5}{2}$

ORAL EXERCISES

State the slope and the coordinates of a point of each line described by the following equations.

1. $y + 1 = \frac{2}{3}(x - 3)$

2. $y + 4 = -(x + 1)$

3. $y = x - 1$

4. $y - 6 = -\frac{3}{4}(x - 5)$

State the y-intercept of each line described by the following equations.

5. $y = -2x + 6$

6. $y = 3x$

7. $y - 5 = x$

8. $y = -\frac{1}{4}(x - 8)$

9. What is the slope of the line whose equation is $2x + y - 5 = 0$?

10. What is the y-intercept of the line whose equation is $x - 2y + 5 = 0$?

WRITTEN EXERCISES

A. For Exercises 1–5, write the equation of each line described in point-slope form.

1. The line that has a slope of -2 and passes through $P(1, -1)$.
2. The line that has a slope of $\frac{3}{4}$ and passes through $Q(2, 6)$.
3. The line that passes through $O(0, 0)$ and $H(8, 4)$.
4. The line that passes through $S(1, 1)$ and $T(3, -1)$.
5. The line that has a slope of 4 and intercepts the y-axis at -2.

For Exercises 6–10, write each equation in Exercises 1–5 in standard form.

Identify a point on the graph of each of the following equations, and give the slope of the line.

11. $y - 5 = 3(x + 2)$ **12.** $y + 2 = x + 1$ **13.** $2y + 18 = 8(x + 3)$

Give the slope and y-intercept of each equation.

14. $y = -x + 2$ **15.** $x + y - 3 = 0$ **16.** $2x + 3y - 10 = 0$

Sketch the graphs of the following equations.

17. $y + 1 = \frac{1}{2}(x - 3)$ **18.** $y = -x + 2$

B. Find the common solution by drawing the graphs of the following pairs of equations.

19. $y = x$ and $x + y = 4$ **20.** $y = x - 3$ and $x + y = 7$

Use the following equations for Exercises 21–23:

a. $y = x + 2$ **b.** $y = x + 1$ **c.** $2x - 2y + 2 = 0$ **d.** $y = -x + 2$

21. Which pair(s) represent the graphs of parallel lines?

22. Which pair(s) represent the graphs of intersecting but not dependent lines?

23. Which pair(s) represent the graphs of coincident lines?

C. 24. What pair of conditions will determine the interior of the angle shown in the figure?

25. Write a narrative proof of Theorem 11.9.

26. Write a narrative proof of Theorem 11.10.

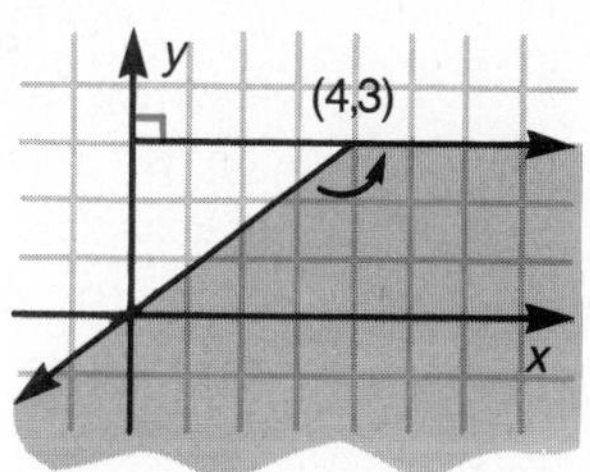

Written Exercises

1. $y + 1 = -2(x - 1)$
2. $y - 6 = \frac{3}{4}(x - 2)$
3. $y = \frac{1}{2}x$
4. $y - 1 = -(x - 1)$ or $y + 1 = -(x - 3)$
5. $y + 2 = 4x$
6. $2x + y - 1 = 0$
7. $3x - 4y + 18 = 0$
8. $x - 2y = 0$
9. $x + y - 2 = 0$
10. $4x - y - 2 = 0$
11. $m = 3, P(-2, 5)$
12. $m = 1, P(-1, -2)$
13. $m = 4, P(-3, -9)$
14. $m = -1, b = 2$
15. $m = -1, b = 3$
16. $m = -\frac{2}{3}, b = \frac{10}{3}$

17, 19. See *Teacher's Manual,* p. T61

18, 20. See *Selected Answers,* p. 639

21. a and b, a and c
22. a and d, b and d, c and d
23. b and c
24. $y \leq 3$ and $y \leq \frac{3}{4}x$
25. (Theorem 11.9) If l is vertical, $x = a$, so $x + (0)y - a = 0$, where $A = 1, B = 0, C = -a$. If l is not vertical, $y = mx + b$, so $mx - y + b = 0$, where $A = m, B = -1, C = b$.
26. (Theorem 11.10) Given $Ax + By + C = 0$ the equation for l, if $B = 0$, l is vertical and $x = \frac{-C}{A}$. If $B \neq 0$, $y = \frac{-A}{B}x - \frac{C}{B}$, and l is a line with $m = \frac{-A}{B}$, $b = \frac{-C}{B}$.

Skills Maintenance

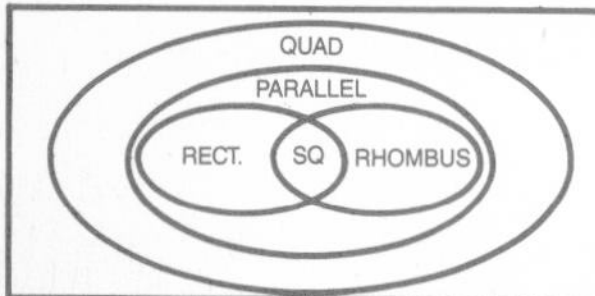

2. F

3. T

4. $x = 2\sqrt{2}$

5. $x = 2\sqrt{3}$

6. $x = \sqrt{7}$

Exploration

the hypotenuse of each triangle

where the two hypotenuses intersect

$3\frac{1}{2}$ or $3\frac{2}{3}$

$x = 3.6$

Write the equation of each line and solve the system to find the y-coordinate of point of intersection.

Horizontal distance does not matter; it is a constant for both lines and cancels out in solving the system.

SKILLS MAINTENANCE

1. Draw a Venn diagram showing how parallelograms, squares, rectangles, and rhombuses are related to each other and to the set of all quadrilaterals.

Are the following true or false?

2. If two lines in a plane are cut by a transversal, the alternate interior angles are congruent.

3. If $\triangle PDQ \sim \triangle FYI$, then $\frac{PD}{FY} = \frac{PQ}{FI} = \frac{DQ}{YI}$.

Find x in each of the following:

4.

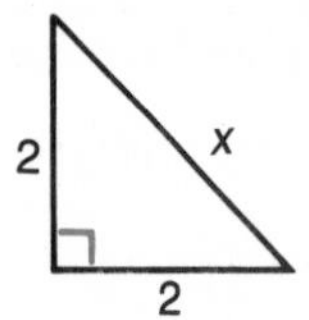

5.

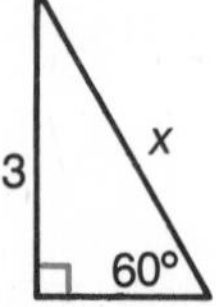

6.

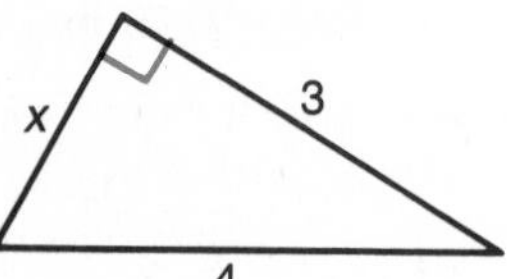

EXPLORATION/Work Problems

Many algebraic problems can be solved using coordinate geometry. Consider a typical work problem of the type you learned to solve in first-year algebra:

John can paint a house in 9 hours. Elise can paint the same house in 6 hours. How long will it take them working together to paint the house?

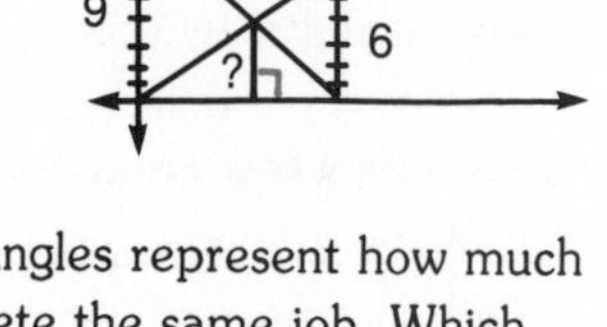

In the figure, the legs of two right triangles represent how much time it takes John and Elise to complete the same job. Which lines represent their rates of work? If John and Elise begin at the same time working at their individual rates, at what point on the figure will they complete the job?

Copy the figure on your graph paper. Can you estimate the distance from the point of intersection of the two lines to the x-axis? Solve the algebraic equation and see if the resulting value of x is close to your estimation. How could you use coordinate geometry to find an exact answer to this problem? Does the distance between the vertical segments affect your calculation? Explain.

MATH HERITAGE/Grace Murray Hopper

Grace Murray Hopper, who pioneered the development of the computer programming language COBOL, has been called a living legend. Born in 1906 in New York, Grace Hopper graduated from Vassar College and received a Ph.D. from Yale University. Her career began in college teaching, but in 1943, with the world at war, she entered the Naval Reserve. There she learned to program the first large-scale digital computer—the Mark I.

In a few short years, the UNIVAC I surpassed the Mark I in speed and became the first commercial electronic computer. Comprised of 200 miles of wiring, 5,000 tubes, and 975,000 parts, the UNIVAC filled a large room.

When Hopper began programming UNIVAC I, she tackled a problem that no other programmer had been able to solve. With the explosion of interest in computers, many new and diverse computer languages were being developed, but these languages were not easily interchangeable. A great need existed for a translating device that could adapt a given program for different computers. Facing considerable skepticism, Hopper succeeded in creating a compiler that would perform this task, making it possible for computers not yet invented to someday utilize outdated programming languages.

Among Hopper's many other accomplishments were her contributions to the invention of COBOL and to the wide acceptance of other, new languages like FORTRAN. While advancing in the Navy to the rank of Commodore, Hopper has published more than 50 papers and received as many awards, including the Society of Women Engineers Award (1964), the Legion of Merit Award (1973), and the Living Legacy Award (1984).

TEACHER'S RESOURCE MASTERS

Computer Master 11

Computer

Block 1 is at $(-3, 4)$;
avg. distance = 7.24
Block 2 is at $(1, 3)$;
avg. distance = 5.23
Block 3 is at $(3, -1)$;
avg. distance = 4.94
Block 4 is at $(0, -6)$;
avg. distance = 7.69.
Location 3 is the closest to all three fixed points.

Additional exercise: Ask students to find a location for a subway nearest all three buildings. Show that the blocks nearest the concurrence of the altitudes of $\triangle LSP$ are the ones most likely to be nearest all three fixed points. The block at (2, 0) is most nearly equidistant to L, P, and S.

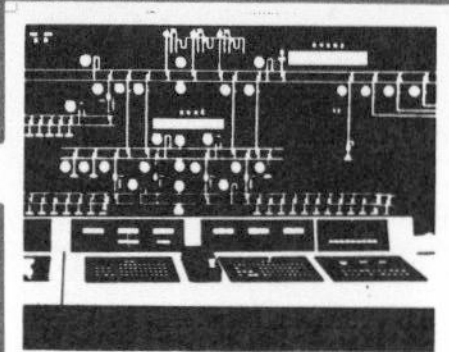

COMPUTER

The Grid City, U.S.A., city planners are selecting a site for a new fire station. The city owns four blocks on which it may build. The site should be close to three public buildings: the library (L), the school (S), and the post office (P). With a coordinate map of the city, as shown at the right, the planners will use the computer program below to find the average distances from blocks 1, 2, 3, and 4 to the public buildings. City center square (red) is the origin.

	−5	−4	−3	−2	−1	0	1	2	3	4	5	
6												6
5									S			5
4			1									4
3							2					3
2												2
1												1
0						X						0
−1			L						3			−1
−2												−2
−3											P	−3
−4												−4
−5												−5
−6						4						−6
	−5	−4	−3	−2	−1	0	1	2	3	4	5	

Enter the coordinates of the test locations in order. Which location is best-suited for the fire station?

```
100 REM FIND THE CLOSEST
    LOCATION IN RELATION TO
    THREE FIXED POINTS
110 PRINT"HOW MANY TEST
    LOCATIONS?";: INPUT T
140 FOR I=1 TO T
150 PRINT:PRINT"TYPE THE
    COORDINATES FOR TEST
    LOCATION # " I" IN THE
    FORM X, Y. ";: INPUT X1, Y1
160 REM FIND DISTANCE TO THE
    THREE FIXED POINTS
170 FOR J=1 TO 3
180 READ X2,Y2
190 D(J)=SQR(((X2-X1)↑2)+
    ((Y2-Y1)↑2))
200 L$(1)="LIBRARY":L$(2)=
    "SCHOOL": L$(3)="POST
    OFFICE"
210 PRINT"DISTANCE
    TO"L$(J)"="D(J)
220 NEXT J
230 REM FIND AVERAGE
    DISTANCE TO THE THREE
    FIXED POINTS
240 M(I)=(D(1)+D(2)+D(3))/3
250 PRINT"AVERAGE
    DISTANCE="M(I)
260 REM KEEP TRACK OF
    SHORTEST AVERAGE
    DISTANCE FOR EACH
    LOCATION
264 REM FARTHEST POSSIBLE
    DISTANCE ON GRID IS 16
268 B= 16
270 IF M(I)<=B THEN B=M(I):L=I
280 REM RESET DATA FOR NEXT
    LOCATION
290 RESTORE
300 NEXT I
310 PRINT"LOCATION" L "IS
    CLOSEST TO ALL THREE
    FIXED POINTS."
320 DATA -3,-1,3,5,5,-3
330 END
```

CHAPTER 11 REVIEW

VOCABULARY

Cartesian plane (11.1)	oblique (11.2)	slope (11.2)
coordinate (11.1)	ordered pair (11.1)	slope-intercept form (11.8)
distance formula (11.4)	origin (11.1)	standard form (11.8)
graph (11.1)	point-slope form (11.8)	unit (11.1)
linear equation (11.8)	quadrant (11.1)	x-axis (11.1)
midpoint formula (11.5)	rectangular coordinate system (11.1)	y-axis (11.1)
		y-intercept (11.8)

REVIEW EXERCISES

11.1 **What are the coordinates of each labeled point in the rectangular coordinate system at the right?**

1. *A* **2.** *B* **3.** *C* **4.** *D*

5. *E* **6.** *F* **7.** *G* **8.** *O*

9. In which quadrant are both the x and y coordinates positive numbers?

10. In which quadrant are both the x and y coordinates negative numbers?

11.2 **11.** Find the slope of the line that contains the points (3, 4) and (1, 6).

12. What is the slope of a horizontal line?

13. What is the slope of a vertical line?

14. Supply the missing value that will make the line through (5, 3) and (x −1) have the slope $m = 2$.

11.3 **In square *ABCD*, the slope of *BC* is $\frac{5}{4}$.**

15. What is the slope of *AD*? **16.** What is the slope of *AB*?

17. If the slope of diagonal *AC* is $\frac{1}{9}$, what is the slope of diagonal *BD*?

The vertices of a triangle are (2, 0), (4, 4), and (8, −2).

18. Find the slopes of its sides. **19.** Find the slopes of its altitudes.

20. Is the triangle a right triangle?

11.4 **21.** Find the lengths of the sides. **22.** Find the perimeter.

TEACHER'S RESOURCE MASTERS

Enrichment Master 8

ENRICHMENT

See Activities 21-22, p. T50

Chapter 11 Review

1. (−1, 2) 2. (2, 3)
3. (3, 0) 4. (2, −4)
5. (0, −2) 6. (−3, −1)
7. (−1, −4) 8. (0, 0)
9. I 10. III
11. $m = -1$
12. 0
13. no slope
14. 3
15. $\frac{5}{4}$
16. $\frac{-4}{5}$
17. −9
18. 2, $\frac{-1}{3}$, $\frac{-3}{2}$
19. $\frac{-1}{2}$, 3, $\frac{2}{3}$
20. no
21. $2\sqrt{5}, 2\sqrt{13}, 2\sqrt{10}$
22. $2\sqrt{5} + 2\sqrt{13} + 2\sqrt{10}$

23. $\sqrt{13}$

24. $(3\frac{1}{2}, 6)$

25. (14, −7)

26. (10, 12)

27. $c = b\sqrt{3}$

28. $A(a, 0)$, $B(2a + b, c)$, $C(a + 2b, 2c)$, $D(b, c)$ Show $DB \perp AC$ or $AB \ncong BC$

29. 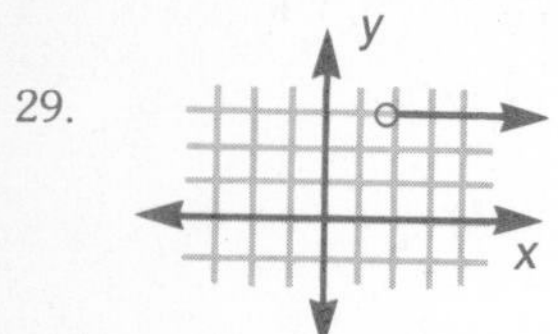

30. 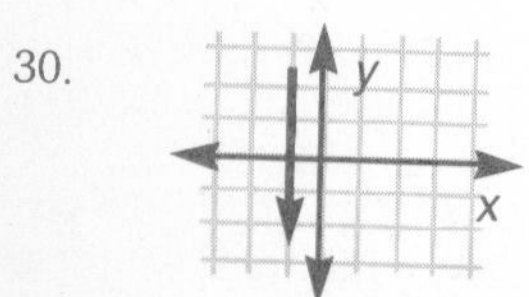

31. 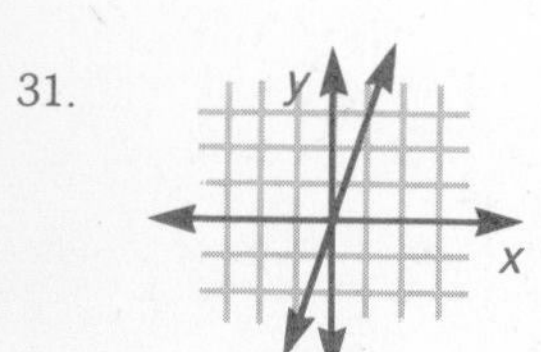

32. 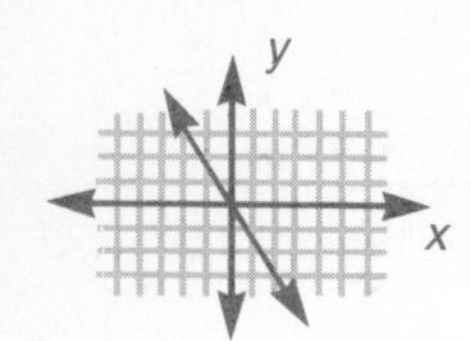

33. $y \geq x$

34. $y + 5 = \frac{2}{3}(x - 3)$

35. $y = \frac{1}{3}x - 2$

36. (−1, 2)

23. Find the length of $\overline{PQ}$, given $P(1, 5)$ and $Q(3, 2)$.

11.5 **Find the coordinates of the missing point.**

24. Given $A(-7, 9)$ and $B(14, 3)$, the midpoint of $\overline{AB}$ is at (_____, _____).

25. Given $A(-6, 3)$ and B(_____, _____), the midpoint of $\overline{AB}$ is at $(4, -2)$.

26. Given A(_____, _____) and $B(-2, -6)$, the midpoint of $\overline{AB}$ is at (4, 3).

27. If the triangle shown is equilateral, express the value of c in terms of b.

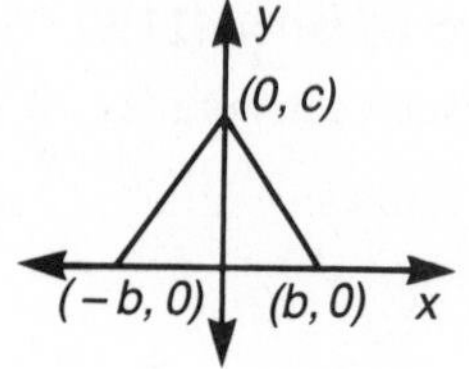

11.6 **28.** Prove that the coordinates of the midpoints A, B, C, and D of the sides of rhombus $PQRS$ cannot be the vertices of a second rhombus.

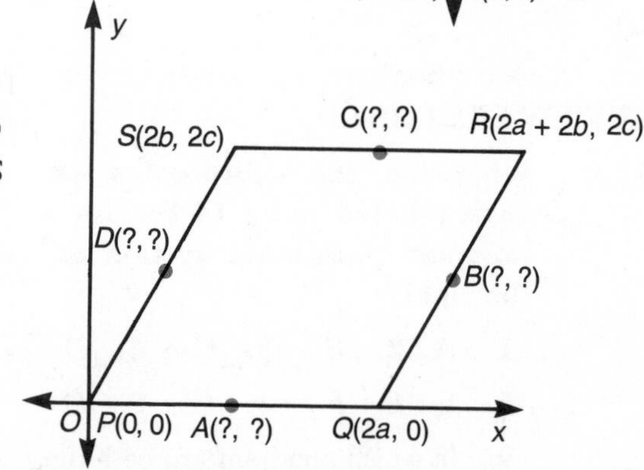

11.7 **Sketch and describe the graphs of the conditions described below.**

29. $x > 2$ and $y = 3$

30. $y \leq 3$ and $x = -1$

31. $y = 3x$

32. $x = \frac{-1}{2}y$

33. State the algebraic condition describing the shaded region of the figure on the right.

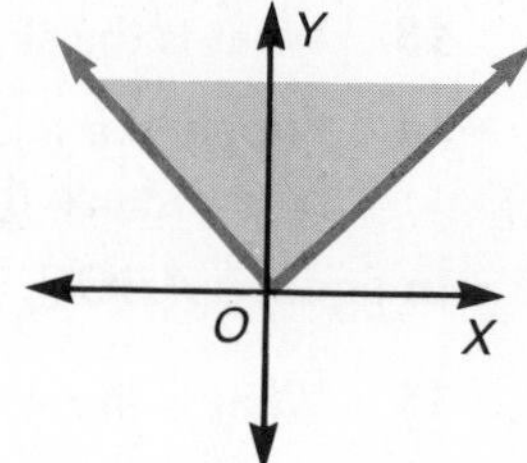

11.8 **34.** Write in point-slope form the equation of the line that contains the point $(3, -5)$ and has slope $\frac{2}{3}$.

35. Write the equation $x - 3y = 6$ in slope-intercept form.

36. Find the common solution of the following pair of equations by means of graphing $y = x + 3$ and $x + y = 1$.

CHAPTER 11 TEST

TEACHER'S RESOURCE MASTERS

Chapter 11 Test
Multiple Choice Test—Chapter 11

Chapter 11 Test

1. Which of the following points does not lie in any quadrant?

a. (1, 3) **b.** (−4, −2) **c.** (0, 5) **d.** (−1, 2) **e.** (2, −1)

2. Given $A(1, 4)$ and $B(3, k)$, if the slope of $\overline{AB}$ is $\frac{3}{2}$, what is the value of k?

a. −7 **b.** 0 **c.** 2 **d.** 3 **e.** 7

3. Which of the following lines has no slope?

a. $y = x$ **b.** $y = 0$ **c.** $y = 1$ **d.** $x = 0$ **e.** $y = -x$

4. Given $P(1, 3)$, $Q(4, 4)$, and $R(7, k)$, if P, Q, and R are collinear points, what is the value of k?

a. 4 **b.** 5 **c.** 6 **d.** 7 **e.** 8

5. Lines l and k are perpendicular. If the slope of l is 2, what is the slope of k?

a. 2 **b.** −2 **c.** $\frac{1}{2}$ **d.** $\frac{-1}{2}$ **e.** 1

6. Line l contains points $A(14, 9)$ and $B(-3, 2)$. Line k is parallel to line l. What is the slope of k?

a. $\frac{7}{17}$ **b.** $\frac{17}{7}$ **c.** $\frac{11}{17}$ **d.** $\frac{11}{9}$ **e.** $\frac{7}{11}$

7. Given $A(5, 4)$ and $B(-4, -3)$, what is the length of $\overline{AB}$?

a. 2 **b.** $\sqrt{2}$ **c.** $\sqrt{15}$ **d.** $\sqrt{19}$ **e.** none of these

8. How far from the origin is the point (12, 5)?

a. $\sqrt{7}$ **b.** 7 **c.** $\sqrt{13}$ **d.** 13 **e.** 17

9. Given $P(8, -3)$ and $Q(-6, 5)$, what is the midpoint of $\overline{PQ}$?

a. (−14, 4) **b.** (2, 1) **c.** (1, 1) **d.** (−1, −1) **e.** (2, 4)

10. Given $\triangle ABC$ with D, E, and F the midpoints of $\overline{AB}$, $\overline{BC}$, and $\overline{AC}$, and the slope of $\overline{AB} = 2$, what would you need to establish to prove that a segment joining the midpoints of two sides of a triangle is parallel to the third side?

a. slope of $\overline{FE} = -2$ **b.** slope of $\overline{FE} = 2$ **c.** slope of $\overline{DE} = \frac{1}{2}$

d. $FD = DE$ **e.** slope of $\overline{FD} = \frac{1}{2}$ the slope of $\overline{FE}$

11. Which of the conditions given below does *not* describe a line?

a. $y = x - 1$ **b.** $y = 0$ **c.** $x + y = 0$ **d.** $y = x$ **e.** $y = |x|$

12. What is the slope of the line $3x - y + 1 = 0$?

a. 3 **b.** 1 **c.** −3 **d.** $\frac{1}{3}$ **e.** $-\frac{1}{3}$

1. c
2. e
3. d
4. b
5. d
6. a
7. e
8. d
9. c
10. b
11. e
12. a

CHAPTER 12

Circles and Spheres

12.1 Introduction and Definitions

In this chapter, you will learn to graph special curves called circles.

Compare the following two definitions:

> **DEFINITIONS: circle, sphere**
> A **circle** is the set of all coplanar points equidistant from a given point C. A **sphere** is the set of all points equidistant from a given point C.

In both definitions, point C is called the **center.** Note how deleting the word "coplanar" in the second definition takes the two-dimensional circle and transforms it into the three-dimensional sphere.

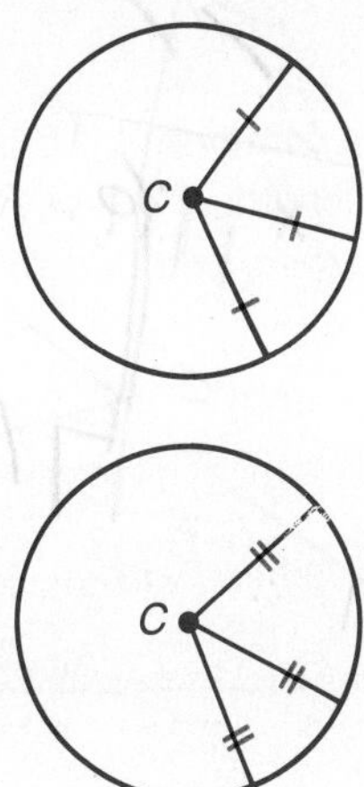

> **DEFINITION: radius**
> A **radius** of a circle or sphere is
> (1) any segment with one endpoint at the center and the other endpoint on the circle or sphere; and
> (2) the distance from the center to the circle/sphere.

Thus, both of the following statements could be true about a given circle or sphere: (1) $\overline{CB}$ is a radius. (2) The radius is 3 inches. The definitions of circle, sphere, and radius together suggest that any two radii in the same circle or sphere are congruent to each other.

> **DEFINITIONS: interior and exterior of a circle**
> The **interior** of a circle is the union of its center and the set of all points in the plane of the circle whose distances from the center are less than the radius. The **exterior** of a circle is the set of all points in the plane of the circle whose distances from the center are greater than the radius.

OBJECTIVE

Identify circles, spheres, radii, interiors and exteriors of circles, great circles, concentric circles, tangents, secants, and chords.

TEACHER'S NOTES

See p. T37

MIXED REVIEW

1. What is the set of all points in a plane equidistant from two points? ⊥ bisecting line
2. In which quadrant is the point $(3, -2)$? 4th
3. Simplify $\sqrt{(x^2 - 8x + 16)}$. $|x - 4|$
4. Multiply $\sqrt{8} \cdot \sqrt{12}$. $4\sqrt{6}$
5. In $\frac{3}{x} + \frac{7}{x-2}$, x can not be equal to ______. 0 or 2

TEACHER'S RESOURCE MASTERS

Practice Master 36, Part 1

DEFINITION: diameter
In the same circle or sphere, two collinear radii form a **diameter.**

A circle is named after its center. The figure illustrates $\odot Y$ with radii $\overline{XY}$ and $\overline{YZ}$ and diameter $\overline{XZ}$. The symbol "$\odot$" means "circle."

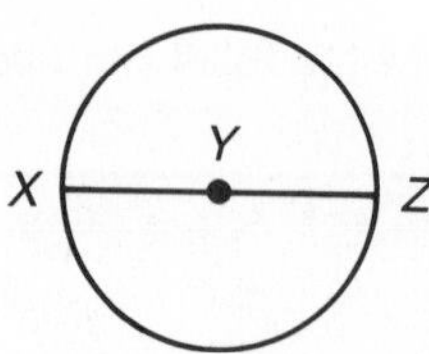

Example: Given $\odot C$ with diameter $\overline{AB}$, find the length of $\overline{AB}$ if $AC = 2x - 7$ and $CB = 5x - 34$.

Solution: Since C is the center and $\overline{AB}$ is a diameter, $\overline{AC}$ and $\overline{CB}$ must be radii of the circle and therefore the same length: $AC = CB$. Algebraic substitution yields $2x - 7 = 5x - 34$, or $x = 9$. Substituting again, you find that $AC = CB = 11$. Since $AB = AC + CB$, $AB = 22$.

THEOREM 12.1
The intersection of a sphere with a plane through its center is a circle with the same center and radius as the sphere.

In the next figure, the center of the sphere, point C, is contained in plane E. $\overline{CA}$ is a radius of the sphere and is therefore also a radius of $\odot C$, the circle determined by the intersection of the plane and the sphere.

If plane E were raised away from the center C, the intersection of the plane and the sphere would be a series of smaller and smaller circles, until finally the plane and the sphere no longer touched. Think of slicing an orange through the middle as opposed to slicing it near one end; the center section yields the largest slice. In a sphere, this center section is called a **great circle.**

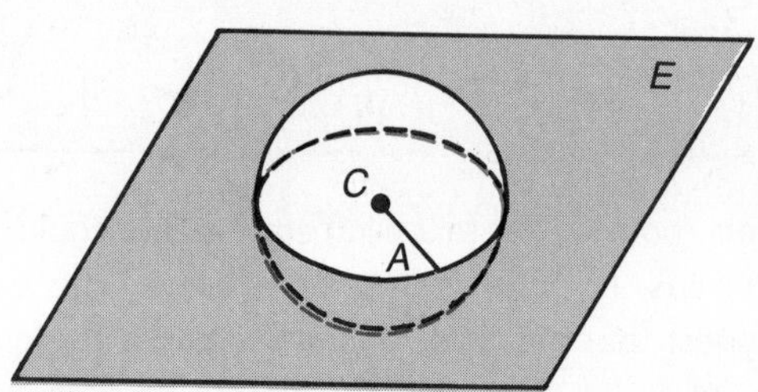

DEFINITION: great circle
The intersection of a sphere with a plane through its center is called a **great circle** of the sphere.

Two or more circles or spheres may be related to each other by position. The three most common relationships are represented in the next figure.

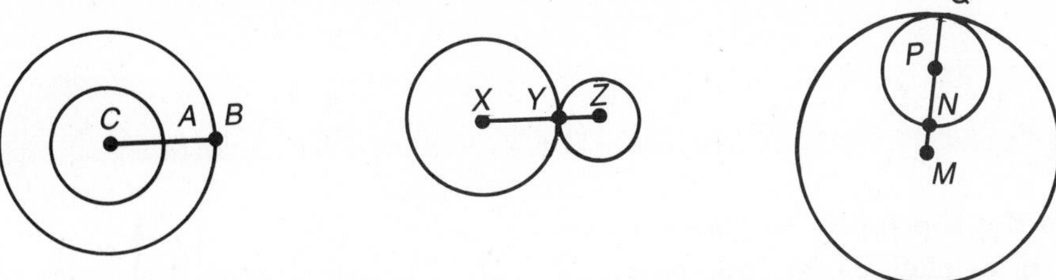

In the figure on the left, the two circles share the same center, C. In the middle figure, radii $\overline{XY}$ and $\overline{YZ}$ are collinear, with the circles intersecting only at Y. In the figure on the right, radius $\overline{MQ}$ contains radius $\overline{PQ}$, with the circles intersecting only at Q.

> **DEFINITIONS: concentric circles, externally tangent, internally tangent, point of tangency**
> Two or more circles (in the same plane) or spheres are **concentric** if they share the same center point. Two or more circles (in the same plane) or spheres are **externally tangent** if they intersect in exactly one point and if their interiors do not intersect. Two or more circles or spheres are **internally tangent** if they intersect in exactly one point and if the interior of one contains the interior of the other. The **point of tangency** (or **point of contact**) in both cases is the point of intersection.

A circle may also be described by its position relative to a line. Two common relationships are shown below.

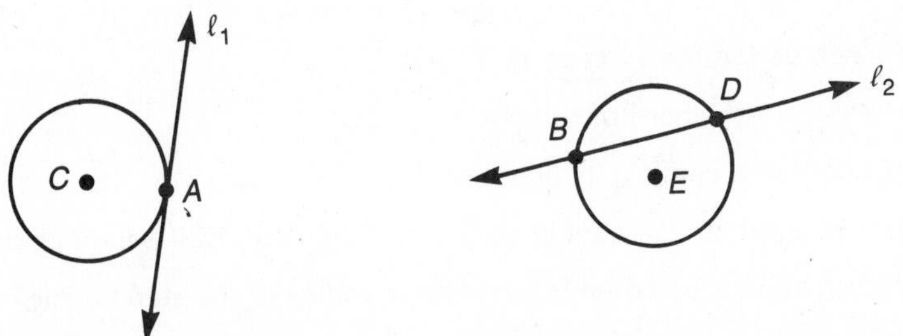

In the figure on the left, l_1 intersects $\odot C$ at exactly one point, A. In the figure on the right, l_2 intersects $\odot E$ at two points, B and D.

> **DEFINITIONS: tangent, secant, chord**
> A line that intersects a circle at exactly one point is called a **tangent**, and the intersection is called the **point of tangency** (or **point of contact**). A **secant** is a line that intersects a circle in exactly two points. A **chord** is a segment whose endpoints are on the circle.

ASSIGNMENT GUIDE

Minimum 1-18
Regular 1-27 odd
Maximum 1-31 odd, 32

In the previous figures, l_1 is a tangent, $\overrightarrow{BD}$ is a secant, and $\overline{BD}$ is a chord. A diameter is often defined as a chord that contains the center of a circle.

ORAL EXERCISES

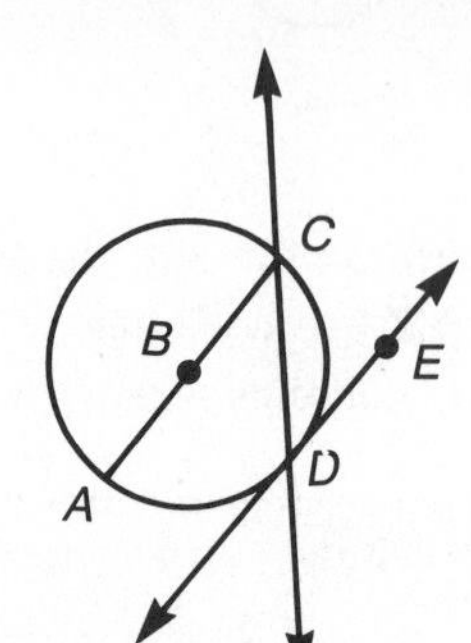

Refer to the top figure to give the correct term for each of the following.

1. B 2. $\overline{AB}$ 3. $\overline{AC}$

4. $\overline{CD}$ 5. $\overleftrightarrow{CD}$ 6. $\overleftrightarrow{DE}$

Refer to the bottom figure to name each of the following.

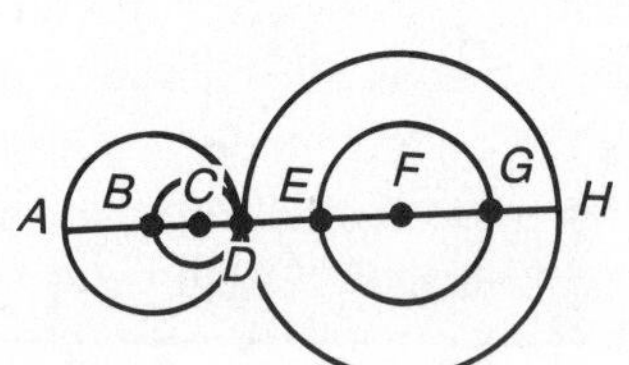

7. the center of $\odot B$
8. the center of $\odot C$
9. two concentric circles
10. two internally tangent circles
11. two externally tangent circles
12. a radius of $\odot C$
13. a radius of small $\odot F$
14. a diameter of large $\odot F$
15. a chord of $\odot B$
16. a point of tangency

State whether each sentence is true or false.

17. A radius of a circle is a chord of the circle.
18. The longest chord in a circle is its diameter.
19. The diameter of a sphere is equal in length to a diameter of its great circle.
20. A chord of a circle may be equal in length to a radius of the same circle.
21. A tangent to a circle may contain the center of the circle.
22. A secant to a circle may contain the center of the circle.
23. A secant always contains a chord.
24. A circle is a convex set.
25. Two externally tangent spheres intersect in exactly one point.
26. The intersection of a line and a circle may contain three points.
27. Two spheres may be internally tangent.
28. The intersection of a plane and a sphere may contain only two points.

Oral Exercises

1. center 2. radius
3. diameter 4. chord
5. secant 6. tangent
7. B 8. C
9. small and large $\odot F$
10. $\odot B$, $\odot C$
11. $\odot B$, large $\odot F$
12. $\overline{CD}$ or $\overline{CB}$
13. $\overline{FG}$ or $\overline{FE}$
14. $\overline{DH}$
15. $\overline{AD}$
16. D
17. F
18. T
19. T
20. T
21. F 22. T
23. T 24. F
25. T 26. F
27. T 28. F

29. The interior of a sphere is a convex set.

30. In a circle, a chord and a diameter may be congruent.

WRITTEN EXERCISES

A. Refer to the figure of ⊙*A* and ⊙*B* to find each length if *AD* = 5 and *BG* = 3.

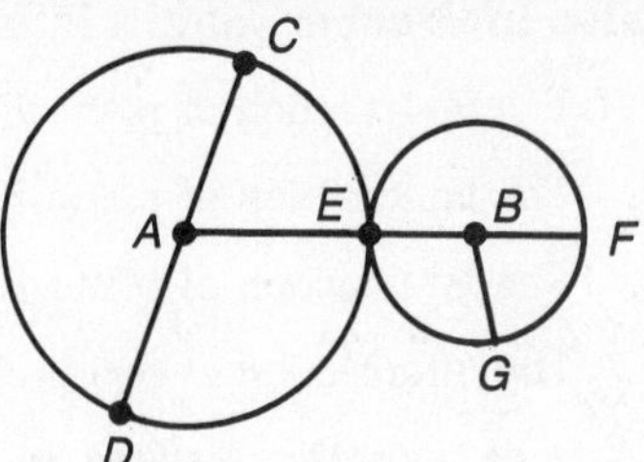

1. *AE*	**2.** *DC*
3. *BF*	**4.** *EF*
5. *AB*	**6.** *AF*

State whether each sentence is true or false.

7. Two different lines may be tangent to a circle at the same point.

8. A secant may contain the diameter of a circle.

9. The longest chord of a circle is its radius.

10. A diameter and a chord may be parallel.

11. A diameter and a radius may be parallel.

12. A sphere has many great circles.

13. If two circles are internally tangent, a radius of one may be a diameter of the other.

14. The intersection of a secant and a circle is a chord.

B. Given that *A* is the center of the two concentric circles, ⊙*B* is externally tangent to small ⊙*A* and intersects large ⊙*A*, *C* bisects $\overline{AD}$, and *BF* = 4, find each length.

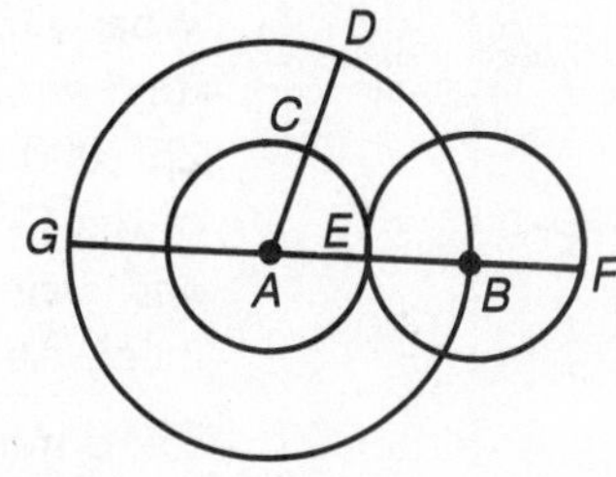

15. *EB*	**16.** *CD*
17. *AB*	**18.** *GF*

Given ⊙*A* with diameter $\overline{BC}$, find each length.

19.	$BA = 2x + 3$	$AC = 5x - 9$	$BA =$ _____
20.	$BC = 5x - 1$	$AB = 2x + 7$	$BC =$ _____
21.	$BA = \frac{1}{2}x + 3$	$AC = 2x$	$BC =$ _____
22.	$BC = 17 - 3x$	$AB = x + 1$	$AC =$ _____

29. T

30. T

Written Exercises

1. 5 2. 10
3. 3 4. 6
5. 8 6. 11
7. F
8. T
9. F
10. T
11. F
12. T
13. T
14. F
15. 4
16. 4
17. 8
18. 20
19. 11
20. 74
21. 8
22. 4

23. 0

24. 1

25. 3

26. a great circle

27. a great circle

28. a line

29. two points

30.

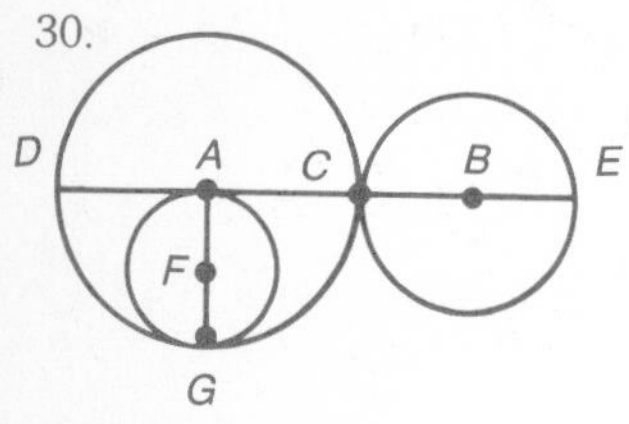

31. 18

32. 72

Calculator

1. ≈606

2. ≈574

3. 16%

4. ≈69 mi

How many lines may be drawn tangent to each of the following?

23. both of two concentric circles

24. both of two internally tangent circles

25. both of two externally tangent circles

Plane *E* intersects sphere *P*, passing through the center of the sphere. Plane *F* also intersects sphere *P*, also passing through the center of the sphere.

26. The intersection of plane E and sphere P is ______________.

27. The intersection of plane F and sphere P is ______________.

28. The intersection of plane E and plane F is ______________.

29. The intersection of two great circles is ______________.

C. **⊙*A* is externally tangent to ⊙*B* at point *C*, such that diameter $\overline{DC}$ of ⊙*A* is twice as long as diameter $\overline{CE}$ of ⊙*B*. ⊙*F* is internally tangent to ⊙*A* at point *G*, such that $\overline{AG}$ is a diameter of ⊙*F*.**

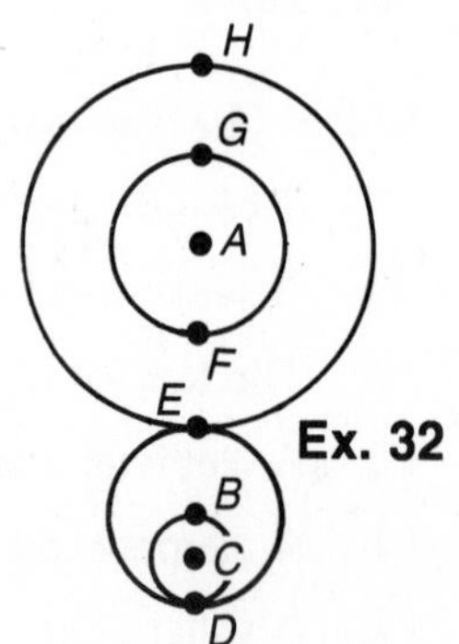

Ex. 32

30. Sketch ⊙A, ⊙B, and ⊙F.

31. Find DE if $FG = 3$.

32. Refer to the figure of small and large ⊙A, ⊙B, ⊙C. F bisects $\overline{AE}$, $\overline{BE} \cong \overline{GH}$, $HF = 7x - 6$, and $BC = \frac{3}{2}x - 3$. Find HD.

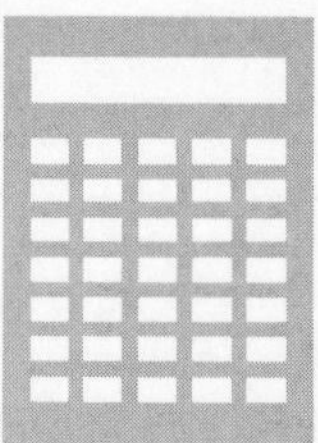

CALCULATOR

1. When Eratosthenes measured the earth in the third century B.C., he found the circumference to be about 250,000 stadia. Although we are not sure of the length of the Greek stadium, using the best current estimate and converting to miles, this would be about 28,700 miles. About how long, in feet, was one stadium?

2. The distance from Aswan to Alexandria was about 5000 stadia. How many miles is this?

3. If the actual circumference of the earth is about 24,800 miles, approximately what was Eratosthenes' percent of error?

4. What is the approximate length, in miles, of one degree of longitude at the equator?

12.2 Tangents and Chords

This lesson focuses on tangents and chords of circles. The next theorem, which concerns tangents, is lengthy but leads to six valuable corollaries concerning both tangents and chords.

THEOREM 12.2
Given a line and a circle in the same plane, let P be the center of the circle and let F be the foot of the perpendicular from P to the line. Then exactly one of the following must be true:

1. Every point of the line is outside the circle.
2. F is on the circle, and the line is tangent to the circle at F.
3. F is inside the circle, and the line intersects the circle in exactly two points, which are equidistant from F.

Given: line l and $\odot P$ in the same plane; point F on l such that $\overline{PF} \perp l$

Prove: Either (1) Any other point Q on l is outside $\odot P$; (2) F is on $\odot P$, and l is tangent to $\odot P$ at F; or (3) F is inside $\odot P$, and l intersects $\odot P$ in exactly two points Q and T, such that $\overline{QF} \cong \overline{TF}$.

Proof: Theorem 12.2 must be proved for all positions of point F. (1) First, consider F to be *outside* $\odot P$, and let r be the radius of $\odot P$. Because F is outside the circle, $PF > r$. By Theorem 6.6, $\overline{PF}$ is the shortest segment between P and $\overline{FQ}$. Therefore, if Q is any other point on l distinct from F, $PQ > PF$. Since $PF > r$ already, $PQ > r$, which means that Q is outside the circle. Finally, since Q represents all points on l other than F, and since F and Q are both outside the circle, it follows that the entire line l is outside the circle, as stated in the first part of Theorem 12.2.

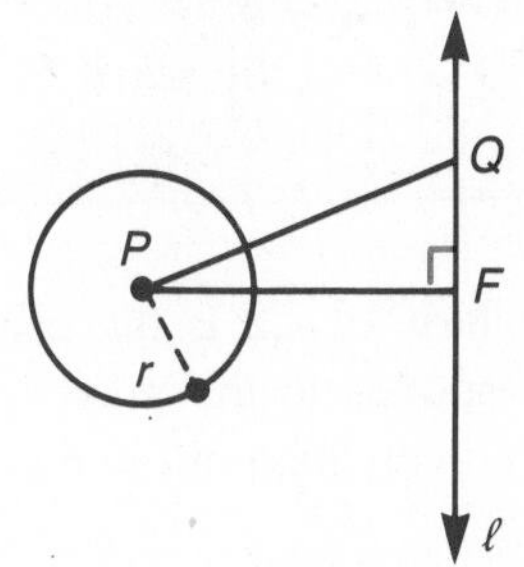

(2) Consider F now to be a point *on* $\odot P$. Here, $PF = r$. By the same reasoning used in (1), if Q is any other point on l, $PQ > r$. Therefore, all points on l other than F are outside the circle, so by the definition of tangent, l is tangent to the circle at F.

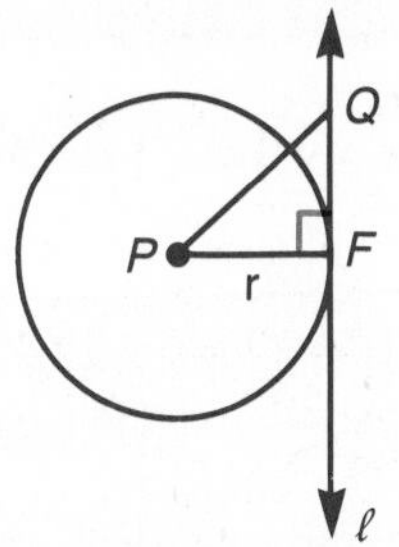

OBJECTIVE

Use Theorem 12.2 and its corollaries and Theorems 12.3 and 12.4 to answer questions regarding tangents and chords and to find the lengths of segments in circles.

TEACHER'S NOTES

See p. T37

MIXED REVIEW

1. Solve $\sqrt{x - 3} = 4$. $x = 1$
2. Simplify $\sqrt{6^2 + 8^2}$. 10
3. Solve $5(20 - x) = 6x + 50$. $x = \frac{50}{11}$
4. Factor $x^2 - 15x - 34$. $(x - 17)(x + 2)$
5. Add $\frac{2x}{3y} + \frac{7}{4x}$. $\frac{8x^2 + 21y}{12xy}$

TEACHER'S RESOURCE MASTERS

Practice Master 36, Part 2

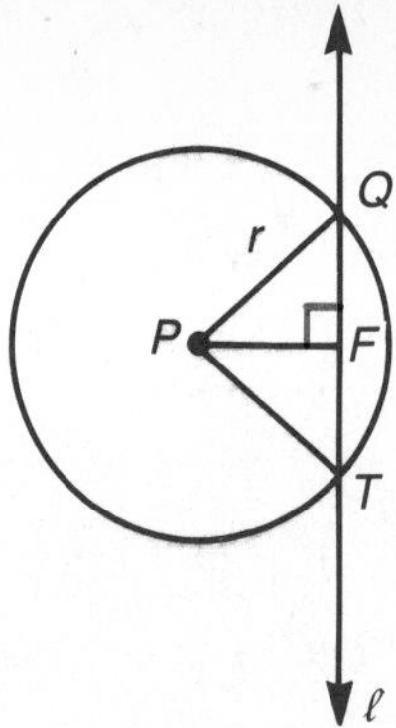

(3) Consider F to be *inside* $\odot P$. In this case, l cannot be entirely outside the circle (because at least one point is inside). The line cannot intersect the circle in three or more points because otherwise there would be three or more radii with collinear endpoints, which is impossible on a circle. Hence, the line intersects the circle in exactly two points. Theorem 12.2 further asserts that these two points are equidistant from F, or $\overline{QF} \cong \overline{TF}$. You know that $\overline{PQ} \cong \overline{PT}$ because each is a radius of the same circle. Considering $\overline{PF}$ as the common side of two right triangles, by *HL*, $\triangle PFQ \cong \triangle PFT$. Thus, their corresponding parts $\overline{QF}$ and $\overline{TF}$ are congruent.

Several corollaries result from Theorem 12.2. Each is based on a particular condition of Theorem 12.2 and may be justified by the theorem.

COROLLARY 12.2.1
Every line tangent to a circle is perpendicular to the radius drawn to the point of tangency.

Corollary 12.2.1 is based on the second condition of Theorem 12.2 and establishes that a radius and tangent that intersect are perpendicular.

COROLLARY 12.2.2
Any line in the plane of a circle perpendicular to a radius at its outer end is a tangent to the circle.

Corollary 12.2.2 is the converse of Corollary 12.2.1. Because the outer end of the radius corresponds to the point called F in Theorem 12.2, Corollary 12.2.2 is also based on the second condition of the theorem.

COROLLARY 12.2.3
Any perpendicular from the center of a circle to a chord bisects the chord.

Corollary 12.2.3 restates the third condition of Theorem 12.2.

COROLLARY 12.2.4
The segment joining the center of a circle to the midpoint of a chord is perpendicular to the chord.

Corollary 12.2.4 is the converse of the previous corollary and is also based on the third condition of Theorem 12.2.

> **COROLLARY 12.2.5**
> In the plane of a circle, the perpendicular bisector of a chord passes through the center of the circle.

Corollary 12.2.5 may be verified by Corollary 12.2.3, Corollary 12.2.4, or the third condition of Theorem 12.2.

> **COROLLARY 12.2.6**
> If a line in the plane of a circle intersects the interior of the circle, then it intersects the circle in exactly two points.

Example: $\overleftrightarrow{BC}$ is tangent to $\odot A$ at B. Find $m\angle ABC$.

Solution: According to Corollary 12.2.1, an intersecting tangent and radius are perpendicular, so $m\angle ABC = 90$.

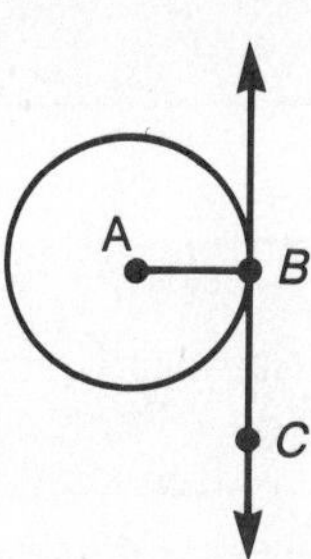

Example: $\overline{AB} \perp \overleftrightarrow{BC}$ at B, which lies on $\odot A$. Is $\overleftrightarrow{BC}$ a tangent, secant, or chord?

Solution: By Corollary 12.2.2, if $\overleftrightarrow{BC} \perp \overline{AB}$ at its outer end (B), then $\overleftrightarrow{BC}$ is a tangent to $\odot A$.

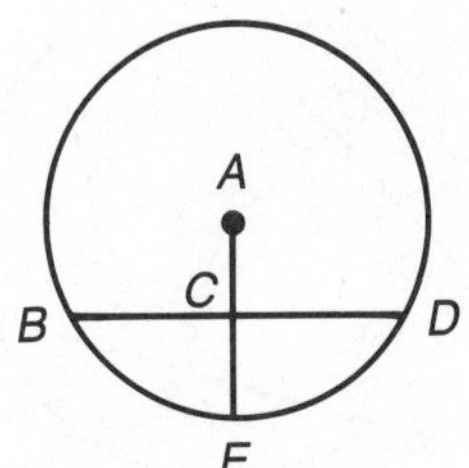

Example: In $\odot A$, $\overline{AE} \perp \overline{BD}$. If $BD = 10$, find CD.

Solution: Corollary 12.2.3 states that a radius perpendicular to a chord bisects the chord; $CD = 5$.

Example: In $\odot A$, $\overline{AE}$ bisects $\overline{BD}$. Find $m\angle ACD$.

Solution: Corollary 12.2.4 states that a radius bisecting a chord is perpendicular to the chord. Therefore, $m\angle ACD = 90$.

Example: $\overline{AB}$ is the perpendicular bisector of $\overline{CD}$; $\overline{EF}$ is the perpendicular bisector of $\overline{HI}$. How do you know that G is the center of the circle?

Solution: By Corollary 12.2.5, the perpendicular bisector of a chord must contain the center of the circle. Since $\overline{AB}$ and $\overline{EF}$ both contain the center, their point of intersection, G, must be the center.

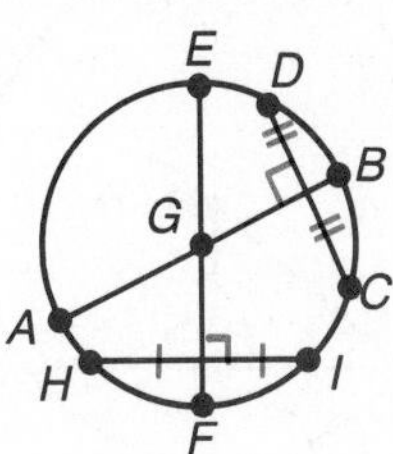

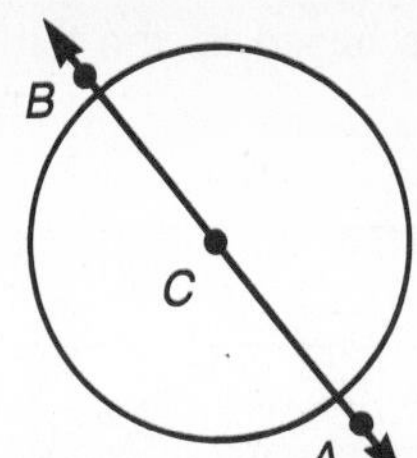

Example: $\overleftrightarrow{AB}$ contains the center of $\odot C$. Is $\overleftrightarrow{AB}$ a tangent, secant, or neither?

Solution: Corollary 12.2.6 states that a line intersecting the interior of the circle intersects the circle itself twice, making $\overleftrightarrow{AB}$ a secant.

DEFINITION: congruent circles
Circles with congruent radii are called **congruent circles.**

THEOREM 12.3
In the same circle or in congruent circles, chords equidistant from the center are congruent.

THEOREM 12.4
In the same circle or in congruent circles, any two congruent chords are equidistant from the center.

Theorem 12.3 states that, in $\odot A$ at the right, if $\overline{AC} \cong \overline{AB}$, then $\overline{XY} \cong \overline{WZ}$. Theorem 12.4 states the converse: if $\overline{XY} \cong \overline{WZ}$, then $\overline{AC} \cong \overline{AB}$. The proofs are left as exercises.

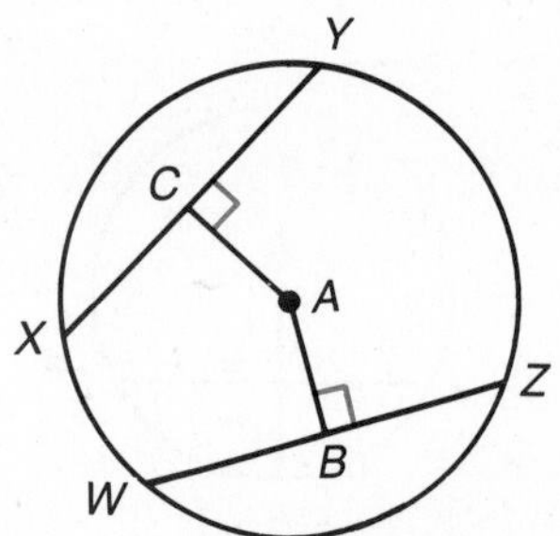

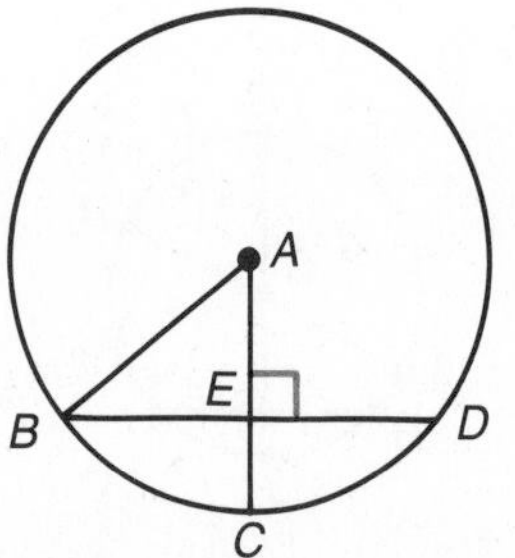

As a final example, consider $\odot A$ with a radius of 5. If $AE = 3$, find BD. Since radius $\overline{AC}$ is perpendicular to chord $\overline{BD}$, it bisects $\overline{BD}$. Using the Pythagorean Theorem, you find BE and then double it to find BD. $AE^2 + BE^2 = AB^2$; $9 + BE^2 = 25$; $BE^2 = 16$. Therefore, $BE = 4$ and $BD = 8$.

ORAL EXERCISES

Refer to the figure of $\odot C$ to fill in the blanks.

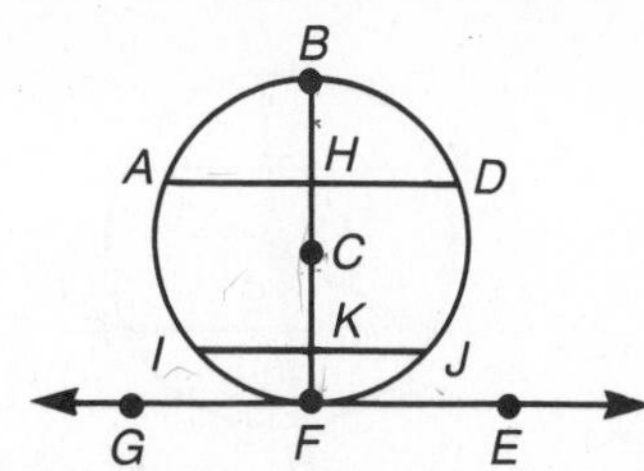

1. If $\overline{CB} \perp \overline{AD}$, then _____ bisects _____.
2. If $\overleftrightarrow{GE}$ is a tangent, then $\angle$ ____ $\cong \angle$ ____.
3. If $\overline{CB} \perp \overline{AD}$ and $AD = 12$, then $AH =$ _____.
4. If $\overline{CF}$ bisects $\overline{IJ}$, then $\angle$ ____ $\cong \angle$ ____.
5. If $\overleftrightarrow{GE}$ is a tangent with $\angle EFK \cong \angle FKI$, then $m\angle IKC =$ _____.

Refer to the figure of $\odot A$ below to decide if each statement is <u>true</u> or <u>false</u>. (Remember that "not necessarily true" means "false.")

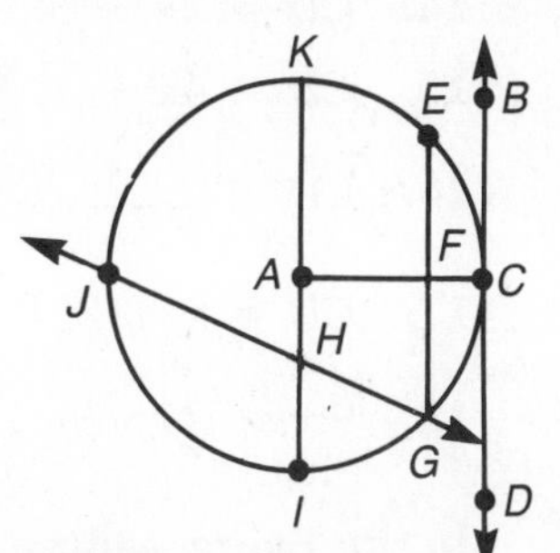

6. $\overleftrightarrow{BD}$ is a tangent; therefore, $\overline{AC} \perp \overline{BD}$.
7. $\overleftrightarrow{JG}$ is a secant; therefore, $\overline{JG}$ cannot bisect $\overline{AI}$.
8. $\overline{EG}$ bisects $\overline{AC}$; therefore, $\overline{EG} \perp \overline{AC}$.
9. A bisects $\overline{KI}$; therefore, $\overline{KI} \perp \overline{AC}$.
10. $\overline{EG} \cong \overline{JG}$; therefore, $\overline{AF} \cong \overline{AH}$.
11. $\overline{AI}$ bisects $\overline{JG}$; therefore, $\overline{AI} \perp \overline{JG}$.
12. $\overline{AC}$ bisects $\overline{EG}$; $\overleftrightarrow{BD}$ is a tangent to $\odot A$ at C; therefore, $\overline{EG} \parallel \overleftrightarrow{BD}$.
13. $\overleftrightarrow{BD}$ is tangent to $\odot A$ at C; $\angle BCA \cong \angle EFA$; therefore, $\overline{AC}$ bisects $\overline{EG}$.

WRITTEN EXERCISES

A. Indicate whether each of the following statements is <u>true</u> or <u>false</u>.

1. In a circle, if a radius bisects a chord, it is perpendicular to the chord.
2. In a circle, a tangent and a diameter that intersect are perpendicular.
3. If a line in the plane of a circle intersects the interior of that circle, the line is a secant.
4. If a line and a radius are perpendicular, the line is a tangent.
5. The diameters of two congruent circles are congruent.
6. If a chord of one circle is congruent to a chord of another circle, then the circles are congruent.
7. If two chords in a circle are congruent, then they are the same distance from the center of the circle.
8. If a radius bisects two chords in a circle, then the chords are parallel.

ASSIGNMENT GUIDE

Day 1
Minimum 1-13
Regular 1-18
Maximum 1-19
Day 2
Minimum 20-24
Regular 20-26
Maximum 20-27

Oral Exercises

1. $\overline{CB}, \overline{AD}$ 2. *GFB, EFB*
3. 6 4. *IKC, JKC*
5. 90 6. T
7. F 8. F
9. F 10. F
11. T 12. T
13. T

Written Exercises

1. T 2. T
3. T 4. F
5. T 6. F
7. T
8. F (One of the chords could be a diameter.)

9. T　10. 90
11. 90　12. $\overline{AC} \parallel \overline{DF}$
13. *EXD*　14. 38
15. 5　16. 14
17. 24

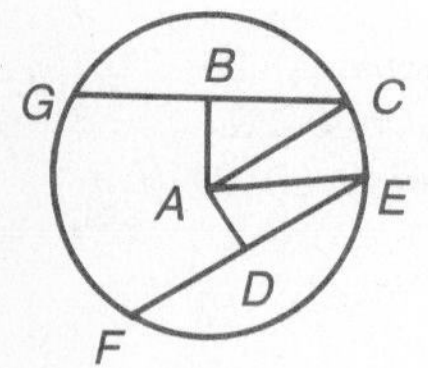

18. Given: $\overline{AB} \perp \overline{BC}$, $\overline{AD} \perp \overline{DE}$, $\overline{AB} \cong \overline{AD}$
Prove: $\overline{CG} \cong \overline{EF}$
Proof: *1.* $\overline{AC} \cong \overline{AE}$ (Radii of the same ⊙ are ≅.); *2.* $\overline{AB} \cong \overline{AD}$ (Given); *3.* $\triangle ABC \cong \triangle ADE$ (HL); *4.* $\overline{BC} \cong \overline{DE}$ (CPCTC); *5.* $\overline{CG} \cong \overline{EF}$ (Cor. 12.2.3 and Def. of bisect).

19. Given: $\overline{AB} \perp \overline{BC}$, $\overline{AD} \perp \overline{DE}$, $\overline{CG} \cong \overline{EF}$
Prove: $\overline{AB} \cong \overline{AD}$
Proof: *1.* $\overline{BC} \cong \overline{DE}$ (Cor. 12.2.3 and Def. of bisect); *2.* $\overline{AC} \cong \overline{AE}$ (Radii of the same ⊙ are ≅.); *3.* $\triangle ABC \cong \triangle ADE$ (HL); *4.* $\overline{AB} \cong \overline{AD}$ (CPCTC).

20. 16　21. 5
22. $\sqrt{51}$　23. $2\sqrt{5}$
24. 10
25. Since radii of the same ⊙ are ≅, $\overline{AC} \cong \overline{AD} \cong \overline{AE} \cong \overline{AB}$. $\angle BAC \cong \angle EAD$ (Vert. ∠s are ≅.), so $\triangle BAC \cong \triangle EAD$ by SAS.
26. $BC = 9$
27. See *Teacher's Manual*, p. T61

9. If two chords of a circle are perpendicular to the same radius, then both chords are bisected.

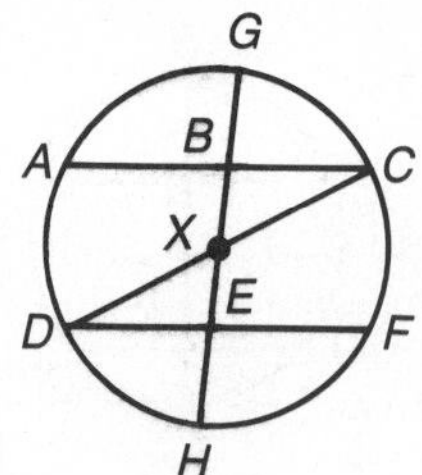

In ⊙*X*, diameter $\overline{GH}$ bisects congruent chords $\overline{AC}$ and $\overline{DF}$.

10. $m\angle ABH =$ _____
11. $m\angle GEF =$ _____
12. Therefore, _____ ∥ _____
13. and $\triangle BXC \cong \triangle$ _____.

B. Find the length of each segment. Radius $\overline{AB} \perp \overline{CE}$.

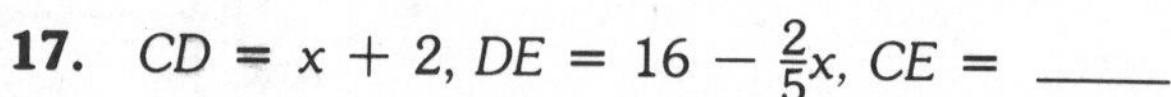
14. $CD = 2x - 3$, $DE = x + 8$, $CE =$ _____

15. $CD = 4x + 1$, $DE =$ _____, $CE = 15 - 5x$

16. $CD =$ _____, $DE = \frac{2}{3}x$, $CE = x + 7$

17. $CD = x + 2$, $DE = 16 - \frac{2}{5}x$, $CE =$ _____

18. Prove Theorem 12.3.　**19.** Prove Theorem 12.4.

In the figure, radius $\overline{AE} \perp \overline{BD}$.

20. If $AB = 10$ and $AC = 6$, find BD.
21. If $AE = 13$ and $BD = 24$, find AC.
22. If $AC = 7$ and $CE = 3$, find BC.
23. If $BC = 4$ and $AC = 2$, find AD.
24. If $BC = 8$ and $CE = 4$, find AB.

C. 25. Given: ⊙*A* with diameters $\overline{BE}$ and $\overline{CD}$
Prove: $\triangle BAC \cong \triangle EAD$

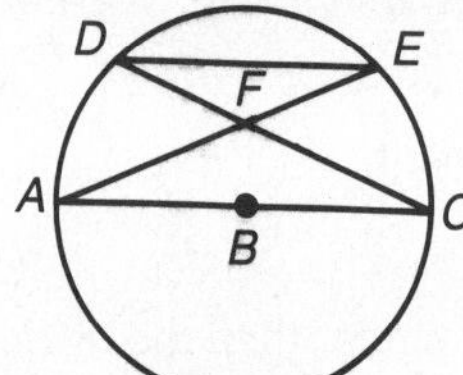
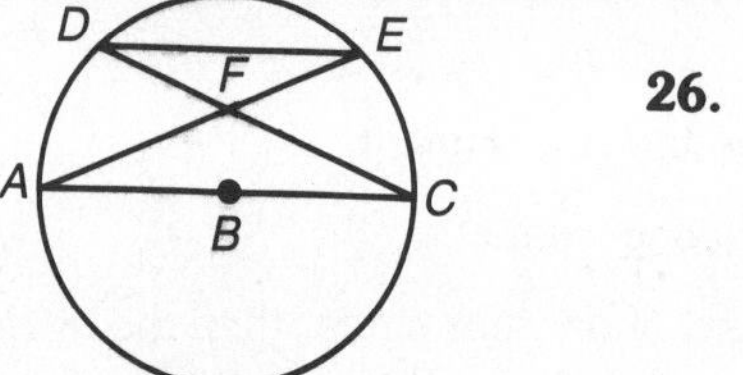

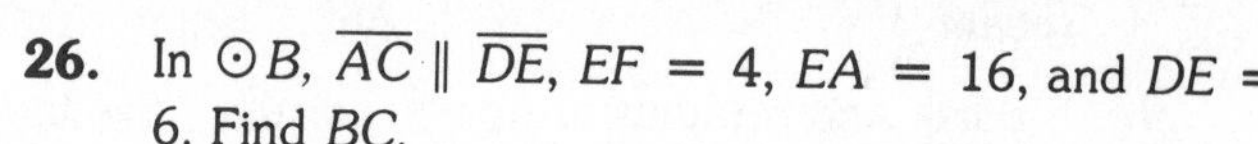
26. In ⊙*B*, $\overline{AC} \parallel \overline{DE}$, $EF = 4$, $EA = 16$, and $DE = 6$. Find BC.

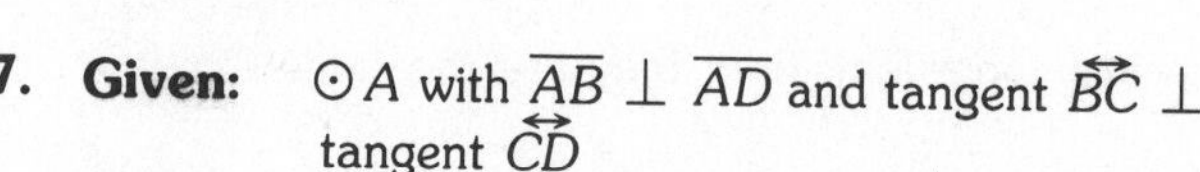
27. Given: ⊙*A* with $\overline{AB} \perp \overline{AD}$ and tangent $\overleftrightarrow{BC} \perp$ tangent $\overleftrightarrow{CD}$
Prove: Quadrilateral *ABCD* is a square.

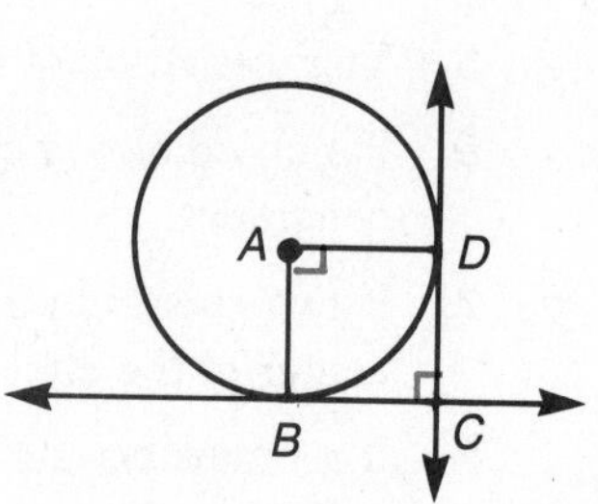

12.3 Planes and Spheres

Most of the vocabulary, theorems, and corollaries in this chapter so far have been limited to circles in the two-dimensional plane. Now you will extend these concepts to three dimensions and spheres.

You know already that a sphere is the set of all points in space equidistant from a given point. This distance is called the *radius of the sphere.* The next definitions follow directly from the vocabulary describing circles.

DEFINITIONS: interior and exterior of a sphere
The **interior** of a sphere is the union of its center and the set of all points whose distances from the center are less than the radius. The **exterior** of a sphere is the set of all points whose distances from the center are greater than the radius.

Extending the idea of tangency to spheres produces the following definitions.

DEFINITIONS: tangent plane, point of tangency
A plane that intersects a sphere in exactly one point is called a **tangent plane** to the sphere. The point where the plane and sphere intersect is called the **point of tangency** (or **point of contact**).

Theorem 12.2, the basis of six corollaries introduced in the last section, has its counterpart in three dimensions as well.

THEOREM 12.5
Given a plane E and a sphere with center P, let F be the foot of the perpendicular segment from P to E. Then exactly one of the following must be true:
1. Every point on E is outside the sphere.
2. F is on the sphere, and plane E is tangent to the sphere at F.
3. F is inside the sphere, and plane E intersects the sphere in a circle with center F.

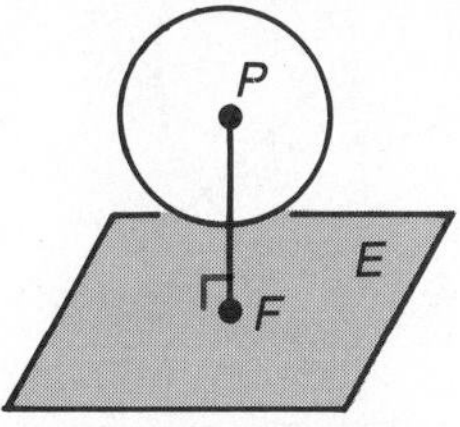

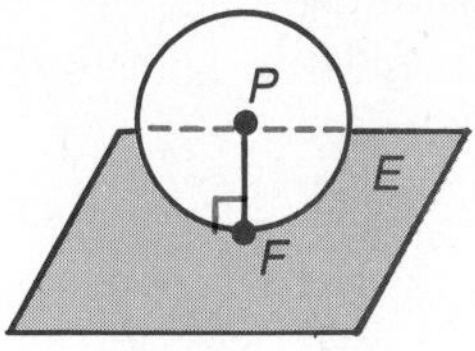

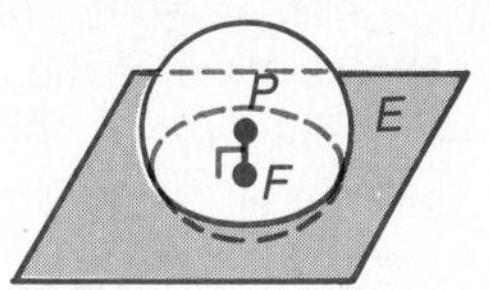

OBJECTIVE

Use Theorem 12.5 and its corollaries to answer questions regarding tangents and chords and to find the lengths of segments in spheres.

TEACHER'S NOTES

See p. T38

MIXED REVIEW

1. Find the area of a square with diagonal of 10. 50
2. Find the legs of a right triangle with a hypotenuse of 12 and a 30° angle. 6 and $6\sqrt{3}$
3. Find the area of an isosceles triangle with base angles of 30 and a base of 20. $\frac{100\sqrt{3}}{3}$
4. Add $\frac{6}{x-3} + \frac{9}{x+2}$. $\frac{15x-15}{(x-3)(x+2)}$
5. Subtract $\frac{4}{x-1} - \frac{2}{x+4}$. $\frac{2x+18}{(x-1)(x+4)}$

TEACHER'S RESOURCE MASTERS

Practice Master 37, Part 1
Quiz 23

If F is *outside* the sphere, then the first condition of Theorem 12.5 holds; if F is *on* the sphere, the second condition holds. The proofs for both are almost identical to the proofs of the first two conditions of Theorem 12.2. If F is *inside* the sphere, apply the third condition of Theorem 12.5. The proof of this third condition relies on the coordinate geometry of circles, which will be covered later in this chapter.

Corollaries 12.5.1–12.5.4 correspond to Corollaries 12.2.1–12.2.4, again extending the concepts from circles to spheres.

COROLLARY 12.5.1
A plane tangent to a sphere is perpendicular to the radius drawn to the point of tangency.

COROLLARY 12.5.2
A plane perpendicular to a radius at its outer end is tangent to the sphere.

COROLLARY 12.5.3
A perpendicular from the center of a sphere to a chord bisects the chord.

COROLLARY 12.5.4
The segment joining the center of a sphere to the midpoint of a chord is perpendicular to the chord.

As with the corollaries to Theorem 12.2, the proofs of these corollaries follow from the three conditions of Theorem 12.5.

Example: Plane E is tangent to sphere P at F. The diameter of the sphere is 18, and $FG = 6$. Find PG. Corollary 12.5.1, states that radius $\overline{PF} \perp \overline{FG}$, allowing application of the Pythagorean Theorem. If the diameter is 18, then $PF = 9$. Since $PF^2 + FG^2 = PG^2$, substitution yields $81 + 36 = PG^2$, $117 = PG^2$ or $PG = \sqrt{117} = 3\sqrt{13}$.

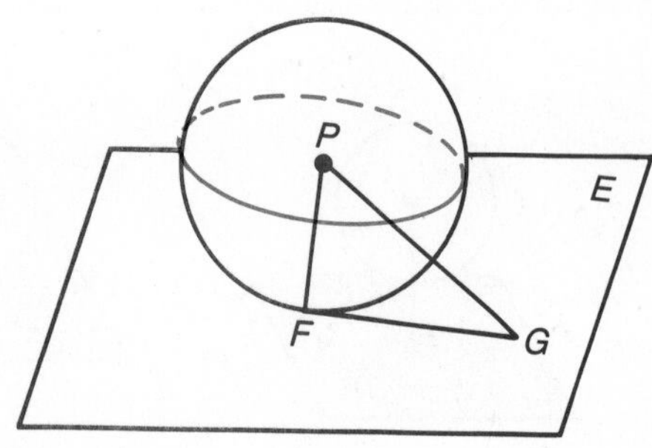

ORAL EXERCISES

Supply the correct vocabulary term to complete each sentence.

1. The center of a sphere lies in the sphere's ______________________.
2. A point lies in the exterior of a sphere if its distance from the center is ____________ the radius.
3. A plane that intersects a sphere at one point is called a ______________________ plane.
4. A tangent plane is ______________________ to the radius it intersects.
5. A radius of a sphere will ______________________ a chord to which it is perpendicular.
6. The intersection of a plane and sphere may be the empty set, one point, or a ______.
7. If a plane contains the center of a sphere, the intersection of the plane and the sphere is called a ______________________.
8. Match each of the corollaries 12.5.1–12.5.4 with the corresponding condition of Theorem 12.5.

Plane *E* is tangent to sphere *A* at *B*. *C* is another point on sphere *A*.

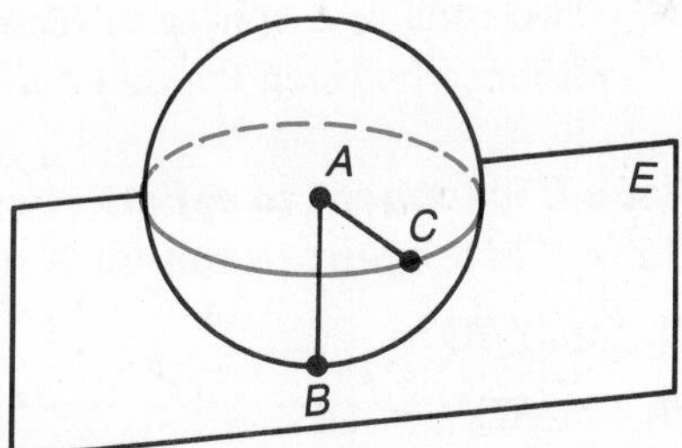

9. The intersection of plane *E* and sphere *A* is ______.
10. $\overline{AC}$ and $\overline{AB}$ are congruent because ______________________.
11. Imagine raising plane *E* until it contains $\overline{AC}$. The intersection of plane *E* and sphere *A* is now ______.

WRITTEN EXERCISES

A. Indicate whether each of the following statements is true or false.

1. Two planes tangent to a sphere at opposite ends of a diameter will be parallel to each other.
2. Two perpendicular planes may be tangent to the same sphere.
3. The only plane perpendicular to a radius of a sphere is a tangent plane.
4. Two different planes may be tangent to the same sphere at the same point.
5. If the radius of a sphere bisects a chord, it is perpendicular to any plane containing the chord.

ASSIGNMENT GUIDE

Minimum 1–18
Regular 1–22
Maximum 1–24

Oral Exercises

1. interior
2. greater than
3. tangent
4. perpendicular
5. bisect
6. circle
7. great circle
8. 12.5.1 → second condition
   12.5.2 → second condition
   12.5.3 → third condition
   12.5.4 → third condition
9. *B*
10. Radii of the same sphere are ≅.
11. ⊙*A*

Written Exercises

1. T
2. T
3. F
4. F
5. F

6. T

7. T

8. F

9. T

10. 10

11. 3.5

12. 5

13. 5

14. 5

15. $3\sqrt{5}$

16. $4\sqrt{5}$

17. It could.

18. $5\sqrt{2}$

19. 90

20. 90

21. They might not be coplanar.

22. SAS or LL

23. No; it is neither reflexive nor transitive.

24. *1.* $\overline{DB} \cong \overline{EC}$ (Radii of $\cong$ $\odot$'s are $\cong$.); *2.* $\overline{AB} \cong \overline{AC}$ (Radii of the same sphere are $\cong$.); *3.* $\triangle DAB \cong \triangle EAC$ (HL).

6. The diameter of a great circle is equal in length to twice the radius of its sphere.

7. If two planes are the same distance from the center of a sphere they intersect, their intersections with the sphere will be two congruent circles.

8. If a radius of a sphere bisects a chord, then the chord bisects the radius.

9. If a diameter of a sphere is bisected by a plane, the plane contains a great circle of the sphere.

B. Points *B, C,* and *D* are on sphere *A* such that $\overline{AC} \perp \overline{BD}$.

10. If $BE = 5$, then $BD =$ _____.

11. If $BD = 7$, then $ED =$ _____.

12. If $AB = 5$, then $AD =$ _____.

13. If $AD = 8$ and $EC = 3$, then $AE =$ _____.

14. If $BE = 4$ and $AE = 3$, then $AB =$ _____.

15. If $BD = 12$ and $AB = 9$, then $AE =$ _____.

16. If $CE = 2$ and $AC = 6$, then $BD =$ _____.

17. State whether Theorem 12.3 could or could not have a counterpart in a theorem relating to spheres.

18. Two radii in a sphere of diameter 10 are perpendicular to each other. Find the distance between the outer endpoints of the radii.

Plane *E* is tangent to sphere *X* at *Q*.
Plane *F* is tangent to sphere *X* at *R*.

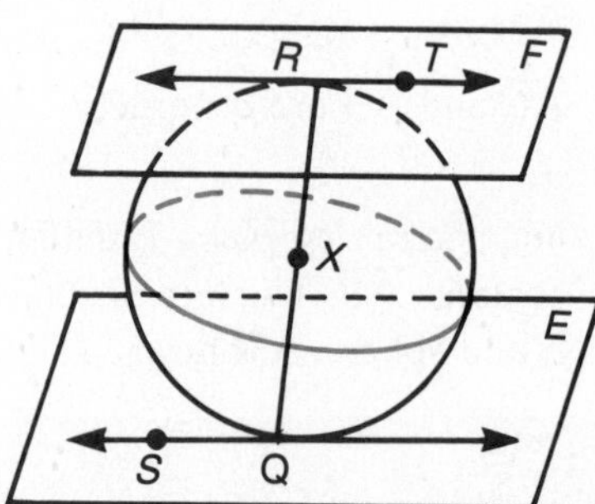

19. $m\angle TRQ =$ _____

20. $m\angle RQS =$ _____

21. Although plane $E \parallel$ plane F, $\overleftrightarrow{RT}$ might not be parallel to $\overleftrightarrow{SQ}$ because _____.

22. If $\overline{RT} \cong \overline{SQ}$, then $\triangle XRT \cong \triangle XQS$ by _____.

23. Is tangency of spheres an equivalence relation? Support your answer.

C. 24. Given: Sphere A with $\odot D \cong \odot E$, $\overline{DE} \perp \overline{DB}$, $\overline{DE} \perp \overline{EC}$

Prove: $\triangle DAB \cong \triangle EAC$

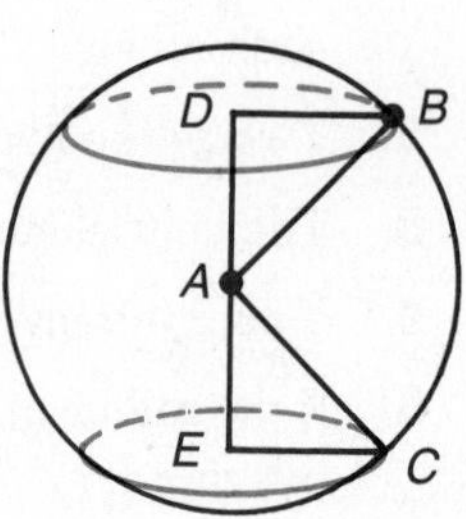

SELF-QUIZ

Complete each sentence with the correct term.

1. A chord that contains the center of a circle is called a _____.
2. Two coplanar circles with the same center are called _____.
3. The set of all points in space equidistant from the same point is a _____.
4. A segment whose endpoints are on a circle is called a _____.
5. Two great circles of a sphere are _____.
6. A tangent and a radius that intersect are _____.
7. In a circle, two congruent chords are _____ from the center.

In $\odot A$, $\overline{AH} \perp \overline{BD}$, $\overline{AI} \perp \overline{GE}$, and $\overline{AH} \cong \overline{AI}$.

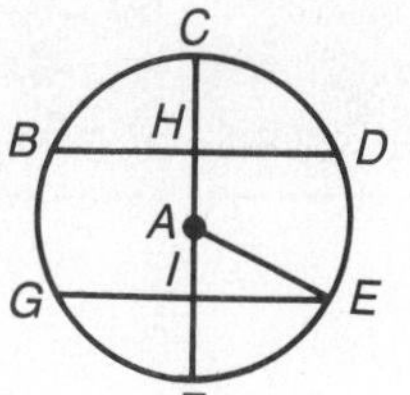

8. If $CH = 5$ and $AI = 3$, find CF.
9. If $AI = 4$ and $AE = 10$, find GE.
10. If $AH = 7$ and $AC = 12$, find BD.

Self-Quiz

1. diameter
2. concentric
3. sphere
4. chord
5. congruent
6. perpendicular
7. equidistant
8. 16
9. $4\sqrt{21}$
10. $2\sqrt{95}$

EXPLORATION
Series that Converge on π

Because it belongs to the set of irrational numbers, π has no repeating or terminating decimal form. How, then, can you obtain an approximation of π to use in applied situations?

Many different series converge on π. The best known are the following:

1. $4 \cdot (1 - \frac{1}{3} + \frac{1}{5} - \frac{1}{7} + \frac{1}{9} \ldots)$
2. $2(\frac{2}{1} \cdot \frac{2}{3} \cdot \frac{4}{3} \cdot \frac{4}{5} \cdot \frac{6}{5} \cdot \frac{6}{7} \cdot \frac{8}{7} \cdot \frac{8}{9} \ldots)$
3. $4 \cdot \cfrac{1}{1 + \cfrac{1^2}{2 + \cfrac{3^2}{2 + \cfrac{5^2}{2 + \cfrac{7^2}{2 + \ldots}}}}}$

Perform the first three calculations in each series. What is your result? If the value of π is actually 3.14159+, which is the better approximation, 3.14 or $3\frac{1}{7}$?

Exploration

1. $3.4\overline{6}$
2. $3.\overline{5}$
3. $3.\overline{6}$

$3\frac{1}{7}$

OBJECTIVE

Identify major and minor arcs, semicircles, and central angles and find their measures.

TEACHER'S NOTES

See p. T38

MIXED REVIEW

1. Can a triangle have sides of 17, 18 and 37? no
2. The supplement of $27\frac{1}{2}$ is ______. $152\frac{1}{2}$
3. Complements of congruent angles are ______. $\cong$
4. Multiply $\frac{x^2+2x+1}{x-2} \cdot \frac{x^2-5x+6}{x^2-2x-3}$. $x+1$
5. Divide $\frac{x+6}{x^2+x-6} \div \frac{x+1}{x-3}$. $\frac{x+6}{(x+1)(x+2)}$

TEACHER'S RESOURCE MASTERS

Practice Master 37, part 2

12.4 Angles and Arcs of Circles

Just as angles can be classified as acute, right, or obtuse, so can portions of a circle, called **arcs,** be measured and classified.

> **DEFINITIONS: minor and major arcs, semicircle**
> Given $\odot P$ with points A and B on the circle, the union of A and B and all the points of the circle in the interior of $\angle APB$ is called a **minor arc.** The union of A and B and points of the circle in the exterior of $\angle APB$ is called a **major arc.** If A, P, and B are collinear (so that $\overline{AB}$ is a diameter), the union of A and B and all the points of the circle in either half-plane determined by edge $\overleftrightarrow{AB}$ is called a **semicircle.**

The names of the three types of arcs suggest their relative sizes. While a semicircle is exactly half a circle, a minor arc is less than a half and a major arc more. A minor arc is named by its endpoints: $\overparen{AB}$, for example.

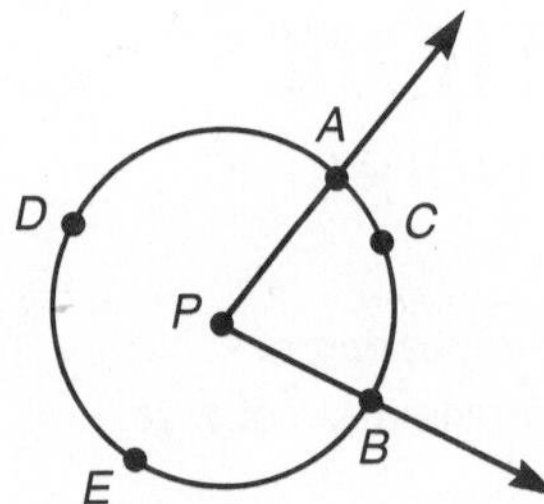

In the figure, $\overparen{AB}$ and $\overparen{BA}$ are the same minor arc, as are $\overparen{ACB}$ and $\overparen{BCA}$. Naming the major arc requires the use of three points. $\overparen{ADB}$, $\overparen{AEB}$, $\overparen{BEA}$, and $\overparen{BDA}$ are all names of the same major arc. $\overparen{DA}$ is yet another arc, as is $\overparen{CBD}$.

In the same figure, $\angle APB$ is called a **central angle,** and $\overparen{AB}$ is an **intercepted arc.** Central angles are used to determine the degree measures of intercepted arcs.

> **DEFINITIONS: central angle, intercept**
> A **central angle** of a given circle is an angle whose vertex is at the center of the circle. An angle **intercepts** an arc if and only if (1) the endpoints of the arc lie on the angle, (2) each side of the angle contains an endpoint of the arc, and (3) except for its endpoints, the arc lies in the interior of the angle.

DEFINITION: measure of an arc

The degree **measure of an arc** ($m\widehat{AXB}$) is as follows:

1. If $\widehat{AXB}$ is a minor arc, then $m\widehat{AXB}$ is the measure of the corresponding central angle.
2. If $\widehat{AXB}$ is a semicircle, then $m\widehat{AXB} = 180$.
3. If $\widehat{AXB}$ is a major arc, and $\widehat{AYB}$ is the corresponding minor arc, then $m\widehat{AXB} = 360 - m\widehat{AYB}$.

By the definition, an arc is major or minor depending on whether its measure is less than or greater than 180. In the figure, therefore, $\widehat{CB}$ is a minor arc, so $m\widehat{CB} = m\angle CAB$. $\widehat{DCB}$ is a semicircle, so $m\widehat{DCB} = m\widehat{DFB} = 180$. $\widehat{DFC}$ is a major arc whose measure is the difference between 360 and $m\widehat{DC}$, or $m\widehat{DFC} = 360 - m\angle DAC$.

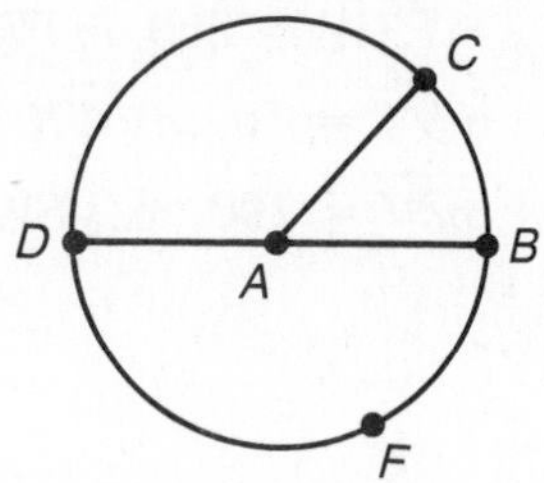

THEOREM 12.6

If $\widehat{AB}$ and $\widehat{BC}$ are arcs of the same circle having only the point B in common, and if their union is $\widehat{AC}$, then $m\widehat{AB} + m\widehat{BC} = m\widehat{AC}$.

Example: In the figure, $m\widehat{AB} = 35$ and $m\widehat{BC} = 85$. Find $m\widehat{AC}$.

Solution: By Theorem 12.6, $m\widehat{AB} + m\widehat{BC} = m\widehat{AC}$. By substituting the given values, $35 + 85 = m\widehat{AC}$. So, $m\widehat{AC} = 130$.

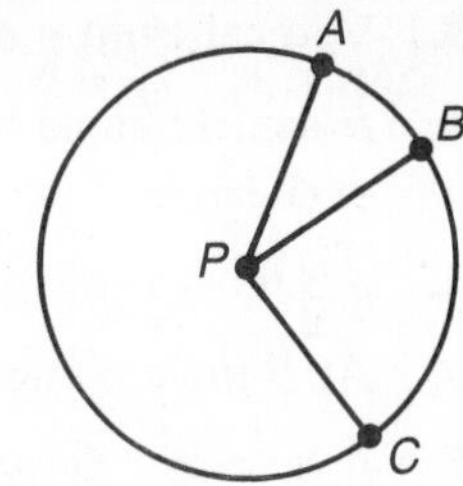

ASSIGNMENT GUIDE

Minimum 1-19 odd
Regular 1-25 odd
Maximum 1-19 odd, 21-26

ORAL EXERCISES

Refer to the figure of $\odot P$ and state whether each arc named is a minor arc, a semicircle, or a major arc.

1. $\widehat{AB}$	**2.** $\widehat{FD}$	**3.** $\widehat{DCB}$	**4.** $\widehat{ECB}$
5. $\widehat{FAD}$	**6.** $\widehat{EFA}$	**7.** $\widehat{DC}$	**8.** $\widehat{FCA}$
9. $\widehat{ADB}$	**10.** $\widehat{EF}$		

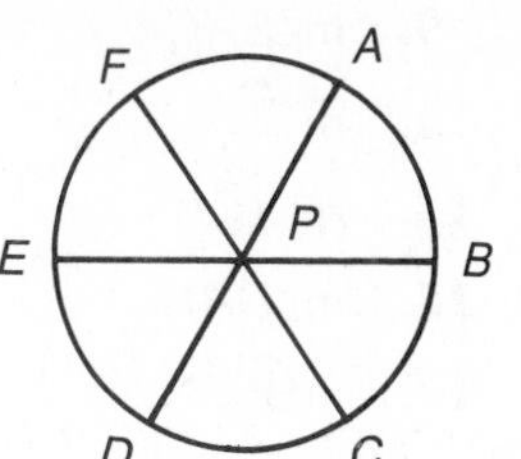

Oral Exercises

1. minor
2. minor
3. minor
4. semicircle
5. major
6. minor
7. minor
8. major
9. major
10. minor

11. 50 12. 320
13. 100 14. 300
15. 100 16. 330
17. 110 18. 120
19. 80 20. 120

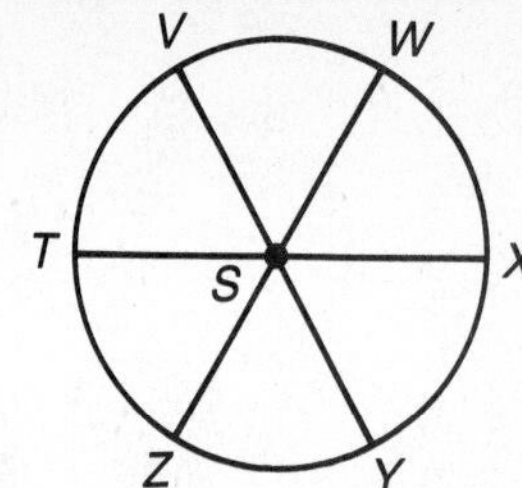

Refer to the figure of $\odot Q$ to supply the missing measure.

11. $m\angle WSX = 50$; $m\overset{\frown}{WX} =$ _____

12. $m\angle TSV = 40$, $m\overset{\frown}{TXV} =$ _____

13. $m\overset{\frown}{VX} = 100$, $m\angle VSX =$ _____

14. $m\overset{\frown}{WX} = 60$, $m\overset{\frown}{WTX} =$ _____

15. $m\overset{\frown}{TXW} = 260$, $m\overset{\frown}{TW} =$ _____

16. $m\angle ZSY = 30$, $m\overset{\frown}{ZVY} =$ _____

17. $m\overset{\frown}{VT} = 70$, $m\overset{\frown}{VWX} =$ _____

18. $m\angle WSX = 60$, $m\overset{\frown}{TW} =$ _____

19. $m\overset{\frown}{ZV} = 100$, $m\angle VSW =$ _____

20. $m\overset{\frown}{ZVX} = 240$, $m\angle ZSX =$ _____

WRITTEN EXERCISES

Written Exercises

1. F 2. T
3. T 4. T
5. T 6. F
7. T 8. T

A. Indicate whether each of the following statements is true or false.

1. A central angle and its intercepted arc are congruent.

2. An acute central angle will always intercept a minor arc.

3. Vertical central angles will intercept arcs of the same measure.

4. A central angle in two concentric circles will intercept arcs of the same measure in each circle.

5. $\overset{\frown}{AB}$ must name a minor arc.

6. $\overset{\frown}{ACB}$ must name a major arc.

7. A diameter determines two semicircles.

8. If two secants to the same circle intersect inside the circle, then four arcs are intercepted.

9. 30 10. 30
11. 150 12. 180
13. 210 14. 30
15. 150 16. 150
17. 330 18. 150

B. In the figure, both circles have centers at A, and $m\overset{\frown}{BC} = 30$. Determine each measure.

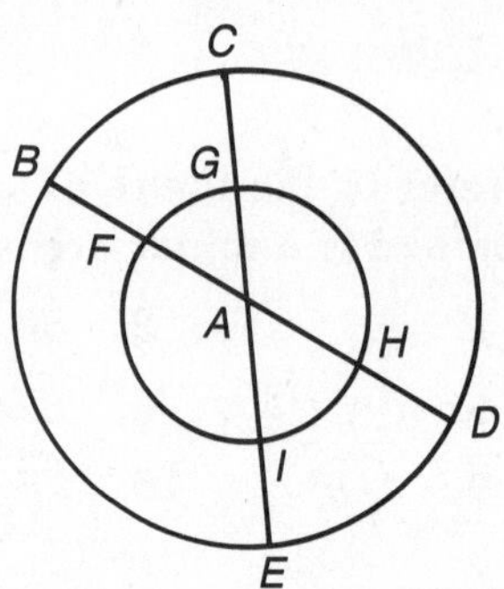

9. $m\angle BAC$

10. $m\overset{\frown}{FG}$

11. $m\overset{\frown}{GH}$

12. $m\overset{\frown}{CBE}$

13. $m\overset{\frown}{CBD}$

14. $m\overset{\frown}{HI}$

15. $m\angle GAH$

16. $m\angle FAI$

17. $m\overset{\frown}{HGI}$

18. $m\overset{\frown}{BE}$

Refer to the figure of $\odot Q$ to determine each measure.

19. $m\angle XQW = 2x - 7$ $\quad$ $m\angle YQZ = 4x - 41$
Find $m\overset{\frown}{WX}$.

20. $m\overset{\frown}{WX} = 12x + 2$ $\quad$ $m\overset{\frown}{YZ} = 9x + 20$
Find $m\angle XQW$.

21. $m\angle XQY = x + 80$ $\quad$ $m\angle WQZ = 4x + 8$
Find $m\overset{\frown}{YZ}$.

22.	$m\overset{\frown}{WX} = 6x + 3$	$m\overset{\frown}{XY} = 2x - 7$	Find $m\angle XQW$.
C. **23.**	$m\overset{\frown}{XW} = \frac{2}{3}x - 6$	$m\overset{\frown}{WZ} = x + 6$	Find $m\angle XQY$.
24.	$m\angle YQZ = 5 + 3x$	$m\angle ZQW = 7x + 15$	Find $m\overset{\frown}{WX}$.
25.	$m\overset{\frown}{XY} = 40 - 2x$	$m\overset{\frown}{WZ} = 12 + 5x$	Find $m\overset{\frown}{XWY}$.
26.	$m\angle XQW = \frac{3}{4}x - 5$	$m\overset{\frown}{XY} = \frac{1}{2}x$	Find $m\overset{\frown}{YXZ}$.

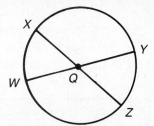

CHALLENGE

Given: $\odot G$ with diameters $\overline{LH}$, $\overline{MI}$, $\overline{NJ}$, and $\overline{PK}$
$m\overset{\frown}{JI} = m\overset{\frown}{HN}$

Prove: $\triangle LGN \cong \triangle IGN$

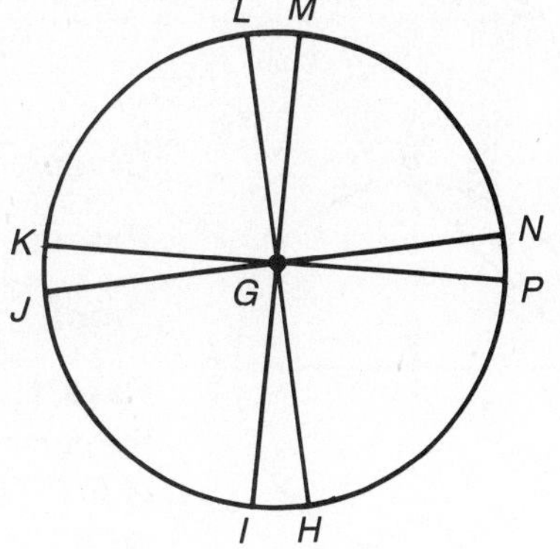

19. 27 $\quad$ 20. 74
21. 76 $\quad$ 22. 141
23. 114 $\quad$ 24. 53
25. 328 $\quad$ 26. 254

Challenge

1. $m\overset{\frown}{JI} = m\overset{\frown}{HN}$ (Given);
2. $m\overset{\frown}{JI} = m\angle JGI$ (Def. of measure of an arc);
3. $m\angle JGI = m\angle MGN$ (Thm. 3.7 and Def. of congruence);
4. $m\overset{\frown}{MN} = m\angle MGN$ (Def. of measure of an arc);
5. $m\overset{\frown}{MN} = m\overset{\frown}{JI}$ (Substitution);
6. $m\overset{\frown}{MN} = m\overset{\frown}{HN}$ (Transitive prop. of equality);
7. $m\overset{\frown}{HN} = m\angle HGN$ (Def. of measure of an arc);
8. $m\angle HGN = m\angle MGN$ (Substitution);
9. $m\angle IGH = m\angle MGL$ (Thm. 3.7 and Def. of congruence);
10. $m\angle HGN + m\angle IGH = m\angle MGN + m\angle MGL$ (Addition property of equality);
11. $m\angle HGN + m\angle IGH = m\angle IGN$
$m\angle MGN + m\angle MGL = m\angle NGL$
(Angle Addition Postulate);
12. $m\angle IGN = m\angle NGL$ (Substitution);
13. $\overline{GI} \cong \overline{GL}$ (Radii of the same circle are $\cong$.);
14. $\overline{GN} \cong \overline{GN}$ (Congruence of segments is reflexive);
15. $\triangle LGN \cong \triangle IGN$ (SAS).

OBJECTIVES

Identify inscribed angles and inscribed polygons.

Use Theorem 12.7 and its corollaries and Theorems 12.8 and 12.9 to find the measure of an arc or an angle.

TEACHER'S NOTES

See p. T38

MIXED REVIEW

1. If $A = (4, 5)$ and $B = (13, 17)$ find AB. 15
2. Find the area of a 45 − 45 right triangle if the hypotenuse is $8\sqrt{2}$. 32
3. Find the area of a rectangle with base of $10\sqrt{2}$ and height of $\sqrt{8}$. 40
4. What is the area of a rhombus with a side of 12 and a 60° angle? $72\sqrt{3}$
5. If $\sqrt{2} \approx 1.414$ and $\sqrt{3} \approx 1.732$, then $\frac{1}{\sqrt{3} - \sqrt{2}} \approx$ ______. 3.145

TEACHER'S RESOURCE MASTERS

Practice Master 38, Part 1

12.5 Inscribed Angles of a Circle

A central angle is equal in measure to its intercepted arc. But a central angle is not the only kind of angle that can intercept arcs.

> **DEFINITION: inscribed angle**
> An angle is **inscribed** in an arc if and only if (1) the two endpoints of the arc lie on the two sides of the angle, and (2) the vertex of the angle is a point, but not an endpoint, of the arc.

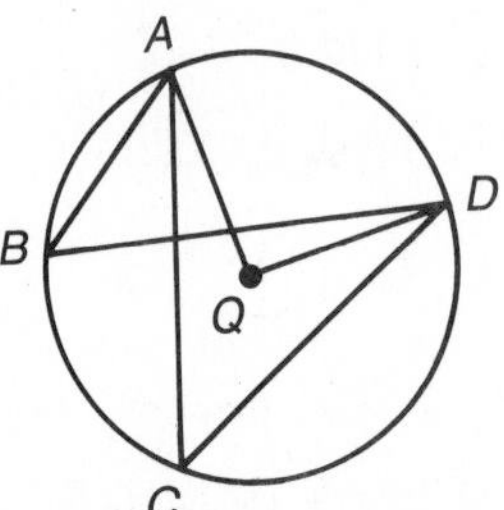

In the figure at the left, $\angle ACD$ and $\angle ABD$ are inscribed in arc $\widehat{ABCD}$.

While a given arc may be intercepted by only one central angle, any number of inscribed angles may intercept the same arc. In the figure, central $\angle Q$ and inscribed $\angle B$ and $\angle C$ all intercept $\widehat{AD}$.

> **THEOREM 12.7**
> The measure of an inscribed angle is half the measure of its intercepted arc.

This important theorem, whose corollaries will be considered later, is most easily proved in three cases.

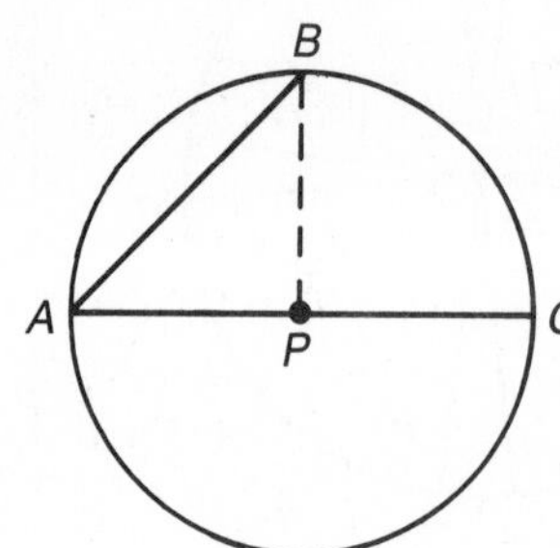

Given: $\odot P$ with inscribed $\angle BAC$

Prove: $m\angle BAC = \frac{1}{2}m\widehat{BC}$

Proof:

Case 1: Assume the inscribed angle contains a diameter of the circle. In the figure, inscribed $\angle A$ contains $\overline{AC}$, a diameter of $\odot P$. Draw radius $\overline{PB}$. Applying Corollary 8.13.3 to $\triangle ABP$, $m\angle A + m\angle B = m\angle BPC$. Since radii of the same circle are congruent, $\triangle ABP$ is isosceles with $m\angle A = m\angle B$. Substitution yields $m\angle A + m\angle A = m\angle BPC$, or $2m\angle A = m\angle BPC$. Finally, because $\angle BPC$ is a central angle, $m\angle BPC = m\overline{BC}$. Hence, $2m\angle A = m\widehat{BC}$, or $m\angle A = \frac{1}{2}m\widehat{BC}$.

Case 2: Suppose that B and C are on opposite sides of the diameter through A. Draw diameter $\overline{AD}$, and $m\angle BAC = m\angle BAD + m\angle DAC$.

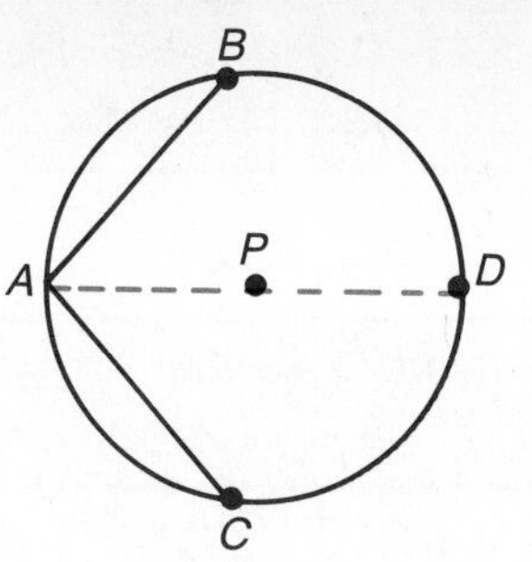

Case 1 proved that $m\angle BAD = \frac{1}{2}m\widehat{BD}$ and that $m\angle DAC = \frac{1}{2}m\widehat{DC}$. Substitution results in $m\angle BAC = \frac{1}{2}m\widehat{BD} + \frac{1}{2}m\widehat{DC}$, or $m\angle BAC = \frac{1}{2}(m\widehat{BD} + m\widehat{DC})$. Theorem 12.6, which states that $m\widehat{BD} + m\widehat{DC} = m\widehat{BDC}$, and the final substitution yields $m\angle BAC = \frac{1}{2}m\widehat{BDC}$.

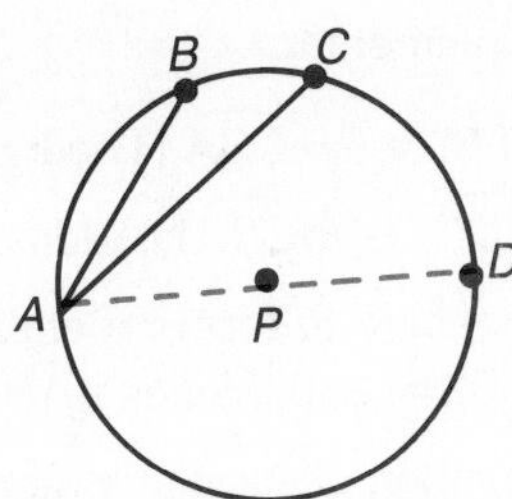

Case 3: Neither the inscribed angle nor its interior contains a diameter of the circle, as shown. Again, you must show that $m\angle BAC = \frac{1}{2}m\widehat{BC}$. First draw diameter $\overline{AD}$. Case 1 proved that $m\angle BAD = \frac{1}{2}m\widehat{BD}$ and $m\angle CAD = \frac{1}{2}m\widehat{CD}$. Then by applying the Angle Addition Postulate, $m\angle BAC = \frac{1}{2}m\widehat{BC}$. Three corollaries are suggested by Theorem 12.7.

$m\angle BAC + m\angle CAD = m\angle BAD$ (Angle Addition Post.); $m\angle BAC + \frac{1}{2}m\widehat{CD} = \frac{1}{2}m\widehat{BD}$ (Substitution); $2m\angle BAC + m\widehat{CD} = m\widehat{BD}$ (Multiplication prop. of equality); $2m\angle BAC = m\widehat{BD} - m\widehat{CD}$ (Subtraction); $2m\angle BAC = m\widehat{BC}$ (Theorem 12.6); $m\angle BAC = \frac{1}{2}m\widehat{BC}$ (Multiplication prop. of equality)

COROLLARY 12.7.1
An angle inscribed in a semicircle is a right angle.

Given: $\odot P$
$\angle BAC$ inscribed in a semicircle

Prove: $\angle BAC$ is a rt. $\angle$.

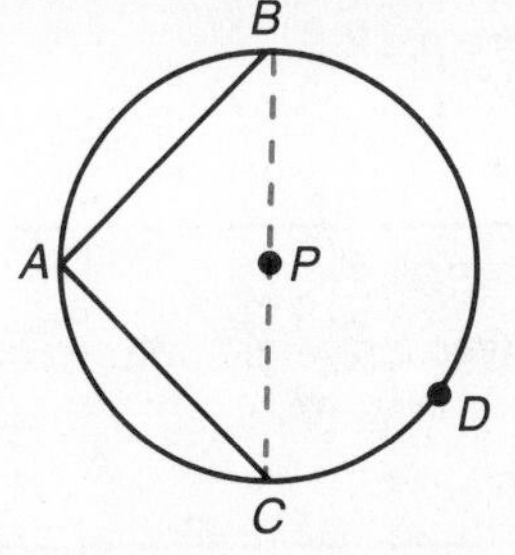

Proof: $m\angle BAC = \frac{1}{2}m\widehat{BDC}$ (Theorem 12.7); $m\widehat{BDC} = 180$ (Def. of semicircle); $m\angle BAC = 90$ (Substitution); $\angle BAC$ is a right angle (Def. of rt. $\angle$).

COROLLARY 12.7.2
Angles inscribed in the same arc are congruent.

Given: $\odot R$
$\angle AXB$ inscribed in $\widehat{AB}$
$\angle AYB$ inscribed in $\widehat{AB}$

Prove: $\angle AXB \cong \angle AYB$

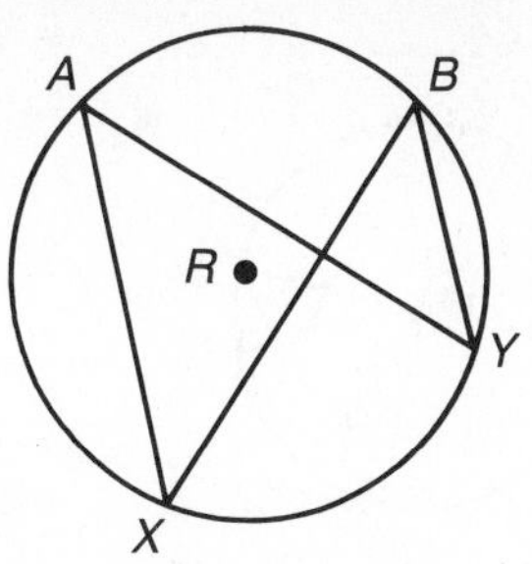

Proof: $m\angle AXB = \frac{1}{2}m\widehat{AB}$ (Theorem 12.7); $m\angle AYB = \frac{1}{2}m\widehat{AB}$ (Theorem 12.7); $m\angle AXB = m\angle AYB$ (Transitive prop. of equality); $\angle AXB \cong \angle AYB$ (Def. of $\cong$ $\angle$s).

DEFINITION: inscribed polygon
A polygon is **inscribed** in a circle if and only if all of its vertices lie on the circle.

COROLLARY 12.7.3
The opposite angles of an inscribed quadrilateral are supplementary.

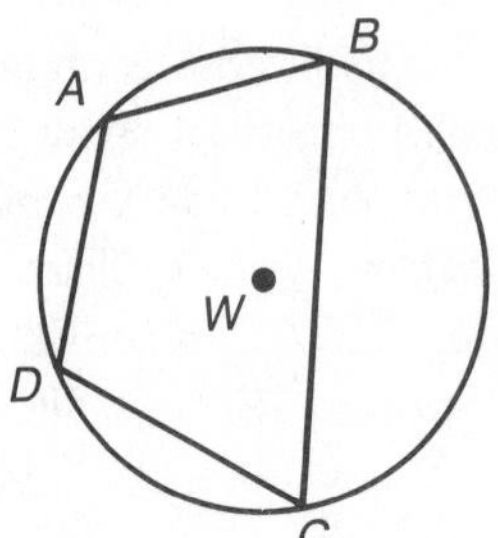

Given: $\odot W$ with inscribed quad. $ABCD$

Prove: $\angle ABC$ and $\angle CDA$ are supplementary.

Proof: $m\angle ABC = \frac{1}{2}m\widehat{ADC}$, $m\angle CDA = \frac{1}{2}m\widehat{CBA}$ (Theorem 12.7); $m\angle ABC + m\angle CDA = \frac{1}{2}(m\widehat{ADC} + m\widehat{CBA})$ (Addition prop. of equality); $\widehat{ADC}$ and $\widehat{CBA}$ combine to form an entire circle, so $m\angle ABC + m\angle CDA = \frac{1}{2}(360) = 180$. Hence $\angle ABC$ and $\angle CDA$ are supplementary by definition of supplementary angles.

A situation similar to that of an inscribed angle exists when one side of an angle contains a chord of the circle while the other side is tangent to the circle. Such an angle is discussed in Theorem 12.8

THEOREM 12.8
Given an angle with vertex on the circle such that the angle is formed by a secant ray and a tangent ray, the measure of the angle is one-half the measure of the intercepted arc.

Theorem 12.8 is proved only for the case where the measure of the angle formed by the secant and tangent is less than 90, like $\angle CAB$ in the next figure.

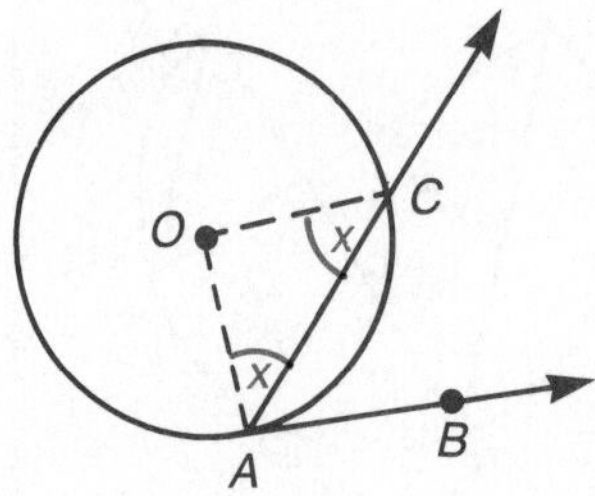

First, draw radii $\overline{OA}$ and $\overline{OC}$. $m\angle O = m\widehat{AC}$. By Corollary 12.2.1, $\overline{OA} \perp \overrightarrow{AB}$, so $m\angle CAB = 90 - x$. Because $\triangle OAC$ is isosceles, $m\angle O = 180 - 2x$. But half of $180 - 2x$ is $90 - x$, so $m\angle CAB = \frac{1}{2}m\angle O$, or $m\angle CAB = \frac{1}{2}m\widehat{AC}$.

Example: In $\odot O$ with tangent $\overrightarrow{BD}$, $m\widehat{ACB} = 7x + 20$ and $m\widehat{AB} = 3x + 80$. Find $m\angle ABD$. Since $\widehat{ACB}$ and AB combine to form $\odot O$, you know that $7x + 20 + 3x + 80 = 360$. Solving for x yields $x = 26$. Therefore, $m\widehat{AB} = 158$, and $m\angle ABD = \frac{1}{2}(158)$ or 79.

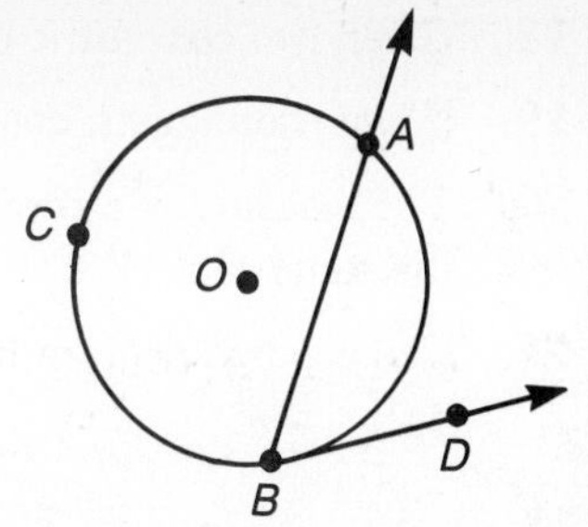

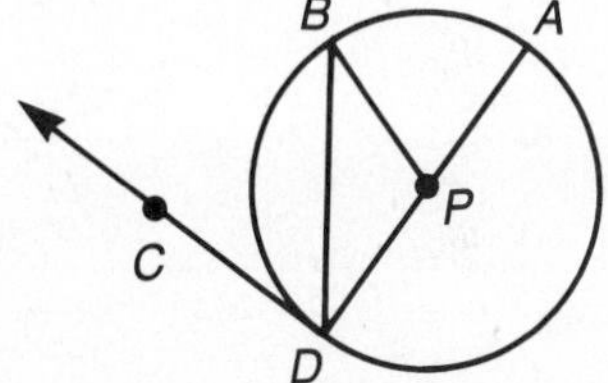

Example: Given $\odot P$ with diameter $\overline{DA}$, tangent $\overrightarrow{DC}$, and $m\angle CDB = 80$, find $m\angle BPA$. Because $m\angle CDB = 80$, $m\widehat{DB} = 160$, and because $\angle CDA$ intercepts a semicircle, $m\widehat{BA} = 20$. Thus, since $\angle BPA$ is a central angle, $m\angle BPA = 20$.

ASSIGNMENT GUIDE

Day 1
Minimum 1-15
Regular 1-23 odd
Maximum 1-27 odd
Day 2
Minimum 21-26
Regular 2-26 even
Maximum 2-32 even

ORAL EXERCISES

Refer to the figure of $\odot P$ for Exercises 1–10.

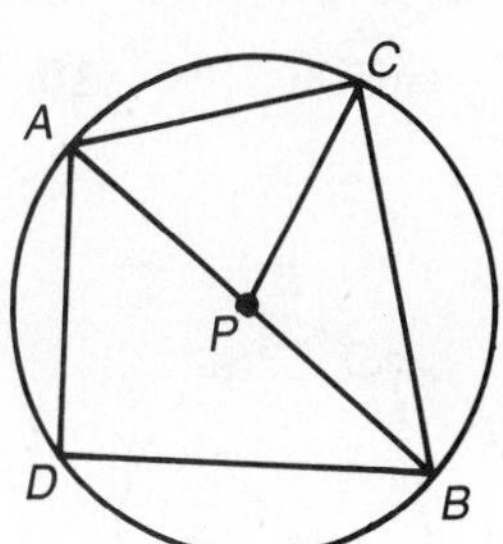

1. Name two inscribed angles.
2. Name two central angles.
3. Name an angle that intercepts $\widehat{BC}$.
4. Name an angle that intercepts $\widehat{AC}$.
5. Name an angle that intercepts $\widehat{ACB}$.
6. Name an angle that intercepts $\widehat{AD}$.
7. If $m\widehat{AC} = 60$, $m\angle ABC =$ _____.
8. If $m\widehat{CB} = 100$, $m\angle CPB =$ _____.
9. If $m\angle CAB = 40$, $m\widehat{BC} =$ _____.
10. If $m\angle CPA = 80$, $m\angle CBA =$ _____.

Indicate whether each of the following statements is true or false.

11. Two angles that intercept the same arc must be congruent.
12. If two congruent angles are inscribed in the same circle, they must intercept congruent arcs.
13. An inscribed right angle must intercept a semicircle.
14. Opposite angles of an inscribed quadrilateral must be supplementary.
15. An inscribed equilateral triangle must separate a circle into three congruent arcs.
16. Each angle of an inscribed square must intercept a semicircle.
17. Given two concentric circles, an inscribed angle of one must be an inscribed angle of the other.

Oral Exercises

1. $\angle ADB$, $\angle DAB$, $\angle BAC$, $\angle DAC$, $\angle ACB$, $\angle CBA$, $\angle ABD$, $\angle CBD$
2. $\angle APC$, $\angle CPB$
3. $\angle CPB$, $\angle CAB$
4. $\angle APC$, $\angle ABC$
5. $\angle ADB$
6. $\angle DBA$
7. 30
8. 100
9. 80
10. 40
11. F
12. T
13. T
14. T
15. T
16. T
17. F

18. T

19. T

20. T

21. only if it is a rectangle or square

Written Exercises

1.	30	2.	75
3.	90	4.	80
5.	35	6.	30
7.	100	8.	250
9.	180	10.	150
11.	100	12.	110
13.	260	14.	25
15.	100	16.	140
17.	25	18.	30
19.	70	20.	230

21. Since $m\angle A = 30$, $m\widehat{BC} = 60$; $\widehat{ABC}$ is a semicircle, so $m\widehat{AB} = 120$.

22. $\widehat{ABC}$ is a semicircle; since $m\widehat{AB} = 90$, $m\widehat{BC} = 90$ also. So $m\angle A = m\angle C = 45$, and $\triangle ACB$ is isosceles.

18. Given two concentric circles, a central angle of one must be a central angle of the other.

19. If two chords each contain the same point of a circle, they must form an inscribed angle.

20. The measure of a central angle is twice the measure of an inscribed angle that intercepts the same arc.

21. Can a parallelogram be inscribed in a circle?

WRITTEN EXERCISES

A. Refer to the figure of $\odot P$ to find each value, given $m\widehat{AE} = 150$ and $m\angle ADC = 55$.

1.	$m\angle APB$	**2.**	$m\angle ABE$
3.	$m\angle C$	**4.**	$m\widehat{BC}$
5.	$m\angle DAC$	**6.**	$m\angle EPD$
7.	$m\widehat{EC}$	**8.**	$m\widehat{AEC}$
9.	$m\widehat{ACD}$	**10.**	$m\angle BPD$

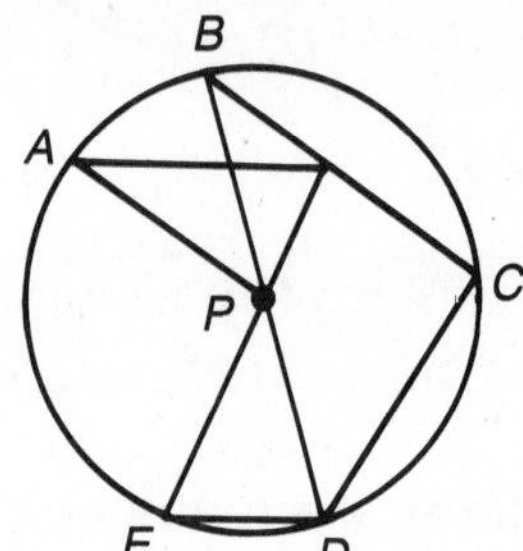

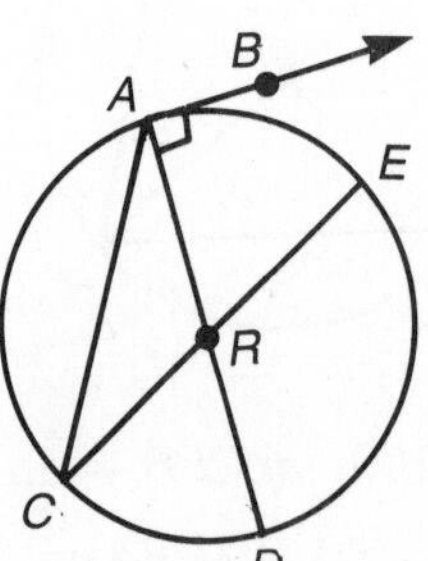

Refer to the figure of $\odot R$ with tangent $\overrightarrow{AB}$ to answer the following questions.

11. If $m\widehat{AC} = 80$, find $m\angle ARE$.

12. If $m\angle ARE = 70$, find $m\widehat{AC}$.

13. If $m\angle CAD = 40$, find $m\widehat{CDA}$.

14. If $m\widehat{AE} = 50$, find $m\angle CAD$.

15. If $m\angle BAC = 130$, find $m\angle ARC$.

16. If $m\widehat{ACE} = 320$, find $m\angle ARC$.

17. If $m\angle ERD = 130$, find $m\angle ACE$.

18. If $m\widehat{EAD} = 210$, find $m\angle ARE$.

19. If $m\angle BAC = 125$, find $m\widehat{AE}$.

20. If $m\widehat{EAD} = 230$, find $m\widehat{AEC}$.

B. 21. Given: $\odot P$ with $m\angle A = 30$

Prove: $m\widehat{AB} = 120$

22. Given: $\odot P$ with $m\widehat{AB} = 90$

Prove: $\triangle ACB$ is isosceles.

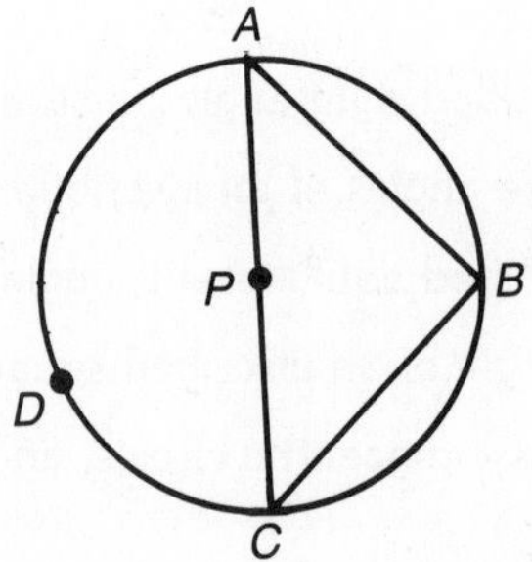

Refer to the figure of $\odot P$ for Exercises 23–27.

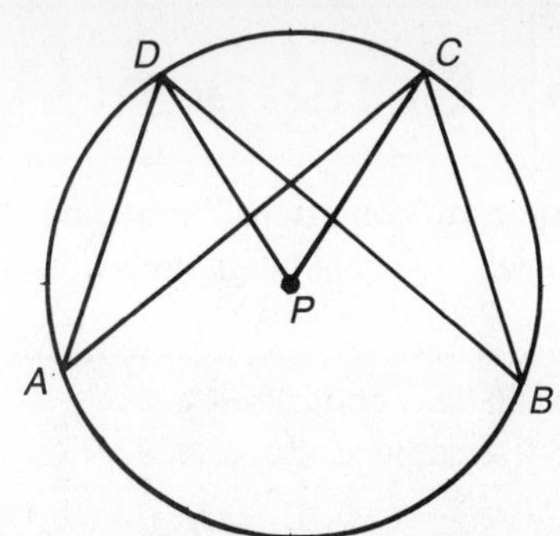

23. $m\widehat{DC} = 96 - x$, $m\angle B = 3x + 20$.
Find $m\angle A$.

24. $m\angle A = 3x - 25$, $m\angle P = 3x + 10$.
Find $m\angle B$.

25. $m\angle P = 2x^2 - 12$, $m\widehat{DC} = x^2 + 4$.
Find $m\angle A$.

26. $m\angle A = x^2 + 7$, $m\angle B = 2x + 22$.
Find $m\angle P$.

27. $m\angle A = 3x + 36$, $m\widehat{DC} = x^2$
Find $m\widehat{DAC}$.

Refer to the figure of $\odot W$ with tangent $\overrightarrow{AB}$ for Exercises 28–29.

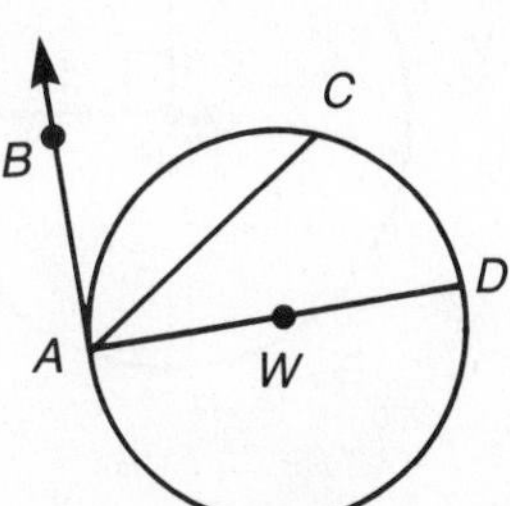

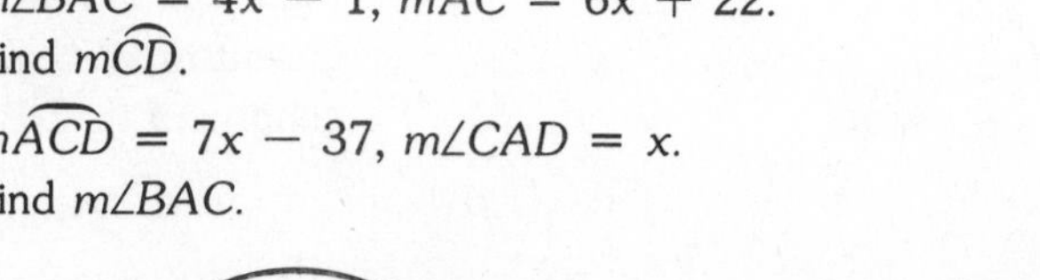

28. $m\angle BAC = 4x - 1$, $m\widehat{AC} = 6x + 22$.
Find $m\widehat{CD}$.

C. **29.** $m\widehat{ACD} = 7x - 37$, $m\angle CAD = x$.
Find $m\angle BAC$.

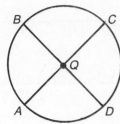

30. Given: $\odot Q$
Prove: $m\widehat{AB} = m\widehat{DC}$

31. Given: Two concentric circles with center P. $\overline{AC}$ tangent to small $\odot P$ at B
Prove: $\overline{BP} \parallel \overline{CD}$

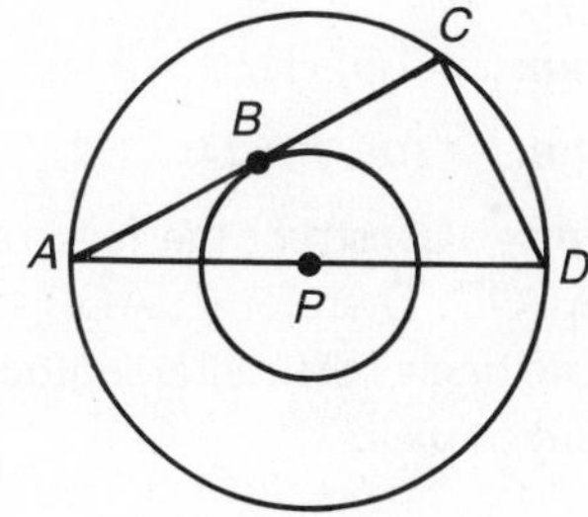

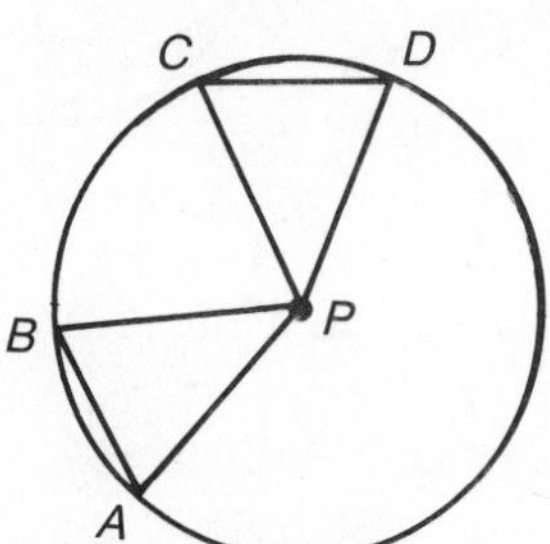

32. Given: $\odot P$ with $m\widehat{AB} = m\widehat{CD}$
Prove: $\overline{AB} \cong \overline{CD}$

23. 44
24. 35
25. 10
26. 32 or 64
27. 216 or 324
28. 86
29. 59
30. $m\angle BQA = m\angle CQD$ since they are vertical angles. Thus, $m\widehat{AB} = m\widehat{DC}$ because the measure of an arc is the measure of the central angle that intercepts it.
31. $m\angle ABP = 90$, since radius $\overline{BP}$ must be perpendicular to tangent $\overline{AC}$. By Corollary 12.7.1, $m\angle C = 90$, because it is inscribed in semicircle $\widehat{AD}$. Therefore, since corres. $\angle$s are $\cong$, $\overline{BP} \parallel \overline{CD}$.
32. Since $m\widehat{AB} = m\widehat{CD}$, $m\angle APB = m\angle CPD$. Radii $\overline{AP} \cong \overline{BP} \cong \overline{CP} \cong \overline{DP}$, so by SAS, $\triangle APB \cong \triangle CPD$. By CPCTC, $\overline{AB} \cong \overline{CD}$.

OBJECTIVE

Use Theorems 12.9–12.11 to find the measure of an arc or an angle.

TEACHER'S NOTES

See p. T38

MIXED REVIEW

1. Multiply $(\sqrt{5} - \sqrt{2})(\sqrt{5} + \sqrt{2})$. 3
2. What is the altitude of an equilateral triangle with side 7? $\frac{7\sqrt{3}}{2}$
3. Solve $3x - y = 10$
   $2x + 3y = 14$ (4, 2)
4. What figure is formed by connecting the midpoints of a rectangle consecutively? rhombus
5. If $ax^2 + bx + c = 0$, then $x = ?$ $\frac{-b \pm \sqrt{b^2 - 4ac}}{2a}$

TEACHER'S RESOURCE MASTERS

Practice Master 38, Part 2

12.6 Congruent Arcs

So far the term "congruent," meaning "the same size and shape," has been applied to segments, angles, polygons, and circles. This lesson explores **congruent arcs.**

DEFINITION: congruent arcs
Within the same circle or congruent circles, **congruent arcs** are arcs of the same degree measure.

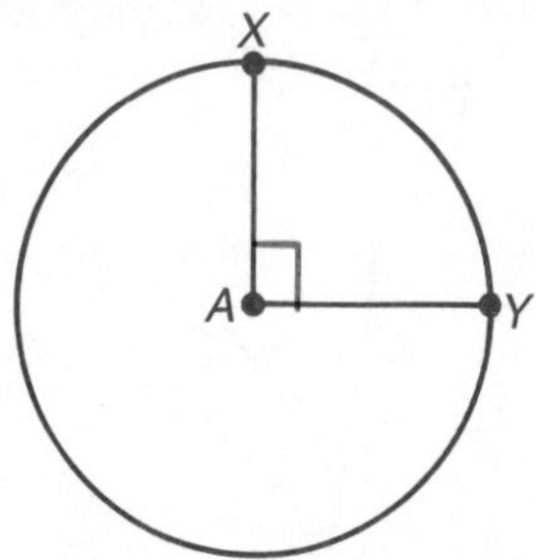

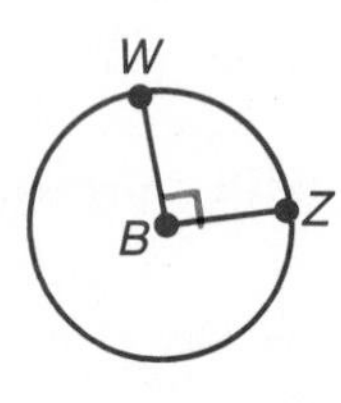

Two arcs of the same measure might not be congruent. Consider $\odot A$ and $\odot B$ in the figure. While $m\widehat{XY} = m\widehat{WZ} = 90$, $\widehat{XY}$ is longer than $\widehat{WZ}$. For $\widehat{XY}$ to be congruent to $\widehat{WZ}$, $\odot A$ must be congruent to $\odot B$.

THEOREM 12.9
In the same circle or in congruent circles, if two chords are congruent, then so are the corresponding minor arcs.

Given: $\odot O$, chord $\overline{AB} \cong$ chord $\overline{CD}$

Prove: $\widehat{AB} \cong \widehat{CD}$

Proof: Construct the four radii as shown. By SSS, $\triangle AOB \cong \triangle COD$. Therefore, $\angle AOB \cong \angle COD$, and because they are central angles their intercepted arcs $\widehat{AB}$ and $\widehat{CD}$ must be congruent as well.

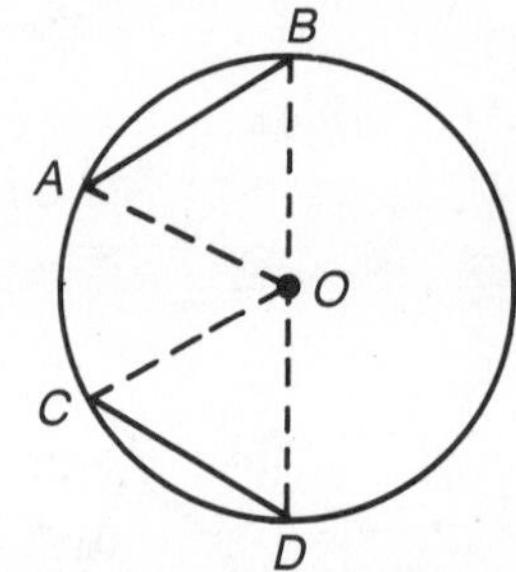

THEOREM 12.10
In the same circle or in congruent circles, if two arcs are congruent, then so are the corresponding chords.

Given: $\odot O$, $\widehat{AB} \cong \widehat{CD}$

Prove: $\overline{AB} \cong \overline{CD}$

Proof: In the figure above, since the arcs are congruent, the central angles, $\angle AOB$ and $\angle COD$, are also congruent. By SAS, using the congruent radii and central angles, $\triangle AOB \cong \triangle COD$. The corresponding parts $\overline{AB}$ and $\overline{CD}$ are congruent.

Another correspondence between chords and arcs occurs in the case of parallel chords.

THEOREM 12.11
If two chords in the same circle are parallel, then the arcs between the two chords are congruent.

Given: $\overline{AB} \parallel \overline{CD}$

Prove: $\widehat{AC} \cong \widehat{BD}$

Proof: Since alternate interior angles on parallel segments are congruent, $\angle ABC \cong \angle DCB$. Both are inscribed angles, and since they are congruent, so too are their intercepted arcs, $\widehat{AC}$ and $\widehat{BD}$.

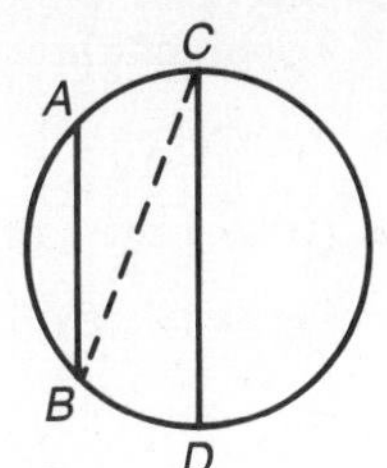

Nothing can be proved about the arcs intercepted by two parallel chords. In this figure, students can see that $\widehat{AB}$ is not congruent to $\widehat{CD}$.

To see how these theorems may be applied, consider the following example.

Example: Given $\overline{AB} \cong \overline{BC}$, $\overline{AB} \parallel \overline{DC}$, and $m\widehat{AD} = 100$ in the figure. Find $m\angle DBC$.

Solution: Since $\overline{AB}$ and $\overline{BC}$ are congruent, $\widehat{AB}$ and $\widehat{BC}$ are congruent. Also, since $\overline{AB}$ and $\overline{DC}$ are parallel, $\widehat{AD}$ and $\widehat{BC}$ are congruent. Consequently, by the transitive property, $\widehat{AB}$, $\widehat{BC}$, and $\widehat{AD}$ are all congruent arcs, and each therefore measures 100. That leaves $m\widehat{DC} = 360 - 300$ or 60, so the measure of inscribed $\angle DBC$ is 30.

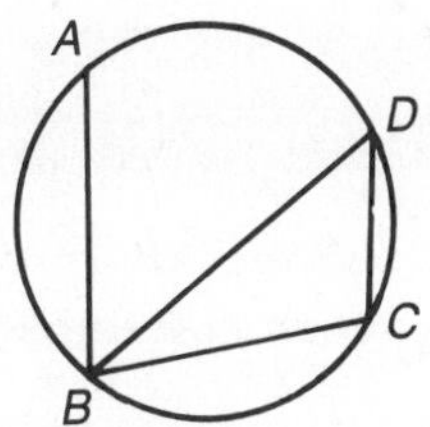

ASSIGNMENT GUIDE

Minimum 1-15
Regular 1-25 odd
Maximum 1-25 odd, 26-27

ORAL EXERCISES

State which pair of arcs in $\odot O$ is congruent for each case.

1. $\overline{AF} \cong \overline{ED}$
2. $\overline{BC} \parallel \overline{FE}$
3. $\overline{BC} \cong \overline{FE}$
4. $\overline{AB} \parallel \overline{ED}$
5. $\overline{FE} \cong \overline{ED}$
6. $\overline{AF} \parallel \overline{CD}$

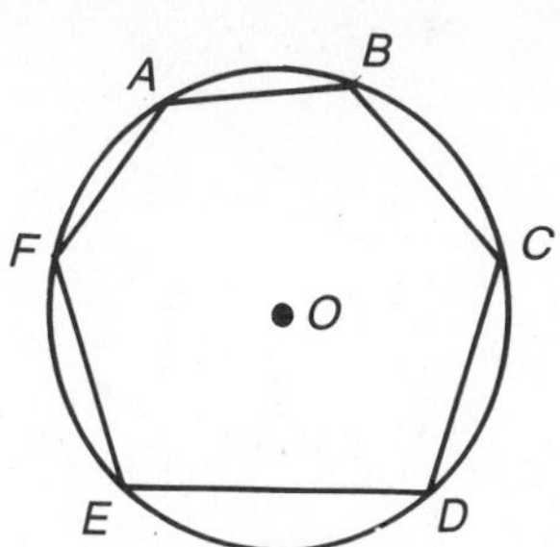

Oral Exercises
1. $\widehat{AF}$, $\widehat{ED}$
2. $\widehat{BF}$, $\widehat{CE}$
3. $\widehat{BC}$, $\widehat{FE}$
4. $\widehat{AE}$, $\widehat{BD}$
5. $\widehat{FE}$, $\widehat{ED}$
6. $\widehat{AC}$, $\widehat{FD}$

7. $\overline{AB} \cong \overline{FE}$

8. $\overset{\frown}{AC} \cong \overset{\frown}{FD}$

9. $\overset{\frown}{AF} \cong \overset{\frown}{CD}$

10. $\overset{\frown}{AC} \cong \overset{\frown}{FD}$

11. $\overset{\frown}{BC} \cong \overset{\frown}{CD}$

12. $\overline{CD} \cong \overline{AF}$

13. F 14. T

15. F 16. T

17. F 18. T

19. T 20. T

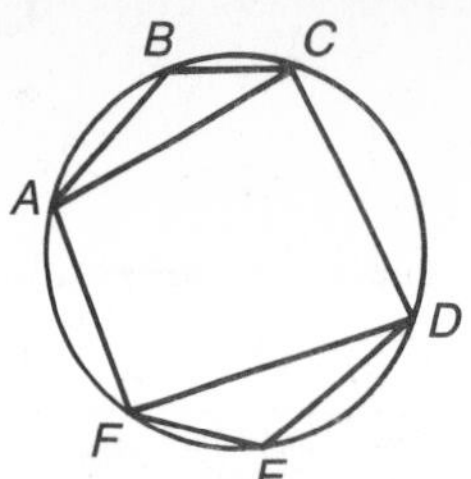

Referring to the figure, state any conclusion you may draw from each of the following.

7. $\overset{\frown}{AB} \cong \overset{\frown}{FE}$ **8.** $\overline{AC} \cong \overline{FD}$

9. $\overline{AC} \parallel \overline{FD}$ **10.** $\overline{AF} \parallel \overline{CD}$

11. $\overline{BC} \cong \overline{CD}$ **12.** $\overset{\frown}{CD} \cong \overset{\frown}{AF}$

For a given circle, state whether each of the following is true or false.

13. Congruent chords are parallel.

14. Congruent chords determine congruent arcs.

15. Congruent arcs determine parallel chords.

16. Parallel chords determine congruent arcs.

17. Arcs of the same degree measure are congruent.

18. Perpendicular chords with the same endpoint intercept a semicircle.

19. An obtuse inscribed angle intercepts a major arc.

20. If an inscribed angle has a diameter as one of its sides, it must be an acute angle.

WRITTEN EXERCISES

Written Exercises

1. Thm 12.9

2. Thm 12.11

3. congruence of arcs is transitive

4. 120

5. 35 6. 90

7. 110 8. 35

9. 180 10. 125

11. 250 12. 290

A. Given $\overline{AB} \cong \overline{BC}$ and $\overline{AB} \parallel \overline{DC}$ in $\odot P$, complete each statement.

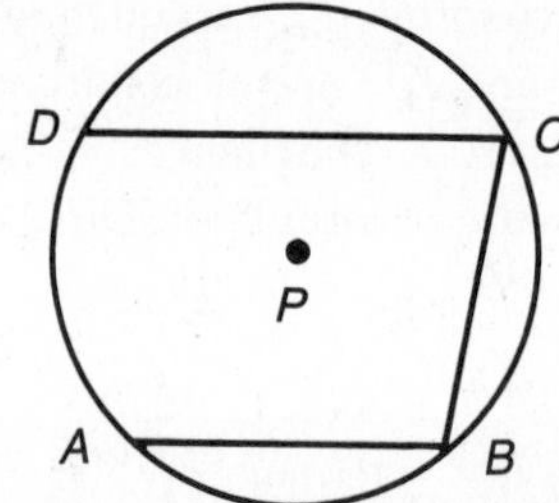

1. $\overset{\frown}{AB} \cong \overset{\frown}{BC}$ because ____________________.

2. $\overset{\frown}{AD} \cong \overset{\frown}{BC}$ because ____________________.

3. Therefore, $\overset{\frown}{AB} \cong \overset{\frown}{AD}$ because ____________________.

4. So if $m\overset{\frown}{AB} = 80$, $m\overset{\frown}{DC} =$ ____________________.

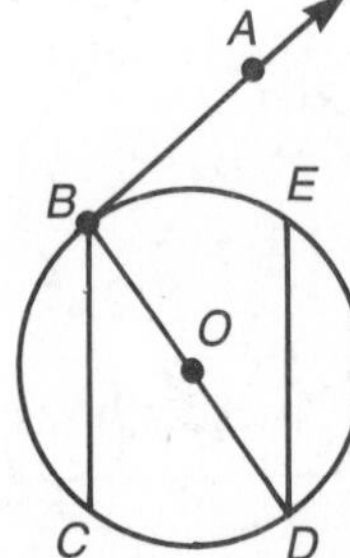

Given $\odot O$ with tangent $\overrightarrow{BA}$, diameter $\overline{BD}$, $m\overset{\frown}{BE} = 70$, and $\overline{BC} \cong \overline{ED}$, find the following values.

5. $m\angle BDE$ **6.** $m\angle ABD$

7. $m\overset{\frown}{ED}$ **8.** $m\angle CBD$

9. $m\overset{\frown}{BCD}$ **10.** $m\angle ABC$

11. $m\overset{\frown}{BEC}$ **12.** $m\overset{\frown}{BCE}$

B. Given $\odot O$ with a diameter $\overline{CD}$, $\overline{AB} \parallel \overline{CD} \parallel \overline{EF}$, and $\overline{AB} \cong \overline{EF}$, complete each statement.

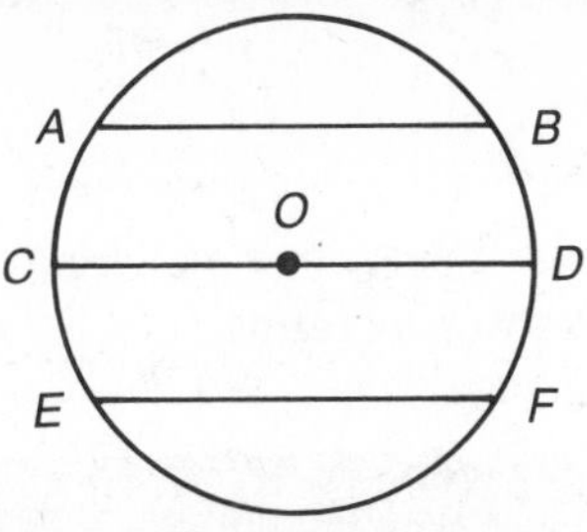

13. If $m\overset{\frown}{AB} = 80$, then $m\overset{\frown}{AC} =$ ____.

14. If $m\overset{\frown}{AE} = 100$, then $m\overset{\frown}{AC} =$ ____.

15. If $m\overset{\frown}{EF} = 60$, then $m\overset{\frown}{ED} =$ ____.

16. If $m\overset{\frown}{AB} = 90$, then $m\overset{\frown}{AE} =$ ____.

17. If $m\overset{\frown}{CE} = 50$, then $m\overset{\frown}{CEB} =$ ____.

18. If $m\overset{\frown}{BD} = 40$, then $m\overset{\frown}{ACD} =$ ____.

19. Given: $\odot Q$ with $\overline{AB} \parallel \overline{DE}$

Prove: $\triangle CAB \sim \triangle CED$

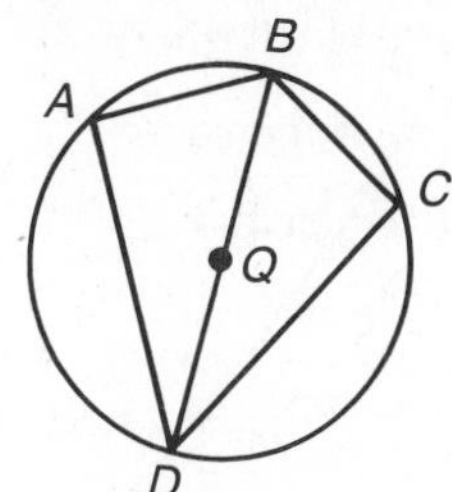

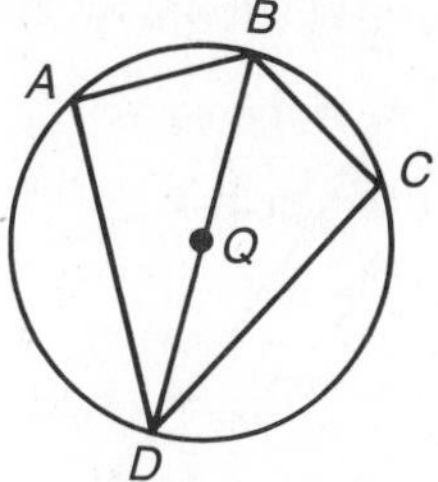

20. Given: $\odot Q$ with diameter $\overline{BD}$ and $\overline{AB} \cong \overline{CB}$

Prove: $\overset{\frown}{AD} \cong \overset{\frown}{CD}$

C. Refer again to the figure of $\odot O$ in Exercises 13–18 to answer the following questions, given $\overline{AB} \parallel \overline{CD} \parallel \overline{EF}$ and $\overline{AB} \cong \overline{EF}$.

21. If $m\overset{\frown}{AB} = 8x + 20$ and $m\overset{\frown}{CA} = 6x$, find $m\overset{\frown}{BD}$.

22. If $m\overset{\frown}{AC} = 4x + 20$ and $m\overset{\frown}{CE} = 3x + 30$, find $m\overset{\frown}{AD}$.

23. If $m\overset{\frown}{AB} = 90 - x$ and $m\overset{\frown}{EF} = 20 + 4x$, find $m\overset{\frown}{BF}$.

24. If $m\overset{\frown}{EC} = 50 + x$ and $m\overset{\frown}{EF} = 8x$, find $m\overset{\frown}{AB}$.

25. If $m\overset{\frown}{AE} = 7x - 20$ and $m\overset{\frown}{BD} = 2x + 20$, find $m\overset{\frown}{BDA}$.

26. Given: $\overset{\frown}{AB} \cong \overset{\frown}{DE}$
$\overset{\frown}{AC} \cong \overset{\frown}{EF}$

Prove: $\triangle ABC \cong \triangle EDF$

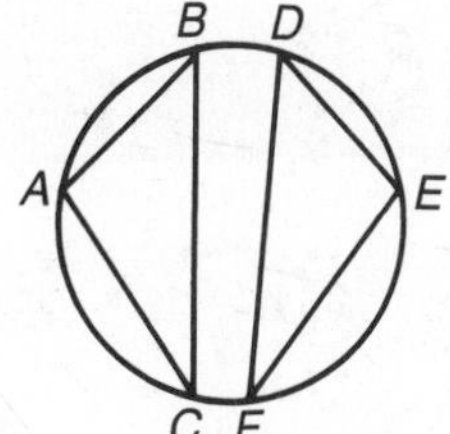

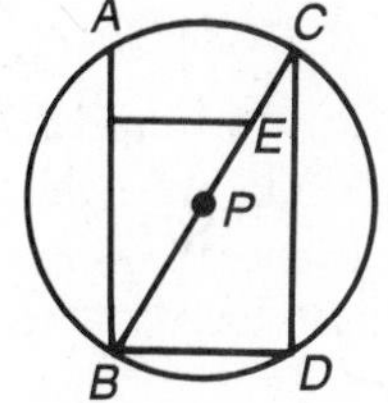

27. Given: $\odot P$, $\overline{AB} \parallel \overline{CD}$

Prove: $\overline{AE} \not\parallel \overline{BD}$

HINT: Use an indirect method.

13. 50 14. 50

15. 120 16. 90

17. 230 18. 220

19. Since $\overline{AB} \parallel \overline{DE}$, $\overset{\frown}{AD} \cong \overset{\frown}{BE}$. So, inscribed $\angle A \cong \angle D \cong \angle B \cong \angle E$. $\triangle CAB \sim \triangle CED$ by AA.

20. Given $\overline{AB} \cong \overline{CB}$, $\overset{\frown}{AB} \cong \overset{\frown}{CB}$, so inscribed $\angle ADB \cong \angle CDB$. Because $\overline{BD}$ is a diameter, inscribed $\angle A \cong \angle C$, and $\triangle ABD \cong \triangle CBD$ by SAA. So, $\angle ABD \cong \angle CBD$ by CPCTC. Since the two inscribed angles are $\cong$, $\overset{\frown}{AD} \cong \overset{\frown}{CD}$.

21. 48 22. 120

23. 104 24. 64

25. 300

26. Since $\overset{\frown}{AB} \cong \overset{\frown}{DE}$, $\overline{AB} \cong \overline{DE}$. Since $\overset{\frown}{AC} \cong \overset{\frown}{EF}$, $\overline{AC} \cong \overline{EF}$. Using Theorem 12.6, $\overset{\frown}{BC} \cong \overset{\frown}{DF}$, so $\overline{BC} \cong \overline{DF}$ and $\triangle ABC \cong \triangle EDF$ by SSS.

27. Since $\overline{AB} \parallel \overline{CD}$, $\angle ABC \cong \angle DCB$ by alt. int. $\angle$s. Assume $\overline{AE} \parallel \overline{BD}$, so that $\angle AEB \cong \angle DBC$. Thus, by AA, $\triangle AEB \sim \triangle DBC$, and $\angle A \cong \angle D$ by corres. parts. But $\angle D$ is inscribed in a semicircle and is a rt. $\angle$, while $\angle A$, when extended, intercepts a minor arc and is therefore acute. This contradicts $\angle A \cong \angle D$, so the assumption $\overline{AE} \parallel \overline{BD}$ is false.

OBJECTIVE

Use Theorems 12.12–12.17 to find the measure of an arc or an angle.

TEACHER'S NOTES

See p. T38

MIXED REVIEW

1. Average 36, 18, and 48. 34
2. Add $2\frac{1}{2} + 3\frac{2}{5}$. $5\frac{9}{10}$
3. Divide $4\frac{1}{2} \div \frac{3}{8}$. 12
4. Simplify $\sqrt{(17-1)^2 + [15-(-15)]^2}$. 34
5. Give six ways to prove any right triangles are congruent. SAS, ASA, SSS, SAA, HL, LL

TEACHER'S RESOURCE MASTERS

Practice Master 39, Part 1

12.7 Power of a Point in Relation to a Circle

In order to continue exploring the relationships between arcs and segments, you will need to know two new terms.

DEFINITION: tangent and secant segments
If the line $\overleftrightarrow{QR}$ is tangent to a circle at R, the segment $\overline{QR}$ is a **tangent segment** from Q to the circle. If the line $\overleftrightarrow{QW}$ is a secant intersecting a circle at W and Y, then $\overline{QW}$ and $\overline{QY}$ are **secant segments** from Q to the circle.

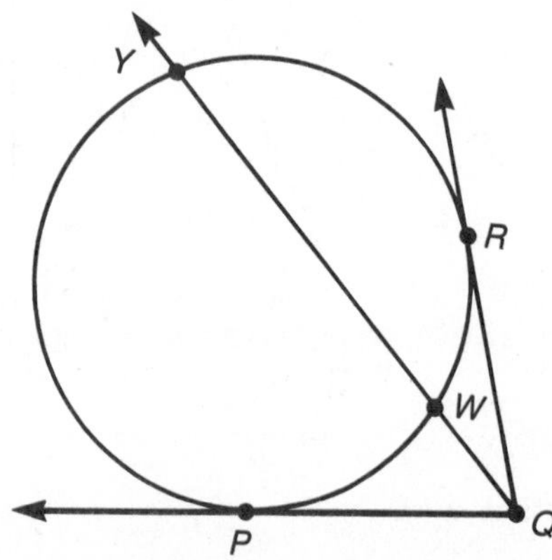

From a given external point, such as Q, there are two lines tangent to a given circle. Hence, there are two tangent segments from that point, while there are an infinite number of secant segments.

THEOREM 12.12
The two tangent segments to a circle from an external point are congruent and form congruent angles with the line joining the external point to the center of the circle.

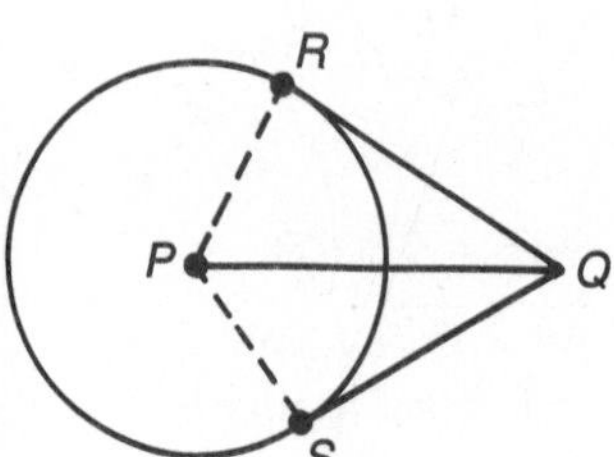

Given: $\odot P$, external point Q, $\overleftrightarrow{QR}$ and $\overleftrightarrow{QS}$ tangent to $\odot P$ at R and S, respectively.

Prove: $\overline{QR} \cong \overline{QS}$, and $\angle RQP \cong \angle SQP$

Proof: Draw radii $\overline{PR}$ and $\overline{PS}$. By Cor. 12.2.1, $\overline{PR} \perp \overline{RQ}$ and $\overline{PS} \perp \overline{SQ}$, so $\triangle PQR$ and $\triangle PQS$ are right triangles. Since $\overline{PR} \cong \overline{PS}$ and $\overline{PQ} \cong \overline{PQ}$, the triangles are congruent by HL. Therefore, $\overline{QR} \cong \overline{QS}$ and $\angle RQP \cong \angle SQP$ because the corresponding parts are congruent.

THEOREM 12.13
Given circle C and an external point Q, let l_1 be a secant through Q intersecting circle C in points R and S, and let l_2 be another secant through Q intersecting circle C in points U and T. Then $QR \cdot QS = QU \cdot QT$.

Given: $\odot C$, external point Q, $\overleftrightarrow{QS}$ a secant intersecting $\odot C$ at R and S, $\overleftrightarrow{QT}$ a secant intersecting $\odot C$ at U and T

Prove: $QR \cdot QS = QU \cdot QT$

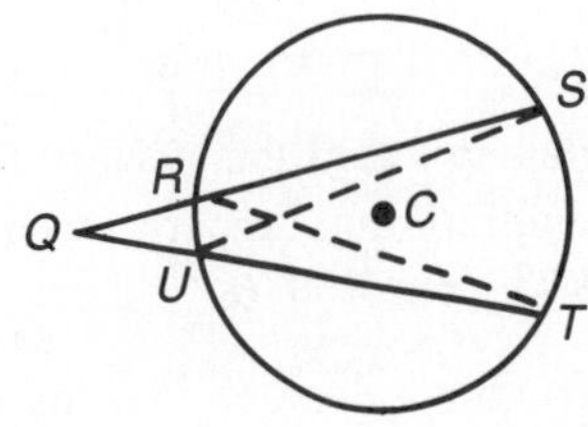

Proof: Draw $\overline{TR}$ and $\overline{SU}$ and consider $\triangle QSU$ and $\triangle QTR$. Because the inscribed angles, $\angle S$ and $\angle T$, both intercept $\overline{RU}$, $\angle S \cong \angle T$. Also, $\angle Q$ is common to both triangles. Thus, using the AA Corollary, $\triangle QSU \sim \triangle QTR$. The corresponding sides of similar triangles are proportional, giving $\frac{QS}{QT} = \frac{QU}{QR}$, which cross-multiplies to yield $QR \cdot QS = QU \cdot QT$.

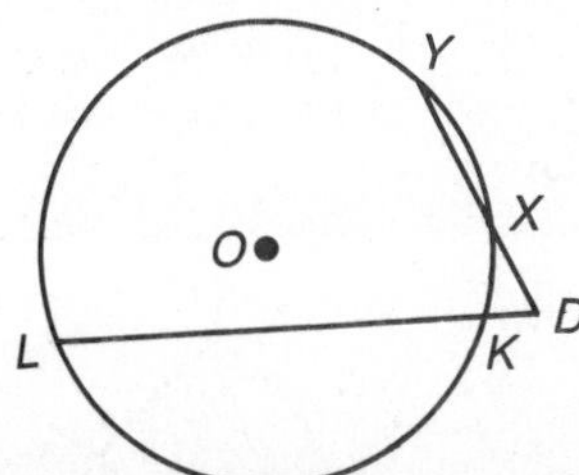

Example: In the figure of $\odot O$, $DX = 6$, $DY = 15$ and $DK = 3$. Find KL.

Solution: By Theorem 12.13, $DX \cdot DY = DK \cdot DL$, or $6 \cdot 15 = 3 \cdot DL$. Solving for DL gives $DL = 30$, so $KL = DL - DK = 27$.

THEOREM 12.14
Given a tangent segment $\overline{QT}$ to a circle and a secant through Q intersecting the circle in points R and S, then $QR \cdot QS = QT^2$.

Given: Tangent segment $\overline{QT}$ and secant $\overleftrightarrow{QS}$ intersecting the circle at R and S

Prove: $QR \cdot QS = QT^2$

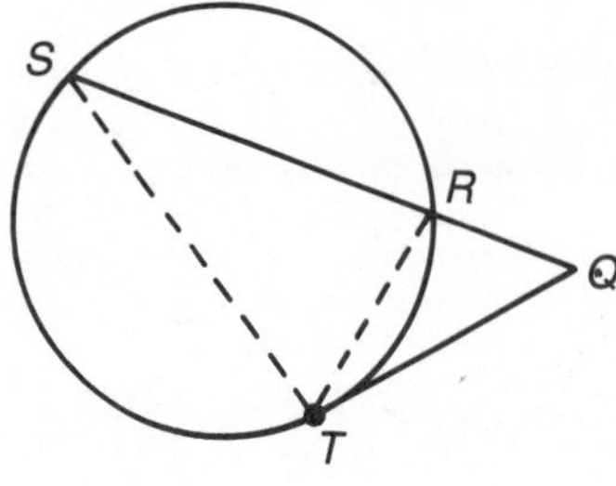

The tangent segment is the geometric mean between the secant segments.

Proof: In the figure shown, draw $\overline{ST}$ and $\overline{RT}$. Since $\angle S$ and $\angle RTQ$ each equal $\frac{1}{2}m\overparen{RT}$, $\angle S \sim \angle RTQ$. Using $\angle Q \cong \angle Q$, $\triangle QRT \sim \triangle QTS$. It follows that $\frac{QR}{QT} = \frac{QT}{QS}$, or $QR \cdot QS = QT^2$.

Since Q has been assumed to be outside the circle, there can be no other combination of secant segments and tangent segments to consider other than those in the last three theorems. In each case, the constant product is called the **power of the point** with respect to the given circle.

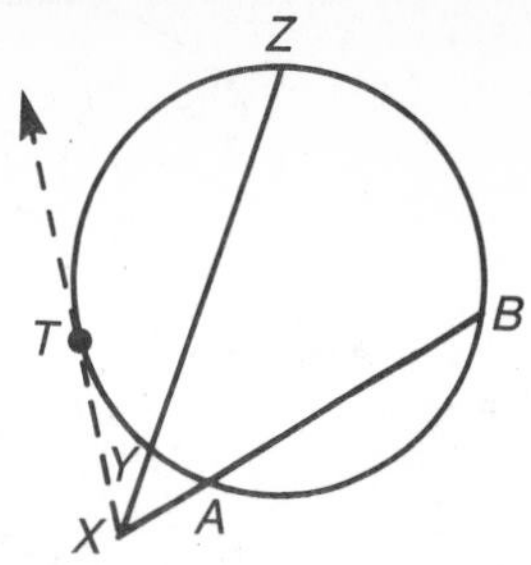

Example: In the figure, $XY = 3$ and $YZ = 9$. If $XA = 4$, find XB and AB.

Solution: Using Theorem 12.13, the power of the point X is the product of the lengths of the secant segments, or $XY \cdot XZ = XA \cdot XB$. Substituting the values known, you obtain $3 \cdot 12 = 4 \cdot XB$. The power of the point X is 36, and $XB = 9$, so $AB = 5$.

Having found the power of point X for this particular circle, you can use it to determine the length of any tangent segment from X to the circle. If T is the point of tangency, then $36 = XT^2$, or $XT = 6$.

You have dealt so far only with a point outside a circle. Consider now two secants that intersect inside a circle.

THEOREM 12.15
If two chords intersect in the interior of a circle, the product of the lengths of the segments of one equals the product of the lengths of the other.

Given: Chords $\overline{AC}$ and $\overline{BD}$ intersecting in point Q in the interior of a circle

Prove: $AQ \cdot QC = DQ \cdot QB$

Proof: Draw $\overline{AD}$ and $\overline{BC}$. Since the inscribed angles, $\angle D$ and $\angle C$, both intercept $\widehat{AB}$, $\angle D \cong \angle C$. Using the congruent vertical angles at Q, $\triangle AQD \sim \triangle BQC$. Thus, $\frac{AQ}{QB} = \frac{DQ}{QC}$, or $AQ \cdot QC = DQ \cdot QB$.

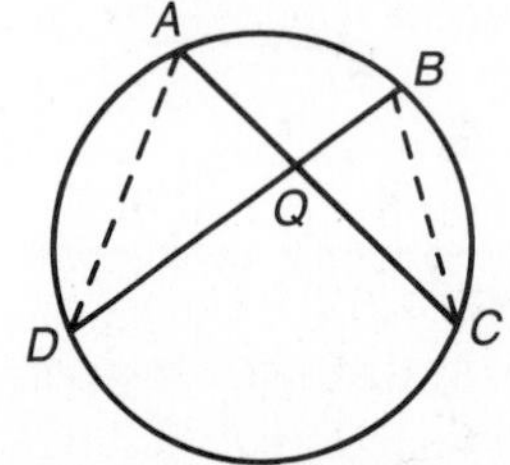

Be careful to differentiate this pattern from the previous one. In the last example, the power of the point X was obtained from $XY \cdot XZ$, not from $XY \cdot YZ$.

Example: In the circle shown above, $DB = 15$, $DQ = 9$, and $AQ = 2$. Find QC.

Solution: $QB = DB - DQ = 15 - 9 = 6$. By Theorem 12.15, $AQ \cdot QC = DQ \cdot QB$, or $2 \cdot QC = 9 \cdot 6$. Solving, $QC = 27$.

THEOREM 12.16
If two tangents, a tangent and a secant, or two secants intersect in the exterior of a circle, the measure of the angle formed is one-half the difference of the measures of the intercepted arcs.

What follows is the proof for the case of two secants only. The other two cases are left as exercises.

Given: Secants $\overline{QC}$ and $\overline{QD}$ intersecting a circle in points B, C, A, and D

Prove: $m\angle Q = \frac{1}{2}(m\widehat{DC} - m\widehat{AB})$

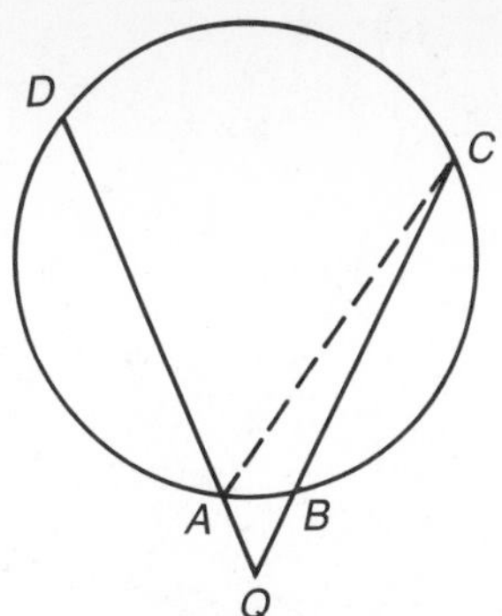

Proof: Draw either $\overline{AC}$ or $\overline{DB}$. ($\overline{AC}$ has been chosen here.) In $\triangle AQC$, $m\angle Q + m\angle C + m\angle CAQ = 180$. Since $\angle C$ is an inscribed angle, the following equation results from substituting the measure of its intercepted arc: $m\angle Q + \frac{1}{2}m\widehat{AB} + m\angle CAQ = 180$. Because $\angle CAQ$ is part of a linear pair: $m\angle CAQ = 180 - m\angle CAD = 180 - \frac{1}{2}m\widehat{DC}$. Thus, the original equation becomes $m\angle Q + \frac{1}{2}m\widehat{AB} + 180 - \frac{1}{2}m\widehat{DC} = 180$. Solving for $m\angle Q$ yields $m\angle Q = \frac{1}{2}(m\widehat{DC} - m\widehat{AB})$.

Example: In the circle shown above, $m\widehat{DC} = 100$ and $m\widehat{AB} = 20$. What is $m\angle Q$?

Solution: By Theorem 12.16, $m\angle Q = \frac{1}{2}(m\widehat{DC} - m\widehat{AB}) = \frac{1}{2}(100 - 20) = \frac{1}{2}(80) = 40$.

Finally, consider the case of two chords intersecting in the interior of a circle.

THEOREM 12.17
If two chords intersect in the interior of a circle, the measure of an angle formed is one-half the sum of the measures of the arcs intercepted by the angle and its vertical angle.

Given: Chords $\overline{AC}$ and $\overline{BD}$ intersect in the interior of a circle, forming $\angle 1$ as shown

Prove: $m\angle 1 = \frac{1}{2}(m\widehat{CB} + m\widehat{DA})$

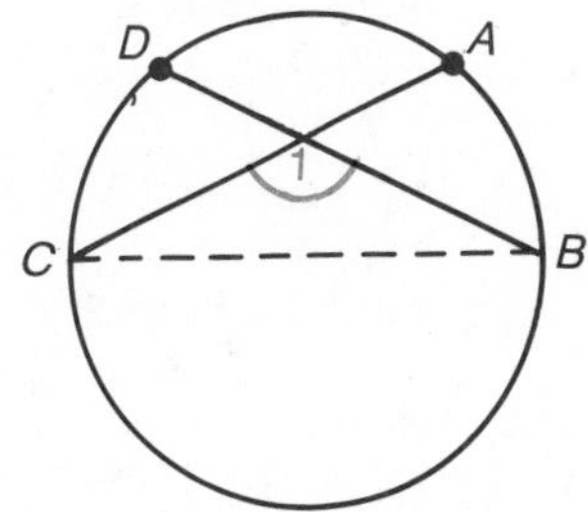

Proof: Draw $\overline{CB}$ and consider the triangle in which $m\angle 1 + m\angle C + m\angle B = 180$. Since $\angle C$ and $\angle B$ are inscribed angles, the measures of the intercepted arcs may be substituted, producing: $m\angle 1 + \frac{1}{2}m\widehat{AB} + \frac{1}{2}m\widehat{DC} = 180$. Multiplying by 2 to clear the fractions and then isolating $m\angle 1$, you find: $2m\angle 1 = 360 - (m\widehat{AB} + m\widehat{DC})$. But 360 is the measure of the whole circle, so $360 - (m\widehat{AB} + m\widehat{DC})$ equals $m\widehat{CB} + m\widehat{DA}$. Hence, $2m\angle 1 = m\widehat{CB} + m\widehat{DA}$, or $m\angle 1 = \frac{1}{2}(m\widehat{CB} + m\widehat{DA})$.

Example: In the figure, $m\angle G = 20$, $m\widehat{BC} = 30$, and $m\widehat{AB} = 90$. Find $m\angle AFB$.

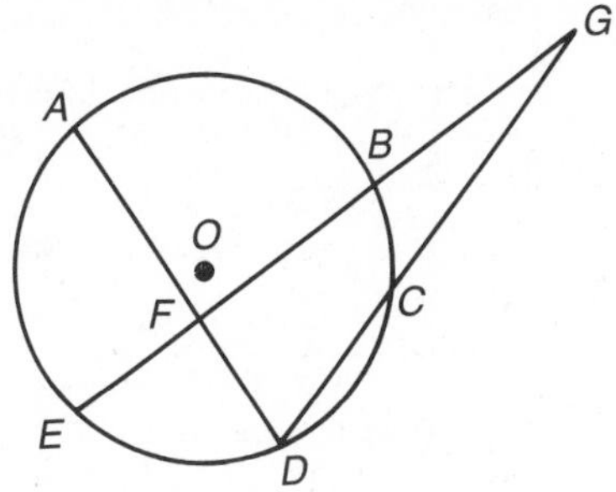

Solution: Theorem 12.16 allows you to state that $m\angle G = \frac{1}{2}(m\widehat{ED} - m\widehat{BC})$, or $20 = \frac{1}{2}(m\widehat{ED} - 30)$. Solving for $m\widehat{ED}$ yields $70 = m\widehat{ED}$. To find $m\angle AFB$, use $m\angle AFB = \frac{1}{2}(m\widehat{AB} + m\widehat{ED})$, or $\frac{1}{2}(90 + 70)$, which is 80.

ASSIGNMENT GUIDE

Day 1
Minimum 1–5
Regular 1–5, 11–15
Maximum 1–5, 11–15, 23–25
Day 2
Minimum 6–15
Regular 16–22, 26–29
Maximum 16–22, 26–29, 36–43

ORAL EXERCISES

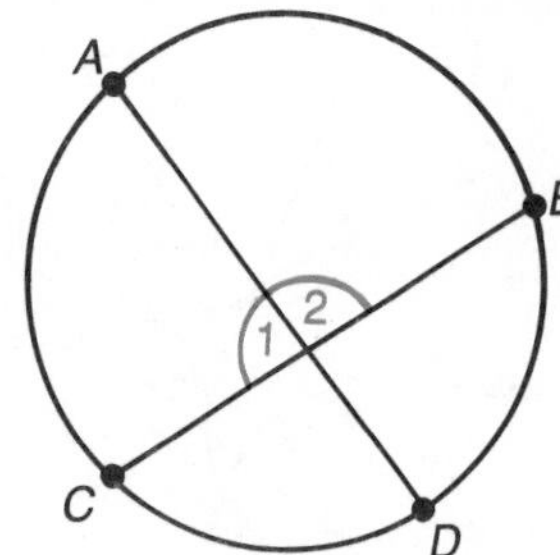

Refer to the figure to supply the missing measures.

1. $m\widehat{AC} = 80$ $\quad m\widehat{BD} = 100$ $\quad m\angle 1 =$ _____
2. $m\widehat{AC} = 80$ $\quad m\widehat{BD} = 60$ $\quad m\angle 1 =$ _____
3. $m\widehat{AC} = 120$ $\quad m\widehat{BD} = 140$ $\quad m\angle 2 =$ _____
4. $m\widehat{AB} = 120$ $\quad m\widehat{CD} = 60$ $\quad m\angle 2 =$ _____
5. $m\widehat{AB} = 70$ $\quad m\angle 2 = 100$ $\quad m\widehat{CD} =$ _____
6. $m\widehat{AB} = 100$ $\quad m\angle 2 = 60$ $\quad m\widehat{DC} =$ _____

Refer to the figure to supply the missing measures.

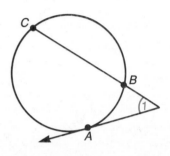

7. $m\widehat{AC} = 100$ $\quad m\widehat{AB} = 40$ $\quad m\angle 1 =$ _____
8. $m\widehat{AC} = 120$ $\quad m\widehat{AB} = 70$ $\quad m\angle 1 =$ _____
9. $m\widehat{AC} = 100$ $\quad m\angle 1 = 30$ $\quad m\widehat{AB} =$ _____
10. $m\widehat{AC} = 120$ $\quad m\angle 1 = 50$ $\quad m\widehat{AB} =$ _____
11. $m\widehat{AB} = 30$ $\quad m\angle 1 = 20$ $\quad m\widehat{AC} =$ _____
12. $m\widehat{AC} = 100$ $\quad m\angle 1 = 20$ $\quad m\widehat{BC} =$ _____

13. State three products that represent the power of point A in the figure below.

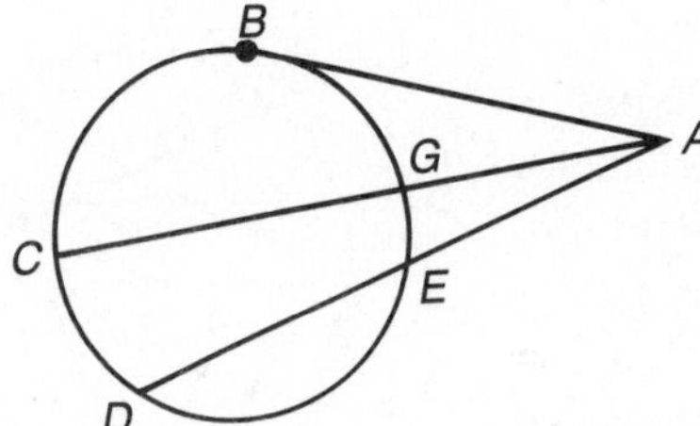

14. State three products that represent the power of point E in the figure below.

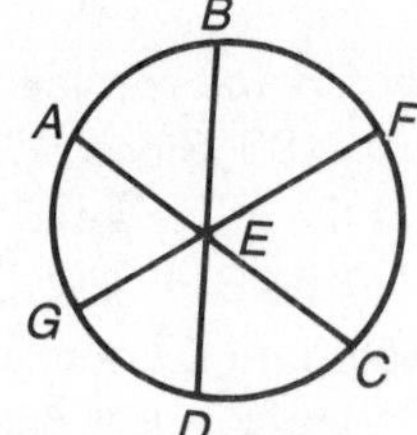

Oral Exercises

1.	90	2.	70
3.	50	4.	90
5.	130	6.	20
7.	30	8.	25
9.	40	10.	20
11.	70	12.	200

13. $AE \cdot AD$, $AG \cdot AC$, AB^2

14. $AE \cdot EC$, $BE \cdot ED$, $FE \cdot EG$

WRITTEN EXERCISES

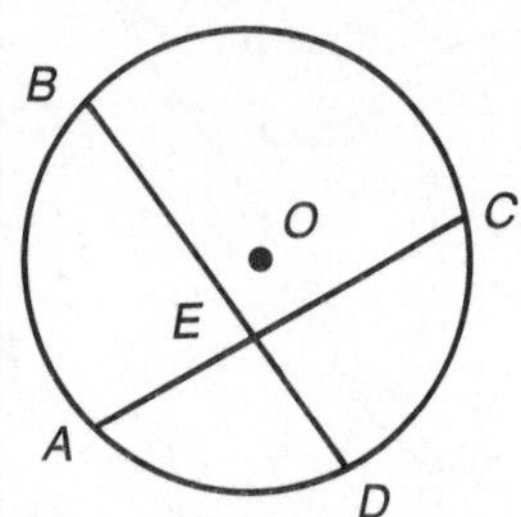

A. Refer to the figure for Exercises 1–10.

1. $AE = 5$ $\quad EC = 4$ $\quad BE = 2$ $\quad ED =$ _____
2. $AE = 5$ $\quad AC = 11$ $\quad BE = 3$ $\quad ED =$ _____
3. $AC = 12$ $\quad EC = 4$ $\quad BE = 2$ $\quad BD =$ _____
4. $AE = EC$ $\quad BE = 3$ $\quad ED = 12$ $\quad AC =$ _____
5. $AC = 15$ $\quad BE = 4$ $\quad ED = 9$ $\quad AE =$ _____

Written Exercises

1. 10
2. 10
3. 18
4. 12
5. 12 or 3

6. $m\widehat{AB} = 80$ $m\widehat{DC} = 120$ $m\angle AEB =$ _____

7. $m\widehat{BC} = 120$ $m\widehat{AD} = 60$ $m\angle AED =$ _____

8. $m\widehat{BC} = 100$ $m\widehat{AD} = 60$ $m\angle AEB =$ _____

9. $m\widehat{DC} = 110$ $m\angle CED = 80$ $m\widehat{BA} =$ _____

10. $m\widehat{DC} = 60$ $m\angle BEC = 100$ $m\widehat{BA} =$ _____

Use $\odot O$ with tangent segments $\overline{AB}$ and $\overline{AG}$ for Exercises 11–22.

11. $AB = 6$ $AC = 4$ $AD =$ _____

12. $AB = 4$ $AC = 3$ $AG =$ _____

13. $AE = 2$ $EF = 6$ $AG =$ _____

14. $AC = 6$ $OD = 2$ $AE = 5$ $AF =$ _____

15. $AC = 8$ $AD = 10$ $AE = 4$ $AF =$ _____

16. $m\widehat{BE} = 80$ $m\widehat{BF} = 160$ $m\angle BAF =$ _____

17. $m\widehat{DF} = 150$ $m\widehat{CE} = 30$ $m\angle DAF =$ _____

18. $m\widehat{FG} = 100$ $m\angle GAF = 40$ $m\widehat{EG} =$ _____

19. $m\widehat{DB} = 120$ $m\angle BAD =$ _____

20. $m\widehat{BG} = 120$ $m\angle BAG =$ _____

21. $m\angle BAG = 50$ $m\widehat{BDG} =$ _____

22. $m\angle DAG = 40$ $m\widehat{CG} = 50$ $m\widehat{DG} =$ _____

B. Refer to $\odot A$ for Exercises 23–25.

23. $RY = 3$ $ZR = 6$ $ZW = 10$
Find XY.

24. $XA = 13$ $RY = 2$ $ZR = 6$
Find ZW.

25. $XA = 5$ $RZ = 1$ $WZ = 22$
Find RY.

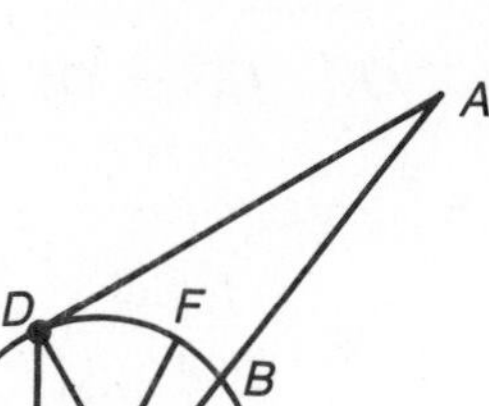

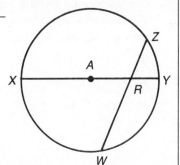

Refer to $\odot C$ with tangent segment $\overline{AD}$ for 26–29.

26. $m\angle DCE = 140$ $m\angle A = 30$ Find $m\widehat{DB}$.

27. $m\angle DEB = 30$ $m\angle A = 40$ Find $m\widehat{DE}$.

28. $m\widehat{EB} = 120$ $m\angle DCF = 50$ Find $m\angle A$.

29. $m\widehat{BE} = 100$ $m\angle A = 30$ Find $m\widehat{DB}$.

6. 100
7. 90
8. 100
9. 50
10. 100
11. 9
12. 4
13. 4
14. 12
15. 20
16. 40
17. 60
18. 20
19. 30
20. 60
21. 230
22. 130
23. 11
24. 14
25. 3
26. 80
27. 140
28. 10
29. 100

30. 36 31. 70

32. If ∠1 is a central ∠, then the chords are both diameters. The measure of an arc is the same as the measure of its central ∠, so $m\widehat{AB} + m\widehat{DC} = m\angle 1 + m\angle 2$. But, vert. ∠s are ≅. Thus, $2m\angle 1 = m\widehat{AB} + m\widehat{DC}$, and $m\angle 1 = \frac{1}{2}(m\widehat{AB} + m\widehat{DC})$.

33. 130 34. 20
35. 120 36. 260
37. 100 38. 90
39. 40 40. 100

41. In the larger circle, $QC \cdot QB = QA^2$. In the smaller circle, $QA^2 = QE \cdot QD$. Using the transitive property, $QC \cdot QB = QE \cdot QD$.

42.

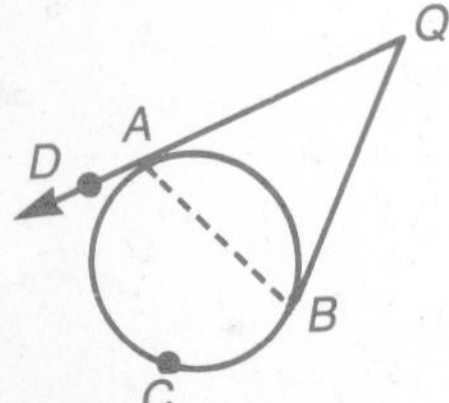

Tangents $\overrightarrow{QA}$ and $\overrightarrow{QB}$ intersect the circle at points A and B respectively (Given); Draw $\overline{AB}$ (Two points determine a line.); $m\angle Q + m\angle QAB + m\angle QBA = 180$ (Theorem 8.13);

$m\angle Q = 180 - m\angle QAB - m\angle QBA$
$= m\angle DAB - m\angle QBA$
$= \frac{1}{2}m\widehat{ACB} - \frac{1}{2}m\widehat{AB}$
$= \frac{1}{2}(m\widehat{ACB} - m\widehat{AB})$.

43. See *Teacher's Manual*, p. T61

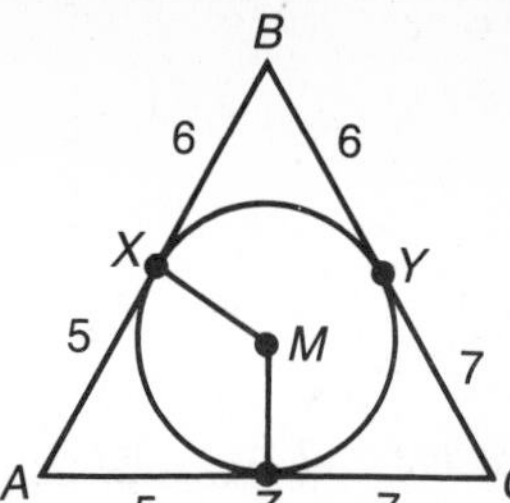

Refer to ⊙M with three tangent segments as shown for Exercises 30–31.

30. $AX = 5$ $BY = 6$ $CZ = 7$
Find the perimeter of △ABC.

31. If $m\angle XMZ = 110$, find $m\angle A$.

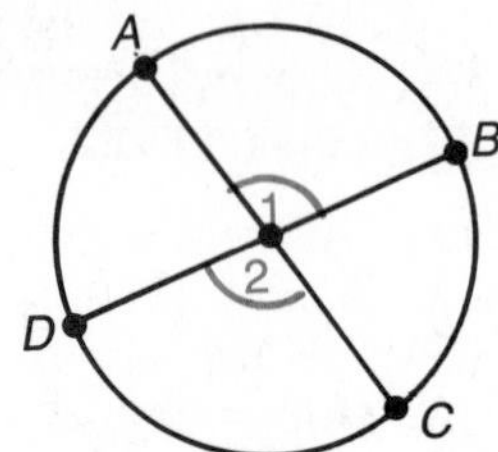

32. Use the figure at the right to explain why Theorem 12.17 holds even when ∠1 is a central angle.

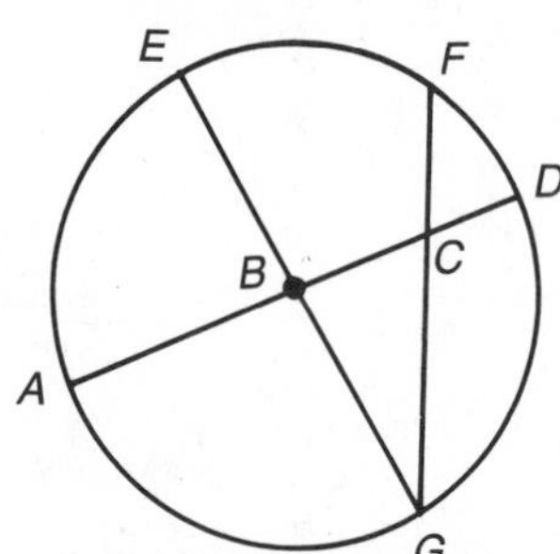

Refer to ⊙B for Exercises 33–35.

33. $m\angle ABG = 80$ $m\widehat{FD} = 20$ Find $m\angle ACF$.

34. $m\angle EGF = 60$ $m\angle FCD = 80$ Find $m\widehat{FD}$.

35. $m\angle DCG = 110$ $m\widehat{AG} = 80$ Find $m\widehat{AF}$.

C. For Exercises 36–40, refer to the figure of the concentric circles with centers at W, tangent segments $\overline{AC}$ and $\overline{CD}$, and $m\angle C = 80$.

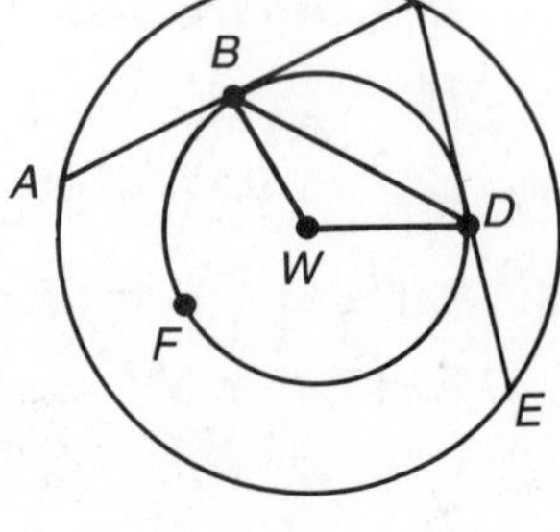

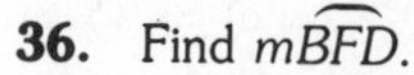

36. Find $m\widehat{BFD}$. **37.** Find $m\angle W$.

38. Find $m\angle WDE$. **39.** Find $m\angle WBD$.

40. Find $m\widehat{AC}$.

41. Given: $\overline{QA}$ tangent to both externally tangent circles.

Prove: $QC \cdot QB = QE \cdot QD$

42. Prove Theorem 12.16 for two tangents.

43. Prove Theorem 12.16 for one tangent and one secant.

12.8 The Coordinate Geometry of a Circle

OBJECTIVE

Given the equation of a circle, write the equation in standard form, determine the center and the radius, and graph the circle.

TEACHER'S NOTES

See p. T38

MIXED REVIEW

1. On a circle with diameter $\overline{AB}$, where would you locate P so that $\triangle PAB$ has the largest possible area. at the end of a radius $\perp$ $\overline{AB}$
2. What is the set of all points in space equidistant from the ends of $\overline{AB}$? $\perp$ bisecting plane of $\overline{AB}$
3. In an isosceles triangle with a vertex angle of 40, what are the base angles? 70
4. If $mx^2 + nx + p = 0$, then $x = ?$ $\frac{-n \pm \sqrt{n^2 - 4mp}}{2m}$
5. Solve $x^2 + x - 1 = 0$. $x = \frac{-1 \pm \sqrt{5}}{2}$

TEACHER'S RESOURCE MASTERS

Practice Master 39, Part 2
Quiz 24

You will now graph a circle by reading information from an equation. The equation of a line, written in its standard form $y = mx + b$, can be used to find the slope and y-intercept. In much the same way, the equation of a circle, written in standard form, can be used to find the center and radius.

THEOREM 12.18
A circle with center at (a, b) and radius $= r$ is the graph of the equation $(x - a)^2 + (y - b)^2 = r^2$.

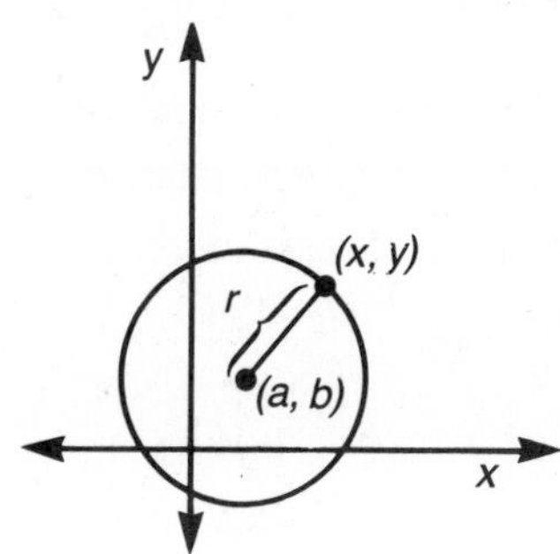

Given: $\odot O$ with center at (a, b) and radius $= r$

Prove: $\odot O$ is the graph of the equation $(x - a)^2 + (y - b)^2 = r^2$.

Proof: A circle is defined as the set of all coplanar points equidistant from a given point called the center. In the figure, (x, y) is any point in any quadrant that lies on the circle whose center is (a, b). The distance from (x, y) to (a, b) is r, the radius of the circle. Applying the distance formula, $r = \sqrt{(x - a)^2 + (y - b)^2}$, and squaring both sides will yield the equation given in Theorem 12.18, $r^2 = (x - a)^2 + (y - b)^2$.

Example: Graph the equation $(x - 1)^2 + (y + 2)^2 = 9$.

Solution: Write the equation in standard form: $(x - 1)^2 + [y - (-2)]^2 = 9$. The center is $(1, -2)$. Since $r^2 = 9$, the radius is 3 units.

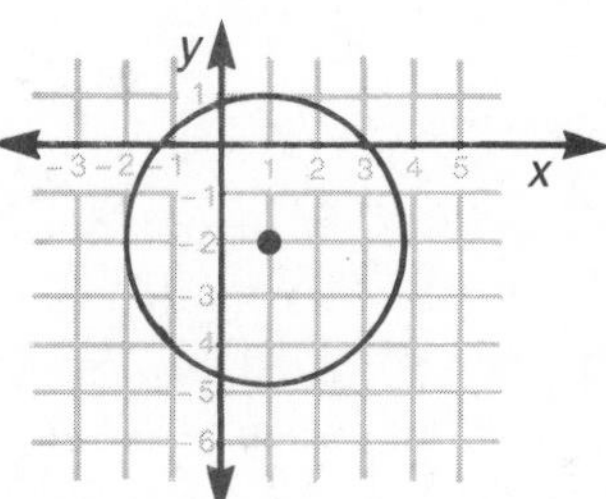

Example: Write the equation for a circle with its center at the origin and a radius of 4 units.

Solution: The origin is $(0, 0)$, so replacing (a, b) and r in the standard equation, $(x - 0)^2 + (y - 0)^2 = 4^2$, which simplifies to $x^2 + y^2 = 16$.

Example: Write the equation for a circle with its center at $(-4, 0)$ and a radius of 5 units.

Solution: Replacing (a, b) and r in the standard equation yields $(x + 4)^2 + y^2 = 25$.

THEOREM 12.19
Every circle is the graph of an equation of the form $x^2 + y^2 + Ax + By + C = 0$.

In Theorem 12.19, A, B, and C represent known constants. To be put in standard form, $x^2 + y^2 + Ax + By + C = 0$ must somehow become $(x - a)^2 + (y - b)^2 = r^2$. This is accomplished by completing the square.

Example: Write $2x^2 + 2y^2 - 8x + 12y - 10 = 0$ in standard form.

1. $2x^2 + 2y^2 - 8x + 12y = 10$	1. Move the constant term away from the others.
2. $x^2 + y^2 - 4x + 6y = 5$	2. Divide the equation so that the coefficients of the squared terms are 1.
3. $x^2 - 4x + y^2 + 6y = 5$	3. Group the x and y terms together.
4. $x^2 - 4x + 4 + y^2 + 6y + 9 = 5 + 4 + 9$	4. Take half of the x-term's coefficient, square it, and add it to both sides of the equation; repeat for the y-term.
5. $(x - 2)^2 + (y + 3)^2 = 18$	5. Factor the x and y terms separately; combine the constant terms on the other side of the equation.

Completing the square on $x^2 + y^2 + Ax + By + C = 0$ yields the following results:

$$x^2 + y^2 + Ax + By + C = 0$$
$$x^2 + Ax + y^2 + By = -C$$
$$x^2 + Ax + \tfrac{A^2}{4} + y^2 + By + \tfrac{B^2}{4} = -C + \tfrac{A^2}{4} + \tfrac{B^2}{4}$$
$$(x + \tfrac{A}{2})^2 + (y + \tfrac{B}{2})^2 = -C + \tfrac{A^2}{4} + \tfrac{B^2}{4}$$

Thus Theorem 12.20 can be made more specific by stating that $x^2 + y^2 + Ax + By + C = 0$ is

(1) a circle if $-C + \frac{A^2}{4} + \frac{B^2}{4} > 0$

(2) a point if $-C + \frac{A^2}{4} + \frac{B^2}{4} = 0$

(3) the empty set if $-C + \frac{A^2}{4} + \frac{B^2}{4} < 0$

Example: Write $4x^2 + 4y^2 + 12y + 4 = 0$ in standard form.

Solution:

$$4x^2 + 4y^2 + 12y = -4$$
$$x^2 + y^2 + 3y = -1$$
$$x^2 + y^2 + 3y + \tfrac{9}{4} = -1 + \tfrac{9}{4}$$
$$x^2 + (y + \tfrac{3}{2})^2 = \tfrac{5}{4}$$

Therefore, $C(0, -\frac{3}{2})$, $r = \sqrt{\frac{5}{4}} = \frac{\sqrt{5}}{2}$

If the steps of completing the square yield $(x - a)^2 + (y - b)^2 = 0$, then $r^2 = 0$. The equation is solved by $x = a$ and $y = b$, so it is just a complicated way of naming the point (a, b). Consider $(x + 3)^2 + (y - 1)^2 = -9$. According to the standard equation, $r^2 = -9$; therefore, no circle exists.

THEOREM 12.20
Given the equation $x^2 + y^2 + Ax + By + C = 0$, the graph of this equation is (1) a circle, (2) a point, or (3) the empty set.

ORAL EXERCISES

Give the center and radius (to the nearest whole number) of each of the circles in Exercises 1-6.

1. $(x-1)^2+(y-2)^2=9$ **2.** $(x+3)^2+(y-1)^2=25$

3. $x^2+(y+5)^2=17$ **4.** $(x-6)^2+y^2=4$

5. $x^2+y^2=35$ **6.** $x^2+y^2=1$

Give the equation of each graphed circle in Exercises 7-12.

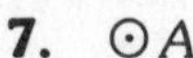

7. $\odot A$ **8.** $\odot B$

9. $\odot C$ **10.** $\odot D$

11. $\odot E$ **12.** $\odot F$

Give the value(s) that would be added to both sides of each equation in Exercises 13-20 to complete the square.

13. $x^2+4x+y^2-6y=1$

14. $x^2-2x+y^2+2y=3$

15. $x^2+x+y^2+4y=5$ **16.** $x^2+10x+y^2=3$

17. $x^2-3x+y^2-7y=5$ **18.** $x^2+y^2+8y=-2$

19. $x^2+x+y^2-y=1$ **20.** $x^2-9x+y^2-\frac{5}{2}y=2$

State whether each of the equations in Exercises 21-25 is the equation of a circle, a point, or the empty set.

21. $(x-3)^2+(y+2)^2=8$ **22.** $(x+1)^2+y^2=-7$

23. $x^2+y^2=10$ **24.** $(x+2)^2+(y-1)^2=0$

25. $x^2+(y+3)^2=\frac{7}{3}$

WRITTEN EXERCISES

A. Write the equation of each circle described in Exercises 1-5. C is the center.

1. $C(-2,-3)$, $r=1$ **2.** $C(1,5)$, $r=5$ **3.** $C(0,4)$, $r=3$

4. $C(0,0)$, $r=\frac{7}{2}$ **5.** $C(4,\frac{-2}{3})$, $r=4\frac{1}{3}$

Graph each of the following.

6. $(x+1)^2+(y+2)^2=4$ **7.** $(x-3)^2+y^2=9$ **8.** $x^2+y^2=25$

9. $(x-1)^2+(y+3)^2=\frac{9}{4}$ **10.** $x^2+(y-3)^2<9$

ASSIGNMENT GUIDE

Minimum 1-19 odd
Regular 1-23 odd
Maximum 1-35 odd

Oral Exercises

1. $C(1,2)$; $r=3$
2. $C(-3,1)$; $r=5$
3. $C(0,-5)$; $r=4$
4. $C(6,0)$; $r=2$
5. $C(0,0)$; $r=6$
6. $C(0,0)$; $r=1$
7. $x^2+y^2=4$
8. $(x-4)^2+y^2=1$
9. $(x+3)^2+(y-3)^2=9$
10. $x^2+(y-4)^2=4$
11. $(x-2)^2+(y+4)^2=1$
12. $(x+3)^2+(y+4)^2=4$

13. 4, 9 14. 1, 1
15. $\frac{1}{4}$, 4 16. 25, 0
17. $\frac{9}{4}$, $\frac{49}{4}$ 18. 0, 16
19. $\frac{1}{4}$, $\frac{1}{4}$ 20. $\frac{81}{4}$, $\frac{25}{16}$
21. circle 22. empty set
23. circle 24. point
25. circle

Written Exercises

1. $(x+2)^2+(y+3)^2=1$
2. $(x-1)^2+(y-5)^2=25$
3. $x^2+(y-4)^2=9$
4. $x^2+y^2=\frac{49}{4}$
5. $(x-4)^2+(y+\frac{2}{3})^2=\frac{169}{9}$

6-10. See *Teacher's Manual*, p. T61

11. circle 12. circle

13. circle 14. point

15. empty set

16. $(x + y)^2 \neq x^2 + y^2$

17. $(x + 2)^2 + (y - 1)^2 = 16$

18. $x^2 + (y - 2)^2 = 16$

19. $(x + 1)^2 + (y - 4)^2 = 40$

20. $(x - 5)^2 + y^2 = 13$

21. $(x - \frac{3}{2})^2 + (y + \frac{3}{2})^2 = \frac{74}{4}$

22. $(x - 2)^2 + (y + 1)^2 = 4$

23. $(x + 1)^2 + y^2 = 3$

24. $(x + \frac{3}{2})^2 + (y + \frac{3}{4})^2 = \frac{77}{16}$

25. $(x - 1)^2 + y^2 = 64$

26. $x^2 + y^2 = 25$

27. $C(\frac{-b}{2a}, \frac{-c}{2a})$,

$r = \sqrt{\frac{b^2 + c^2 - 4ad}{2a}}$

28. $(-1, 4)$

29. $(-2, 3)$

30. $(-1, \frac{-1}{2})$

31. $(a, b + r)$

32. $(a, b - r)$

33. $(a + r, b)$

34. $(a - r, b)$

35. $(0, -4)$ and $(3, -1)$

B. Indicate whether each equation in Exercises 11–15 is the equation of a circle, a point, or the empty set.

11. $x^2 + 6x + y^2 + 2y = 3$

12. $x^2 - 4x + y^2 - 8y = -15$

13. $x^2 + y^2 + 2x - 6y + 9 = 0$

14. $3x^2 + 3y^2 - 6x - 18y + 30 = 0$

15. $5x^2 + 5y^2 + 5x - 20y + 50 = 0$

16. Explain the mistake in the following chain of steps: $(x + y)^2 = 25$ is the same as $x^2 + y^2 = 25$, so the equation describes a circle whose center is $(0, 0)$ and whose radius is 5.

Translate the information in Exercises 17–26 into the standard form for a circle. C is the center and A and B are two points at the opposite ends of a diameter.

17. $C(-2, 1)$, $r = 4$

18. $C(0, 2)$, $A(4, 2)$

19. $C(-1, 4)$, $A(-3, 10)$

20. $A(8, 2)$, $B(2, -2)$

21. $A(5, 1)$, $B(-2, -4)$

22. $3x^2 + 3y^2 - 12x + 6y + 3 = 0$

23. $4x^2 + 4y^2 + 8x - 8 = 0$

24. $2x^2 + 2y^2 + 6x + 3y - 4 = 0$

25. The circle is concentric with $(x - 1)^2 + y^2 = 16$ but its radius is twice as long.

26. The center of the circle is the origin, and it contains the point of intersection of the lines $y = x - 7$ and $y = 2x - 10$.

C. 27. Find the center and radius of this equation:
$ax^2 + bx + ay^2 + cy + d = 0$.

Use the results of Exercise 27 to predict the center of the circles in Exercises 28–30 without completing the square.

28. $x^2 + 2x + y^2 - 8y = 5$

29. $3x^2 + 12x + 3y^2 - 18y = 9$

30. $2x^2 + 2y^2 + 4x + 2y - 3 = 0$

Given $(x - a)^2 + (y - b)^2 = r^2$, find the coordinates of the following points on its graph:

31. the highest point of the circle

32. the lowest point of the circle

33. the farthest right point of the circle

34. the farthest left point of the circle

35. Without graphing, find the points of intersection of the circle $(x - 2)^2 + (y + 3)^2 = 5$ and the line $y = x - 4$.

SKILLS MAINTENANCE

What values, if any, must be excluded from the replacement sets of the variables below?

1. $\frac{9}{x} = \frac{7}{x-4}$ **2.** $\frac{3}{x} - \frac{2}{3x} = \frac{14}{3}$ **3.** $\frac{y}{2} + \frac{y}{3} = 5$ **4.** $\frac{1+k}{3-k} = \frac{3}{5}$

Solve each equation. Remember that multiplying an expression containing a variable may introduce extraneous roots. Check all roots in the original equation.

5. $2 - \frac{1}{x} = \frac{5}{x}$ **6.** $\frac{3}{y-3} = 2 + \frac{y}{y-3}$ **7.** $\frac{5}{s+3} = \frac{3}{s-1}$

8. $\frac{8}{n} = 4$ **9.** $\frac{2y}{y+1} = 2 - \frac{3}{y}$ **10.** $\frac{-x}{x-2} - 2 + \frac{x}{x-2} = 0$

Solve each equation. Remember that squaring both sides may introduce extraneous roots. Check all solutions in the original equation.

11. $\sqrt{x-2} = 3$ **12.** $y = 1 + \sqrt{3-y}$ **13.** $\sqrt{5r-2} = \sqrt{5}$

14. $\sqrt{x+1} = 11$ **15.** $1 + \sqrt{x-1} = x$ **16.** $y = 3 + \sqrt{10-6y}$

CHALLENGE

A record convention is being held in an exhibition hall, which has 4335.48 ft^2 of exhibit space. Booths are arranged along six aisles: 1) Rock 'n Roll, 2) Rhythm & Blues, 3) Easy Listening, 4) Classical, 5) Country/Western, and 6) Golden Oldies. The square booths are 15 × 15 ft. Each rectangular booth is as wide as a square booth, but 20 percent longer. Two sides of each triangular booth are as long as a square booth; the other side is as long as a rectangular booth. The diameter of each circular booth is twice the altitude of a triangular booth.

From the floor plan at the right, find the area of exhibit space in each aisle of booths. Which aisle has the most exhibit space? (HINT: Use the Pythagorean Theorem to find the area of each triangular booth. Use 3.14 as the value for pi.)

Aisle 1 Aisle 2 Aisle 3 Aisle 4 Aisle 5 Aisle 6

EXIT EXIT

Skills Maintenance

1. 0, 4 2. 0
3. none 4. 3
5. $x = 3$ 6. ∅
7. $s = 7$ 8. $n = 2$
9. $y = -3$ 10. ∅
11. $x = 11$ 12. $y = 2$
13. $r = \frac{7}{5}$ 14. $x = 120$
15. $x = 1$ or $x = 2$ 16. ∅

Challenge

The area of one square = 15 × 15 = 225 ft^2. The area of one rectangle is 15 × 18 (15 · 1.2) = 270 ft^2. Therefore, each triangle is 15 × 15 × 18, an isosceles triangle. The altitude must therefore create two right triangles. By the Pythagorean Theorem, if the hypotenuse and base are 15 and 9, then the altitude must be 12 ($15^2 - 9^2 = 12^2$). So the area of one triangle = $\frac{1}{2}(18 \cdot 12) = 108$ ft^2. If the diameter of a circle is twice the altitude of a triangle, then the radius is the same as that altitude, so the area of a circle = $3.14 \cdot 12^2 = 452.16$ ft^2.

Aisle 1 = 108 + 225 + 225 + 108 = 666 ft^2
Aisle 2 = 270 + 108 + 225 = 603 ft^2
Aisle 3 = 225 + 452.16 + 225 = 902.16 ft^2
Aisle 4 = 108 + 108 + 108 + 108 = 432 ft^2
Aisle 5 = 270 + 225 + 225 = 720 ft^2
Aisle 6 = 452.16 + 108 + 452.16 = 1012.32 ft^2

The "Golden Oldies" aisle has the most space.

IN OTHER FIELDS/Astronomy

The concept of alternate interior angles led to a discovery by Erastosthenes, a Greek mathematician who lived in the third century B.C. An individual with many talents, Erastosthenes was also director of the Alexandria Library. It was there that he read: *In Syene, at noon on June 21, vertical sticks cast no shadows. June 21 is the longest day of the year, and at noon the sun is directly overhead.*

Intrigued, Erastosthenes decided to conduct the same experiment in Alexandria. To his surprise, at noon on June 21, sticks *did* cast shadows in Alexandria. In an attempt to decipher this puzzle, Erastosthenes noted that Syene was far to the south of Alexandria. If the sun were directly overhead everywhere, no shadows would be cast in either city. He was forced to conclude that the surface of the Earth is curved and that the greater the difference in shadow lengths, the greater the curvature.

Erastosthenes concluded that because the sun is far away, its rays are parallel when they reach the Earth. The figure below illustrates his reasoning. He pictured the sticks extending down to the center of the Earth. From the shadow length in Alexandria, he calculated $\angle A$ to have a measure of 7. Then, using the concept of alternate interior angles, he knew that $\angle A \cong \angle B$. Thus he concluded that Syene was 7 degrees away from Alexandria on the *circumference* of (or distance around) the Earth, or approximately one-fiftieth of 360°.

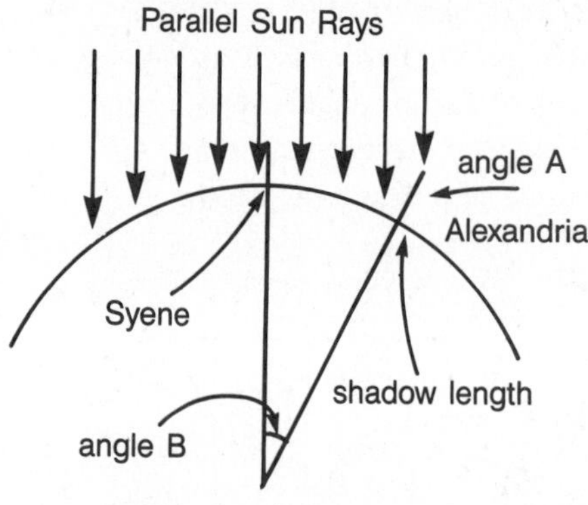

Determined to draw a more general conclusion, he hired a man to pace the distance between the two cities. The result was 800 kilometers. He then multiplied 800 (kilometers in 7 degrees) by 50 (how many angles of 7 degrees are in 360) to arrive at 40,000 kilometers, which he said must be the circumference of the Earth. Amazingly, his conclusion was correct within only a small percentage of error. Using alternate interior angles, Erastosthenes thus became the first person to measure accurately the size of a planet.

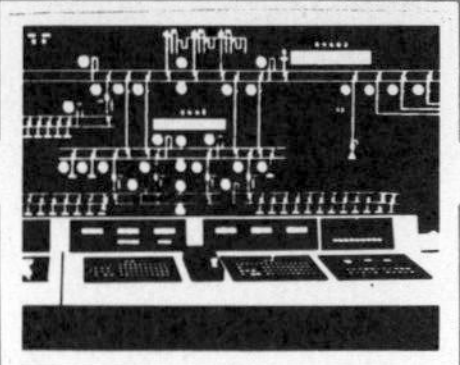

COMPUTER

The creation of coordinate geometry by René Descartes (1596–1650) made it possible to translate geometric relations into algebraic formulas. These formulas can be used with a computer. Consider the two lines at the right, represented by the system of linear equations $Ax + By = C$ and $Mx + Ny = P$. Using the multiplication-addition method to solve the system yields

$$x = \frac{CN - BP}{AN - BM} \text{ and } y = \frac{AP - CM}{AN - BM}.$$

The following program will find the point of intersection for two different lines that do not have the same slope.

```
10  PRINT"INPUT THE COEFFICIENTS OF THE TWO LINES"
20  INPUT A,B,C,M,N,P
30  LET D = A*N - B*M
40  LET X = (C*N - B*P)/D
50  LET Y = (A*P - C*M)/D
60  PRINT"THE INTERSECTION IS X =;X" Y=;Y
70  GOTO 10
80  END
```

This program will work only for lines that have unequal slopes.

1. For coefficients, input 1, 2, 3, 4, 5, 6. Compare the results with an input of 3, 4, 5, 6, 7, 8 and with 5, 6, 7, 8, 9, 10.

2. Create a line after line 20 to allow the user to exit the program.

3. Create a line after line 30 to identify and eliminate lines that have the same slope.

In science and mathematics, you must often solve formulas for a single variable before you can use a computer. Solve the formulas below for the variable shown.

4. If $A = \frac{1}{2}bh$, then $b =$ _____.

5. If $E = mc^2$, then $m =$ _____.

TEACHER'S RESOURCE MASTERS

Computer Master 12

COMPUTER SOFTWARE

Angles, Arcs, and Transformation

1. The results for consecutive coefficients will always be $x = -1$ and $y = 2$.
2. Answers will vary. For example, Line 25 IF A = −9999 THEN GOTO 80.
3. For example, Line 35 IF D = 0 THEN PRINT"INVALID DATA. LINES HAVE THE SAME SLOPE.":GOTO 10.
4. $b = \frac{2A}{h}$
5. $m = \frac{E}{c^2}$

TEACHER'S RESOURCE MASTERS

Enrichment Master 9

ENRICHMENT

See Activities 23-24, p. T51

Chapter 12 Review

1. $\overline{CD}$, $\overline{PT}$, $\overline{PR}$
2. $\overrightarrow{AB}$
3. $\overrightarrow{AF}$
4. $\overline{EF}$
5. S
6. P, S, C
7. $\overline{RT}$
8. $\odot P$, $\odot P$
9. large $\odot P$, $\odot C$
10. $\odot C$, $\odot S$
11. 90
12. YX
13. Q
14. $\overline{RS}$

CHAPTER 12 REVIEW

VOCABULARY

arc (12.4)
center (12.1)
central angle (12.4)
chord (12.1)
circle (12.1)
concentric circles (12.2)
congruent arcs (12.6)
congruent circles (12.2)
diameter (12.1)
exterior of a circle (12.1)
exterior of a sphere (12.3)
externally tangent (12.1)
great circle (12.1)
inscribed angle (12.5)
inscribed polygon (12.5)
intercepted arc (12.4)
interior of a circle (12.1)
interior of a sphere (12.3)
internally tangent (12.1)
major arc (12.4)
measure of an arc (12.4)
minor arc (12.4)
point of contact (12.1)
point of tangency (12.1)
power of the point (12.7)
radius (12.1)
radius of a sphere (12.3)
secant (12.1)
secant segment (12.7)
semicircle (12.4)
sphere (12.1)
tangent (12.1)
tangent plane (12.3)
tangent segment (12.7)

REVIEW EXERCISES

12.1 Refer to the figure at the right to name the following:

1. three radii
2. a tangent line
3. a secant
4. a chord
5. an interior point of $\odot C$
6. three centers
7. a diameter
8. two concentric circles
9. externally tangent circles
10. internally tangent circles

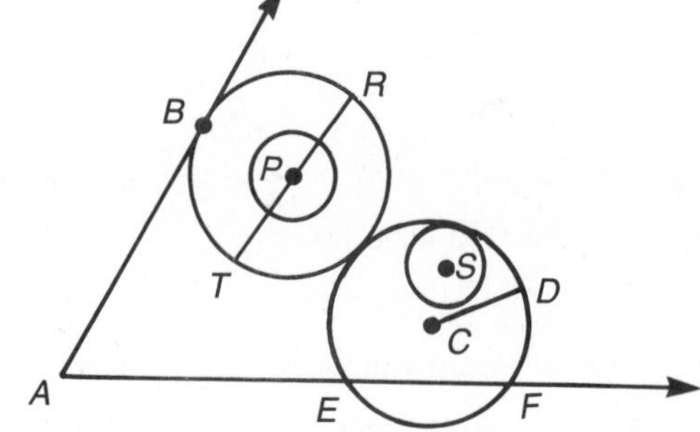

12.2 Refer to the figure of $\odot Q$ for Exercises 11–14.

11. If $\overleftrightarrow{UV}$ is tangent to $\odot Q$ at Z, then $m\angle XZU$ = _____.
12. If $m\angle QXW = 90$, then WX = _____.
13. If $\overline{ZX} \perp \overline{WY}$ and $\overline{WX} \cong \overline{YX}$, then $\overline{ZX}$ contains point _____.
14. If $QX = QT$, then $\overline{WY} \cong$ _____.

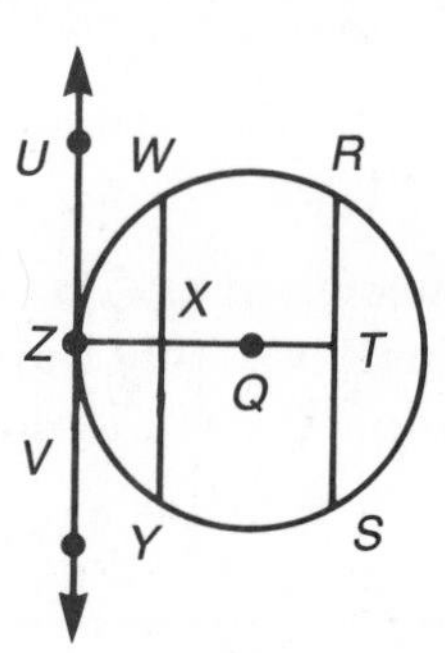

12.3 **Plane L is tangent to sphere M at N.**

15. Name a point exterior to sphere M.

16. Name a point interior to sphere M.

17. $\overline{OR} \cong$ ____ **18.** $\overline{MN}$ is ____ plane J.

12.4 **$\odot P$ has diameters $\overline{AB}$ and $\overline{CD}$. Choose the best answer to complete each statement.**

19. $\widehat{ABC}$ is a ____. **a.** minor arc **b.** major arc **c.** semicircle

20. A central angle is ____. **a.** $\angle ABC$ **b.** $\angle CAB$ **c.** $\angle APC$

21. $\angle DPB$ intercepts ____. **a.** $\widehat{DB}$ **b.** $\angle APC$ **c.** $\widehat{AB}$

22. $m\widehat{AC} + m\widehat{BC} =$ ____. **a.** 180 **b.** $m\widehat{AB}$ **c.** a and b

12.5 **23.** An inscribed triangle is ____. **a.** $\triangle APD$ **b.** $\triangle DAB$ **c.** $\triangle DQA$

24. If $m\angle BCD = 30$, then $m\widehat{BC} =$ ____. **a.** 30 **b.** 60 **c.** 120 **d.** 150

25. $m\angle CBD =$ ____. **a.** 45 **b.** 60 **c.** 90 **d.** 180

26. $m\angle RAD =$ ____. **a.** $m\widehat{AD}$ **b.** $\frac{1}{2}m\widehat{AD}$ **c.** $m\angle APD$

12.6 **27.** If $\overline{AD} \cong \overline{BC}$, then $\widehat{AD} \cong$ ____. **a.** $\widehat{AC}$ **b.** $\widehat{BD}$ **c.** $\widehat{BC}$

28. If $\overline{AD} \parallel \overline{BC}$, then $\widehat{BD} \cong$ ____. **a.** $\widehat{AC}$ **b.** $\widehat{BC}$ **c.** $\widehat{AD}$

12.7 **29.** $QC \cdot QD =$ ____. **a.** QA^2 **b.** $QC \cdot CD$ **c.** $CP \cdot CD$

30. The power of point P is ____. **a.** $CP \cdot DP$ **b.** $BP \cdot AP$ **c.** a and b

31. If $m\widehat{AC} = 70$, then $m\angle AQD$ is ____. **a.** 35 **b.** 20 **c.** 40

32. $m\angle APC =$ ____. **a.** $m\angle DPB$ **b.** $m\widehat{AC}$ **c.** $\frac{1}{2}(m\widehat{AC} + m\widehat{BD})$ **d.** a, b, and c

12.8 **Given the equation $x^2 + y^2 + 10x - 6y + 3 = 0$,**

33. write the equation in standard form.

34. what is the center of the circle?

35. what is the radius of the circle?

Given the equation $3x^2 + 3y^2 - 42x - 12y + 111 = 0$,

36. write the equation in standard form. **37.** what is the center of the circle?

38. what is the radius of the circle? **39.** graph the circle.

15. L
16. M
17. RP
18. $\perp$
19. b
20. c
21. a
22. c
23. b
24. c
25. c 26. b
27. c 28. a
29. a 30. c
31. b 32. d
33. $(x - (-5))^2 + (y - 3)^2 = 31$
34. $(-5, 3)$ 35. $\sqrt{31}$
36. $(x - 7)^2 + (y - 2)^2 = 16$
37. $(7, 2)$ 38. 4
39.

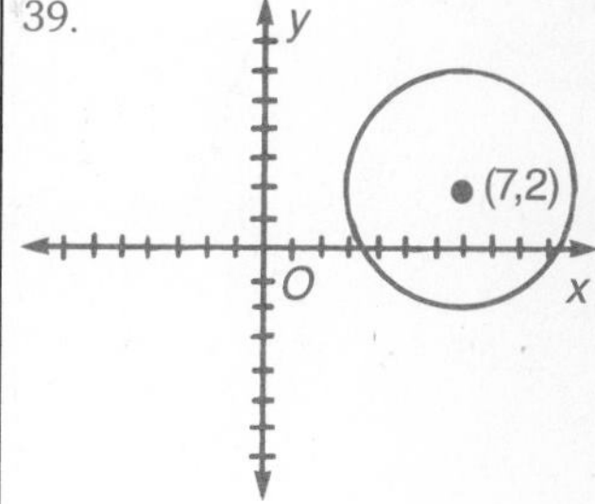

TEACHER'S RESOURCE MASTERS

Chapter 12 Test
Multiple Choice Test—Chapter 12

Chapter 12 Test

1. F
2. T
3. T
4. T
5. F
6. T
7. F
8. F
9. F
10. T
11. F
12. T
13. T
14. F
15. 25
16. $\overset{\frown}{CD}$
17. 40
18. 8
19. 8
20. 20
21. $C(-2, 3)$ $r = 3$
22. $x^2 + y^2 = 25$

CHAPTER 12 TEST

Tell whether each statement is <u>true</u> or <u>false</u>.

1. Concentric circles have the same radius.

2. If a secant passes through the center of a circle, then it contains a diameter of the circle.

3. The diameter of a great circle is a diameter of its sphere.

4. Lines tangent to the opposite ends of a diameter are parallel.

5. Chords equidistant from the center of a circle are parallel.

6. A radius perpendicular to a chord bisects the chord.

7. A plane perpendicular to the radius of a sphere is a tangent plane.

8. A chord perpendicular to the radius of a sphere bisects the radius.

9. A major arc may be named by its two endpoints.

10. A central angle can be measured by the arc it intercepts.

11. If two arcs of the same circle intersect in more than one point, the measure of their union is the sum of their measures.

12. If an arc is intercepted by each of two inscribed angles, the angles are congruent.

13. If two chords of a circle are perpendicular at their common endpoint, their other endpoints determine a diameter.

14. Opposite angles of an inscribed quadrilateral are congruent.

Refer to the figure to answer Exercises 15–20.

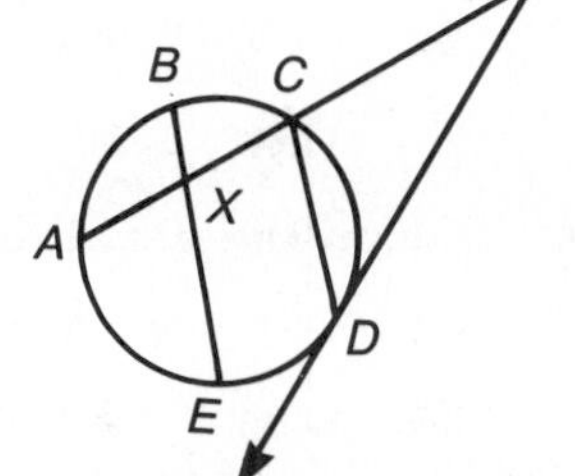

15. If $m\overset{\frown}{BC} = 50$, then $m\angle BDC =$ _____.

16. If $\overline{BE} \cong \overline{CD}$, then $\overset{\frown}{BE} \cong$ _____.

17. If $\overline{BE} \parallel \overline{CD}$, and $m\overset{\frown}{ED} = 80$, then $m\angle BDC =$ _____.

18. $PA = 16$, $PC = 4$, $PD =$ _____.

19. $BX = 2$, $EX = 8$, $AX = 4$, $AC =$ _____.

20. $m\overset{\frown}{AD} = 100$, $m\overset{\frown}{CD} = 60$, $m\angle APD =$ _____.

21. Determine the center and radius of the circle whose equation is $2x^2 + 2y^2 + 8x - 12y + 8 = 0$.

22. Determine the equation of the circle whose center is the origin and whose diameter is 10.

CUMULATIVE REVIEW: CHAPTERS 9–12

1. In $\triangle ABC$, the area of $\triangle ABD = 10$, the area of $\triangle BEC = 13$, and the area of $\triangle DEC = 12$. If $\triangle ABC \cong \triangle XYZ$, find the area of $\triangle XYZ$.

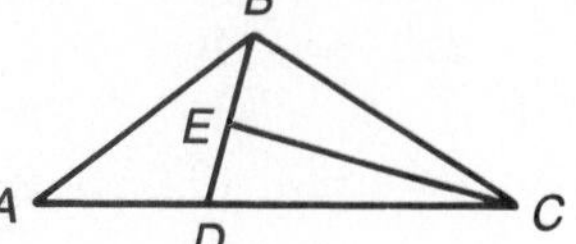

a. 70 **b.** 35 **c.** 15 **d.** 140

2. The area of a rectangle is 32 cm^2. The length is 8 less than 4 times as long as the width. Find the length and width of the rectangle.

a. $-16, -2$ **b.** 16, 2 **c.** 8, 4 **d.** 1, 32

3. In right $\triangle JKL$, $\angle K$ is a right $\angle$. If $JK = 9$ and $LK = 6$, find the area of $\triangle JKL$.

a. 27 **b.** 54 **c.** 28 **d.** 56

4. Find the area of ▱$PQRS$.

a. 85 **b.** 42.5 **c.** 160 **d.** 170

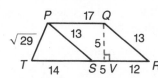

5. Find the area of trapezoid $PQRT$.

a. 170 **b.** 120 **c.** 90 **d.** 240

6. In right $\triangle MNP$, $MN = 9$, $NP = 13$, and $\angle N$ is a right $\angle$. Find MP.

a. 21 **b.** 25 **c.** $5\sqrt{10}$ **d.** $10\sqrt{5}$

7. In right $\triangle GHK$, $m\angle G = 30$ and $m\angle K = 60$. If $GK = 36$, find GH.

a. 18 **b.** $18\sqrt{2}$ **c.** $36\sqrt{3}$ **d.** $18\sqrt{3}$

8. What is the ratio of 5 feet to 7 yards?

a. $\frac{5}{21}$ **b.** $\frac{5}{7}$ **c.** $\frac{15}{21}$ **d.** $\frac{15}{7}$

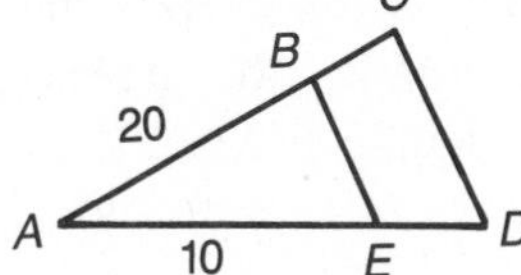

9. In the figure, $\overline{EB} \parallel \overline{DC}$. Find AC.

a. 6 **b.** 26 **c.** 13 **d.** 33

10. How would you prove the triangles at the right are similar?

a. AA **b.** AAA **c.** ASA **d.** SSS

11. $\triangle ABC \sim \triangle DEF$. $BC = x$ and $EF = 3x$. If $AC = \frac{x}{5}$, find DF.

a. $\frac{x}{3}$ **b.** $\frac{x}{15}$ **c.** $\frac{x}{5}$ **d.** $\frac{3x}{5}$

12. $\triangle JKN \sim \triangle MNO$. If $JK = 4$, $MN = 12$, and the area of $\triangle JKN = 6$, find the area of $\triangle MNO$.

a. 18 **b.** 54 **c.** 24 **d.** 96

TEACHER'S RESOURCE MASTERS

Cumulative Test—Chapters 1-12
Form A or B

Cumulative Review: Chapters 9-16

1. b
2. c
3. a
4. a
5. b
6. c
7. d
8. a
9. b
10. a
11. d
12. b

For Exercises 13–17, refer to the coordinate system below.

13. d

13. What are the coordinates of *A*? **a.** (−1, 5) **b.** (5, −1) **c.** (1, −5) **d.** (−5, 1)

14. c

14. What is the slope of $\overrightarrow{AB}$?

a. $\frac{-1}{3}$ **b.** −3 **c.** $\frac{1}{3}$ **d.** 3

15. b

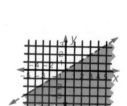

15. Given *D*(−6, −5) and *J*(6, −1), find *DJ*.

a. 6 **b.** $4\sqrt{10}$ **c.** 2 **d.** $6\sqrt{5}$

16. d

16. In △*BHJ*, if *BK* is a median, find the coordinates of *K* given *H*(−2, 2) and *J*(6, −1).

a. $(4, \frac{3}{2})$ **b.** $(\frac{3}{2}, 4)$ **c.** $(\frac{1}{2}, 2)$ **d.** $(2, \frac{1}{2})$

17. c

17. To prove △*BCA* is a right △, you could show that *m* of $\overline{AB}$ and *m* of $\overline{BC}$ are
a. inverses. **b.** equal. **c.** negative reciprocals.
d. reciprocals.

18. c

18. What equation matches the graph at the right?

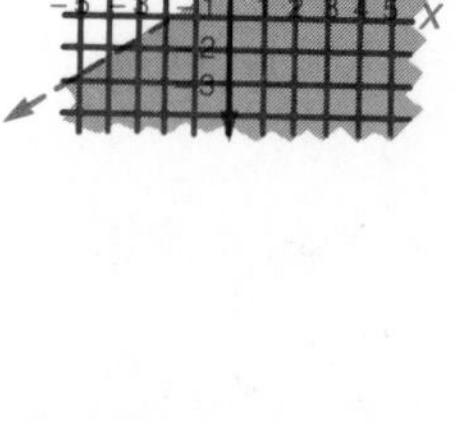

a. $x = 2y$ **b.** $x \geq 2y$

c. $x > 2y$ **d.** $x < 2y$

19. a

19. In the equation $3y = 2x + 15$, what is the slope of the line?

a. $\frac{2}{3}$ **b.** $\frac{3}{2}$ **c.** $\frac{-2}{3}$ **d.** 2

20. b

20. If the radius of one circle is the diameter of another circle, the circles are

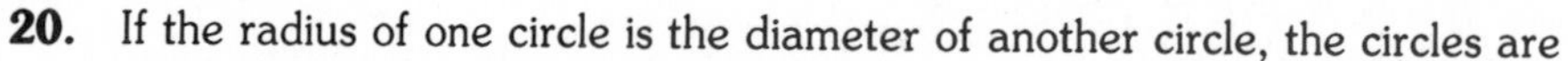

a. concentric. **b.** internally tangent. **c.** externally tangent.
d. congruent.

For Exercises 21–23, refer to the figure of ⊙*D*.

21. c

21. If $m\angle ADB = 55$, then $m\widehat{AB} =$ _____.

a. $27\frac{1}{2}$ **b.** 28 **c.** 55 **d.** 110

22. b

22. If $m\angle AEB = 22$, $m\widehat{AB} =$ _____.

a. 22 **b.** 44 **c.** 11 **d.** 88

23. c

23. If *HA* = 4 and *AE* = 12, find *HG*.

a. 4 **b.** $4\sqrt{3}$ **c.** 8 **d.** $8\sqrt{3}$

24. a

24. The equation of ⊙*A* is $x^2 + (y + 3)^2 - 25 = 0$. Find the center of ⊙*A*.

a. (0, −3) **b.** (0, 3) **c.** (−5, 3) **d.** (5, −3)

PREPARING FOR COLLEGE ENTRANCE EXAMS

Select the correct answer for each of the following questions.

1. The area of $\triangle ABC = 18$ and $m\angle A = 45$. Find $\overline{AC}$.

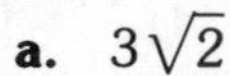

a. $3\sqrt{2}$ **b.** $6\sqrt{2}$ **c.** $9\sqrt{2}$

d. $12\sqrt{2}$ **e.** $18\sqrt{2}$

2. In $\triangle ABC$, $\overline{DE} \parallel \overline{AC}$, $\overline{BE} = 2$, $\overline{CE} = 4$, and $\overline{DE} = 3$. Find $\overline{AC}$.

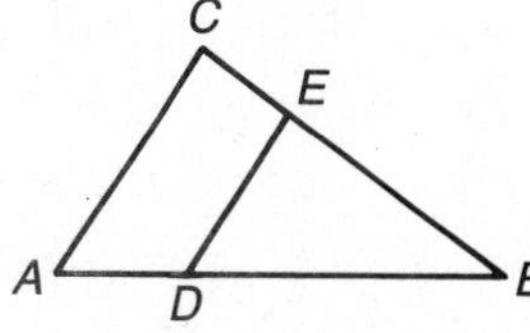

a. 5.4 **b.** 6 **c.** 7.2

d. 7.6 **e.** 9

3. Point $M(a, b)$ is the midpoint of the line segment connecting point $A(2a, b)$ and point $B(x, y)$. Find $x + y$.

a. a **b.** b **c.** $a + b$ **d.** $a - 2b$ **e.** $-a$

4. What is the area of quadrilateral $ABCD$?

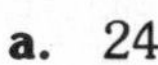

a. 24 **b.** 30

c. 35 **d.** 36

e. 48

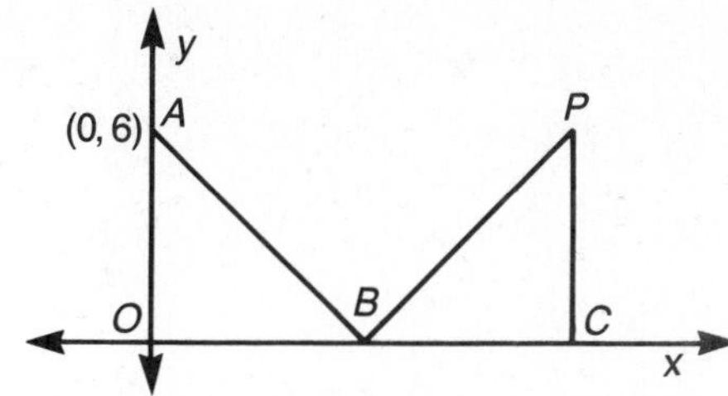

5. $\triangle AOB$ and $\triangle PCB$ are right isosceles $\triangle$s with equal areas. What are the coordinates of point P?

a. (12, 6) **b.** (6, 12)

c. (12, 5) **d.** (0, 12)

e. (6, 0)

Preparing for College Entrance Exams

1. b

2. e

3. b

4. d

5. a

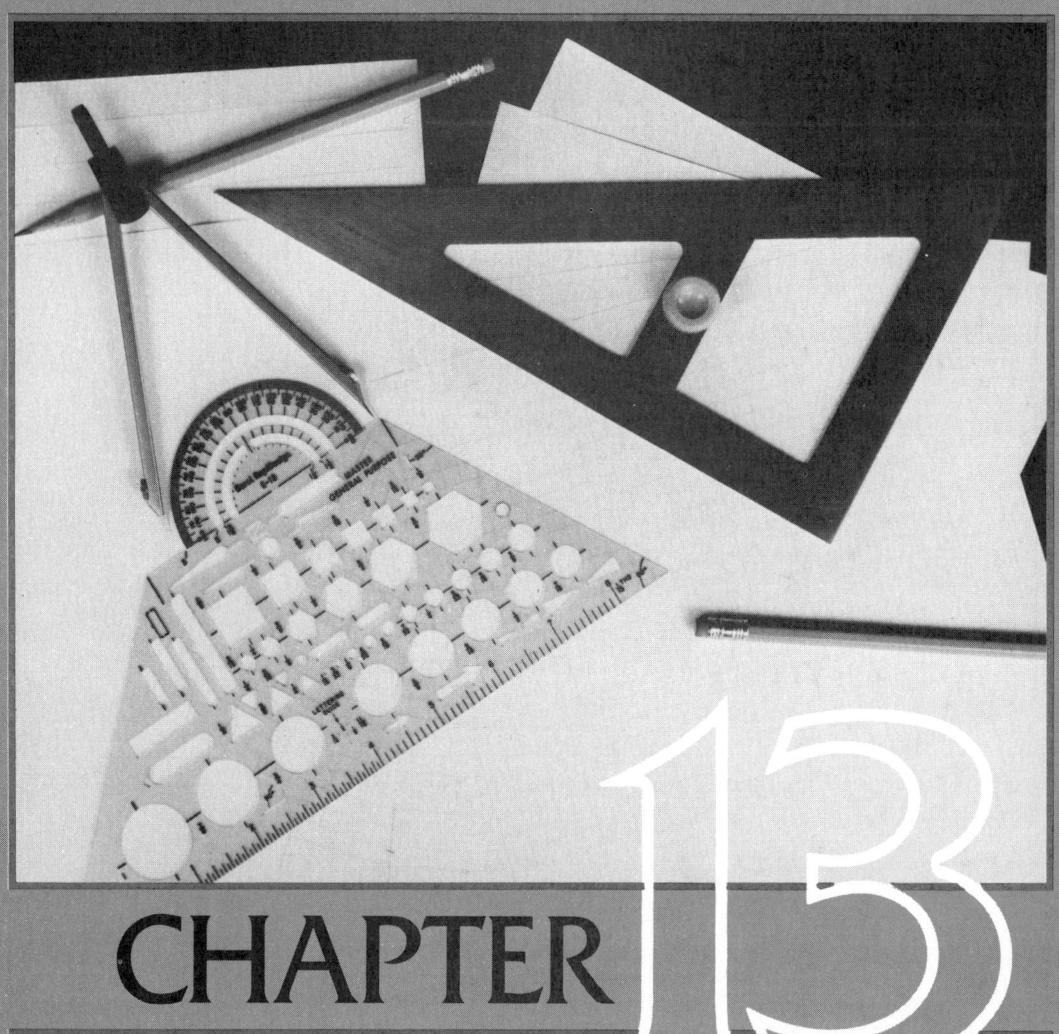

CHAPTER 13

Constructions

13.1 Loci/Set Characterizations

Sets come in an infinite variety, and every set is characterized by a condition. This means that each member of a set shares a condition, and no element satisfying the condition exists outside that set.

Many geometric concepts are easier to understand when characterized as sets of points. In Chapter 5, you proved that the perpendicular bisector of a segment, in a plane, is the set of all points of the plane that are equidistant from the endpoints of the segment.

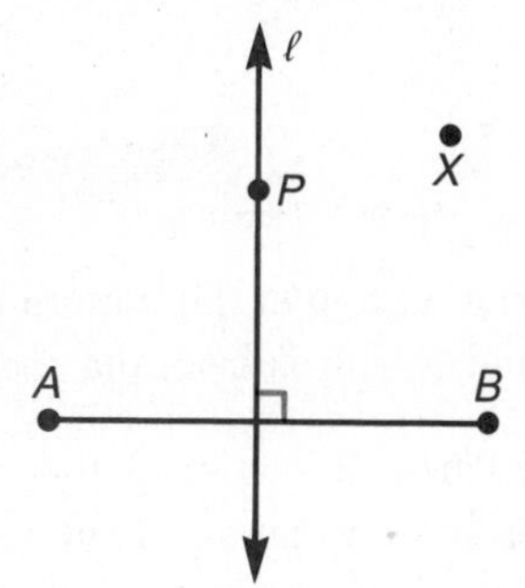

As shown in the figure at the right, all points characterized by the above statement form a line, l. If a point P in the plane of l is equidistant from A and B, then it lies on l. If a point X does not lie on l, then it is not equidistant from A and B.

A figure formed by all points that satisfy a given condition is called a **locus of points** (plural, **loci**). Different conditions may produce different geometric figures as loci. In a plane, a locus of points could be a point, a ray, two lines, or some other figure. In space, the possibilities increase. For example, the set of all points in space equidistant from the endpoints of a segment is the perpendicular bisecting plane of the segment.

Example: In a plane, what is the locus of points 3 units from a given point P?

Solution: Sketch several points that satisfy the condition. Then see if any identifiable figure emerges.

Only five points have been sketched in the figure shown at the right. Already, you can see that a circle is beginning to take shape. Its center is at P, and its radius is 3.

Now it remains for you to answer the question. Words may vary, but the characterization must be precise, and it must contain two parts. The first part names the figure, and the second part describes it:

> "In a plane, *the locus of points* three units from a point P *is a circle* with its *center on* P and a *radius of 3 units.*"

OBJECTIVE

Describe and sketch geometric figures that satisfy a given condition.

TEACHER'S NOTES

See p. T38

MIXED REVIEW

1. Solve $7 \leq 2x - 1 \leq 15$. $4 \leq x \leq 8$
2. Solve $|2x - 4| = 12$. $\{8, -4\}$
3. What is the area of an equilateral triangle with an altitude of $7\sqrt{3}$ $49\sqrt{3}$
4. Solve $|x - 1| < 8$. $-7 < x < 9$
5. Factor $15x^2 - 7x - 2$. $(5x + 1)(3x - 2)$

TEACHER'S RESOURCE MASTERS

Practice Master 40, Part 1

Example: Locus problems become more challenging when two or more conditions are imposed on points. Imagine that you have found this piece of a treasure map:

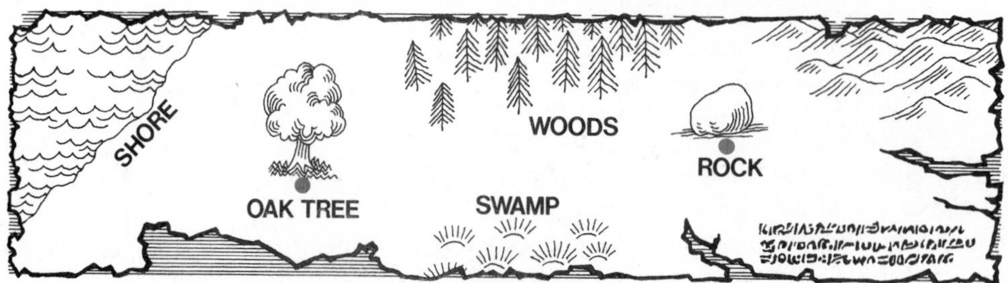

The writing at the bottom of the map states that the treasure is buried 30 yards from the oak and 50 yards from the rock. Given this information, where should you dig?

Solution: You know that the locus of points at a given distance from a point is a circle. Does this mean that you have to dig two huge circular trenches, one with a radius of 30 yards and the other with a radius of 50 yards? This would be a formidable job.

The map states that *both* characterizations have to apply, and two circles can intersect in at most two points. The figure at the right shows that only two points meet both conditions. At most, you must dig two holes.

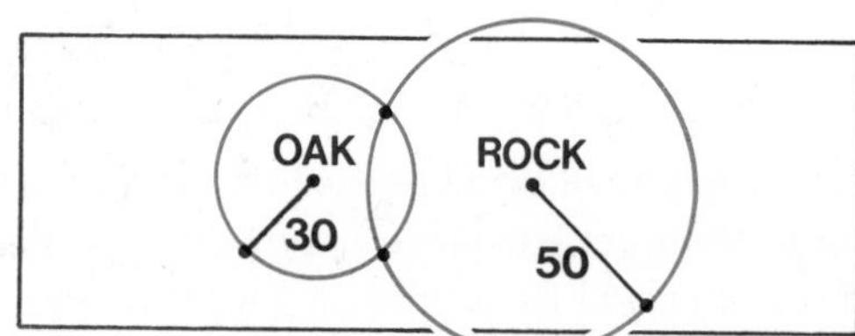

ASSIGNMENT GUIDE

Minimum 1-6
Regular 1-9 odd
Maximum 1-7 odd, 8-11

Oral Exercises

1. a) two lines parallel to, and one inch on either side of the given line
   b) a cylinder of radius 1 in. around the given line
2. a line parallel to and half the distance between the two given lines
3. point C
4. the point of intersection of the two diagonals
5. the line that is the intersection of the two planes that bisect the other two walls
6. an oval surrounding $\overline{AB}$ at a distance of 1 cm
7. if the circles were tangent

ORAL EXERCISES

1. What is the locus of points that are 1 inch from a given line
(a) in a plane? (b) in space?

2. What is the locus of points in a plane P that are equidistant from two parallel lines in P?

3. What is the locus of points in a plane P that are equidistant from every point on circle C lying in P?

4. What is the locus of points equidistant from the vertices of a rectangle?

5. What is the locus of points equidistant from the ceiling, floor, and two opposite walls of your classroom?

6. $\overline{AB}$ is a segment of length 2 cm in a plane P. What is the locus of points in P that are 1 cm from $\overline{AB}$?

7. Referring back to the treasure map example, under what circumstance would you only need to dig one hole?

WRITTEN EXERCISES

A. **1.** Sketch and describe the locus of points in a plane S that lie in the interior of an angle, $\angle A$, and are equidistant from its sides.

2. Write a statement characterizing the set of points on the red circles in relation to the black circle, O.

3. Sketch the following characterization and tell whether it is true or false. *The locus of points that are midpoints of the radii of a given circle is a circle concentric with the given circle and with a radius equal to one-half the radius of the given circle.*

B. **4.** Sketch and describe the locus of points that are midpoints of all possible chords of a circle, where the chords share a given point of the circle as a common endpoint.

5. Name the locus of the centers of all circles that are concentric with a circle having the center A.

6. Name the locus of points in a plane that are 2 cm from each of two points 5 cm apart.

7. Describe the locus of points that are a units from $\odot C$, which has radius r. There are three possible answers. Explain why and give all three.

8. What equation describes the locus of points equidistant from the x-axis and the y-axis in a coordinate system.

9. A narrow plank lies on the ground perpendicular to the wall of a building, as shown at the right. If the end of the plank, P, were moved up the wall to any point above point X, what locus of points is described by all possible locations for the plank's midpoint, Q?

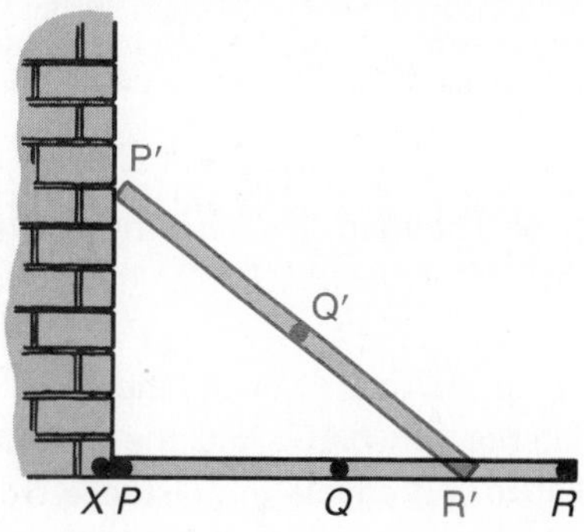

10. If the other end of the plank, point R, was raised instead, and P remained fixed at X, what locus of points would then be described by any location of midpoint Q?

C. **11.** Mr. Wilson lives in a house set back from the road. In the attic, he finds a note written by the previous owner of the house. The note states that a coin collection is buried at a point equidistant from the house and the road. Sketch a figure showing the locus of points where the collection could be buried. HINT: Let the house be a point, and let the road be a straight line. Remember the definitions of distance from a point to a point and from a point to a line.

Written Exercises

1. the bisector of $\angle A$, *not* including the vertex
2. the locus of points 1 in. from $\odot O$
3. true

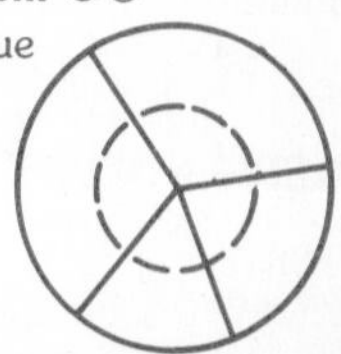

4. an internally tangent circle whose diameter equals the radius of the given circle

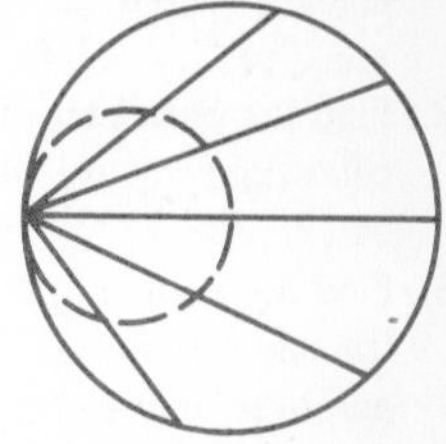

5. point A
6. the empty set
7. If $a < r$, the locus is two concentric circles with radii $r + a$ and $r - a$. If $a = r$, the locus is a concentric circle with radius $2r$ and the point C. If $a > r$, the locus is two concentric circles of radius $a + r$ and $a - r$.
8. $|x| = |y|$
9. The locus is a 90-degree arc of $\odot X$ with radius PQ.
10. The locus is also a 90-degree arc of $\odot X$ with radius PQ.
11. Students will draw a curve as shown below. The teacher may explain that this shape is called a *parabolic* curve.

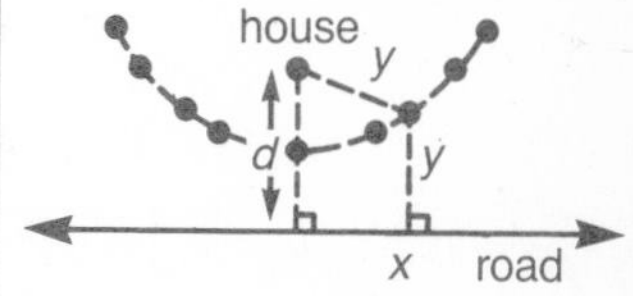

OBJECTIVE

Use Theorems 13.1–13.4 to answer questions regarding angle bisectors, points of concurrence, and set characterizations.

TEACHER'S NOTES

See p. T38

MIXED REVIEW

1. The supplement of an acute angle is always ________. obtuse
2. Find the perimeter of an isosceles right triangle with legs of 12. $P = 24 + 12\sqrt{2}$
3. Find the area of an isosceles triangle with a base of 12 and base angles of 30. $12\sqrt{3}$
4. What are skew lines? lines that do not intersect and are not parallel
5. If a rectangle has a perimeter of 64, what is its largest possible area. 256

TEACHER'S RESOURCE MASTERS

Practice Master 40, Part 2
Quiz 25

13.2 Concurrency Theorems

The following is a restatement of some of the characterizations you have already learned. Some characterizations are definitions, and some are theorems.

1. A sphere is the set of points in space at a given distance from a given point.
2. A circle is the set of points in a given plane at a given distance from a given point in the plane.
3. The perpendicular bisecting plane of a given segment is the set of points in space equidistant from the endpoints of the segment.
4. The perpendicular bisector in a given plane of a given segment in the plane is a set of points in the plane equidistant from the endpoints of the segment.

The next theorem adds another characterization to this list.

THEOREM 13.1
The bisector of an angle, excluding its endpoint, is the set of points in the interior of the angle equidistant from the sides of the angle.

The proof of Theorem 13.1 has two parts. Given that $\overrightarrow{AD}$ bisects $\angle BAC$, you must prove:

(1) If P is on $\overrightarrow{AD}$ but $P \neq A$, then P is in the interior of $\angle BAC$, and the distance from P to $\overleftrightarrow{AB}$ equals the distance from P to $\overleftrightarrow{AC}$.

(2) If P is in the interior of $\angle BAC$ and the distance from P to $\overleftrightarrow{AB}$ equals the distance from P to $\overleftrightarrow{AC}$, then P lies on $\overrightarrow{AD}$ and $P \neq A$.

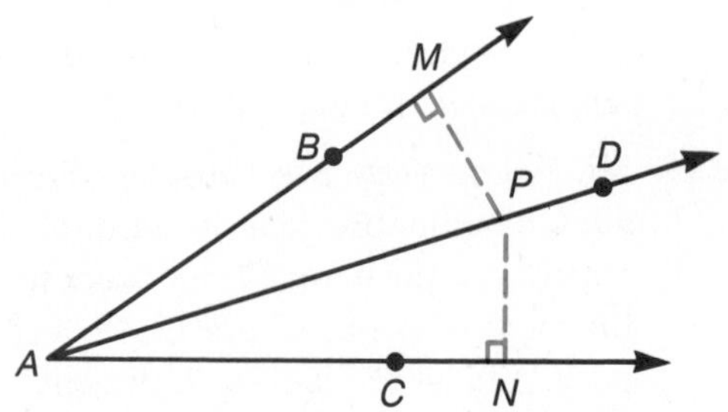

(1) **Given:** P is on $\overrightarrow{AD}$, $P \neq A$, $\overline{PM} \perp \overleftrightarrow{AB}$, $\overline{PN} \perp \overleftrightarrow{AC}$

Prove: P is in the interior of $\angle BAC$, $PM = PN$

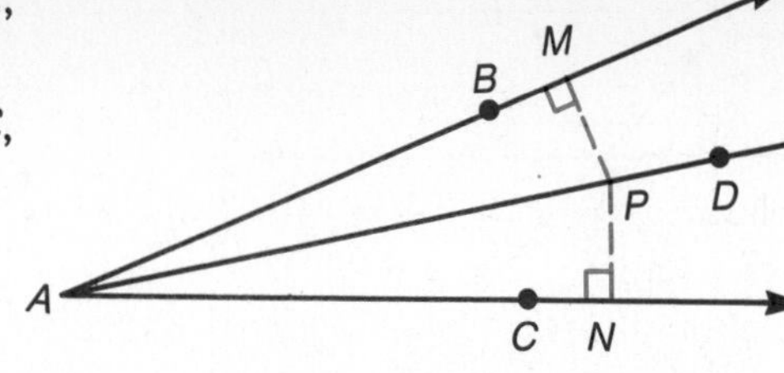

Proof:

STATEMENTS	REASONS
1. P is in the interior of $\angle BAC$.	1. P is on $\overrightarrow{AD}$; $P \neq A$; and definition of angle bisector
2. $\overline{AP} \cong \overline{AP}$	2. Congruence of segments is reflexive.
3. $\angle PAM \cong \angle PAN$	3. Definition of angle bisector
4. $\overline{PM} \perp \overleftrightarrow{AB}$, $\overline{PN} \perp \overleftrightarrow{AC}$	4. Given
5. $\angle PMA \cong \angle PNA$	5. All rt. $\angle$s are $\cong$ (Theorem 3.3).
6. $\Delta PMA \cong \Delta PNA$	6. SAA
7. $\overline{PM} \cong \overline{PN}$	7. Corres. parts of $\cong$ Δs are $\cong$.
8. $PM = PN$	8. Definition of $\cong$ segments

(2) **Given:** P is in the interior of $\angle BAC$, $\overline{PM} \perp \overleftrightarrow{AB}$, $\overline{PN} \perp \overleftrightarrow{AC}$, $PM = PN$

Prove: $P \neq A$, and P lies on $\overrightarrow{AD}$.

Proof:

STATEMENTS	REASONS
1. $P \neq A$	1. Definition of interior of an angle
2. $PM = PN$	2. Given
3. $\overline{PM} \cong \overline{PN}$	3. Definition of $\cong$ segments
4. $\overline{PA} \cong \overline{PA}$	4. Congruence of segments is reflexive.
5. $\overline{PM} \perp \overleftrightarrow{AB}$, $\overline{PN} \perp \overleftrightarrow{AC}$	5. Given
6. $\angle PMA$ and $\angle PNA$ are rt. $\angle$s.	6. Definition of $\perp$
7. $\Delta PMA \cong \Delta PNA$	7. HL
8. $\angle PAM \cong \angle PAN$	8. Corres. parts of $\cong$ Δs are $\cong$.
9. P lies on $\overrightarrow{AD}$.	9. Definition of angle bisector

The bisector of an angle was defined in Chapter 3 as a ray that divides an angle into two congruent angles. Theorem 13.1 strengthens the definition. It describes the bisecting ray in terms of point characterization. You can now think of an angle bisector as a locus of points.

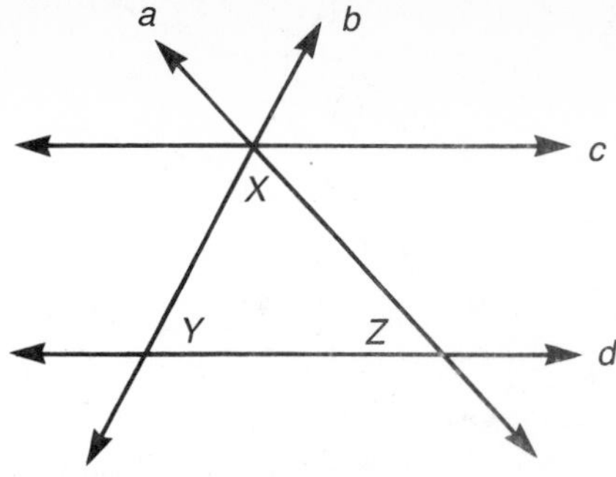

Now you are ready to prove three theorems dealing with *concurrence* of lines. Recall from Chapter 6 that two or more lines are *concurrent* if and only if there is a *single* point that lies on *all* of them. The common point of intersection is called the *point of concurrency.*

In the figure, lines a, b, c are concurrent at X, lines b and d are concurrent at Y, and lines a and d are concurrent at Z.

THEOREM 13.2
The perpendicular bisectors of the sides of a triangle are concurrent in a point equidistant from the three vertices of the triangle.

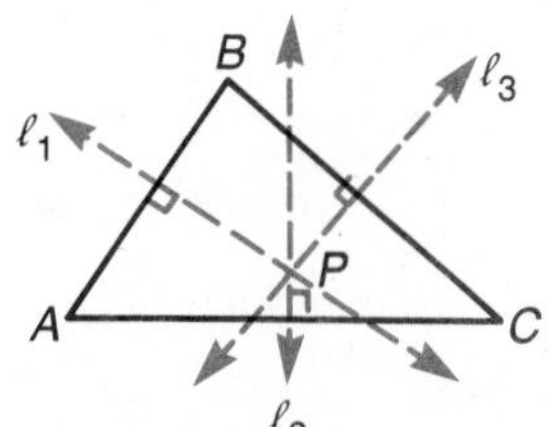

Given: ΔABC, l_1, l_2, and l_3 the perpendicular bisectors of $\overline{AB}$, $\overline{AC}$ and $\overline{BC}$

Prove: l_1, l_2, and l_3 are concurrent at P, and $AP = BP = CP$.

Proof: l_1 is not parallel to l_2, or $\overline{AB}$ would be parallel to $\overline{AC}$. Therefore, l_1 intersects l_2 at some point P. By Theorem 5.2, $AP = BP$, and $AP = CP$. Thus, $BP = CP$. Again by Theorem 5.2, this means that P lies on l_3. Therefore, P is on all three of the perpendicular bisectors.

COROLLARY 13.2.1
There is one and only one circle through three noncollinear points.

COROLLARY 13.2.2
Two distinct circles intersect in at most two points.

The proofs of these corollaries are left as exercises.

THEOREM 13.3
The lines containing the three altitudes of a triangle are concurrent.

Given: ΔABC, altitude l_1 from vertex A

Prove: The altitudes of ΔABC are concurrent.

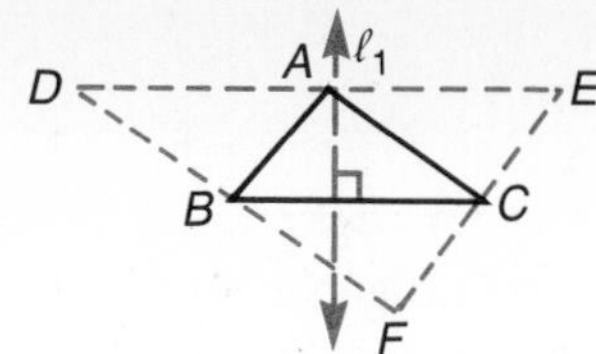

Proof: Through each vertex, draw a line parallel to the opposite side. These three lines determine ΔDEF and parallelograms $DACB$ and $AECB$. Since opposite sides of a parallelogram are congruent, $BC = AE$ and $BC = DA$. Thus, $DA = AE$, meaning that l_1, the altitude from A in ΔABC is the perpendicular bisector of $\overline{DE}$ in ΔDEF. In similar fashion, the other two altitudes of ΔABC are perpendicular bisectors of sides of ΔDEF. Since perpendicular bisectors are concurrent, by Theorem 13.2, it follows that the three altitudes of a triangle are concurrent.

> **THEOREM 13.4**
> The angle bisectors of a triangle are concurrent at a point equidistant from the three sides.

Given: ΔABC, $\overrightarrow{AD}$ the bisector of $\angle A$, $\overrightarrow{BE}$ the bisector of $\angle B$, and P the intersection of the two bisectors

Prove: The angle bisectors from A, B, and C are concurrent at P, and P is equidistant from $\overleftrightarrow{AB}$, $\overleftrightarrow{AC}$, and $\overleftrightarrow{BC}$.

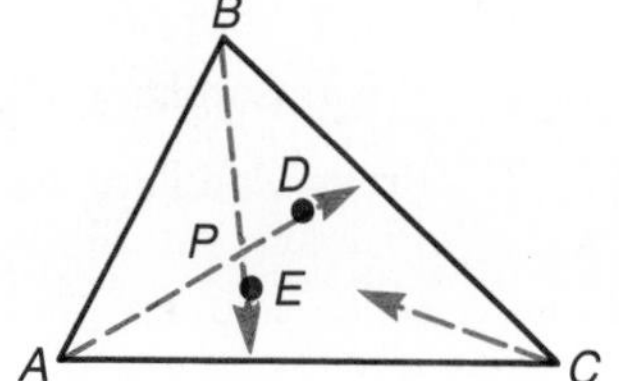

Proof: By Theorem 13.1, P is equidistant from (1) $\overleftrightarrow{AB}$ and $\overleftrightarrow{AC}$ and (2) $\overleftrightarrow{AB}$ and $\overleftrightarrow{BC}$, so P is equidistant from $\overline{AC}$ and $\overleftrightarrow{BC}$. This means that P is on the bisector of $\angle C$. Thus, the three bisectors have point P in common, and P is equidistant from $\overleftrightarrow{AB}$, $\overleftrightarrow{AC}$, and $\overleftrightarrow{BC}$.

ASSIGNMENT GUIDE

Minimum 1-4
Regular 1-5
Maximum 1-7 odd, 9-10

ORAL EXERCISES

Using only rough sketches as a basis of decision, discuss the following possibilities.

1. A triangle in which the three perpendicular bisectors of the sides, the three angle bisectors, and the three altitudes are all concurrent at the same point.

2. A triangle in which the three perpendicular bisectors of the sides are concurrent at a point outside the triangle.

3. A triangle in which the three angle bisectors are concurrent at a point outside the triangle.

4. A triangle in which the three altitudes are concurrent at one of the vertices of the triangle.

Oral Exercises

1. equilateral
2. obtuse triangle
3. impossible
4. rt. Δ at the rt. ∠ vertex

Written Exercises

1. at the center of the circle

2. Form a triangle and apply Theorem 13.2.

3. No; it would form two isos. Δs that share one leg and whose bases are contained in the same line, which is impossible.

4. It would be the point at which $\overleftrightarrow{PQ}$ intersects the bisector of $\angle ABC$.

5. It would be the point at which the bisector of $\angle B$ intersects the $\perp$ bisector of $\overline{DC}$.

6. See *Selected Answers*, p. 641

7. *Two distinct circles can intersect in at most two points.* If $\odot P$ and $\odot Q$ intersect in three points A, B, and C, then because they lie on a circle, A, B, and C are noncollinear. By Cor. 13.2.1, there is one and only one circle through 3 noncollinear points. Contradiction.

8. $P(-2, 0)$, $Q(1, 3)$, and $R(-3, 3)$ are the midpoints of $\overline{AB}$, $\overline{BC}$, and $\overline{AC}$. Because $\overline{SP} \perp \overline{AB}$, the x-coordinate of S is -2. By Thm. 13.2, $AS = BS = CS$, so $\sqrt{16 + y^2} = \sqrt{4 + (6 - y)^2}$, which yields $y = 2$. So $S(-2, 2)$.

9. The diagonals and sides of the quadrilateral are chords of the circle. Cor. 12.2.5 states that the perpendicular bisector of a chord passes through the center of the circle.

10. See *Selected Answers*, p. 641

WRITTEN EXERCISES

A. 1. Trace a circle. Locate three points on the circle, not too close to each other, and draw a triangle having those three points as vertices. Sketch the perpendicular bisectors of the three sides of the triangle. Where do the bisectors appear to be concurrent?

2. Sketch and describe the locus of points equidistant from three noncollinear points.

3. Could there be a point equidistant from three collinear points? Use a drawing to help explain your answer.

4. A line intersects the sides of $\angle ABC$ in P and Q. Where would you find a point of $\overleftrightarrow{PQ}$ that is equidistant from the sides of the angle?

B. 5. Imagine that the sides of this figure are the boundaries of a farm. The farmer wants to sink a well at a point equidistant from $\overline{AB}$, $\overline{BC}$, D, and C. Explain, with the help of a drawing, how to find this point.

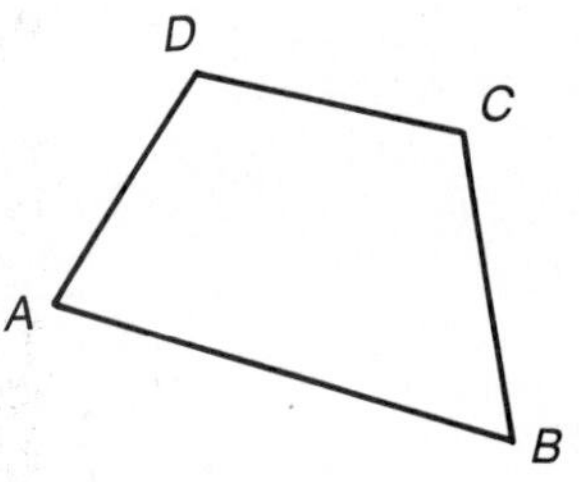

6. Prove Corollary 13.2.1.

7. Prove Corollary 13.2.2.

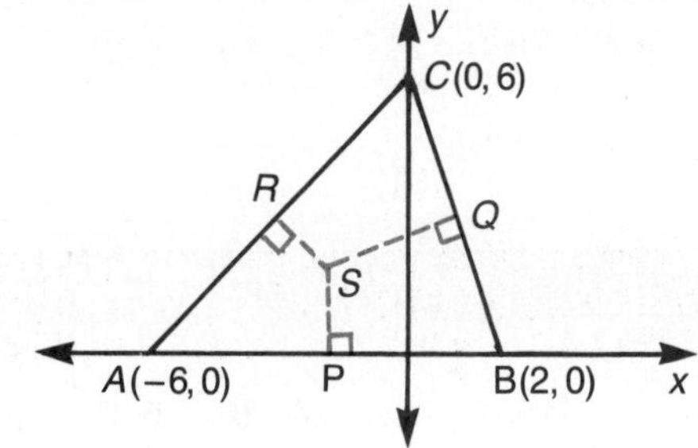

8. Given the coordinates of ΔABC as shown and the perpendicular bisectors $\overline{SR}$, $\overline{SQ}$, and $\overline{SP}$, find the coordinates of S using Theorem 13.2 and the distance formula.

C. 9. A quadrilateral is *cyclic* if its four vertices lie on a circle. Explain why the perpendicular bisectors of the four sides and the perpendicular bisectors of the two diagonals of a cyclic quadrilateral are concurrent.

10. Given the three lines determined by the sides of a triangle, show by a careful drawing that there are exactly four points each of which is equidistant from all three lines.

13.3 Constructions

In this chapter you have been asked to solve several problems by sketching a figure. This instruction implicitly assumes a certain degree of error. Still, accurate drawings are essential at times.

An accurate drawing is called a **construction** in geometry. Since the time of the ancient Greeks, only two instruments have been permitted for use in constructions. These are the *compass* and the *straightedge*. In general, geometric constructions are *never* based on any kind of measuring device.

Most geometric constructions depend on the intersection of (1) two lines, (2) a line and a circle, or (3) two circles. The first two cases have been considered already in previous theorems and postulates. Case 3 is presented in the next theorem.

THEOREM 13.5 (The Two Circle Theorem)
If two circles have radii a and b, and if c is the distance between their centers, then the circles intersect in two points, one on each side of the line of centers, provided each one of a, b, and c is less than the sum of the other two.

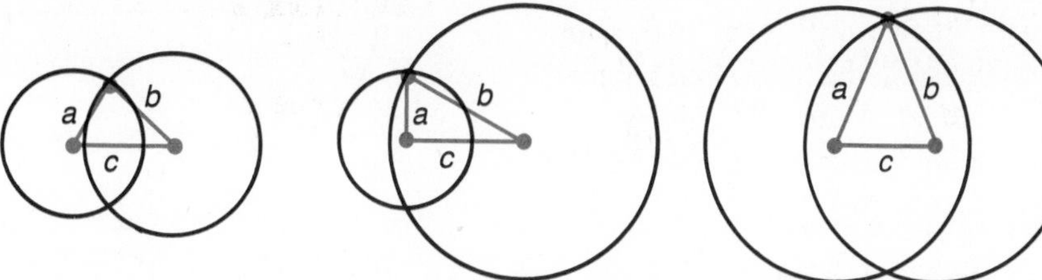

Remember that a and b are the radii of the two circles, and that c is the *line of centers,* the segment that joins the centers of the two circles. The inequality condition imposed on a, b, and c is important. Note that in each of the following figures, neither a, b, nor c is greater than the sum of the other two, and the circles do not intersect in two points.

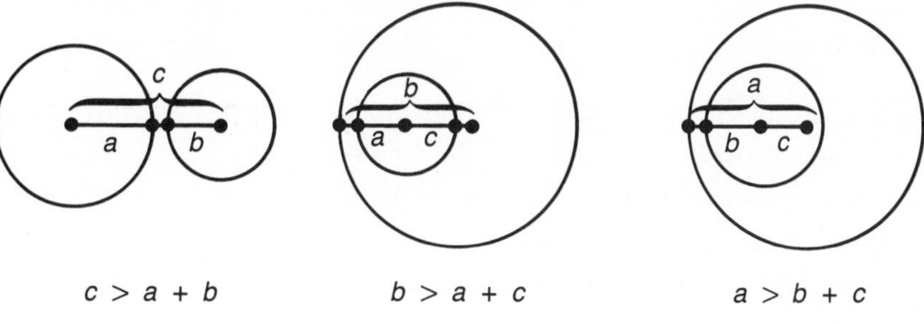

$c > a + b$ $\qquad$ $b > a + c$ $\qquad$ $a > b + c$

OBJECTIVES

Use a compass and straightedge to perform Constructions 1–7, the basic geometric constructions.

Apply Theorem 13.5 to the construction of a perpendicular bisector of a segment.

TEACHER'S NOTES

See p. T38

MIXED REVIEW

1. What is the sum of all of the exterior angles of a triangle? a square? 360, 360
2. Find the base of a rectangle that has an altitude of 8 and a diagonal of 17. 15
3. What is the slope of the line with the equation $2y = 4x - 3$? 2
4. Solve $2x - 3y = 17$
   $3x + 2y = 6$
   $(4, -3)$
5. In a parallelogram, if one angle measures 120, find the other three angles. 60, 120, 60

TEACHER'S RESOURCE MASTERS

Practice Master 41, Part 1

You now have sufficient background to perform the constructions that follow. All constructions are in a given plane.

CONSTRUCTION 1
Copy a given triangle.

Given: ΔABC

Construct: $\Delta DEF \cong \Delta ABC$

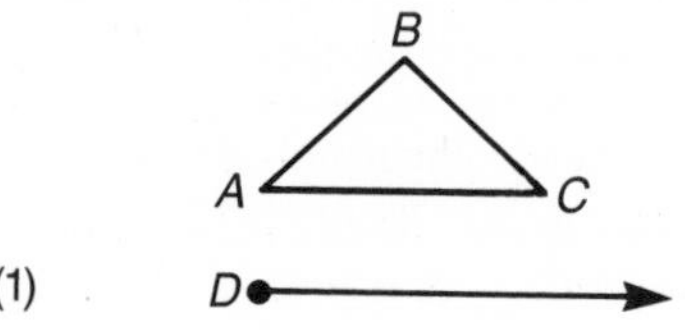

Step 1: Draw a ray and label the endpoint D. Vertex D will correspond to vertex A.

Step 2: Place the compass point at A and pencil tip at C on ΔABC to measure $\overline{AC}$. Transfer compass point to D and draw an arc of radius AC on the ray. Label the point of intersection F.

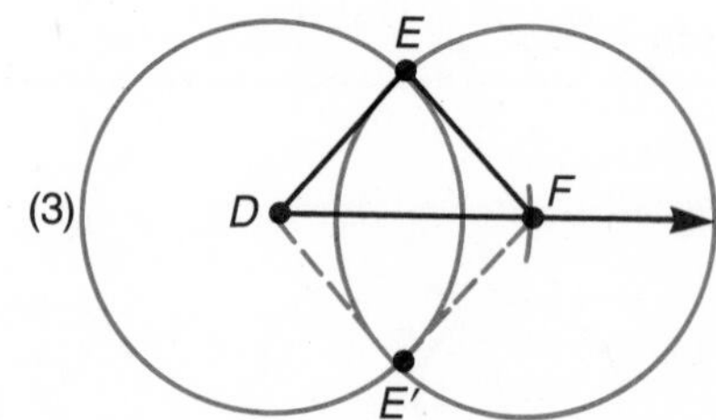

Step 3: Using the compass, construct $\odot D$ with radius AB and $\odot F$ with radius BC, the two circles intersecting at E and E'. Using the straightedge, draw $\overline{DE}$ and $\overline{FE}$.

The Two Circle Theorem ensures that $\odot D$ and $\odot F$ intersect at two points, here labeled E and E'. By connecting these points with D and F, you have ΔDEF congruent to ΔABC by SSS (Theorem 4.5). You should be able to see that $\overline{DF} \cong \overline{AC}$ (Step 2), $\overline{DE} \cong \overline{AB}$ (Step 3), and $\overline{EF} \cong \overline{BC}$ (Step 3).

The mechanics of the remaining constructions are left to you. In each case, a summary and figures are provided.

CONSTRUCTION 2
Copy a given angle.

Given: $\angle A$

Construct: $\angle F \cong \angle A$

Summary: (1) With A as center, draw an arc intersecting the sides of $\angle A$ at B and C. (2) Draw a ray with endpoint F. With F as center, draw an arc of radius AC intersecting the ray at G. (3) With G as center, draw an arc of radius CB intersecting the second arc at E. Draw $\overline{FE}$.

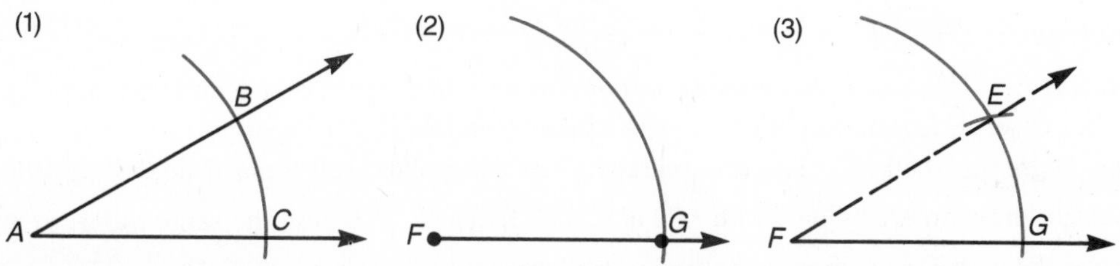

Conclusion: $\angle EFG \cong \angle BAC$

CONSTRUCTION 3
Construct the perpendicular bisector of a given segment.

Given: $\overline{AB}$

Construct: $\perp$ bisector of $\overline{AB}$

Summary: (1) With A as center, draw an arc of radius r, where $r > \frac{1}{2}AB$. (2) With B as center, draw an arc of radius r intersecting the first arc at points C and D. (3) Draw $\overline{CD}$ intersecting $\overline{AB}$ at P.

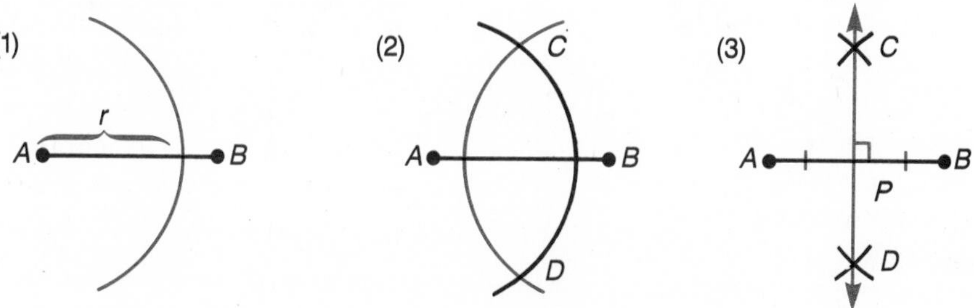

Conclusion: $\overline{CD}$ is the perpendicular bisector of $\overline{AB}$.

CONSTRUCTION 4
Bisect a given segment.

Construction 4 is a corollary to Construction 3, which has already determined the midpoint of a given segment.

CONSTRUCTION 5
Construct a perpendicular to a given line through a given point.

Given: Line l and point P

Construct: $\overleftrightarrow{PT} \perp l$

Summary: Two cases are possible; either P is on l, or P is not on l. The same steps apply in either case. (1) Locate any point Q (other than P) on l. With P as center, draw an arc whose radius is greater than PQ. The arc intersects l at two points, call them R and S. (2) With R as center, draw an arc below l with radius r, such that $r > \frac{1}{2}RS$. Use the same radius to draw another arc with S as center. Label the point where the arcs intersect T. Draw $\overleftrightarrow{PT}$.

CASE 2

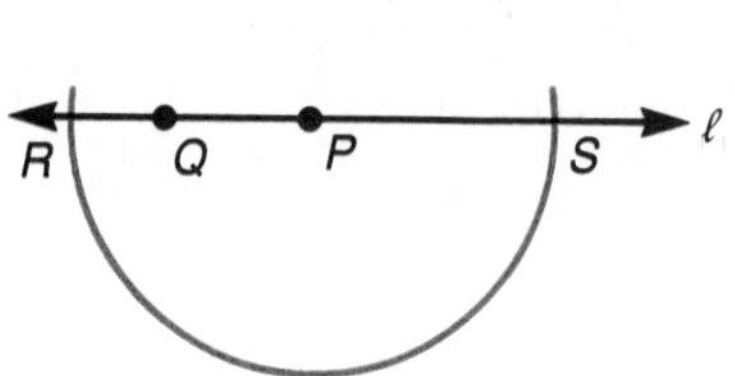

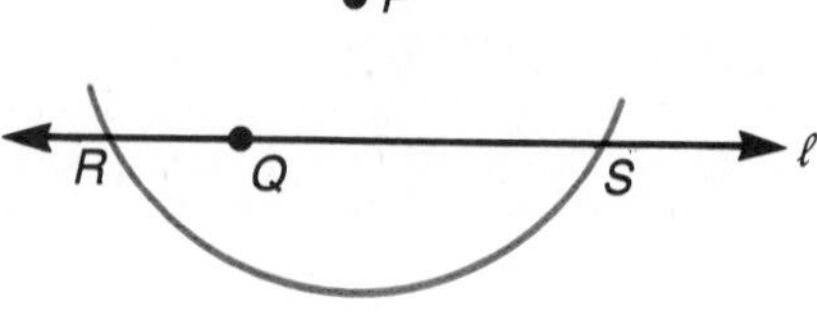

(2)

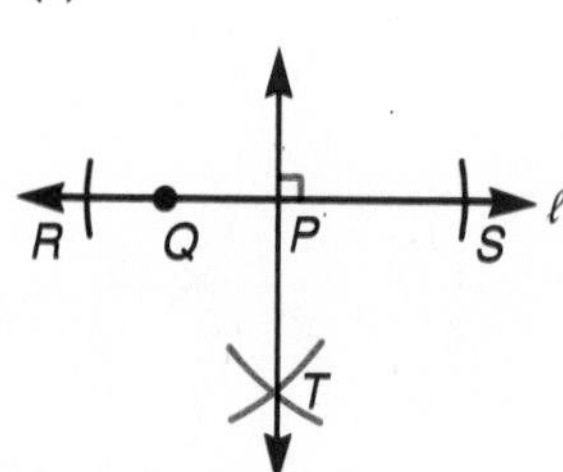

Conclusion: $\overleftrightarrow{PT} \perp l$

CONSTRUCTION 6
Construct a parallel to a given line through a given external point.

Given: Line l and point P not on l

Construct: $\overleftrightarrow{PT} \parallel l$

Summary: (1) Locate any point Q on l and draw $\overline{PQ}$. (2) Using P as a vertex, construct an alternate interior angle at P congruent to the angle formed by $\overleftrightarrow{PQ}$ and l, following the method of Construction 2. Let the new line be determined by P and T.

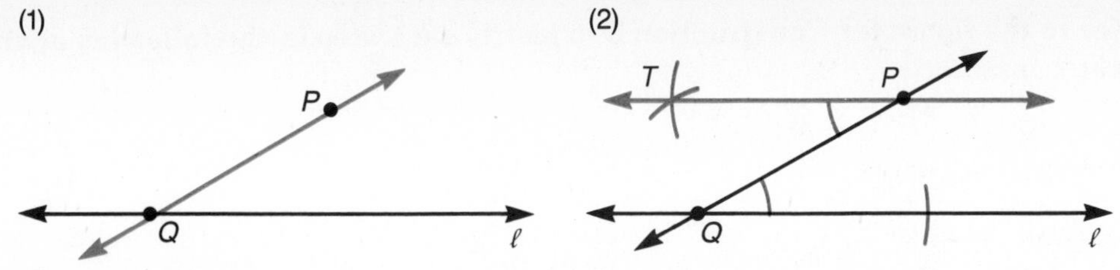

Conclusion: $\overleftrightarrow{PT} \parallel l$

CONSTRUCTION 7
Divide a segment into a given number of congruent segments.

Given: $\overline{AB}$

Construct: n congruent segments on $\overline{AB}$

Summary: (1) With A as the endpoint, draw any ray that does not contain $\overline{AB}$. (2) Using a compass, mark off n congruent segments on the ray, intersecting it at $P_1, P_2, \ldots P_n$. Draw $\overline{BP_n}$. (3) Following the method of Construction 6, construct lines parallel to $\overline{BP_n}$ through $P_1, P_2 \ldots P_{n-1}$, intersecting $\overline{AB}$ in $Q_1, Q_2, \ldots Q_{n-1}$.

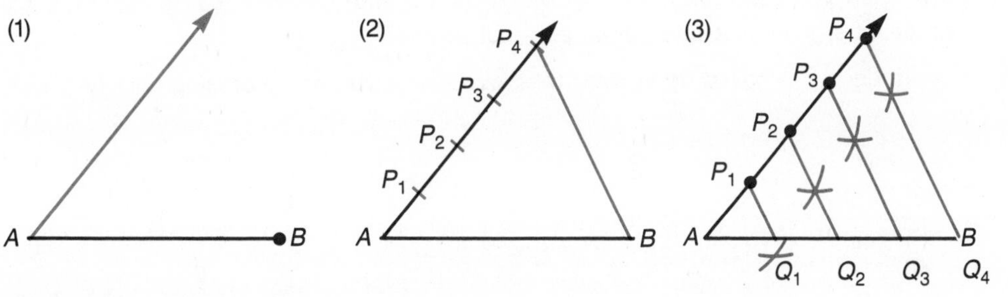

Conclusion: $AQ_1 = Q_1Q_2 = \ldots = Q_{n-1}B$.

ORAL EXERCISES

1. Which earlier theorems or postulates deal with the intersection of two lines?
2. Which earlier theorems or postulates deal with the intersection of a line and a circle?
3. In terms of the Two Circle Theorem, what is the relationship between a, b, and c in two circles that are internally tangent? externally tangent?
4. In Construction 3, why is it necessary to choose $r > \frac{1}{2}AB$? Could you choose $r > AB$?
5. In Construction 3, what kind of figure is formed by the segments $\overline{AC}$, $\overline{BC}$, $\overline{AD}$, and $\overline{BD}$?

ASSIGNMENT GUIDE

Minimum 1-6
Regular 1-10
Maximum 6-12

Oral Exercises

1. Theorems 2.1, 2.4, 3.8, and 7.3
2. Theorem 12.2
3. $a = b + c$ or $b = a + c$; $c = a + b$
4. Theorem 13.5 says that two circles with centers A and B will intersect in two points only if a (radius of $\odot A$) + b (radius of $\odot B$) $> AB$, $a + AB > b$, and $b + AB > a$. These conditions are ensured if $a = b = r$ and $r > \frac{1}{2}AB$ (or $r > AB$).
5. a rhombus

6. Postulate 1
7. SSS
8. CPCTC
9. SAS
10. CPCTC
11. Def. of bisect
12. CPCTC
13. Theorem 3.4; Def. of $\perp$
14. Def. of $\perp$ bisector
15. Constructions 3 and 4
16. Theorem 8.5; Theorem 8.7
17. Construct the perpendicular h to l from P, then construct the perpendicular to h at P. Two lines perpendicular to the same line are parallel by the theorem.
18. Theorem 8.7 and Corollary 8.26.1

Refer to the figure for Construction 3 to justify each step in the following analysis of the construction.

6. Draw $\overline{CA}$, $\overline{CB}$, $\overline{DA}$, and $\overline{DB}$.

7. $\triangle CAD \cong \triangle CBD$

8. $\angle ACP \cong \angle BCP$

9. $\triangle ACP \cong \triangle BCP$

10. $\overline{AP} \cong \overline{BP}$

11. P bisects $\overline{AB}$.

12. $\angle CPA \cong \angle CPB$

13. $\overleftrightarrow{CD} \perp \overleftrightarrow{AB}$

14. $\overline{CD}$ is the $\perp$ bisector of $\overline{AB}$.

15. Construction 5 resembles which previous constructions in its use of congruent triangles to determine a perpendicular line?

16. Construction 6 is based upon what theorem? What other theorem could be used to complete the same construction?

17. How could you use both cases of Construction 5 and Theorem 8.2 to construct a line parallel to a given line through an external point P?

18. Construction 7 is based upon what theorems or corollaries concerning parallel lines?

Written Exercises

Teacher's Note: Using the first seven constructions as a basis, students can perform many other interesting constructions. Students should be reminded that they may use only a compass and a straight-edge to perform constructions. Also, they should be able to prove the validity of each construction.

1. Steps 1 and 2, Construction 1
2. Construction 2
3. Construction 1
4. Constructions 1 and 2
5. Construction 3
6. Constructions 1 and 5
7. Constructions 1 and 6
8. Construction 7

WRITTEN EXERCISES

A. Draw each of the following figures and then construct a figure congruent to your drawing.

1. line segment

2. acute angle

3. scalene triangle

4. quadrilateral containing no right angle

5. Draw a segment of arbitrary length and bisect it.

6. Draw an obtuse triangle and construct the altitude from the vertex of the obtuse angle.

B. **7.** Draw an acute triangle and then, through one of its vertices, construct a line parallel to the opposite side.

8. Draw a segment roughly 6 inches long and divide it into three congruent segments.

9. Draw a segment roughly 5 cm long and, using it as one of the sides, construct an equilateral triangle.

10. Construct a 45-45-90 triangle.

C. 11. Draw $\overline{AB}$ about 6 inches long. Then construct an isosceles triangle such that AB is its perimeter and each congruent side is twice the length of its base.

12. This figure illustrates another way to construct one line parallel to another. Use the method to construct a line parallel to a given line, and explain why the method is correct.

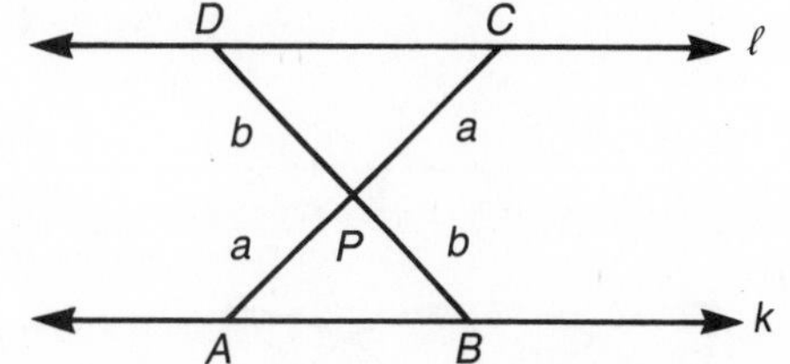

9. Construction 1
10. Constructions 5 and 1
11. If $AB = p$, the perimeter, $b =$ the base, and $s =$ the two congruent sides, then $2b = s$ and $5b = p$. Using Construction 7, divide $\overline{AB}$ into five congruent segments. Each will have measure b. Then construct a triangle having sides b, $2b$, and $2b$.
12. Choose any two points A and B on the given line. Use an arc of radius $r > \frac{1}{2}AB$ to find point P on the $\perp$ bisector of $\overline{AB}$. Draw $\overrightarrow{AP}$ and $\overrightarrow{BP}$. Using P as center, draw an arc of radius AP (or BP), intersecting $\overrightarrow{AP}$ and $\overrightarrow{BP}$ in C and D. Then $\overleftrightarrow{CD} \parallel \overleftrightarrow{AB}$. Reason: $\Delta APB \cong \Delta CPD$ by SAS, so alt. int. $\angle$s are $\cong$.

SELF-QUIZ

1. Sketch and describe the locus of points consisting of the vertices of all isosceles triangles having $\overline{AB}$ as base.

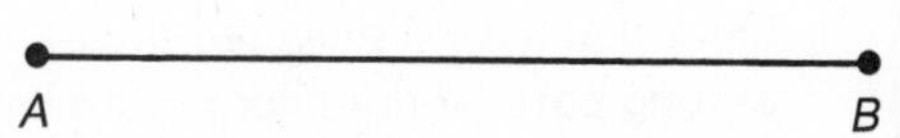

Name each locus of points.

2. The set of points in a given plane at a given distance from a given point of the plane.
3. The set of points in a given plane equidistant from the endpoints of a given segment in the plane.
4. The set of points equidistant from the endpoints of a given segment.
5. The set of points at a given distance from a given point.
6. The set of points in the interior of an angle equidistant from the sides.

Fill in the blanks.

7. The angle bisectors of a triangle meet at a point equidistant from the three ______ of the triangle.
8. The perpendicular bisectors of the sides of a triangle meet at a point equidistant from the three ______ of the triangle.
9. There is one and only one circle through ______ noncollinear points.
10. To construct the perpendicular bisector of $\overline{AB}$, you would use an arc whose radius is at least greater than ______.

Self-Quiz

1. the $\perp$ bisector of $\overline{AB}$
2. a circle
3. the $\perp$ bisector of the segment
4. the $\perp$ bisecting plane of the segment
5. a sphere
6. the angle bisector, excluding the endpoint
7. sides
8. vertices
9. three
10. $\frac{1}{2}AB$

EXPLORATION/
Geometric Art

Do you have artistic talent? Many people do. But other people say that they can't draw a straight line.

The fact is that anyone can create beautiful designs using a compass and a straightedge. Here is just one example:

Study the figure carefully. It was drawn on graph paper using only one compass setting. See if you can duplicate it on a blank sheet of graph paper.

Once you have discovered a basic design, you can create new designs by erasing parts of the figure or adding new parts. You might also try shading different areas in different colors. Here are two designs developed from the original:

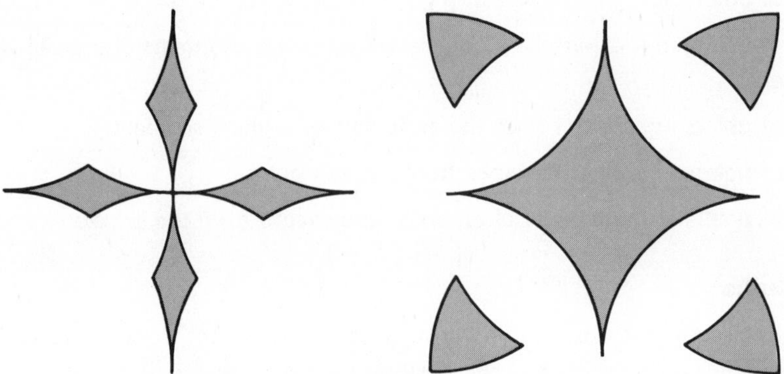

The possibilities are infinite. (1) Construct a basic design. (2) Modify it. (3) Use color for artistic effect. For best results, use a good compass and sharpened drawing pencils.

As a project, your class could hold a geometric art show in which all entries are created using only a compass and straightedge.

13.4 Circle Relationships

A polygon is **inscribed** in a circle if each of its vertices lies on the circle, as shown in the figure on the left below. A polygon is **circumscribed** about a circle if each side of the polygon is tangent to the circle, as shown in the figure on the right below. (Referring to the circle, you could say that the left circle is circumscribed about the polygon and that the right circle is inscribed in the polygon.)

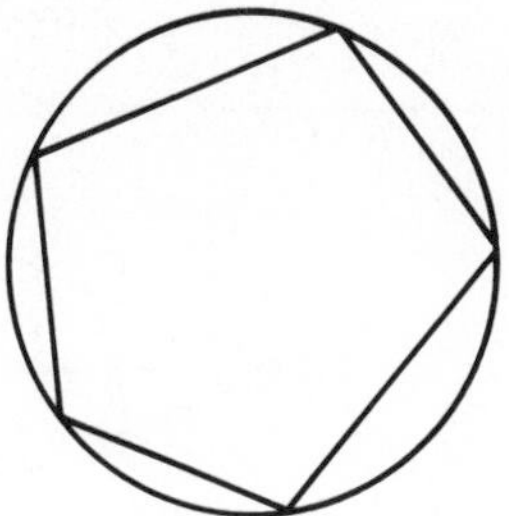

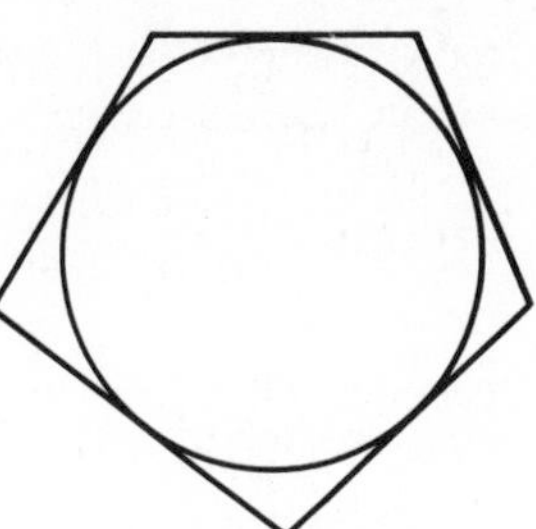

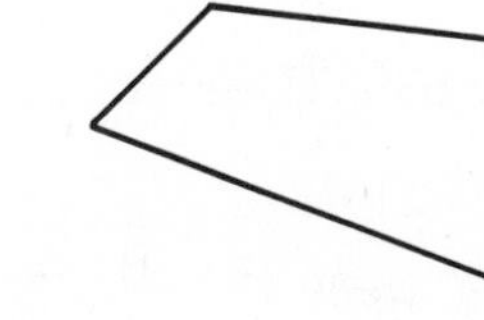

In many cases, a polygon cannot have a circle inscribed in it or circumscribed about it. Such is the case with the polygon shown on the right.

For every triangle, a circle can be inscribed in it, and a second circle can be circumscribed about it. The following constructions show you how.

CONSTRUCTION 8
Circumscribe a circle about a given triangle.

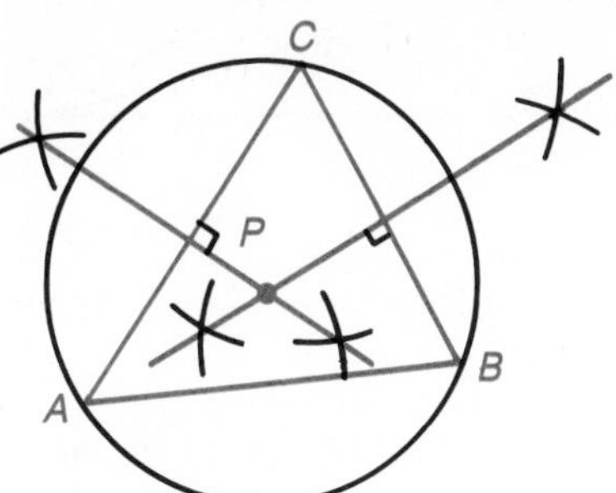

Given: ΔABC

Construct: $\odot P$ that contains A, B, and C

Summary: Construct the perpendicular bisectors of $\overline{AC}$ and $\overline{BC}$. Label their intersection P.

Conclusion: By Theorem 13.2, $AP = BP = CP$, so P is the center of a circle containing A, B, and C.

OBJECTIVES

Use compass and straightedge to perform Constructions 8–10, regarding circles.

Recognize and identify impossible constructions.

TEACHER'S NOTES

See p. T39

MIXED REVIEW

1. If the perimeter of a square is 32, find the diagonal length. $8\sqrt{2}$
2. Solve $5x - 3y = 1$
   $2x + y = -4$
   $(-1, -2)$
3. Solve $x^2 - 3x = 0$. $\{0, 3\}$
4. Factor $4x^2 - 8x - 60$. $4(x - 5)(x + 3)$
5. Add $\frac{5x}{y} + \frac{3}{2y^2}$. $\frac{10xy + 3}{2y^2}$

TEACHER'S RESOURCE MASTERS

Practice Master 41, Part 2
Quiz 26

In Construction 8, P is called the **circumcenter** of ΔABC, or the point of concurrency of the perpendicular bisectors of the sides. In the case of an inscribed triangle, therefore, the circumcenter of the triangle is the center of the circle that circumscribes it.

An interesting corollary can be deduced from Construction 8. The perpendicular bisector of any chord of a circle contains the center of the circle.

In order to inscribe a circle in a triangle, you must be able to perform one more basic construction.

CONSTRUCTION 9
Bisect a given angle.

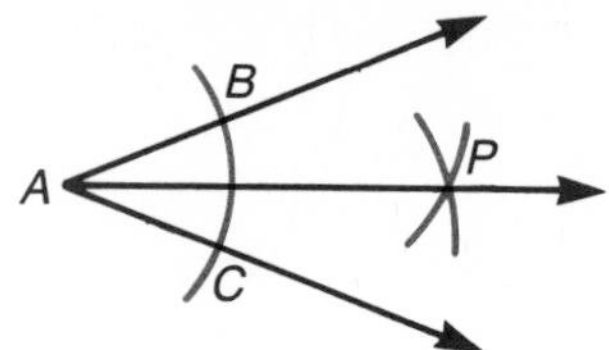

Given: $\angle A$

Construct: the bisector of $\angle A$

Summary: Draw an arc with A as center intersecting the sides of $\angle A$ at B and C. Now draw arcs of equal radius using B and C as centers so that the arcs intersect at P. Draw $\overrightarrow{AP}$.

Conclusion: By SSS (Theorem 4.5), $\Delta ABP \cong \Delta ACP$, so $\angle BAP \cong \angle CAP$.

CONSTRUCTION 10
Inscribe a circle in a given triangle.

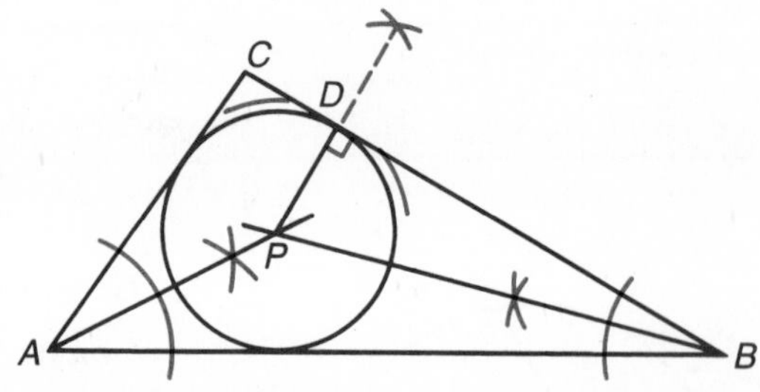

Given: ΔABC

Construct: $\odot P$ inscribed in ΔABC

Summary: Construct the bisectors of $\angle A$ and $\angle B$ and label their intersection P. By Theorem 13.4, P also lies on the bisector of $\angle C$. Now construct the perpendicular, $\overline{PD}$, from P to $\overline{BC}$. Finally, construct a circle with center P and radius PD.

Conclusion: $\odot P$ is tangent to the three sides of ΔABC and is therefore inscribed in the triangle.

In Construction 10, P is the **incenter** of ΔABC, or the point of concurrency of its angle bisectors. The incenter of a triangle is also the center of the circle inscribed in it.

Construction techniques are only as good as your ability to verify them. Mathematical proof can also be used to show that some things are *impossible*. For example, three famous constructions have tormented geometricians for two thousand years. It is now known that all three are impossible, but even today some stubborn spirits keep trying. As you study them, keep in mind that the only tools allowable in geometric construction are a compass and an unmarked straightedge.

1. The Angle-Trisection Problem

Given $\angle BAC$, the challenge is to construct two rays, $\overrightarrow{AD}$ and $\overrightarrow{AE}$ (with points D and E in the interior of $\angle BAC$), that trisect $\angle BAC$. That is, you want $\angle BAD \cong \angle DAE \cong \angle EAC$.

In 1837 an American mathematician named Wantzel published a proof that the construction is impossible. Note that the construction applies to angles in general. It is true, for example, that angles of 90 degrees and 45 degrees *can* be trisected, since angles of 30 degrees and 15 degrees can be constructed.

The Wantzel proof is an impressive example of how modern abstract algebra can be used to prove classical problems in mathematics. A good source on this topic is W.W. Sawyer, *A Concrete Approach to Abstract Algebra* (San Francisco: Freeman, Cooper, and Co., 1959).

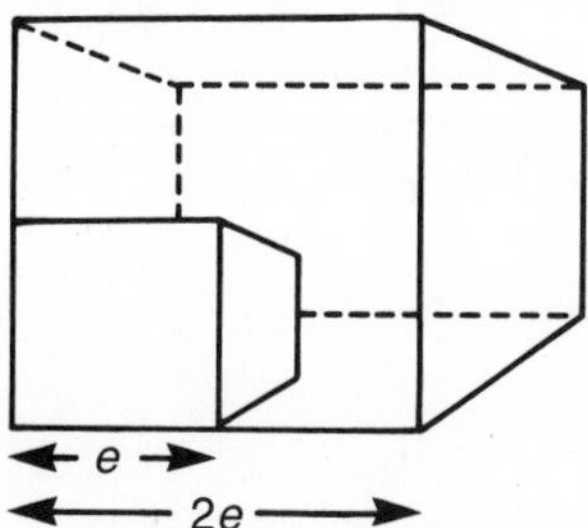

2. Doubling the Cube

Assume that you are asked to double the volume of a cube having an edge measuring e units. Your first reaction might be to construct a second cube with an edge measuring $2e$ units. This reaction, unfortunately, would be wrong. $(2e)^3 = 8e^3$, meaning that the second cube would have a volume 8 times the volume of the first.

In algebraic terms, you are looking for a number, b, such that $b^3 = 2a^3$. Solving for b, you find that $b = a\sqrt[3]{2}$. Now $\sqrt[3]{2}$ is an irrational number, but it is approximately 1.26. This means that b must be 1.26 times the length of a in order for the volume of the second cube to be *close* to twice the volume of the first.

Still, this calculation doesn't meet the challenge at hand. Using segment a as a basis, you have not constructed a segment b such that a cube with edge b will have twice the volume as a cube with edge a.

3. Squaring the Circle

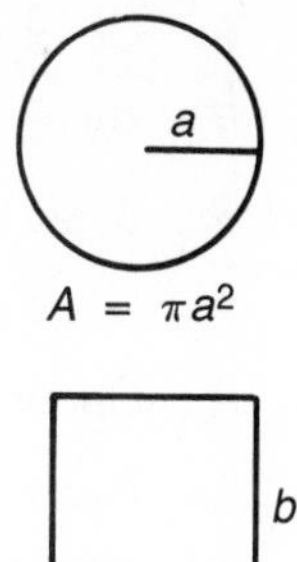

This construction challenges you to construct a square that has exactly the same area as the circle.

Algebraically, if $b^2 = \pi a^2$, then $b = a\sqrt{\pi}$. According to a hand calculator, $\sqrt{\pi} \approx 1.77$, so you'll come close if you make b about 1.77 times the length of a. Again, however, there is no way of solving the problem through geometric construction.

ASSIGNMENT GUIDE

Minimum 1-11 odd
Regular 1-7 odd, 10-12
Maximum 1-7 odd, 12-17

Oral Exercises

1. Construct an equilateral triangle on both sides of the angle. The overlapping 60° angles at the common vertex create three 30° angles.
2. Bisect a 90° ∠.
3. 45° − 30° 4. 45° + 30°
5. 90° + 30° 6. 45° + 60°
7. Bisect a 45° ∠.
8. $67\frac{1}{2}$°, 135°, for example
9. XYZ 10. ⊙A
11. ⊙P 12. A
13. P 14. A
15. P

Written Exercises

1. Construction 5
2. Constructions 5, 9
3. Constructions 5, 9, 2
4. Construction 5 and Construction 9 applied twice
5. First construct an equilateral triangle; then bisect one angle.
6. Construction 8, 10
7. When the triangle is equilateral
8. Construction 8
9. Construction 10
10. Construct the ⊥ bisectors of two adjacent sides; the point of intersection is the center; the distance from the center to any vertex is the radius of the circumscribed circle.
11. Bisect the adjacent angles; the point at which they meet is the center of the inscribed circle whose radius is the length of a ⊥ to any side.
12. See *Selected Answers*, p. 641

ORAL EXERCISES

1. It is possible to trisect a right angle using only a compass and straightedge. Discuss techniques that you think might work.

Describe how you would construct angles of the following measures.

2. 45 **3.** 15 **4.** 75

5. 120 **6.** 105 **7.** $22\frac{1}{2}$

8. Are there any other angles you could construct besides the ones named in Exercises 2–7? If so, name one.

Refer to the figure of ⊙*A* and ⊙*P* to name the following.

9. a polygon inscribed in a circle

10. a circle circumscribing a polygon

11. an inscribed circle

12. a circumcenter

13. an incenter

14. a point where the perpendicular bisectors of the sides of a triangle meet

15. a point where the angle bisectors of a triangle meet

WRITTEN EXERCISES

A. Using only straightedge and compass, construct angles having the following measures.

1. 90 **2.** 45 **3.** 135

4. Bisect a 45° angle.

B. **5.** Construct an angle of 60° and an angle of 30°.

6. Construct an equilateral triangle, then its circumscribed and inscribed circles.

7. When are the circumcenter and the incenter of a triangle concurrent?

8. Draw any scalene triangle and construct its circumscribed circle.

9. Draw any scalene triangle and construct its inscribed circle.

10. Circumscribe a circle about a given square.

11. Inscribe a circle inside a given rhombus that is not a square.

12. Construct a right triangle, given one acute angle and the radius of the circumscribed circle.

C. **13.** Construct an isosceles triangle, given the base and the radius of the inscribed circle.

14. Write a short narrative proof of Construction 10.

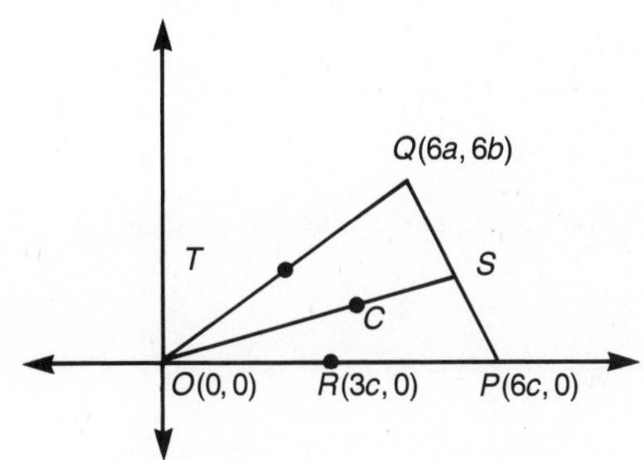

Refer to the figure at the left for Exercises 15–16.

15. Prove the following theorem using coordinate geometry: *The medians of a triangle are concurrent, and their point of concurrency is two-thirds of the way along each median, from the vertex to the opposite side.*

16. Use the theorem in Exercise 15 to construct an isosceles triangle, given the vertex angle and the radius of the inscribed circle.

17. It is possible to trisect any angle if you allow yourself to make two marks on the straightedge. The figure below shows how to trisect $\angle CBA$. The dotted lines are construction lines, and CB is the distance between the two marks on your straightedge. By studying the drawing, analyze, describe, and verify the construction technique. (HINT: Prove $z = 3u$.)

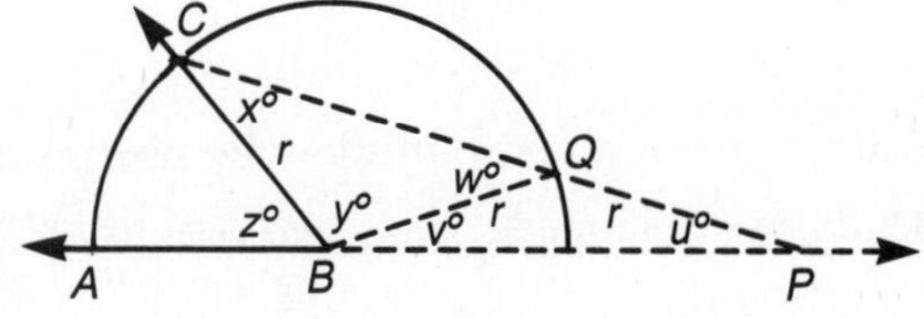

CALCULATOR

1. Suppose you accept a job which will take you 20 days to complete. For the first day you are paid 1 penny. Each day after that your pay is doubled. How much will you earn on the 20th day? How much will you earn for the whole job?
2. If a sheet of newspaper is 0.003 inches thick and you build a pile of newspapers by starting with one sheet and doubling the number of sheets in the pile 30 times, how many miles high would the pile be when you finished?

13. Draw the circle having the given radius. Draw any line tangent to the circle. Construct the radius $\perp$ the tangent. Bisect the given base and measure off half the base on either side of the point of tangency. Draw the two tangents to the circle from the determined endpoints of the base to form the third vertex.
14. By Theorem 13.4, the angle bisectors of a $\triangle$ are concurrent in a point equidistant from the sides. By drawing the $\perp$ from the incenter to one side, you establish the radius, by Cor. 12.2.1, of a $\odot$ that is tangent to all three sides.
15. If S is the midpoint of $\overline{PQ}$, its coordinates are $(3a + 3c, 3b)$. Let C be the point on the median $\overline{OS}$ such that $OC = 2CS$. The coordinates of C are therefore $\left(\frac{0 + 2(3a + 3c)}{3}, \frac{0 + 2(3b)}{3}\right) = (2a + 2c, 2b)$. Likewise if $QD = \frac{2}{3}QR$, then $D = \left(\frac{6a + 2(3c)}{3}, \frac{6b + 2(0)}{3}\right) = (2a + 2c, 2b)$. Thus, $C = D$. You can also determine that $\overline{OS}$ and $\overline{PT}$ are concurrent with the median $\overline{QR}$ at C, and that C is therefore two-thirds of the way along any median from the corresponding vertex.
16. See *Selected Answers*, p. 641
17. See *Teacher's Manual*, p. T62

Calculator

1. \$5242.88, \$10,485.75
2. 3,221,225.2 in., 51 mi

Skills Maintenance

1. proportional
2. bc
3. extremes, means
4. geometric mean
5. 3
6. 6
7. 17.5
8. $\sqrt{39}$
9. $\frac{2y}{3}$
10. $\frac{1}{2}$ and extraneous root of 6
11. 750, 40 min.
12. 126
13. 10 ft from the center
14. $26\frac{2}{3}$ lb, 84 lb

Calculator

≈1050 mph

≈740 mph

SKILLS MAINTENANCE

Fill in the blank with the correct word or phrase.

1. Given two sequences $a, b, c \ldots$ and $p, q, r \ldots$ of positive numbers, if $\frac{a}{p} = \frac{b}{q} = \frac{c}{r} = \ldots$ then the two sequences are _____.

2. If $\frac{a}{b} = \frac{c}{d}$, then $ad =$ _____.

3. In the expression $\frac{a}{b} = \frac{c}{d}$, a and d are called the _____ and b and c are called the _____.

4. In the expression $\frac{x}{y} = \frac{y}{z}$, y is called the _____ of x and z.

Find x in each equation below.

5. $\frac{x}{9} = \frac{5}{15}$

6. $\frac{4}{x} = \frac{x}{9}$

7. $\frac{4}{10} = \frac{7}{x}$

8. $\frac{3}{x} = \frac{x}{13}$

9. $\dfrac{2 + \frac{x}{4}}{x} = \dfrac{3 + \frac{y}{4}}{y}$

10. $\frac{x - 1}{2x - 12} = \frac{-x}{2x - 12}$

Answer each question below by writing and solving a proportion.

11. Joan can type 50 words per minute. How many words can she type in 15 minutes? How long will it take her to type a 2000-word essay?

12. Jack received 3 votes for every 2 received by his opponent in an election. If 210 votes were cast, how many did he get?

13. On a seesaw, weight varies inversely with distance. If a 105-lb boy sits 8 feet from the center, where would an 84-lb boy have to sit to balance the seesaw?

14. The ratio of weight on the moon to weight on earth is 1:6. If a man weighs 160 lb on earth, what will he weigh on the moon? What will a stone that weighs 14 lb on the moon weigh on earth?

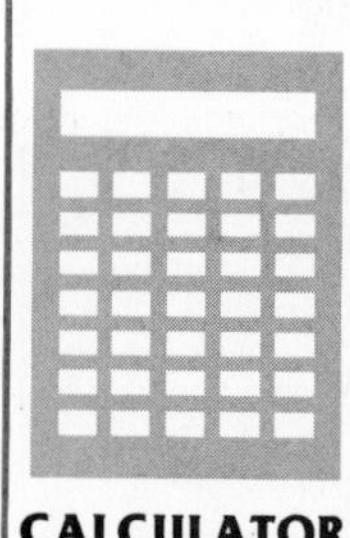

CALCULATOR

1. As the earth rotates, objects on its surface travel at different speeds with respect to the earth's axis, depending on the latitude of each object. If the radius of the earth is about 4000 mi, what is the approximate speed of an object near the equator? At latitude 45° North?

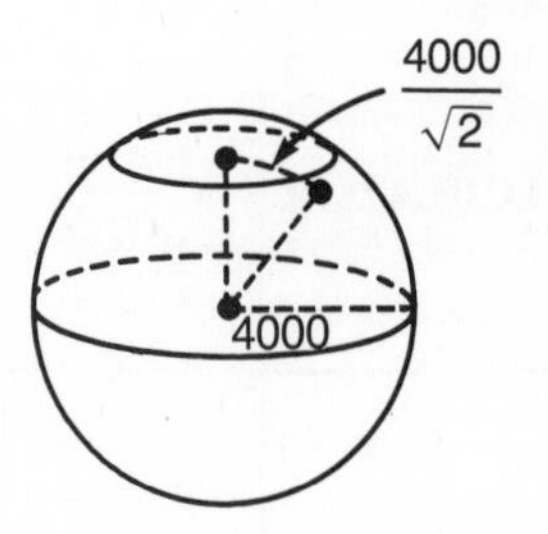

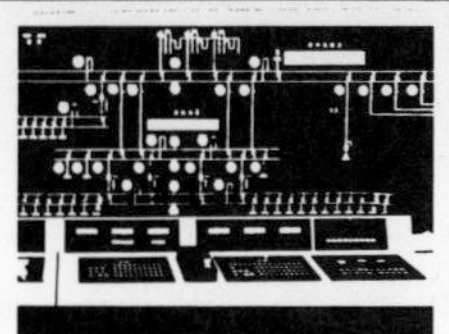

COMPUTER

Standardized mathematics tests will require you to use the relations in special triangles (30°-60°-90° and 45°-45°-90°) and in right triangles whose side lengths have integral values. These integral values are called *Pythagorean Triples.* If x and y are positive integers with $x > y$, then prove that $x^2 + y^2$ will be the length of the hypotenuse if the legs have lengths of $2xy$ and $x^2 - y^2$. These values can be used to create sets of triples in the following program:

```
10  PRINT"LEG 1","LEG 2",
    "HYPOTENUSE"
20  FOR X=2 to 5
30  FOR Y=1 TO X−1
40  LET A=X↑2−Y↑2
50  LET B=2*X*Y
60  LET C=X↑2+Y↑2
70  PRINT A,B,C
80  NEXT Y
90  NEXT X
100 END
```

Your program should give you ten sets of triples (3-4-5, 8-6-10, and so on). Modify line 20 by changing the 5 to other integral values greater than 1.

Can you detect a pattern that will allow you to predict the number of triples if line 20 is changed to "FOR X=2 TO 50" or "FOR X=2 TO 100" without running the program and counting the triples? Can you write a program to check this pattern?

Another important concept is to determine if three given numbers can be the lengths of the sides of a triangle, and what type of triangle is formed. How might you modify the following program to identify *obtuse* and *acute* triangles as well?

```
10  PRINT"INPUT THE LENGTHS
    OF THE TWO SHORTER
    SIDES"
20  INPUT A,B
30  PRINT"INPUT THE LENGTH
    OF THE LONGEST SIDE"
40  INPUT C
50  IF A+B<=C THEN 150
60  IF A+C<=B THEN 150
70  IF B+C<=A THEN 150
80  PRINT"WILL WORK"
90  IF C↑2=A↑2+B↑2 THEN 120
100 PRINT"NOT A RIGHT
    TRIANGLE":GOTO 160
120 PRINT"RIGHT
    TRIANGLE":GOTO 160
150 PRINT"WILL NOT WORK"
160 END
```

TEACHER'S RESOURCE MASTERS

Computer Master 13

Computer

There is an arithmetic pattern, where the number of triples is the sum of the last number of triples and the last value for x. The following program will quickly give the values in the pattern:

```
10 Y=1
20 FOR X=2 TO 100
30 PRINT X,Y
40 Y=X+Y
50 NEXT X
```

If the highest value for x is 50, there will be 1225 sets of triples. If the highest value of x is 100, there will be 4950 sets of triples.

To identify all three angle types, delete line 100 and insert the following lines:

```
100 IF C↑2>A↑2+B↑2
THEN 130
110 IF C↑2<A↑2+B↑2
THEN 140
130 PRINT"OBTUSE
    TRIANGLE":GOTO 160
140 PRINT"ACUTE
    TRIANGLE":GOTO 160
```

EXPLORATION/ The Golden Rectangle

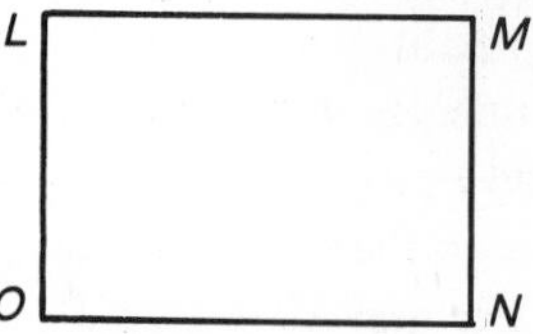

Which of the two rectangles above is more pleasing to your eye? Most people choose the one on the left. The reason may be that rectangle *LMNO* can be seen in its entirety at one glance, while rectangle *STUV* requires scanning from one end to the other. Rectangle *LMNO* is called a *golden rectangle,* because the lengths of its sides are in a special ratio called the *golden ratio.* To find the golden ratio, consider the line segment below.

Point P divides $\overline{AB}$ into two segments, $\overline{AP}$ and $\overline{PB}$, such that $\frac{AP}{PB} = \frac{AB}{AP}$. If you make AP the length of a rectangle and PB its width, then the sides of the rectangle are in the proportion $\frac{l}{w} = \frac{w+l}{l}$. This is called the *divine proportion,* and $\frac{l}{w}$ is called the golden ratio. Any rectangle formed by this ratio is a golden rectangle.

To construct a golden rectangle, draw a square *EFGH*, as shown at the right, and label the midpoint M of $\overline{HG}$. Now with center M and radius $\overline{MF}$, draw an arc intersecting $\overleftrightarrow{HG}$ at I. A line perpendicular to $\overleftrightarrow{HG}$ at I intersects $\overleftrightarrow{EF}$ at J. The result is the golden rectangle *EJIH*.

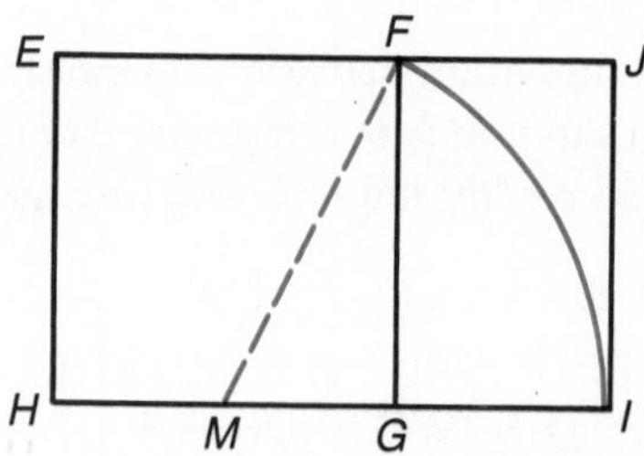

You can verify that rectangle *EJIH* satisfies the golden ratio by letting each side of the original square *EFGH* equal 1. Then MG is $\frac{1}{2}$, and by the Pythagorean Theorem MF is $\frac{\sqrt{5}}{2}$. Since $\overline{MF}$ and $\overline{MI}$ are radii of the same arc, they have the same measure, so GI is $MI - MG$, or $\frac{\sqrt{5}}{2} - \frac{1}{2}$, and $HI = \frac{1}{2} + \frac{\sqrt{5}}{2}$. Now you can verify the divine proportion as follows:

$\frac{l}{w} = \frac{w+l}{l}$, or $\frac{HI}{EH} = \frac{EH + HI}{HI}$.

Thus, $\dfrac{\frac{1}{2} + \frac{\sqrt{5}}{2}}{1} = \dfrac{\frac{3}{2} + \frac{\sqrt{5}}{2}}{\frac{1}{2} + \frac{\sqrt{5}}{2}}$

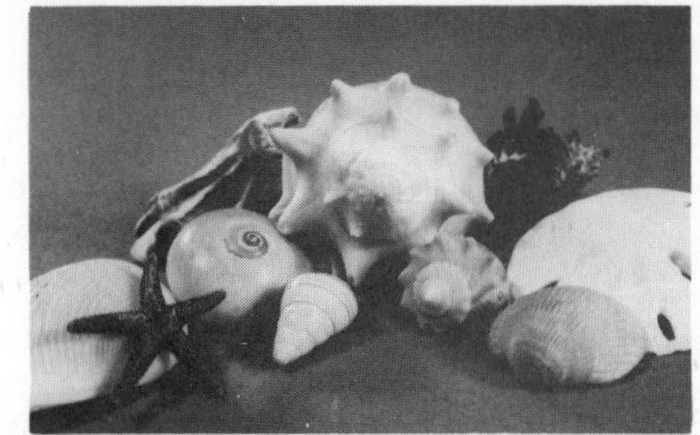

When you cross-multiply and simplify, you obtain $\frac{3}{2} + \frac{\sqrt{5}}{2} = \frac{3}{2} + \frac{\sqrt{5}}{2}$, so the proportion is valid for rectangle *EJIH*. By the same method you could show that the smaller rectangle *GFJI* is also a golden rectangle.

An interesting pattern results when you construct golden rectangles within golden rectangles. If you mark off a square with sides of length *GI* in rectangle *GFJI*, you create yet another golden rectangle *FJLK*. Continuing this process produces golden rectangles *KFNU, OPUK, RQPU,* and *QPTS*.

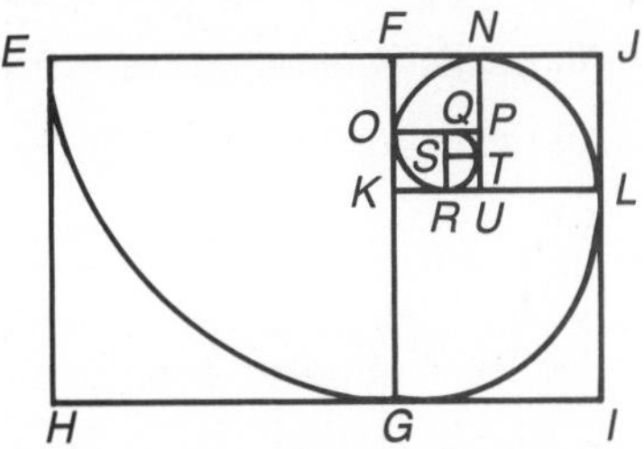

Now draw the quarter circles having (a) center *F*, radius *FE*; (b) center *K*, radius *KG*; (c) center *U*, radius *UL*; and so on. The result is called a *logarithmic spiral.* Spirals generated from the golden ratio are found in many natural wonders, including the pinecone and the sea shell pictured above. Other examples are the galaxies of the stars, ocean waves, and the cochlea of the human ear.

The golden ratio also exists in some triangles. For example, an isosceles triangle with a vertex angle of 36° is a *golden triangle.* If one base angle is bisected, the opposite side will be divided into two segments that are in the golden ratio. Another isosceles golden triangle is also created within the original triangle. By repeating the process and connecting the vertices of all the consecutive golden triangles, you can produce a logarithmic spiral.

You can estimate the value of the golden ratio using numerical values you have already determined. In rectangle *EJIH*, the ratio of length to width has the value $\frac{1}{2} + \frac{\sqrt{5}}{2}$. Using your calculator, verify that this expression reduces to 1.61803. . . . The golden ratio therefore is often rounded off to 1.6, although this is only an approximation of the "golden number" that has an almost magical quality.

TEACHER'S RESOURCE MASTERS

Enrichment Master 10

ENRICHMENT

See Activities 25–26, p. T51–T52

Chapter 13 Review

1. a line parallel to and midway between l and m
2. two lines parallel to m, each 3 cm on either side of m
3. the interior of the circle with center S and radius 5 cm
4. two lines through the origin having slopes of 1 and -1
5.

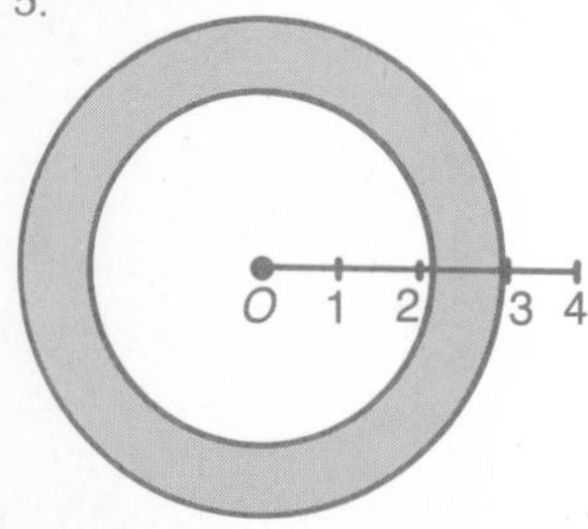

6. the two points at which $\odot P$ with radius d intersects the line
7. the perpendicular bisector of RS
8. the bisector of $\angle A$, which also bisects $\angle C$
9. the point of concurrency of the perpendicular bisectors of the sides
10. the center of the circle containing the 3 points
11. the empty set
12. the point of concurrency of the angle bisectors
13. No; one circle could also be inside the other.
14. Construction 1
15. Construction 2
16. Draw arcs from each endpoint of a given segment with radii the same length as the segment. Their intersection forms the third vertex of an equilateral triangle.

CHAPTER 13 REVIEW

VOCABULARY

circumcenter (13.4)
circumscribed (13.4)
construction (13.3)
incenter (13.4)
inscribed (13.4)
loci (13.1)
locus of points (13.1)

REVIEW EXERCISES

13.1 Sketch and describe the following loci of points in a plane.

1. All points equidistant from two parallel lines, l and m.
2. All points 3 cm from a given line, m.
3. All points less than 5 cm from a given point, S.
4. All points equidistant from the x-axis and y-axis.
5. All points further than 2 units from point C but less than 3 units from C.
6. All points at a given distance, d, from point P and contained in a line through P.

13.2

7. The locus of points equidistant from two given points, R and S.
8. In square $ABCD$, the locus of points equidistant from adjacent sides $\overline{AB}$ and $\overline{AD}$.
9. The locus of points equidistant from the vertices of a triangle.
10. The locus of points equidistant from three given noncollinear points.
11. The locus of points equidistant from three collinear points.
12. The locus of points equidistant from the three sides of a triangle.

13.3

13. Given two circles, $\odot A$ with radius a and $\odot B$ with radius b, both circles lying in the same plane, if $a + b > AB$, must the circles intersect? Explain and support your answer with a sketch.

In the following construction problems, use only a compass and a straightedge.

14. Copy ΔABC, shown below.

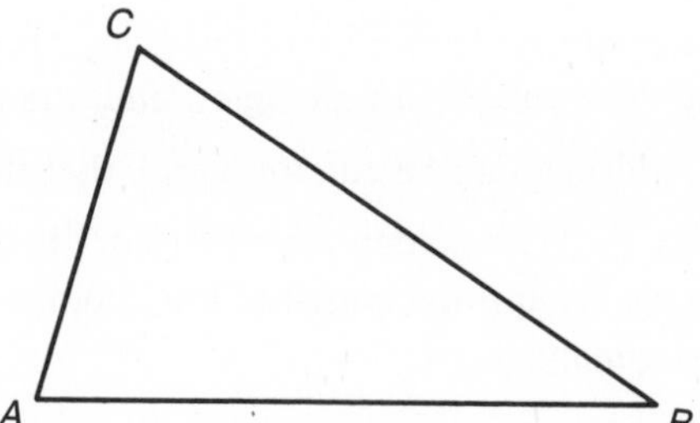

15. Copy $\angle X$, shown below.

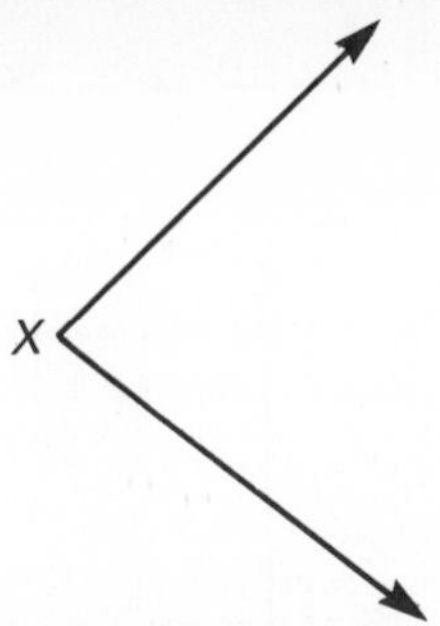

16. Construct an equilateral triangle.

17. Construct an isosceles triangle.

18. Construct a square given a diagonal.

19. Construct a 30-60-90 triangle.

20. Draw an obtuse triangle. Then construct the altitude from the vertex of either acute angle.

21. Construct a parallelogram given one side, one acute angle, and the longer diagonal.

22. Draw a segment about 5 or 6 inches long. Then divide the segment into 5 equal segments.

13.4 **23.** Circumscribe a circle about a right triangle.

24. Construct a right triangle with a given segment as the hypotenuse.

25. Construct a 45-45-90 triangle.

26. Inscribe a circle in an acute triangle.

27. Draw a circle. Then circumscribe a square about it.

28. Draw a circle. Then find the center of the circle by construction.

29. The three vertices of a triangle are at (0, 0), (4, 0), and (0, 4). Find the coordinates of the center of the circumscribed circle. What is the measure of the radius of the circle?

30. A circle has its center at the origin of a rectangular coordinate system, and it contains the point (3, 4). Find the equation of the line that is tangent to the circle at that point. Then draw the circle and construct the tangent.

17. Construction 3; construct the $\perp$ bisector of a given segment; join the endpoints of the segment to any point on the perpendicular.
18. Construction 4; construct the $\perp$ bisector of the given diagonal so that the bisector is the same length as the diagonal and is bisected itself; join the endpoints of the two diagonals.
19. Construct an equilateral Δ; from one endpoint construct a perpendicular; extend the other side of the Δ to intersect the perpendicular.
20. Construction 5
21. Construct an obtuse ΔABC, with obtuse $\angle A$ the supplement of the given $\angle$, and with AB equal to the given side and BD equal to the given diagonal. Then construct a line through B $\parallel$ AD. On it locate C so that $BC = AD$. Draw $\overline{CD}$.
22. Construction 7
23. Construction 8
24. See *Selected Answers*, p. 642
25. See *Teacher's Manual*, p. T62
26. Construction 10
27. Construct $\perp$ diameters; construct tangents to endpoints of the diameters; extend tangents until they intersect to form a square.
28. Draw 2 non-parallel chords. Their $\perp$ bisectors intersect at the center.
29. $C(2, 2)$, radius $= 2\sqrt{2}$
30. Slope of tangent $= \frac{-3}{4}$. Equation of tangent is $(y - 4) = \frac{-3}{4}(x - 3)$.

TEACHER'S RESOURCE MASTERS

Chapter 13 Test
Multiple Choice Test—Chapter 13

Chapter 13 Test

1. e
2. b
3. b
4. d
5. b
6. d
7. Construction 3
8. Construction 5
9. Construction 6
10. Construction 9
11. Construction 8

CHAPTER 13 TEST

1. Which set characterization best describes the figure?

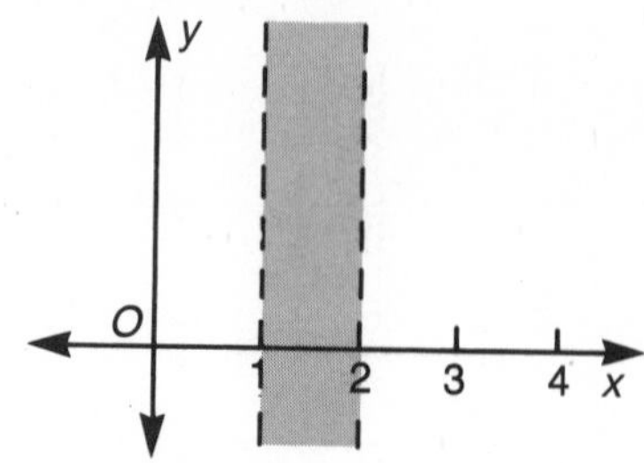

a. $x < 2$

b. $x > 1$

c. $1 > x > 2$

d. $1 < y < 2$

e. $1 < x < 2$

2. The locus of points in a plane equidistant from three given noncollinear points is _____.

a. a line **b.** a point **c.** a circle
d. a triangle **e.** the interior of a circle

3. The locus of points in space a given distance from a given point is _____.

a. a circle **b.** a sphere **c.** a line **d.** a point **e.** a cylinder

4. The set of midpoints of all the radii of a circle is _____.

a. an arc **b.** a chord **c.** a point **d.** a circle **e.** the empty set

5. To find a point equidistant from the three sides of a triangle you must _____.

a. bisect two segments **b.** bisect two angles
c. construct two altitudes **d.** construct two medians
e. use a protractor

6. For any given triangle, which of the following are *not* concurrent at a point?

a. the angle bisectors **b.** the perpendicular bisectors of the sides
c. the lines containing the altitudes **d.** the sides
e. the medians

For each construction use only a compass and a straightedge.

7. Draw a segment and construct its perpendicular bisector.

8. Construct a perpendicular line to a segment through a point on the segment.

9. Draw an obtuse triangle. Then, through the vertex of the obtuse angle, construct a line parallel to the opposite side.

10. Draw an acute angle and bisect it.

11. Circumscribe a circle about an equilateral triangle.

CHAPTER 14

Area and Volume

OBJECTIVES

Identify polygons, their vertices, sides, angles, apothems, and perimeters.
Determine central angles of a polygon.
Use formulas for deriving angles of a polygon.

TEACHER'S NOTES

See p. T39

MIXED REVIEW

1. How many degrees are in a triangle? 180
2. Each angle of a square has ______degrees. 90
3. Solve $|2x - 1| = 9$. $\{5, -4\}$
4. Solve $13 < 4x - 3 < 25$. $4 < x < 7$
5. Solve $(x - 2)(x + 3)(2x + 1) = 0$. $\{2, -3, -\frac{1}{2}\}$

TEACHER'S RESOURCE MASTERS

Practice Master 42, Part 1

14.1 Polygons

Your experience with polygons up to now is probably sufficient to tell you which set of figures below are polygons and which are not.

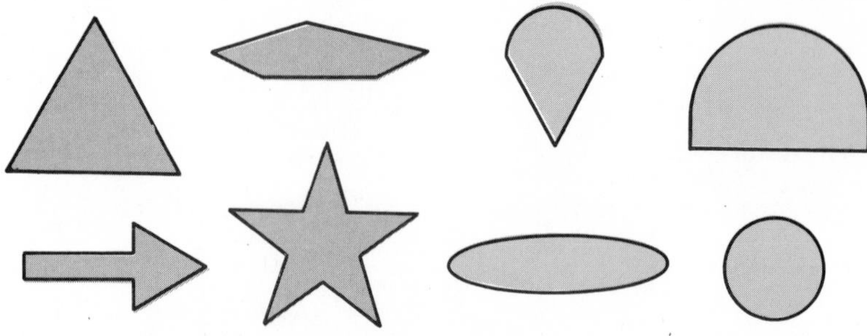

If you identified the shaded figures as polygons, you were correct. Perhaps unconsciously you recognized that the sides of these figures are formed by segments that intersect only at their endpoints, and that no two segments with a common endpoint are collinear. The figures on the right do not satisfy these conditions.

It is now possible to define *polygon* formally. Recall that when you learned to divide a segment into any number of congruent segments, the notation $P_1, P_2, \ldots, P_n$ was used to denote any number of points. The definition of *polygon* uses the same notation, with n being an unspecified number of points and P_{n-1} denoting the next-to-last point in the sequence.

DEFINITIONS: polygon, vertices, sides, angles of a polygon
Let $P_1, P_2, P_3, \ldots, P_{n-1}, P_n$ be n distinct points in a plane ($n \geq 3$). Let the n segments $\overline{P_1P_2}, \overline{P_2P_3}, \ldots, \overline{P_{n-1}P_n}, \overline{P_nP_1}$ have the properties:
(1) no two segments intersect except at their endpoints, as specified, and
(2) no two segments with a common endpoint are collinear.
Then the union of the n segments is a **polygon.** The n given points are **vertices** (plural of **vertex**) of the polygon, the n segments are **sides** of the polygon. By (2), any two segments with a common vertex determine an angle, which is called an **angle of the polygon.**

Polygons having n vertices and n sides are sometimes called **n-gons.** Thus, a triangle is a 3-gon and a quadrilateral is a 4-gon, although these familiar figures are seldom named as n-gons. Other special n-gons are the **pentagon** (5-gon), **hexagon** (6-gon), **octagon** (8-gon), **decagon** (10-gon), and **dodecagon** (12-gon).

Each side of a polygon lies on a line that separates the plane of the polygon into two half-planes. If, for each side, the rest of the polygon lies entirely in one of the half-planes having that side on its edge, then the polygon is called a **convex polygon.** In the figure at the right, the sides of the polygon have been extended to show that the condition for a convex polygon is satisfied.

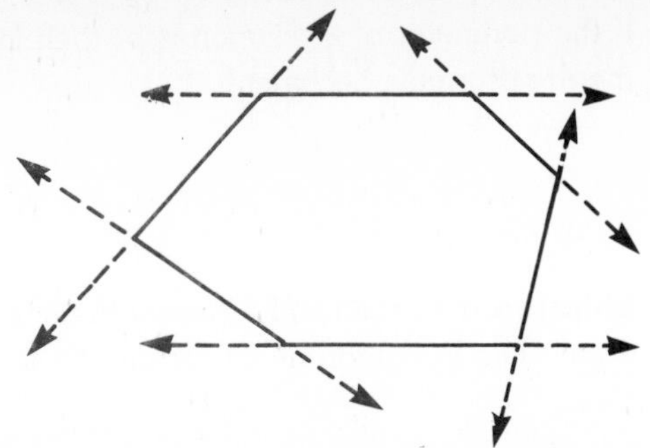

If a polygon is convex, the union of the polygon and its interior is a *convex set,* as defined in Chapter 2. The first figure of this chapter shows four polygons. You should be able to explain why the star and arrow-shaped polygon are not convex.

Some special properties of polygons follow from the definition of convex.

DEFINITION: regular polygon
A polygon is **regular** if and only if it is convex and all of its sides and all of its angles are congruent.

Every regular polygon can be inscribed in a circle (or a circle can be circumscribed about any regular polygon), and a circle can be inscribed in any regular polygon. A **radius** of a regular polygon is a radius of its circumscribed circle.

If $P_1P_2 \ldots P_n$ is a regular polygon inscribed in $\odot Q$, then the triangles formed by two consecutive radii and a side of the polygon are congruent by SSS (Theorem 4.5). By corresponding parts, the angles formed about Q are also congruent and are called the **central angles** of the polygon. Because the sum of their measures is 360, an n-gon will have central angles measuring $\frac{360}{n}$.

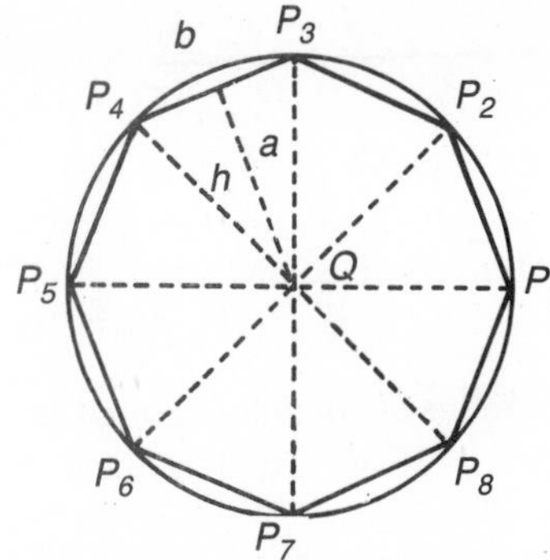

The triangles formed by radii of $\odot Q$ have the same base (b) and altitude (a). The area of each triangle is therefore $\frac{1}{2}ab$, and the total area of the regular n-gon is

$$A_n = n(\tfrac{1}{2}ab).$$

DEFINITIONS: apothem, perimeter of a polygon
The altitude a of a triangle formed by consecutive radii of a regular polygon is the **apothem** of the polygon. The sum of the lengths of the sides of the polygon is the **perimeter.**

If the perimeter of a polygon is p, then in a regular polygon $p = n \cdot b$. Using this notation, the area formula becomes

$$A_n = \tfrac{1}{2}a(nb) = \tfrac{1}{2}ap.$$

Example: Find the area of a regular hexagon if a side measures 4 cm.

Solution: Two radii and a base of the hexagon form an equilateral triangle with sides of length 4 cm. The Pythagorean Theorem can be applied to find that the apothem measures $2\sqrt{3}$. Thus,

$$A = \tfrac{1}{2}(2\sqrt{3})(p) = \tfrac{1}{2}(2\sqrt{3})(24)$$
$$= 24\sqrt{3}\text{ cm}^2.$$

Is it possible to determine the sum of the measures of the interior angles of a polygon? You have proved that the sum of the measures of the angles of a triangle is 180. You also know that a triangle has no diagonals and that any polygonal region can be subdivided into triangular regions by drawing the diagonals from one vertex. These diagonals form 2 triangles in a convex quadrilateral, 3 triangles in a convex pentagon, and so on.

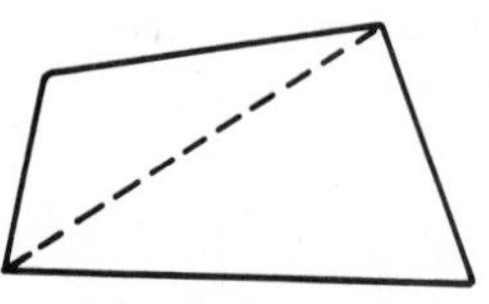

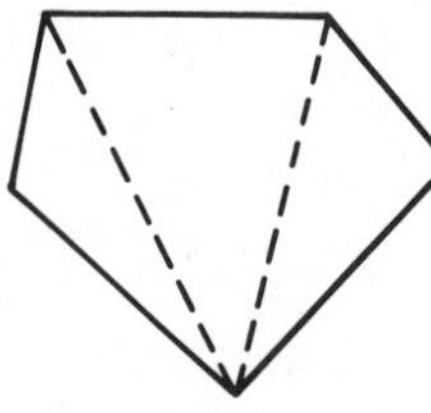

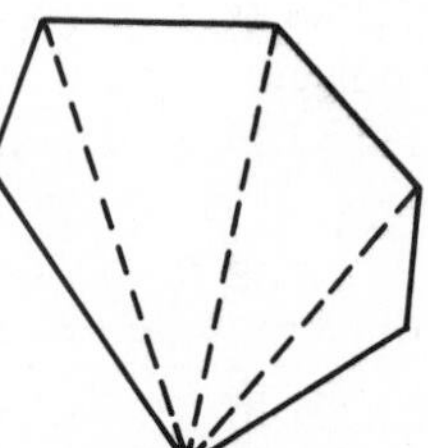

If the number of triangles formed in a convex polygon is n, then the sum of the measures of its angles is $180n$. To determine n without drawing a figure for each case, consider the pattern:

sides	3	4	5	6	. . .	n
triangles	1	2	3	4	. . .	$n - 2$

In each case, the number of triangles formed is two less than the number of sides. Thus, the formula for the total measure of the interior angles of a convex polygon with n sides is $S = (n - 2)180$.

Exterior angles of a convex polygon are formed by extending each side of the polygon in one direction. Unlike the interior angle sum, which varies depending on the number of sides of a polygon, the sum of the measures of the exterior angles of a convex polygon is constant.

You can see that the interior and exterior angle at each vertex are supplementary, so $m\angle 1 + m\angle 2 = m\angle 3 + m\angle 4 = 180$ for all angles of a polygon. If the polygon has n vertices, it has n pairs of supplementary angles whose measures total $180n$. Therefore,

$180n$ = interior angle sum + exterior angle sum

$180n = (n - 2)180$ + exterior angle sum

$180n = 180n - 360$ + exterior angle sum

360 = exterior angle sum

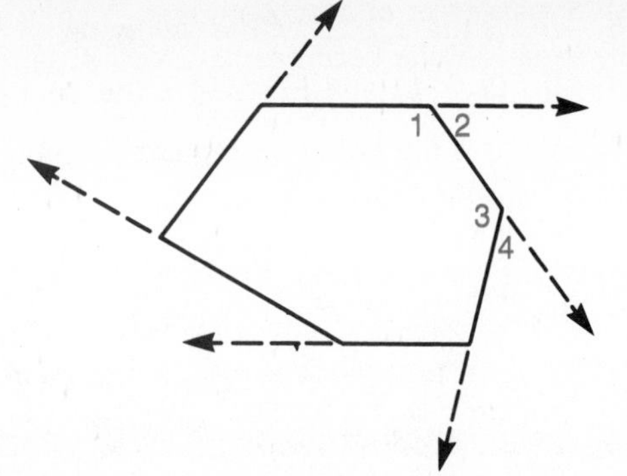

Thus, the exterior angle sum of a convex polygon does not depend on the number of sides; it is always 360.

ORAL EXERCISES

1. Which figures below are convex polygons?

(a)

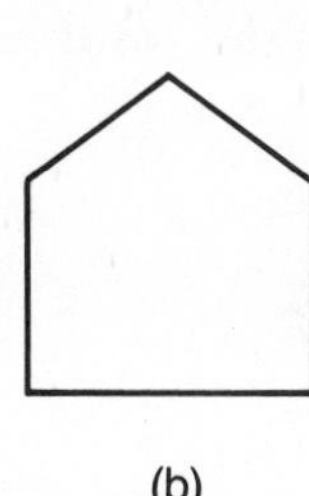

(b)

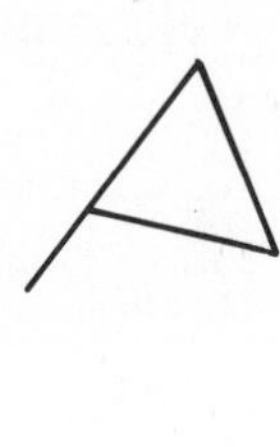

(c)

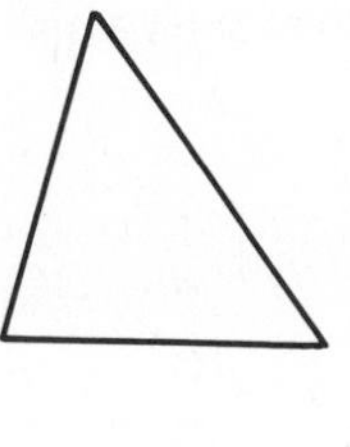

(d)

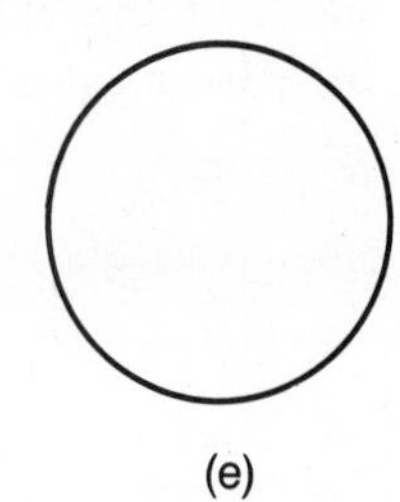

(e)

2. Define a regular polygon.

3. Is the figure at the right a polygon? How many sides does it have? Could you use the formula $S = (n - 2)180$ to determine the sum of the interior angles?

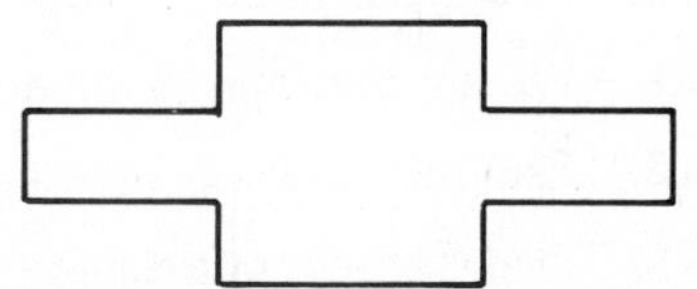

4. A formula for the sum of the measures of the interior angles of a convex polygon of n sides is $(n - 2)180$. What would be the formula for the measure of each angle of a regular n-gon? for the measure of each exterior angle of regular n-gon?

Given regular pentagon *ABCDE* with center *F*, answer the following.

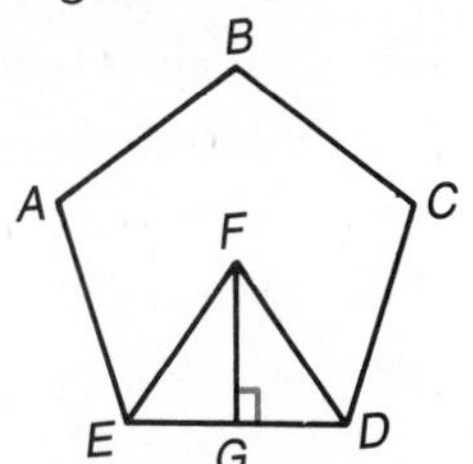

5. Name a radius.

6. Name a central angle.

7. The measure of $\angle EFD$ is ______.

ASSIGNMENT GUIDE

Minimum 1-19
Regular 1-25 odd
Maximum 1-19 odd, 21-30

Oral Exercises

1. b and d are convex polygons.
2. convex with all sides and all $\angle$s $\cong$
3. yes; 12; no
4. $\frac{(n - 2)180}{n}$, $\frac{360}{n}$
5. $\overline{FE}$ or $\overline{FD}$
6. $\angle EFD$, $\angle DFC$, $\angle CFB$, $\angle BFA$, or $\angle AFE$
7. 72

8. apothem

9. 440

10. 75 cm^2

8. $\overline{FG}$ is the ____ of the pentagon.

9. If $FG = 11$ and $ED = 16$, the area of the pentagon is ____.

10. What is the area of a regular polygon with perimeter 60 and apothem 2.5 cm?

Written Exercises

1. S
2. A
3. S
4. N
5. 1080
6. 540
7. 720
8. 1260
9. 360
10. 144
11. $\frac{1}{8}$
12. 100
13. 128
14. $96\sqrt{3}$
15. $81\sqrt{3}$
16. (a) 2; (b) $\sqrt{3}$; (c) $6\sqrt{3}$
17. 18
18. 5

WRITTEN EXERCISES

A. Complete each sentence with the word sometimes, always, or never.

1. An interior angle of a convex quadrilateral is ____ greater than 90.
2. The total measure of the exterior angles of a convex polygon is ____ equal to 360.
3. The total measure of the interior angles of a pentagon is ____ equal to 540.
4. The total measure of the central angles of a regular polygon is ____ equal to 260.

Each of the following polygons is convex. What is the total measure of the interior angles?

5. octagon
6. pentagon
7. hexagon
8. 9-gon
9. What is the total measure of the exterior angles of each polygon in Exercises 5–8?

B. 10. Find the measure of each angle in a regular decagon.

11. What is the ratio of the apothem of a square to its perimeter?
12. Find the area of a square with perimeter 40.
13. Find the area of a square with diagonal 16.
14. Find the area of a regular hexagon with apothem $4\sqrt{3}$.
15. Find the area of an equilateral triangle if the radius of the circle that circumscribes it is $6\sqrt{3}$.
16. The sides of a regular hexagon are each 2 cm long. If it is inscribed in a circle, find (a) the radius of the circle, (b) the apothem of the hexagon, and (c) the area of the hexagon.
17. Each angle of a polygon is 160. How many sides does the polygon have?
18. In a regular polygon, the ratio of the measure of an interior angle to the measure of an exterior angle is $\frac{3}{2}$. How many sides does the polygon have?

19. Given regular pentagon $ABCDE$ with $FA = FB = FC = FD = FE$, find the measures of $\angle 1$ and $\angle 2$.

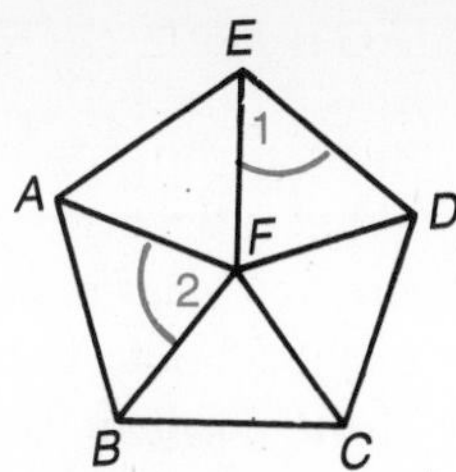

19. 54, 72

20. Find the area of the shaded square at the right.

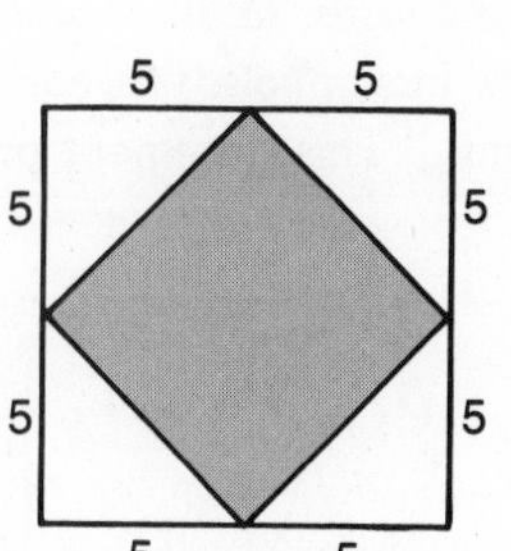

20. 50

C. Given square $ABCD$, find the missing values if $CB = 12$, and $\overline{AF} \cong \overline{EF} \cong \overline{FB}$.

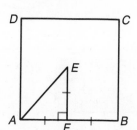

21. $EF =$ _____

22. $EA =$ _____

23. perimeter of square $ABCD =$ _____

24. area of square $ABCD =$ _____

21. 6

22. $6\sqrt{2}$

23. 48

24. 144

Given equilateral $\triangle ABC$ with center E, find the missing values if $CB = 8$.

25. $AE =$ _____

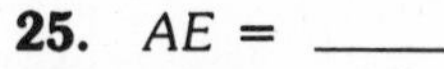

26. $ED =$ _____

27. perimeter $\triangle ABC =$ _____

28. area $\triangle ABC =$ _____

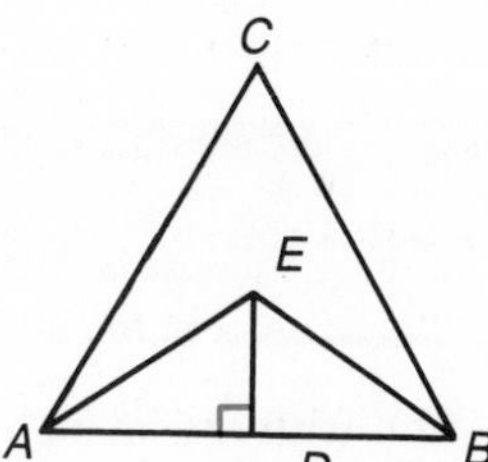

25. $\frac{8\sqrt{3}}{3}$

26.  $\frac{4\sqrt{3}}{3}$

27. 24

28. $16\sqrt{3}$

29. Find the ratio of the area of the smaller figure to the larger figure, if both are regular pentagons.

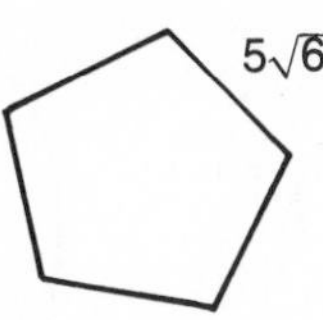

19

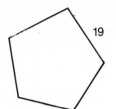

29. $\frac{150}{361}$

30. What is the area of a square with radius $10y$?

30. $200y^2$

OBJECTIVE

Use Theorems 14.1 and 14.2 to answer questions regarding circles and their arcs.

TEACHER'S NOTES

See p. T39

MIXED REVIEW

1. If $ax^2 + c = 0$, then $x = ?$ $\pm\sqrt{\frac{c}{a}}$
2. Solve $5x - 3(4 - x) = 12$. 3
3. Solve $|x| = -9$. $\varnothing$
4. Multiply $(5x - 3)(2x + 1)$. $10x^2 - x - 3$
5. Divide $\frac{x^2 - x - 2}{x + 3} \div \frac{x^2 + 2x + 1}{x^2 + 2x - 3}$. $\frac{(x - 2)(x - 1)}{(x + 1)}$

TEACHER'S RESOURCE MASTERS

Practice Master 42, Part 2

14.2 Circumference and Area of Circles

Suppose you want to measure the distance around, or **circumference** (C) of a given circle. You might consider inscribing a regular polygon in the circle and then calculating the perimeter of the polygon. The perimeter (p) should be a close approximation of C if the polygon has many sides. In other words, you can find p as close to C as you want by making n large enough. In symbols, this concept is expressed as "$p \rightarrow C$," which means "p approaches C as a limit." This statement provides a definition of **circumference.**

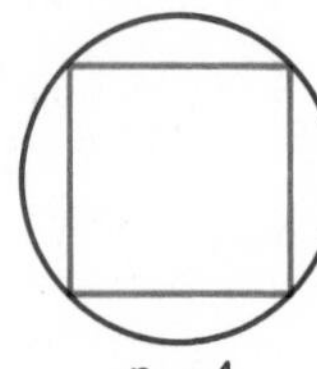

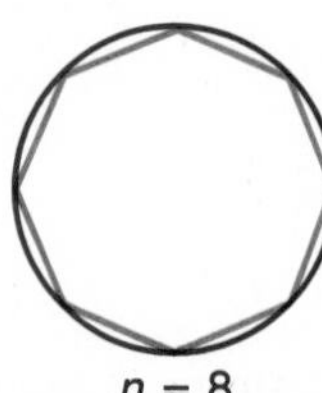

DEFINITION: circumference of a circle
The **circumference of a circle** is the limit of the perimeters of the inscribed regular polygons.

The circumference of a circle has a special relationship to the radius, in that $\frac{C}{2r}$ equals the number π**(pi)**. In order to define π, it is necessary to establish that $\frac{C}{2r}$ is constant for all circles, regardless of their size.

THEOREM 14.1
The ratio $\frac{C}{2r}$ of the circumference to the radius is the same for all circles.

Given: $\odot X$ with radius r and circumference C, $\angle X'$ with radius r' and circumference C'

Prove: $\frac{C}{2r} = \frac{C'}{2r'}$

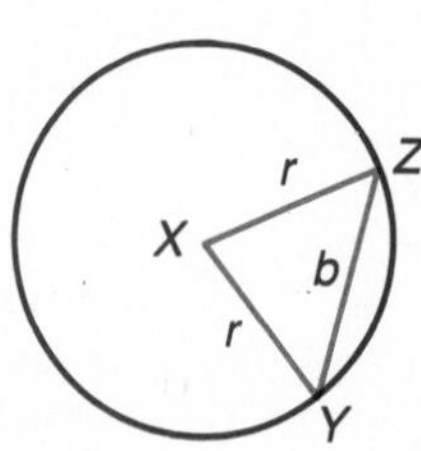

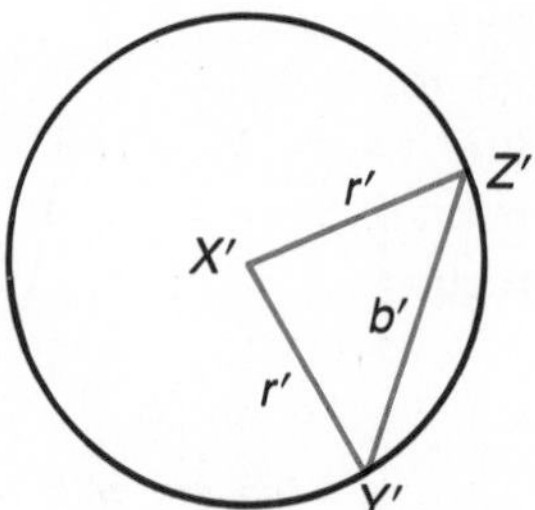

Proof: The proof is by similar triangles. Inscribe a regular n-gon in each circle, using the same value of n for both. Draw the radii of the n-gon to form congruent triangles about the centers X and X' (only one triangle is shown for each circle).

Because each central angle of the given n-gons has a measure of $\frac{360}{n}$, $\angle YXZ \cong \angle Y'X'Z'$. Also, adjacent sides of $\triangle XYZ$ and $\triangle X'Y'Z'$ are proportional. Therefore, $\triangle XYZ \sim \triangle X'Y'Z'$ by SAS (Theorem 10.4), and $\frac{b}{r} = \frac{b'}{r'}$. Since $p = nb$ is the perimeter of the first n-gon, and $p' = nb'$ is the perimeter of the second, substitution yields $\frac{p}{r} = \frac{p'}{r'}$.

By definition, $p \to C$ and $p' \to C'$. Therefore, $\frac{C}{r} = \frac{C'}{r'}$ and $\frac{C}{2r} = \frac{C'}{2r'}$.

The number $\frac{C}{2r}$, which is the same for all circles, is designated by π. Theorem 14.1 can therefore be restated in the familiar form $C = 2\pi r$.

Because π is an irrational number, it cannot be represented exactly in fractional form. It can, however, be approximated closely by such rational numbers as 3.14, $\frac{22}{7}$, and 3.1416.

As with a polygon, the area of a circle refers to the area of the region determined by the circle. In order to find a formula for this area, it is necessary first to define **circular region.**

DEFINITION: circular region
A **circular region** is the union of a circle and its interior.

The formula for the area of an inscribed regular n-gon: $A_n = \frac{1}{2}ap$, where a is the apothem and p is the perimeter.

Example: $A_n \to$? As the figure illustrates, the area of the inscribed n-gon (A_n) will always be less than the area of the circle that circumscribes it (A), even when n is quite large. As n increases, though, the difference between A_n and A decreases, or $A_n \to A$. Like the definition of circumference, a definition of **area** follows from this statement about approaching limits.

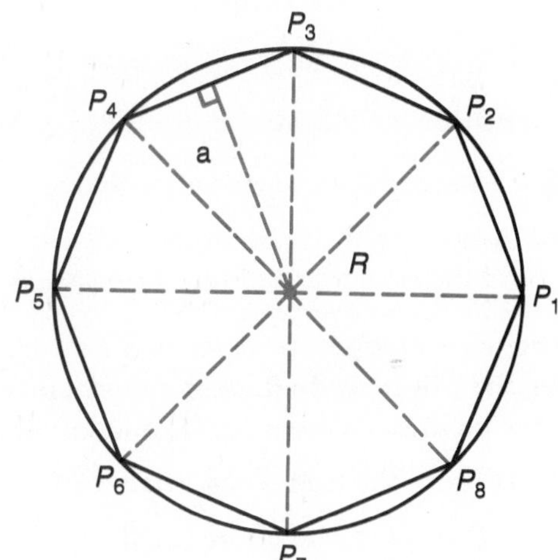

DEFINITION: area of a circle
The **area of a circle** is the limit of the areas of the inscribed regular polygons.

Example: $a \to$? Referring to the figure of $\odot R$, you can see that the apothem (a) will always be shorter than the radius (RP_1, RP_2, . . . , RP_n) of an n-gon (because either leg of a right triangle is always shorter than the hypotenuse). Again, however, as n increases, the difference between a and r decreases, so $a \to r$.

Example: $p \to$? By the definition of circumference, you know that $p \to C$.

By combining Examples 2 and 3, you can conclude that $ap \to rC$, or $\frac{1}{2}ap \to \frac{1}{2}rC$. Since $A_n = \frac{1}{2}ap$, substitution yields $A_n \to \frac{1}{2}rC$. But from Example 1 you know that $A_n \to A$, so $A = \frac{1}{2}rC$. Substituting $2\pi r$ for C yields the familiar formula for area of a circle: $A = \pi r^2$.

> **THEOREM 14.2**
> The area of a circle of radius r is πr^2.

Example: Find the area of a circle with a radius of 3 cm.

Solution:
$$\begin{aligned} A &= r^2 \\ &= 3.14(3^2) \\ &= 3.14 \cdot 9 \\ &= 28.26 \text{ cm}^2 \end{aligned}$$

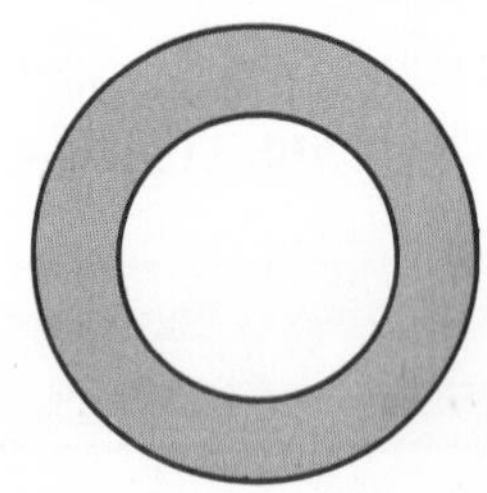

Closely related to a circular region is the **annulus,** from the Latin word for *ring.* The shaded portion of the figure is an annulus, whose area is the difference between the areas of the larger and smaller concentric circles.

ASSIGNMENT GUIDE

Minimum 1-13
Regular 1-23 odd
Maximum 1-15 odd, 20-25

Oral Exercises

1. 20π or 62.8 cm, 100π or 314 cm^2
2. Because as n increases, the perimeter approaches the circumference.
3. the radius of the circle
4. 0
5. 180°
6. the circumference of the circle
7. 100 yards

ORAL EXERCISES

1. What are the circumference and area of a circle with a radius of 10 cm?
2. State why the circumference of a circle can be described as the limit of the perimeter of the circumscribed regular polygons.

A regular polygon is inscribed in a circle, then another with one more side than the first is inscribed, and so on endlessly, each time increasing the number of sides by one. Answer the following about the inscribed polygons.

3. What is the limit of the length of an apothem?
4. What is the limit of the length of a side?
5. What is the limit of the measure of an angle?
6. What is the limit of the perimeters of the polygons?
7. Taking steps that measure 1 yard in length, you can walk around a circular pool close to the edge in 628 steps. What is the approximate radius of the pool? (Use 3.14 for π)

8. If you know the area of a circle, can you determine the circumference? Why or why not?

9. What is the formula for the circumference of a circle in terms of its diameter? for the area of a circle in terms of its diameter?

10. Define π.

11. If a regular octagon has the same area as a circle, can it be inscribed in the circle?

8. Yes; you can find r from the area and use it to find C.

9. $C = \pi d$; $A = \frac{\pi d^2}{4}$

10. $\frac{C}{2r}$

11. no

WRITTEN EXERCISES

A. Find the circumference and area of a circle with the given radius in terms of π.

1. 6 m **2.** 11 mm **3.** n units **4.** 7.83 cm **5.** $6\sqrt{3}$ ft

Find the radius of a circle with the given circumference.

6. 16π in. **7.** $10\sqrt{3}\pi$ cm **8.** $12k\pi$ ft

B. 9. The moon is about 240,000 miles from the earth, and its path around the earth is nearly circular. Find the circumference of the circle the moon describes every month in terms of π.

10. What is the area of a circle in which the longest possible chord is 8 inches long? Use $\pi = 3.14$.

11. Find the area of the annulus if the diameter of an iron washer is 6 cm and the diameter of the hole is 3 cm. Use $\pi = 3.14$.

12. The radius of the larger of two circles is four times the radius of the smaller. Find the ratio of the area of the first to that of the second.

13. The side of a square is 16 m. In terms of π, what is the circumference of its inscribed circle? of its circumscribed circle?

14. The circumference of a circle and the perimeter of a square are equal to 20 inches. Which has the greater area? How much greater is it?

15. The radius of a circle is 10 feet. By how much is its circumference changed, in terms of π, if its radius is increased by 1 foot? If the radius were originally 1000 feet, what would be the change in the circumference when the radius is increased by one foot?

16. Given a square whose side is 20 cm, what is the area between its circumscribed and inscribed circles? Use $\pi = 3.14$.

17. An equilateral triangle is inscribed in a circle. If the side of the triangle is 18 in., in terms of π, what is the radius of the circle? the circumference? the area?

Written Exercises

1. $C = 12\pi$ m, $A = 36\pi$ m^2

2. $C = 22\pi$ mm, $A = 121\pi$ mm^2

3. $C = 2\pi n$ units, $A = \pi n^2$ units^2

4. $C = 15.66\pi$ cm, $A = 61.3089\pi$ cm^2

5. $C = 12\pi\sqrt{3}$ ft, $A = 108\pi$ ft^2

6. 8 in.

7. $5\sqrt{3}$ cm

8. $6k$ ft

9. $480{,}000\pi$ mi

10. 16π in.$^2 \approx 50.24$ in.^{2}

11. 6.75π cm$^2 \approx 21.2$ cm^2

12. $\frac{16}{1}$

13. 16π m, $16\pi\sqrt{2}$ m

14. The circle has the greater area by approx. 6.85 in.^{2}.

15. 2π ft, 2π ft

16. 100π cm$^2 = 314$ cm^2

17. $r = 6\sqrt{3}$ in., $C = 12\pi\sqrt{3}$ in., $A = 108\pi$ in.^{2}

18. Area of circle = 40π; area outside cross = $40\pi - 80$

18. The cross inside the circle is divisible into 5 squares. In terms of π, what is the area inside the circle? What is the area outside the cross?

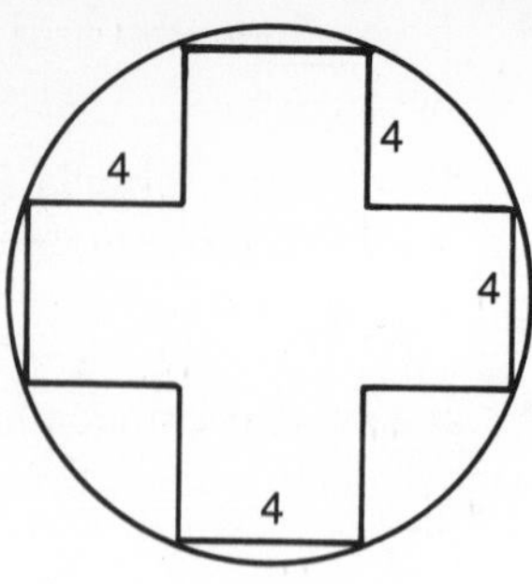

19. The circle 3 in. from the center has an area 16π in.^{2} larger.

20. $4h - \frac{\pi h^2}{4}$

21. $r = 40$ in., $\frac{A_1}{A_2} = \frac{25}{64}$; The circumferences of two circles are proportional to their radii; the areas of two circles are proportional to the squares of their radii.

22. $48\pi - 36\sqrt{3}$ cm^2

23. $\frac{3}{4}$

C. 19. In a sphere whose radius is 10 inches, circles are intercepted by planes 3 in. and 5 in. from the center. Which circle has the larger area? How much larger?

20. An isosceles trapezoid whose bases are 2 in. and 6 in. is circumscribed about a circle. If h is the altitude of the trapezoid, express in terms of h the area of the trapezoid that lies outside the circle.

21. The ratio of the circumferences of two circles is 5 to 8. If the smaller circle has a radius of 25 in., find the radius of the larger circle. What is the ratio of the areas of the two circles? State a corollary you might deduce regarding the ratio of the circumferences of two circles given the radii. State a corollary you might deduce regarding the ratio of the areas of two circles given their radii.

22. An equilateral triangle with perimeter of 36 cm is inscribed in a circle. Find the area of the region bounded by the circle but containing no points in the interior of the triangle.

23. Given a regular hexagon, find the ratio of the areas of the inscribed to the circumscribed circles.

The Earth is about 9.3×10^7 miles from the sun. Assume the path of the Earth around the sun is nearly circular. Use your calculator to answer Exercises 24–25.

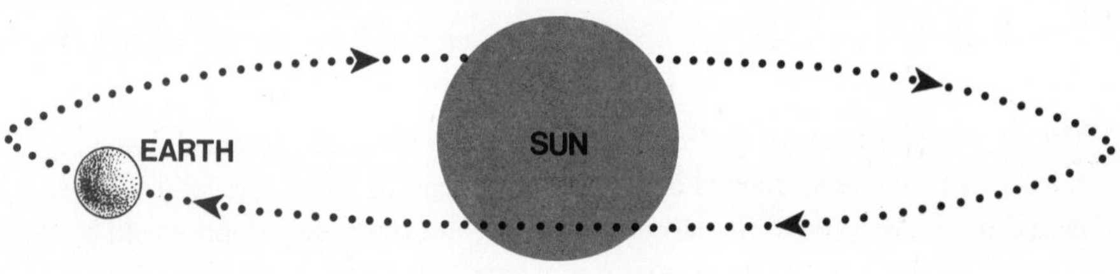

24. $d = (1.86 \cdot 10^8)\pi$ mi $\approx$ 584 million mi

25. $r \approx 66{,}626$ mph

24. How far do we travel in orbit every year?

25. What is our speed in orbit in miles per hour? (There are 365.25 days in a year.)

14.3 Lengths of Arcs

The idea that the perimeter of an inscribed, regular n-gon approaches circumference as a limit can be used to define the length of an arc. In the figure below, QR is an arc of $\odot O$. By Postulate 12, you can take points $P_1, P_2, \ldots, P_{n-1}$ on $\widehat{QR}$ so that each of the angles formed about O has a measure of $\frac{m\widehat{QR}}{n}$.

You can see that as n is increased, the fraction $\frac{m\widehat{QR}}{n}$ (the measure of each central angle) will decrease. As the central angles become smaller, the congruent segments $\overline{QP_1}$, $\overline{P_1P_2}$, $\ldots$, $\overline{P_{n-1}R}$ draw closer to the arcs they intercept, $\widehat{QP_1}$, $\widehat{P_1P_2}$, $\ldots$, $\widehat{P_{n-1}R}$. The sum of the lengths of these segments therefore approaches the measure of the larger arc as a limit.

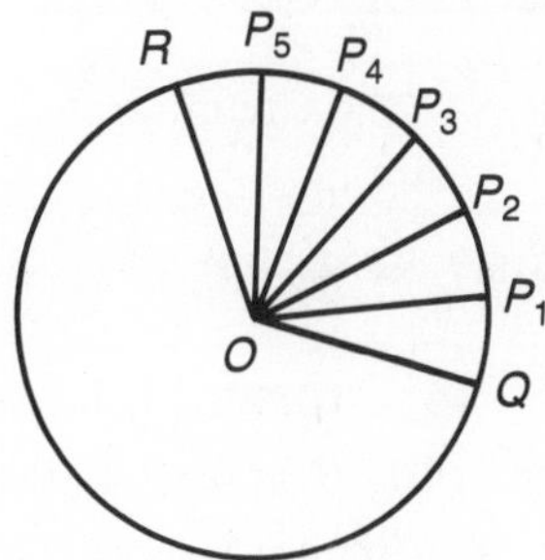

DEFINITION: length of an arc
The length of $\widehat{QR}$ is the limit of $QP_1 + P_1P_2 + \cdots + P_{n-1}R$ as n is taken larger and larger.

An entire circle is considered to be an arc of measure 360, and any point on the circle may be considered both endpoints of the arc. The circumference of a circle is thus the length of an arc measuring 360.

The relationship between the length and measure of an arc is stated in Theorem 14.3, the basic theorem on arc length.

THEOREM 14.3
If two arcs have equal radii, then their lengths are proportional to their measures.

The theorem states that, for the two arcs shown,

$$\frac{\text{length } \widehat{XY}}{m\widehat{XY}} = \frac{\text{length } \widehat{X'Y'}}{m\widehat{X'Y'}}$$

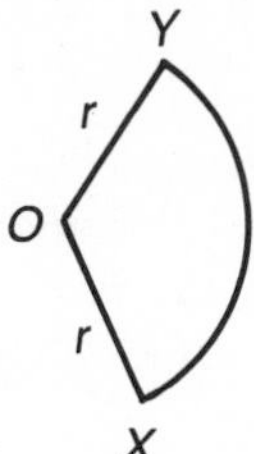

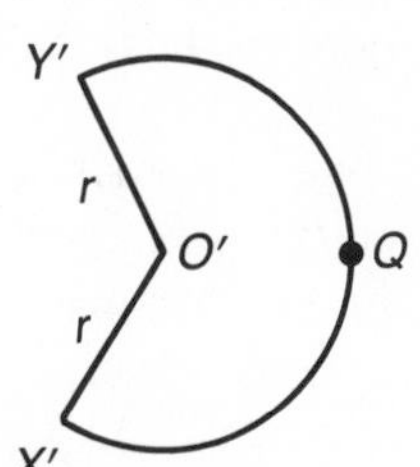

OBJECTIVE

Use Theorems 14.3 and 14.4 to answer questions regarding the lengths of arcs.

TEACHER'S NOTES

See p. T40

MIXED REVIEW

1. Evaluate $a^2 + 2a - 6 + a$ if $a = 5$. 34
2. Solve $x^2 - 7x + 10 = 0$. $\{5, 2\}$
3. Subtract $\frac{3}{x+2} - \frac{2}{x-3}$. $\frac{x-13}{(x+2)(x-3)}$
4. Multiply $(x + 2)(x - 4)(x - 2)$. $x^3 - 4x^2 - 4x + 16$
5. Find the distance between $(5, -3)$ and $(11, 5)$. 10

TEACHER'S RESOURCE MASTERS

Practice Master 43, Part 1

The proof of Theorem 14.3 is difficult and beyond the scope of this geometry course. Therefore, it is presented here without proof.

Given the relationships established in Theorems 14.1 and 14.3, you can derive a general formula for the length of any arc.

THEOREM 14.4

An arc of measure q and radius r has length $\frac{\pi}{180}(qr)$.

Given: C, the circumference of circle O of radius r, L the length of any arc AB with measure q

Prove: $L = \frac{\pi}{180}(qr)$

Proof: By Theorem 14.3, $\frac{L}{q} = \frac{C}{360}$, and by Theorem 14.1, $C = 2\pi r$. Substitution yields $\frac{L}{q} = \frac{2\pi r}{360}$, $L = \frac{2\pi rq}{360}$, $L = \frac{\pi}{180}(qr)$.

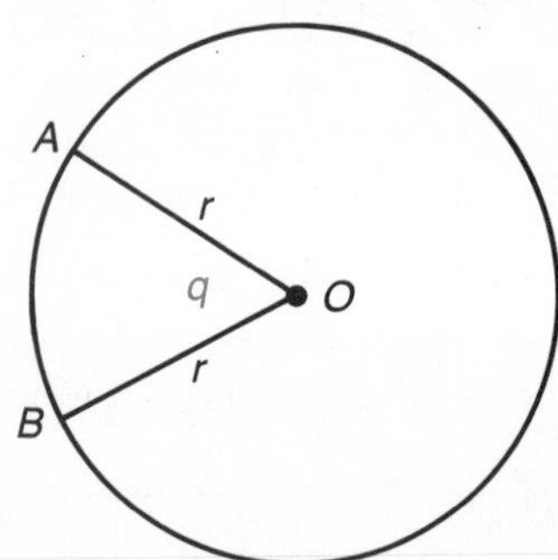

Remember that the circumference of a circle is $2\pi r$, so the length of any arc will be a fraction of that number.

Example: Find the length of an 80° arc in a circle of radius 6 inches.

Solution: Applying Theorem 14.4, $L = \frac{\pi}{180}(qr) = \frac{\pi}{180}(480)$, or $L = \frac{8\pi}{3}$ in.

As shown in the figure, any region bounded by two radii and an arc is called a **sector** of the circle.

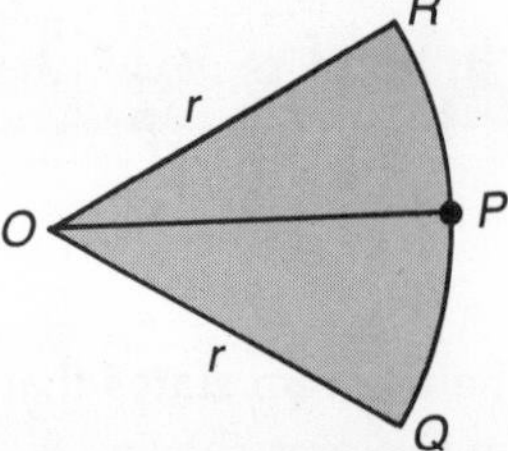

DEFINITIONS: sector, arc and radius of the sector

If $\widehat{QR}$ is an arc of a circle with center O and radius r, then the union of all segments $\overline{OP}$, where P is any point of $\widehat{QR}$, is a **sector.** $\widehat{QR}$ is the **arc of the sector,** and r is the **radius of the sector.**

ORAL EXERCISES

For Exercises 1–12, given the degree measure of an arc, state what fractional part of the circumference of a circle it represents.

1. 10	**2.** 40	**3.** 60	**4.** 90	**5.** 120	**6.** 135
7. 150	**8.** 180	**9.** 225	**10.** 270	**11.** 315	**12.** 45

13. State the formula for finding the length of an arc.

14. If an arc has a degree measure of 180 and radius of 10 units, what is the length of the arc?

15. f an arc has degree measure of 360 and a radius of 1 unit, what is the length of the arc? What is another name for this length?

16. What is the length of an arc in a circle with radius 6 and central angle of 120?

17. If the length of a 180° arc is 10 cm, what is the radius?

WRITTEN EXERCISES

A. The radius of a circle is 18 inches. In terms of π, what is the length of the arcs having the following degree measures?

1. 60	**2.** 90	**3.** 120	**4.** 72	**5.** 144	**6.** 270

7. Find the radius of a circle in which a 30° arc is 4π inches long.

8. If the length of a 60° arc is 4 cm, find the radius of the circle and the length of the chord of the arc in terms of π.

A wheel of radius 12 inches rotates through an angle of 45°.

9. How many inches does a point on the rim of the wheel move, in terms of π?

10. How many inches does a point on the wheel 5 inches from the center move, in terms of π?

B. 11. How far does the tip of a 2-inch minute hand on a clock travel in 20 minutes, in terms of π?

12. If the angular velocity of a fly-wheel with a 10-inch radius is 450° per second, how far does a point on the wheel travel in a minute, in terms of π?

13. What is the radius of a circle if the length of a 40° arc is 18π?

ASSIGNMENT GUIDE

Day 1
Minimum 1–8
Regular 1–8
Maximum 1–8
Day 2
Minimum 9–15
Regular 9–16
Maximum 9–18

Oral Exercises

1. $\frac{1}{36}$ 2. $\frac{1}{9}$ 3. $\frac{1}{6}$

4. $\frac{1}{4}$ 5. $\frac{1}{3}$ 6. $\frac{3}{8}$

7. $\frac{5}{12}$ 8. $\frac{1}{2}$ 9. $\frac{5}{8}$

10. $\frac{3}{4}$ 11. $\frac{7}{8}$ 12. $\frac{1}{8}$

13. $L = \frac{\pi}{180}(qr)$ 14. 10π

15. 2π; circumference

16. 4π 17. $\frac{10}{\pi}$ cm

Written Exercises

1. 6π in. 2. 9π in.

3. 12π in. 4. $\frac{36\pi}{5}$

5. $\frac{72\pi}{5}$ 6. 27π in.

7. 24 in. 8. $\frac{12}{\pi}$ cm; $\frac{12}{\pi}$ cm

9. 3π in. 10. $\frac{5\pi}{4}$ in.

11. $\frac{4\pi}{3}$ 12. 1500π in.

13. 81

14. $\frac{5\pi}{2}$

14. Given square *UVXY* with a side of 10 inches, find the length of $\widehat{AB}$ in terms of π.

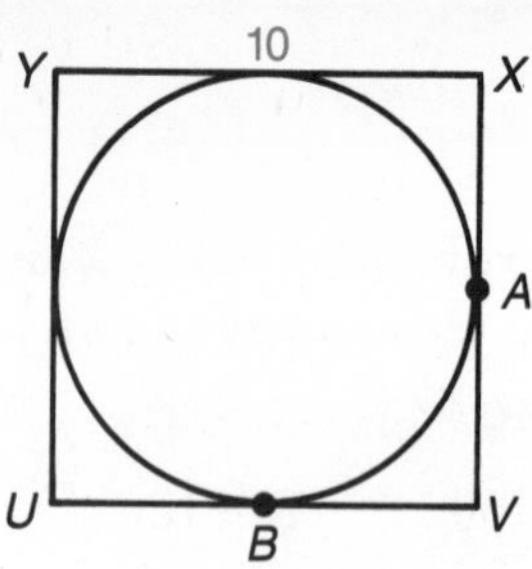

15. $\frac{5\sqrt{3}\pi}{3}$ in.

15. Given regular hexagon *CDEFGH* with a side of 10 inches, find the length of $\widehat{AB}$ in terms of π.

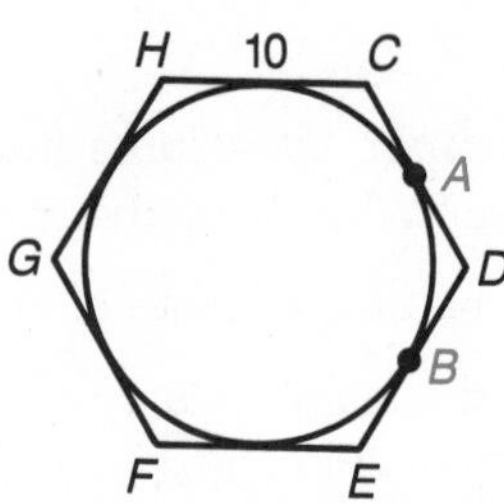

16. $\approx$5.8 m

16. In designing skyscrapers, engineers must allow for the swaying motion of the building. The Sears Tower in Chicago has a height of 443.2 meters. If the top of the building sways along an arc of $\frac{3}{4}°$, how many meters does it move in all? (Use π = 3.14.)

17. $\frac{63,360}{13\pi}$ times

C. 17. How many times does a bicycle wheel with a diameter of 26 inches make a complete turn in traveling 2 miles, in terms of π?

18. $44\pi + 48\sqrt{3}$

18. A continuous belt runs around two wheels of radius 6 in. and 30 in. The centers of the wheels are 48 inches apart. Find the length of the belt in terms of π.

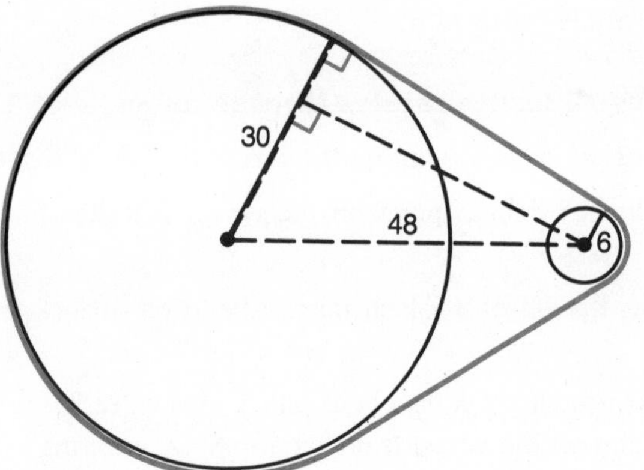

14.4 Areas of Sectors and Segments

In a circle of fixed radius r, the area of a sector is proportional to the length of its corresponding arc. You can see this concept illustrated in the figure. If you know that the arcs labeled $\overset{\frown}{AB}$ have lengths $\frac{1}{4}$, $\frac{1}{3}$, and $\frac{1}{2}$ the circumference of the circle, then you might deduce that the areas of the shaded sectors are $\frac{1}{4}$, $\frac{1}{3}$, and $\frac{1}{2}$ the area of the circle.

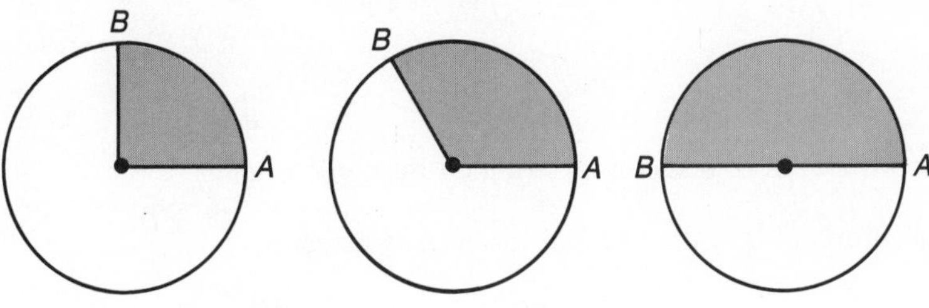

The next theorem states how the area of a sector is related to the length of its arc.

> **THEOREM 14.5**
> The area of a sector is half the product of its radius and the length of its arc.

In other words, $A = \frac{1}{2}rL$. To derive the formula, remember that when an arc is the whole circle, $A = \pi r^2$ or $\frac{2\pi r^2}{2}$. Substituting C for $2\pi r$, you find $A = \frac{Cr}{2}$ or $\frac{1}{2}Cr$. You now have a formula for the area of a given circle in terms of its total arc length, or circumference. The fact that the area (A) of a circle or any of its sectors is proportional to the corresponding arc length (L) can be expressed:

$$\frac{A}{L} = \frac{\frac{1}{2}Cr}{C}.$$

$$\text{Thus,} \quad A = \frac{\frac{1}{2}CrL}{C} \text{ or } A = \frac{1}{2}rL.$$

Therefore, if you know the length of an arc, you can determine the area of the corresponding sector, and vice versa. You can also derive a formula for the area of a sector given only radius and arc measure, as stated in Theorem 14.6.

OBJECTIVE

Use formulas derived from Theorems 14.5 and 14.6 to find the areas of sectors and segments of circles.

TEACHER'S NOTES

See p. T40

MIXED REVIEW

1. Solve $3 + \frac{x}{x-2} = \frac{6}{x-2}$ if $x \neq 2$. 3
2. Multiply $\sqrt{50} \cdot \sqrt{2}$. 10

Given $A = (-2, 7)$, $B = (3, 15)$.

3. Find AB. $\sqrt{89}$
4. Find the midpoint of $\overline{AB}$. $(\frac{1}{2}, 11)$
5. Find the slope of $\overline{AB}$. $\frac{8}{5}$

TEACHER'S RESOURCE MASTERS

Practice Master 43, Part 2
Quiz 27

THEOREM 14.6

The area of a sector of radius r and arc measure q is $\frac{\pi}{360}(qr^2)$.

Algebraically, the formula is derived by substituting $\frac{\pi}{180}(qr)$ (Theorem 14.4) for L in the formula $A = \frac{1}{2}rL$ (Theorem 14.6):

$$\begin{aligned} A &= \tfrac{1}{2}rL \\ &= \tfrac{1}{2}r(\tfrac{\pi}{180})(qr) \\ &= \tfrac{1}{2}(\tfrac{1}{180})(\pi)(qr^2) \\ &= \tfrac{\pi}{360}(qr^2) \end{aligned}$$

Example: Find the area of a sector determined by a 90° angle.

Solution: Substituting 90 in the formula for area of a sector,

$$A = \tfrac{\pi}{360}(90r^2) = \tfrac{90}{360}\pi r^2 = \tfrac{\pi r^2}{4}.$$

In addition to sectors, which are defined by two radii and an arc, circles contain other regions called **segments.** You have learned about segments as they relate to lines. Now you will define a different kind of segment related to circles.

DEFINITION: segment of a circle

A **segment of a circle** is the region bounded by a chord and an arc of the circle.

To find the area of a segment, subtract from (1) the area of the sector (2) the area of the triangle formed by the given chord and the radii to its endpoints.

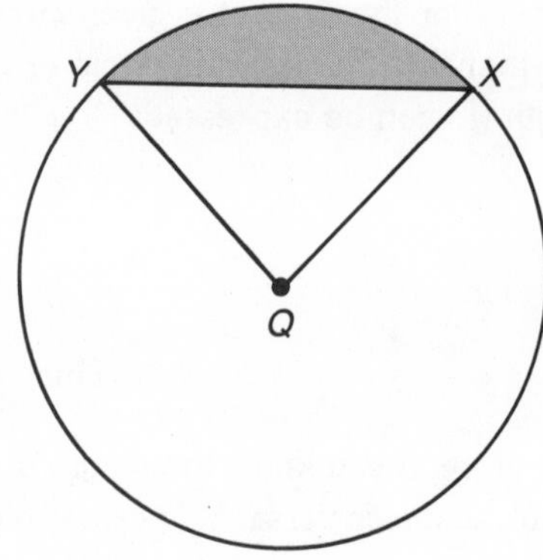

Example: In $\odot Q$, if $m\angle XQY = 90$ and $QX = 6$, find the area of the segment bounded by $\overline{XY}$ and $\overset{\frown}{XY}$.

Solution: The area of sector XYQ is $\frac{1}{4}\pi(6^2) = 9\pi$. The area of $\triangle XQY = \frac{1}{2}(6)(6) = 18$. The area of the segment is therefore $9\pi - 18$. The perimeter of the segment can be found by adding the length of the chord $\overline{XY}$ to the length of the arc $\overset{\frown}{XY}$.

ORAL EXERCISES

1. In a circle with fixed radius, what is the effect on the area of a sector if the length of its arc is doubled?

2. Two circles, each with a sector having an arc of x degrees, have radii a and b. What is the ratio of the areas of the sectors?

3. If the area of a sector is $\frac{1}{6}$ that of a circle, what is the degree measure of its arc?

4. In a given circle is it possible for a sector and its segment to have the same area?

WRITTEN EXERCISES

A. The radius of a circle is 6 m. Find the area of a sector in terms of π, given the following measure of its arc.

1. 90 **2.** 10 **3.** 36 **4.** 150

5. In a circle of radius 2 units, a sector has area π. What is the the measure of its arc?

Find the area of the shaded sector in terms of π, given the following measures.

6. $m\angle APB = 60; r = 10$

7. $m\angle APB = 120; r = 8$

8. $m\angle APB = 45; r = 12$

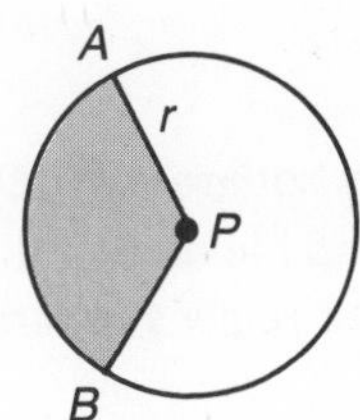

B. 9. Find the area of a sector, in terms of π, with a 45° arc and a $5\sqrt{2}$-ft radius.

10. An equilateral triangle is inscribed in a circle with a 10-inch radius. In terms of π, find the area of a segment cut off by one side of the triangle.

11. In terms of π, what is the area of the smaller segment whose chord is 9 inches long in a circle with a 9-inch radius?

12. A segment of a circle has a 120° arc and a chord $4\sqrt{3}$ inches long. Find the area of the segment in terms of π.

13. Find the perimeter of a segment of a circle, in terms of π, having a radius of 16 in. and a 120° arc.

14. Two circles, each with a 6-in. radius, intersect so that their common chord is 6 in. long. Find the area of the region bounded by the two minor arcs in terms of π.

ASSIGNMENT GUIDE

Minimum 1-17 odd
Regular 1-21 odd
Maximum 1-13 odd, 14-16, 21-22

Oral Exercises

1. The area doubles.
2. $\frac{a^2}{b^2}$
3. 60
4. Yes, if the arc is a semicircle.

Written Exercises

1. 9π 2. π
3. $\frac{18}{5}\pi$ 4. 15π
5. 90 6. $\frac{50\pi}{3}$
7. $\frac{64\pi}{3}$ 8. 18π
9. $\frac{25}{4}\pi$ ft
10. $\frac{100\pi}{3} - 25\sqrt{3}$ in.^{2}
11. $\frac{27}{2}\pi - \frac{81}{4}\sqrt{3}$ in.^{2}
12. $\frac{16\pi}{3} - 4\sqrt{3}$ in.^{2}
13. $\frac{32\pi}{3} + 16\sqrt{3}$ in.
14. $12\pi - 18\sqrt{3}$ in.^{2}

15. $16\sqrt{3} - 8\pi$

15. Find the area of the shaded portion of the figure at the right in terms of π.

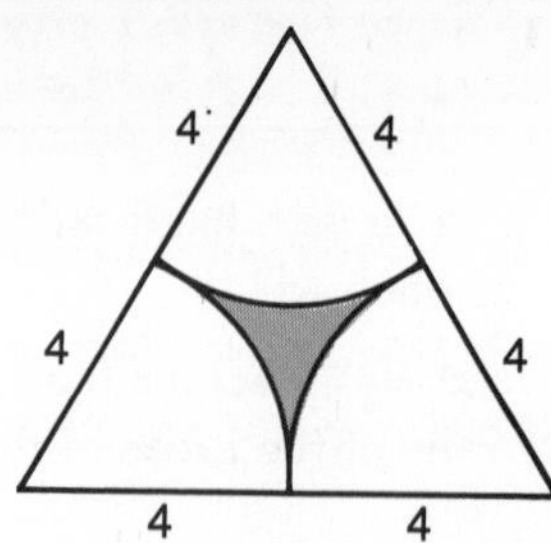

The radius of a circle is 4 cm, and $m\angle AOB = 60$.

16. 4 cm

16. Find $\widehat{AB}$.

17. $\frac{4\pi}{3}$ cm

17. Find the length of ACB in terms of π.

18. $\frac{8\pi}{3}$ cm^2

18. Find the area of the sector defined by O and $\widehat{ACB}$ in terms of π.

19. $\frac{8\pi}{3} - 4\sqrt{3}$

19. Find the area of segment ACB in terms of π.

20. $\frac{40\pi}{3}$ cm^2

20. Find the area of the sector defined by O and $\widehat{ADB}$ in terms of π.

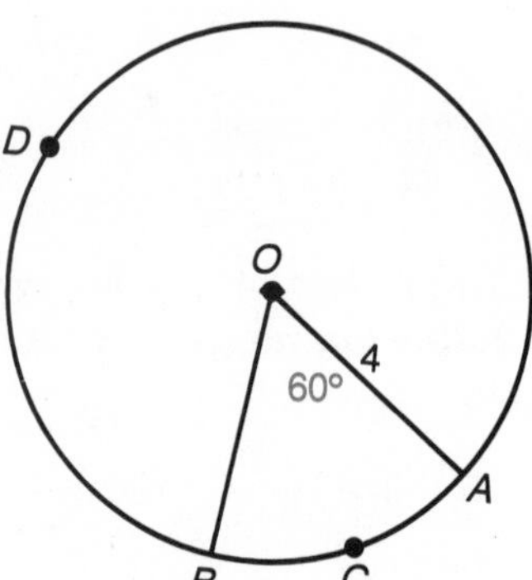

21. $100\pi - 200$

C. 21. Given square $ABCD$ and $AP = 10$, find the area of the union of the shaded regions in terms of π.

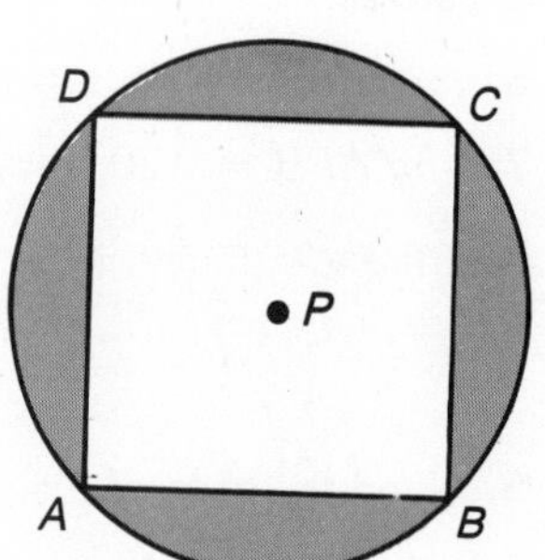

22. $64\pi - 96\sqrt{3}$

22. Given regular hexagon $ABCDEF$ with $AP = 8$, find the area of the union of the shaded regions in terms of π.

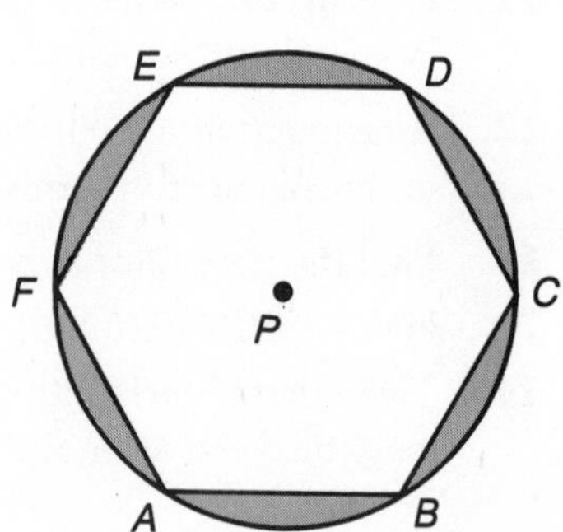

SELF-QUIZ

What is the measure of an angle of each of the following regular polygons?

1. octagon **2.** hexagon **3.** pentagon **4.** decagon

5. If both a square and a regular octagon are inscribed in the same circle, which has the greater apothem? the greater perimeter?

6. Find the measure of an exterior angle of a regular octagon.

7. What is the radius of a circle if its circumference is equal to its area?

8. One regular 7-sided polygon has an area of 8 and another regular 7-gon has an area of 18. What is the ratio of a side of the smaller to a side of the larger?

9. Find the area of a regular hexagon with a perimeter of 72 cm.

10. If a regular hexagon is inscribed in a circle of radius 5, what is the length of each side? What is the length of the arc of each side in terms of π?

11. A wheel has a 20-inch diameter. In terms of π, how far will it roll if it turns 270°?

12. Given a circle with an 18-cm radius, find the area of a segment in terms of π that has a 120° arc.

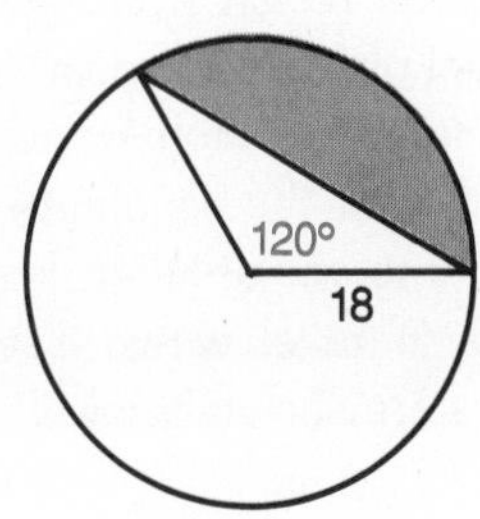

13. Find the area and perimeter in terms of π of a sector with a 30° arc in a circle with a radius of 14 cm.

CHALLENGE

Draw a circle with center O, and construct $\perp$ diameters $\overline{AF}$ and $\overline{BG}$. In $\triangle AOB$, inscribe $\odot C$. If $AF = 28$, find the area of $\odot C$ in terms of π. (HINT: Perform constructions on graph paper, and use coordinate geometry.)

Self-Quiz

1. 135 2. 120

3. 108 4. 144

5. octagon; octagon

6. 45

7. 2

8. $\frac{2}{3}$

9. $216\sqrt{3}$ cm^2

10. 5; $\frac{5\pi}{3}$

11. 15π in.

12. $108\pi - 81\sqrt{3}$ cm^2

13. $\frac{49\pi}{3}$ cm^2; $28 + \frac{7}{3}\pi$ cm

Challenge

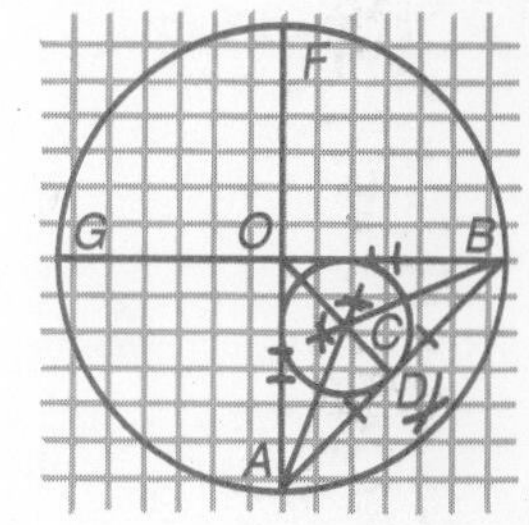

$AO = BO = 14$, so $AB = 14\sqrt{2}$. Let D be the midpoint of $\overline{AB}$. $AD = 7\sqrt{2}$, and $OD = AD$ ($\triangle AOD$ is an isos. rt. $\triangle$.), so $OD = 7\sqrt{2}$. From the graph, we can determine that the diameter of C is $6\sqrt{2}$, so the area of $\cdot$ C is 18π.

OBJECTIVES

Identify prisms, their bases, altitudes, cross sections, lateral edges, and lateral faces.

Use Theorems 14.7–14.9 and Corollaries 14.7.1 and 14.8.1 to answer questions regarding the lateral surface areas and total surface areas of prisms.

TEACHER'S NOTES

See p. T40

MIXED REVIEW

1. If the perimeter of a regular hexagon is 36, find its radius. 6
2. If the diagonal of a square is $7\sqrt{2}$, what is the area of the square? 49
3. Solve $3x^2 - 2x - 5 = 0$. $\{\frac{5}{3}, -1\}$
4. Add $\frac{1}{11} + \frac{1}{13}$. $\frac{24}{143}$
5. Subtract $\frac{1}{11} - \frac{1}{13}$. $\frac{2}{143}$

TEACHER'S RESOURCE MASTERS

Practice Master 43, Part 3

14.5 Prisms

In the figure at the right, A_1 and A_2 are two parallel planes. A_1 contains a polygonal region named R. Imagine a line segment, s, connecting any point in R to a point in plane A_2. Now imagine drawing segments parallel to s connecting all the other points in R to points in A_2, as shown in the figure. The intersection of these segments with A_2 would be a region congruent to R in A_2; in other words, you have reflected all the points of R into A_2.

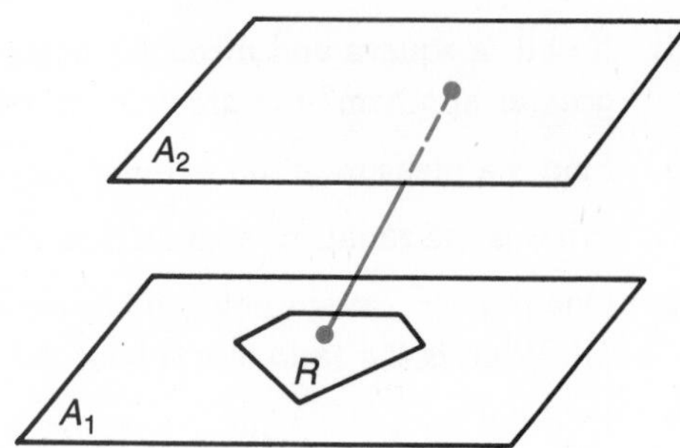

The union of s and all the segments you have mentally drawn parallel to it form a solid figure called a **prism.** You can think of a prism as the solid area carved out by moving a polygonal region from one plane to another parallel plane. Each point in the first region is reflected into another point of the parallel region, and the segments they form are all parallel to one another, like a bundle of pencils or parallel wires. Several examples of prisms are shown below.

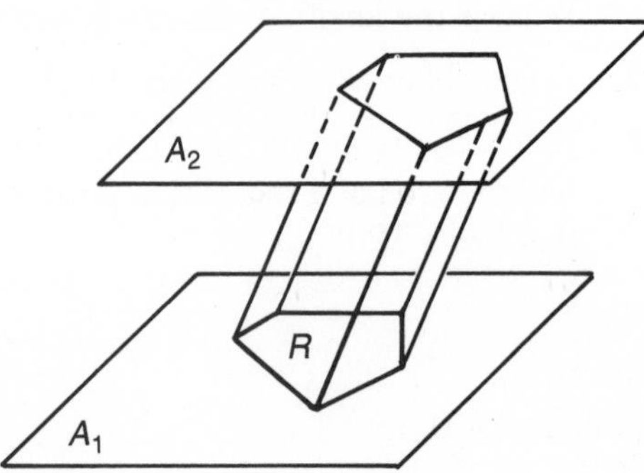

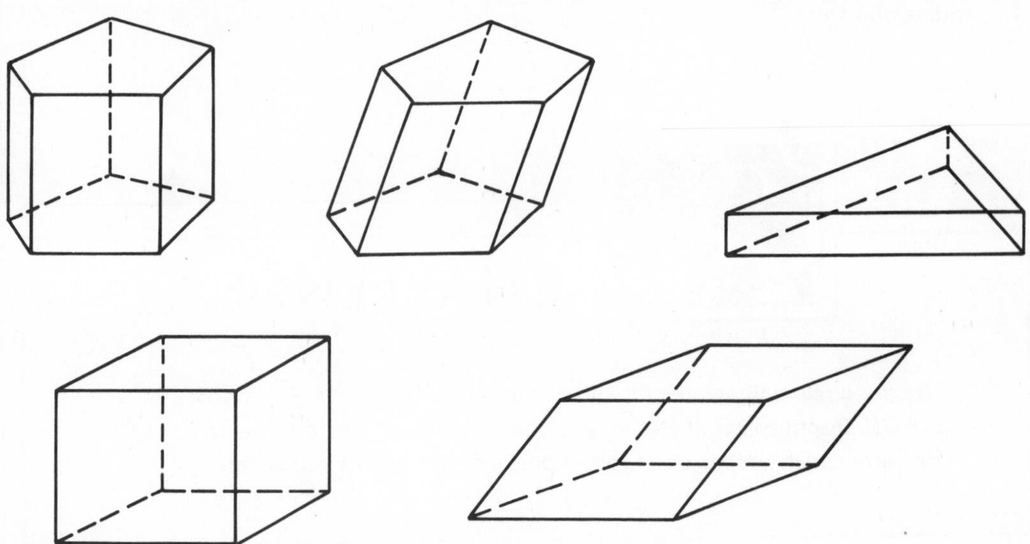

The following definitions describe a prism more precisely.

DEFINITIONS: prism, lower base, upper base, altitude, right prism
Let A_1 and A_2 be two parallel planes, t a transversal, and R a polygonal region in A_1 that does not intersect t. For each point X of R let $\overline{XY}$ be a segment parallel to t with Y in A_2. The union of all such segments is called a **prism.** The polygonal region R is called the **lower base,** or just *base,* of the prism. The set of all the points Y, that is the part of the prism that lies in A_2, is called the **upper base.** The distance h between A_1 and A_2 is the **altitude** of the prism. If t is perpendicular to A_1 and A_2, the prism is called a **right prism.**

Prisms are further classified according to the shapes of their bases: a triangular prism is one whose base is a triangular region, a rectangular prism has a rectangular base, and so on. When a plane parallel to the bases intersects a prism, a cross-sectional region is intercepted.

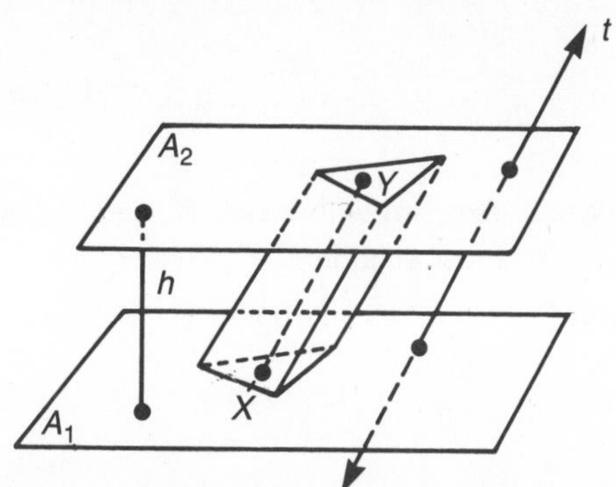

DEFINITION: cross section of a prism
A **cross section of a prism** is the intersection of a prism with a plane parallel to its base, provided this intersection is not empty.

THEOREM 14.7
All cross sections of a triangular prism are congruent to the base.

Given: A prism with triangular bases PQR and $P'Q'R'$ and a cross section intersecting the prism in a region bounded by $\overline{FG}$, $\overline{GH}$, and $\overline{FH}$.

Prove: $\triangle PQR \cong \triangle FGH$

Proof: $\overline{PF} \parallel \overline{QG}$ by definition of a prism, and $\overline{PQ} \parallel \overline{FG}$ by Theorem 8.27. Hence, ▱$PQGF$ is a parallelogram, and so $\overline{PQ} \cong \overline{FG}$, because opposite sides of a parallelogram are congruent. Similarly, $\overline{PR} \cong \overline{FH}$ and $\overline{QR} \cong \overline{GH}$. By SSS (Theorem 4.5), $\triangle PQR \cong \triangle FGH$.

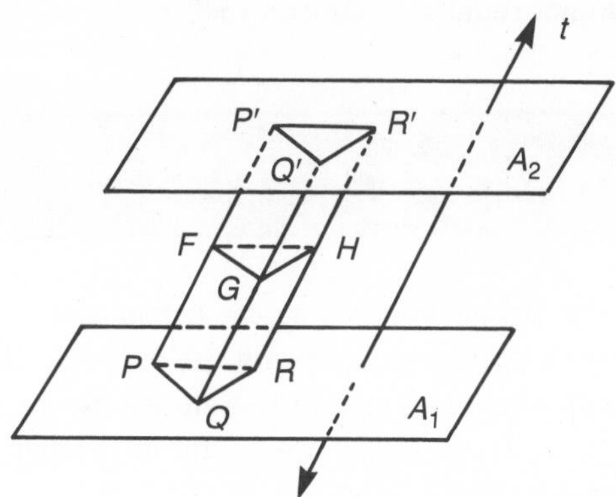

The same reasoning can be used to prove the corollary.

COROLLARY 14.7.1
The upper and lower bases of a triangular prism are congruent.

If two cross sections of a prism are congruent, then they have the same area.

THEOREM 14.8 (Prism Cross Section Theorem)
All cross sections of a prism have the same area.

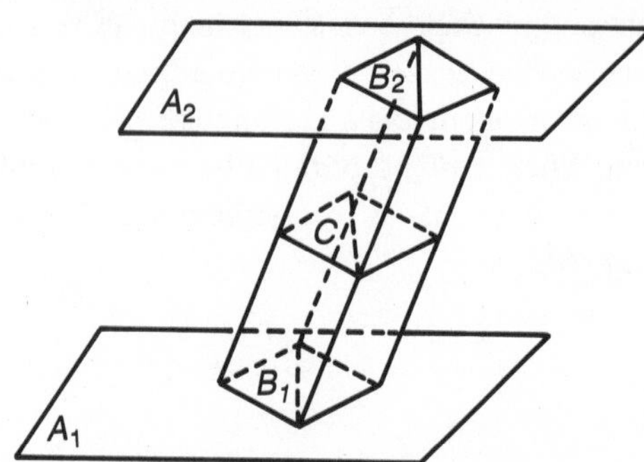

Given: A prism with bases B_1 and B_2 and cross section C

Prove: The area of region B_1 = area of region C

Proof: By definition of a polygonal region, B_1 is comprised of triangular regions. Thus, the prism is the union of triangular prisms whose bases are these triangular regions.

By Theorem 14.7, each triangle in the base is congruent to the corresponding triangle in the cross section. The area of the base is the sum of the areas of its triangular regions, and the area of the cross section is the sum of the areas of its corresponding triangular regions. Since congruent triangles have the same area, the theorem follows.

Because the upper base can be considered a cross section, the corollary to Theorem 15.8 does not require separate proof.

COROLLARY 14.8.1
The two bases of a prism have equal areas.

All the prisms you will study in this course are *convex prisms,* or prisms whose bases are **convex polygonal regions.** (A *convex polygonal region* is comprised of a convex polygon and its interior.) You can therefore refer to a "side" or a "vertex" of the base of a convex polygon. These terms are useful in the following definitions and theorem, which identify a special class of prisms.

DEFINITIONS: lateral edge, lateral face, lateral surface, total surface
A **lateral edge** of a prism is a segment $\overline{PP'}$, where P is a vertex of the base of the prism. A **lateral face** is the union of all segments $\overline{SS'}$ for which S is a point in a given side of the base. The **lateral surface** of a prism is the union of the lateral faces. The **total surface** of a prism is the union of its lateral surface and its bases.

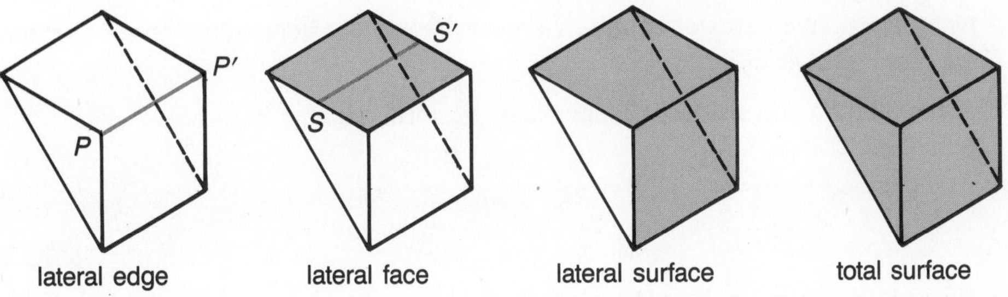

THEOREM 14.9
The lateral faces of a prism are parallelogram regions, and the lateral faces of a right prism are rectangular regions.

The formal proof of Theorem 14.9 is long and tedious. It is omitted here.

When all the faces of a prism (including the bases) are parallelogram regions, the prism has a special name. The prism is further distinguished if all of its faces are rectangular regions.

DEFINITIONS: parallelepiped, rectangular parallelepiped
A **parallelepiped** is a prism whose base is a parallelogram region. A **rectangular parallelepiped** is a right rectangular prism.

The figure shows an example of each of these special prisms.

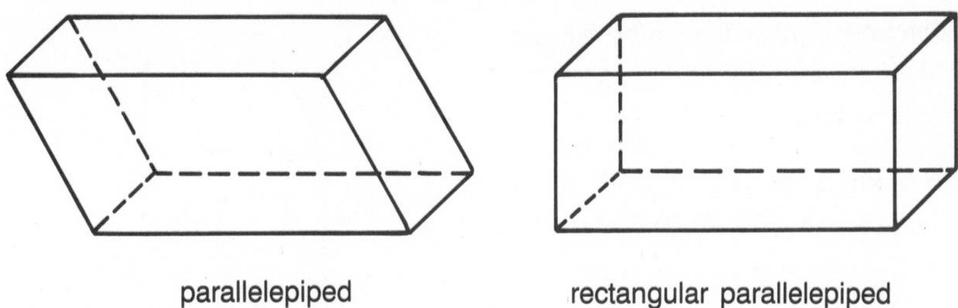

ASSIGNMENT GUIDE

Minimum 1–7
Regular 1–11 odd
Maximum 1–5 odd, 8–12

Oral Exercises

1. no 2. no
3. 5 4. yes
5. no 6. no; yes

Written Exercises

1. F 2. F 3. T 4. F

5.

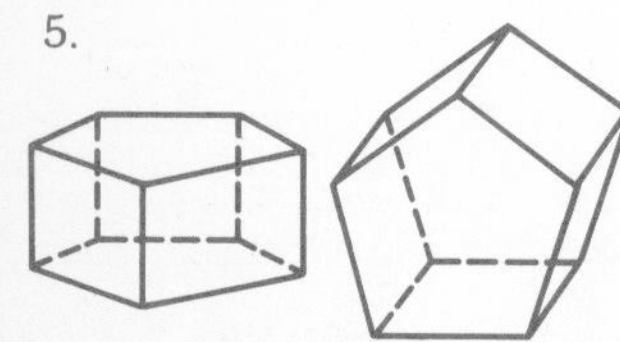

6.

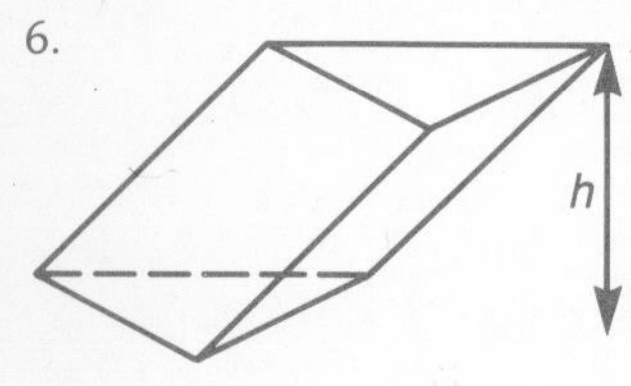

7. 210
8. $240 + 32\sqrt{3}$ in.^{2}
9. 5.2 cm
10. $4, 8, 4\sqrt{3}$; 30, 60, 90; $8\sqrt{3}$
11. A cube is a rectangular parallelepiped all of whose edges are congruent.
12. 384

ORAL EXERCISES

1. Can the two bases of a prism differ in the number of sides?
2. Can a prism have lateral faces that are hexagonal regions?
3. How many lateral faces does a prism have if its bases are pentagonal regions?
4. Can the base of a right prism be bounded by an isosceles trapezoid?
5. If two prisms have bases of equal area must the polygons bounding those bases have the same number of sides?
6. Can the altitude of a prism be longer than a lateral edge? a base edge?

WRITTEN EXERCISES

A. Indicate whether each statement in Exercises 1–4 is true or false.

1. Each lateral face of a prism is a rectangular region.
2. Every prism has at least four lateral faces.
3. A prism must have at least 6 base edges.
4. Each lateral face of a cube is twice the area of a base.

B. Sketch the figures described in Exercises 5 and 6.

5. a right pentagonal prism
6. a triangular prism in which the altitude is *not* the length of a lateral edge
7. Find the area of the lateral surface of a right prism whose altitude is 10 if the sides of the pentagonal base are 2, 3, 4, 5, and 7.
8. Find the total surface area of a right triangular prism if the base is an equilateral triangle 8 inches on a side and the height of the prism is 10 inches.
9. The length of a lateral edge of a right prism is 10 cm and its lateral area is 52 cm^2. What is the perimeter of the base?
10. If the sides of a cross section of a triangular prism are 4, 8, and $4\sqrt{3}$, then any other cross section will be a triangle whose sides are ____, ____, ____, whose angles measure ____, ____, ____, and whose area is ____.

C. 11. Given the figure of a cube at the right, define *cube* as a type of parallelepiped.

12. If the diagonal $\overline{XY}$ of the given cube is $8\sqrt{3}$, find its total surface area.

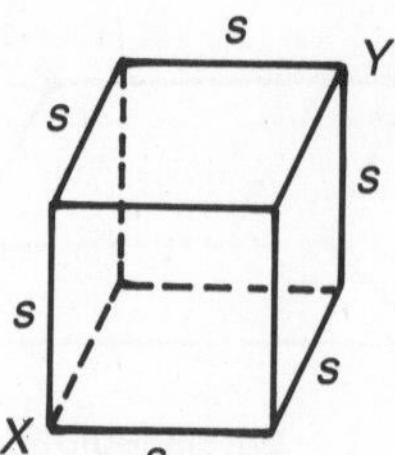

14.6 Pyramids

If you have studied or seen the Great Pyramids of Egypt, then you may already be familiar with the geometric shape that gave these ancient structures their name. The figures below show a geometric pyramid compared to a prism.

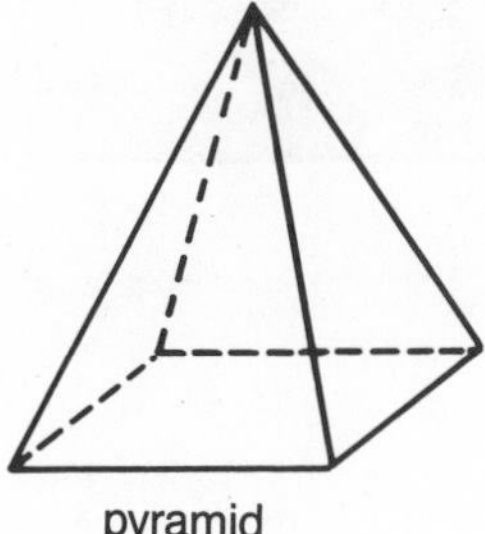
pyramid

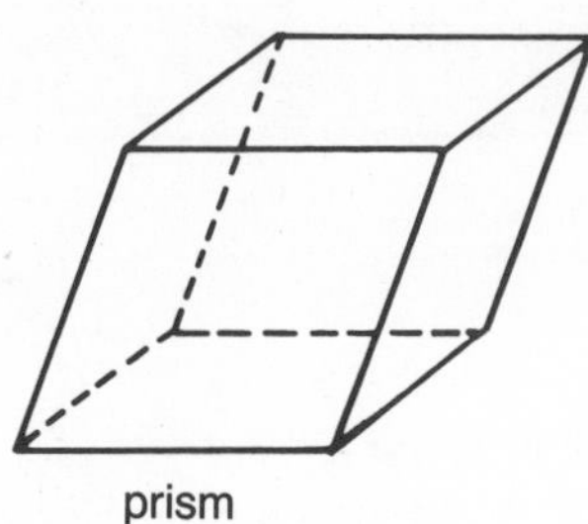
prism

DEFINITIONS: pyramid, base, vertex, altitude of a pyramid
Let R be a polygonal region in a plane E, and let P be a point not in E. For each point Q in R there is a segment $\overline{QP}$. The union of all such segments is called a **pyramid,** with **base** R and **vertex** P. The distance h from P to E is the **altitude** of the pyramid.

DEFINITIONS: regular pyramid, slant height
A **regular pyramid** is a pyramid whose base is a regular polygonal region having for its center the foot of the perpendicular from the vertex to the base. The **slant height** of a regular pyramid is the length of the altitude of any of the lateral faces.

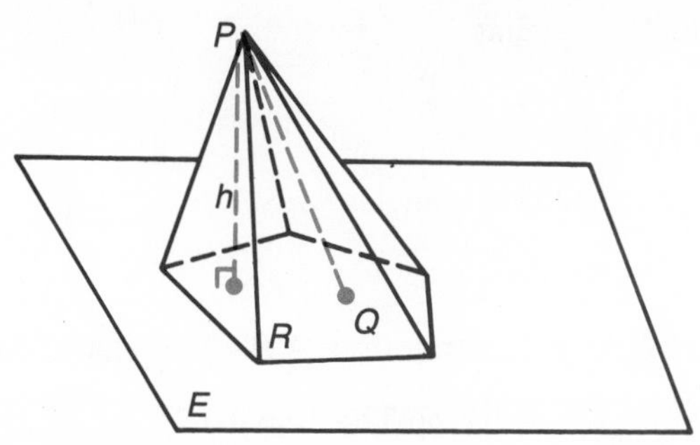

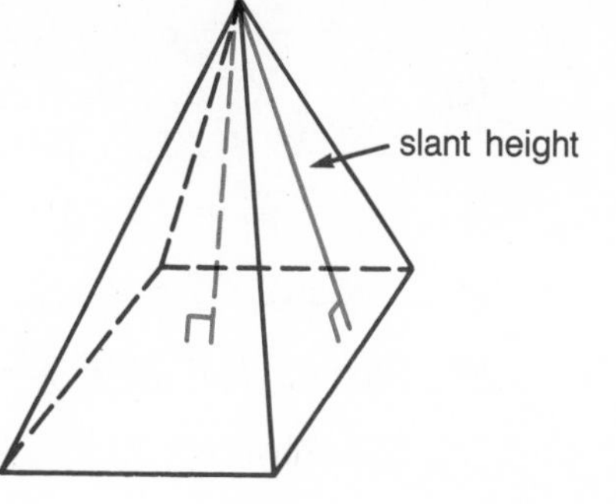

OBJECTIVES

Identify pyramids, their bases, vertices, altitudes, slant heights, and cross sections.

Use Theorems 14.10–14.12 to answer questions regarding the areas of lateral surfaces and cross sections of pyramids.

TEACHER'S NOTES

See p. T40

MIXED REVIEW

1. Solve $\sqrt{3x - 2} - 5 = 0$. 9

Given two similar triangles with corresponding sides in a ratio of 4:3.

2. What is the ratio of perimeters? 4:3
3. What is the ratio of corresponding altitudes? 4:3
4. What is the ratio of their areas? 16:9
5. Solve $4(3x - 2) = 5(8 - x)$. $2\frac{14}{17}$

TEACHER'S RESOURCE MASTERS

Practice Master 44, Part 1

Because prisms and pyramids share certain features, other terms already applied to prisms will also be used in reference to pyramids without formal definition.

The next two theorems correspond to Theorems 14.7 and 14.8 for prisms.

THEOREM 14.10
A cross section of a triangular pyramid, by a plane between the vertex and the base, is a triangular region similar to the base. If the distance from the vertex to the cross section plane is k and the altitude is h, then the ratio of the area of the cross section to the area of the base is $(\frac{k}{h})^2$.

Given: $\triangle XYZ$ in plane E
Point P is distance h from E.
Plane $E' \parallel$ plane E at a distance k from P.
E' intersects $\overline{PX}$, $\overline{PY}$, and $\overline{PZ}$ in X', Y', and Z', respectively.

Prove: $\triangle X'Y'Z' \sim \triangle XYZ$, and $\frac{\text{the area of } \triangle X'Y'Z'}{\text{the area of } \triangle XYZ} = (\frac{k}{h})^2$

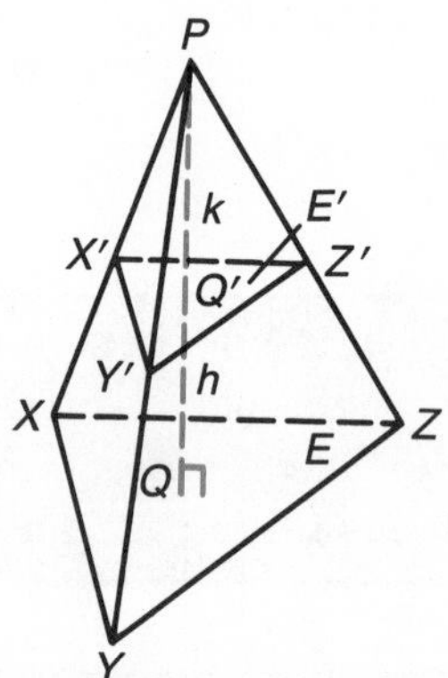

Proof: Let $\overline{PQ} \perp E$ and let $\overline{PQ}$ intersect E' at Q'. Then $h = PQ$, $k = PQ'$.

(1) $\overline{XQ} \parallel \overline{X'Q'}$ by Theorem 8.27.
$\triangle PX'Q' \sim \triangle PXQ$ by Corollary 10.3.2.
$\frac{PX'}{PX} = \frac{PQ'}{PQ} = \frac{k}{h}$ by definition of similar triangles.

(2) $\overline{X'Y'} \parallel \overline{XY}$ by Theorem 8.27.
$\triangle PX'Y' \sim \triangle PXY$ by Corollary 10.3.2.
$\frac{X'Y'}{XY} = \frac{PX'}{PX} = \frac{k}{h}$ by (1) and definition of similar triangles.

(3) Similarly, $\frac{Y'Z'}{YZ} = \frac{k}{h}$ and $\frac{Z'X'}{ZX} = \frac{k}{h}$.

(4) From (2) and (3), $\frac{X'Y'}{XY} = \frac{Y'Z'}{YZ} = \frac{Z'X'}{ZX} = \frac{k}{h}$. Therefore, $\triangle A'B'C' \sim \triangle ABC$ by SSS (Theorem 10.5), and $\frac{\text{the area of } \triangle X'Y'Z'}{\text{the area of } \triangle XYZ} = (\frac{k}{h})^2$ by Theorem 10.7.

THEOREM 14.11

In any pyramid, the ratio of the area of a cross section and the area of the base is $(\frac{k}{h})^2$, where h is the altitude of the pyramid and k is the distance from the vertex to the plane of the cross section.

Given: Pyramid with base R, vertex P, and cross section R'. The distance from P to R is h, the distance from P to R' is k, the area of R' is A', the area of $R = A$.

Prove: $\frac{A'}{A} = (\frac{k}{h})^2$

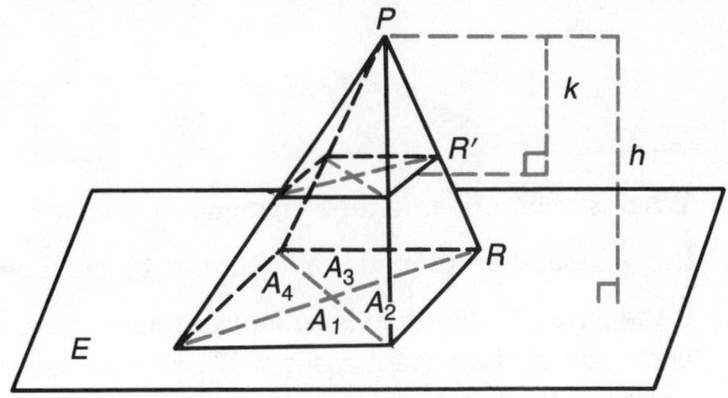

Proof: Divide the base into triangular regions and call their areas $A_1, A_2, \ldots, A_n$. (In the figure, $n = 4$) Call the areas of the corresponding triangular regions in the cross section $A_1', A_2', \ldots, A_n'$. Then,

$$A = A_1 + A_2 + \cdots + A_n, \text{ and}$$
$$A' = A_1' + A_2' + \cdots + A_n'.$$

By Theorem 14.10, $A_1' = (\frac{k}{h})^2 A_1$, $A_2' = (\frac{k}{h})^2 A_2$, and so on.

Therefore, $A' = (\frac{k}{h})^2(A_1 + A_2 + \cdots + A_n)$

$$A' = (\tfrac{k}{h})^2(A)$$
$$\frac{A'}{A} = (\tfrac{k}{h})^2.$$

This result suggests a theorem for pyramids similar to the Cross Section Theorem for prisms.

THEOREM 14.12 (The Pyramid Cross Section Theorem)

Given two pyramids with the same altitude, if the bases have the same area, then cross sections equidistant from the bases also have the same area.

For convenience, the pyramids shown here are triangular, but the proof applies to any base that is divisible into triangular regions. A special name given to a triangular pyramid is **tetrahedron.**

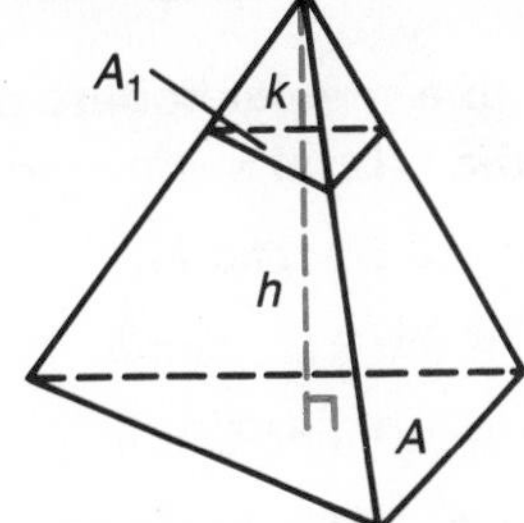

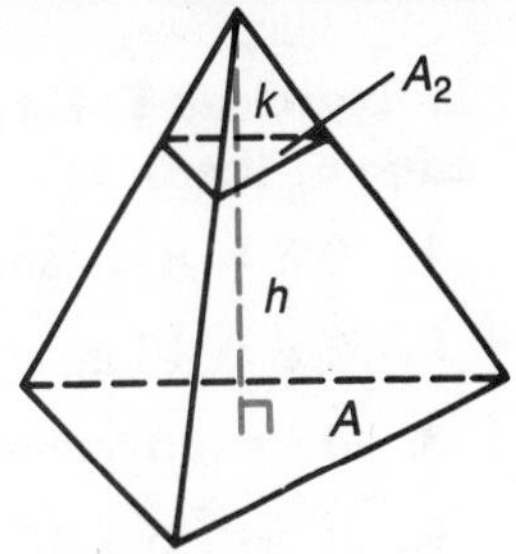

ASSIGNMENT GUIDE

Minimum 1–11
Regular 1–15 odd
Maximum 1–11 odd, 12–16

Given: Two pyramids with altitudes h and bases with area A; A_1 and A_2 are the areas of cross sections, each distance k from the vertex; $d = h - k$.

Prove: $A_1 = A_2$

Proof: $\frac{A_1}{A} = \left(\frac{k}{h}\right)^2 = \frac{A_2}{A}$ by Theorem 14.11. Thus,

$$\frac{A_1}{A} = \frac{A_2}{A}, \text{ and } A_1 = A_2.$$

ORAL EXERCISES

1. What is another name for a triangular pyramid?
2. If the base of a pyramid is a square, each cross section will form a _____.
3. If the base of a pyramid is an equilateral triangle, each cross section will form _____. If each side of the base measures 15, a cross section one-third of the distance from the vertex to the base will have sides each measuring _____.
4. Can the base of a pyramid be an octagon?
5. How many lateral faces does a pyramid have if its base is bounded by a hexagon? a decagon? an n-gon?
6. Each lateral face of a pyramid forms a _____.

Refer to the figure for Exercises 7–10.

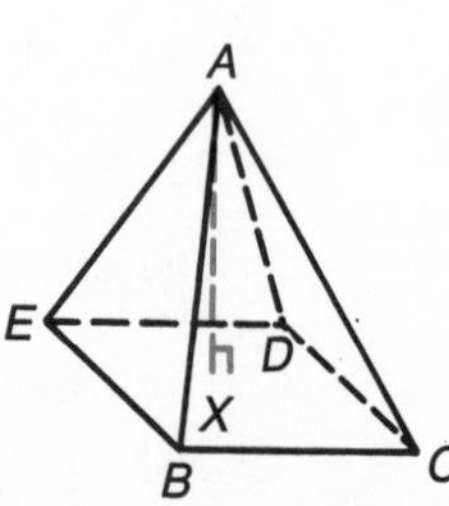

7. Point A is the _____ of the pyramid.
8. $\overline{AX}$ is the _____ of the pyramid.
9. _____ is the base of the pyramid.
10. If the pyramid is regular, then $\triangle ABC$ is _____.
11. True or false? *All lateral edges of a pyramid are congruent.*
12. True or false? *The height of a triangular pyramid is always less than the length of any lateral edge.*

Oral Exercises

1. tetrahedron
2. square
3. an equilateral △; 5
4. yes
5. 6; 10; n
6. triangle
7. vertex
8. altitude
9. quadrilateral $BCDE$
10. isosceles
11. F
12. F

WRITTEN EXERCISES

A. In Exercises 1–4, refer to a regular square pyramid; e is a lateral edge, b is an edge of the base, S is the lateral surface area, and l is the slant height.

1. If $h = 8$ cm and $b = 12$ cm, find l.
2. If $e = 13$ in. and $b = 5\sqrt{2}$ in., find h.
3. If $l = 25$ mm and $b = 40$ mm, find h.
4. If $S = 144$ in.^{2} and $l = 12$ in., find b and e.

Written Exercises

1. 10 cm
2. 12 in.
3. 15 mm
4. 6 in.; $3\sqrt{17}$ in.

B. Refer to the regular hexagonal pyramid in the figure for Exercises 5–7; *e* is a lateral edge, *b* is an edge of the base, *S* is the lateral surface area, *l* is the slant height, and *T* is the total surface area.

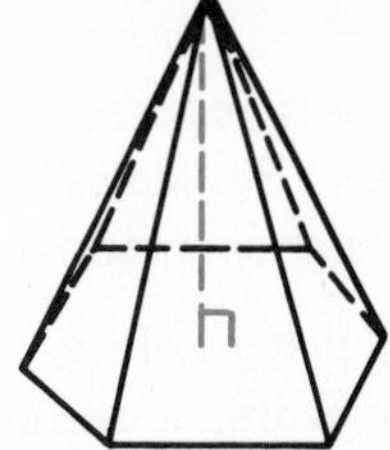

5. If $h = 3\sqrt{3}$ ft and $b = 8$ ft, find l and S.

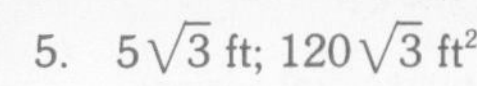
5. $5\sqrt{3}$ ft; $120\sqrt{3}$ ft^2

6. If $e = 26$ in. and $b = 10$ in., find h.

6. 24 in.

7. If $b = 6$ ft and $l = 25$ ft, find T.

7. $450 + 54\sqrt{3}$ ft^2

8. Two pyramids, one triangular and one hexagonal, have equal base areas. In each the altitude is 6 cm. The area of a cross section of the triangular pyramid 2 cm from the base is 25 cm^2. What is the area of a cross section 2 cm from the base of the hexagonal pyramid?

8. 25 cm^2

In the pyramid shown, $\triangle ABC$ is equilateral. A plane parallel to the base intersects the lateral edges in *D*, *E*, and *F*, such that $PE = \frac{1}{2}EB$.

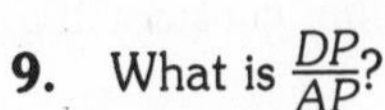

9. What is $\frac{DP}{AP}$?

9. $\frac{1}{3}$

10. What is $\frac{DE}{AB}$?

10. $\frac{1}{3}$

11. If $BC = 6$, what is the area of $\triangle DEF$?

11. $\sqrt{3}$

12. The altitude of a square pyramid is 20 m, and a side of the base is 30 m. Find the area of a cross section at a distance 12 from the vertex.

12. 324 m^2

13. The area of the base of a pentagonal pyramid is 144 ft^2. The altitude of the pyramid is 24 ft. What is the area of the cross section 8 ft from the base?

13. 64 ft^2

14. A regular pyramid has a square base, 10 in. on a side, and is one foot tall. Find the lateral surface area of the pyramid and the area of a cross section 3 inches above the base.

14. 260 in.^{2}; 56.25 in.^{2}

C. 15. Base B_2 is parallel to base B_1 in the pyramid shown with altitude $PQ = 7$ m and altitude $PQ' = 4$ m. If the area of B_1 is 336 m^2, what is the area of B_2?

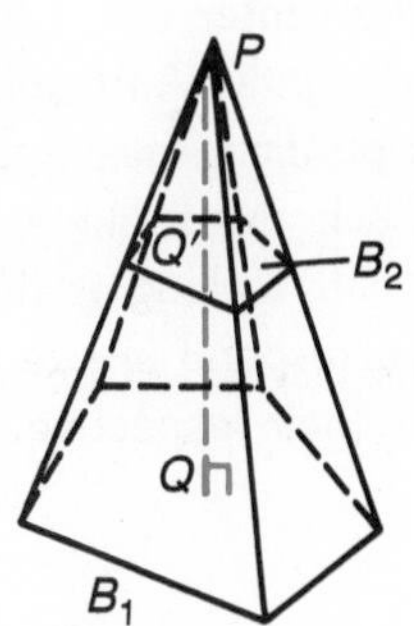

15. $\frac{768}{7}$ m^2

16. Find the total surface area, to the nearest tenth, of a right pyramid whose base is a regular hexagon 4 inches on a side and whose altitude is 6 inches.

16. 124.7 in.^{2}

OBJECTIVES

Identify polyhedral regions.

Use Postulates 21 and 22, and Theorems 14.13–14.16, to find the volumes of polyhedral regions.

TEACHER'S NOTES

See p. T40

MIXED REVIEW

Find the hypotenuse of a right triangle if the legs are

1. 12 and 16. 20
2. 15 and 8. 17
3. 14 and 48. 50
4. $\frac{3}{4}$ and 1. 1.25
5. 10 and 24. 26

TEACHER'S RESOURCE MASTERS

Practice Master 44, Part 2

14.7 Cavalieri's Principle

Chapter 9 introduced the concept of a *polygonal region* and its area with the four "area postulates." Postulate 20 gives the area of a rectangle as bh. Using this information, you were able to determine formulas for the areas of different polygonal regions.

In space, polygonal regions form the bases and sides of **polyhedral regions.** (Compare the term to *di*hedral, a word you applied to angles formed when *two* planes or surfaces intersect. *Poly*hedral means "having *many* surfaces.") The measure of a polyhedral region is called its **volume.**

POSTULATE 21

The volume of a rectangular parallelepiped is the product of the altitude and the area of the base. ($V = Ah$, where A represents the area of the base and h the height.)

Another postulate is needed to make a connection between the volume of a rectangular parallelepiped and the volume of other solids. To understand the connection, consider the physical model illustrated below.

Imagine a flat metal disk having exactly the same diameter as the lid of a tin can and with a tiny hole precisely in its center. If you had many such disks sufficiently thin, you could stack them on a table to exactly the same height as a tin can to form a model of the can. Since the two figures would be the same size, their volumes would also be the same.

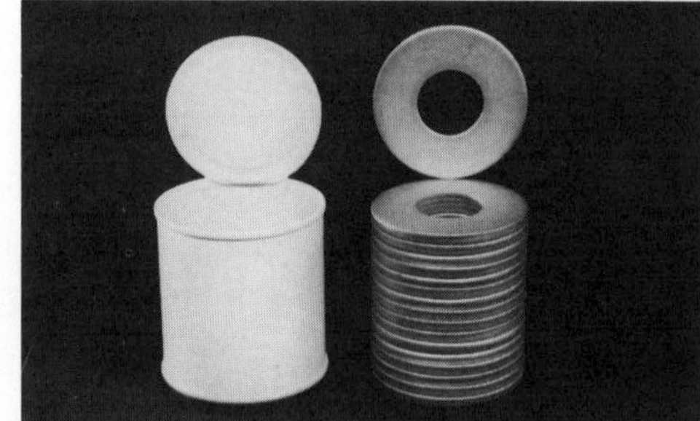

Now suppose you insert a long metal pin through the center of the stack of disks and tilt the pin slightly. Although the disks shift to a skewed position, their total volume will not change. Each disk is like a thin cross section of the tin can; as long as the disks and cross sections correspond in size and number, the volumes of their respective figures will be the same.

The idea represented by this model is called **Cavalieri's Principle.** It is stated as a postulate, without proof.

POSTULATE 22 (Cavalieri's Principle)
Given two solids and a plane, if for every plane that intersects the solids and is parallel to the given plane the two intersections have equal areas, then the two solids have the same volume.

The significance of Cavalieri's Principle in determining volumes is demonstrated in the next theorem.

THEOREM 14.13
The volume of any prism is the product of the altitude and the area of the base ($V = Ah$).

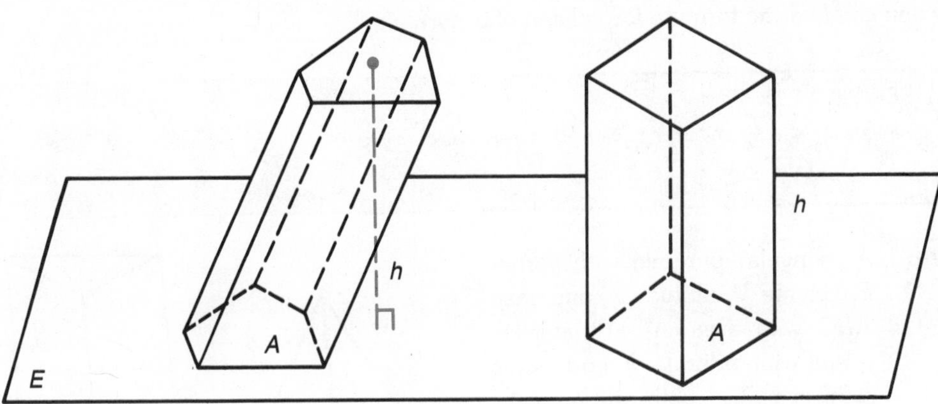

Given: A prism and a parallelepiped, each with altitude h and base area A and each lying in plane E.

Prove: The volume (V) of the prism is the product of its altitude (h) and the area of its base (A).

Proof: By the Prism Cross Section Theorem (Theorem 14.8), you know that all cross sections of both prisms have area A. Then by Cavalieri's Principle, the two prisms have the same volume (V). Since the volume of the rectangular parallelepiped is Ah by Postulate 21, the volume of the other prism is also Ah. Thus, for any prism, $V = Ah$.

Cavalieri's Principle applied to the Pyramid Cross Section Theorem allows you to determine the volume of a pyramid. First, though, you must prove that two pyramids having the same altitude and base area have the same volume.

THEOREM 14.14
If two pyramids have the same altitude and the same base area, then they have the same volume.

Given: Two pyramids, each with altitude h and base area A

Prove: The pyramids have the same volume.

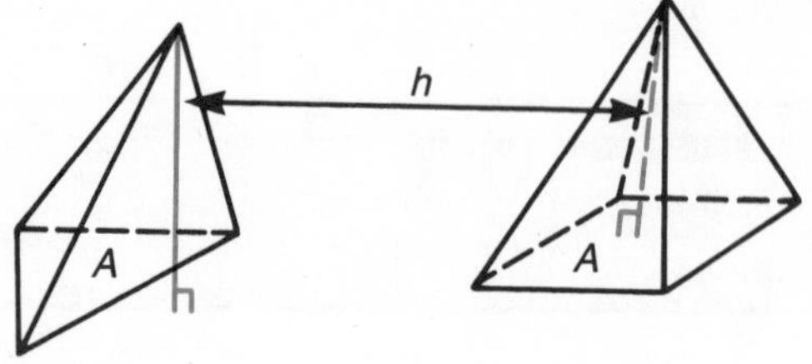

Proof: By the Pyramid Cross Section Theorem (Theorem 14.12), corresponding cross sections of the two pyramids have the same area. So, by Cavalieri's Principle, their volumes are also the same.

Now you can find the formula for volume of a pyramid.

THEOREM 14.15
The volume of a triangular pyramid is one-third the product of its altitude and its base area ($V = \frac{1}{3}Ah$).

Given: A triangular pyramid with vertex E, volume V, altitude h, and base ABC with area A; a triangular prism with altitude h and bases ABC and DEF, both with area A.

Prove: $V = \frac{1}{3}Ah$.

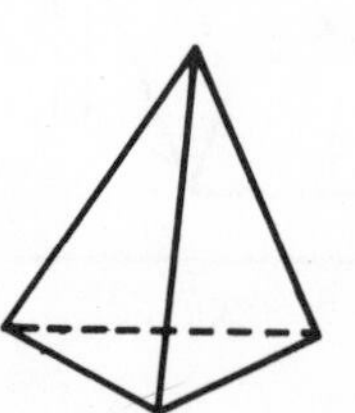

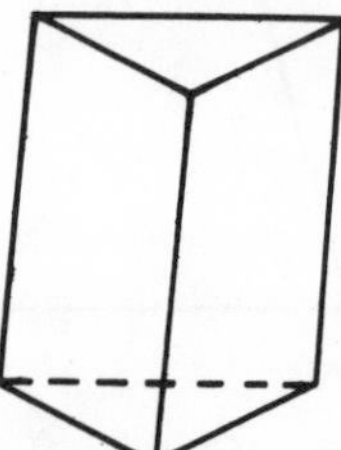

Proof: Divide the prism into three triangular pyramids, one of them corresponding to the given pyramid, as shown:

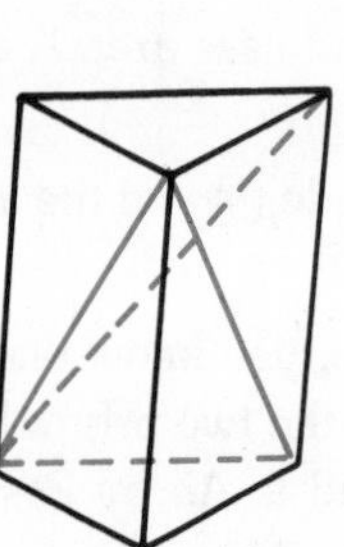

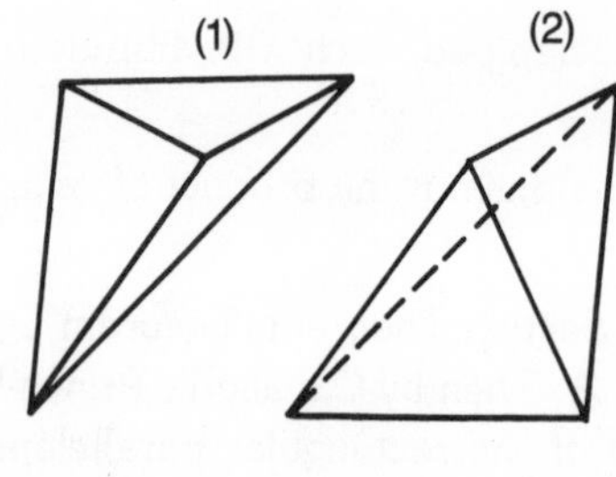

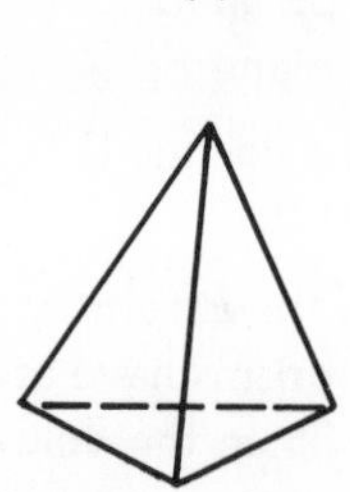

Pyramids 1 and 2 have bases ADF and FCA and common vertex E. Since $\triangle ADF$ and $\triangle FCA$ are the two triangles formed when ▱$ACFD$ is divided by diagonal $\overline{AF}$, $\triangle ADF$ and $\triangle FCA$ lie in the same plane and are congruent. Therefore, pyramids 1 and 2 have the same base area and the same altitude, so by Theorem 14.14 they have the same volume.

Now think of pyramids 1 and 3 as having bases *DEF* and *ABC*. It is given that $\triangle DEF \cong \triangle ABC$, and you know that the altitude (h) from vertex A to the plane of $\triangle DEF$ is the same as the altitude from vertex E to the plane of $\triangle ABC$. Thus, pyramids 1 and 3 have the same volume. By the transitive property, all three pyramids (1, 2, and 3) have the same volume V.

By Theorem 14.13, the volume of the given prism is Ah. Therefore, $3V = Ah$, and $V = \frac{1}{3}Ah$.

The next theorem states that this formula applies to all pyramids.

THEOREM 14.16
The volume of a pyramid is one-third the product of its altitude and its base area ($V = \frac{1}{3}Ah$).

Given: A triangular pyramid with altitude h and base area A; another pyramid with altitude h and base area A in the same plane.

Prove: The two pyramids have the same volume (V), and $V = \frac{1}{3}Ah$.

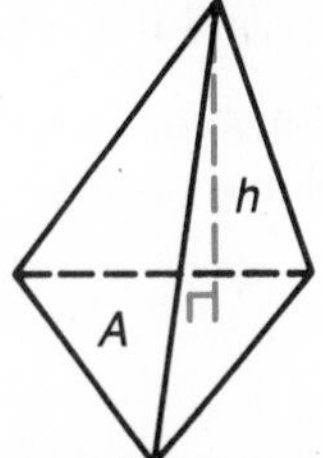

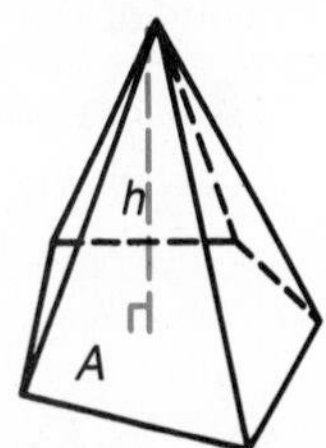

Proof: By the Pyramid Cross Section Theorem (Theorem 14.12), cross sections of the pyramids at the same height have the same area. Therefore, by Cavalieri's Principle (Postulate 22), the two pyramids have the same volume. Since $V = \frac{1}{3}Ah$ for the triangular pyramid by Theorem 14.15, $V = \frac{1}{3}Ah$ for the other pyramid as well.

ASSIGNMENT GUIDE

Minimum 1-8
Regular 1-13 odd
Maximum 1-7 odd, 8-14

ORAL EXERCISES

1. If two pyramids have the same base area, must they have the same volume?
2. A rectangular parallelepiped has an altitude of 6 and base edges measuring 3 and 4. What is its volume?
3. If a cube has total surface area of $18x^2$, what is the volume of the cube?
4. What is the volume of a right rectangular prism with dimensions $2x$, $3x$, and $4x$?
5. If a prism and pyramid have the same base area and the same altitude, how do their volumes compare?
6. If two pyramids have the same total surface area, must they have the same volume?

Oral Exercises

1. no
2. 72
3. $3x^3\sqrt{3}$
4. $24x^3$
5. 3:1
6. no

Written Exercises

1. 120
2. $8k^2$; $24k^3$
3. $60\sqrt{3}$ cm^3
4. 3 in.
5. 54 in.^{2}
6. $3\sqrt{3}$
7. 18
8. ≈ 11.2 gal
9. $30\sqrt{5}$
10. The right △ formed by the edge, half-diagonal, and altitude is a 30-60-90 △, with hypotenuse 12 and legs 6 and $6\sqrt{3}$. So the altitude of the pyramid is $6\sqrt{3}$. Since the diagonals of the square base are ⊥, the area of the base with diagonals 12 is $\frac{12 \cdot 12}{2}$, or 72. Then the volume of the pyramid is $\frac{1}{3}(72)(6\sqrt{3})$, or $144\sqrt{3}$ in^3.
11. 600 in.^{3}
12. 8; $\frac{8}{27}$
13. $V = \frac{s^3\sqrt{2}}{6}$
14. $\frac{1}{24}$

WRITTEN EXERCISES

A. **1.** The dimensions of a rectangular parallelepiped are 4, 5, and 6. Find its volume.

2. A prism has total surface area $72k^2$ and lateral surface area $56k^2$. What is the area of each base? If its altitude is $3k$, what is its volume?

3. The base of a right prism is a regular hexagon with edges 2 cm long. If the height of the prism is 10 cm, find the volume.

The volume of a cube is 27 in^3.

4. Find the length of a lateral edge.

5. Find the total surface area.

6. Find the length of a diagonal.

B. **7.** The lengths of the edges of a rectangular box are in the ratio 4:7:9. If the volume of the box is 2016, find the length of the longest edge.

8. A rectangular metal can, 1 × 1 × 1.5 ft, is filled with water. Given that 1 gallon of water has a volume of 231 in.^{3}, how many gallons of water does the can hold?

9. Find the volume of the right prism in the figure if the bases are isosceles trapezoids.

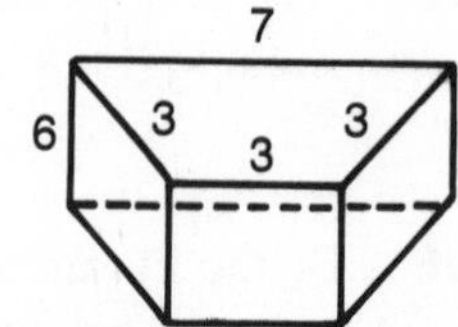

10. In a regular square pyramid, a lateral edge is 12 in. long. Each lateral edge determines a 60° angle with the diagonals of the base. Find the volume of the pyramid.

11. The base of a right prism is a rhombus with diagonals 10 and 24 in. long. If the height of the prism is 5 in., find the volume.

12. The area of a cross section of a pyramid is 40, and the area of the base of the pyramid is 90. If the altitude of the pyramid is 12, how far from the vertex is the cross section? What is the ratio of the volumes of the two pyramids?

C. **13.** Derive a formula for the volume of a regular square pyramid whose lateral faces are equilateral triangles of side s.

14. In the cube shown, A and B are the midpoints of $\overline{XY}$ and $\overline{YZ}$, forming a pyramid with vertex D and base AYB. Find the ratio of the volume of the pyramid to the volume of the cube.

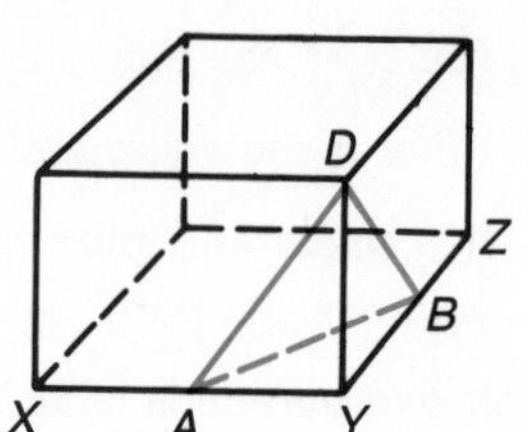

14.8 Cylinders and Cones

You have seen that prisms and pyramids are formed from bases that are polygonal regions. Suppose you applied the same methods used to form prisms and pyramids using instead a circular region as base. The results would be as illustrated below.

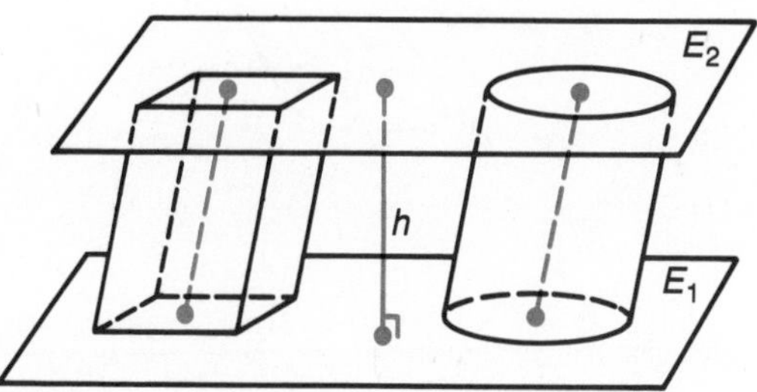

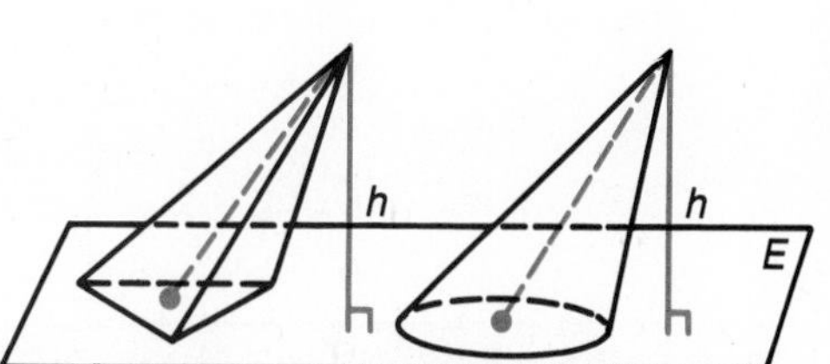

The figure on the left above compares a rectangular prism to a **cylinder.** Cylinders may be constructed with other curved bases, such as ovals, but the circular cylinder is the only one you will study in this text. The figure on the right above compares a triangular pyramid to a **cone.**

> **DEFINITION: right circular cylinder**
> If the line joining the centers of the base circles of a cylinder is perpendicular to the planes of both bases, then the cylinder is a **right circular cylinder.**

> **DEFINITION: right circular cone**
> If the center of the base circle of a cone is the foot of the perpendicular from the vertex to the plane of the base, then the cone is a **right circular cone.**

Right circular cylinder

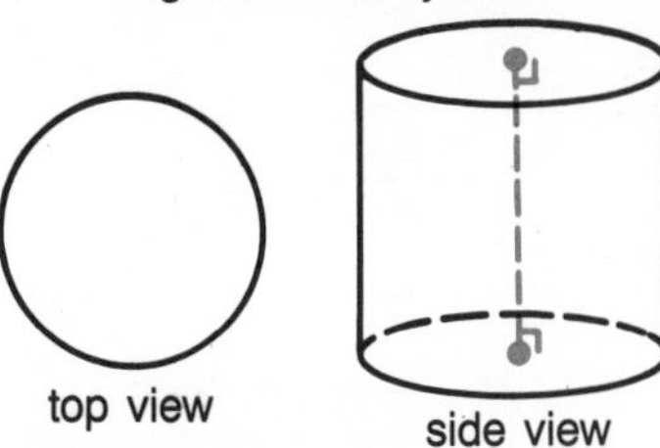

Right circular cone

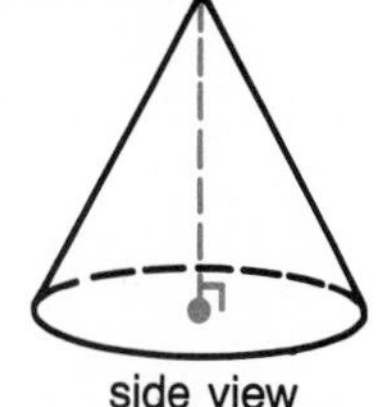

OBJECTIVES

Identify cylinders and cones and their cross sections.

Use Theorems 14.17–14.21 to find the volumes of cylinders and cones.

TEACHER'S NOTES

See p. T40

MIXED REVIEW

1. Which points in a plane are equidistant from the endpoints of a segment? the ⊥ bisecting line
2. Given a circle with a circumference of 12π, find the radius, diameter and area. 6, 12, 36π
3. What is the area of an equilateral triangle with a side of 14? $49\sqrt{3}$
4. How many degrees in a pentagon? 540
5. Can a polygon have congruent sides and not be a regular polygon? yes

TEACHER'S RESOURCE MASTERS

Practice Master 45, Part 1

THEOREM 14.17
A cross section of a circular cylinder is a circular region congruent to the base.

Proof Plan: Let C be the center and r the radius of the base. Using parallelograms, $A_1C_1 = AC = r$.

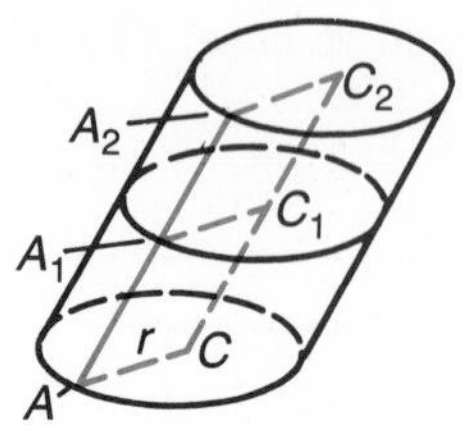

THEOREM 14.18
The area of a cross section of a circular cylinder is equal to the area of the base.

Proof Plan: The theorem follows directly from Theorem 14.17 and the fact that congruent circles have equal areas.

THEOREM 14.19
A cross section of a cone with altitude h, made by a plane at a distance k from the vertex, is a circular region whose area has a ratio to the area of the base of $(\frac{k}{h})^2$.

Proof Plan: Let $h = PR$. Then,

$$\triangle PC_1R_1 \sim \triangle PCR$$

$$\frac{PC_1}{PC} = \frac{k}{h}, \triangle PC_1A_1 \sim \triangle PCA, \frac{C_1A_1}{CA} = \frac{k}{h}, \text{ or } C_1A_1 = \frac{k}{h}(CA).$$

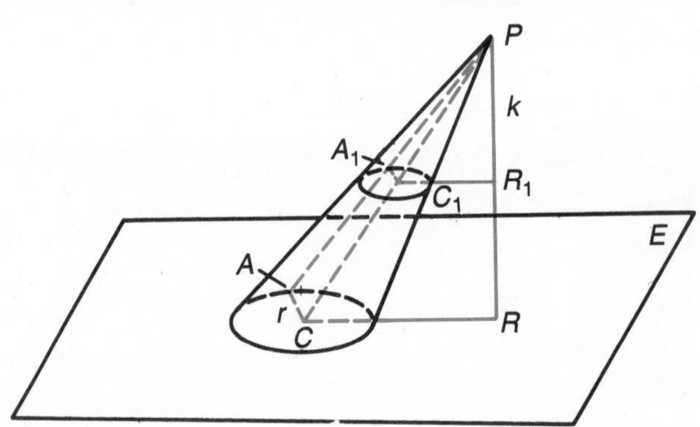

Since CA (r), k, and h are constant values, C_1A_1 is also constant. This means that C_1A_1 is the radius of a circle that describes a cross section of the cone. Thus,

$$\frac{\text{area} \odot C_1}{\text{area} \odot C} = \frac{\pi(C_1A_1)^2}{\pi(CA)^2} = \left(\frac{k}{h}\right)^2.$$

Now, using Cavalieri's Principle (Postulate 22), you can determine the volumes of cylinders and cones. The proofs follow the logic of the corresponding proofs for prisms and pyramids.

THEOREM 14.20
The volume of a circular cylinder is the product of the altitude and the area of the base. ($V = Ah$).

THEOREM 14.21
The volume of a circular cone is one-third the product of the altitude and the area of the base ($V = \frac{1}{3}Ah$).

ORAL EXERCISES

1. If a circular cone and a circular cylinder have congruent bases and altitudes, what is the ratio of the volume of the cone to the volume of the cylinder?

2. Find the volume of a cone having radius 4 and height 8 in terms of π.

3. Find the volume of a cylinder having radius 4 and height 8 in terms of π.

4. The ratio of the volumes of two similar cones is $\frac{27}{125}$. What is the ratio of their altitudes?

5. The ratio of the total surface area of two similar cylinders is $\frac{4}{25}$. What is the ratio of their altitudes? of their volumes?

WRITTEN EXERCISES

A. Find the volume of a circular cone in terms of π, given the radius and measure of the altitude.

1. $r = 3; h = 4$ **2.** $r = 6; h = 8$ **3.** $r = \frac{5}{3}; h = 9$ **4.** $r = 11.7; h = 6.4$

5. Find the number of gallons of water a conical tank will hold if it is 30 inches deep and the radius of the circular base is 14 inches. (There are 231 cubic inches in a gallon. Use $\frac{22}{7}$ as an approximation of π.)

ASSIGNMENT GUIDE

Day 1
Minimum 1-11
Regular 1-21 odd
Maximum 1-19 odd, 23-26
Day 2
Minimum 20-26
Regular 23-31 odd
Maximum 27-32

Oral Exercises

1. $\frac{1}{3}$
2. $\frac{128\pi}{3}$
3. 128π
4. $\frac{3}{5}$
5. $\frac{2}{5}$; $\frac{8}{125}$

Written Exercises

1. 12π
2. 96π
3. $\frac{25\pi}{3}$
4. $\approx 292\pi$
5. ≈ 26.7 gal

Find the volume of a circular cylinder in terms of π, given the radius (r) and the measure of the altitude (h).

6. $r = 4$; $h = 10$ **7.** $r = 16$; $h = 40$

8. $r = 1.5$; $h = 6$ **9.** $r = 22.45$; $h = 8.63$

B. 10. A cylinder of height 10 cm has a volume of 180π cm^3. Find the radius of the cylinder.

11. A solid metal cylinder of radius 3 cm and height 12 cm is melted down and recast as a cone with radius 5 cm. Find the height of the cone.

12. A cone and a cylinder have equal volumes. The radius of the cone is three times that of the cylinder. What is the ratio of the height of the cone to that of the cylinder?

13. How would you determine the lateral surface area of a right circular cylinder? of a right circular cone?

14. A tile drainage pipe is a cylindrical shell 20 inches long. The inside and outside diameters are 5 and 5.8 inches, respectively. Find the volume of the clay necessary to make the pipe.

In a right circular cylinder, the radius of the base is one foot and the altitude is 20 inches.

15. Find the area of the base. **16.** Find the lateral surface area.

17. Find the total surface area. **18.** Find the volume.

19. A certain cone has a volume of 27 in^3. Its height is 5 inches. A second cone is cut from the first by a plane parallel to the base and two inches below the vertex. Find the volume of the second cone.

Find the ratio of the volumes of two similar right circular cones given the radii of their bases.

20. 2 and 5 **21.** 4 and 16

22. 8 and 10 **23.** x and y

24. State the pattern you observed in Exercises 20-23.

25. Would the same pattern you described in Exercise 24 be observed for right circular cylinders?

26. A grocery store sells two brands of canned fruit juice. Brand A comes in a container twice as tall as that of Brand B, but the Brand B container has a diameter twice that of the Brand A container. If Brand B costs twice as much as Brand A, which is the better buy, assuming equal quality?

6. 160π
7. $10{,}240\pi$
8. 13.5π
9. $\approx 4{,}349.54\pi$
10. $3\sqrt{2}$ cm
11. 12.96 cm
12. $\frac{1}{3}$
13. circumference times altitude (Ch); $\frac{1}{2}$ times circumference times slant height
14. 43.2π in.^{3}
15. 144π in.^{2}
16. 480π in.^{2}
17. 768π in.^{2}
18. $2{,}880\pi$ in.^{3}
19. $\frac{216}{125}$ in.^{3}
20. $\frac{8}{125}$
21. $\frac{1}{64}$
22. $\frac{64}{125}$
23. $\frac{x^3}{y^3}$
24. The volumes of two similar right circular cones are proportional to the cubes of their altitudes (h^3) or the cubes of their radii (r^3).
25. yes
26. They are equal in value.

27. The figure at the right shows the profile view of a pyramid whose base is a square. The pyramid is inscribed in a right circular cone. If the altitudes of the cone and the pyramid both measure 36 and a base edge of the pyramid measures 20, find the volume of each.

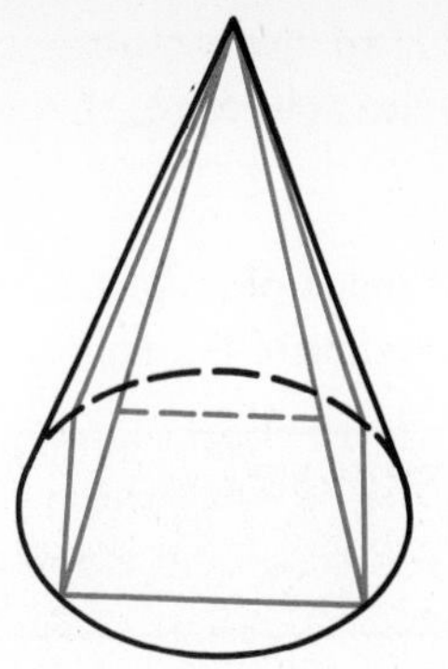

27. $V_p = 4800$, $V_c = 2400$

28. Consider a cone in a cylinder and two congruent cones in another cylinder, as shown at the right. If the cylinders are the same size, compare the volume of the single cone with the combined volume of the other two cones. Would your conclusion change if the two cones in the right-hand cylinder were not congruent?

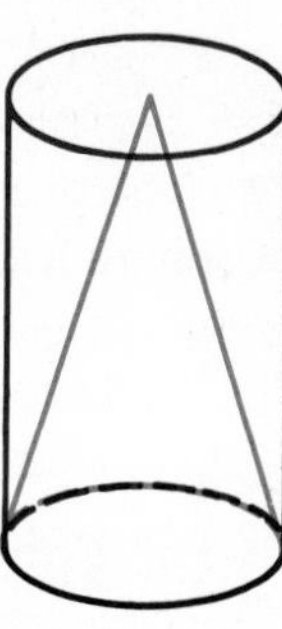

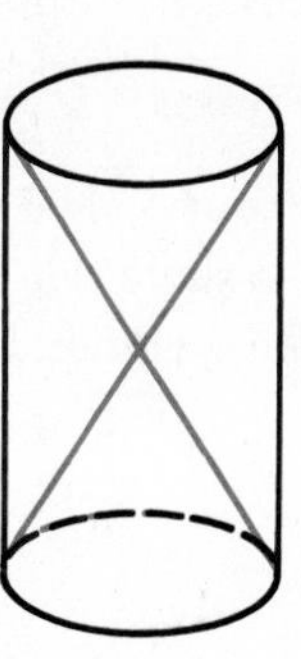

28. The volumes are equal whether or not the cones are congruent.

29. A right circular cone stands inside a right circular cylinder having the same base and height. Write a formula for the volume of the space between the cylinder and the cone.

29. $\frac{2}{3}\pi r^2 h$

30. If a plane parallel to the base of a cone or pyramid cuts off another cone or pyramid, then the solid between the parallel plane and the base is called a **frustum.** The frustum of the cone at the right has a lower radius of 6 in., an upper radius of 4 in., and a height of 8 in. Find its volume.

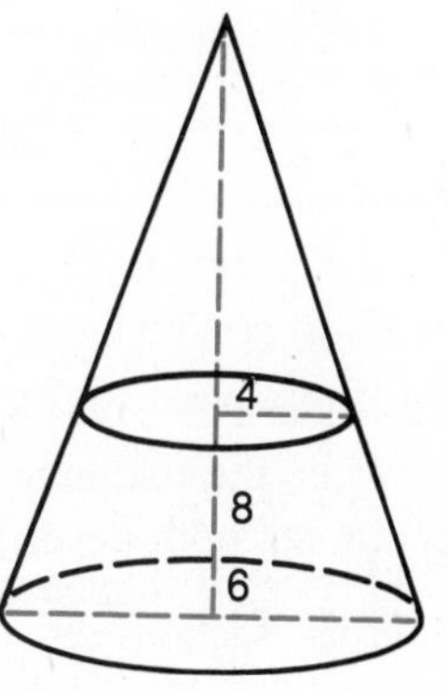

30. $\frac{608\pi}{3}$ in.^{3}

C. 31. The radius of the base of a cylinder is increased 30 percent and the altitude is increased 20 percent. By what percentage is the volume increased?

31. 102.8 percent

32. A conical tent is made by using a semicircular piece of canvas of radius 12 yards. Find the number of cubic feet of air inside the tent.

32. $1944\pi\sqrt{3}$ ft^3

OBJECTIVES

Identify the annulus of a sphere and a spherical shell.
Use Theorems 14.22 and 14.23 to find the volume and surface area of a sphere.

TEACHER'S NOTES

See p. T40

MIXED REVIEW

1. If the ratio of the areas of two squares is 36 to 16 what is the ratio of their perimeters? 6:4
2. Solve $12x^2 + 60x + 75 = 0$. $-\frac{5}{2}$
3. Given two cubes of sides 2 and 4, what is the ratio of their diagonals, surface areas and volumes? 1:2, 1:4, 1:8
4. Solve $2x + 5y = 14$
   $x - y = -7$
   $(-3, 4)$
5. Solve $x^2 - 6x + 8 = 0$. $\{4, 2\}$

TEACHER'S RESOURCE MASTERS

Practice Master 45, Part 2
Quiz 28

14.9 Spheres

The union of a sphere and its interior is a solid whose volume can be measured if you know the radius of the sphere.

THEOREM 14.22
The volume of a sphere of radius r is $\frac{4}{3}\pi r^3$ ($V = \frac{4}{3}\pi r^3$).

Given: Sphere R with radius r, volume V; E a tangent plane

Prove: $V = \frac{4}{3}\pi r^3$

Proof: In E construct a circle of radius r. Using this circle as base, construct a cylinder on the same side of E as the sphere with altitude $2r$. The cylinder and the sphere thus have the same altitude.

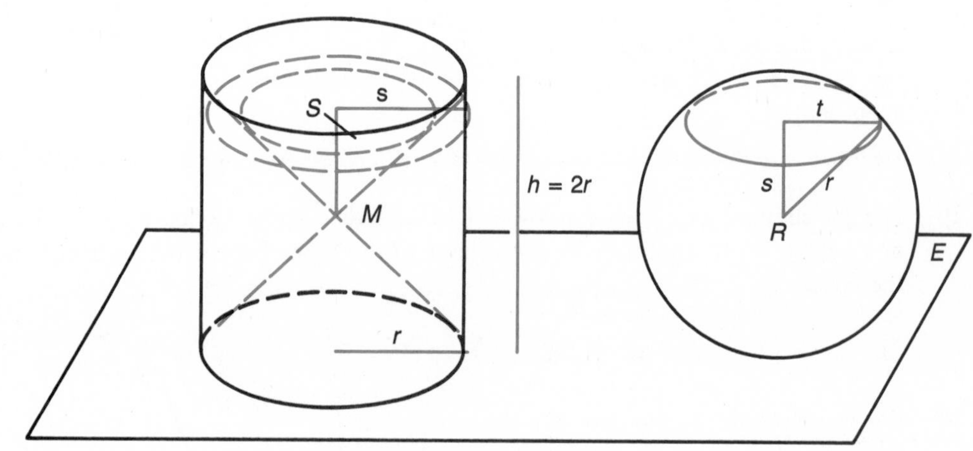

Now consider two cones having as their bases the two bases of the cylinder. Let their common vertex M be the midpoint of the *axis* of the cylinder. (The *axis* is the vertical segment joining the centers of both bases.)

Take cross sections of the sphere and the cylinder by a plane parallel to E and at a distance s from M:

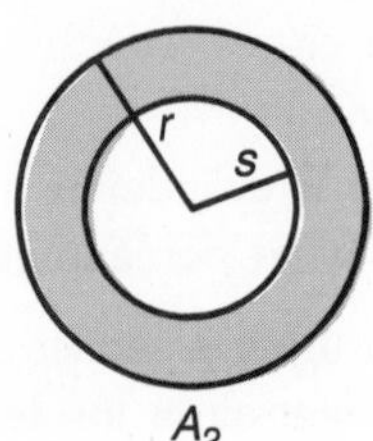

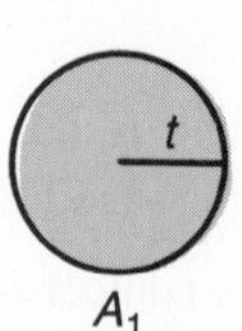

The area of the cross section of the sphere (A_1) is πt^2, or $\pi(r^2 - s^2)$ by the Pythagorean Theorem. Compare the cross section of the sphere with a cross section of the solid region between the cones and the cylinder. This cross section is an *annulus* whose outer radius is r and whose inner radius is s. Hence, its area (A_2) is $\pi r^2 - \pi s^2$, or $\pi(r^2 - s^2)$. Thus, $A_1 = A_2$. By Cavalieri's Principle, the volume of the sphere is equal to the volume of the region between the cones and the cylinder. Therefore, the volume of the sphere (V_s) is the difference between the volume of the cylinder and twice the volume of one cone:

$$V_s = (\pi r^2)(2r) - 2(\tfrac{1}{3}\pi r^2)(r) = \tfrac{4}{3}\pi r^3.$$

With this information, you can now derive a formula for the surface area of a sphere. Given a sphere of radius r, enclose it in a slightly larger sphere of radius $r + h$ having the same center. The solid region lying between the two spherical surfaces is called a **spherical shell.** Call the surface area of the inner sphere S. You can reason that volume V of the shell is approximately hS. (If the inner sphere were a globe, how much lacquer would you need to give the globe a quarter-inch coating over all its surface? $V \approx \frac{1}{4}S$.) Stated another way, $S = \frac{V}{h}$, approximately. The thinner the shell, the closer the approximation, so as h becomes smaller, $\frac{V}{h} \to S$.

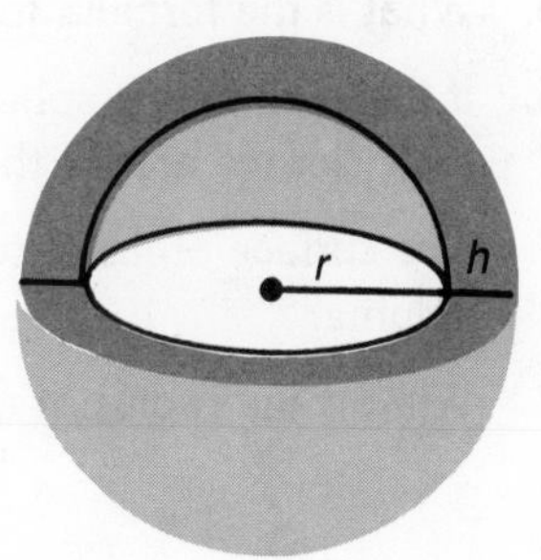

Since you can calculate $\frac{V}{h}$ exactly, you can see what it approaches as h becomes smaller and smaller. This will tell you what S is. The volume V of the spherical shell is the difference of the volumes of the two spheres:

Note: This would be a good time to review multiplication of $(r + h)^3$.

$$\begin{aligned} V &= \tfrac{4}{3}\pi(r+h)^3 - \tfrac{4}{3}\pi r^3 \\ &= \tfrac{4}{3}\pi[(r+h)^3 - r^3] \\ &= \tfrac{4}{3}\pi[r^3 + 3r^2h + 3rh^2 + h^3 - r^3] \\ &= \tfrac{4}{3}\pi[3r^2h + 3rh^2 + h^3] \end{aligned}$$

$$\begin{aligned} \text{Therefore, } \tfrac{V}{h} &= \tfrac{4}{3}\pi(3r^2 + 3rh + h^2) \\ &= 4\pi r^2 + h(4\pi r + \tfrac{4}{3}\pi h). \end{aligned}$$

As h approaches zero ($h \to 0$), the entire second term approaches zero. So, $\frac{V}{h} \to 4\pi r^2$, and $S = 4\pi r^2$. This conclusion is stated as a thoerem.

THEOREM 14.23
The surface area of a sphere of radius r is $4\pi r^2$ ($S = 4\pi r^2$).

ASSIGNMENT GUIDE

Minimum 1–10
Regular 1–15 odd
Maximum 1–11 odd, 13–17

Oral Exercises

1. F
2. four times as large
3. annulus
4. $\frac{1}{16}$; $\frac{1}{64}$
5. πd^2
6. $\frac{2}{5}$; $\frac{4}{25}$; $\frac{8}{125}$
7. $\frac{2}{3}$; $\frac{8}{27}$
8. $\frac{1}{2}k$

Written Exercises

1. 144π, 288π
2. 12π, $4\pi\sqrt{3}$
3. 100π, $\frac{500}{3}\pi$
4. $32\pi\sqrt{3}$ cm^3
5. $\frac{256}{3}\pi y^6$
6. $\frac{34{,}496}{3}$ ft^3 = 86,240 gal
7. No; $V(\text{cone}) = \frac{5}{3}\pi$ in.^{3} $V(\text{ice cream}) = \frac{4}{3}\pi$ in.^{3}
8. 34 gal

ORAL EXERCISES

1. True or false? *A sphere is a solid.*

2. How does the surface area of a sphere compare with the area of a great circle of the sphere?

3. A spherical shell is like what region in a plane?

4. Assume that the earth and the moon are spherical. The radius of the earth is approximately 3960 miles, and the radius of the moon is approximately 1000 miles. What is the approximate ratio of their surface areas? their volumes?

5. What is the formula for the surface area of a sphere in terms of its diameter?

6. If the radii of two spheres are 2 and 5, respectively, what is the ratio of their diameters? their surface areas? their volumes?

7. The surface areas of two spheres are 36π and 81π. What is the ratio of their radii? their volume?

8. What is the radius of a sphere inscribed in a cylinder of height k?

WRITTEN EXERCISES

A. Find the surface area and volume of a sphere with the given radius.

1. 6 **2.** $\sqrt{3}$

3. Find the surface area and the volume of a sphere having diameter 10.

4. Find the volume of a sphere that has surface area of 48π cm^2.

5. Find the volume of a sphere that has surface area $64\pi y^4$.

B. 6. A spherical storage tank has a radius of 14 feet. How many gallons will it hold? (Use $\pi = \frac{22}{7}$ and 7.5 gal in a ft^3)

7. An ice cream cone 5 in. deep and 2 in. in top diameter has placed on top of it two hemispherical scoops of ice cream also of 2 in. diameter. If the ice cream melts into the cone, will it overflow? Why or why not?

8. A large storage shed in the shape of a hemisphere must be painted. If the floor of the shed requires 17 gal of paint, how much paint will be needed to cover the exterior of the shed?

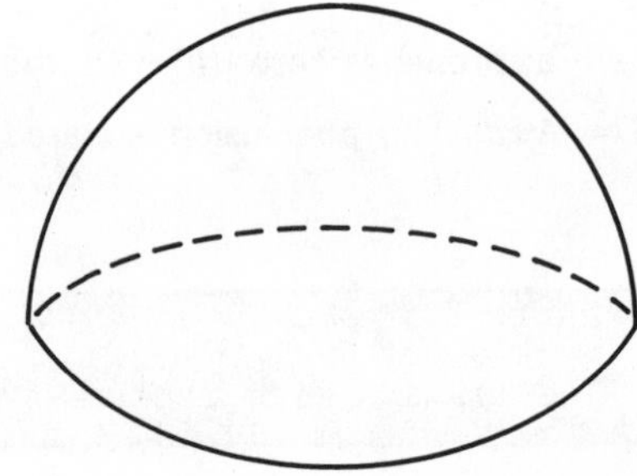

9. Find the surface area and volume of the snowman pictured at the right.

10. Find the volume of a hemisphere of diameter 20 m.

11. Two solid metal spheres of radii $2k$ and $3k$ are melted and recast as a solid circular cylinder of height $5k$. Find the radius of the cylinder.

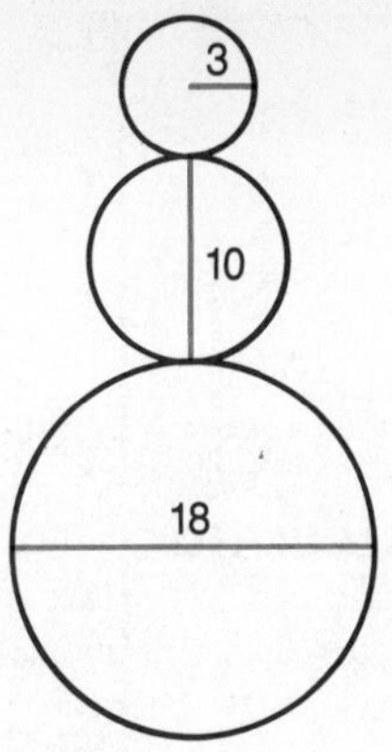

12. The cross section shown at the right is that of a spherical shell with center O, inner radius 4 in., and outer radius 7 in. Find the volume of the shell.

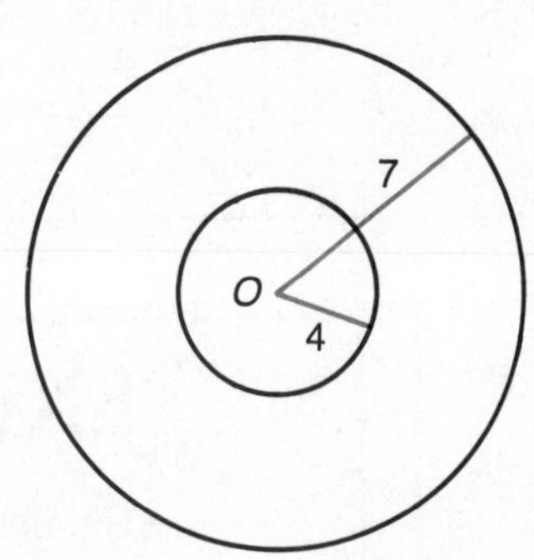

13. Half the air is let out of a spherical rubber balloon. If it retains its spherical shape, how does the resulting radius compare with the original radius?

14. A cylinder of height 12 in. is inscribed in a sphere of radius 8 in. Find the volume of the cylinder.

15. A cone is inscribed in a sphere as shown at the right. If the sphere has radius 4, and the cone has altitude 6, find the volume of the cone.

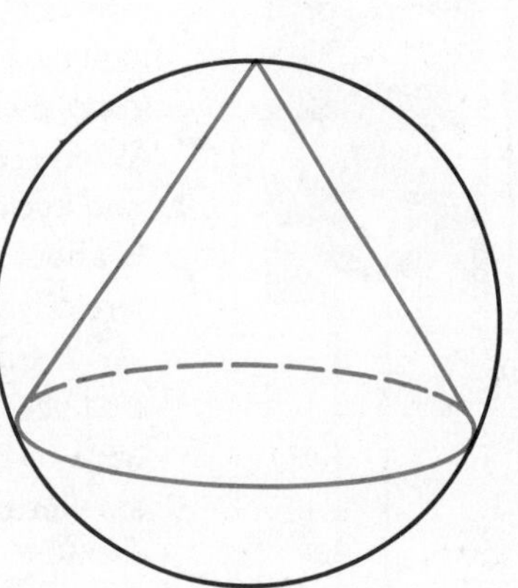

C. 16. A sphere has twice the volume of a right circular cylinder. The radius of the sphere is twice that of the radius of the base of the cylinder. Compare the surface area of the sphere with the total surface area of the cylinder.

17. Archimedes (287–212 B.C.) showed that the volume of a sphere is two-thirds the volume of the smallest right circular cylinder that can contain it. Verify this.

9. 460π; $1174\frac{2}{3}\pi$

10. $\frac{2000}{3}\pi$ m^3

11. $\frac{2\sqrt{21}}{3}k$

12. 372π in.^{3}

13. $\frac{\sqrt[3]{4}}{2}$ times as large

14. 336π in.^{3}

15. 24π

16. $\frac{24}{19}$

17. $V(\text{cylinder}) = \pi r^2 h = 2\pi r^3$

$V(\text{sphere}) = \frac{4}{3}\pi r^3$

$\frac{V(\text{sphere})}{V(\text{cylinder})} = \frac{2}{3}$

Calculator

1. $d = 8000,\ r = 4000$
$A = 4\pi r^2$
$= 200{,}960{,}000$
$A \cdot 0.25 = 50.24$ million mi^2

2. $V = \frac{1}{3}bh$, so $\frac{3V}{h} = b$
$\frac{3 \cdot 5600}{4} = 4200$
$\sqrt{4200} = 64.807406$ in.

3. $V = \frac{4}{3}\pi r^3$, so $\frac{V}{\frac{4}{3}\pi} = r^3$
$\frac{113{,}097.34}{\frac{4}{3}\pi} = 27{,}013.696$
$\sqrt[3]{27{,}013.696} = 30$

4. $s = 4\pi r^2$, so $r^2 = \frac{s}{4\pi}$
$r^2 = \frac{7853.9816}{4\pi} = 625.317$
$\sqrt{625.317} = 25.006 = 25$
$V = \frac{4}{3}\pi r^3$
$= \frac{4}{3}\pi 25^3$
$= 65{,}449.847$

Exploration

See *Teacher's Manual*, p. T62

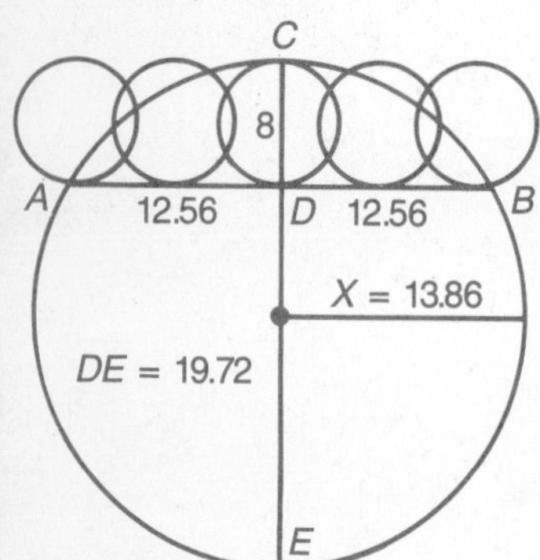

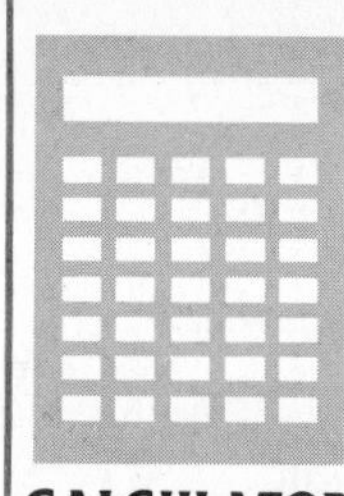

CALCULATOR

1. About three-quarters of the earth's surface is covered with water. How many million square miles of its surface are covered by land? (Use 8000 mi as the diameter of the earth and the $\boxed{\pi}$ button on your calculator, or 3.14.)
2. A metal roofing panel for a sports arena is a square pyramid with a volume of 5600 in.^{3} The height of the pyramid is 4 in. How long is one edge of the base?
3. Using the π button on her calculator, Elizabeth found the volume of a sphere to be 113,097.34. What was the radius of the sphere? (Use the $\boxed{\pi}$ button, or 3.14, and the $\boxed{y^x}$ button.)
4. Find the radius of a sphere if the surface area is 7853.9816 cm^2. Using this radius, find the volume.

EXPLORATION/Cycloids

The figure below shows the path traced by a fixed point on a circle rolling left-to right along a straight line. This path is called a cycloid. The Italian scientist Galileo Galilei (1542-1642) hypothesized that the area under one cycloid arc equals π times the area of the circle that produced it. The ratio is closer to 3:1. The English architect Sir Christopher Wren (1632-1723) discovered that the ratio of one length of one cycloid arc to the diameter of the circle that produced it is about 4:1. Given what you know about the chords of a circle, can you find the radius of the larger circle of which $\overparen{AB}$ is a part? Assume the diameter of the smaller circle is 8, and use 3.14 for π. Knowing this radius, find the ratio of the area of the larger circle containing $\overparen{AB}$ to the area of the smaller circle.

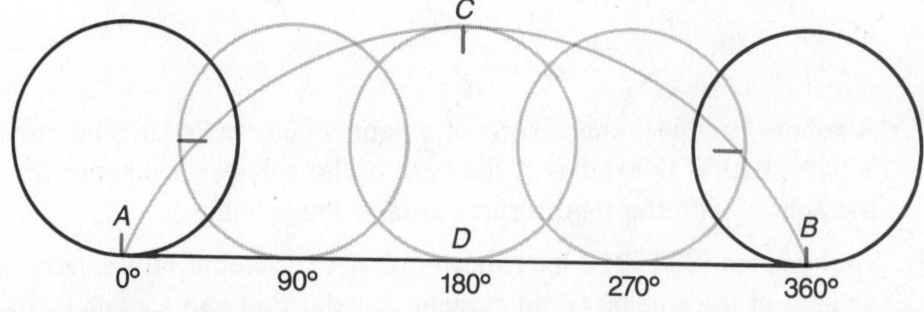

SKILLS MAINTENANCE

1. A rectangular field is 40 m longer than twice its width. It is enclosed by 1040 m of fencing. Find its dimensions.

2. A rectangle whose area is 160 ft^2 is 12 ft longer than it is wide. Find its dimensions.

3. One leg of a right triangle is 2 m longer than the second leg. If the hypotenuse is 10 m long, how long is the second leg?

4. With two presses running, the morning paper can be printed in 5 hours. The faster press working alone can print the paper in 7 hours. How long would it take the slower press working alone?

5. A group of 40 students must be separated into two groups so that one group contains four more than five times the number of students in the other. How many students should be in each group?

Skills Maintenance

1. 160×360 m
2. 8×20 ft
3. 6 m
4. $17\frac{1}{2}$ hours
5. 6, 34

CHALLENGE

Sheila's veterinarian has recommended that Sheila's dog, Starshine, be kept outside during the day so it can get more exercise. The doctor says the dog should have at least 1000 ft^2 of running room. Because her yard is not fenced, Sheila will have to chain the dog to the corner of the house, point C as shown below. Sheila has a 20-foot chain to attach to the dog.

How much exercise area will this length of chain provide for the dog? Can Sheila use a shorter chain, or will she need a longer one? Assume that the corners of the house form right angles. The lengths of the outside walls are shown in the figure. Use 3.14 for pi.

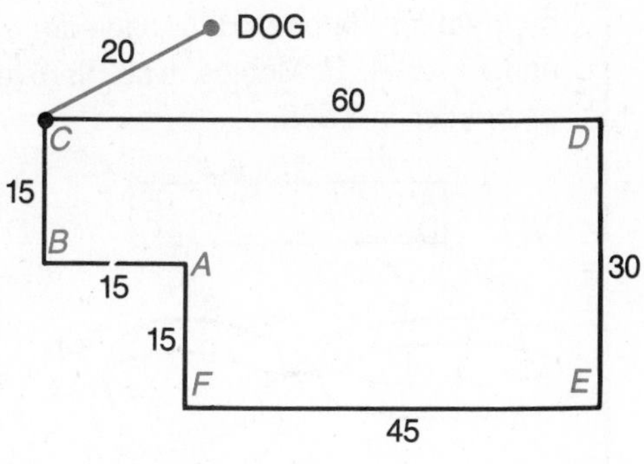

Challenge

Use the formula for area of a sector to find the area of one quadrant of a circle with radius of 20 ft and a central angle measure of 90. Three such quadrants can be measured, so that

$a = \frac{90}{360} \cdot 3.14(20^2) = 314;$
$314 \cdot 3 = 942$ ft^2.

Because the chain will run along the edge of the house, CB, the radius of the last sector will be $20 - 15$, or 5, as measured from B, so that

$a = \frac{90}{360} \cdot 3.14(5^2) = 19.625$

$942 + 19.625 = 961.625$ ft^2. Sheila will need a slightly longer chain to get 1000 ft^2 of exercise area for the dog.

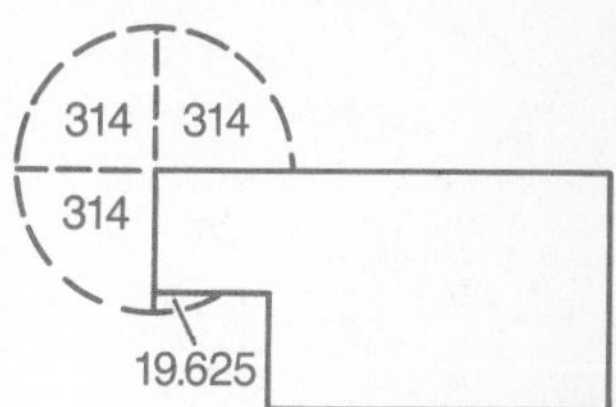

EXPLORATION
Topology

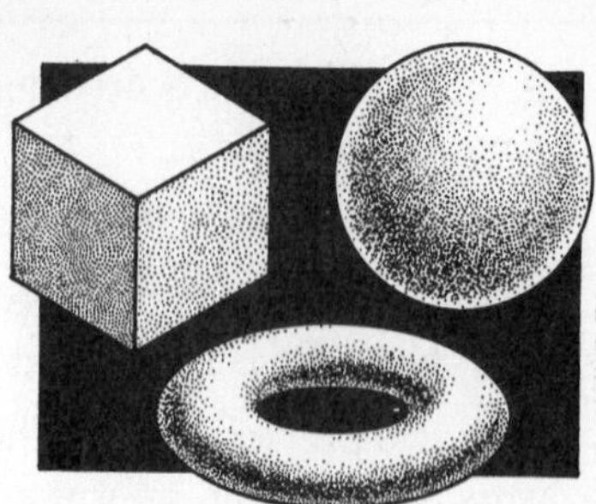

A special branch of mathematics, called **topology,** deals with figures whose geometrical properties are unchanged by *continuous transformations,* such as stretching, bending, or twisting. (Continuous transformations do not include tearing, cutting, or folding.)

Topology is often called "rubber sheet geometry" because it can be illustrated by drawing figures on a sheet of rubber and then stretching, shrinking, or twisting it.

Geometric figures that are topological transformations of each other are said to be homeomorphic. The sphere and cube shown above are homeomorphic, because the edges of the cube can be smoothed into a sphere. Likewise, the sphere can be flattened on six sides until it forms a cube. Neither figure, however, is homeomorphic with the donut-shaped figure, because neither can be transformed into a donut shape without tearing or cutting.

Three topological properties are (1) the number of sides of a figure, (2) the number of edges, and (3) the genus. The **genus** is the largest number of closed curves that can be drawn on a surface without separating it. Simply stated, the genus is the number of "holes" the figure has. For example, the sphere and cube above both have a genus 0 (no holes); the donut has genus 1; the capital letter "B" has genus 2, and so on. The other two properties, number of edges and sides, can best be illustrated by creating the one-sided, one-edge surface called a **Mobius strip,** named for A. F. Mobius, who discovered its particular topological properties in 1858.

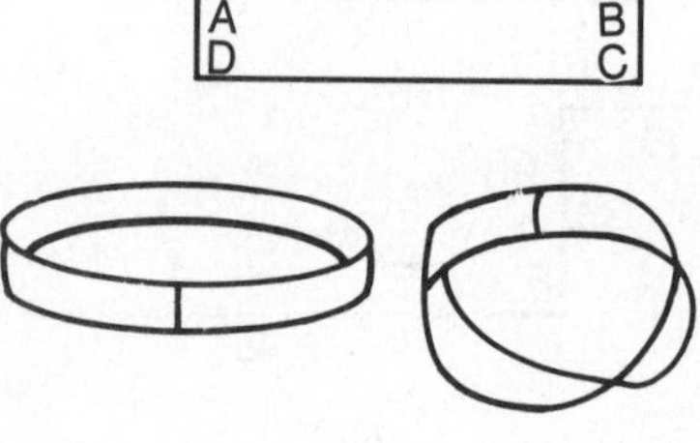

As shown at the left, let A, B, C, and D be vertices of a rectangular strip of paper or metal. If point A is joined to point B and point D is joined to point C, a band is formed with an inner and outer surface and two edges. However, if the strip is twisted so that A joins C and D joins B, a continuous edge and surface is formed.

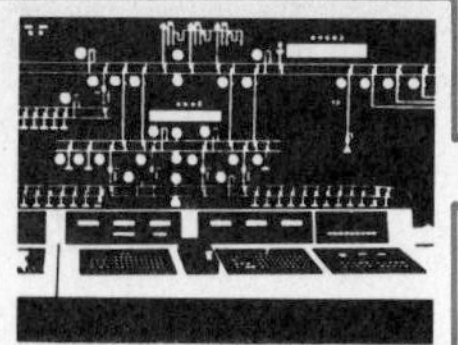

COMPUTER

Because a computer can solve the same problem over and over again with slight variations in a short time, it is an ideal way to identify trends. If all the possibilities are investigated, the trend can be established as a fact in a **proof by exhaustion.**

For example, the formula for the area of a sector of a circle is $A = \frac{q}{360}\pi r^2$. (A simpler way to rewrite this for the computer is $A = (Q{*}3.14{*}R\uparrow 2)/360$.) Clearly, as q (the measure of the arc) changes, the area will change. Similarly, as the value of r (the radius) changes, the area will change. A computer might be used to explore how changing the degrees of arc measure or the radius length would affect the area. The following program allows you to manipulate these variables.

```
100  REM AREA OF A SECTOR
110  PRINT"WHAT IS THE RADIUS OF THE SECTOR?";:INPUT R
120  PRINT"WHAT ARE THE MINIMUM AND MAXIMUM VALUES?"
130  PRINT"FOR THE ARC MEASURE?":INPUT X,Y
140  PRINT"WHAT INCREMENT BETWEEN THESE VALUES?":INPUT I
150  PRINTTAB(1)"RADIUS"TAB(10)"ARC MEASURE"TAB(25)"AREA"
160  PRINTTAB(1)"------"TAB(10)"-----------"TAB(25)"----------"
170  FOR Q=X TO Y STEP I
180  LET A=(Q*3.14*R↑2)/360
190  PRINTTAB(1)R TAB(10)Q TAB(25)A
200  NEXT Q
210  PRINT"RUN AGAIN WITH DIFFERENT VALUES? (Y/N)":INPUT R$
220  IF R$="Y" THEN GOTO 110
230  END
```

With wise choices for the radius, minimum and maximum arc measure, and the increment, a variety of cases can be computed and tested. For example, $X = 1$, $Y = 360$, and $I = 1$ will go around an entire circle at one-degree intervals.

1. If the radius is doubled, will the area of the sector with the same arc measure be doubled?

2. If the arc measure is tripled, will the area of the sector with the same radius be tripled?

TEACHER'S RESOURCE MASTERS

Computer Master 14

Computer

1. No; the area quadruples when the radius is doubled.

2. Yes; the area triples.

TEACHER'S RESOURCE MASTERS

Enrichment Master 11

ENRICHMENT

See Activities 27–28, p. T52

Chapter 14 Review

1. 256
2. 540
3. 10
4. 6
5. 11π
6. 40 in.
7. 4π
8. $16\pi - 32$

CHAPTER 14 REVIEW

VOCABULARY

annulus (14.2)
apothem (14.1)
central angle of a polygon (14.1)
circular region (14.2)
circumference (14.2)
cone (14.8)
convex polygon (14.1)
convex polygonal region (14.5)
cross section (14.5)
cylinder (14.8)
decagon (14.1)
dodecagon (14.1)
hexagon (14.1)
lateral edge (14.5)
lateral face (14.5)
length of an arc (14.3)
n-gon (14.1)
octagon (14.1)
parallelepiped (14.5)
pentagon (14.5)
perimeter (14.1)
pi (14.2)
polyhedral region (14.7)
prism (14.5)
pyramid (14.6)
radius of a polygon (14.1)
radius of a sector (14.3)
rectangular parallelepiped (14.5)
regular polygon (14.1)
regular pyramid (14.6)
right circular cone (14.8)
right circular cylinder (14.8)
right prism (14.5)
sector of a circle (14.3)
segment of a circle (14.4)
slant height (14.6)
spherical shell (14.9)
tetrahedron (14.6)
volume (14.7)

REVIEW EXERCISES

14.1

1. The perimeter of a regular polygon is 64 and its apothem is 8. What is its area?

2. What is the total measure of the interior angles of a pentagon?

3. How many sides does a regular polygon have if the measure of each exterior angle is 36?

14.2

4. The center of a wheel rolling along a straight track travels 12π units each time the wheel makes one revolution. What is the radius of the wheel?

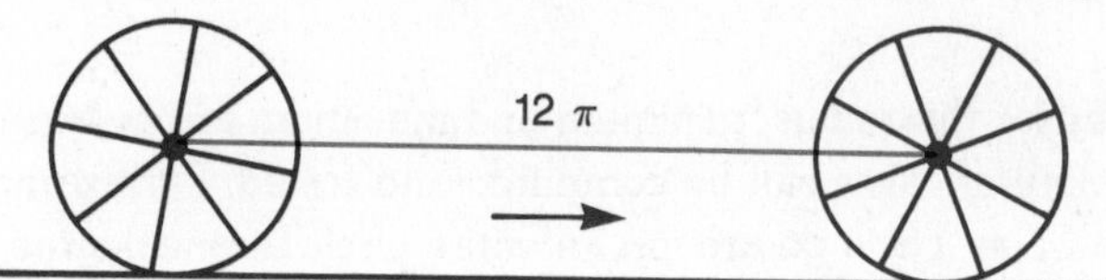

5. Given two concentric circles, one with radius 5 and one with radius 6, what is the area of the annulus in terms of π?

14.3

6. In a circle, an arc measuring 72° has a length of 8 inches. What is the circumference of the circle?

14.4

7. The area of a sector of a circle is 12π and the measure of its central angle is 120°. What is the length of its arc?

8. In $\odot O$ of radius 8, radii $\overline{OA}$ and $\overline{OB}$ form a central angle of 90°. What is the area of the segment determined by $\overline{AB}$ and $\widehat{AB}$ in terms of π?

14.5 **9.** If the lower base of a right prism is bounded by an equilateral triangle of perimeter 24 cm, what is the area of a cross section parallel to and 4 cm from the upper base? 9. $16\sqrt{3}$ cm^2

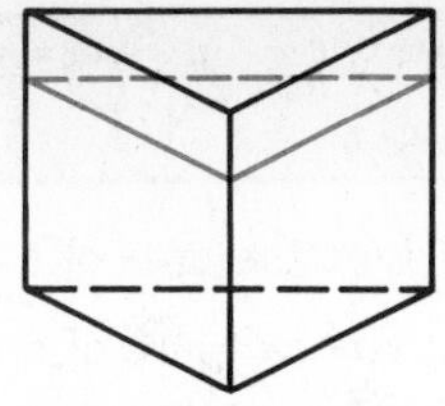

10. A rectangular parallelepiped has altitude 8 and base edges measuring 4 and 5. What is its lateral surface area? 10. 144

14.6 **11.** The base of a pyramid is bounded by a rhombus measuring 24 on a side. What is the length of the side of a cross section one-fourth of the distance from the vertex to the base? 11. 6

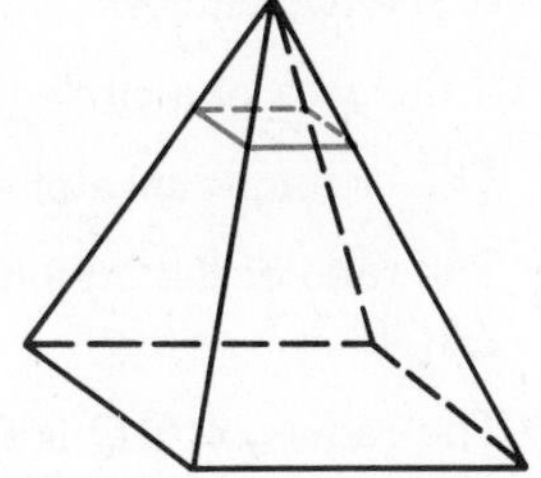

14.7 **12.** A pyramid has an altitude of 12 inches and a volume of 432 cubic inches. What is the area of a cross section 4 inches above the base? 12. 48 in.^{2}

14.8 **13.** In terms of π, what is the altitude of a cone whose radius is 10 cm and whose volume is 500 cm^3? 13. $\frac{15}{\pi}$

14.9 **14.** A cylinder of radius 22 in. and height 30 in. is filled with water. If a sphere of radius 15 in. is lowered into the cylinder and then removed, what volume of water will remain in the cylinder in terms of π? 14. $10{,}020\pi$ in.^{3}

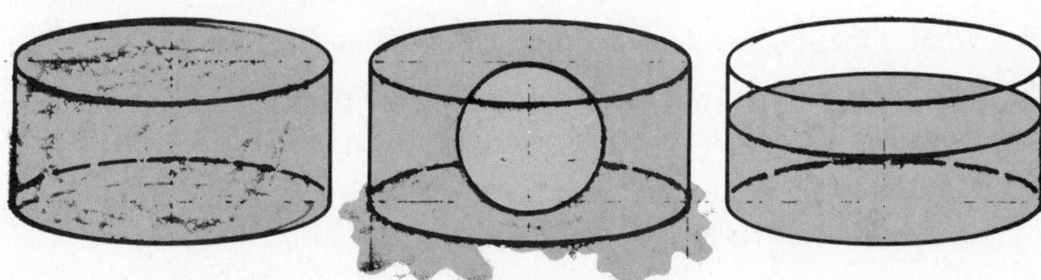

15. A spherical ball of diameter 6 cm has a hollow center of diameter 3 cm. What is the volume of the shell in terms of π? 15. 31.5π cm^3

16. What is the ratio of the surface area of a sphere to the lateral area of a circumscribed right circular cylinder? 16. 1:1

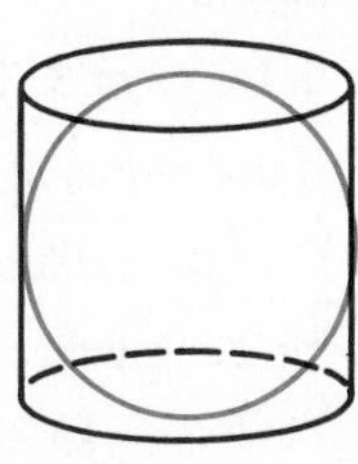

TEACHER'S RESOURCE MASTERS

Chapter 14 Test
Multiple Choice Test—Chapter 14

Chapter 14 Test

1. $\frac{3}{2}a^2\sqrt{3}$
2. 9
3. 900
4. 9:4
5. 8
6. 3π
7. 80°
8. $9\pi - 18$
9. 5
10. 240
11. 36 in.^{2}
12. $50\sqrt{3}$ in.^{3}
13. $\frac{28}{3}$
14. $50\pi\sqrt{2}$
15. It becomes eight times larger.
16. 3
17. 1458π

CHAPTER 14 TEST

1. Find the area of a regular hexagon whose perimeter is $6a$.

2. The measure of an exterior angle of a regular polygon is 40. Find the number of sides of the polygon.

3. Find the sum of the measures of the interior angles of a polygon with 7 sides.

4. If the ratio of the circumferences of two circles is 9:4, what is the ratio of the diameters of the two circles?

5. If the area of a circle is 16π, what is its diameter?

6. The circumference of a circle is 12π. Find the length of an arc whose measure is 90°.

7. The ratio of the area of sector AOB to the area of circle O is 2:9. Find the measure of $\angle AOB$.

8. The radius of $\odot Q$ is 6. $m\angle XQY = 90$. Find the area of the segment defined by $\overline{XY}$ and $\widehat{XY}$ in terms of π.

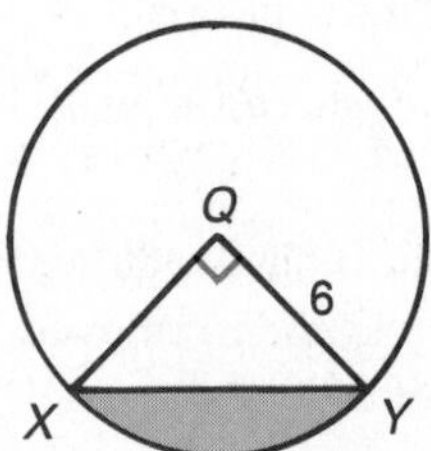

9. What is the smallest number of faces a prism may have?

10. Find the lateral surface area of a rectangular parallelepiped if the volume is 320, the altitude is 10, and the base edges are in a ratio of 2:1.

11. The altitude of a square pyramid is 5 in., and a side of the base is 10 in. Find the area of a cross section 3 in. from the vertex.

12. What is the volume of a pyramid whose base is an equilateral triangle 10 inches on a side and whose altitude is 6 inches?

13. The volume of a cylinder is 28. Find the volume of a cone with the same base and altitude.

14. In terms of π, find the volume of a cone whose altitude is $6\sqrt{2}$ and whose radius is 5.

15. If the radius of a sphere is doubled, what happens to its volume?

16. Find the radius of a sphere if its volume equals its surface area.

17. Find the volume of a right cylinder in terms of π if the radius of an inscribed sphere is 9 cm.

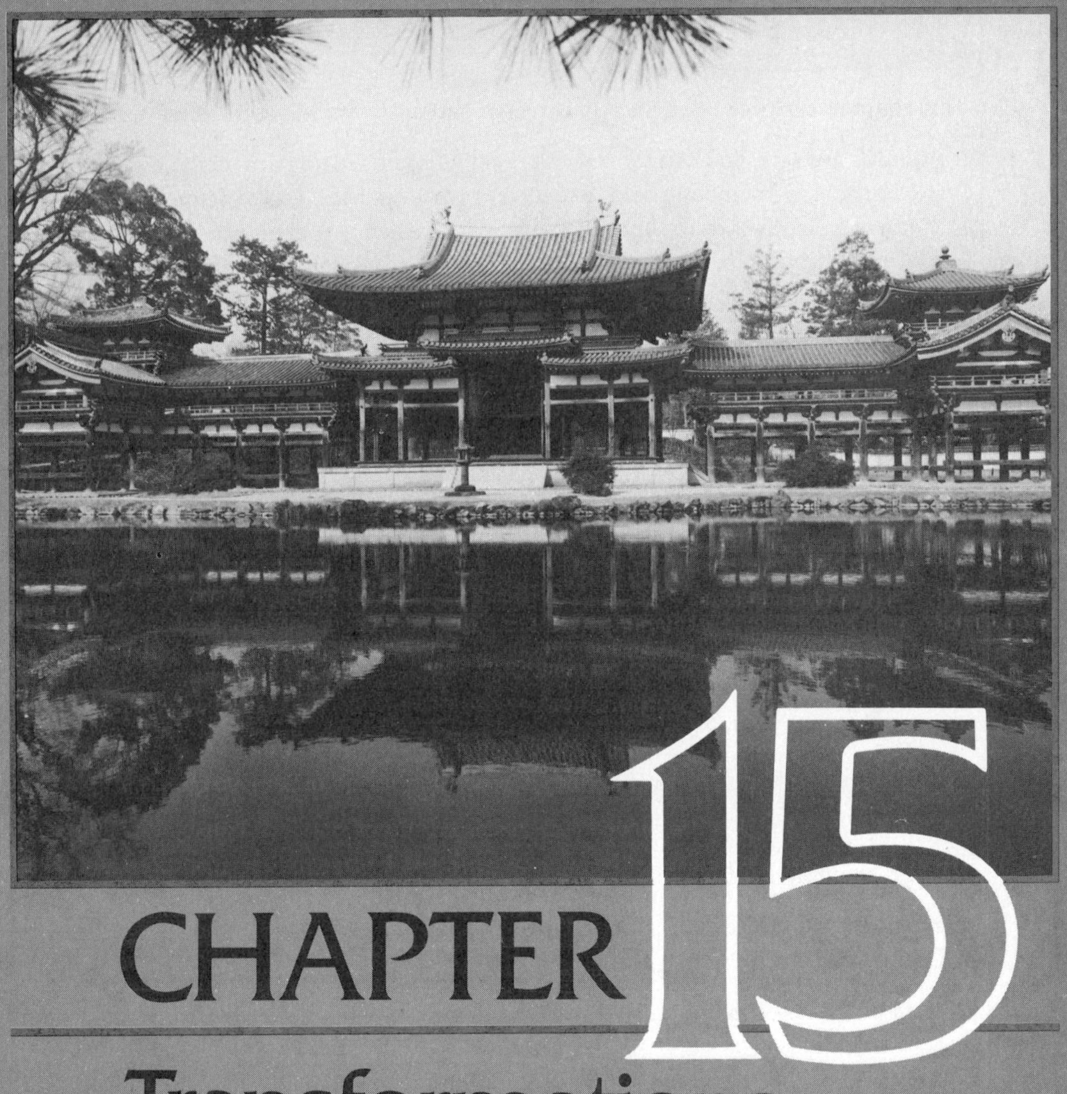

CHAPTER 15

Transformations

OBJECTIVES

Find the Cartesian product of two sets.

Identify a relation, its domain, range, inverse, function, and inverse function.

TEACHER'S NOTES

See p. T40

MIXED REVIEW

1. Solve for x if $A = xa^2 - xc^2$. $x = \frac{A}{a^2 - c^2}$
2. Subtract $\frac{4}{5} - \frac{1}{3}$. $\frac{7}{15}$
3. Solve $x + 4y = -1$
   $2x - 4y = -8$.
   $(-3, \frac{1}{2})$
4. Solve $x^2 - x - 1 = 0$. $\frac{1 \pm \sqrt{5}}{2}$
5. Multiply $\sqrt{32} \cdot \sqrt{8}$. 16

TEACHER'S RESOURCE MASTERS

Practice Master 46, Part 1

15.1 Relations and Functions

This chapter explores relationships between geometry and algebra called *transformations*.

If A and B are sets, you can form another set whose elements are all the ordered pairs whose first components (members) belong to A and whose second components (members) belong to B. For example, if $A = \{a, b, c\}$ and $B = \{5, 8\}$, then you can form the set of ordered pairs $\{(a, 5), (a, 8), (b, 5), (b, 8), (c, 5), (c, 8)\}$. This new set is called the **Cartesian product** of A and B.

DEFINITION: Cartesian product
If A and B are any two sets, then the **Cartesian product** of A and B, denoted by $A \times B$, is the set of all ordered pairs (x, y) such that x is an element of A and y is an element of B. This set is represented as $\{(x, y): x \in A, y \in B\}$.

Other Cartesian products you can form using sets A and B above are

$$B \times A = \{(5, a), (5, b), (5, c), (8, a), (8, b), (8, c)\};$$
$$A \times A = \{(a, a), (a, b), (a, c), (b, a), (b, b), (b, c), (c, a), (c, b), (c, c)\};$$
$$B \times B = \{(5, 5), (5, 8), (8, 5), (8, 8)\}.$$

The last example $B \times B$, would be described as $\{(x, y): x \in B, y \in B\}$.

The Cartesian product $R \times R$ where R is the set of real numbers, establishes the coordinate or Cartesian plane.

Subsets of Cartesian products that satisfy a given condition are called **relations.**

DEFINITIONS: relation, domain, range
A **relation** is a set of ordered pairs. The **domain** of a relation is the set containing the first members of its ordered pairs. The **range** of a relation is the set containing the second members of its ordered pairs.

Example: $A = \{(1, 4), (2, 5), (2, 6), (3, 4), (4, 7)\}$. What are the domain and range of A?

Solution: The domain of $A = \{1, 2, 3, 4\}$.
The range of $A = \{4, 5, 6, 7\}$.

Relations can be described in many different ways. For example, a subset of $R \times R$ can be described in all the ways shown below.

Set Listing

$\{(1, 4), (2, 5), (3, 6), (4, 7)\}$

Table

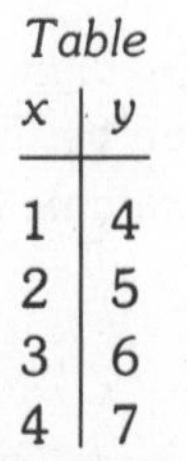

x	y
1	4
2	5
3	6
4	7

Diagram

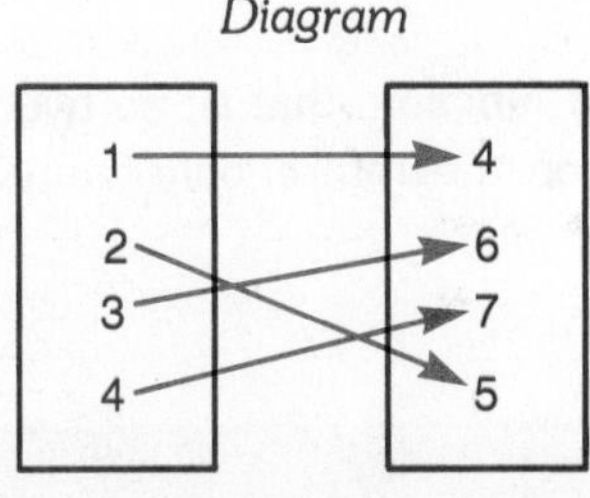

Graph

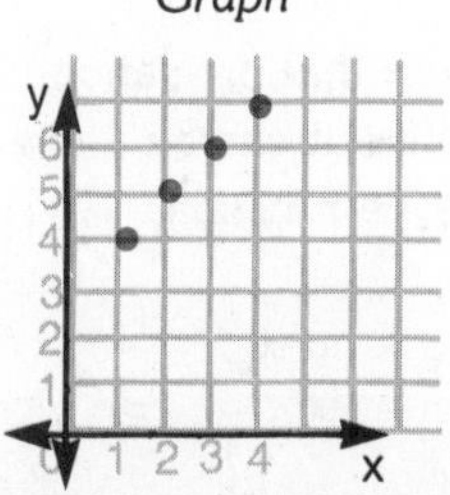

Another way to describe a relation is by a rule. A rule for the relation described above could be "The second member of each ordered pair is three more than the first member." This rule can also be written $\{(x, y): y = x + 3\}$.

A new relation can be formed by interchanging the first and second members of each ordered pair of a given relation. This new relation is the **inverse relation** of the given relation. The inverse relation of a relation A is denoted by A^{-1}.

Example: Given the relation $T = \{(2, 4), (3, 9), (4, 16)\}$, what is T^{-1}?

Solution: $T^{-1} = \{(4, 2), (9, 3), (16, 4)\}$

If you were using a rule to describe the relation T in the above example, then you would simply interchange the variables to write the rule for its inverse. That is, if $T = \{(x, y): y = x^2\}$, then $T^{-1} = \{(x, y): x = y^2\}$

DEFINITION: function
A relation is a **function** if and only if no two orderd pairs have the same first member.

Example 3: Determine which of the following relations are functions.

$$A = \{(3, 8), (2, 7), (3, 5), (4, 9)\}$$
$$B = \{(1, 7), (2, 9), (3, 11), (4, 9)\}$$
$$C = \{(2, 5), (3, 4), (5, 6), (7, 9)\}$$

Solution: Relations B and C are functions, but A is not.

Now examine the inverse of each relation in the example.

$$A^{-1} = \{(8, 3), (7, 2), (5, 3), (9, 4)\}$$
$$B^{-1} = \{(7, 1), (9, 2), (11, 3), (9, 4)\}$$
$$C^{-1} = \{(5,, 2), (4, 3), (6, 5), (9, 7)\}$$

Notice that A is not a function, but its inverse A^{-1} is. B is a function, but B^{-1} is not. Both C and C^{-1} are functions.

ASSIGNMENT GUIDE

Day 1
Minimum 1-9
Regular 1-17 odd
Maximum 1-15 odd, 17-22
Day 2
Minimum 10-24
Regular 19-35 odd
Maximum 23-33 odd, 35-37

Oral Exercises

1. $A \times B = \{(a, 1), (a, 2), (a, 3), (b, 1), (b, 2), (b, 3)\}$
   $B \times A = \{(1, a), (1, b), (2, a), (2, b), (3, a), (3, b)\}$
2. No; when $p \neq q$, $(p, q) \neq (q, p)$.
3. 15, 15
4. $A \times A = \{(1, 1), (1, 2), (2, 1), (2, 2)\}$
5. 36
6. A relation is a set of ordered pairs.
7. A function is a relation in which no two ordered pairs have the same first element.
8. A one-to-one function is a function in which no two ordered pairs have the same second element.
9. The inverse of a relation is the relation formed by exchanging the elements of each ordered pair.
10. A: $D = \{0, 1\}$, $R = \{0, 1, -1\}$
    B: $D = \{4, 5, 6\}$, $R = \{5\}$
    C: $D = \mathrm{R}$, $R = \mathrm{R}$
    D: $D = \mathrm{R} \geq 0$, $R = \mathrm{R}$
11. B, C 12. C
13. $A^{-1} = \{(0, 0), (1, 1), (-1, 1)\}$
    $B^{-1} = \{(5, 4), (5, 5), (5, 6)\}$
    $C^{-1} = \{(x, y): y = x\}$
    $D^{-1} = \{(x, y): y = |x|\}$
14. A^{-1}, C^{-1} 15. C
16. Answers will vary.

DEFINITION: inverse function, one-to-one function
A function has an **inverse function,** or is a **one-to-one function,** if and only if no two ordered pairs have the same second number.

Note that a relation must first be a function, that is, no two first members can be the same, before it can be a one-to-one function. Therefore, only the relation C in the example is a one-to-one function.

ORAL EXERCISES

1. If $A = \{a, b\}$ and $B = \{1, 2, 3\}$, name both $A \times B$ and $B \times A$.

2. For any two different sets A and B, does $A \times B = B \times A$? Explain.

3. If A contains 3 elements and B contains 5 elements, how many elements are in $A \times B$? in $B \times A$?

4. If $A = \{1, 2\}$, name all ordered pairs in $A \times A$.

5. If A contains 6 elements, how many elements are in $A \times A$?

6. State the definition of *relation.*

7. State the definition of *function.*

8. State the definition of *one-to-one function.*

9. State the definition of *inverse relation.*

Use the following relations to answer Exercises 10-15.

$A = \{(0, 0), (1, 1), (1, -1)\}$ $B = \{(4, 5), (5, 5), (6, 5)\}$

$C = \{(x, y): y = x\}$ $D = \{(x, y): x = |y|\}$

10. State the domain and range of each relation.

11. Which of the relations are functions?

12. Which of the relations are one-to-one functions?

13. Name the inverse of each relation.

14. Which of the inverse relations are also functions?

15. Which relation is its own inverse?

16. Name a relation from everyday life that can be considered as a set of ordered pairs.

WRITTEN EXERCISES

A. Fill in the blanks to make each statement true.

1. Any subset of $S \times T$ is called a ____.

2. The relations obtained by interchanging the first and second elements of each ordered pair in a relation is called its ____ relation.

3. A relation in which no two ordered pairs have the same first element is called a ____.

4. A function in which no two ordered pairs have the same second element is called a ____ function.

In Exercises 5 and 6, name both $A \times B$ and $B \times A$.

5. $A = \{\text{Tom, Bill}\}$; $B = \{\text{Lois, Sue}\}$

6. $A = \{4\}$; $B = \{-1, -2, -3, -4, -5\}$

7. How can the number of ordered pairs in the Cartesian product of any two finite sets by determined?

In Exercises 8 and 9, a set S and a relation in S are given. List the elements of $S \times S$ that satisfy the relation.

8. $S = \{-3, 0, 3\}$; "x is greater than y"

9. $S = \{0, 1, 2, 3, 4\}$; "x is the square of y"

Use the following relations to answer Exercises 10-12.

$A = \{(1, 3), (2, 5), (3, 7)\}$ $\quad B = \{(\frac{1}{2}, 2), (\pi, 2), (\sqrt{3}, 2)\}$

$C = \{(6, 1), (6, 2), (6, 3), (6, 4)\}$ $\quad D = \{(x, y): y = 3x\}$

$E = \{(x, y): y = |x|\}$ $\quad F = \{(x, y): y = x^2 + 5\}$

10. Name the domain and range of each relation.

11. Which of the relations are functions?

12. Which of the relations are one-to-one functions?

B. 13. Suppose F is a function. Is F^{-1} always a function? Explain.

14. Suppose R is a relation that is not a function. Can R^{-1} be a function? Explain.

15. Suppose G is a one-to-one function. What can you conclude regarding G^{-1}?

16. State the inverse relations of $S = \{(x, y): x = 2y\}$ and $T = \{(x, y): x = 2|y|\}$. Is either S^{-1} or T^{-1} a function?

Written Exercises

1. relation 2. inverse

3. function 4. one-to-one

5. $A \times B = \{(\text{Tom, Lois}), (\text{Tom, Sue}), (\text{Bill, Lois}), (\text{Bill, Sue})\}$
$B \times A = \{(\text{Lois, Tom}), (\text{Lois, Bill}) (\text{Sue, Tom}), (\text{Sue, Bill})\}$

6. $A \times B = \{(4, -1), (4, -2), (4, -3), (4, -4), (4, -5)\}$
$B \times A = \{(-1, 4), (-2, 4), (-3, 4), (-4, 4), (-5, 4)\}$

7. $n(A) \times n(B) = n(A \times B) = n(B \times A)$

8. $\{(3, -3), (3, 0), (0, -3)\}$

9. $\{(0, 0), (1, 1), (4, 2)\}$

10. A: $D = \{1, 2, 3\}$, $R = \{3, 5, 7\}$
B: $D = \{\frac{1}{2}, \pi, \sqrt{3}\}$, $R = \{2\}$
C: $D = \{6\}$, $R = \{1, 2, 3, 4\}$
D: $D = \{\text{reals}\}$, $R = \{\text{reals}\}$
E: $D = \{\text{reals}\}$, $R = \{y: y \geq 0\}$
F: $D = \{\text{reals}\}$, $R = \{y: y \geq 5\}$

11. A, B, D, E, F

12. A, D

13. No; only if F is one-to-one.

14. Yes; if no two ordered pairs of R have the same second element.

15. G^{-1} is a function.

16. $S^{-1} = \{(x, y): y = 2x\}$
$T^{-1} = \{(x, y): y = 2|x|\}$
Both S^{-1} and T^{-1} are functions.

Each table in Exercises 17–22 defines a relation. Which relations are functions? Write an equation for each relation that expresses y in terms of x.

17.

x	2	3	4	5	6
y	5	6	7	8	9

18.

x	1	2	3	4	5
y	1	8	27	64	125

19.

x	0	1	2	3	4
y	0	$\frac{1}{2}$	1	$\frac{3}{2}$	2

20.

x	−4	−3	−2	−1	0
y	4	3	2	1	0

21.

x	−2	−2	−2	−2	−2
y	0	1	2	3	4

22.

x	0	1	1	4	4
y	0	1	−1	2	−2

Write a formula to define each of the following functions.

23. The circumference of a circle, C, is the product of pi and the diameter, d.

24. The volume, V, of a cube is the third power of its edge, e.

25. The measure of the supplement, s, of an angle having a measure of x is the difference of 180 and x.

26. The area of a square, A, is the square of its side, s.

Graph each relation in Exercises 27–34.

27. $\{(1, 3), (2, 2), (3, 1), (4, 0)\}$

28. $\{(0, 0), (-1, 2), (4, 0)\}$

29. $\{(x, y): y = 2x - 3\}$

30. $\{(x, y): x = 5\}$

31. $\{(x, y): y = -4\}$

32. $\{x, y): x^2 + y^2 = 25\}$

33. $\{(x, y): y < x\}$

34. $\{(x, y): y \geq -3x + 4\}$

C. 35. A shortcut mathematicians use to determine if a relation is a function, given its graph, is called the *vertical line test.* A relation is a function if and only if it is impossible to draw a vertical line that intersects the graph in two or more points. Use the vertical line test to determine which of the relations in Exercises 27–34 are functions.

36. Another shortcut, called the *horizontal line test,* can be used to determine whether or not a function is one-to-one. State the horizontal line test.

37. $\{(x, y): y = x\}$ is called the *identity function.* Explain why.

17. $y = x + 3$
18. $y = x^3$
19. $y = \frac{1}{2}x$
20. $y = -x$
21. $x = -2$
22. $x = y^2$
23. $C = \pi d$
24. $V = e^3$
25. $s = 180 - x$
26. $A = s^2$

27-33. odd See *Teacher's Manual,* p. T62

28-34. even See *Selected Answers,* p. 643-644

35. 27, 28, 29, and 31 are functions.
36. A function is one-to-one if and only if it is impossible to draw a horizontal line that intersects the graph of the function in two or more points.
37. because the function pairs each real number with itself

15.2 Transformations

Two concepts that are similar to relations and functions, and especially important in the study of modern geometry, are **mappings** and transformations.

> **DEFINITIONS: mapping, domain, codomain**
> A **mapping** is a rule that assigns to each element of one set (the **domain**) exactly one element of a second set (the **codomain**).

The figure illustrates the idea of a mapping of A (the domain) into B (the codomain), written $A \rightarrow B$. In the figure, 1 is the **image** of a, and a is the **preimage** of 1; 3 is the image of both b and c, and b and c are both preimages of 3. The set of images $\{1, 3\}$ is called the *range*. If the number of elements in the range equals the number of elements in the codomain, the mapping is said to be **onto.** In the example, two elements of the codomain are not images. Therefore, the range does not equal the codomain, and $A \rightarrow B$ is not onto.

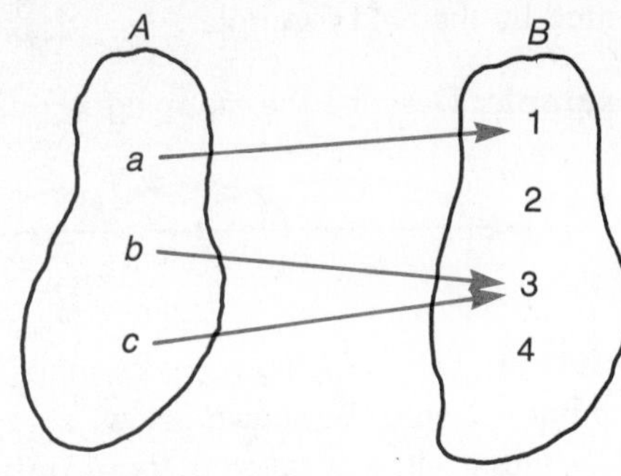

Example: Is $A \rightarrow B$ onto?

Solution: The range equals the codomain, so the mapping is onto. Notice that two preimages have the same image.

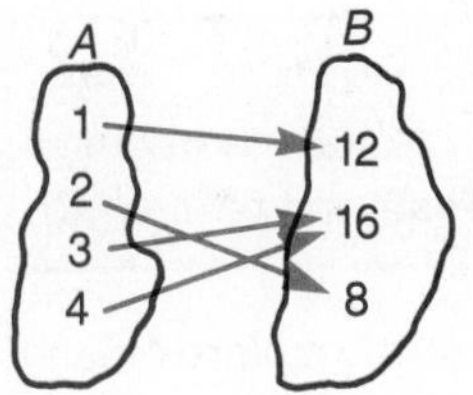

Example: Is $A \rightarrow B$ onto?

Solution: The mapping is not onto. Notice, however, that each image has exactly one preimage. This mapping is called a **one-to-one mapping.**

> **DEFINITION: one-to-one mapping**
> A mapping is **one-to-one** if and only if no two preimages have the same image.

OBJECTIVES

Identify the domain and codomain of a mapping.
Identify and graph a transformation.

TEACHER'S NOTES

See p. T41

MIXED REVIEW

1. Write an equation for the line through (3, 5) and (1, 7). $y = -x + 8$
2. Write an equation for a circle with center at (2, 3) and radius 4. $(x - 2)^2 + (y - 3)^2 = 16$
3. Multiply $(2x - 1)(x + 3)(x - 2)$. $2x^3 + x^2 - 13x + 6$
4. At what point does the graph of $y = |x - 2| + 1$ cross the x-axis? It does not cross the x-axis.
5. Solve $2|x - 3| \leq 18$. $-6 \leq x \leq 12$

TEACHER'S RESOURCE MASTERS

Practice Master 46, Part 2

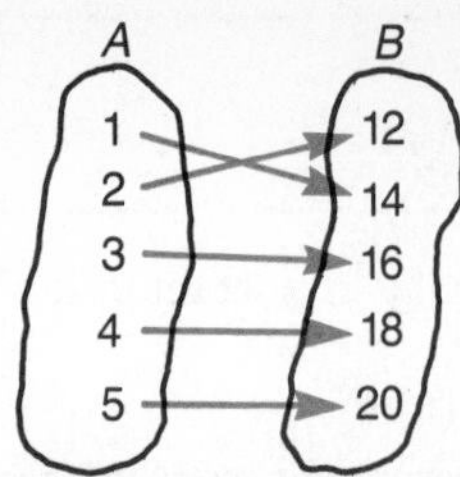

Example: Is $A \to B$ onto? Is it one-to-one?

Solution: This mapping is both onto and one-to-one.

A mapping has an *inverse* if and only if it is both one-to-one and onto. Study the examples above to see that $A \to B$ has an inverse only in Example 3.

Mappings can be represented in ways other than diagrams. Another common method is illustrated by the next example.

Example: Describe the mapping $x \to 2x$ in the set of integers.

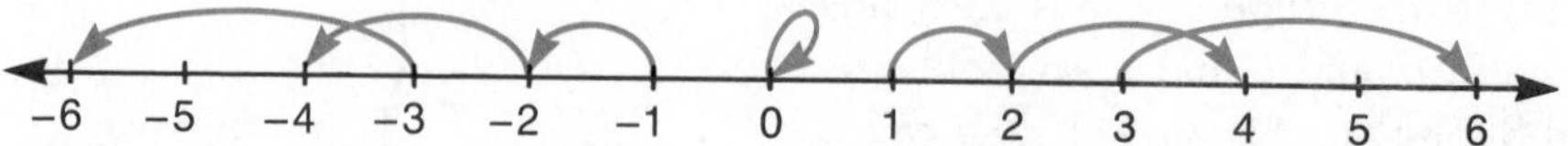

Solution: The mapping $x \to 2x$ maps each integer into its double. This mapping is one-to-one but not onto. As shown below, $x \to 2x$ can be illustrated on the number line. Because 0 maps into itself, it is called a **fixed point.** If a mapping maps every element into itself, then it is an **identity mapping.**

Of particular interest in geometry are mappings of sets of points into sets of points. These mappings are called **transformations.**

> **DEFINITION: transformation**
> A **transformation** is a mapping of a set of points into a set of points that is both one-to-one and onto.

Geometry explores many different kinds of transformations. In this chapter, you will be concerned primarily with transformations like those shown below.

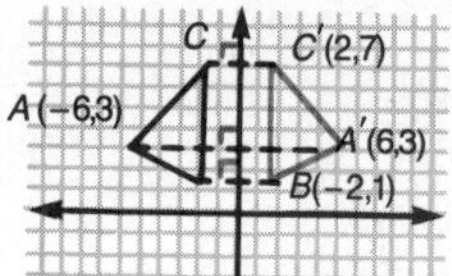

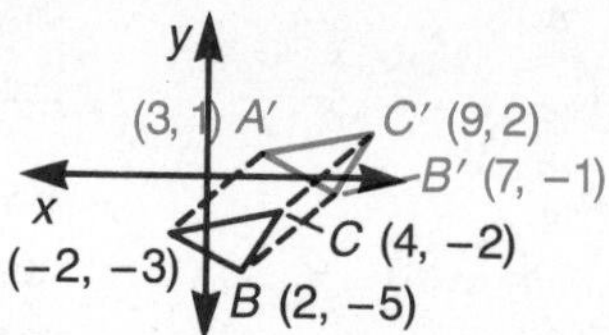

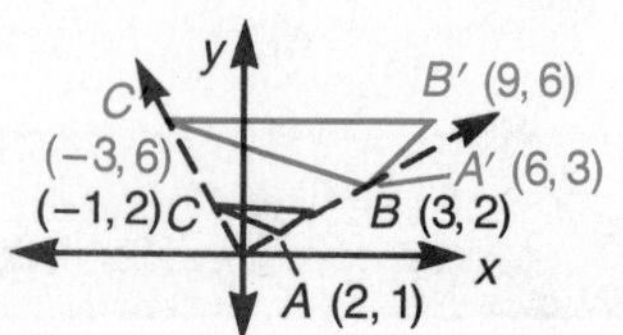

ORAL EXERCISES

A partial diagram for a mapping from the set of whole numbers into the set of whole numbers is shown at the right.

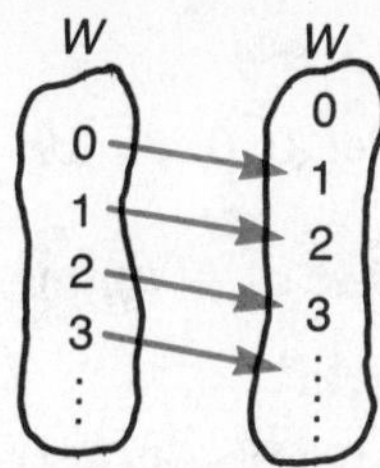

1. What is the domain?
2. What is the codomain?
3. What is the range?

A table for a mapping is shown.

0	→	0
1	→	2
2	→	4
3	→	6
4	→	8
5	→	10

4. What is the image of 3?
5. What is the preimage of 2?
6. Name the domain of the mapping.
7. Name the range of the mapping.
8. What is the rule for the mapping?

Explain why neither of the following is a mapping.

9.

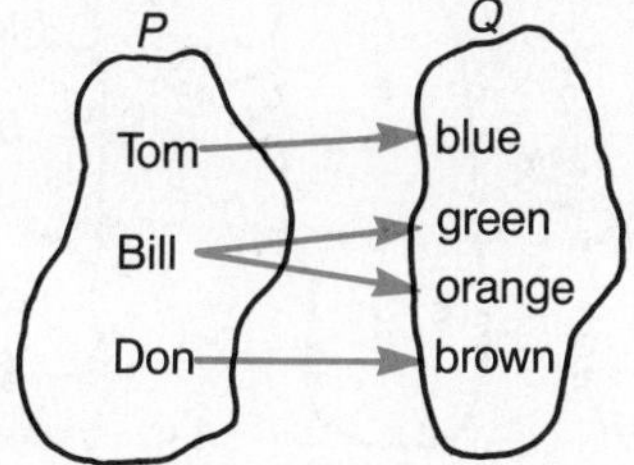

10.

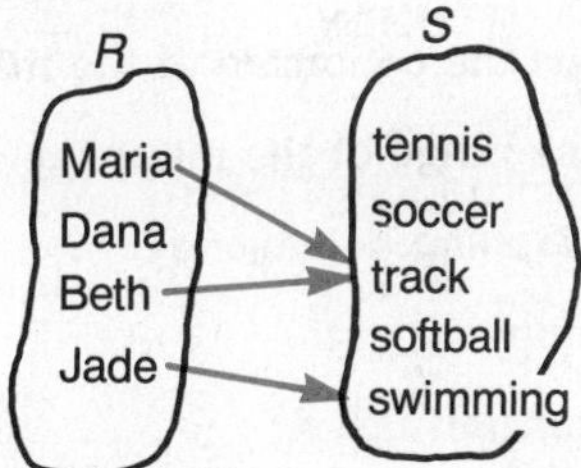

Refer to the figures below to determine which one of the figures is

11. both one-to-one and onto.
12. onto but not one-to-one.
13. one-to-one but not onto.
14. neither one-to-one nor onto.

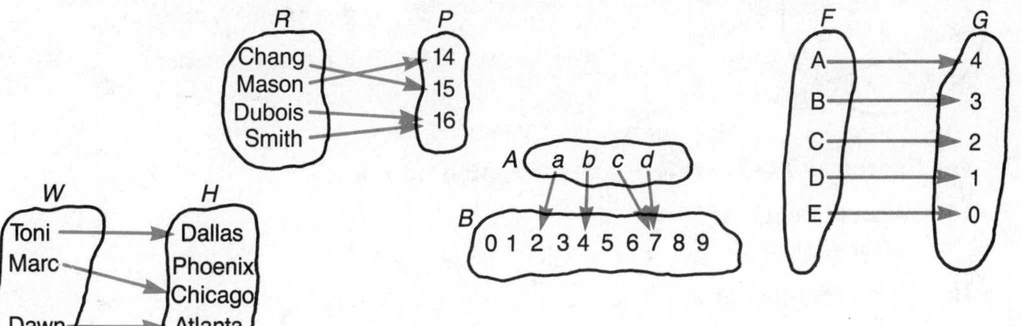

ASSIGNMENT GUIDE

Minimum 1–20
Regular 1–31 odd
Maximum 1–29 odd, 36–39

Oral Exercises

1. {whole numbers}
2. {whole numbers}
3. {natural numbers}
4. 6 5. 1
6. {0, 1, 2, 3, 4, 5}
7. {0, 2, 4, 6, 8, 10}
8. $x \to 2x$
9. Bill has 2 different images.
10. Dana has no images.
11. $F \to G$
12. $R \to P$
13. $W \to H$
14. $A \to B$

15. It must be one-to-one and onto.

16. (3, − 9) 17. (0, −5)

18. (0, 5)
19. $(x, y) \rightarrow (x, y + 5)$
20. The preimage does not exist.
21. (2, 1) → (0, 1), (3, 1) → (0, 1)
22. No. neither 1:1 nor onto
23. Yes. The converse is true only if both the domain and codomain are sets of points and the mapping is both 1:1 and onto.

Written Exercises

1. {1, 2, 3, 4}
2. {a, b, c, d, e}
3. {a, b, c, e}
4. yes 5. no
6. no
7. △*ABC*
8. ⊙*O*
9. yes
10. yes
11. $x \rightarrow 0$
12. No; not 1:1
13. (0, 3)
14. (−1, −4)
15. $(x, y) \rightarrow (-x, y)$
16. yes
17.

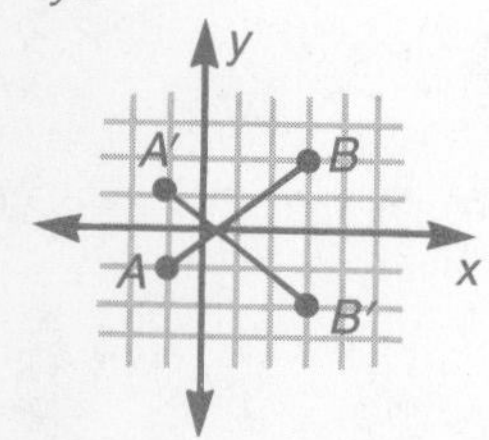

15. What properties must a mapping have in order to have an inverse mapping?

Consider the plane transformation $(x, y) \rightarrow (x, y - 5)$.

16. Name the image of (3, −4). **17.** Name the image of (0, 0).

18. Name the preimage of (0, 0). **19.** State the inverse rule.

Consider the mapping $(x, y) \rightarrow (0, y)$.

20. Name the preimage of (1, 2).

21. Name the images of (2, 1) and (3, 1).

22. Is this mapping a transformation? Explain.

23. Are all transformations mappings? Is the converse true?

WRITTEN EXERCISES

A. Refer to the mapping from *A* to *B* for Exercises 1–6.

1. Name the domain of the mapping.

2. Name the the codomain of the mapping.

3. Name the range of the mapping.

4. Is this mapping one-to-one?

5. Is this mapping onto?

6. Is it a transformation?

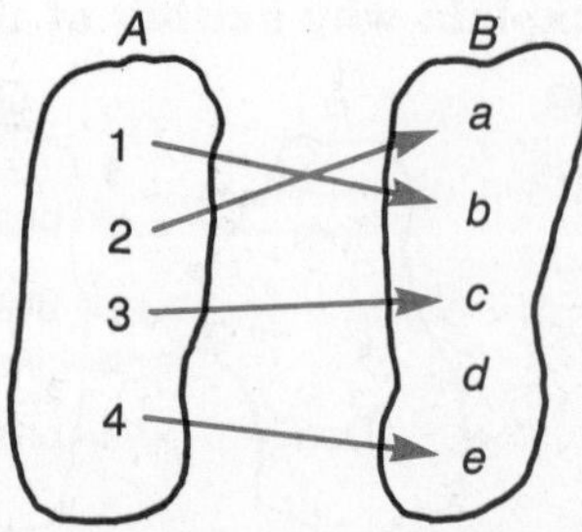

For Exercises 7–10, refer to △*ABC* mapped into the circle.

7. Name the domain of the mapping.

8. Name the range of the mapping.

9. Is this mapping onto?

10. Is it a transformation?

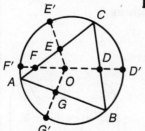

For Exercises 11–12, refer to the mapping on a line.

11. What is the rule of this mapping?

12. Is it a transformation?

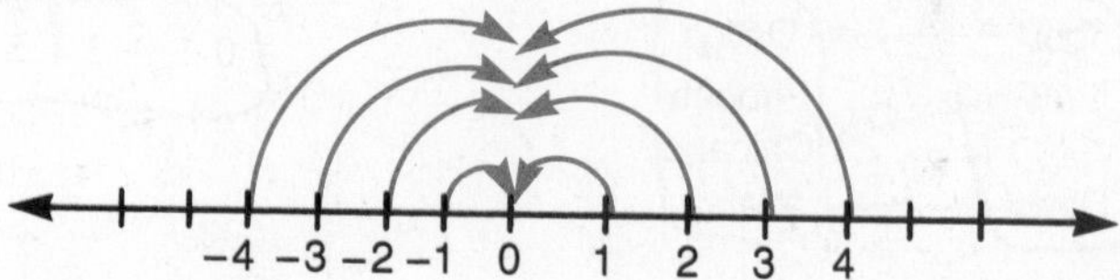

At the right is a mapping on a plane.

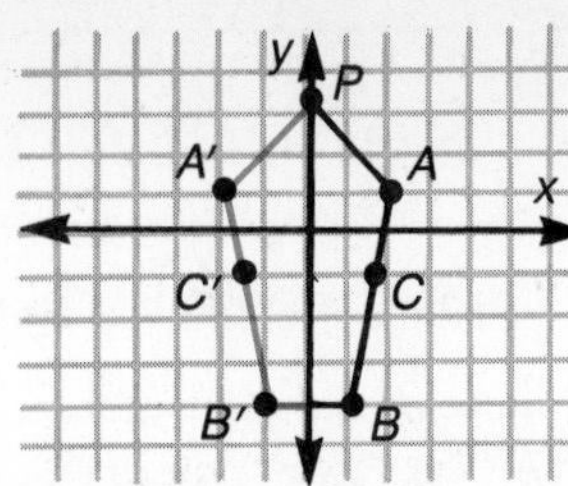

13. Name the image of (0, 3).

14. Name the preimage of (1, −4).

15. What is the rule of this mapping?

16. Is it a transformation? Explain.

B. On graph paper, plot $A(-1, -1)$, $B(3, 2)$, and the images of A and B under the mapping $(x, y) \to (x, -y)$.

17. Draw $\overline{AB}$ and $\overline{A'B'}$.

18. Find AB and $A'B'$.

19. Is $\overline{AB} \cong \overline{A'B'}$?

20. Is this a transformation?

On graph paper, plot $A(-1, -2)$, $B(2, -2)$, $C(-1, 2)$ and their images under the transformation $(x, y) \to (3x, 3y)$.

21. Draw $\triangle ABC$ and $\triangle A'B'C'$.

22. Is $\triangle ABC \sim \triangle A'B'C'$?

23. Find the area of each one.

24. How do the areas compare?

On graph paper, plot $A(-2, -2)$, $B(-2, 4)$, $C(1, 4)$, $D(1, -2)$ and their images under the transformation $(x, y) \to (x, x + y)$.

25. Draw quadrilaterals $ABCD$ and $A'B'C'D'$.

26. Are the quadrilaterals similar?

27. Find the area of each quadrilateral.

28. How do the areas compare?

State whether each of the following are rules of plane transformations.

29. $(x, y) \to (3x, y)$

30. $(x, y) \to (x, 0)$

31. $(x, y) \to (y, x)$

32. $(x, y) \to (x, -y)$

33. $(x, y) \to (4x, 4y)$

34. $(x, y) \to (x + 2, y - 3)$

35. $(x, y) \to (x + y, y)$

36. $(x, y) \to (0, y)$

C. Suppose that the number of sides of any polygon, n, is mapped into the number of diagonals that can be drawn for the polygon.

37. What is the rule for this mapping?

38. Is it a transformation? Explain.

39. A sphere with center O is circumscribed about a cube. If P is any point of the cube, its image P' is the intersection of $\overrightarrow{OP}$ and the sphere. Is this a transformation? Explain.

18. $AB = A'B' = 5$
19. yes 20. yes
21.

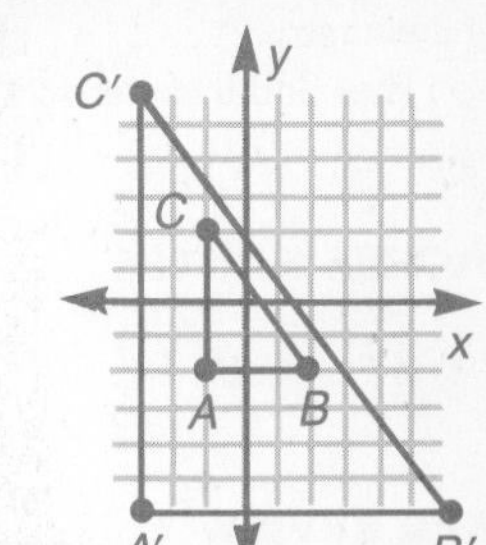

22. yes
23. area of $\triangle ABC = 6$, area of $\triangle A'B'C' = 54$
24. area of image is 9 times original
25.

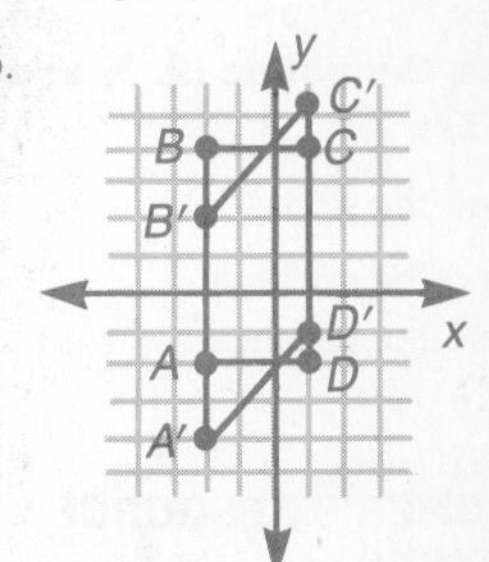

26. No; $ABCD$ is a rectangle, $A'B'C'D'$ is a parallelogram.
27. Both are 18.
28. They are equal.
29. yes 30. yes
31. yes 32. yes
33. no 34. yes
35. yes 36. no
37. $n \to \frac{n(n-3)}{2}$
38. No; it is not a mapping of points to points.
39. Yes; it is a mapping from the cube to the sphere that is both one-to-one and onto.

OBJECTIVES

Identify line reflections and lines of symmetry.

Graph lines and their reflections.

TEACHER'S NOTES

See p. T41

MIXED REVIEW

1. Given a circle with radius 15 find the diameter, circumference and area. 30, 30π, 225π
2. Factor $30x^2 + 7x - 2$ $(6x - 1)(5x + 2)$

Given the points (2, 3) and (14, 17),

3. find the slope. $\frac{5}{6}$
4. find the midpoint. (8, 2)
5. find the distance. $2\sqrt{61}$

TEACHER'S RESOURCE MASTERS

Practice Master 47, Part 1

15.3 Reflections

One type of transformation is a **line reflection,** also called a **reflection in a line.**

> **DEFINITION: line reflection, reflection in a line, line of reflection**
> A **line reflection,** or a **reflection in a line,** is a transformation that maps each point of line l to itself and each point P not on l to its image P', such that l is the perpendicular bisector of $\overline{PP'}$. The line l is the **line of reflection.**

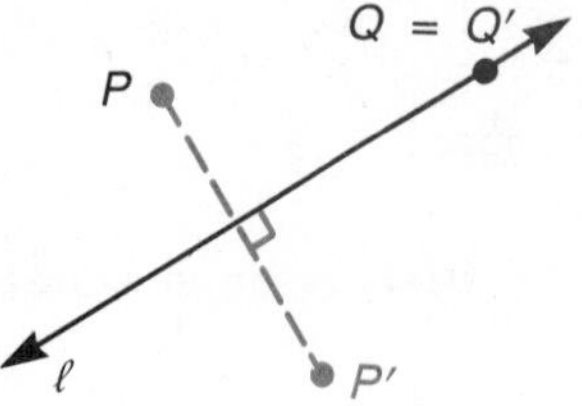

In the figure, P' is the image of P under reflection in l. Since $Q = Q'$; Q is a fixed point. Line l is the line of reflection and the perpendicular bisector of $\overline{PP'}$.

The next two figures illustrate the properties of line reflections.

The image of a geometric figure is the set of images of the points making up the figure. Here, the image of $\overline{PS}$ is $\overline{P'S'}$. The images of the collinear points P, Q, R, and S are likewise collinear. Q is between P and R, and its image Q' is between P' and R'. Thus, collinearity and betweenness of points are *preserved* under line reflection. Distance between points is also preserved under reflection, so $PS = P'S'$.

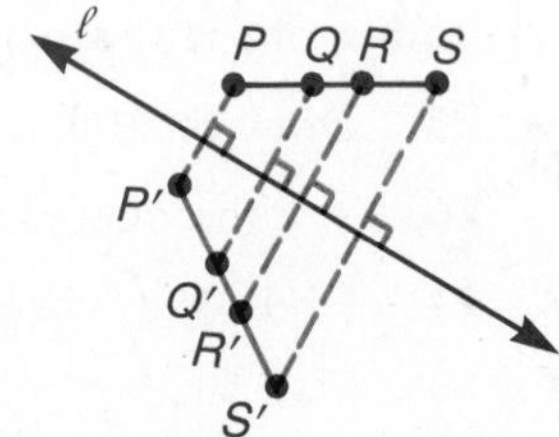

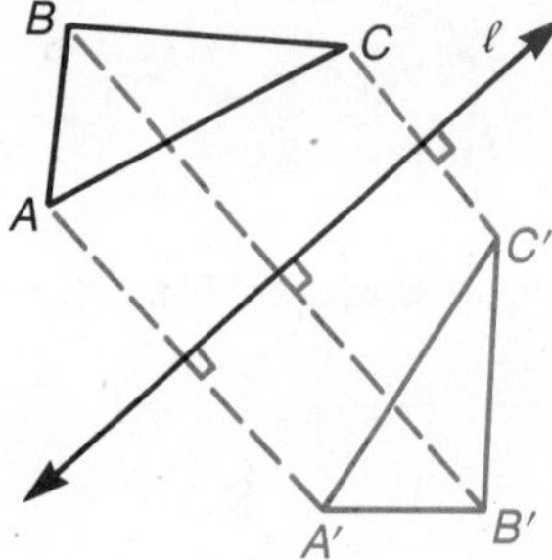

In this figure, the image of $\triangle ABC$ is $\triangle A'B'C'$. Line reflection maps angles onto angles and preserves their measures, so $m\angle A = m\angle A'$. The three noncollinear points A, B, and C are arranged clockwise, while their images A', B', and C' are arranged counterclockwise. Reflection in a line reverses the arrangements or orientation of three noncollinear points.

You can determine the rule for a reflection in a line by using the coordinate plane.

Example: The image of $A(-1,2)$ is $A'(7,2)$; the image of $B(4,-2)$ is $B'(2,-2)$. Determine the equation of the line of reflection and the rule for reflecting in this line.

Solution: You know that the midpoints of $\overline{AA'}$ and $\overline{BB'}$ must lie on the line of reflection. These midpoints are (3,2) and (3,−2), respectively. Therefore, the equation of the line of reflection is $x = 3$. The rule for reflecting in this line is $(x,y) \rightarrow (6 - x, y)$.

Now examine isosceles $\triangle ABC$ with base $\overline{AB}$. If you reflect any point on the triangle in the line $x = 5$, you find that its image is also on the triangle. This interesting result leads to the following definition.

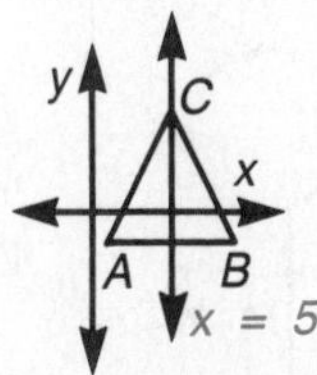

> **DEFINITION: line of symmetry, symmetric**
> If a plane figure is its own image under reflection in a line, then the line of reflection is a **line of symmetry** of the figure. The figure is said to be **symmetric** with respect to the line.

Example: How many lines of symmetry does a regular octagon have?

Solution: There are four perpendicular bisectors of the sides (each bisects a pair of sides) and four lines containing the diagonals joining opposite vertices. Thus, there are 8 lines of symmetry.

ASSIGNMENT GUIDE

Minimum 1-19 odd
Regular 1-27 odd, 28-33
Maximum 1-27 odd, 28-33, 36-41

ORAL EXERCISES

Determine whether each statement is true or false.

1. A point and its image under a line reflection are the same distance from the line of reflection.
2. If a point is located on the line of reflection, then it is its own image.
3. Under a line reflection, a line is parallel to its image.
4. Line reflections preserve betweenness of points.
5. Line reflections preserve the orientation of a set of three or more noncollinear points.

Oral Exercises

1. T
2. T
3. F
4. T
5. F
6. T

7. T 8. F

9. T 10. 1

11. 6 12. 0

13. 4

Written Exercises

1.

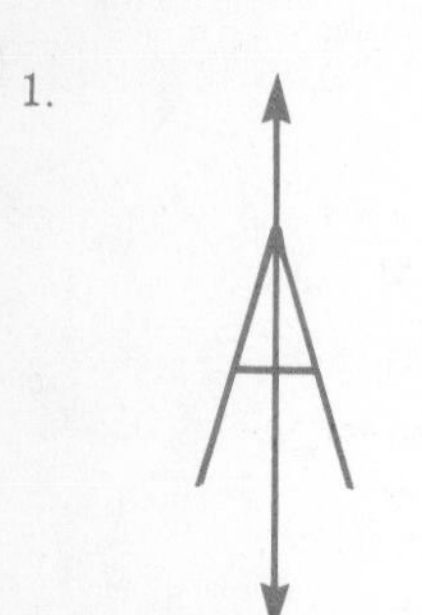

2.

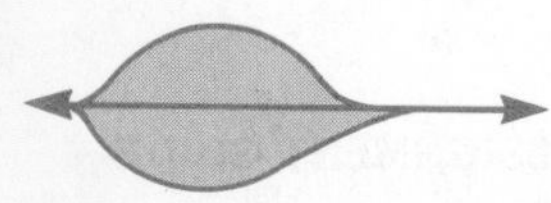

3.

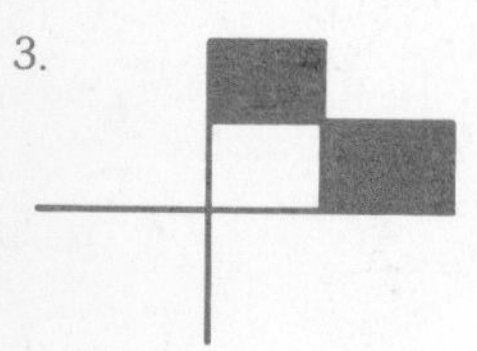

4. 2 5. 1
6. 0 7. 4
8. 2 9. 2
10. infinite 11. 6
12. $A'(0, -4)$, $B'(2, -5)$, $C'(-3, 0)$, $D'(-4, 6)$
13. $A'(0, 4)$, $B'(-2, 5)$, $C'(3, 0)$, $D'(4, -6)$
14. $A'(4, 0)$, $B'(5, 2)$, $C'(0, -3)$, $D'(-6, -4)$
15. $A'(-4, 0)$, $B'(-5, -2)$, $C'(0, 3)$, $D'(6, 4)$

6. If a line is perpendicular to the line it is reflected through, then the line is its own image.

7. The image of a right triangle under a line reflection is a congruent triangle.

8. An angle cannot be mapped onto itself by a line reflection.

9. An equilateral triangle has three lines of symmetry.

How many lines of symmetry does each figure below have?

10.

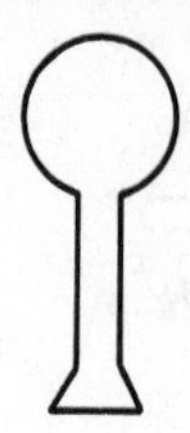

11.

12.

S

13.

WRITTEN EXERCISES

A. Transfer each figure onto your own graph paper. Then draw its image under reflection in *l*.

1.

2.

3.

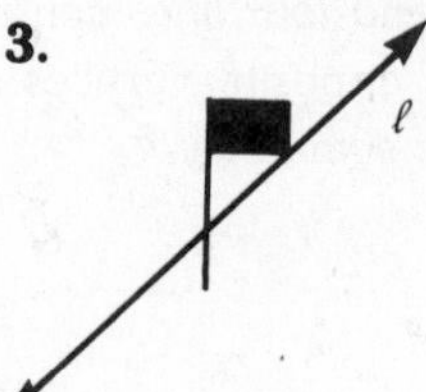

How many lines of symmetry does each figure have?

4. rectangle **5.** angle **6.** parallelogram **7.** square
8. rhombus **9.** line segment **10.** circle **11.** regular hexagon

Use the following points in Exercises 12–15. *A*(0,4) *B*(2,5) *C*(−3,0) *D*(−4,−6)

12. Plot each point on a rectangular coordinate plane. Then plot the image of each point under reflection in the x-axis. Label the image points A', B', C', and D'.

13. Plot the images of A, B, C, and D using the y-axis as the line of reflection.

14. Plot the images of A, B, C, and D reflecting in the line $y = x$.

15. Plot the images of A, B, C, and D using $y = -x$ as the line of reflection.

The coordinate rule for reflecting in the x-axis is $(x,y) \rightarrow (x,-y)$. State the rule for reflecting in the given line.

16. y-axis **17.** $y = x$ **18.** $y = -x$

B. A point and its image under a line reflection are given. State the equation of the line of reflection.

19. $A(4, -2)$; $A'(-2, 4)$ **20.** $B(7, 0)$; $B'(-7, 0)$ **21.** $C(-6, 3)$; $C'(-4, 3)$

22. $D(1, 0)$; $D'(0, -1)$ **23.** $E(2, 3)$; $E'(2, 0)$ **24.** $F(-5, 4)$; $F'(-5, -4)$

Use the following equations of lines for Exercises 25–27.

a. $y = 5$ **b.** $y = x$ **c.** $y = -3x + 2$ **d.** $y = \frac{1}{2}x - 1$

25. Graph each line and its image under reflection in the x-axis. Then state the equation of the image line.

26. Using a reflection in the y-axis, state the equation of each image line.

27. What effect does reflecting a line in each axis have on its slope? on its y-intercept?

State whether each of the following is preserved under line reflections.

28. collinearity **29.** orientation **30.** angle measure

31. betweenness **32.** parallelism **33.** distance

Copy each figure. Then use a compass and straightedge to construct the images under reflection in *l*.

34.

35.

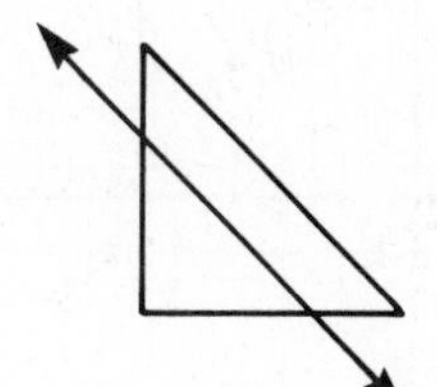

C. Use the following points for Exercises 36–37:

***A*(−1, 2)** ***B*(1, −4)** ***C*(2, 4)** ***D*(5, 1)** ***E*(0, 0)** ***F*(8, 2).**

36. Plot each point on graph paper. Then find the images under a reflection in the vertical line $x = 3$. What is the coordinate rule for this line reflection?

37. Find the images of the same points ($A - F$) reflecting in the horizontal line $y = -2$. What is the coordinate rule for this line reflection?

Graph each line and its image under reflection in the line $y = x$. Then state the equation of the image line.

38. $y = 5$ **39.** $x = -2$ **40.** $y = x$ **41.** $y = 3x + 1$

16. $(x, y) \rightarrow (-x, y)$
17. $(x, y) \rightarrow (y, x)$
18. $(x, y) \rightarrow (-y, -x)$
19. $y = x$ 20. $x = 0$
21. $x = -5$ 22. $y = -x$
23. $y = 1.5$ 24. $y = 0$
25. a. $y = -5$
b. $y = -x$
c. $y = 3x - 2$
d. $y = -\frac{1}{2}x + 1$
26. a. $y = 5$
b. $y = -x$
c. $y = 3x + 2$
d. $y = -\frac{1}{2}x - 1$
27. Reflecting in the x-axis changes slope and y-intercept to their opposites. Reflecting in the y-axis changes slope to opposite but preserves y-intercept.
28. yes 29. no
30. yes 31. yes
32. yes 33. yes
34.

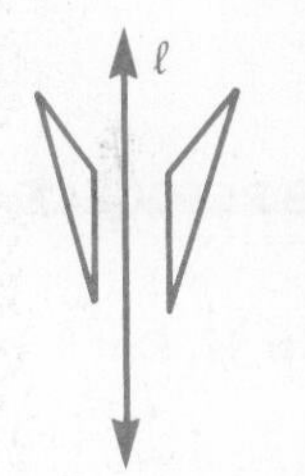

35.

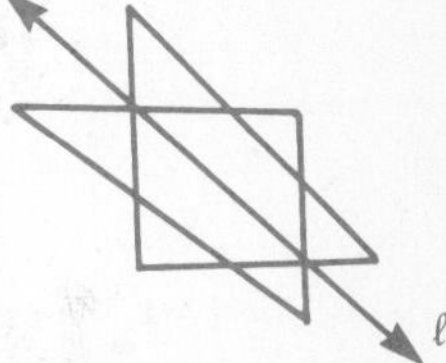

36. $A'(7, 2)$, $B'(5, -4)$, $C'(4, 4)$, $D'(1, 1)$, $E'(6, 0)$, $F'(-2, 2)$; $(x, y) \rightarrow (6 - x, y)$
37. $A'(-1, -6)$, $B'(1, 0)$, $C'(2, -8)$, $D'(5, -5)$, $E'(0, -4)$, $F'(8, -6)$; $(x, y) \rightarrow (x, -y - 4)$
38. $x = 5$ 39. $y = -2$
40. $y = x$
41. $y = \frac{1}{3}x - \frac{1}{3}$

OBJECTIVE

Identify and plot translations and determine their rules and magnitudes.

TEACHER'S NOTES

See p. T41

MIXED REVIEW

1. Find the area of an equilateral triangle with a side of 20. $100\sqrt{3}$
2. What is the longest side of a right triangle? hypotenuse
3. Give the equation for a line with a slope of 3 that goes through (0, 5). $y = 3x + 5$
4. Find the diagonal of a cube with an edge of 3. $3\sqrt{3}$
5. Solve $-1 < 3x + 2 < 11$. $-1 < x < 3$

TEACHER'S RESOURCE MASTERS

Practice Master 47, Part 2
Quiz 29

15.4 Translations

A second plane transformation results from the *product* or **composition** of two reflections in parallel lines. This transformation is called a **translation.** The symbol for composition is "o". Under composition, the operation on the right of the symbol is performed first, and then the operation on the left. The following figures illustrate translations in the parallel lines *l* and *m*.

$\triangle ABC$ is first reflected in *l*, creating the image $\triangle A'B'C'$. Then $\triangle A'B'C'$ is reflected in *m*, creating the image $\triangle A''B''C''$. Therefore, the image of $\triangle ABC$ under translation is $\triangle A''B''C''$. The rule for the translation is $(x, y) \rightarrow (x + 20, y)$.

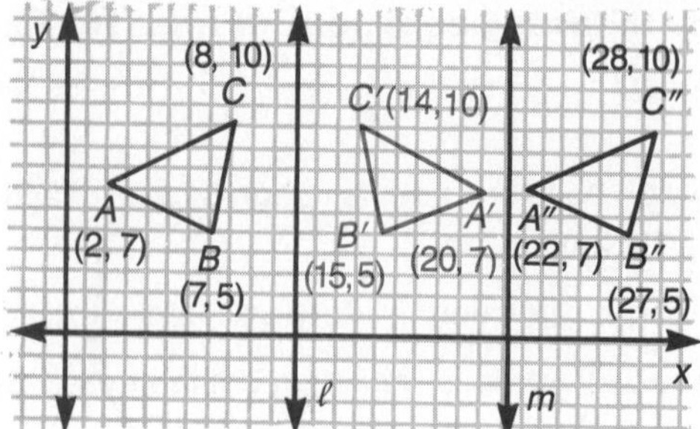

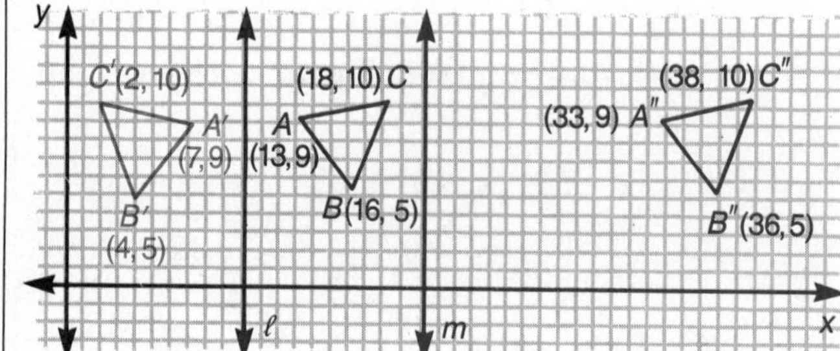

Now positioned between *l* and *m*, $\triangle ABC$ is first reflected in *l*. Its image $\triangle A'B'C'$ is then reflected in *m*. The image of $\triangle ABC$ under translation is $\triangle A''B''C''$. The rule for the translation is again $(x, y) \rightarrow (x + 20, y)$.

In this figure $\triangle ABC$ is reflected in *m* first, and then its image is reflected in *l*. $\triangle A''B''C''$ is the image of $\triangle ABC$ under translation. The rule for this translation is $(x, y) \rightarrow (x - 20, y)$.

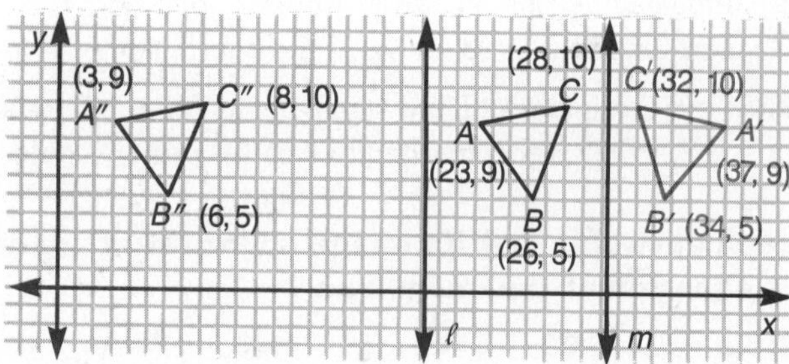

Notice that, in each case, all points of $\triangle ABC$ move the same number of units in the same direction. The distance between any point and its image is called the **magnitude** of the translation. The magnitude is always twice the distance between the parallel lines l and m. The parallel lines of reflection are not always shown in a figure of a translation, and they need not be vertical. The next figure shows a translation in which the parallel lines are neither vertical nor shown in the figure. The rule for this translation is $(x, y) \rightarrow (x + 6, y + 9)$.

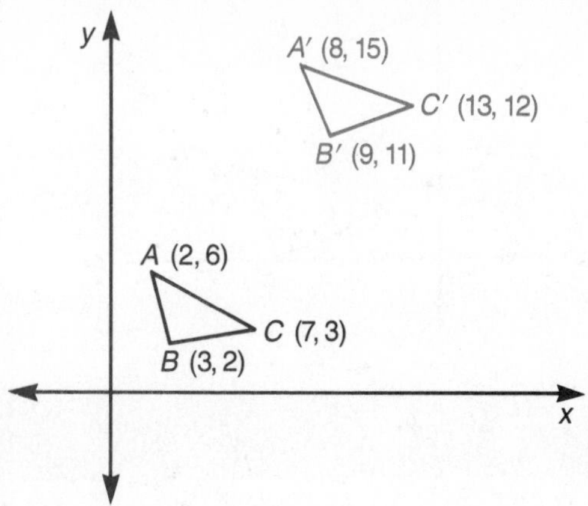

All of these examples of translations suggest the following definition.

DEFINITION: translation
A **translation** is a transformation of the plane that is a composition of reflections in lines l and m, where $l \parallel m$ or $l = m$. The general rule for a translation is $(x, y) \rightarrow (x + a, y + b)$, where a and b are real numbers and (x, y) is any point in the plane.

If you restrict your attention to a line, then the general rule for a translation is $x \rightarrow x + a$, where a is a real number and x is the coordinate of any point on the line.

A translation of the plane preserves lines, parallelism, collinearity, betweenness of points, distance between points, and angle measure. Translation also preserves the orientation of three noncollinear points, or their positions relative to each other.

Example: Given $A(4, -6)$ and its image under translation $A'(-2, 2)$, determine the rule and magnitude of the translation.

Solution: The rule is $(x, y) \rightarrow (x - 6, y + 8)$. The magnitude is given by the distance formula: $d = \sqrt{36 + 64} = 10$.

Example: Under translation, $A(-3, 4)$ is mapped to $A'(-8, 7)$. What is the rule for the translation, and what is the rule for its inverse?

Solution: The rule for the translation is $(x, y) \rightarrow (x - 5, y + 3)$, the rule for its inverse is $(x, y) \rightarrow (x + 5, y - 3)$. In general, the inverse T^{-1} of a transformation T restores every image under T to its original preimage. Thus,

$$(x, y) \xrightarrow{T} (x - 5, y + 3) \xrightarrow{T^{-1}} (x, y).$$

If the transformation (S) is $(x, y) \rightarrow (2x, 2y)$, then S^{-1} is $(x, y) \rightarrow (\frac{1}{2}x, \frac{1}{2}y)$.

ASSIGNMENT GUIDE

Minimum 1-14
Regular 1-19 odd, 20-25
Maximum 1-19 odd, 20-28

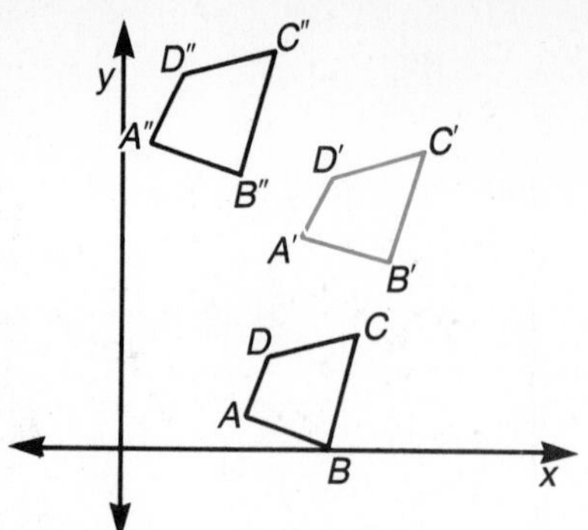

Is the composition of two translations a translation? Consider this example. Quadrilateral *ABCD* is first translated using the rule $(x, y) \rightarrow (x + 2, y + 6)$. The image is then translated using the rule $(x, y) \rightarrow (x - 5, y + 3)$. Do you see that the result is a translation with the rule $(x, y) \rightarrow (x - 3, y + 9)$? You should also see that the result would be the same if the order of the translations were changed. Therefore, composition of translations is commutative.

ORAL EXERCISES

Name the image of each point under the translation with the rule $(x, y) \rightarrow (x + 3, y - 5)$.

1. $A(0, 0)$ **2.** $B(2, -1)$ **3.** $C(-4, 6)$ **4.** $D(-3, 5)$

5. Name the rule for the inverse of the translation above.

Name the preimage of each point under the translation with the rule $(x, y) \rightarrow (x - 5, y - 2)$.

6. $A'(0, 0)$ **7.** $B'(4, -3)$ **8.** $C'(5, 2)$ **9.** $D'(-2, -6)$

10. Name the rule for the inverse of the translation above.

For each figure, name the translation that maps $\triangle ABC$ onto $\triangle A'B'C'$.

11.

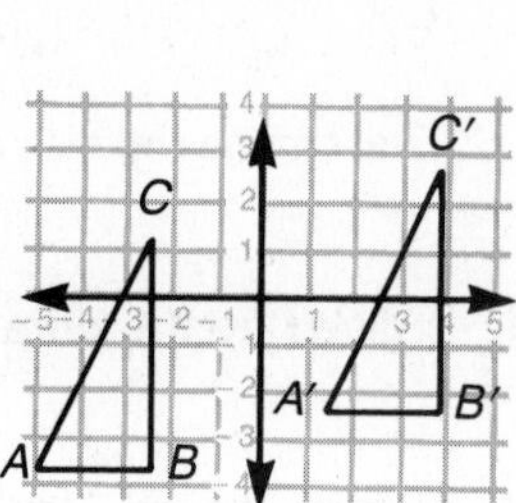

12.

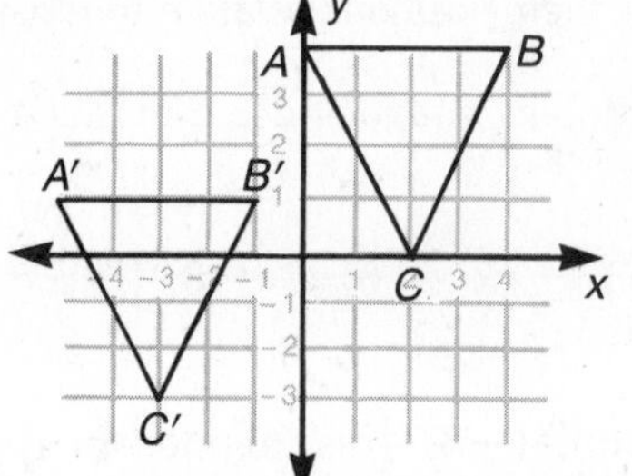

13.

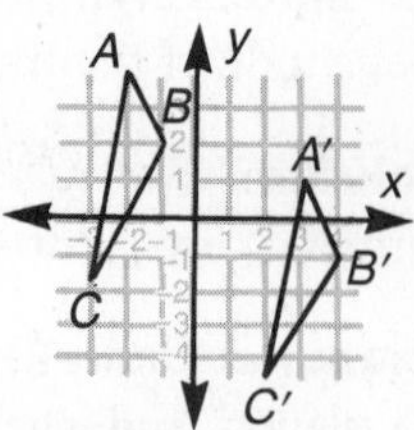

Name the inverse translation that would restore each image to $\triangle ABC$ for

14. Exercise 11. **15.** Exercise 12. **16.** Exercise 13.

17. A translation maps (6, 3) onto (−2, 5). What is the image of (−1, 4) under the same translation.

18. A translation maps the line $y = x + 5$ onto the line $y = x - 2$. Name the rule for the translation.

Oral Exercises

1. (3, −5) 2. (5, −6)
3. (−1, 1) 4. (0, 0)
5. $(x, y) \rightarrow (x - 3, y + 5)$
6. (5, 2) 7. (9, −1)
8. (10, 4) 9. (3, −4)
10. $(x, y) \rightarrow (x + 5, y + 2)$
11. $(x, y) \rightarrow (x + 5, y + 1)$
12. $(x, y) \rightarrow (x - 5, y - 3)$
13. $(x, y) \rightarrow (x + 5, y - 3)$
14. $(x, y) \rightarrow (x - 5, y - 1)$
15. $(x, y) \rightarrow (x + 5, y + 3)$
16. $(x, y) \rightarrow (x - 5, y + 3)$
17. (−9, 6)
18. $(x, y) \rightarrow (x, y - 7)$

WRITTEN EXERCISES

A. Plot each point on a rectangular coordinate plane. Then plot the image of each point under the translation with the rule $(x, y) \rightarrow (x + 4, y - 1)$. Label each image point.

1. $A(-5, 2)$ **2.** $B(0, -1)$ **3.** $C(-3, 0)$ **4.** $D(-2, 3)$

5. On a piece of graph paper, plot the parallelogram with vertices $A(-4, 4)$, $B(-3, 1)$, $C(1, 4)$, and $D(2, 1)$. Then graph its image under the translation with the rule $(x, y) \rightarrow (x + 5, y - 3)$.

A point and its image under a translation are given. State the rule for the translation that maps the point onto its image.

6. $A(0, 0)$; $A'(6, -5)$ **7.** $B(-4, 1)$; $B'(0, 4)$

8. $C(-3, 2)$; $C'(-3, 8)$ **9.** $D(6, -6)$; $D'(-1, -7)$

10. Is composition of reflecting in parallel lines commutative?

11. In a plane, what is the rule for the identity translation?

12. What is the rule for the inverse of $(x, y) \rightarrow (x + a, y + b)$?

B. Graph each line and its image under the translation with the rule $(x, y) \rightarrow (x - 4, y + 6)$.

13. $y = -3$ **14.** $x = 3$ **15.** $y = x$

16. $y = x - 2$ **17.** $y = 3x + 1$ **18.** $y = -4x - 1$

19. Compare each line in Exercises 13–18 with its image. What effect did the translation have on the slope? on the y-intercept?

State whether each of the following is preserved under translation.

20. collinearity **21.** orientation **22.** angle measure

23. betweenness **24.** parallelism **25.** distance

26. Given $A(-4, -1)$ and $B(6, 4)$, find the image of $\overline{AB}$ under the translation having the rule $(x, y) \rightarrow (x + 5, y - 2)$. Use the distance formula to show that $A'B' = AB$. Then use slopes to show that $\overline{A'B'} \parallel \overline{AB}$.

C. 27. What is the rule for the identity translation in space?

28. Name the inverse rule for $(x, y, z) \rightarrow (x + a, y + b, z + c)$.

Written Exercises

1. $A'(-1, 1)$ 2. $B'(4, -2)$

3. $C'(1, -1)$ 4. $D'(2, 2)$

5. $A'(1, 1)$, $B'(2, -2)$, $C'(6, 1)$, $D'(7, -2)$
6. $(x, y) \rightarrow (x + 6, y - 5)$
7. $(x, y) \rightarrow (x + 4, y + 3)$
8. $(x, y) \rightarrow (x, y + 6)$
9. $(x, y) \rightarrow (x - 7, y - 1)$
10. no
11. $(x, y) \rightarrow (x, y)$
12. $(x, y) \rightarrow (x - a, y - b)$

13-17. odd See *Teacher's Manual*, p. T62

14-18. even See *Selected Answers*, p. 644

19. The slope remains the same; y-intercept changes by 6 plus the value for y in the original equation when $x = 4$.

20. yes 21. yes
22. yes 23. yes
24. yes 25. yes
26. $A \rightarrow A'(1, -3)$; $B \rightarrow B'(11, 2)$; $A'B' = AB = 5\sqrt{5}$; slopes of both $= \frac{1}{2}$
27. $(x, y, z) \rightarrow (x, y, z)$
28. $(x, y, z) \rightarrow (x - a, y - b, z - c)$

SELF-QUIZ

$S = \{(0, 0), (-1, 0), (1, 1)\}$

1. Name the domain **2.** Name the range. **3.** Is S a function?

4. Explain why only one-to-one functions have inverse functions.

Give the coordinate rule for each of the following.

5. reflection in the x-axis **6.** reflection in the y-axis

7. translation 5 units upward **8.** reflection in $y = x$

9. translation 3 units to the left and 4 units downward

Are the following types of quadrilaterals symmetric about a diagonal?

10. parallelogram **11.** rectangle **12.** rhombus **13.** trapezoid

Are the following preserved by both translation and line reflection?

14. collinearity **15.** betweenness **16.** distance

17. orientation **18.** parallelism **19.** angle measure

GEOMETRY IN USE/Mirrors

You are familiar with the fact that if an object is placed in front of a mirror, its image appears to lie as far behind the mirror as the object is in front of it. Suppose $\overline{MN}$ is the edge of a plane mirror. If a ray of light from an object located at A strikes the mirror at B, it is reflected off the mirror to the eye at E. The human mind projects $\overline{EB}$ through the mirror to A'.

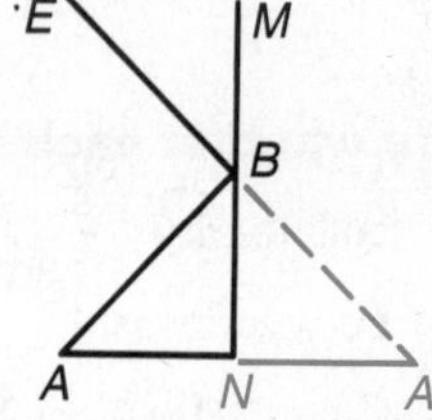

1. If you stand two feet in front of the mirror, how far behind the mirror does your reflection appear to be located?

2. If you hold a notebook in your left hand, which hand appears to be holding it in the mirror?

Self-Quiz

1. $D = \{0, 1, -1\}$
2. $R = \{0, 1\}$
3. S is a function because no two ordered pairs have the same first element.
4. If a function f is not 1:1, the relation obtained by reversing the elements of each ordered pair of f will be such that some of the ordered pairs will have the same first element.
5. $(x, y) \rightarrow (x, -y)$
6. $(x, y) \rightarrow (-x, y)$
7. $(x, y) \rightarrow (x + 5, y)$
8. $(x, y) \rightarrow (y, x)$
9. $(x, y) \rightarrow (x - 3, y - 4)$
10. no 11. no
12. yes 13. no
14. yes 15. yes
16. yes 17. no
18. yes 19. yes

Geometry in Use

1. 2 ft
2. right

15.5 Rotations

Like a translation, the next transformation is also a composition of line reflections. While a translation is a composition of two reflections in parallel lines, a **rotation** is a composition of two reflections in intersecting lines.

DEFINITIONS: rotation, center, magnitude, direction
A **rotation** is a transformation of the plane that is a composition of two reflections in intersecting lines. The point of intersection of the lines of reflection is the **center of rotation.** If point P is the center and A' the image of A under rotation, then the **magnitude of the rotation** is $\theta = m\angle APA'$. The **direction of a rotation** is the direction from the first line of reflection to the second. If the rotation is counterclockwise, then the magnitude is positive. If the rotation is clockwise, then the magnitude is negative.

Unless otherwise stated, it will be assumed that all rotations in this lesson are in a counterclockwise direction. The Greek letter θ (theta) will be used to refer to the magnitude of the rotation. The notation for a rotation is $r[(x, y), \theta]$ where x and y are the coordinates of the center of the rotation, P, and θ is the magnitude of rotation.

In this figure, $\triangle ABC$ is first reflected in the line $y = x$. Its image is then reflected in the y-axis. The lines of reflection intersect at $P(0, 0)$, and a protractor verifies that $m\angle APA'' = 90$, which is the magnitude. (Also, $m\angle APA'' = m\angle BPB'' = m\angle CPC'' = \theta$.) Therefore, $\triangle A''B''C''$ is the image of $\triangle ABC$ under a rotation with center $P(0, 0)$ and magnitude 90, written $r[(0, 0), 90]$. A rotation of 90 is often called a **quarter-turn.**

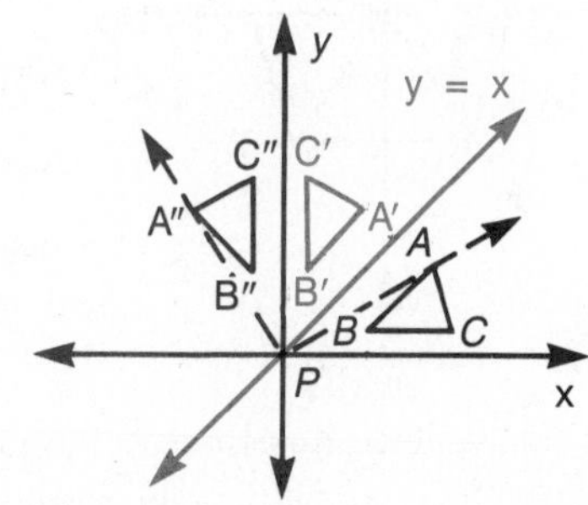

Rotation preserves lines, betweenness of points, distance, and angle measure. Rotation also preserves the orientation of three noncollinear points. The magnitude of a rotation is always twice the measure of the right or acute angle determined by the lines of reflection. It follows that any pair of lines of reflection making the same angle at P determine the same rotation.

OBJECTIVE

Identify rotations and determine their centers, magnitudes, and directions.

TEACHER'S NOTES

See p. T41

MIXED REVIEW

1. What is the volume of a sphere with a diameter of 6? 36π
2. Can a circle have the same number for its radius as it has for its area? yes; $\frac{1}{\pi}$
3. What is the diameter of a circle whose circumference and area are the same number? 4
4. Solve $4x - (x + 5) = -18$. $-4\frac{1}{3}$
5. Solve $x^2 - 8x + 15 = 0$. 3, 5

TEACHER'S RESEARCH MASTERS

Practice Master 48, Part 1

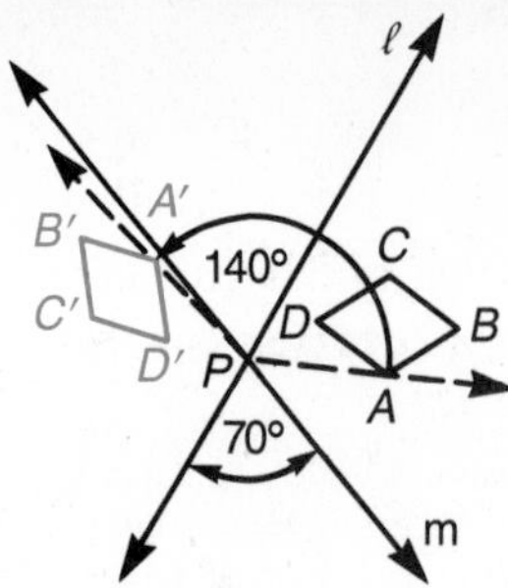

In this figure, the angle determined by the lines of reflection l and m is 70. Therefore, the magnitude of the rotation is 140, and the image of ▱$ABCD$ is as shown.

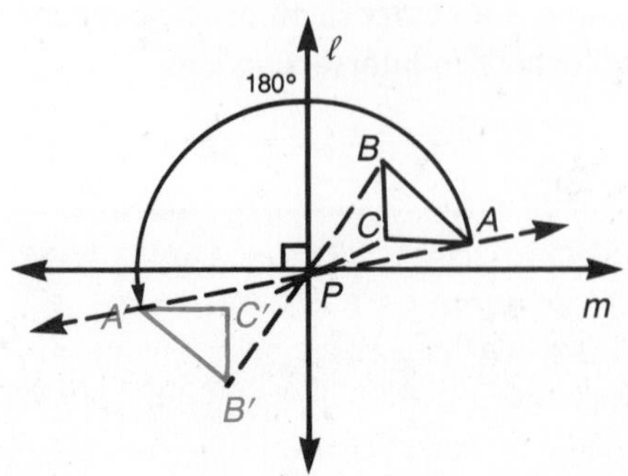

If the two lines of reflection are perpendicular, the rotation will have a magnitude of 180 and is called a **half-turn** or a **reflection in a point.** The figure illustrates a half-turn with center at the origin.

Usually, only the center of the rotation is a fixed point, but a rotation of 360 (or a multiple of 360) results in every point being its own image. This is the identity transformation for rotation.

Earlier you learned that a figure is symmetric with respect to a line if it is its own image under reflection in the line. Similarly, a figure may be its own image under a rotation about a point. Such a symmetry is a **rotational symmetry,** as illustrated in the next figure.

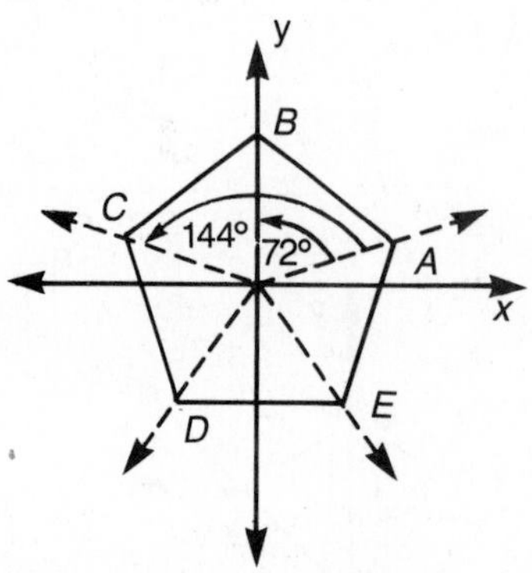

Regular pentagon $ABCDE$ has its center at the origin. Rotations about (0, 0) with magnitudes of 72, 144, 216, 288, and 360 map the pentagon onto itself. A regular pentagon therefore is said to have five rotational symmetries about its center.

The last figure illustrates that a composition of rotations about a given point results in a rotation about that point. Quadrilateral $A'B'C'D'$ is the image of quadrilateral $ABCD$ under $r[(0, 0), 75]$, and quadrilateral $A''B''C''D''$ is the image of quadrilateral $A'B'C'D'$ under $r[(0, 0), 55]$. Is quadrilateral $A''B''C''D''$ the image of □$ABCD$ under $r[(0, 0), 130]$? Yes. Thus composition of rotations about a given point is commutative.

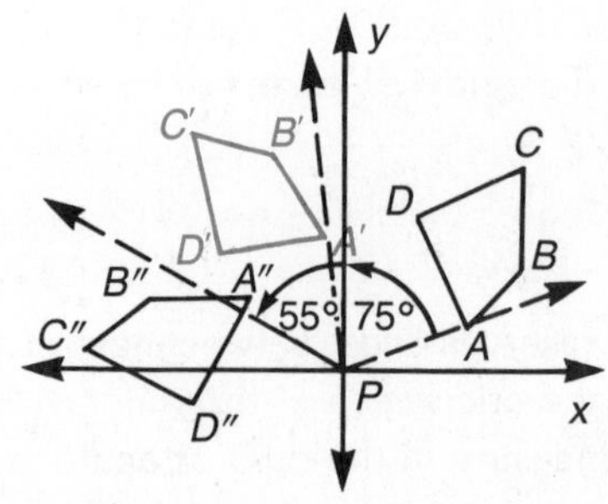

ORAL EXERCISES

State whether each of the following figures are symmetric about *P*.

1.

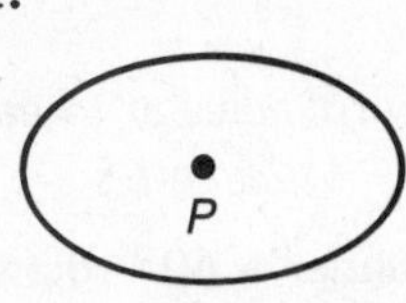

2.

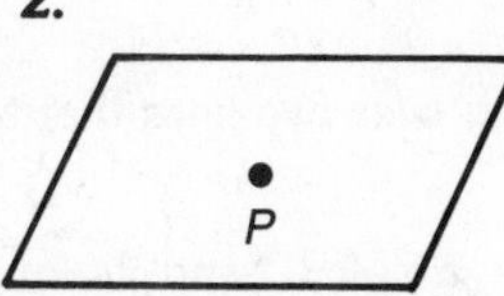

3.

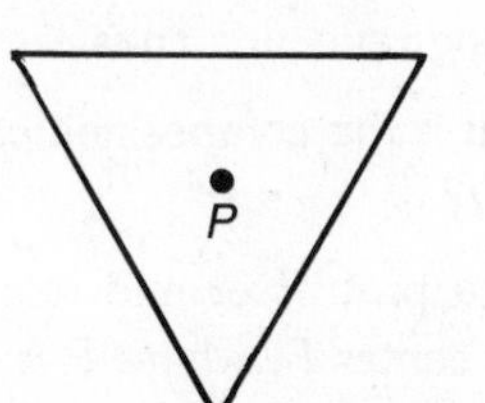

4.

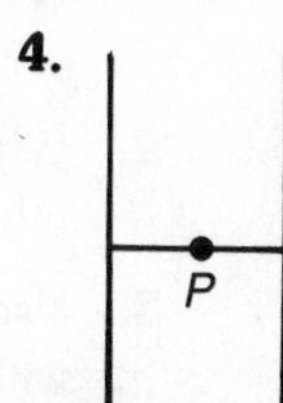

State whether each of the following figures are their own images under a quarter-turn about *P*.

5.

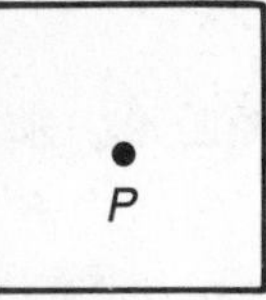

6.

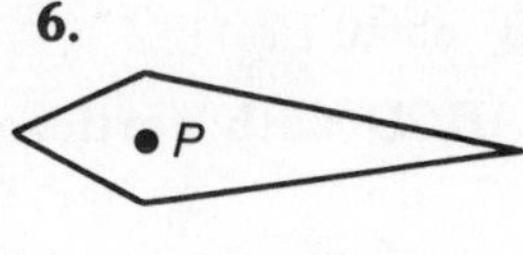

7.

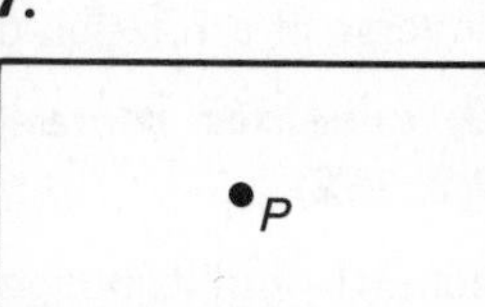

8.

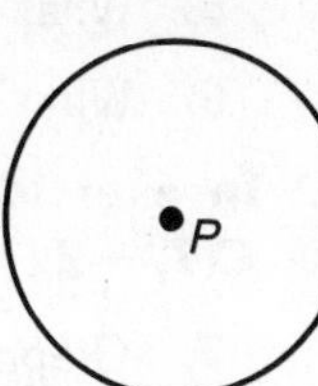

Name the rotation that maps $\triangle ABC$ onto $\triangle A'B'C'$.

9.

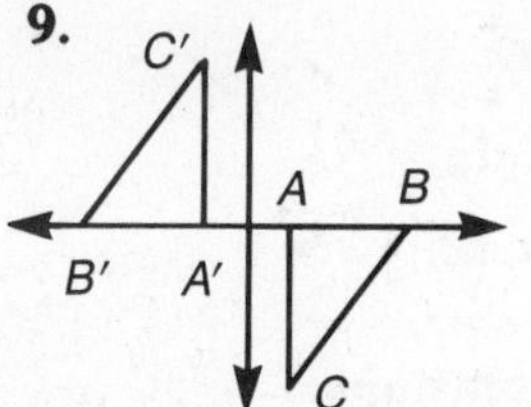

10.

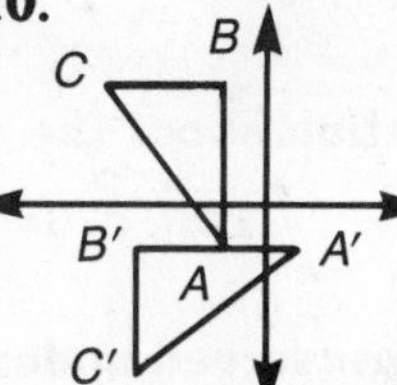

11.

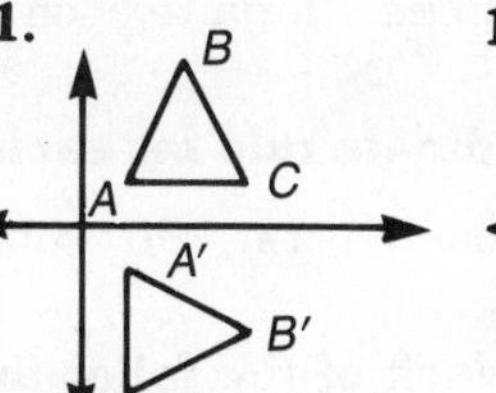

12.

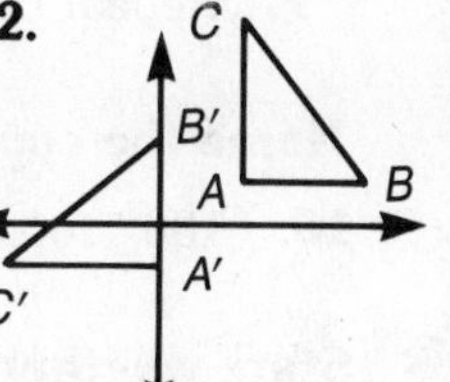

Name all of the rotational symmetries for each figure.

13.

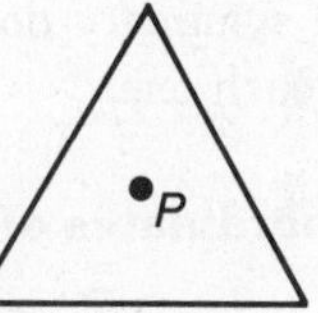

14.

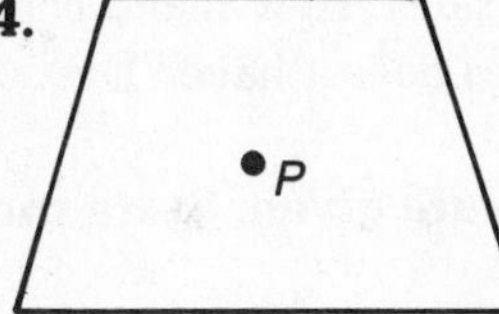

15.

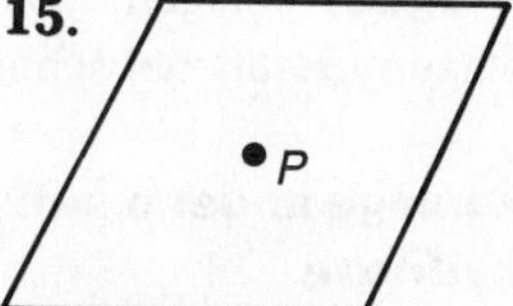

16.

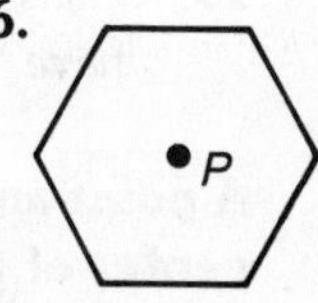

Suppose that two lines *l* and *m* intersect at point *P*, forming an angle of 40°. Successively reflecting over the lines determines a rotation.

17. What is the center of the rotation?

18. What is the magnitude of the rotation?

19. What is the direction of the rotation?

ASSIGNMENT GUIDE

Minimum 1-12
Regular 1-19
Maximum 1-11 odd, 13-19, 21-23

Oral Exercises

1. yes
2. yes
3. yes
4. yes
5. yes
6. no
7. no
8. yes
9. *r*[(0, 0), 180]
10. *r*[(0, 0), 90]
11. *r*[(0, 0), 270]
12. *r*[(2, −1), 90]
13. *r*[*P*, 0], *r*[*P*, 120], *r*[*P*, 240]
14. *r*[*P*, 0]
15. *r*[*P*, 0], *r*[*P*, 180]
16. *r*[*P*, 0], *r*[*P*, 60], *r*[*P*, 120], *r*[*P*, 180], *r*[*P*, 240], *r*[*P*, 300]
17. *P*
18. 80°
19. same as from the 1st reflection line to the 2nd

Written Exercises

1. The center is the point where the two lines intersect. The magnitude is $m\angle APA'$, where P is the center and $A \to A'$. The direction is the direction from the first line to the second.
2. a half-turn (rotation of 180°) about the point where the lines intersect
3. 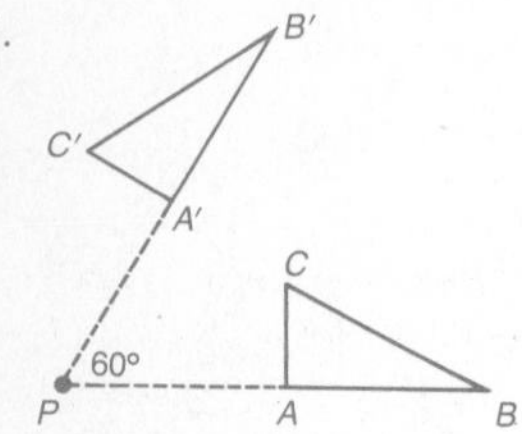

4. Yes, $r[P, 70]$
5. 360° or any multiple of 360°
6. $r[P, 260]$
7. $A'(-2, 0)$, $B'(-7, 0)$, $C'(-7, 2)$, $D'(-2, 2)$
8. $A'(0, 2)$, $B'(0, 7)$, $C'(2, 7)$, $D'(2, 2)$
9. $A'(0, -2)$, $B'(0, -7)$, $C'(-2, -7)$, $D'(-2, -2)$
10. $(x, y) \to (-x, -y)$
11. $(x, y) \to (-y, x)$
12. $(x, y) \to (y, -x)$
13. yes 14. yes
15. yes 16. yes
17. yes 18. yes
19. n; n; $r[P, 0]$, $r[P, \frac{360}{n}]$, $r[P, 2(\frac{360}{n})]$, $r[P, 3(\frac{360}{n})]$, ... $r[P, (n-1)(\frac{360}{n})]$
20. $(0, -3)$ 21. $(1, 3)$
22. $A'(-2, 0)$, $B'(-7, 0)$, $C'(-7, 2)$, $D'(-2, 2)$; $A''(2, 4)$, $B''(7, 4)$, $C''(7, 2)$, $D''(2, 2)$; translation $(x, y) \to (x, y + 4)$
23. No; $A''(2, -4)$, $B''(7, -4)$, $C''(7, -6)$, $D''(2, -6)$; translation $(x, y) \to (x, y - 4)$; not commutative

WRITTEN EXERCISES

A. **1.** A rotation is the composition of reflections in two intersecting lines. How are the center, magnitude, and direction of the rotation determined when the two intersecting reflection lines are known?

2. What is the composition of reflecting over two lines that are perpendicular to each other?

3. Use a protractor and ruler to draw a $\triangle ABC$ and its image under a 60° rotation with center P, where P is in the exterior of $\triangle ABC$.

4. Is the composition of a 40° rotation about P and a 30° rotation about P a rotation? If so, what are its center and magnitude?

5. What is the magnitude of the identity rotation about a point P?

6. What is the inverse of a rotation of 100° about P?

B. **In exercises 7-9, consider rectangle $ABCD$ with vertices $A(2, 0)$, $B(7, 0)$, $C(7, -2)$, and $D(2, -2)$.**

7. Graph the rectangle and its image under a half-turn about the origin, and name the coordinates of A', B', C', and D'.

8. Repeat Exercise 7 for a rotation of 90°.

9. Repeat Exercise 7 for a rotation of 270°.

Name the coordinate rule for each rotation about the origin.

10. 180° rotation **11.** 90° rotation **12.** 270° rotation

State whether each of the following is preserved under rotations.

13. collinearity **14.** orientation **15.** angle measure

16. betweenness **17.** parallelism **18.** distance

19. Consider a regular polygon having n sides. How many lines of symmetry does it have? How many rotational symmetries does it have? Describe each one.

A point and its image under a half-turn are given. State the coordinates of the center of the half-turn.

20. $A(3, -4)$; $A'(-3, -2)$ **21.** $B(4, -1)$; $B'(-2, 7)$

C. **22.** Using rectangle $ABCD$ again, with vertices as given in Exercise 7, draw the rectangle and its image $A'B'C'D'$ under a half-turn about the origin. Next draw the image of $A'B'C'D'$ under a half-turn about $(0, 2)$ and call it $A''B''C''D''$. Finally describe the transformation that maps $ABCD$ onto $A''B''C''D''$.

23. Repeat the directions for Exercise 22, reversing the order in which the half-turns are composed. Are the results the same? Is composition of rotations commutative?

15.6 Isometries

Another transformation of the plane is the **glide reflection.** Like the translation and the rotation, it is a composition of line reflections.

> **DEFINITION: glide reflection**
> A **glide reflection** is a transformation of the plane that is a composition of a line reflection and a translation in a direction parallel to the line of reflection.

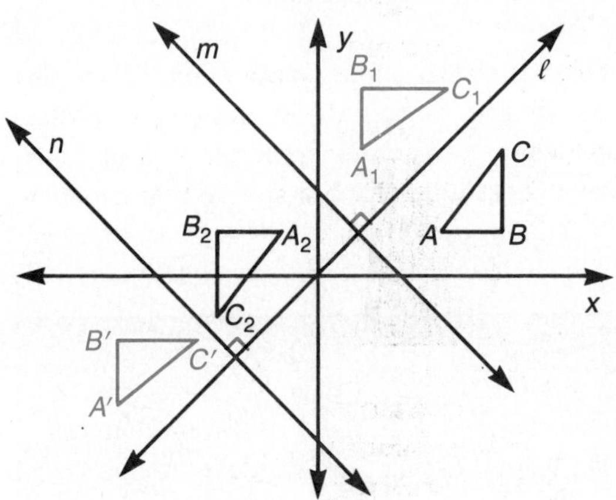

In the figure, $\triangle ABC$ is first reflected in l. This image is then translated in a direction parallel to l by reflection in m and n, where m and n are both perpendicular to l. The image of $\triangle ABC$ under this glide reflection is $\triangle A'B'C'$. The same image would result if $\triangle ABC$ were first translated and then reflected.

A glide reflection preserves collinearity, betweenness of points, distance, and angle measure. The orientation of noncollinear points is reversed under a glide reflection.

You have now examined four transformations of the plane: line reflection, translation, rotation, and glide reflection. Each of these transformations is distance-preserving, and each is either a reflection or a composition of reflections. Such transformations are called **isometries.**

> **DEFINITION: isometry**
> An **isometry** is a line reflection or a composition of line reflections.

OBJECTIVES

Identify glide reflections and isometries.
Identify Abelian groups.

TEACHER'S NOTES

See p. T41

MIXED REVIEW

1. In $\frac{3}{x^2 - x - 2}$, x is never equal to ______. 2, −1
2. Find the area of a regular hexagon with an edge of 8. $96\sqrt{3}$
3. Solve $x + y = 7$
   $2x + 2y = 12$.
   parallel lines
4. Multiply $\sqrt{50} \cdot \sqrt{8}$. 20
5. $\frac{1}{\sqrt{3} - \sqrt{2}} = ?$ $\sqrt{3} + \sqrt{2}$

TEACHER'S RESOURCE MASTERS

Practice Master 48, Part 2

Since the composition of two isometries is also an isometry, the set of isometries is closed under composition. It can be shown that composing an odd number of line reflections produces a line reflection or a glide reflection; composing an even number of line reflections produces a translation or rotation.

The following properties of geometric figures are preserved by isometries:

1. collinearity of points
2. betweenness of points.
3. distance between points
4. angle measure
5. parallelism of lines
6. perpendicularity of lines

It follows that two figures are congruent if and only if one maps onto the other under an isometry. In fact, every isometry is a composition of at most three reflections. Therefore, a figure can be mapped onto a congruent figure in three or fewer reflections.

It has already been stated that the set of isometries is closed under composition. It can also be shown that the composition of isometries is associative. Since each isometry is a transformation, it follows that each has an inverse and an identity transformation $(x, y) \rightarrow (x, y)$. Thus, the set of isometries together with the operation of composition form a special mathematical system called a **group.**

DEFINITIONS: group, Abelian group
A **group** is a mathematical system consisting of a set of elements subject to one binary operation and having these properties: (1) the system is closed under the operation; (2) the operation obeys the associative law; (3) the system has an identity element; and (4) each element has an inverse. A group that also has the commutative property is an **Abelian group**.

The notation $(S, +)$ means the set of elements S subject to the operation of addition.

Example: Given $A = \{0, 1\}$. Is $(A, \cdot)$ a group? Is it an Abelian group?

Solution: The operation is multiplication. A is closed under multiplication, it is associative, and it has an identity element (1), but each element does not have an inverse. No multiplicative inverse exists for 0. A is therefore not a group.

Example: Given $A = \{0, 1\}$, is $(A, +)$ a group?

Solution: A is not closed under addition ($1 + 1$ is not in A), and the element 1 does not have an inverse in A. Therefore, A is not a group.

DEFINITION: symmetry set
The set of transformations that map a geometric figure onto itself is called the **symmetry set** of the figure.

The nonequilateral isosceles triangle at the left has two elements in its symmetry set: the identity transformation (e), and a reflection in $l(r_l)$, where l is the perpendicular bisector of the base.

Example: Is $A = \{e, r_l\}$ a group under composition?

Solution: Let ∘ represent the operation of composition. (A, ∘) produces the elements $e \circ r_l$, $e \circ e$, $r_l \circ e$, and $r_l \circ r_l$. As shown in the table, the compositions form a group. Because the operations are commutative, this set of two isometries is also an Abelian group.

∘	e	r_ℓ
e	e	r_ℓ
r_ℓ	r_ℓ	e

ASSIGNMENT GUIDE

Day 1
Minimum 1-11 odd
Regular 1-10
Maximum 1-10
Day 2
Minimum 2-12 even
Regular 11-15
Maximum 11-17, 18

ORAL EXERCISES

1. Define *isometry*.

State whether each of the following are isometries.

2. rotations
3. line reflections
4. translations
5. glide reflections

State whether each of the following are preserved by all isometries.

6. collinearity
7. orientation
8. angle measure
9. betweenness
10. parallelism
11. distance

12. Is the transformation having the coordinate rule $(x, y) \rightarrow (2x, 2y)$ an isometry? Explain.

Do the following properties hold for any group?

13. closure
14. identity
15. associative
16. commutative
17. inverse

Oral Exercises

1. An isometry is a line reflection or a composition of line reflections.
2. yes 3. yes
4. yes 5. yes
6. yes 7. no
8. yes 9. yes
10. yes 11. yes
12. No; it does not preserve distance.
13. yes 14. yes
15. yes 16. no
17. yes

Let W = {whole numbers}, Z = {integers}, and R = {real numbers}. State whether each of the following are groups.

18. $(W, +)$ **19.** $(Z, +)$ **20.** $(R, +)$ **21.** $(R, -)$

22. $(W, \div)$ **23.** $(Z, \cdot)$ **24.** $(R, \cdot)$ **25.** $(R - \{0\}, \cdot)$

26. Define *Abelian group.*

27. Is $(R, +)$ an Abelian group, where R = {real numbers}?

18. no 19. yes
20. yes 21. yes
22. no 23. no
24. no 25. yes
26. commutative group
27. yes

WRITTEN EXERCISES

A. Fill in the blank(s) to make the sentence true in Exercises 1–12.

1. A plane transformation that preserves distance is called a(n) _____.

2. A group is a mathematical system for which the following properties hold: _____, _____, _____, and _____.

3. A group for which the commutative property also holds is called a(n) _____ group.

4. Every isometry maps a figure onto a(n) _____ figure.

B. **5.** A glide reflection is the composition of a line reflection and a(n) _____ that is _____ to the line of reflection.

6. The composition of an even number of line reflections is either a(n) _____ or a(n) _____.

7. The composition of an odd number of line reflections is either a(n) _____ or a(n) _____.

8. The composition of two translations is a(n) _____.

9. The composition of two rotations about the same point is a(n) _____.

10. The composition of two rotations about different points is either a(n) _____ or a(n) _____.

11. If two figures are congruent, then one can be mapped onto the other by a composition of at most _____ line reflections.

12. The isometry that maps every point onto itself is the _____.

C. How many isometries are in the symmetry set of each figure?

13. parallelogram **14.** square **15.** equilateral triangle

16. rhombus **17.** circle **18.** regular pentagon

Written Exercises

1. isometry
2. closure, associative, identity; inverse
3. Abelian
4. congruent
5. translation; parallel
6. translation; rotation
7. line reflection; glide reflection
8. translation
9. rotation
10. translation; rotation
11. 3
12. identity
13. 2 14. 8
15. 3 16. 4
17. infinite 18. 10

15.7 Dilations

Not every transformation of the plane is an isometry. An example is a **dilation.**

DEFINITIONS: dilation image, center, magnitude
Given a point P in the plane and a positive real number k, the **dilation image** of $A \neq P$ is the point A' on $\overrightarrow{PA}$ such that $PA' = k \cdot PA$. If $A = P$, then the image and preimage coincide. The point P is called the **center** of the dilation, and k is the **magnitude.** A dilation with center $P(x, y)$ and magnitude k is written $d[(x, y), k]$.

In the figure, the center of the dilation is $P(0, -4)$. By the distance formula, $PA = \sqrt{73}$ and $PA' = 2\sqrt{73}$. Thus, the magnitude is 2. The distance formula will verify that $PB' = 2 \cdot PB$ and $PC' = 2 \cdot PC$.

Under $d[(0, -4), 2]$, the image of $\overleftrightarrow{AC}$ is $\overleftrightarrow{A'C'}$, and $\overleftrightarrow{AC} \parallel \overleftrightarrow{A'C'}$. Also, $A'C' = 2 \cdot AC$, $A'B' = 2 \cdot AB$, and $B'C' = 2 \cdot BC$. You could also show that $m\angle ABC = m\angle A'B'C'$, $m\angle BAC = m\angle B'A'C'$, and $m\angle ACB = m\angle A'C'B'$. Thus, $\triangle ABC \sim \triangle A'B'C'$. Finally, the image of $\overleftrightarrow{PA}$ is $\overleftrightarrow{PA}$, the image of $\overleftrightarrow{PC}$ is $\overleftrightarrow{PC}$, and the image of $\overleftrightarrow{PB}$ is $\overleftrightarrow{PB}$.

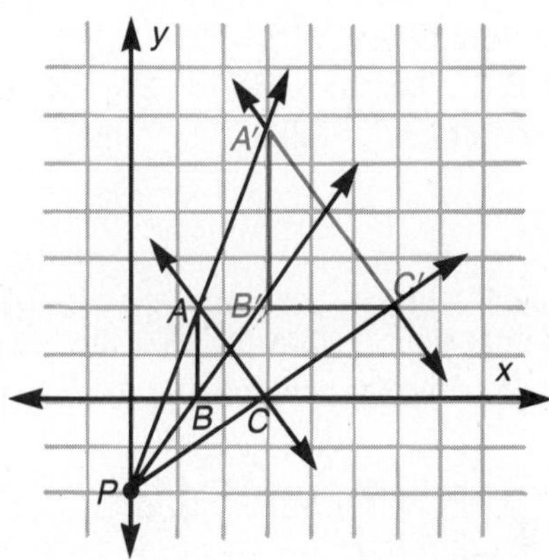

To summarize the properties of a dilation:

1. The image of the center P is P, and the center is the only fixed point.
2. All lines containing the center are their own images and are thus fixed lines.
3. Under a dilation with magnitude k, the distance $A'B'$ between the images of A and B is $k \cdot AB$.
4. Dilation preserves collinearity, betweenness of points, angle measure, and the orientation of noncollinear points.
5. Dilation is a *similarity transformation.*

OBJECTIVE

Identify dilations and determine their centers and magnitudes.

TEACHER'S NOTES

See p. T41

MIXED REVIEW

1. Simplify $\frac{16x^2y^4}{4x^3y^3}$. $\frac{4y}{x}$
2. Solve $\frac{4}{x+3} = \frac{6}{x-2}$. $x = -13$
3. If the area ratio of two circles is 9:49, what is the ratio of their diameters? 3:7
4. Multiply $\sqrt{27} \cdot \sqrt{12}$. 18
5. $\frac{1}{\sqrt{8}} =$ ______. $\frac{\sqrt{2}}{4}$

TEACHER'S RESOURCE MASTERS

Practice Master 49, Part 1

Example: Determine the image of $\triangle ABC$ under $d[(0, 0), \frac{1}{2}]$.

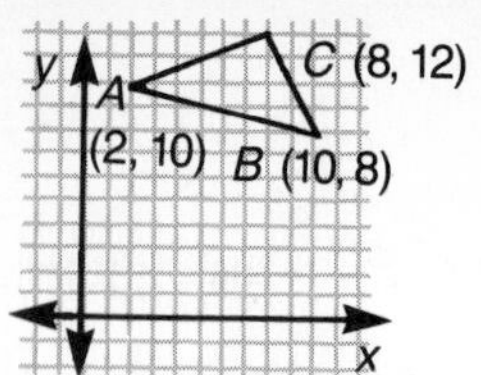

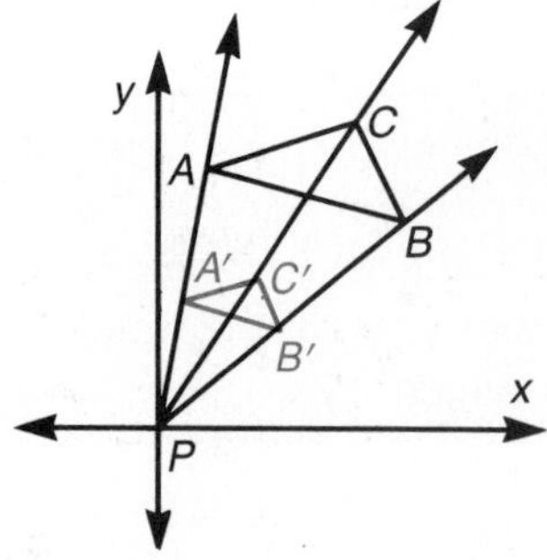

Solution: Since the magnitude is $\frac{1}{2}$, A' will be the midpoint of $\overline{PA}$, B' the midpoint of $\overline{PB}$, and C' the midpoint of $\overline{PC}$. By the midpoint formula, the coordinates of A', B', and C' are (1, 5), (5, 4), and (4, 6), respectively. Thus, $\triangle A'B'C'$ is the image of $\triangle ABC$.

Example: $\triangle XYZ$ and its image $\triangle X'Y'Z'$ under a dilation are given. Determine the center and magnitude of the dilation.

Solution: Since $X'Z' = 3 \cdot XZ$, the magnitude is 3. Therefore, $PX' = 3 \cdot PX$, making the center $(-2, -3)$.

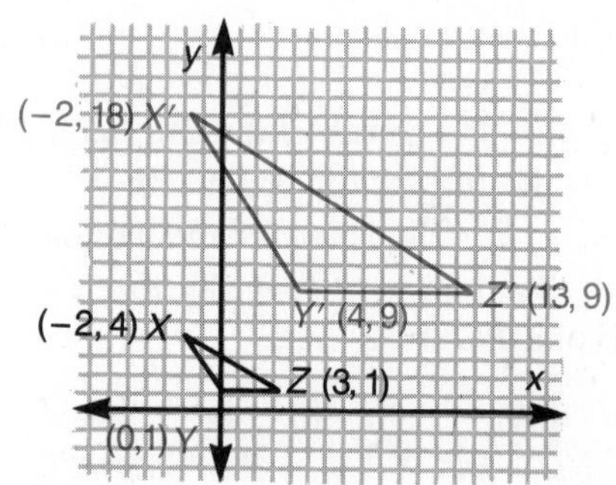

The next figures illustrate that the composition of two dilations with a given center is also a dilation with that center.

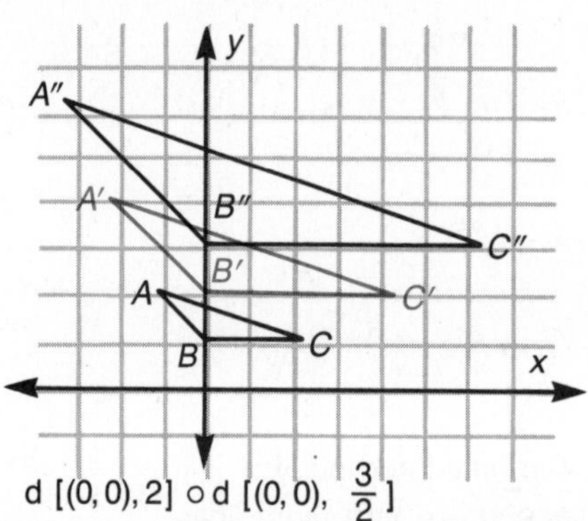

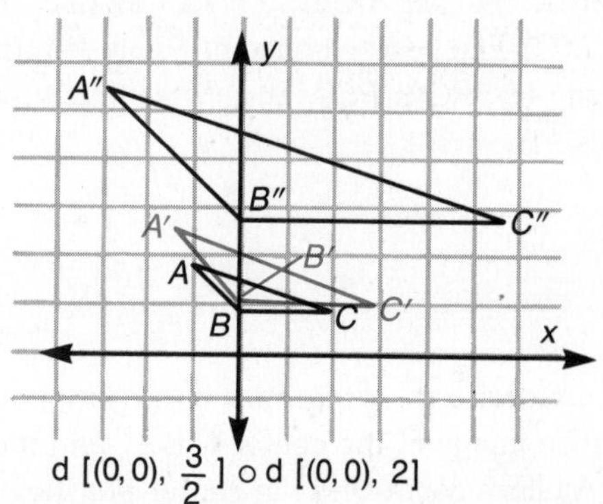

The result of each composition is $d[(0, 0), 3]$. Now examine the same composition in terms of coordinate rules: $d_{3/2}[(0, 0), \frac{3}{2}] = (x, y) \rightarrow (\frac{3}{2}x, \frac{3}{2}y)$, and $d_2[(0, 0), 2] = (x, y) \rightarrow (2x, 2y)$. You can see that $d_2 \circ d_{3/2} = d_{3/2} \circ d_2$, or $(x, y) \rightarrow (3x, 3y)$. In general, the composition of two dilations having the same center and magnitudes a and b respectively is given by $(x, y) \rightarrow (abx, aby)$.

ORAL EXERCISES

Name the dilation that maps $\overline{AB}$ onto $\overline{A'B'}$, given that $\overline{AB} \parallel \overline{A'B'}$.

1.

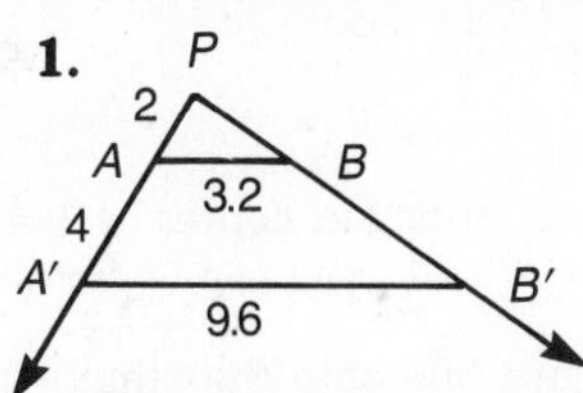

2.

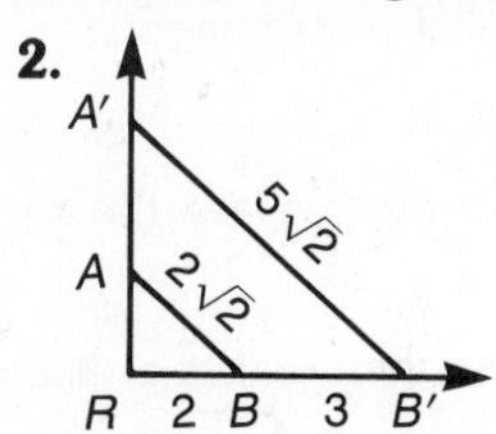

3.

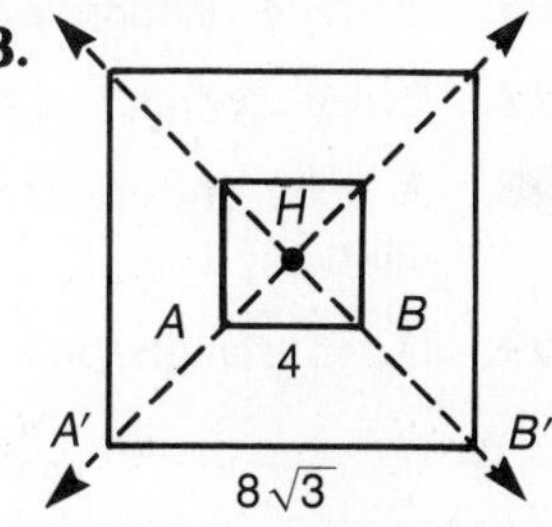

4.

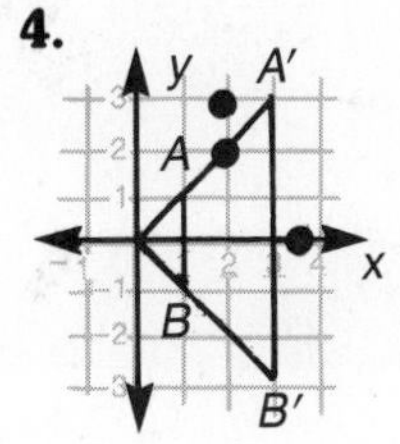

5.

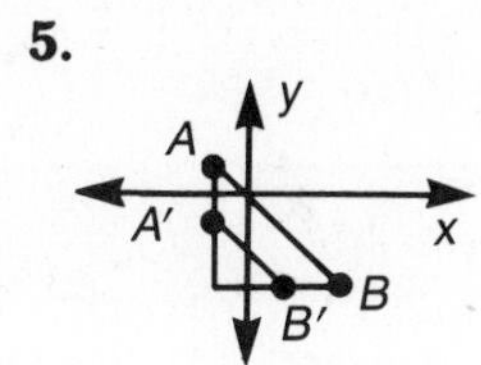

6.

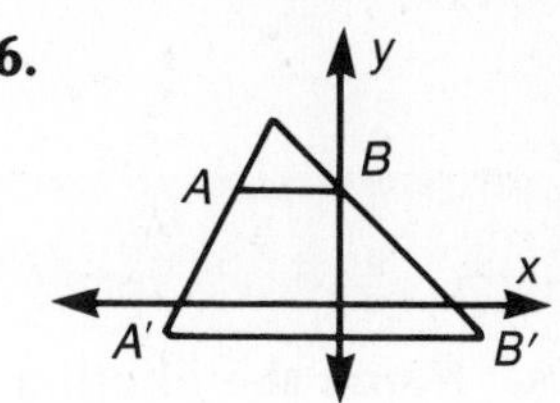

Name the image of each point under the dilation that has the coordinate rule $(x, y) \to (5x, 5y)$.

7. $A(0, 0)$ **8.** $B(4, 0)$ **9.** $C(0, -3)$ **10.** $D(-6, 7)$

Name the preimage of each point under the dilation having the coordinate rule $(x, y) \to (\frac{1}{2}x, \frac{1}{2}y)$.

11. $A'(0, 0)$ **12.** $B'(4, 0)$ **13.** $C'(0, -3)$ **14.** $D'(-6, 7)$

A point and its image under a dilation with center (0, 0) are given. State the coordinate rule for the dilation.

15. $A(5, -2)$; $A'(10, -4)$

16. $C(0, \pi)$; $C'(0, \frac{2\pi}{9})$

17. $B(-7, 0)$; $B'(-49, 0)$

18. $D(\sqrt{2}, -3)$; $D'(\frac{\sqrt{2}}{3}, -1)$

19. What is the coordinate rule for the identity dilation?

20. What is the coordinate rule for the inverse of a dilation with center at the origin and magnitude $\frac{3}{5}$?

Indicate whether each statement is true or false.

21. Dilations map figures onto similar figures.

22. The center of a dilation is its only fixed point.

ASSIGNMENT GUIDE

Minimum 1-15 odd
Regular 1-19 odd
Maximum 1-13 odd, 15-21

Oral Exercises

1. $[P, 3]$ 2. $[R, \frac{5}{2}]$
3. $[H, 2\sqrt{3}]$ 4. $[(0, 0), 3]$
5. $[(-1, -3), \frac{1}{2}]$
6. $[(-2, 5), 3]$
7. $A'(0, 0)$
8. $B'(20, 0)$
9. $C'(0, -15)$
10. $D'(-30, 35)$
11. $A(0, 0)$ 12. $B(8, 0)$
13. $C(0, -6)$ 14. $D(-12, 14)$
15. $(x, y) \to (2x, 2y)$
16. $(x, y) \to (\frac{2}{9}x, \frac{2}{9}y)$
17. $(x, y) \to (7x, 7y)$
18. $(x, y) \to (\frac{1}{3}x, \frac{1}{3}y)$
19. $(x, y) \to (x, y)$
20. $(x, y) \to (\frac{5}{3}x, \frac{5}{3}y)$
21. T
22. T (excluding the identity)

23. T 24. F

25. T 26. T

27. T 28. F

29. F

23. Dilations map angles onto congruent angles.

24. Dilations map segments onto congruent segments.

25. The magnitude of a dilation must be a positive number.

26. Under a dilation, a line is parallel to its image.

27. Every dilation is a transformation.

28. A point and its image under a dilation are the same distance from the center of the dilation.

29. If two triangles are similar, then there exists a dilation that maps one onto the other.

Written Exercises

1. $d[P, 2]$

2. $d[D, \frac{4}{11}]$

3. $d[A, \frac{7}{3}]$

4. $A'(0, 0)$, $B'(8, 0)$, $C'(0, -6)$

5. $A'(-3, 3)$, $B'(-12, 3)$, $C(-6, -9)$

6. $A'(1, -3)$, $B'(5, -3)$, $C'(3, 1)$

7. $A'(5, 0)$, $B'(1, -4)$, $C'(1, 6)$

8. $A'(-18, 0)$, $B'(-9, -12)$, $C'(-9, 0)$. No; it is a composition of the dilation $d[(0, 0), 3]$ and the rotation $r[(0, 0), 180]$.

9. $P'(-1, 9)$, $Q'(-1, -3)$, $R'(2, -3)$. not a dilation; does not produce a similar △

10. $D[P, \frac{1}{k}]$

WRITTEN EXERCISES

A. Name the dilation that maps △*ABC* onto △*A′B′C′*.

1.

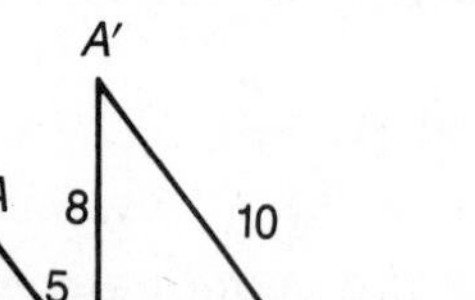

2.

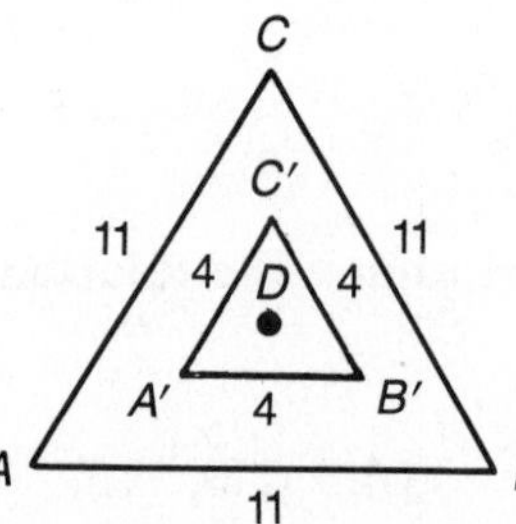

3.

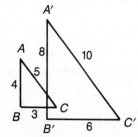

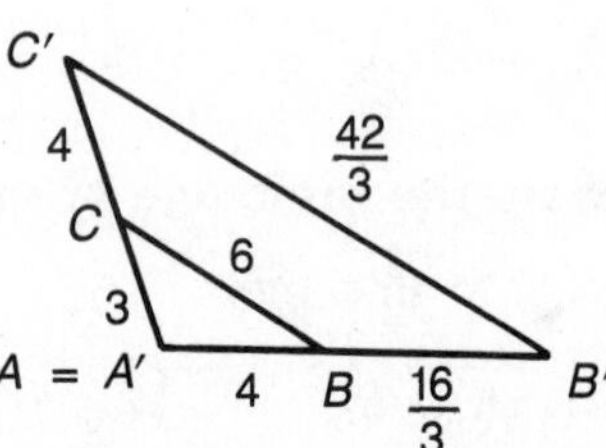

Plot △*ABC*. Then graph its image under the given dilation.

4. $A(0, 0)$, $B(4, 0)$, $C(0, -3)$; $d[(0, 0), 2]$

5. $A(-1, 1)$, $B(-4, 1)$, $C(-2, -3)$; $d[(0, 0), 3]$

6. $A(-1, -5)$, $B(7, -5)$, $C(3, 3)$; $d[(3, -1), \frac{1}{2}]$

7. $A(1, 0)$, $B(-1, -2)$, $C(-1, 3)$; $d[(-3, 0), 2]$

8. Plot △*ABC* with vertices $A(6, 0)$, $B(3, 4)$, and $C(3, 0)$. Then graph its image under the transformation having the coordinate rule $(x, y) \to (-3x, -3y)$. Is it a dilation? Explain.

9. Plot △*PQR* with vertices $P(-1, 3)$, $Q(-1, -1)$, and $R(2, -1)$. Then graph its image under the transformation having the coordinate rule $(x, y) \to (x, 3y)$. Is it a dilation? Explain.

10. What is the inverse of $d[P, k]$?

B. Graph each line and its image under the dilation $d[(0, 0), 3]$. Then state the equation of each image line.

11. $y = 2$ **12.** $y = x$

13. $y = -3x + 2$ **14.** $y = \frac{1}{2}x - 1$

15. Graph the line $y = x + 2$ and its image under the dilation $d[(0, 0), 2]$. What effect does the dilation have on the slope of the line? on its y-intercept?

The dilation $d[(0, 0)\ 4]$ maps $\triangle ABC$ onto $\triangle A'B'C'$.

16. What is the ratio of the perimeters of the triangles?

17. What is the ratio of the areas of the triangles?

C. The figure below illustrates a dilation in space. Suppose $d[P, 3]$ maps the smaller rectangular prism onto the larger one.

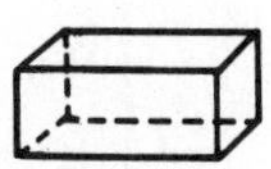

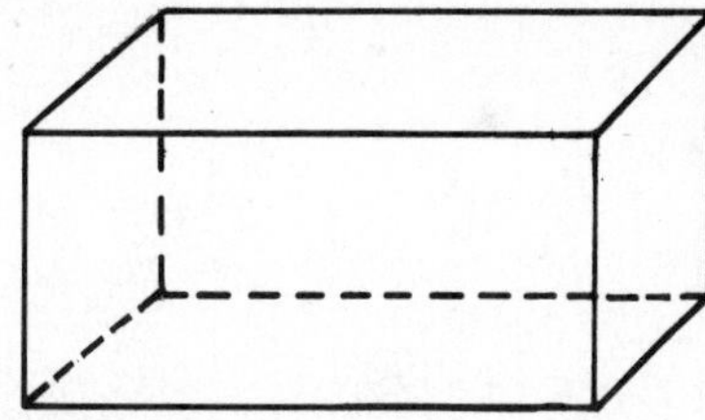

18. What is the ratio of the volumes of the prisms?

19. What is the ratio of the surface areas of the prisms?

Under the dilation $d[(0, 0), k]$, $P(x_1, y_1) \to P'(kx_1, ky_1)$ and $Q(x_2, y_2) \to Q'(kx_2, ky_2)$.

20. Use the distance formula to prove that $P'Q' = k(PQ)$.

21. Use slopes to prove that $\overline{P'Q'} \parallel \overline{PQ}$.

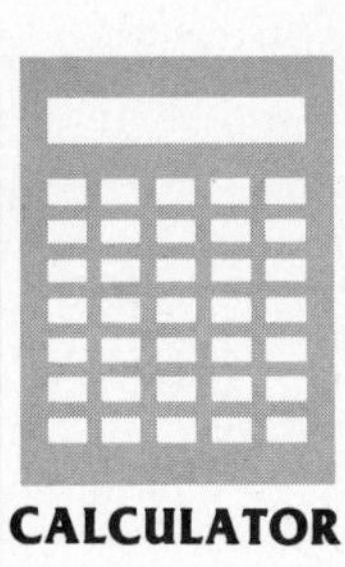

Suppose we could wrap a band around the earth (assuming it is a perfect sphere) at the equator. The band would have a circumference of roughly 25,000 miles and a radius of about 4000 miles. Now suppose we enlarge the band by 6 feet so that it stands out slightly from the sphere. About how far would it stand out? Can you do this problem without using 25,000 or 4000?

11. $y = 6$

12. $y = x$

13. $y = -3x + 6$

14. $y = \frac{1}{2}x - 3$

15. The slope of the image is the same as the slope of its preimage. The y-intercept of the image is 2 times the y-intercept of the preimage.

16. 1:4 17. 1:16

18. 1:27 19. 1:9

20.
$PQ = \sqrt{(x_2 - x_1)^2 + (y_2 - y_1)^2}$
$P'Q'$
$= \sqrt{(kx_2 + kx_1)^2 + (ky_2 - ky_1)^2}$
$= \sqrt{k^2(x_2 - x_1)^2 + k^2(y_2 - y_1)^2}$
$= \sqrt{k^2[(x_2 - x_1)^2 + (y_2 - y_1)^2]}$
$= k\sqrt{(x_2 - x_1)^2 + (y_2 - y_1)^2}$

21. slope of $\overline{PQ} = \frac{y_2 - y_1}{x_2 - x_1}$
slope of $\overline{P'Q'} = \frac{ky_2 - ky_1}{kx_2 - kx_1}$
$= \frac{k(y_2 - y_1)}{k(x_2 - x_1)}$
$= \frac{y_2 - y_1}{x_2 - x_1}$
Since the slopes are equal, $\overline{P'Q'} \parallel PQ$.

Calculator

1 ft

Yes; $r = \frac{c}{2\pi}$; $r' = \frac{c+6}{2\pi} = 0.96 \approx 1$ ft

OBJECTIVE

Identify similarity transformations and their properties.

TEACHER'S NOTES

See p. T41

MIXED REVIEW

1. Find the volume of a cone with a radius of 3 and a height of 4. 12π
2. Subtract $\frac{6}{x-2} - \frac{3}{x+2}$. $\frac{3x+18}{(x-2)(x+2)}$
3. Solve $x^2 + bx + c = 0$. $x = \frac{-b \pm \sqrt{b^2 - 4c}}{2}$
4. Solve $(2x - 3)(x + 2)(x - 4) = 0$. $\{\frac{3}{2}, -2, 4\}$
5. Simplify $\frac{\sqrt{10}}{\sqrt{45}}$. $\frac{\sqrt{2}}{3}$

TEACHER'S RESOURCE MASTERS

Practice Master 49, Part 2
Quiz 30

15.8 Similarities

Reflections, translations, rotations, glide reflections, and dilations are all **similarity transformations,** or **similarities.** The properties of similarities are common to both isometries and dilations. These types of transformations preserve betweenness of points, angle measure, ratio of distances, perpendicularity, and parallelism of lines.

Other similarities are neither isometries nor dilations but result from compositions of isometries and dilations. The next figure shows the composition of a translation and a dilation. The translation t has the coordinate rule $(x, y) \rightarrow (x + 5, y - 4)$, and the dilation $d[(0, 0), 2]$ has the coordinate rule $(x, y) \rightarrow (2x, 2y)$. The composition of $t \circ d$ results in a transformation having coordinate rule $(x, y) \rightarrow (2x + 5, 2y - 4)$, while $d \circ t$ results in a transformation with coordinate rule $(x, y) \rightarrow (2x + 10, 2y - 8)$. Although $t \circ d \neq d \circ t$, $\triangle ABC \sim \triangle A'B'C'$ in either case.

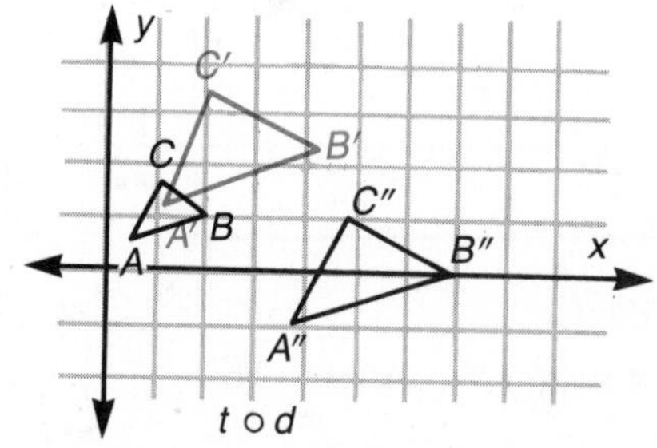

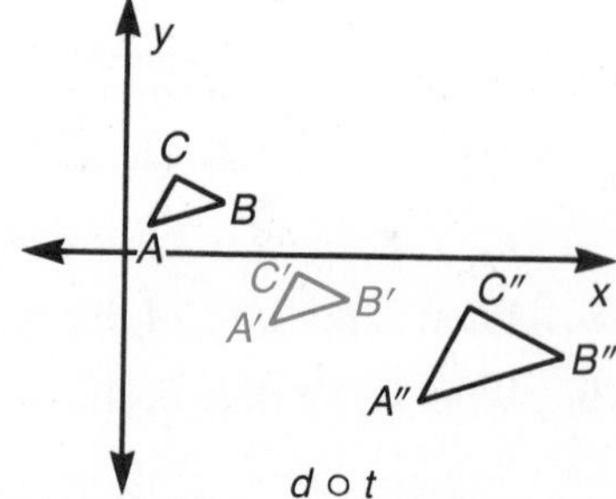

Now consider the composition of a reflection, a translation, and a dilation. The reflection (r) has coordinate rule $(x, y) \rightarrow (x, -y)$, the translation (t) has rule $(x, y) \rightarrow (x - 5, y + 4)$, and the dilation (d) has rule $(x, y) \rightarrow (2x, 2y)$.

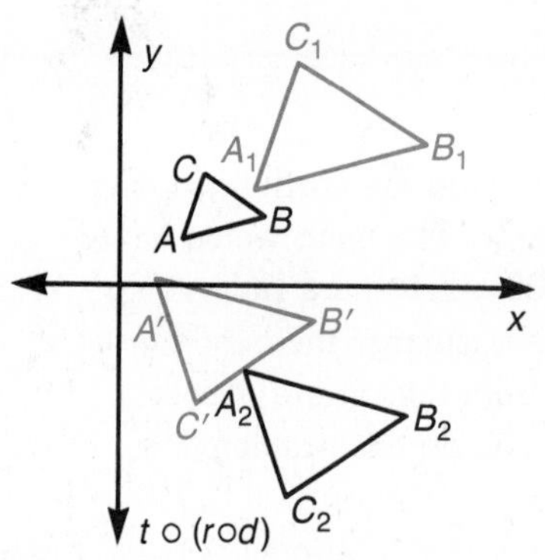

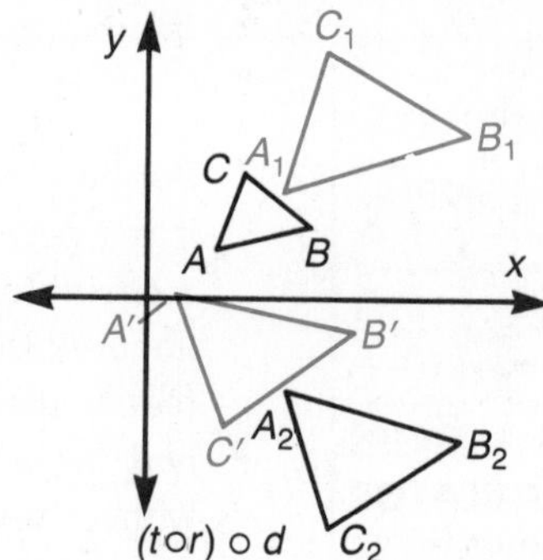

In the figure on the left, $r \circ d$ results in $(x, y) \rightarrow (2x, -2y)$. Translation of $r \circ d$ by t produces the similarity $(x, y) \rightarrow (2x - 5, -2y + 4)$. In the figure on the right, $t \circ r$ results in the rule $(x, y) \rightarrow (x - 5, -y + 4)$. Applying this rule to the dilation produces $(x, y) \rightarrow (2x - 5, -2y + 4)$. You can see that $t \circ (r \circ d) = (t \circ r) \circ d$. It appears, therefore, that the set of similarities is associative under composition.

The next example illustrates that the composition of two similarities is also a similarity.

Example: Given the coordinate rules for a reflection, two dilations, and a translation, determine whether $(t \circ d_2) \circ (d_1 \circ r)$ is a similarity.

$$r(x, y) \rightarrow (x, 12 - y) \qquad d_1[(0, 0), \tfrac{3}{2}] = (x, y) \rightarrow (\tfrac{3}{2}x, \tfrac{3}{2}y)$$

$$t(x, y) \rightarrow (x - 5, y) \qquad d_2[(0, 0), \tfrac{1}{3}] = (x, y) \rightarrow (\tfrac{1}{3}x, \tfrac{1}{3}y)$$

Solution: $(d_1 \circ r) = (x, y) \rightarrow (\frac{3}{2}x, 18 - \frac{3}{2}y)$. The image of $\triangle ABC$ under this similarity is $\triangle A_1B_1C_1$.
$(t \circ d_2) = (x, y) \rightarrow (\frac{1}{3}x - 5, \frac{1}{3}y)$. The image of $\triangle A_1B_1C_1$ under this similarity is $\triangle A'B'C'$. Thus, $(t \circ d_2) \circ (d_1 \circ r)$ is $(x, y) \rightarrow (\frac{1}{2}x - 5, 6 - \frac{1}{2}y)$, and the image of $\triangle ABC$ under $(t \circ d_2) \circ (d_1 \circ r)$ is $\triangle A'B'C'$. This composition of similarities is equal to the similarity $d \circ g$, where d is a dilation and g is a glide reflection having the following rules:

$$g(x, y) \rightarrow (x - 10, 12 - y)$$

$$d[(0, 0), \tfrac{1}{2}] = (x, y) \rightarrow (\tfrac{1}{2}x, \tfrac{1}{2}y)$$

$$(d \circ g) = (x, y) \rightarrow (\tfrac{1}{2}x - 5, 6 - \tfrac{1}{2}y)$$

Therefore, $(t \circ d) \circ (d \circ r) = (d \circ g)$.

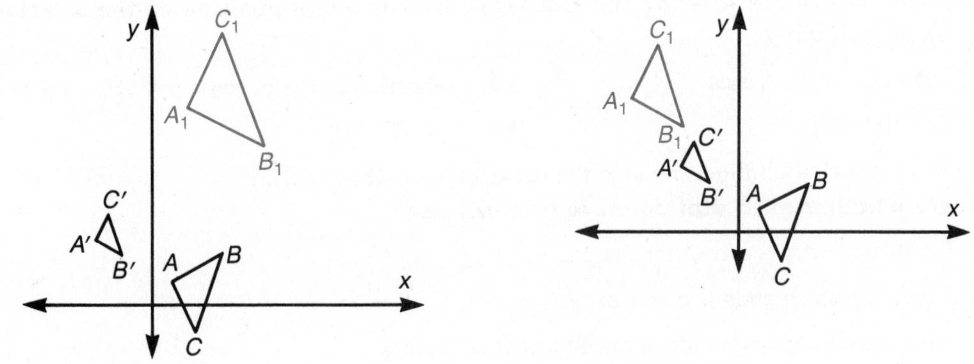

The set of similarity transformations is closed under composition, and composition is associative. Each similarity has an identity transformation and an inverse. Therefore, the set of similarity transformations forms a group under composition.

ASSIGNMENT GUIDE

Minimum 1-8
Regular 1-11 odd, 12-16, 17-23 odd
Maximum 1-9 odd, 11-16, 23-24

Oral Exercises

1. $d[(0, 0), 2]$
2. $d[(0, 0), 2] \circ r_{y\text{-axis}}$ or $r_{y\text{-axis}} \circ d[(0, 0), 2]$
3. $d[(1, 1), \frac{1}{2}] \circ r[(0, 0), 180]$ or $r[(0, 0), 180] \circ d[(1, 1), \frac{1}{2}]$
4. $d[(0, 0), \frac{1}{2}] \circ r_{x\text{-axis}}$ or $r_{x\text{-axis}} \circ d[(0, 0), \frac{1}{2}]$
5. $A'(0, 0)$ 6. $B'(16, 0)$
7. $C'(0, 12)$ 8. $D'(-24, -28)$
9. $A'(0, 0)$ 10. $B'(-1, -1)$
11. $C'(0, 3)$ 12. $D'(\frac{1}{2}, -4)$
13. $(x, y) \to (3x, -3y)$
14. $(x, y) \to (-3x, 3y)$
15. $(x, y) \to (-3x, -3y)$
16. $(x, y) \to (-3y, 3x)$
17. The rules are each the same.
18. T 19. F
20. F 21. T
22. F 23. T
24. T 25. F
26. T

ORAL EXERCISES

Name the similarity that maps the smaller triangle onto the larger one.

1.

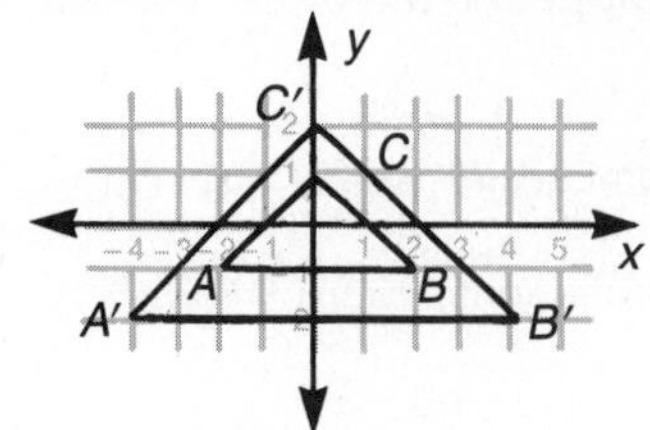

2.

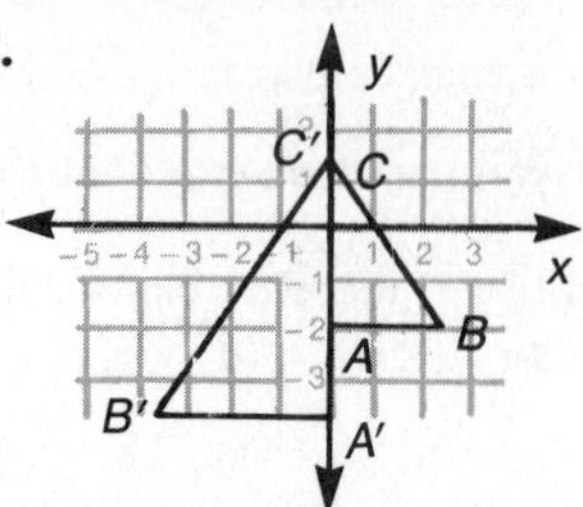

Name the similarity that maps the larger triangle onto the smaller one.

3.

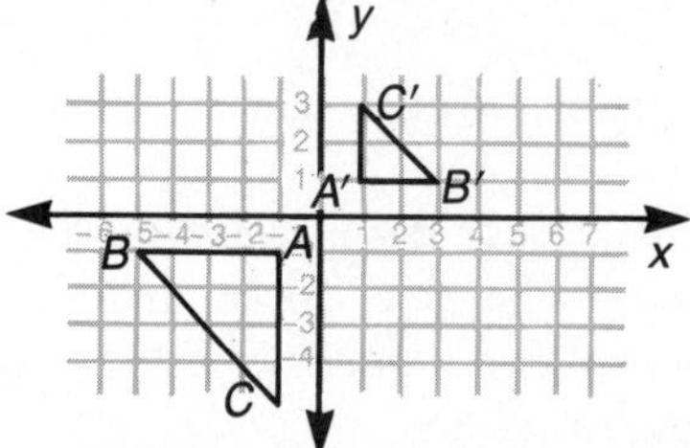

4.

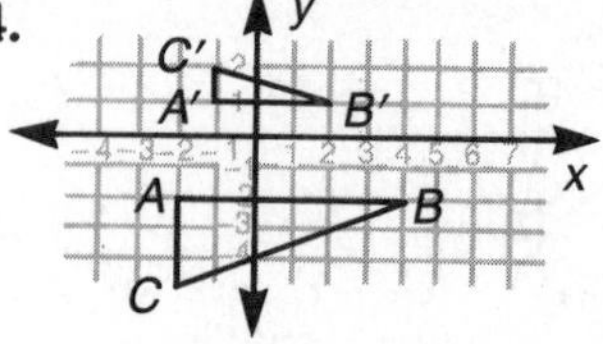

Name the image of each point under the similarity that has the coordinate rule $(x, y) \to (4x, -4y)$.

5. $A(0, 0)$ **6.** $B(4, 0)$ **7.** $C(0, -3)$ **8.** $D(-6, 7)$

Name the preimage of each point under the similarity having the coordinate rule $(x, y) \to (-2y, -2x)$.

9. $A(0, 0)$ **10.** $B(2, 2)$ **11.** $C(0, -6)$ **12.** $D(-1, 8)$

Name the coordinate rule for the similarity that is a composition of the dilation $d[(0, 0), 3]$ following

13. reflection in the x-axis.

14. reflection in the y-axis.

15. $r[(0, 0), 180]$.

16. $r[(0, 0), 90]$.

17. What is the result if you reverse the order of each composition?

Indicate whether each statement is true or false.

18. Every similarity is a transformation.

19. Every transformation is a similarity.

20. Similarities map segments onto congruent segments.

21. Similarities map perpendicular lines onto perpendicular lines.

22. Under a similarity, a line is parallel to its image.

23. Similarities map parallel lines onto parallel lines.

24. Every isometry is a similarity.

25. Every similarity is an isometry.

26. The set of all similarities, under the operation of composition, form a group.

WRITTEN EXERCISES

A. Name the similarity that maps $\triangle ABC$ onto $\triangle A'B'C'$ and give the coordinate rule for each.

1.

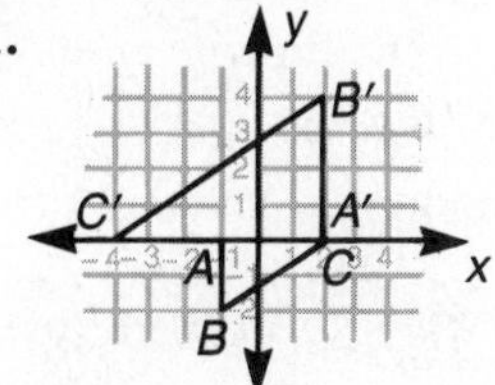

2.

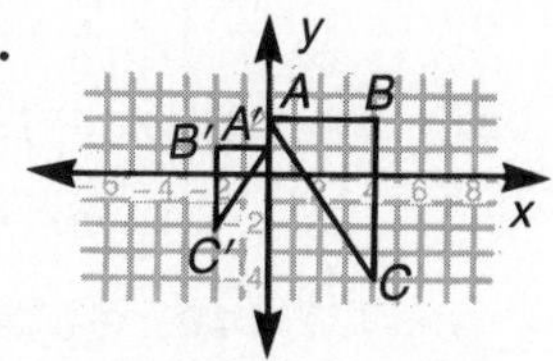

3.

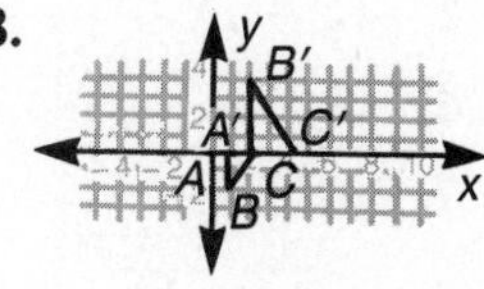

4. What is the effect of the dilation $d[(0, 0), 1]$?

B. Plot $\triangle ABC$ with vertices $A(1, 0)$, $B(5, 0)$, and $C(1, 3)$.

5. Draw the image, $\triangle A'B'C'$, under a dilation with center at the origin and magnitude 2. Now draw the image of $\triangle A'B'C'$ (label it $A''B''C''$) under the translation having the rule $(x, y) \rightarrow (x - 6, y - 8)$.

6. Repeat Exercise 5, reversing the order of the composition. How do $t \circ d$ and $d \circ t$ compare?

Plot $\triangle ABC$ with vertices $A(-2, -1)$, $B(2, 0)$, and $C(-1, 1)$.

7. Find the image of $\triangle ABC$ under $d[(0, 0), 2]$ following reflection in the x-axis.

8. Name the coordinate rule for the similarity $d \circ r$ in 7.

Plot $\triangle ABC$ with vertices $A(-7, -3)$, $B(-1, -3)$, and $C(-4, 5)$.

9. Find the image of $\triangle ABC$ under $d[(0, 0), \frac{1}{3}] \circ r[(0, 0), 180]$.

10. Name the coordinate rule for the similarity $d \circ r$ in 9.

State whether each of the following is preserved by all similarities.

11. collinearity **12.** orientation **13.** angle measure

14. betweenness **15.** parallelism **16.** distance

C. Name the coordinate rule for the similarity that is a composition of the dilation $d[(0, 0), k]$ following

17. reflection in the x-axis. **18.** reflection in the y-axis.

19. translation 3 units upward. **20.** 90° rotation about (0, 0).

21. 180° rotation about (0, 0). **22.** reflection in $y = x$.

Under the similarity rule $(x, y) \rightarrow (-4x, -4y)$, $\triangle ABC \rightarrow \triangle A'B'C'$.

23. What is the ratio of the perimeters of the triangles?

24. What is the ratio of the areas of the triangles?

Written Exercises

1. $d[(0, 0), 2] \circ r[(0, 0), 180]$ or $r[(0, 0), 180] \circ d[(0, 0), 2]$ $(x, y) \rightarrow (-2x, -2y)$
2. $d[(0, 0), \frac{1}{2}] \circ r_{y\text{-axis}}$ or $r_{y\text{-axis}} \circ d[(0, 0), \frac{1}{2}]$ $(x, y) \rightarrow (-\frac{1}{2}x, \frac{1}{2}y)$
3. $d[(0, 0), 2] \circ r_{x\text{-axis}}$ or $r_{x\text{-axis}} \circ d[(0, 0), 2]$ $(x, y) \rightarrow (2x, -2y)$
4. identity dilation
5. $A'(2, 0)$, $B'(10, 0)$, $C'(2, 6)$; $A''(-4, -8)$, $B''(4, -8)$, $C''(-4, -2)$
6. $A'(-5, -8)$, $B'(-1, -8)$, $C'(-5, -5)$; $A''(-10, -16)$, $B''(-2, -16)$, $C''(-10, -10)$ Composition of a dilation and translation does *not* commute.
7. $A''(-4, 2)$, $B''(4, 0)$, $C''(-2, -2)$
8. $(x, y) \rightarrow (2x, -2y)$
9. $A''(\frac{7}{3}, 1)$, $B''(\frac{1}{3}, 1)$, $C''(\frac{4}{3}, -\frac{5}{3})$
10. $(x, y) \rightarrow (-\frac{1}{3}x, -\frac{1}{3}y)$
11. yes 12. no
13. yes 14. yes
15. yes 16. no
17. $(x, y) \rightarrow (kx, -ky)$
18. $(x, y) \rightarrow (-kx, ky)$
19. $(x, y) \rightarrow (kx, ky + 3k)$
20. $(x, y) \rightarrow (-ky, kx)$
21. $(x, y) \rightarrow (-kx, -ky)$
22. $(x, y) \rightarrow (ky, kx)$
23. 1:4 24. 1:16

Skills Maintenance

1. $-x-y$ 2. $4y^2+3y$

3. $3n^8$ 4. $8y^3$

5. $16n^2-1$

6. $a+2ab+b^2$

7. m^9 8. $\frac{3m}{m-3}$

9. $2x^3yz^2\sqrt{5y}$ 10. $\frac{1}{2}$

11. -6 12. $\frac{2h}{t^2}$

13. $x>2$ 14. 8, 2

15. 0, 3 16. 2

17. $2\pm\sqrt{3}$ 18. 6, -2

19. 28

Exploration

1. glide reflection or translation
2. line reflection or rotation
3. line reflection or translation
4. line reflection
5. rotation or line reflection
6. translation

SKILLS MAINTENANCE

Simplify these expressions.

1. $(x+y)-2(x+y)$ **2.** $-3y+4y^2+6y$ **3.** $n^6\cdot 3n^2$

4. $(2y)^3$ **5.** $(4n-1)(4n+1)$ **6.** $(a+b)^2$

7. $m^6\div m^{-3}$ **8.** $[m^2\div(m^2-9)][(3m+9)\div m]$

9. $\sqrt{20x^6y^3z^4}$ **10.** $3y\div(2y-8)-(y+2)\div(y-4)$

Solve each equation, inequality, or system of equations.

11. $6x-20=10x+4$ **12.** Solve for g: $h=\frac{1}{2}gt^2$ **13.** $4-5x<3x-12$

14. $x=y+6$
$x+3y=14$ **15.** $2x-y=-3$
$4x+5y=15$ **16.** $\frac{2y-7}{y}+3=\frac{3}{y}$

17. $x^2-4x=-1$ **18.** $x^2=4x+12$ **19.** $\sqrt{m-3}=5$

EXPLORATION/Transformations in Designs

Many national flags use transformations in their designs. State the type of transformation that appears in each flag below.

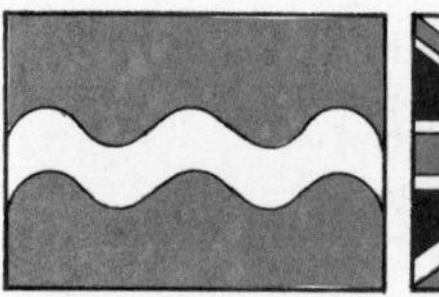

1. Seychelles

2. United Kingdom

3. Syria

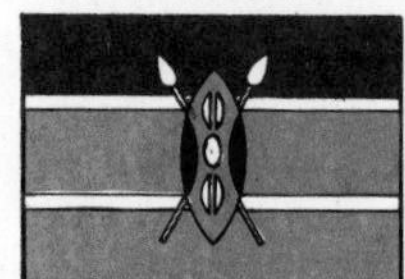

4. Kenya

5. Micronesia

6. Panama

EXPLORATION
Tessellations

The figure on the right is called a tessellation. A tesselation is created by repeating the same shape so that they interlock without gaps. The simplest tessellation shapes are polygons, all triangles, all quadrilaterals, some pentagons, and some hexagons. Octagons, however, don't work.

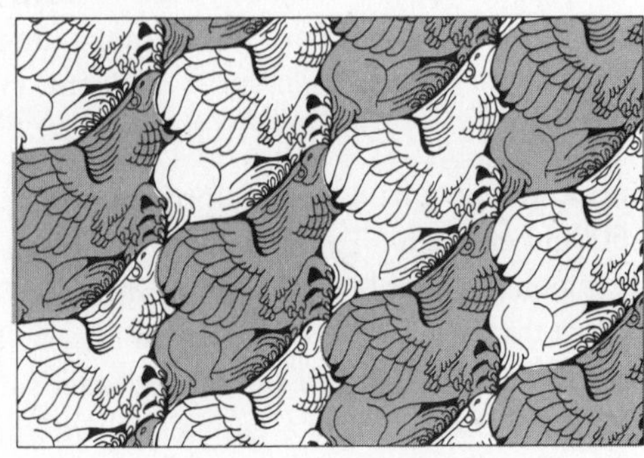

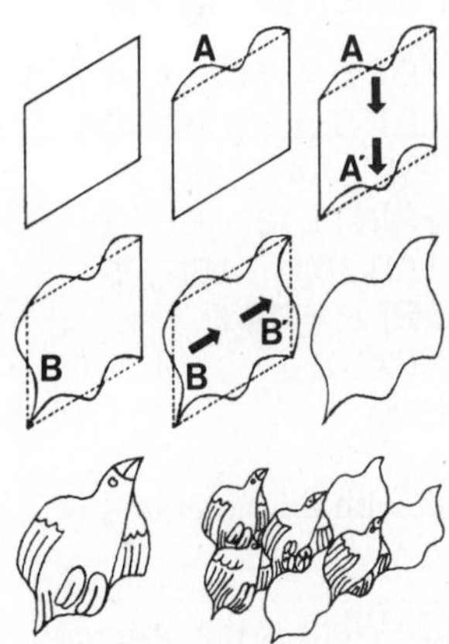

Intrigued by tessellations, a man named M. C. Escher designed about one hundred and fifty tessellations in the 1940's and 50's. He had two rules when drawing:

Without recognizability, no meaning.
Without shade contrast, no visibility.

In his tesselations, the repeating shapes are always living creatures. Simple shapes can be created by modifying polygons as illustrated at the left. Escher used shade contrast as a simple necessity and as a logical way of visualizing the individual components of his patterns.

There are two types of tesselations; periodic and nonperiodic. A periodic tessellation repeats the same shape with the same orientation. If you were to trace a portion of a periodic pattern, you could move your tracing paper, without rotating it, to a new position where the lines would match. In a nonperiodic tesselation, the shapes are repeated, but their orientation changes. The figure at the right shows a nonperiodic tessellation.

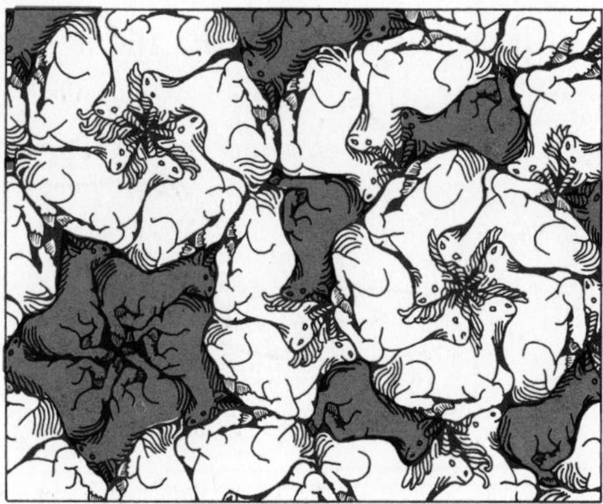

TEACHER'S RESOURCE MASTERS

Computer Master 15

COMPUTER SOFTWARE

Angles, Arcs, and Transformations

Computer

The total surface area is the lateral surface area plus the areas of the bases. $S = 2\pi rh + 2\pi r^2$.

Surface area of cylinder A = 339.12
Surface area of cylinder B = 282.60
Surface area of cylinder C = 270.04
Surface area of cylinder D = 466.29

Cylinder C has the least surface area.

1. 6 cm
2. 6 cm; 6.2 cm; It is more effective to change I.
3. The optimal radius is 4.3 cm.

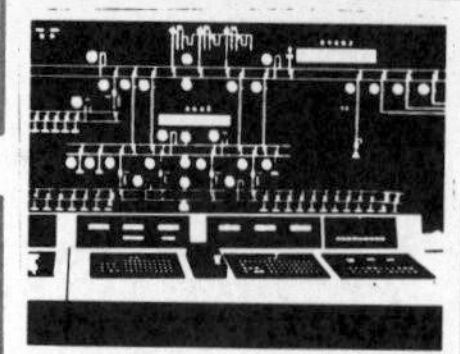

COMPUTER

The cylinders below might appear to have nothing in common, other than being right cylinders. However, all four have identical volumes ($V = \pi r^2 h$). The *total surface area* of each cylinder is different. How would you find the one with the *least* area?

Suppose that a fruit juice company must manufacture uniform cans with a 1500-ml capacity. To minimize costs, each can's surface area should use as little aluminum as possible. This is an **optimization** problem; that is, find a size that makes the best use of available materials. The program below creates a table of values that can be read to find the least surface area for a constant volume of 1500 ml. The radius is a variable which in turn determines the height. The radius for each new calculation increases by an increment chosen by the user.

```
100 REM MINIMIZE CAN SURFACE AREA
110 PRINT"WHAT RADIUS?";:INPUT R
120 PRINT"WHAT INCREMENT?";:INPUT I
130 PRINTTAB(1)"RADIUS"TAB(10)"HEIGHT"
    TAB(25)"SURFACE AREA"
140 PRINTTAB(1)"------"TAB(10)"------
    -----"TAB(25)"------------"
150 FOR J=1 TO 15
160 LET H=1500/(3.14*R↑2)
170 LET S=(2*3.14*R*H)
    +(2*3.14*R↑2)
180 PRINTTAB(1)R
    TAB(10)H TAB(25)S
190 LET R=R+I
200 NEXT J
210 END
```

1. Use 3 as a starting point for the measure of the radius, with an increment of 1. What is the optimal length of the radius?
2. Rerun the program with 0.5 as the increment, then 0.1. What is the optimal radius in each case? Is it more effective to change the value of R or I?
3. Change the volume in line 160 to 500. In increments of 0.1, what radius is best?

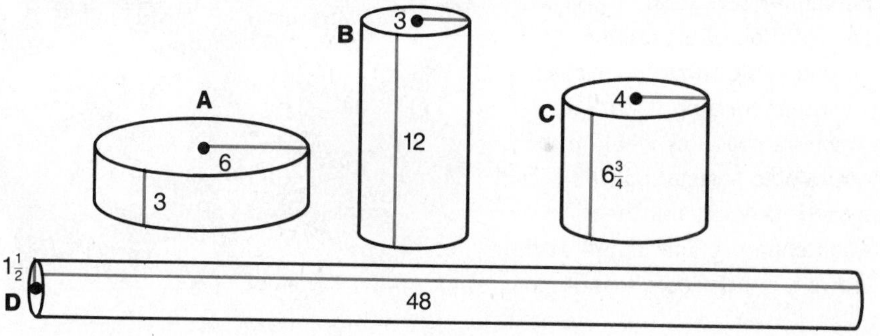

CHAPTER 15 REVIEW

VOCABULARY

Abelian group (15.6)
Cartesian product (15.1)
center (15.5, 15.7)
codomain (15.2)
composition (15.4)
dilation (15.7)
dilation image (15.7)
direction of rotation (15.5)
domain (15.1, 15.2)
fixed point (15.2)
function (15.1)
glide reflection (15.6)
group (15.6)
half-turn (15.5)
identity mapping (15.2)
image (15.2)
inverse relation (15.1)
isometry (15.6)
line of symmetry (15.3)
line reflection (15.3)
magnitude (15.4, 15.5, 15.7)
mapping (15.2)
one-to-one function (15.1)
one-to-one mapping (15.2)
onto (15.2)
preimage (15.2)
quarter-turn (15.5)
range (15.1)
reflection in a point (15.5)
relation (15.1)
rotation (15.5)
rotational symmetry (15.5)
similarity (15.8)
similarity transformation (15.8)
symmetric (15.3)
symmetry set (15.6)
transformation (15.2)
translation (15.4)

REVIEW EXERCISES

15.1 **Let $A = \{a, b, c\}$ and $B = \{2, 4, 6, 8\}$. Name the indicated Cartesian products.**

1. $A \times B$ **2.** $B \times A$ **3.** $A \times A$

4. If M contains 12 elements and N contains 3 elements, how many elements are in $M \times N$?

Refer to sets R and S for exercises 5-9.
$R = \{(2, 3), (-2, 5), (0, -1), (4, 3)\}$ $S = \{(-4, 7), (2, 6), (3, 8), (-5, 0)\}$

5. List the domain of R. **6.** List the range of R

7. List the inverse of S.

8. Which relations, if any, are functions?

9. Which relations, if any, have inverse functions?

15.2 **10.** What name is given to the mapping $(x, y) \rightarrow (x, y)$?

11. Given $A = (0, 2)$ and $B = (1, 3)$, graph the images A' and B' under the coordinate rule $W = (x, y) \rightarrow (x - 1, y)$.

12. In Exercise 11, is W a transformation?

13. In Exercise 11, does W have a fixed point?

ENRICHMENT

See Activities 29-30, p. T53

1. $\{(a, 2), (a, 4), (a, 6), (a, 8)$ $(b, 2), (b, 4), (b, 6), (b, 8),$ $(c, 2), (c, 4), (c, 6), (c, 8)\}$

2. $\{(2, a), (2, b), (2, c), (4, a),$ $(4, b), (4, c), (6, a), (6, b),$ $(6, c), (8, a), (8, b), (8, c)\}$

3. $\{(a, a), (a, b), (a, c), (b, a),$ $(b, b), (b, c), (c, a), (c, b)$ $(c, c)\}$

4. 36
5. $\{-2, 0, 2, 4\}$
6. $\{-1, 3, 5\}$
7. $S^{-1} = \{(7, -4), (6, 2), (8, 3), (0, -5)\}$
8. R, S 9. S

10. the identity mapping or transformation
11. $A'(-1, 2)$ $B'(0, 3)$

12. yes 13. no fixed point

14. $\{a, b, c, d\}$

15. $\{2, 4, 8, 10\}$

16. $\{15\}$

17. $A \rightarrow B$, $E \rightarrow F$

18. $A \rightarrow B$, $C \rightarrow D$

19. $A \rightarrow B$

20. one

21. $(x, y) \rightarrow (-x, y)$

22. yes 23. no

24. yes

25. a translation

26. $T^{-1} = (x, y) \rightarrow (x, y + 3)$

27. when the lines of reflection intersect

28. (0, 0) 29. 180°

30. $(x, y) \rightarrow (-x, -y)$

31. 6

32. isometry

33. three

34. two

35. No; the set has no multiplicative inverses.

36. distance 37. $A'(6, -9)$

38. T 39. F

40. T

Refer to the three mappings below for Exercises 14–19.

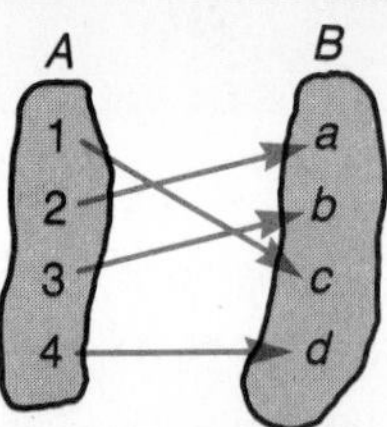

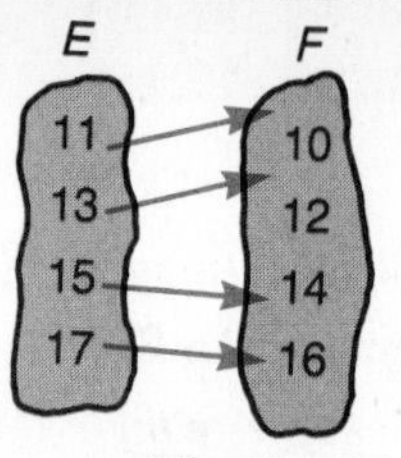

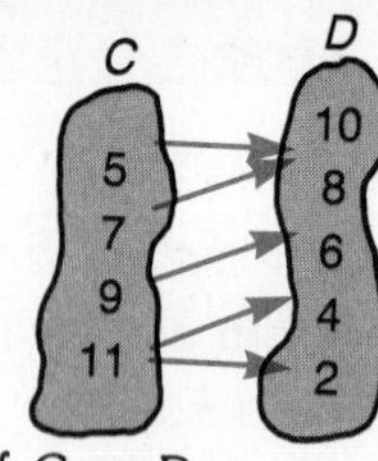

14. List the range of $A \rightarrow B$. **15.** List the codomain of $C \rightarrow D$.

16. In $E \rightarrow F$, what is the preimage of 12?

17. Which of the mappings, if any, are onto?

18. Which of the mappings, if any, are one-to-one?

19. Which mapping has an inverse?

15.3 **20.** How many lines of symmetry does a nonequilateral isosceles triangle have?

21. Give the coordinate rule for a reflection in the y-axis.

State whether each of the following are preserved by a line reflection.

22. distance **23.** orientation **24.** parallelism

25. What is the product of two reflections in parallel lines?

15.4 **26.** T maps $A(-6, 4)$ onto $A'(-6, 1)$. What is the rule for T^{-1}?

15.5 **27.** When is the product of two line reflections a rotation?

28. What is the center of the rotation $r[(0, 0), 180]$?

29. What is the magnitude of r? **30.** Give the coordinate rule for r.

31. How many rotational symmetries does a regular hexagon have?

15.6 **Complete each statement correctly in Exercises 32–35.**

32. Any composition of line reflections is a(n) ______.

33. Any figure can be mapped onto a congruent figure applying ______ or fewer reflections.

34. How many isometries are in the symmetry set of an isosceles trapezoid?

35. Given $S = \{\text{integers}\}$, is $(S, \cdot)$ a group? Explain.

15.7 **36.** What property preserved by isometries is *not* preserved by a dilation?

37. Give the image of $A(16, -24)$ under $d[(0, 0), \frac{3}{8}]$.

15.8 **Answer <u>true</u> or <u>false</u> in Exercises 38–40.**

38. Every isometry is a similarity.

39. Every similarity is an isometry.

40. A dilation is a similarity.

CHAPTER 15 TEST

Fill in the blanks to make each sentence true in 1–13.

1. A relation is any set of _____ pairs.
2. A transformation is a mapping of a set of points to a set of points that is both _____ and _____.
3. A point that is its own image under a transformation is called a _____ point.
4. The transformation that maps every point of the plane onto itself is called the _____.
5. The coordinate rule for reflecting in the x-axis is _____.
6. The coordinate rule for reflecting in the y-axis is _____.
7. The coordinate rule for a translation 4 units to the right is _____.
8. The composition of reflecting in two parallel lines is a _____.
9. The composition of reflecting in two intersecting lines is a _____.
10. Two figures are congruent if and only if there is a(n) _____ that maps onto the other.
11. An isometry may not preserve _____ of noncollinear points.
12. The coordinate rule for $d[(0, 0), 3]$ is _____.
13. A similarity may be a composition of an isometry and a(n) _____.

State whether the transformation that maps $\triangle ABC$ onto $\triangle A'B'C'$ can be best described as a line reflection, rotation, translation, glide reflection, dilation, or similarity.

14.

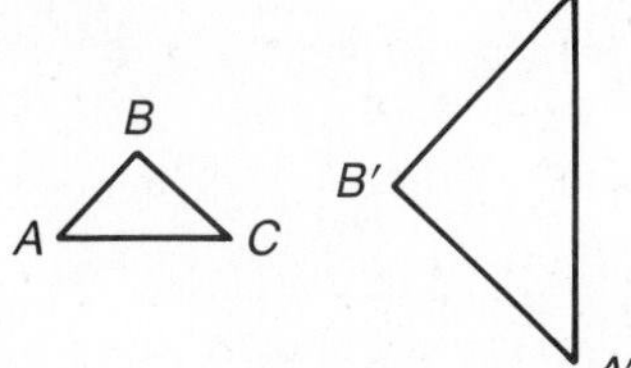

15.

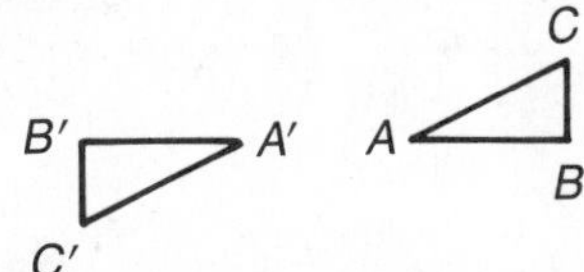

16.

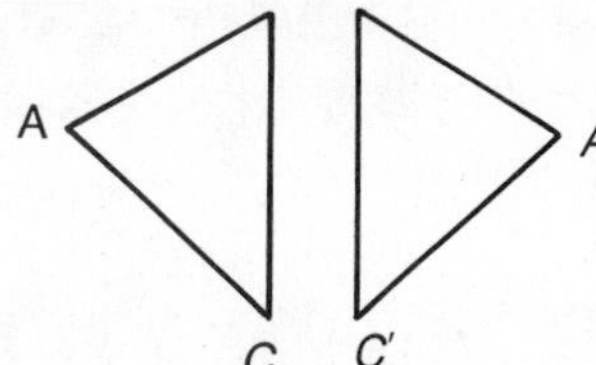

17.

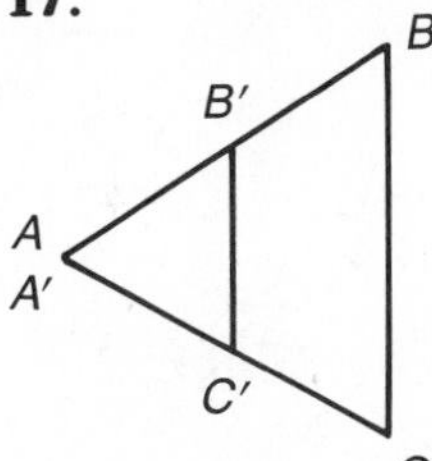

18.

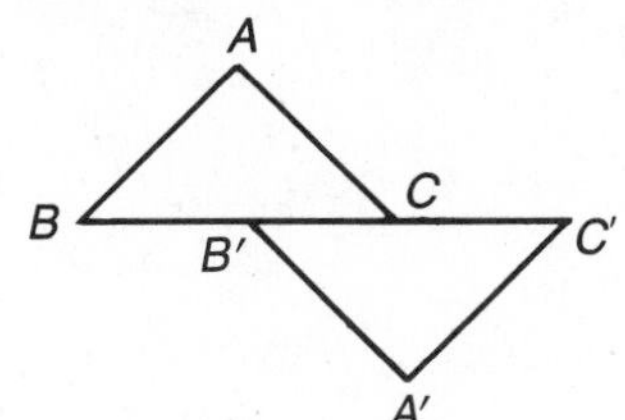

19.

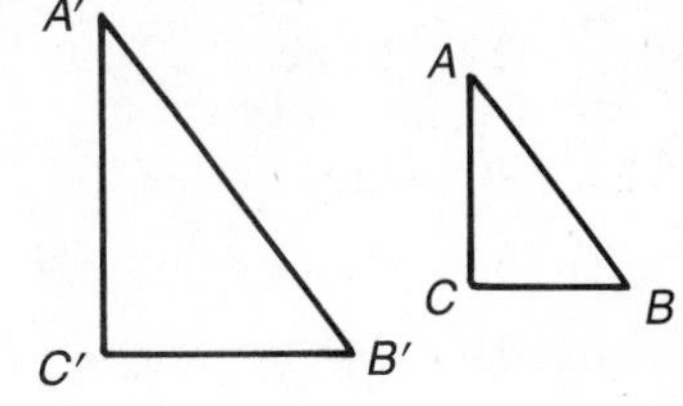

TEACHER'S RESOURCE MASTERS

Chapter 15 Test
Multiple Choice Test—Chapter 15

Chapter 15 Test

1. ordered
2. one-to-one, onto
3. fixed
4. identity
5. $(x, y) \rightarrow (x, -y)$
6. $(x, y) \rightarrow (-x, y)$
7. $(x, y) \rightarrow (x + 4, y)$
8. translation
9. rotation
10. isometry
11. orientation
12. $(x, y) \rightarrow (3x, 3y)$
13. dilation
14. similarity
15. rotation
16. line reflection
17. dilation
18. glide reflection
19. similarity

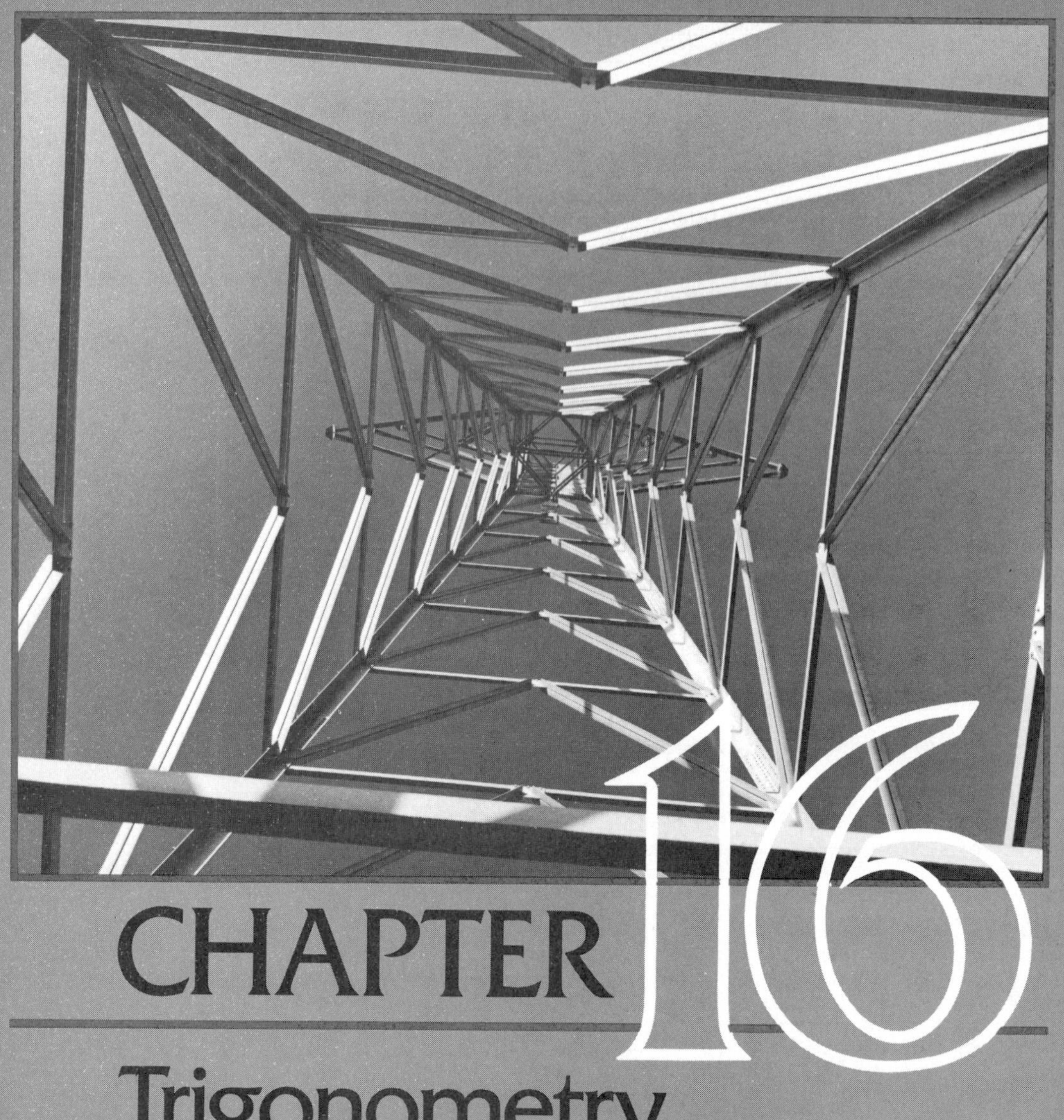

CHAPTER 16

Trigonometry and Vectors

16.1 Trigonometric Ratios

In Chapter 10, two triangles are defined as similar if (a) their corresponding angles are congruent, and (b) their corresponding sides are proportional.

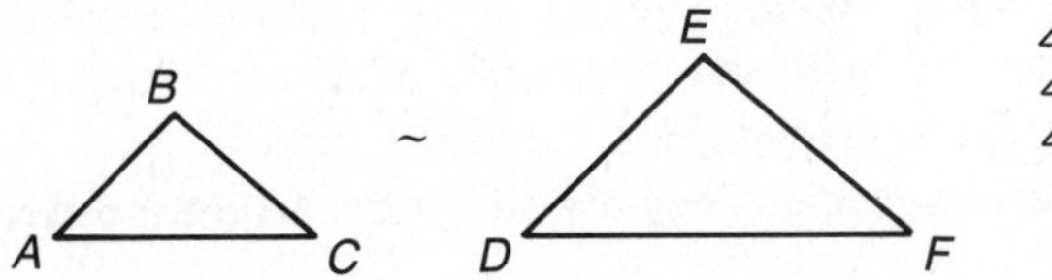

$\angle A \cong \angle D$
$\angle B \cong \angle E$
$\angle C \cong \angle F$

$$\frac{AB}{DE} = \frac{BC}{EF} = \frac{AC}{DF}$$

The terms of any proportion can be rearranged according to algebraic rules. For example, using the multiplication property of equality, $\frac{AB}{DE} = \frac{BC}{EF}$ can be rewritten as:

$$\frac{AB}{DE} \cdot \frac{DE}{BC} = \frac{BC}{EF} \cdot \frac{DE}{BC}, \text{ so } \frac{AB}{BC} = \frac{DE}{EF}$$

Thus, the ratio between two sides of the same triangle equals the ratio between the *corresponding* sides of a similar triangle. The new equation is another way of expressing that the corresponding sides are proportional.

A powerful relationship can be derived from these proportions. Consider the following problem.

Example: The telephone company is searching for trees tall enough to be telephone poles. How can the height of a tree be determined without actually climbing it?

Solution: If the surveyor measures the length of the shadow of the tree at noon and sights the top of the trunk to find the measure of $\angle A$, a right triangle is formed with the height of the trunk as one of the sides. The surveyor can then form another right triangle with the same measure for $\angle A$. $\Delta ABC \sim \Delta ADE$, so $\frac{BC}{AC} = \frac{DE}{AE}$. If the surveyor has measured and found that $AC = 50$ m, $AE = 10$ m, and $DE = 3$ m, then $\frac{x}{50} = \frac{3}{10}$, and $x = 15$ m. Since telephone poles measure approximately 10 meters, this tree is tall enough to be used.

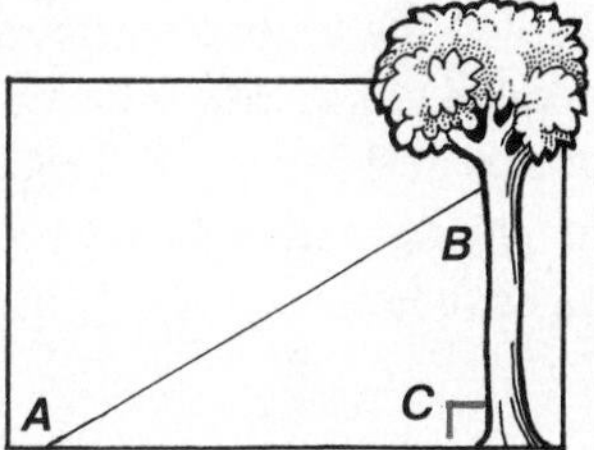

It is important that $\angle A$ have the same measure in both triangles in the example. All right triangles that have one acute angle of the same measure are a "family" of similar triangles whose corresponding sides are proportional.

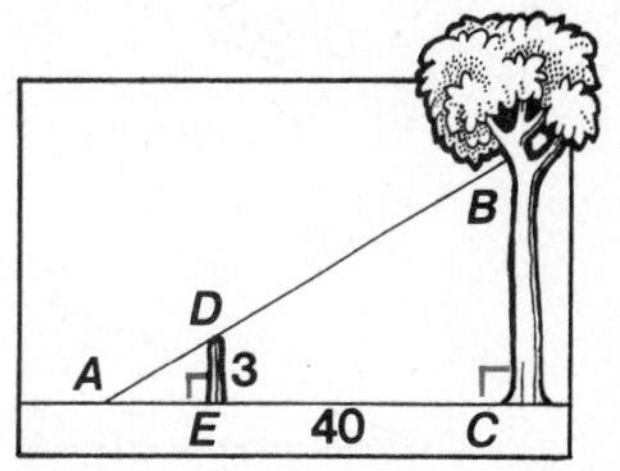

OBJECTIVE

Identify sine, cosine, and tangent values given the measures of the sides of a right triangle.

TEACHER'S NOTES

See p. T41

MIXED REVIEW

1. Simplify $\sqrt{[1 - (-4)]^2 + (-6 - 6)^2}$. 13
2. Find the midpoint between (1, 8) and (7, −12). (4, −2)
3. Find the area of an isosceles right triangle with a hypotenuse of 8. 16
4. Solve $\frac{6}{x} = \frac{9}{25}$. $x = 16\frac{2}{3}$
5. Factor $21x^2 + x - 2$. $(7x - 2)(3x + 1)$

TEACHER'S RESOURCE MASTERS

Practice Master 50, Part 1

$$\frac{7}{10} = \frac{9.1}{13} = \frac{12.6}{18} = 0.7$$

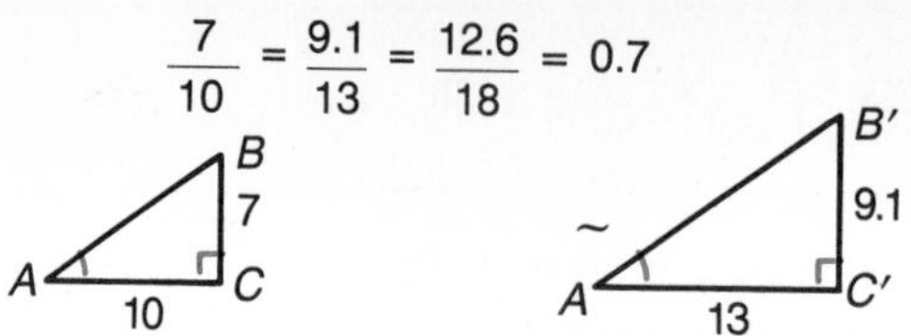

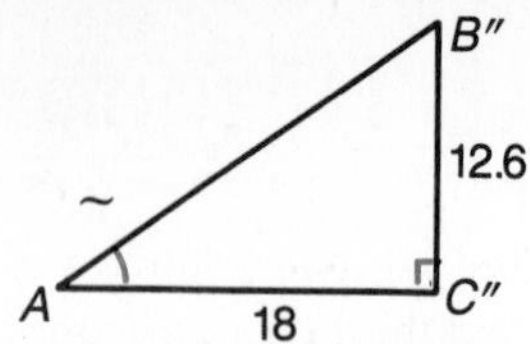

The three right triangles in the figure above have $\angle A$ of the same measure (and therefore $m\angle B$ also). These similar triangles are members of a family of similar triangles whose angles are congruent to $\angle A$, $\angle B$, and $\angle C$ and whose sides are in the ratio $\frac{7}{10}$. Such ratios of corresponding sides are useful in problem-solving. They are called the **trigonometric ratios.**

DEFINITIONS: sine, cosine, tangent

Let C be a right angle in right ΔABC, and let a, b, and c name the lengths of the sides opposite $\angle A$, $\angle B$, and $\angle C$, respectively. Then,

$$\textbf{sine } \angle A = \frac{a}{c} = \frac{\text{length of the opposite side}}{\text{length of the hypotenuse}}$$

$$\textbf{cosine } \angle A = \frac{b}{c} = \frac{\text{length of the adjacent side}}{\text{length of the hypotenuse}}$$

$$\textbf{tangent } \angle A = \frac{a}{b} = \frac{\text{length of the opposite side}}{\text{length of the adjacent side}}$$

The ratios are abbreviated *sin* $\angle A$, *cos* $\angle A$, and *tan* $\angle A$.

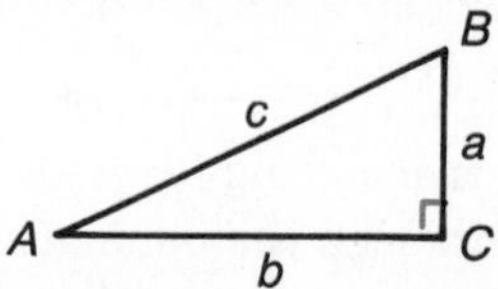

To find the trigonometric ratios for the other acute angle, you redefine the sides of ΔABC in relation to $\angle B$. Side a becomes the adjacent side, and b becomes the opposite side. In a family of similar triangles, the trigonometric ratios are constant for each of the acute angles. Thus, for any right triangle having an $\angle B'$ whose measure equals $m\angle B$, the trigonometric ratios would be as follows:

$\angle B \cong B'$

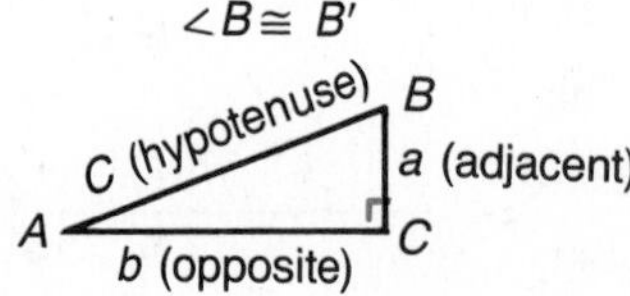

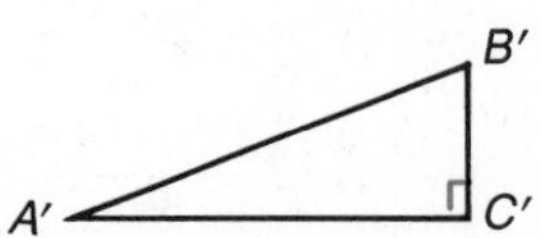

$$\sin \angle B' = \sin \angle B = \frac{b}{c} = \frac{\text{length of opposite side}}{\text{length of hypotenuse}}$$

$$\cos \angle B' = \cos \angle B = \frac{a}{c} = \frac{\text{length of adjacent side}}{\text{length of hypotenuse}}$$

$$\tan \angle B' = \tan \angle B = \frac{b}{a} = \frac{\text{length of opposite side}}{\text{length of adjacent side}}$$

Example: Write sin $\angle A$ as a ratio and a decimal.

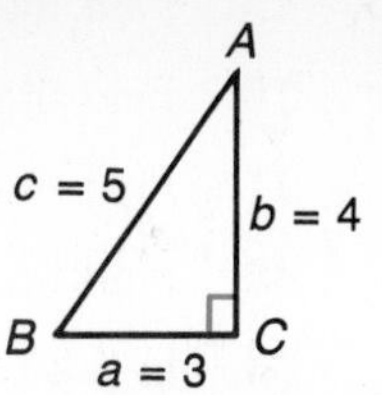

Solution: sin $\angle A$ = $\frac{\text{length of the opposite side}}{\text{length of the hypotenuse}} = \frac{a}{c} = \frac{3}{5} = 0.6$

Example: Write tan $\angle B$ as a ratio and a decimal.

Solution: tan $\angle B$ = $\frac{\text{length of the opposite side}}{\text{length of the adjacent side}} = \frac{b}{c} = \frac{4}{3} = 1.\overline{3}$

ORAL EXERCISES

1. Explain why the definition of the trigonometric ratios has been restricted to right triangles.

Complete each statement by referring to the figures of ΔMNP and ΔXYZ.

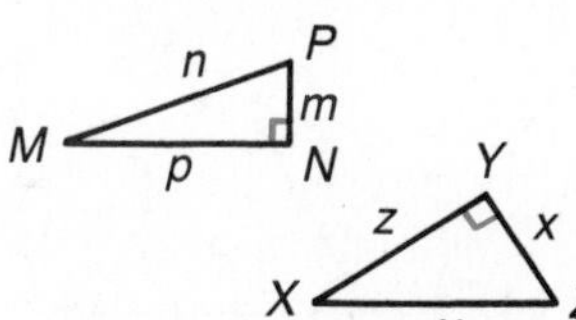

2. sin $\angle P = \frac{?}{n}$ **3.** cos $\angle X = \frac{z}{?}$

4. tan $\angle M = \frac{?}{p}$ **5.** sin $\angle Z = \frac{z}{?}$

6. tan $\angle X = \frac{x}{?}$ **7.** cos $\angle ? = \frac{p}{n}$

8. sin $\angle ? = \frac{x}{y}$ **9.** _____ $\angle Z = \frac{x}{y}$

10. _____ $\angle P = \frac{p}{m}$ **11.** sin $\angle M$ = _____ $\angle P$

WRITTEN EXERCISES

A. Refer to the figures below to find the trigonometric ratio in Exercises 1–18.

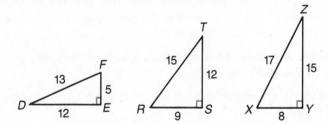

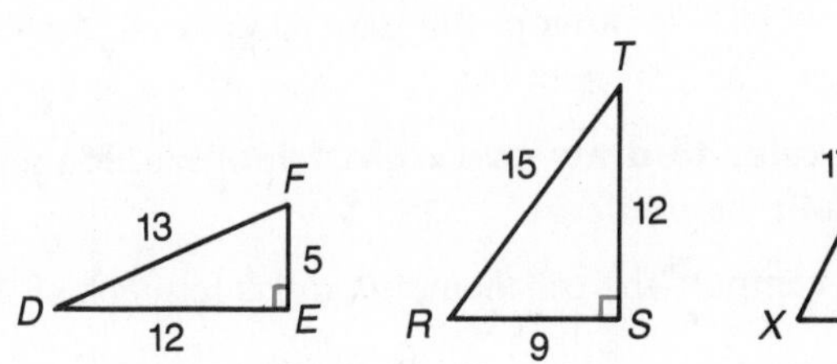

1. sin $\angle D$ =	**2.** cos $\angle F$ =	**3.** sin $\angle F$ =	**4.** tan $\angle D$ =
5. tan $\angle F$ =	**6.** cos $\angle D$ =	**7.** cos $\angle R$ =	**8.** tan $\angle T$ =
9. sin $\angle T$ =	**10.** tan $\angle R$ =	**11.** sin $\angle R$ =	**12.** cos $\angle T$ =
13. tan $\angle X$ =	**14.** sin $\angle X$ =	**15.** cos $\angle Z$ =	**16.** cos $\angle X$ =
17. tan $\angle Z$ =	**18.** sin $\angle Z$ =		

ASSIGNMENT GUIDE

Day 1
Minimum 1–15
Regular 1–21 odd
Maximum 1–15 odd, 19–21
Day 2
Minimum 16–25
Regular 22–28
Maximum 23–29 odd, 30–31, 34–35

Oral Exercises

1. Ratios of sides will vary if the triangles are not similar.

2.	p	3.	y
4.	m	5.	y
6.	z	7.	M
8.	X	9.	cos
10.	tan	11.	cos

Written Exercises

1.	$\frac{5}{13}$	2.	$\frac{5}{13}$
3.	$\frac{12}{13}$	4.	$\frac{5}{12}$
5.	$\frac{12}{5}$	6.	$\frac{12}{13}$
7.	$\frac{3}{5}$	8.	$\frac{3}{4}$
9.	$\frac{3}{5}$	10.	$\frac{4}{3}$
11.	$\frac{4}{5}$	12.	$\frac{4}{5}$
13.	$\frac{15}{8}$	14.	$\frac{15}{17}$
15.	$\frac{15}{17}$	16.	$\frac{8}{17}$
17.	$\frac{8}{15}$	18.	$\frac{8}{17}$

19. $XY = 5$

20. $XY'' = 20$

21. $Y'Z' = 8$

22. $Y''Z'' = 16$

23. $\frac{4}{5}, \frac{4}{5}$ 24. $\frac{4}{5}, \frac{4}{5}$

25. $\frac{4}{5}$

26. $XY = 12$ cm, $YZ = 16$ cm

27. $\frac{\sqrt{3}}{2}, \frac{\sqrt{3}}{3}$

28. $10\sqrt{2}$ cm

29. $16\sqrt{3}$

30. $h = 9.9, A = 158.4$

31. $h \approx 9.27, A \approx 148.32$

32. Answers will vary.

33. The sin of an acute ∠ and the cos of its complement are equal. Complementary angles have reciprocal tangents.

34. $\frac{a}{b} = \frac{a}{c} \div \frac{b}{c}$ for all sides a, b, and c of a right triangle.

35. The ratio of the sides is 3:4:5, so AB is a multiple of 5.

B. 19. Find the length of $\overline{XY}$.

20. Find the length of $\overline{XY''}$.

21. Find the length of $\overline{Y'Z'}$.

22. Find the length of $\overline{Y''Z''}$.

23. In ΔXYZ, $\sin \angle X =$ _____ and $\cos \angle XYZ =$ _____.

24. In $\Delta XY'Z'$, $\sin \angle X =$ _____ and $\cos \angle XY'Z' =$ _____.

25. In $\Delta XY''Z''$, $\cos \angle Y'' =$ _____.

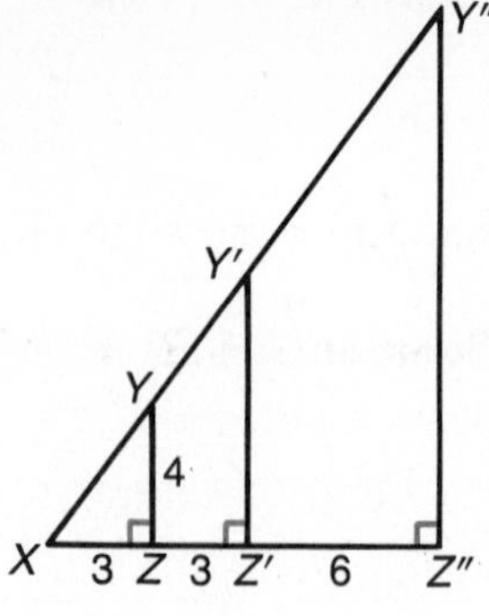

In ΔXYZ, the measure of hypotenuse $\overline{XZ}$ is 20 cm.

26. If $\cos \angle Z = \frac{4}{5}$, find the measures of the two legs.

27. If $\sin \angle X = 0.5$, find $\cos \angle X$ and $\tan \angle X$.

28. If $\tan \angle Z = 1$, find the measures of the two legs.

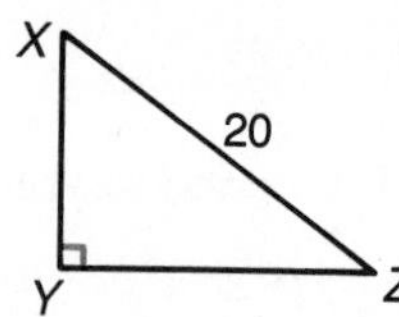

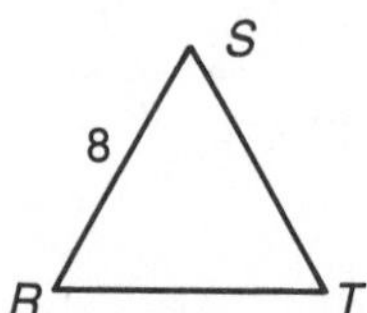

29. ΔRST is equilateral. If $\tan R = \sqrt{3}$ and $RS = 8$, find the area of ΔRST.

30. In trapezoid $ABCD$, $\sin \angle A = 0.99$. If $BC = 14$, $AD = 18$, and $AB = 10$, find the area of the trapezoid.

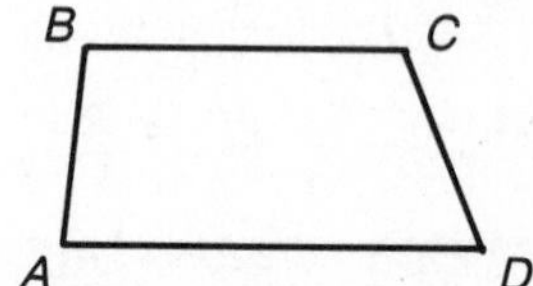

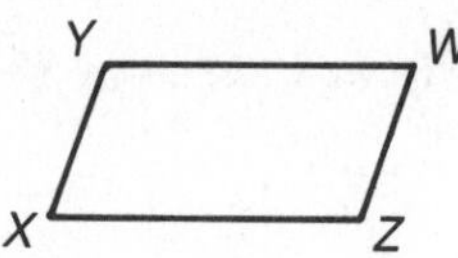

31. In parallelogram $XYWZ$, $XZ = 16$, $\cos \angle W = 0.375$, and $WZ = 10$. Find the area of the parallelogram to the nearest hundredth.

Use a protractor and ruler to draw two right triangles. Measure the sides of the triangles as carefully as you can.

32. Use a calculator to compute the trigonometric ratios for each of the acute angles in the right triangles.

33. What relationship exists in the trigonometric ratios for the complementary angles within each right triangle?

C. 34. Show that $\tan \angle X = \frac{\sin \angle X}{\cos \angle X}$ for all acute angles X.

35. Given a right ΔABC, with $\angle C$ the right angle, if $\tan \angle A = \frac{3}{4}$, why does $AB = 5x$, where x is some natural number?

16.2 Values of Trigonometric Ratios

The power of the idea of *trigonometric ratios* is that they apply to *all* triangles within a family of similar triangles.

Consider first that each trigonometric ratio represents an equation with three unknowns: the angle measure and the numerator and denominator of the ratio. At least two of the three unknown values must be found to solve the equation.

In the case of a small triangle or a figure, you can usually measure the sides accurately enough to determine the ratio. Thus, by measuring the sides of the triangles shown in the figure, you can state that

$$\sin \angle B = \tfrac{5}{13} \approx 0.3846$$

$$\tan \angle A = \tfrac{12}{5} = 2.400$$

$$\cos \angle Z = \tfrac{15}{17} \approx 0.8824$$

$$\cos \angle X = \tfrac{8}{17} \approx 0.4706$$

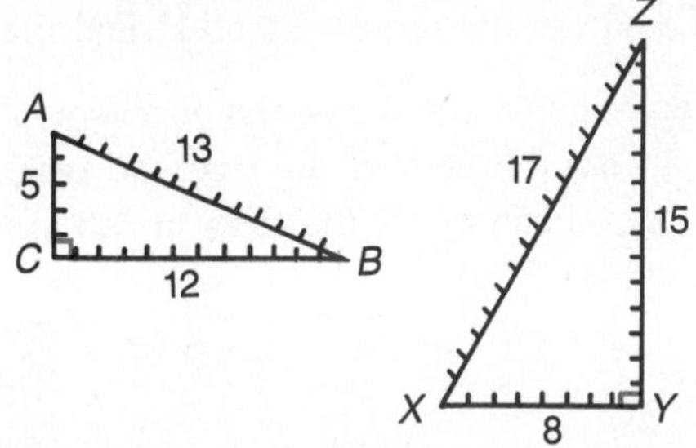

Notice that if you know the numerator and denominator of the ratio, you can express two of the variables as a single value by performing the indicated division. Still, the equation is left with one unknown: the angle measure. A family of similar right triangles cannot be identified until the measure of one of the acute angles is known. A direct relationship exists between a given trigonometric ratio and a particular angle measure, as you will see when you apply the Pythagorean Theorem in two special cases.

Example: What are the values of the sine, cosine, and tangent of any isosceles right triangle?

Solution: In any isosceles right triangle, the angles measure 45-45-90, so a family of similar triangles is described. Since the legs are congruent, you can label the measure of each leg x. By the Pythagorean Theorem,

$$x^2 + x^2 = c^2,$$
$$2x^2 = c^2,$$
$$x\sqrt{2} = c.$$

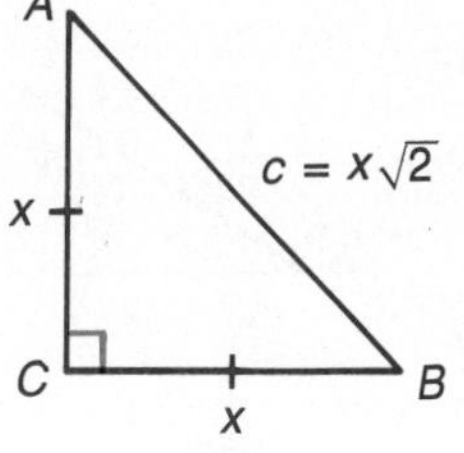

$$\text{So, } \sin \angle A = \frac{x}{x\sqrt{2}} = \frac{1}{\sqrt{2}} = \frac{\sqrt{2}}{2}$$

$$\cos \angle A = \frac{x}{x\sqrt{2}} = \frac{1}{\sqrt{2}} = \frac{\sqrt{2}}{2}$$

$$\tan \angle A = \frac{x}{x} = 1$$

OBJECTIVES

Find trigonometric ratios for special right triangles (30-60-90, 45-45-90).

Use trigonometric tables or a calculator to

(1)determine trigonometric ratios, given angle measures;

(2)determine angle measure's given ratios;

(3)determine the area of a figure given a side and an angle.

TEACHER'S NOTES

See p. T42

MIXED REVIEW

1. An angle inscribed in a semicircle is a (n) ______ angle. right
2. Solve $2x + y = 3$, $x - 3y = -23$. $(-2, 7)$
3. The acture angles of a right triangle are ________. complementary
4. Find $|-12 - 3|$ 15
5. Solve $x^2 - 121 = 0$. ± 11

TEACHER'S RESOURCE MASTERS

Practice Master 50, Part 2

Example: What are the values of the sine, cosine, and tangent of any 30-60-90 triangle?

Solution: By Theorem 9.9, the leg opposite the 30° angle measures half the hypotenuse. So, applying the Pythagorean Theorem,

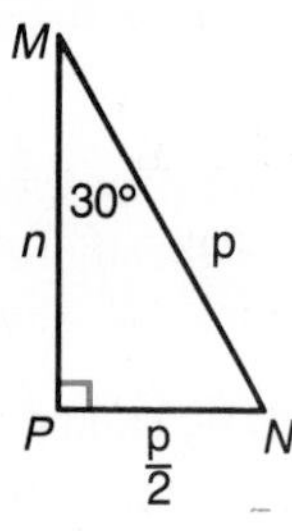

$$n^2 + \frac{p^2}{4} = p^2$$

$$n^2 = \frac{4p^2}{4} - \frac{p^2}{4}$$

$$n^2 = \frac{3p^2}{4}$$

$$n = \frac{p\sqrt{3}}{2}$$

So, $\sin \angle N = \sin 60° = \dfrac{\frac{p\sqrt{3}}{2}}{p} = \dfrac{\sqrt{3}}{2}$

$\cos \angle N = \cos 60° = \dfrac{\frac{p}{2}}{p} = \frac{1}{2}$

$\tan \angle N = \tan 60° = \dfrac{\frac{p\sqrt{3}}{2}}{\frac{p}{2}} = \sqrt{3}$

You could use the same method to find the trigonometric ratios for 30°.

So, returning to the surveying problem, if you pace off 10 meters from the base of the tree and read the angle at A to be 60°, you can apply the tangent ratio to find the height of the tree:

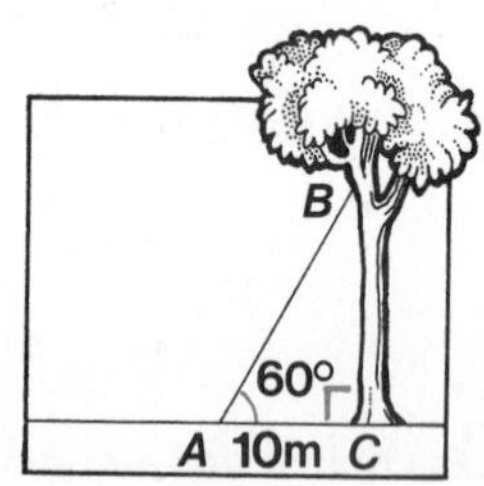

$$\tan \angle A = \tan 60° = \frac{BC}{AC},$$

$$\sqrt{3} \approx 1.732 \approx \frac{BC}{10},$$

$$17.32 \approx BC.$$

At 17.32 meters, the tree is tall enough to be a telephone pole.

Calculating the values for the table requires advanced mathematics beyond the Pythagorean Theorem. It was not, however, too advanced for the Greeks. Hipparchus (c. 140 B.C.) wrote about constructing a table of chords, which led to sine values. This was important in the Greeks' study of astronomy.

The examples above consider only two special cases of right triangles. To find the trigonometric ratios for an acute angle of any right triangle, you can refer to a table listing the sine, cosine, and tangent values for acute angles whose measures are whole degrees. Such a table, accurate to three decimal places, is provided on page 628 of this text. Given two unknowns of a trigonometric relationship, you can calculate the third value by referring to the table.

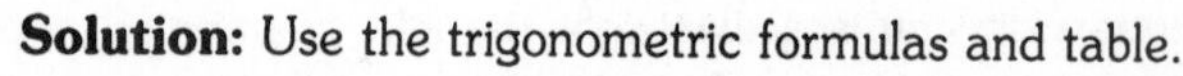
Example: If $m\angle L = 32$ and $JK = 13$, find JL.

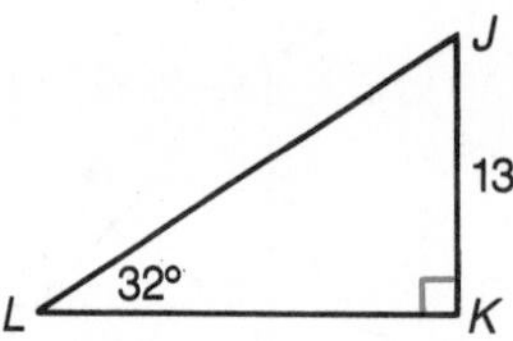

Solution: Use the trigonometric formulas and table.

$$\sin \angle L = \frac{JK}{LJ}$$

$$\sin 32° = \frac{13}{x}$$

Referring to the table, we find sin 32° = 0.5299. So,

$$0.5299 = \frac{13}{x}$$

$$x \approx 24.53$$

Many calculators have the sine, cosine, and tangent ratios as built-in functions. You enter the angle measure and then select the desired trigonometric ratio. Although the accuracy of the ratio may be expressed to the full digit display of the calculator, it can be rounded off to whatever degree of accuracy is required.

ORAL EXERCISES

1. Find the three trigonometric ratios for an angle whose measure is 30°, using the 30-60-90 triangle.

Find each of the following trigonometric ratios from the table on page 628 or using a calculator.

2. sin 74° 3. tan 16° 4. cos 49°
5. sin 33° 6. cos 86° 7. tan 57°

Use the table on page 628 or a calculator to find the measure of the angle having the indicated trigonometric ratio.

8. $\cos \angle A = 0.2250$ 9. $\sin \angle B = 0.6293$ 10. $\tan \angle C = 0.0349$
11. $\sin \angle D = 0.8910$ 12. $\cos \angle E = 0.9135$ 13. $\tan \angle F = 1.235$
14. Study the three columns in the table of trigonometric functions. Describe how the ratios change values as the angle measures increase from 1 to 89.

WRITTEN EXERCISES

A. Use the table of trigonometric ratios or a calculator to give each value in decimal form.

1. sin 11° 2. sin 52° 3. cos 82°
4. tan 68° 5. cos 60° 6. sin 70°
7. cos 46° 8. tan 19° 9. tan 9°

Find $m\angle X$ to the nearest degree, given the following trigonometric values. Use the table or a calculator.

10. $\sin \angle X = 0.9659$ 11. $\tan \angle X = 1.0000$ 12. $\sin \angle X = 0.5736$
13. $\cos \angle X = 0.5736$ 14. $\cos \angle X = 0.8910$ 15. $\tan \angle X = 7.1150$

B. Solve each of the following right triangles. (*Solving a triangle* means calculating the measures of all the unknown parts.)

16.

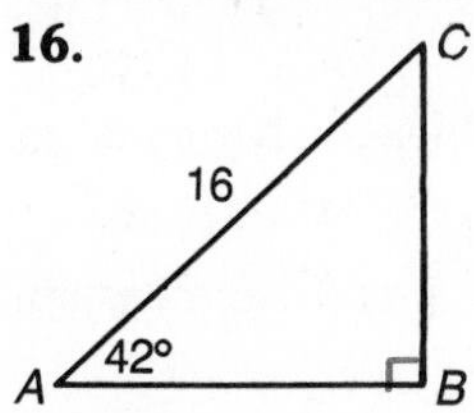

17.

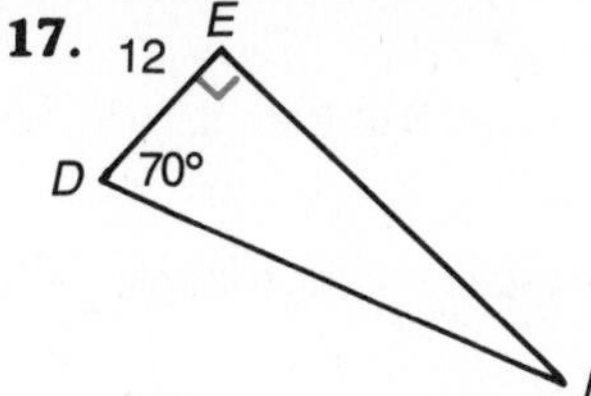

18.

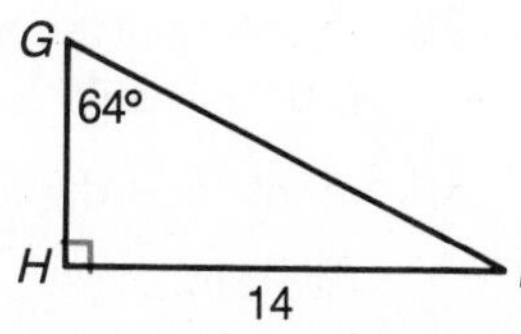

ASSIGNMENT GUIDE

Minimum 1-21 odd
Regular 1-29 odd
Maximum 1-21 odd, 25-27, 30-33

Oral Exercises

1. $\sin 30° = \frac{1}{2}$ $\cos 30° = \frac{\sqrt{3}}{2}$ $\tan 30° = \frac{\sqrt{3}}{3}$
2. 0.9613 3. 0.2867
4. 0.6561 5. 0.5446
6. 0.0698 7. 1.5400
8. 77° 9. 39°
10. 2° 11. 63°
12. 24° 13. 51°
14. Sine values increase from near 0 to 1. Cosine decreases from 1 to near 0. Tangent increases from near 0 to large numbers.

Written Exercises

1. 0.1908 2. 0.7880
3. 0.1392 4. 2.4750
5. 0.5000 6. 0.9397
7. 0.6947 8. 0.3443
9. 0.1584
10. 75° 11. 45°
12. 35° 13. 55°
14. 27° 15. 82°
16. $m\angle C = 48$, $AB \approx 11.15$, $BC \approx 10.04$
17. $m\angle F = 20$, $DF \approx 35.09$, $EF \approx 32.97$
18. $m\angle I = 26$, $GH \approx 6.83$, $GI \approx 15.58$

19. alt. ≈ 10.28

20. the area of ▱$ABCD$ = $65\sqrt{3}$

21. base ≈ 4.08
area ≈ 16.32

22. alt. ≈ 7.25
area ≈ 58

23. alt. ≈ 4.84
area ≈ 60.5

24. 37°, 53°

25. 28°, 62°

26. $r \approx 18.93$
area ≈ 49.77π

27. Alt. to base ≈ 16.48
Alts. to legs ≈ 11.28

28. no 29. yes

30. no 31. yes

32. the area of the triangle
$= \frac{1}{2}(1)(\frac{\sqrt{3}}{2})$
$= \frac{1}{2}(\frac{\sqrt{3}}{2})$
$= \cos 60° \cdot \sin 60°$

33. the area of the triangle
$= \frac{1}{2}(1)(1)$
$= \frac{1}{2}$
$= \frac{1}{2} \tan 45°$

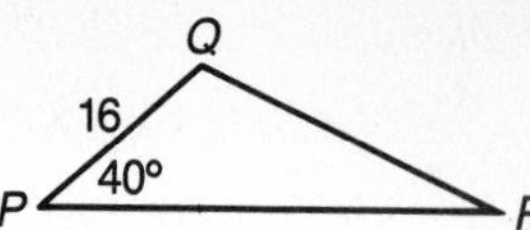

19. In ΔPQR, $m\angle P = 40$ and $PQ = 16$. Find the altitude to $\overline{PR}$.

20. In parallelogram $ABCD$, $m\angle A = 30$, $AB = 10$, and $DE = 8\sqrt{3}$. Find the area of ▱$ABCD$.

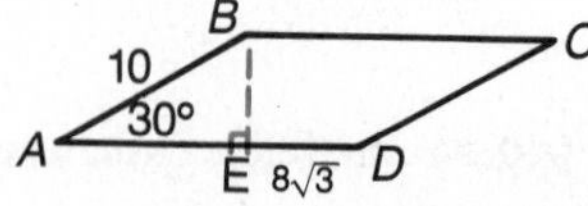

Find the areas of the following triangles.

21.

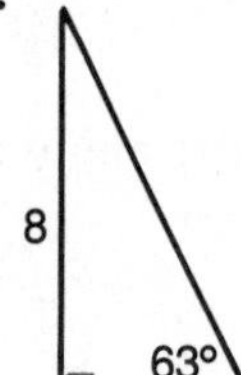

22.

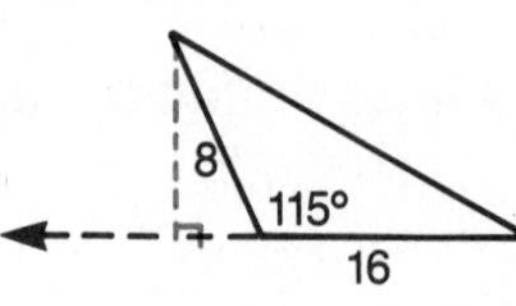

23.

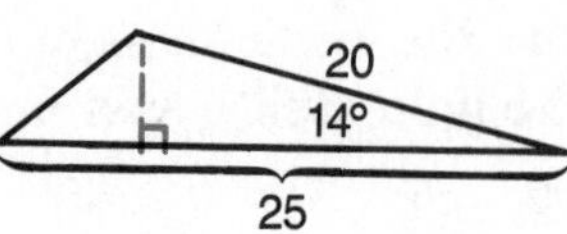

24. To the nearest degree, find the measures of the acute angles of all right triangles whose sides are proportional to the Pythagorean triple 6, 8, 10.

25. To the nearest degree, find the measures of the acute angles of all right triangles whose sides are proportional to the Pythagorean triple 8, 15, 17.

26. In ⊙P, central $\angle QPR$ measures 50°. If chord $\overline{QR}$ measures 16, find the area of the sector.

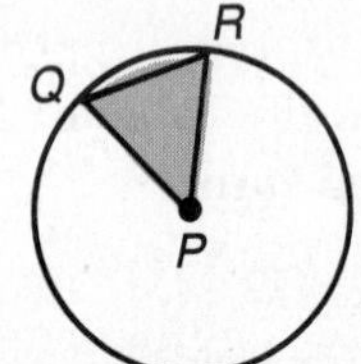

27. ΔABC is isosceles with a vertex angle of 40°. If the base of the triangle measures 12, find the lengths of the three altitudes.

C. Using values from the table or from a calculator, investigate the following relationships. Five affirmative answers are sufficient to suggest the validity of the relationship. One counterexample is sufficient to disprove the statement.

28. Does $\frac{1}{2}(\sin x) = \sin \frac{1}{2}x$?

29. Does $\sin 2x = 2 \sin x \cdot \cos x$?

30. Does $\cos (x + y) = \cos x + \cos y$?

31. Does $\tan x = \frac{\sin x}{\cos x}$?

32. Show that the area of an equilateral triangle with a side of length 1 is equal to sin 60° · cos 60°.

33. Show that the area of an isosceles right triangle with legs $\overline{XY}$ and $\overline{XZ}$ measuring 1 is $\frac{1}{2} \tan \angle Y$.

16.3 Applications of Trigonometry

Trigonometric ratios are useful in solving practical problems. One common example, introduced in the surveying problem, involves **line of sight.**

Suppose that a person standing at point X focuses or sights up to point Y. The angle formed with the horizontal line is called the **angle of elevation.** In a different setting, a person at point Y may sight a point below at X. The angle formed with the horizontal is called the **angle of depression.**

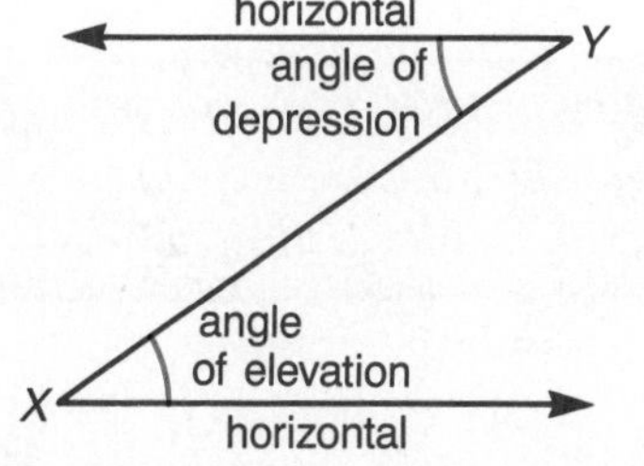

Example: A person stands in a 10th floor window of a building across the street from a skyscraper. The street is 100 feet wide. If the angle of elevation to the top of the building is 32° and the angle of depression to the bottom of the building is 43°, find the height of the skyscraper.

Solution:

$$\tan 32° = \frac{x}{100} \qquad \tan 43° = \frac{y}{100}$$

$$0.6249 \approx \frac{x}{100} \qquad 0.9325 \approx \frac{y}{100}$$

$$62.49 \approx x \qquad 93.25 \approx y$$

$62.49 + 93.25 \approx 155.74$ ft, the approximate height of the skyscraper

Example: The pilot of an airplane wants to calculate the amount of time it will take to land from the aircraft's present position. The plane starts its descent from an altitude of 3000 feet, flying at 190 feet per second. The plane is headed toward the runway at an angle of 6° from the horizontal. Find how long it will be until touchdown.

Solution: Since the runway and the original horizontal motion of the plane are parallel, congruent alternate interior angles are formed (each measuring 6°).

$$\sin 6° = \frac{3000}{d}$$

$$0.1045 \approx \frac{3000}{d}$$

$$28{,}708 \approx d$$

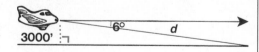

Since rate · time = distance ($r \cdot t = d$), or $t = \frac{d}{r}$, it follows that $t \approx \frac{28{,}708}{190} \approx 151$ seconds or 2.5 minutes.

OBJECTIVE

Apply trigonometric ratios to practical problem solving.

TEACHER'S NOTES

See p. T42

MIXED REVIEW

1. What is the ratio of a diagonal to any side of a square? $\sqrt{2}:1$
2. Find the perimeter of an equilateral triangle with an altitude of $4\sqrt{3}$. 24
3. Solve $3x - 2y = 3$
   $2x + y = -5$
   $(-1, -3)$
4. Which parallelogram has congruent sides? rhombus
5. Solve $x^2 - 8x + 12 = 0$. $\{6, 2\}$

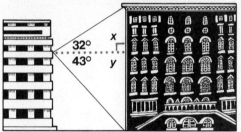

TEACHER'S RESOURCE MASTERS

Practice Master 51, Part 1
Quiz 31

The trigonometric ratios have been defined for *all* acute angles between 0 and 90. Statements in mathematics other than definitions, theorems, or postulates that are true for all replacements of the variable are called **identities**. Identities are similar to theorems because they can be proven. In a certain sense, they are stronger than theorems, because they hold for all values of the variable.

THEOREM 16.1 (The Pythagorean Identity)
Given a right triangle with sides a and b and hypotenuse c, $\sin^2 \angle A + \cos^2 \angle A = 1$ for any acute $\angle A$ of the triangle.

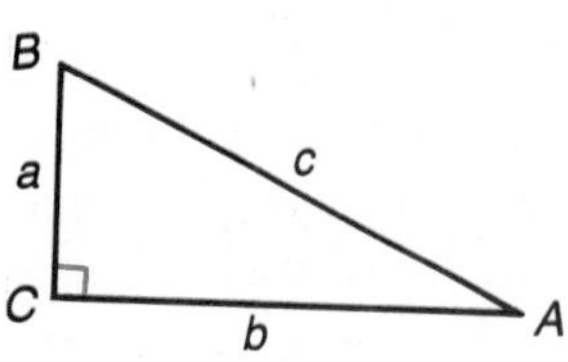

Given: Right ΔABC, as shown

Prove: $\sin^2 \angle A + \cos^2 \angle A = 1$

Proof: By the Pythagorean Theorem, $a^2 + b^2 = c^2$. Dividing each side of the equation by c^2 results in

$$\frac{a^2}{c^2} + \frac{b^2}{c^2} = \frac{c^2}{c^2} = 1.$$

By definition, $\sin \angle A = \frac{a}{c}$ and $\cos \angle A = \frac{b}{c}$, so

$$\sin^2 \angle A + \cos^2 \angle A = 1 \text{ for any acute } \angle A.$$

Note that the exponent 2 is written before the angle name. Sin $\angle A^2$ suggests that the measure of the angle should be squared before the trigonometric ratio is applied.

THEOREM 16.2
Given a right triangle with sides a and b and hypotenuse c, $\tan \angle A = \frac{\sin \angle A}{\cos \angle A}$ for any acute $\angle A$ of the triangle.

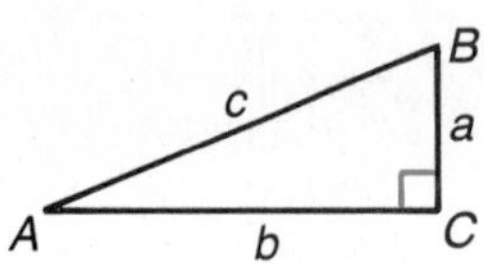

Given: Right ΔABC with legs a and b and hypotenuse c

Prove: $\tan \angle A = \frac{\sin \angle A}{\cos \angle A}$

Proof: By the definition of sine and cosine, $\sin \angle A = \frac{a}{c}$ and $\cos \angle A = \frac{b}{c}$. So, $\frac{\sin \angle A}{\cos \angle A} = \frac{\frac{a}{c}}{\frac{b}{c}} = \frac{a}{b}$. By the definition of tangent, $\tan \angle A = \frac{a}{b}$, so $\tan \angle A = \frac{\sin \angle A}{\cos \angle A}$.

Another identity, Theorem 16.3, follows from the fact that the acute angles in a right triangle are complementary.

THEOREM 16.3
Given right ΔXYZ, if $\angle X$ and $\angle Y$ are complementary, then $\sin \angle X = \cos \angle Y$, and $\cos \angle X = \sin \angle Y$.

Sine and cosine are often called **cofunctions.** So, Theorem 16.3 can be restated as "*Cofunctions of complementary angles are equal.*" The proof is left as an exercise.

Many other identities can be derived from the few introduced here. To establish an identity, you first conjecture the equality you wish to prove. Then, by regrouping and restating terms, you transform each side of the conjecture equation independently until the two sides match.

Example: Prove that $1 - (\cos \angle X - \sin \angle X)^2 = 2 \cdot \sin \angle X \cdot \cos \angle X$

Solution:

$$1 - (\cos \angle X - \sin \angle X)^2 = 2 \cdot \sin \angle X \cdot \cos \angle X$$
$$1 - (\cos \angle X - \sin \angle X)(\cos \angle X - \sin \angle X) = 2 \cdot \sin \angle X \cdot \cos \angle X$$
$$1 - (\cos^2 \angle X - 2 \cdot \sin \angle X \cdot \cos \angle X + \sin^2 \angle X) = 2 \cdot \sin \angle X \cdot \cos \angle X$$
$$1 - (1 - 2 \cdot \sin \angle X \cdot \cos \angle X) = 2 \cdot \sin \angle X \cdot \cos \angle X$$
$$1 - 1 + 2 \cdot \sin \angle X \cdot \cos \angle X = 2 \cdot \sin \angle X \cdot \cos \angle X$$
$$2 \cdot \sin \angle X \cdot \cos \angle X = 2 \cdot \sin \angle X \cdot \cos \angle X$$

This relationship between sine and cosine now holds for *all* values of x

ASSIGNMENT GUIDE

Minimum 1-7
Regular 1-13 odd
Maximum 1-7 odd, 9-15

ORAL EXERCISES

1. Name the angle of elevation from point X to point Y; from point Z to point Y.
2. Name the angle of depression from point Y to point Z.
3. How would you prove the identity $\frac{\tan \angle A}{\tan \angle B} = \frac{\sin \angle A \cdot \cos \angle B}{\sin \angle B \cdot \cos \angle A}$?

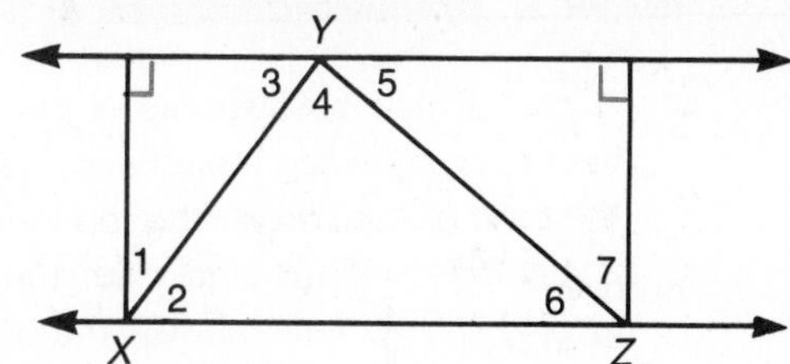

Oral Exercises

1. $\angle 2$, $\angle 6$
2. $\angle 5$
3. Show $\frac{\sin \angle A \cdot \cos \angle B}{\sin \angle B \cdot \cos \angle A} = \frac{\tan \angle A}{\tan \angle B}$.

WRITTEN EXERCISES

A. 1. A surveyor needs to find the width of a river. Sighting a tree across the river, the surveyor walks 100 yards along the river bank. If the line of sight to the tree is 64°, find the width of the river.

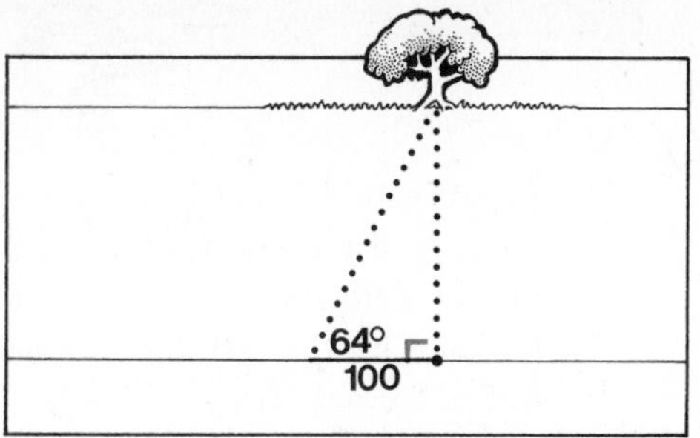

Written Exercises

1. 205 yd

2. ≈28.79 ft

3. ≈975.9 mi

4. 84°

5. ≈17 ft

6. ≈41.8 ft

7. ≈1018.9 ft

8. $m\angle = 34$, 6.6 ft

2. A couple, planning to elope, needs an extension ladder tall enough to reach the second floor, 20 feet from the ground. If the ladder has an angle of elevation of 44° to the window, how long must the ladder be?

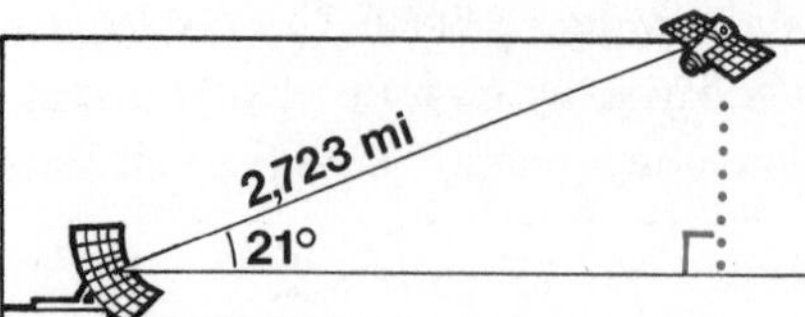

3. A radar station tracking the path of a satellite, shows the angle of elevation to be 21°. If the line of sight distance is 2,723 miles, what is the altitude of the satellite?

B. **4.** The blades of a pair of scissors are 6 inches in length from their point of intersection. If the opening from the point of one blade to the point of the other measures 8 inches, find the angle measurement at the point of intersection of the blades.

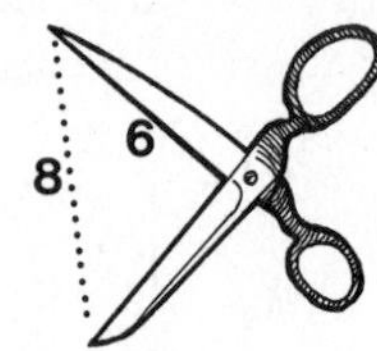

5. A ham radio operator has a tall transmitter on the roof of the house, which is 35 feet tall. If the angle of elevation to the tip of the transmitter from a point 30 feet along the ground is 60°, how tall is the transmitter?

6. A tree struck by lightning is partially broken and bent over, touching the ground. If the distance from the base of the tree to the top (now on the ground) is 12 feet, and the angle the top makes with the ground is 58°, how tall was the tree?

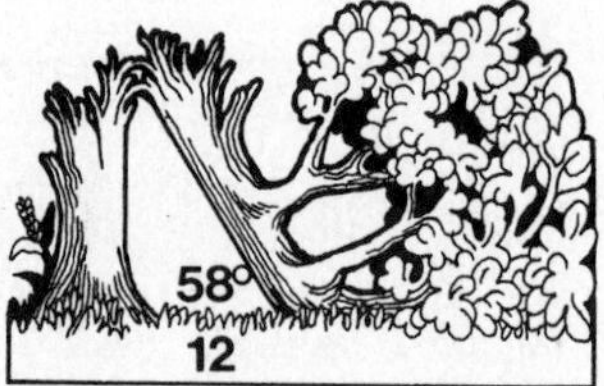

7. A pilot approaching the airport for a landing sees a traffic helicopter below at an angle of depression of 11°. If the line of sight distance is 5340 feet, what is the altitude difference of the two aircraft?

8. A guy wire 12 feet long is attached to a tree for support. If the guy wire is fixed to the ground 10 feet from the base of the tree, what is the angle that the wire makes with the ground? How far up the tree is the guy wire attached?

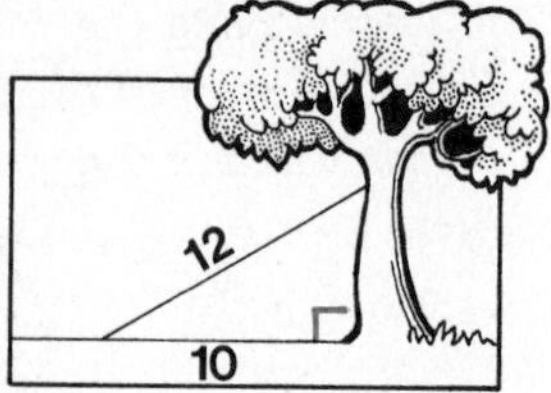

C. **9.** Prove Theorem 16.3.

Verify each of the following identities.

10. $\cos \angle X \cdot \tan \angle X = \sin \angle X$

11. $(1 + \tan^2 \angle X) \sin^2 \angle X = \tan^2 \angle X$

12. $\dfrac{\cos \angle X}{1 - \sin \angle X} = \dfrac{1 + \sin \angle X}{\cos \angle X}$

13. $\dfrac{\sin^4 \angle X - \cos^4 \angle X}{\sin \angle X - \cos \angle X} = \sin \angle X + \cos \angle X$

14. $(1 - \sin^2 \angle X)(1 + \tan^2 \angle X) = 1$

15. $\dfrac{\cos \angle X}{\cos \angle X - \sin \angle X} = \dfrac{1}{1 - \tan \angle X}$

SELF-QUIZ

Complete each statement in Exercises 1–6.

1. The sine of an acute angle in a right triangle is the ratio between the _____ and the length of the hypotenuse.

2. The cosine of an acute angle in a right triangle is the ratio between the _____ and the length of the hypotenuse.

3. The tangent of an acute angle in a right triangle is the ratio between the _____ and the _____.

4. In a family of similar right triangles, the trigonometric ratios for any corresponding congruent angles are _____.

5. The maximum value for the cosine of an angle is _____.

6. The statement $\sin^2 \angle A + \cos^2 \angle A = 1$ is called a(n) _____.

Solve ΔABC and use a trigonometric table or calculator to answer Exercises 7 through 10.

A, 5, 13, B, C

7. $\cos \angle C =$ _____ **8.** $\sin \angle A =$ _____

9. $m\angle A \approx$ _____ **10.** $m\angle C \approx$ _____

11. From a window 150 feet high above the ground, a person sees two newspaper stands below. One has an angle of depression of 20°, and the other has an angle of depression of 58°. How far apart are the two stands?

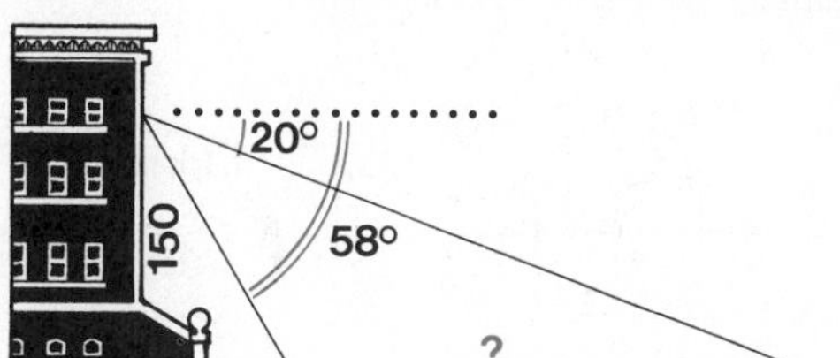

9. By definition, $\sin \angle X = \frac{a}{c}$, $\cos \angle Y = \frac{a}{c}$, $\sin \angle Y = \frac{b}{c}$, $\cos \angle X = \frac{b}{c}$.

10. $\cos \angle X \cdot \tan \angle X = \cos \angle X \cdot \frac{\sin \angle X}{\cos \angle X} = \sin \angle X$.

11. $(1 + \tan^2 \angle X) \sin^2 \angle X = \frac{\cos^2 \angle X + \sin^2 \angle X}{\cos^2 \angle X} \cdot \sin^2 \angle X = \frac{1}{\cos^2 \angle X} \cdot \sin^2 \angle X = \tan^2 \angle X$.

12. $\frac{\cos \angle X}{1 - \sin \angle X} = \frac{\cos \angle X(1 + \sin \angle X)}{(1 - \sin \angle X)(1 + \sin \angle X)} = \frac{\cos \angle X(1 + \sin \angle X)}{1 - \sin^2 \angle X} = \frac{\cos \angle X(1 + \sin \angle X)}{\cos^2 \angle X} = \frac{1 + \sin \angle X}{\cos \angle X}$

13. $\frac{\sin^4 \angle X - \cos^4 \angle X}{\sin \angle X - \cos \angle X} = \frac{(\sin^2 \angle X - \cos^2 \angle X)(\sin^2 \angle X + \cos^2 \angle X)}{\sin \angle X - \cos \angle X} = \frac{(\sin \angle X - \cos \angle X)(\sin \angle X + \cos \angle X)(1)}{\sin \angle X - \cos \angle X} = \sin \angle X + \cos \angle X$

14. $(1 - \sin^2 \angle X)(1 + \tan^2 \angle X) = \cos^2 \angle X\left(\frac{\cos^2 \angle X + \sin^2 \angle X}{\cos^2 \angle X}\right) = \cos^2 \angle X + \sin^2 \angle X = 1$

15. $\frac{1}{1 - \tan \angle X} = \frac{1}{\frac{\cos \angle X - \sin \angle X}{\cos \angle X}} = \frac{\cos \angle X}{\cos \angle X - \sin \angle X}$

Self-Quiz

1. length of the opposite side
2. length of the adjacent side
3. length of the opposite side, length of the adjacent side
4. equal
5. 1
6. identity
7. $\frac{12}{13}$
8. $\frac{12}{13}$
9. 67°
10. 23°
11. ≈318 ft

OBJECTIVE

Find magnitude and direction of a given vector.

TEACHER'S NOTES

See p. T42

MIXED REVIEW

1. Solve $\sqrt{4x} = 6$. 9
2. Find the volume of a sphere with a diameter of 12. 288π
3. If a circle has a circumference of 18π, what is its area? 81π
4. Solve $\frac{x+2}{5} = \frac{6}{7}$. $x = 2\frac{2}{7}$
5. Factor $18x^2 + 25x - 3$. $(9x - 1)(2x + 3)$

TEACHER'S RESOURCE MASTERS

Practice Master 51, Part 2

16.4 Vectors

Trigonometry is often useful in solving problems that involve velocity, gravity, and other forces of nature. In such problems, knowing the magnitude of the force alone may not be sufficient; you may also need the direction of the force.

For example, a train leaves St. Louis at a speed of 65 miles per hour. You can determine how many miles the train will travel in four hours, but, unless you know the direction of its motion, you cannot predict where the train will be.

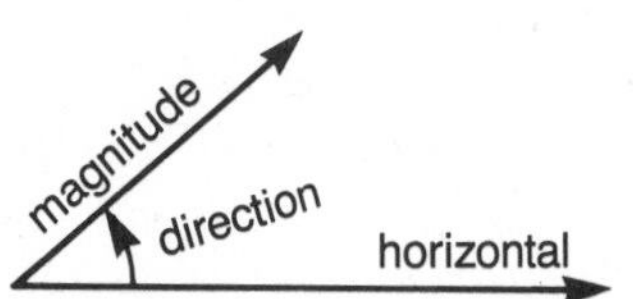

Vectors are used to express mathematical values when both the magnitude and the direction of a quantity are involved. A vector represents movement from an initial point to a terminal point. The distance between these points is the **magnitude of the vector.** The angle formed between a horizontal line and the line segment joining the initial point and the terminal point is the **direction of the vector.**

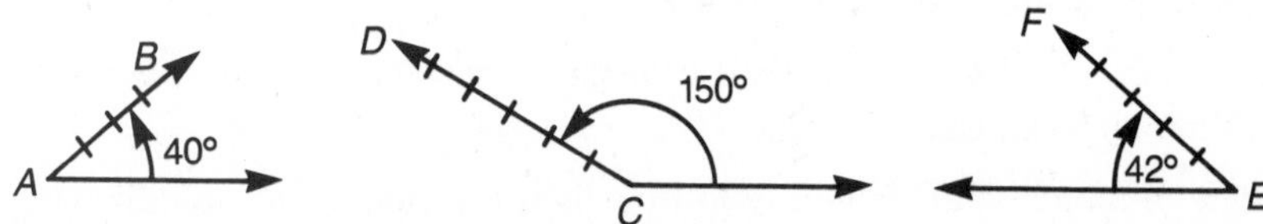

The notation used to name a vector emphasizes the idea of motion. The vectors shown above are named $\overrightarrow{AB}$, $\overrightarrow{CD}$, and $\overrightarrow{EF}$. In each case, an arrowhead drawn from the initial point to the terminal point indicates the motion. This representation is often called a **directed line segment.** Although the notation is identical to the symbol for a ray in geometry, there is an important difference between the two. A vector has a specific terminal endpoint, but a ray continues indefinitely. You will be able to determine from the context of a problem whether $\overrightarrow{AB}$ refers to a vector or a ray.

The Cartesian plane is an ideal way to represent directed line segments. Using the positive x-axis as the horizontal baseline, you can draw the angle of a vector's direction with a protractor. The grid marks on your graph paper allow you to represent any magnitude according to a ratio you select. So, on a scale of 1:25, a vector 4 units long represents a magnitude of 100 units.

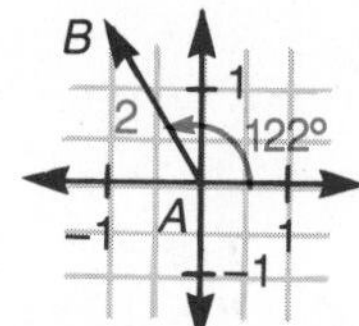

Example: What are the magnitude and direction of $\overrightarrow{AB}$?

Solution: $\overrightarrow{AB}$ has a magnitude of 2 units and an angle of direction of 122°.

Drawing vectors on graph paper also offers a logical way to calculate magnitude without using tools of measurement. If the initial point is at the origin, the terminal point can be labeled by the appropriate x- and y-coordinates. The Pythagorean Theorem is then applied to the resulting right triangle, and the magnitude of the vector (or length of the hypotenuse) can be calculated.

Example: What is the magnitude of $\overrightarrow{OX}$?

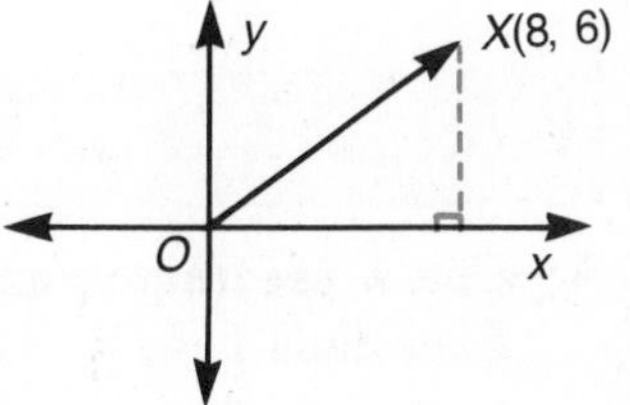

Solution: By the Pythagorean Theorem, $(OX)^2 = 8^2 + 6^2 = 100$, so the magnitude is 10, written as $|\overrightarrow{OX}| = 10$.

The distance formula can be applied to the two endpoints of a vector regardless of its location on the grid.

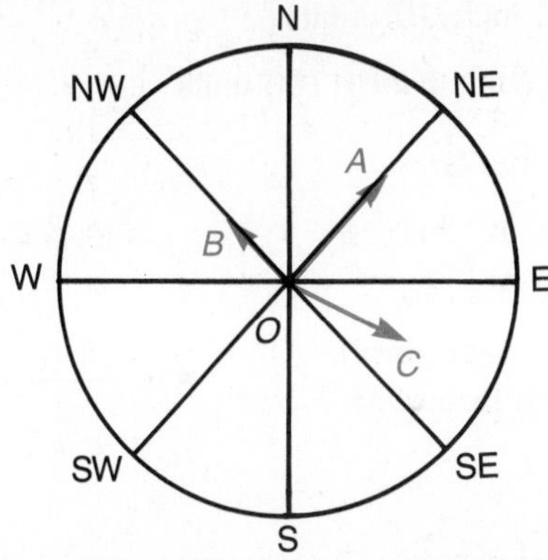

The marks on a compass may also be used to represent the direction of a vector.

Thus, in the figure, $\overrightarrow{OA}$ has a northeast direction, while $\overrightarrow{OB}$ has a northwest direction. The direction of $\overrightarrow{OC}$ is difficult to identify from the compass shown, but you can see that $\overrightarrow{OA} \neq \overrightarrow{AO}$, for any vector $\overrightarrow{OA}$. Since their directions are different, the two vectors cannot be equal. Only if two vectors have equal magnitude and the same direction can they be called **equal vectors.**

Since direction is determined by a horizontal line and a directed line segment, vectors can be translated throughout the coordinate plane. This will prove useful in the next lesson, where arithmetic operations of vectors are explained.

ASSIGNMENT GUIDE

Minimum 1-7
Regular 1-13 odd
Maximum 1-9 odd, 11-14

ORAL EXERCISES

Refer to the figure to answer the following questions.

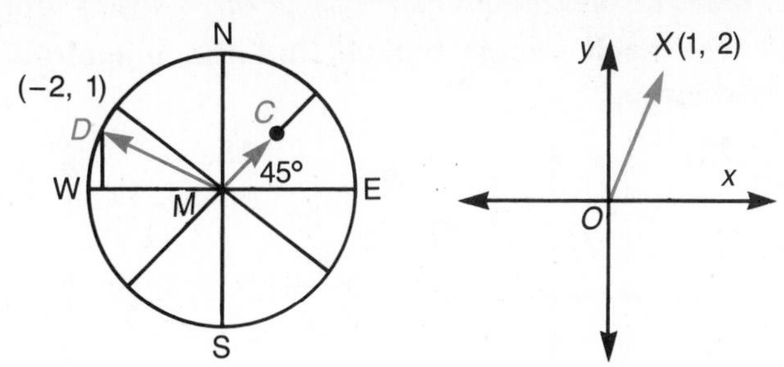

1. Does $\overrightarrow{MC}$ have the same direction as $\overrightarrow{OX}$?
2. Does $\overrightarrow{MD}$ have the same magnitude as $\overrightarrow{OX}$?

Oral Exercises

1. No; $\overrightarrow{OX}$ is not at 45°.
2. yes, $\sqrt{5}$

Can the following numerical quantities be represented by vectors?

3. the current in a river
4. velocity of the wind
5. 5% sales tax
6. your age in 10 years
7. gravity on a 150-pound adult

WRITTEN EXERCISES

A. Use a protractor and the indicated scale to draw the vectors described in Exercises 1–4.

1. a speed of 50 miles per hour at 48°; 1 inch:100 units

2. the pull of gravity with a magnitude of 350; 1 inch:100 units

B. 3. a pull of 75 pounds at 145°; $\frac{1}{2}$ inch:50 units

4. a velocity of 1000 miles per hour at 74°; $\frac{1}{2}$ inch:250 units

5. Copy the figure at the right onto your own graph paper. Then, on the same graph, sketch three vectors equal to the given vector.

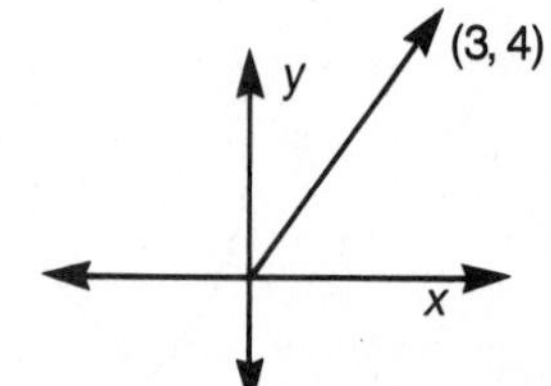

Find the magnitude of each vector shown.

6.

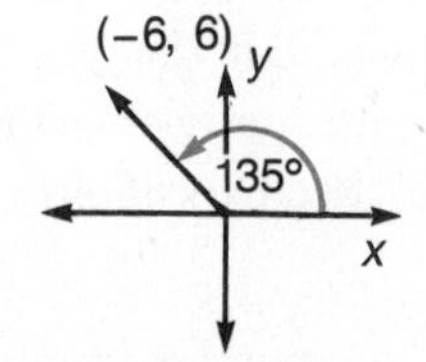

7.

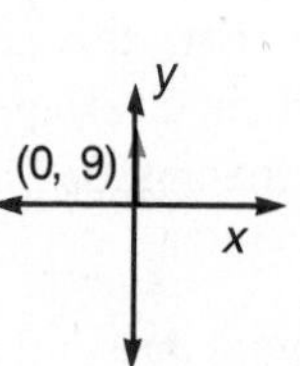

8.

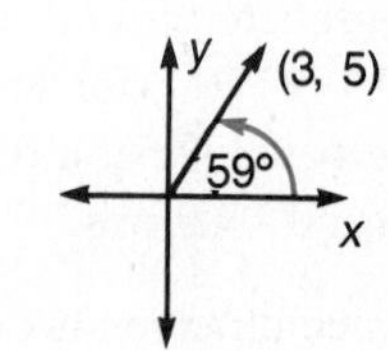

9.

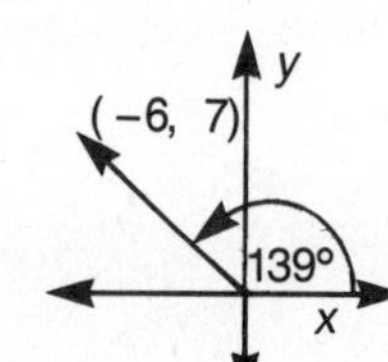

10.

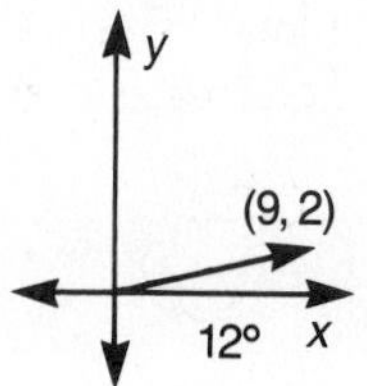

11.

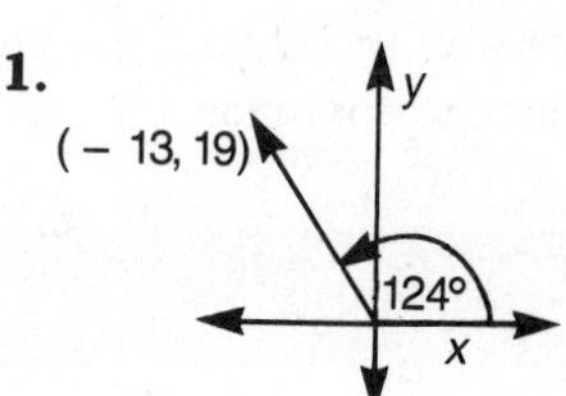

C. For each vector below, find the magnitude and direction to the nearest degree.

12.

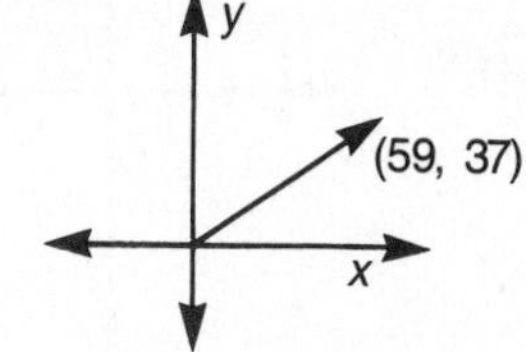

13.

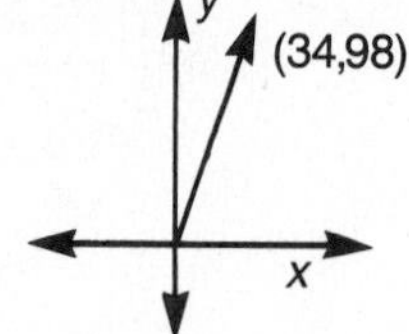

14.

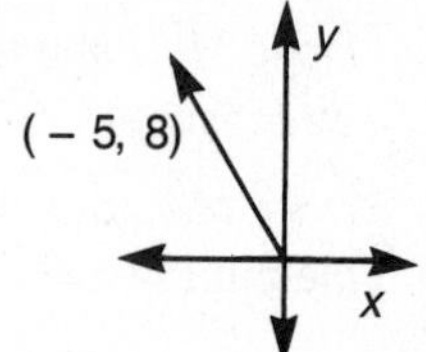

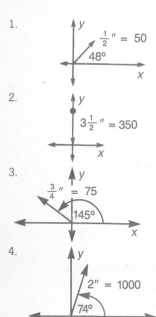

3. yes 4. yes
5. no 6. no
7. yes

Written Exercises

1. $\frac{1}{2}'' = 50$, 48°
2. $3\frac{1}{2}'' = 350$
3. $\frac{3}{4}'' = 75$, 145°
4. $2'' = 1000$, 74°
5. Sketches will vary.
6. $6\sqrt{2}$ 7. 9
8. $\sqrt{34}$ 9. $\sqrt{85}$
10. $\sqrt{85}$ 11. $\sqrt{530}$
12. 32°, $5\sqrt{194}$
13. 71°, $2\sqrt{2690}$
14. 122°, $\sqrt{89}$

16.5 Addition of Vectors

When vectors are combined, both their magnitudes and their directions must be considered.

Example: A shopper is impatiently walking up the steps of a moving escalator in the same direction as the escalator's motion. The escalator is moving at 3 miles per hour and the shopper is walking at 1.5 mph. What is the person's total rate of speed?

Solution: Those standing still on the escalator are moving at 3 mph. A person moving 3 mph by the escalator's power and 1.5 mph by leg power is moving at a total rate of 4.5 mph.

When a reference to motion involves both speed and direction, as in the example above, the rate of speed is called **velocity**. Velocity is a vector quantity.

Example: You are a movie stunt person in a scene on the roof of a moving train. You are walking toward the caboose. The train is travelling at 75 mph and you are walking at 3 mph. What is your total velocity?

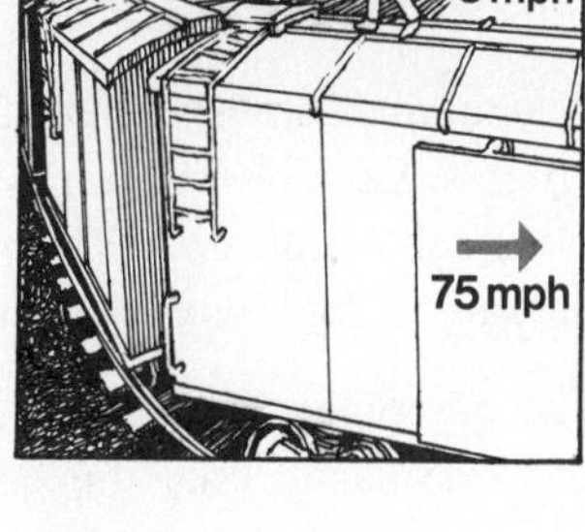

Solution: Walking in the direction opposite that of the train's motion offsets some of the train's forward advance relative to how much ground you, the stunt person, are covering. If the train is moving forward at 75 mph, and you are moving backward at 3 mph, then your net velocity is 75 − 3, or 72 mph in a forward direction.

In these two examples, it is important to notice that the second motion is in either exactly the same or exactly the opposite direction as the first. As a result, in these cases, combining the vectors is similar to combining numbers.

1. If two vectors moving in the *same direction* are added, the result is a vector with the same direction and a magnitude equal to the arithmetic sum of the given magnitudes.

2. If two vectors moving in exactly *opposite* directions are added, the result is a vector moving in the direction of the original vector with greater magnitude. The magnitude of the sum, or **resulting vector,** is the absolute value of the difference of the original magnitudes.

These rules are valid as long as the forces represented by the vectors are moving in the same or opposite directions. Not all sets of vectors fall neatly into these two categories.

OBJECTIVES

Add vectors.
Find net velocity and force by parallelogram method.

TEACHER'S NOTES

See p. T42

MIXED REVIEW

1. At what point does the graph of $y = x^2$ cross the x-axis? (0, 0)
2. Solve $2x - 3(4 - x) = 14$. $x = 5\frac{1}{5}$
3. Multiply $(2x - 3)(5x + 4)$. $10x^2 - 7x - 12$
4. Multiply $\sqrt{9} \cdot \sqrt{25}$. 15
5. Simplify $\sqrt{[6 - (-2)]^2 + (7 - 1)^2}$. 10

TEACHER'S RESOURCE MASTERS

Practice Master 52, Part 1

Example: A ferry is crossing a river, moving due north at a speed of 40 mph. The river current is flowing due east at a rate of 4 mph. What is the net velocity of the ferry?

Solution: The net velocity must be represented by a new vector that has the same effect on motion as the original two vectors combined. The figure at the right shows the two vectors originating at the same point. Vector addition considers first the full motion of one vector and, where it ends, adds the full motion of the second vector. This is accomplished by translating one vector to the endpoint of the other, as shown in the figure. Then, a new vector can be drawn to connect the initial point of one original vector to the terminal point of the other. This new vector represents the sum of the two original vectors. You can see from the figure why this is called the **parallelogram method for addition of vectors.**

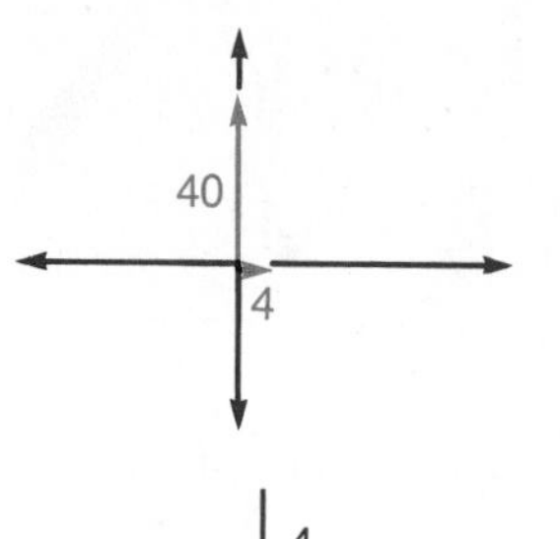

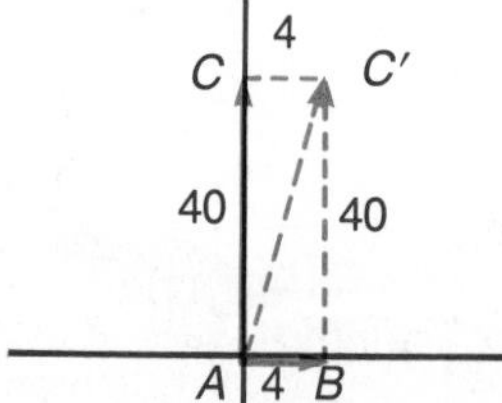

In terms of the example, if $\overrightarrow{AB}$ is the vector representing the motion of the current, and $\overrightarrow{BC'}$ is the translated vector representing the motion of the ferry, then $\overrightarrow{AC'}$ has the same effect as the sum of $\overrightarrow{AB}$ and $\overrightarrow{AC}$. Applying the Pythagorean Theorem, $4^2 + 40^2 = x^2$, so $x = 4\sqrt{101}$.

Any number of vectors can be combined using this translation process. Each new vector is translated to start where the previous one terminated. The final terminal point and the origin determine the resultant vector.

The parallelogram method is strictly a graphical representation that shows only the general direction and approximate magnitude of the sum. The next lesson will use trigonometry to find the exact values for the magnitude and direction of a resultant vector.

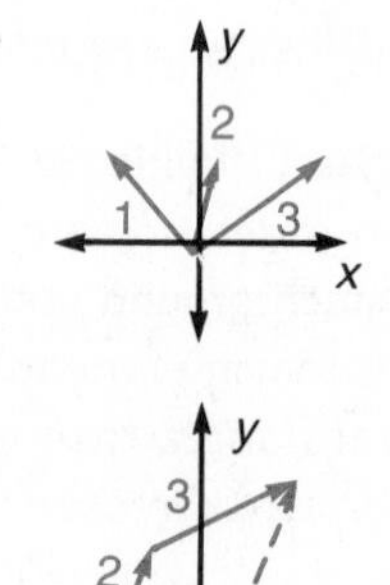

ASSIGNMENT GUIDE

Minimum 1-6
Regular 1-11 odd
Maximum 1-7 odd, 8-11

ORAL EXERCISES

Oral Exercises

1. The person pulling with a force of 75 lb will win with an advantage of 25-lb pull in his or her direction.

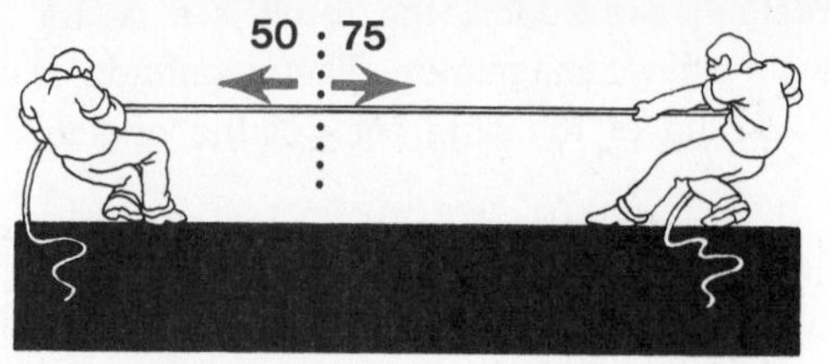

1. In a tug-of-war game, one person is pulling the rope with a force of 75 pounds, while the other is pulling in the opposite direction with a force of 50 pounds. Who will win the game and why?

2. State the rules for adding forces that have the same or opposite directions.

3. John had to run some errands on the way to the library. Describe how the resultant vector of John's travels can be found.

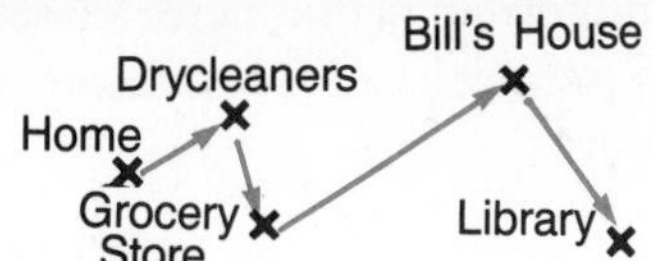

WRITTEN EXERCISES

A. **1.** On a moving sidewalk at the airport, Bill realizes that he needs to move quickly in order to catch his plane. If he walks 3.5 miles per hour, and the sidewalk is moving 7 miles per hour, how fast is Bill moving relative to the stationary floor?

On a flight from New York to Los Angeles, a plane encounters a head wind blowing from the west at 80 miles per hour.

2. If the absolute velocity of the plane is 600 mph, what is the actual velocity of the aircraft while meeting the head wind?

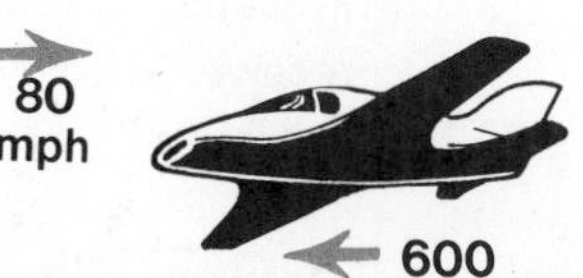

3. Travel time is estimated at $5\frac{1}{2}$ hours. What is the distance of the flight?

4. A family purchased a sofa for a room on the second floor of their house. Since the sofa will not fit through the doorway, the decision is made to haul the sofa up by a rope through a window. Three people are pulling on the rope with forces of 75 pounds, 90 pounds, and 50 pounds, as shown. What is the total pull on the rope?

B. **Copy the following pairs of vectors on your own graph paper. Then use the parallelogram method to add each pair.**

5.

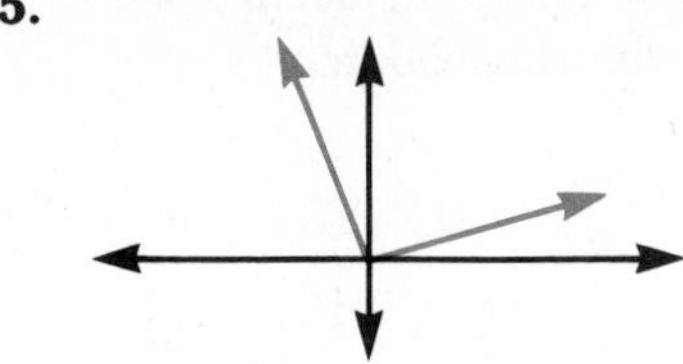

6.

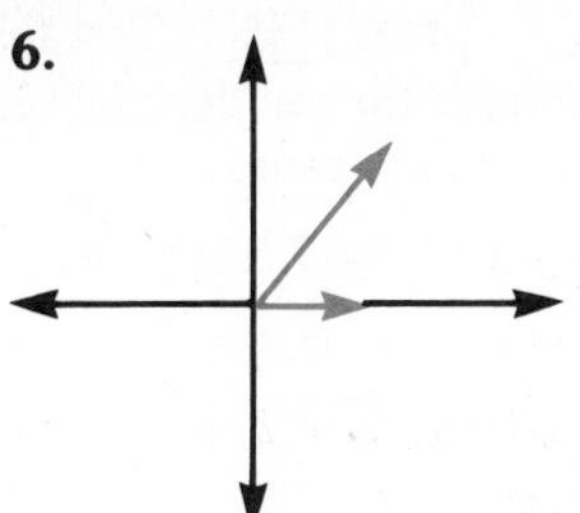

7.

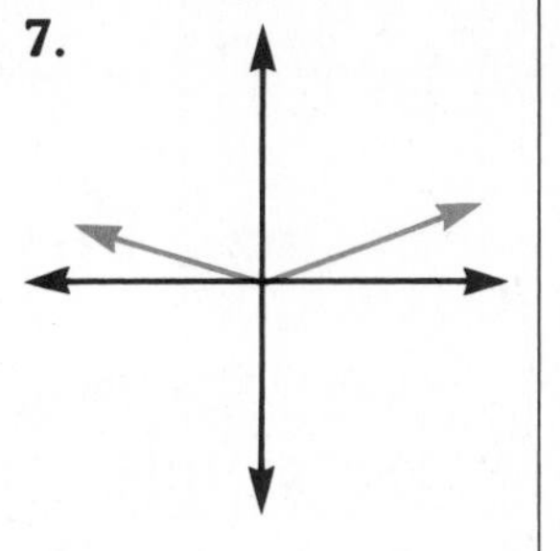

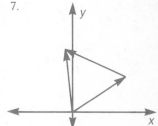

2. If the vectors are in the same direction, the resultant vector has a magnitude that is the total of the given vector magnitudes and has the same direction. If the vectors are in opposite directions, the resultant vector has a magnitude that is the absolute value of the difference between the magnitudes of the given vectors and has the direction of the vector of greater magnitude.
3. The resultant vector of John's travels will be the vector whose beginning point is John's home and whose terminal point is the library.

Written Exercises
1. 10.5 mph 2. 520 mph
3. 2,860 mi 4. 215 lb
5.

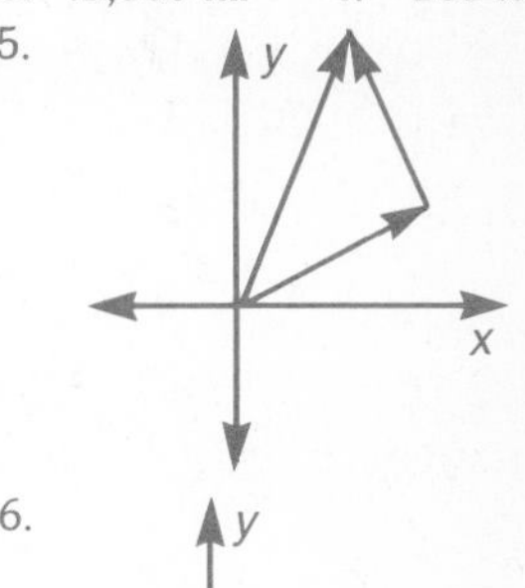

6.

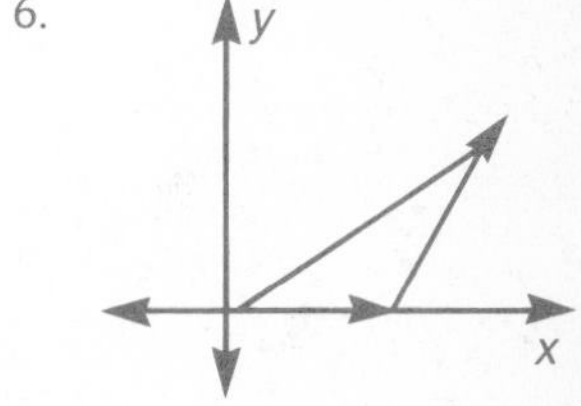

7.

8. 215.87 mph

9. the vector $\overrightarrow{AE}$

10.

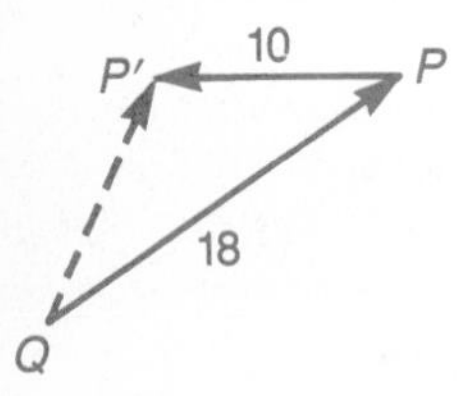

11.

Calculator

1. 82.3°
2. 12.5°
3. 67.4°
4. 40.4°
5. 22.2°
6. 69.8°

8. A pilot is flying a plane due west at 210 miles per hour. The wind is blowing 50 mph from a due north direction. What is the approximate velocity of the plane? (Use a calculator to achieve as much accuracy as possible.)

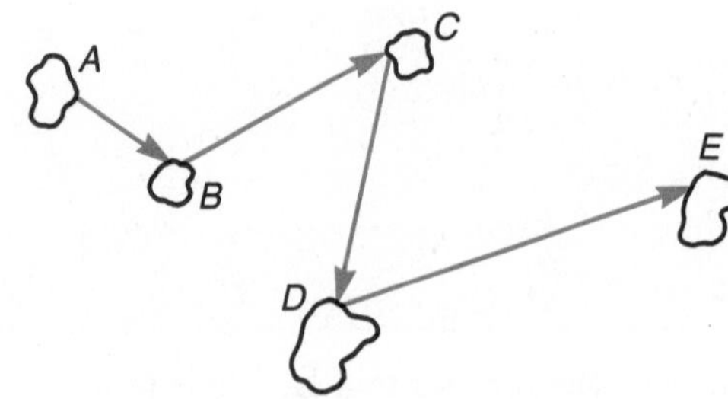

9. A cruise ship is stopping at various ports for the vacationers aboard, as represented by the figure. What single vector is the result of the whole trip?

C. 10. A quarterback lobs a ball to the pass receiver, who is 18 yards away in the position shown. Just as the ball goes into the air, a 10 mph gust of wind blows from due east. Ignoring the force of gravity, make a sketch showing where the pass receiver should move to catch the ball.

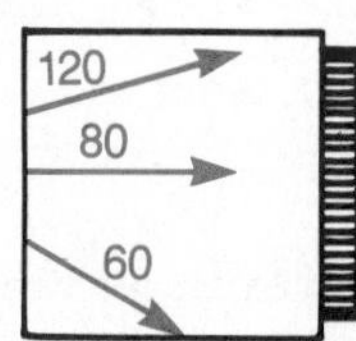

11. Three people are pushing a piano into place. Let the force of friction be negligible and the forces of the three people as given in the figure. Sketch how the piano will actually move along the floor.

CALCULATOR

If your calculator has an inverse function key (INV), you can find the angle if you know the sine. Enter the sine, press INV , press SIN . Test this for the other functions. Find the angles (to one decimal place) with the following trigonometric ratios.

1. $\tan \angle X = 7.3948$ **2.** $\sin \angle A = 0.2167$

3. $\cos \angle J = 0.3849$ **4.** $\cos \angle Y = 0.7618$

5. $\tan \angle C = 0.4081$ **6.** $\sin \angle F = 0.9384$

16.6 Solving Problems Using Vectors

The trigonometric ratios are especially useful in solving problems involving vectors. Consider a vector in **standard vector position,** with its initial point at the origin (P) and its terminal point at R. To determine the ordered pair that names R, draw the perpendicular from R to the x-axis. $\triangle PQR$ is a right triangle whose sides correspond to the x- and y-coordinates of point R. You can, therefore, find the coordinates of R by solving $\triangle PQR$, using the trigonometric ratios:

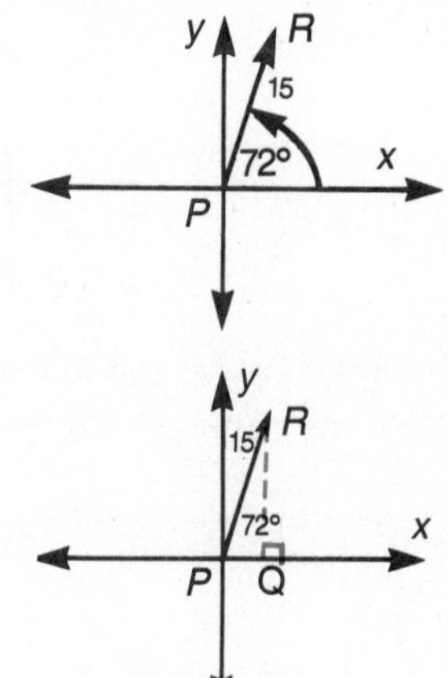

$$\sin 72° = \frac{y}{15} \qquad \cos 72° = \frac{x}{15}$$

$$0.9511 = \frac{y}{15} \qquad 0.3090 = \frac{x}{15}$$

$$14.2665 = y \qquad 4.6350 = x$$

It follows that R is the point (4.635, 14.2665). The distance formula can be applied to $\overrightarrow{PR}$ to check the accuracy of the magnitude.

$$\begin{aligned} |\overrightarrow{PR}| &= \sqrt{(14.2665)^2 + (4.635)^2} \\ &= \sqrt{203.53 + 21.48} \\ &= \sqrt{225.01} \\ &\approx 15 \end{aligned}$$

The slight inexactness between the solution of the distance formula and the given magnitude arises from rounding off the trigonometric ratios. The solution is close enough to be acceptable, though.

According to the methods in the last section, you know that $\overrightarrow{PQ} + \overrightarrow{QR} = \overrightarrow{PR}$ from the definition of vector addition. By a translation, you can find a vertical component to $\overrightarrow{QR}$ along the y-axis of the Cartesian plane. $\overrightarrow{PS}$ and $\overrightarrow{PQ}$ are called **vector components** of $\overrightarrow{PR}$, because $\overrightarrow{PS}$ and $\overrightarrow{PQ}$ have the same effect of motion on point P as $\overrightarrow{PR}$ has. Although vector components are often defined along the x- and y-axes, by the translation of equal vectors, *any* two vectors that combine to give the third are considered components.

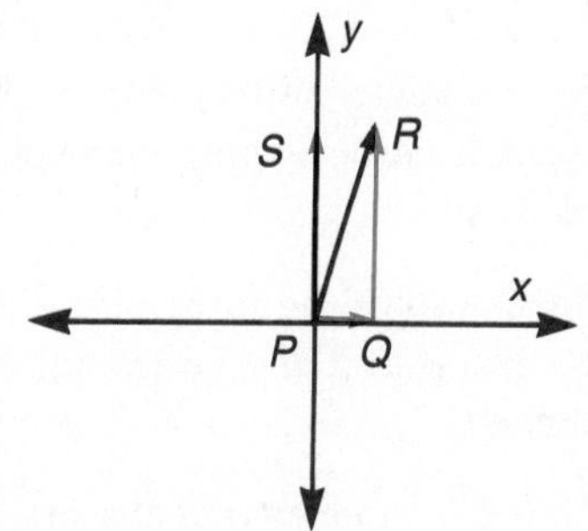

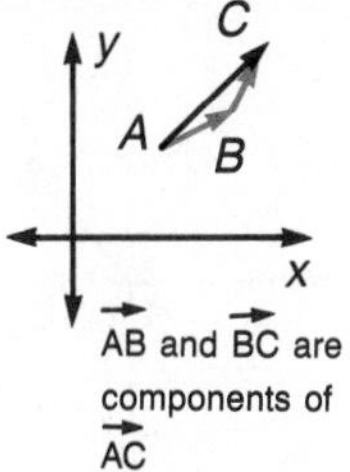

$\overrightarrow{AB}$ and $\overrightarrow{BC}$ are components of $\overrightarrow{AC}$

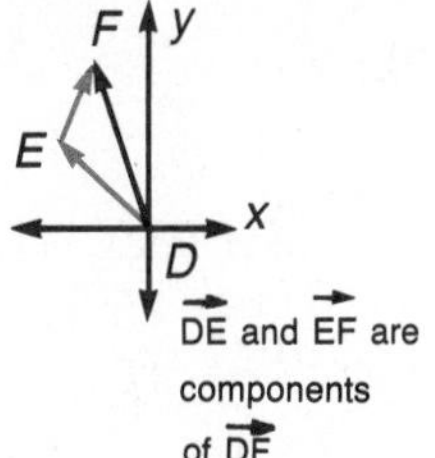

$\overrightarrow{DE}$ and $\overrightarrow{EF}$ are components of $\overrightarrow{DF}$

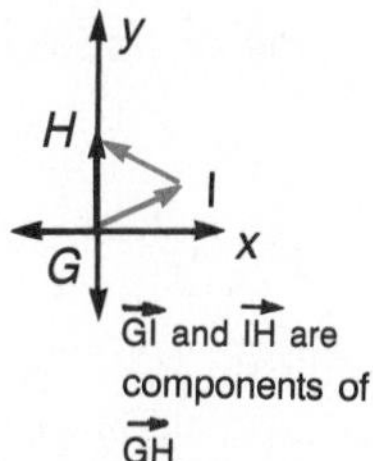

$\overrightarrow{GI}$ and $\overrightarrow{IH}$ are components of $\overrightarrow{GH}$

OBJECTIVES

Add and subtract nonperpendicular vectors and find magnitude and direction of a resultant vector.

Find vector components.

TEACHER'S NOTES

See p. T42

MIXED REVIEW

1. Solve $-18 < 5x - 18 < 5x - 3 < 22$. $-3 < x < 5$
2. Divide $3x^2 + x - 10$ by $x + 2$. $3x - 5$
3. If the area of a circle is 36π, what is its circumference? 12π
4. Solve $\frac{12}{5x} = \frac{3}{7}$. $x = 5\frac{3}{5}$
5. Add $\frac{7}{8x} + \frac{3}{5x}$. $\frac{59}{40x}$

TEACHER'S RESOURCE MASTERS

Practice Master 52, Part 2

Quiz 32

Because the trigonometric ratios are defined for right triangles, the most useful components are the horizontal and vertical ones. For the previous figures, horizontal and vertical components can be selected to represent $\overrightarrow{AC}$, $\overrightarrow{DF}$ and $\overrightarrow{GH}$, as shown below.

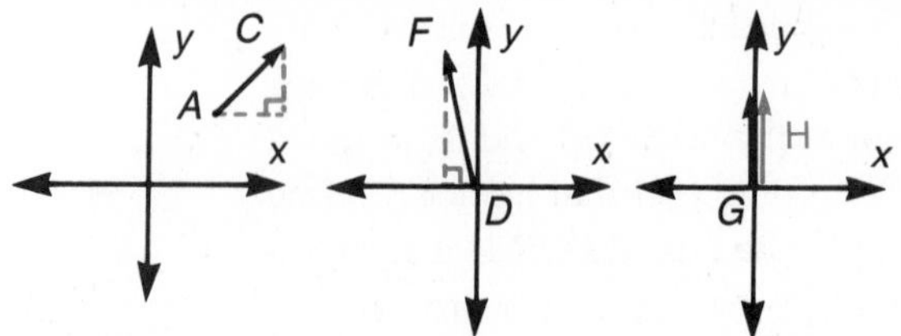

Now reconsider the following example from the last lesson. Apply the trigonometric ratios to solve the resultant vector *completely*, beyond a graphic solution.

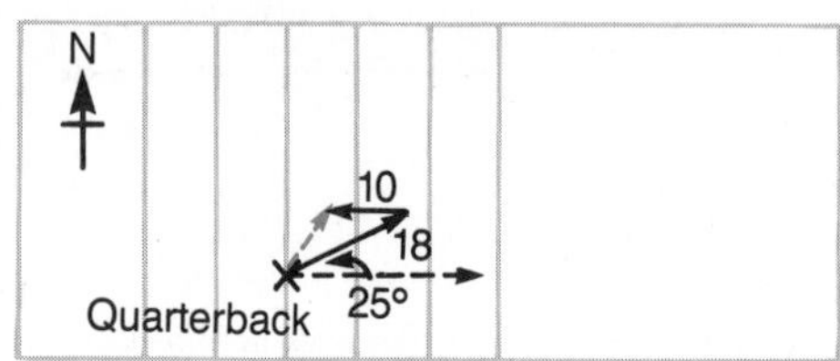

Example: A quarterback lobs a ball to a pass receiver who is 18 yards away. Just as the ball goes into the air, a gust of wind, 10 miles per hour, blows from due east. If the pass receiver ignores the force of gravity, where should the player move to catch the ball?

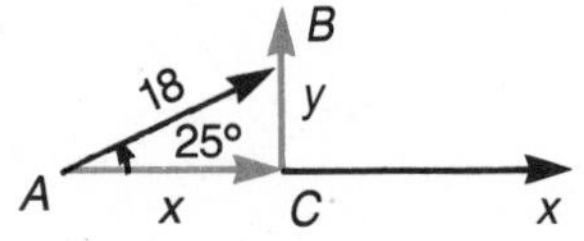

Solution: A graphic resultant estimates where the ball will land, but trigonometry can pinpoint a specific location. First, resolve the pass of the ball into its vertical and horizontal components.

$$\sin 25° = \frac{y}{18} \qquad \cos 25° = \frac{x}{18}$$

$$0.4226 = \frac{y}{18} \qquad 0.9063 = \frac{x}{18}$$

$$7.6068 = y \qquad 16.3134 = x$$

So, the vector of magnitude 18 and direction 25° can be written as the sum of two components: a vertical component of magnitude 7.6068 and a horizontal component of magnitude 16.3134.

Next, resolve the force of the wind into its components. Since the force is horizontal already, it is comprised of a horizontal component of magnitude 10 and a vertical component of magnitude 0.

All the components of the original two vectors being added should now be combined. Since the two forces have been resolved into vertical and horizontal parts, the rules for adding vectors in the same or opposite directions apply.

	VERTICAL	HORIZONTAL
ball	↑ 7.6068	→ 16.3134
wind	↑ 0	← 10
resultant	↑ 7.6068	→ 6.3134

All that remains is to find the magnitude and direction of the resultant vector.

$$\begin{aligned}|\overrightarrow{AB}| &= \sqrt{(7.6068)^2 + (6.3134)^2}\\ &= \sqrt{57.86 + 39.86}\\ &= \sqrt{97.72}\\ &\approx 9.89\end{aligned}$$

$$\tan \angle A = \tfrac{a}{b} = \tfrac{7.6068}{6.3134} = 1.205$$

$$\angle A \approx 50°$$

Now, compare the pass receiver's original position with the location where the ball will actually land.

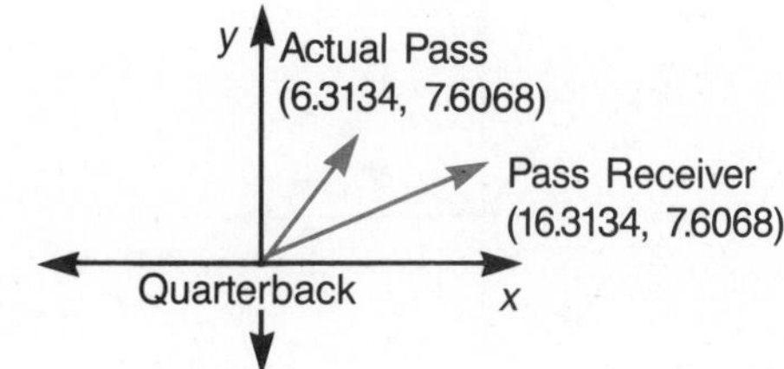

Vector addition, for any vectors, can now be summarized as follows:

1. Resolve every vector into its vertical and horizontal components using the trigonometric ratios.
2. Add the corresponding horizontal and vertical components according to the rules for adding vectors in the same or opposite direction.
3. For the resultant vector, still in component form, apply the tangent ratio to find the angle of direction and the Pythagorean Theorem to find the magnitude.

Throughout mathematics, addition and subtraction are inverse operations. For the system of vectors to be consistent with this concept, a vector subtracted from itself must give a $\vec{0}$ vector, or a vector with magnitude of zero length. Therefore, for $\overrightarrow{AB} - \overrightarrow{AB}$ (or $\overrightarrow{AB} + -\overrightarrow{AB}$) to equal $\vec{0}$, $-\overrightarrow{AB}$ must have the same magnitude as $\overrightarrow{AB}$ but in the opposite direction. Thus, in the figure, $-\overrightarrow{AB} = \overrightarrow{BA}$.

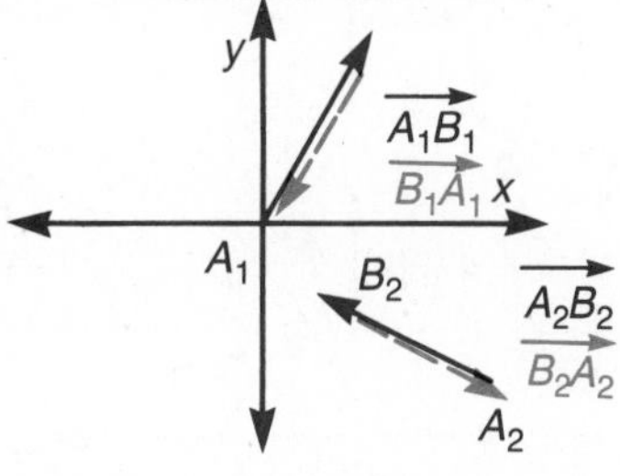

As with numbers, to subtract vectors you *add* the *opposite* of one vector to the other.

Example: The magnitude of $\overrightarrow{OX}$ is 7.78, and the magnitude of $\overrightarrow{OY}$ is 14.62. Determine $\overrightarrow{OY} - \overrightarrow{OX}$.

Solution: $\overrightarrow{OY} - \overrightarrow{OX} = \overrightarrow{OY} + -\overrightarrow{OX} = \overrightarrow{OY} + \overrightarrow{XO}$.
Using translation, draw $\overrightarrow{YZ}$ equal to $\overrightarrow{XO}$. The resulting vector is $\overrightarrow{OZ}$ with magnitude 10 and angle of direction 0.

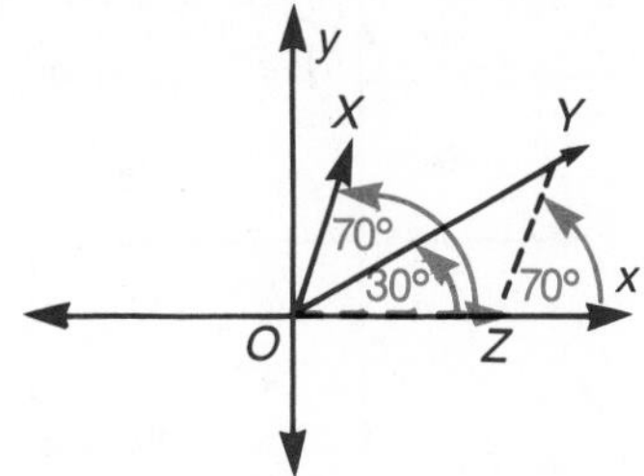

ORAL EXERCISES

1. How many components does any one vector have?
2. From the ordered pair naming the terminal point of a vector in standard position, how would you find the direction of the vector? How would you find the magnitude?
3. Given the magnitude and direction of a vector in standard position, how would you find the ordered pair naming the terminal point of the vector?

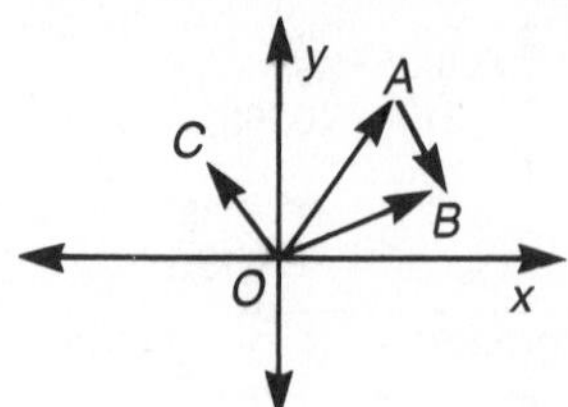

In the figure at the left, $\vec{OC} = \vec{AB}$.

4. What is $\vec{OA} - \vec{OC}$?
5. What is $\vec{OB} - \vec{CO}$?

WRITTEN EXERCISES

A. Find the ordered pair naming the terminal point of each vector.

1. 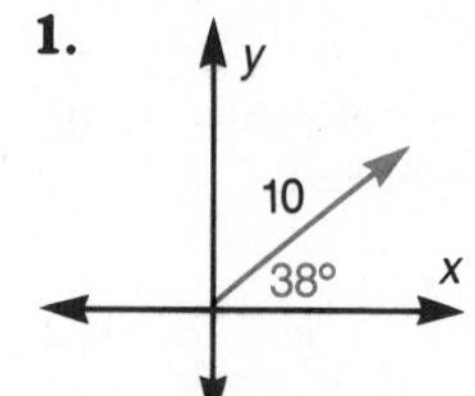

2. 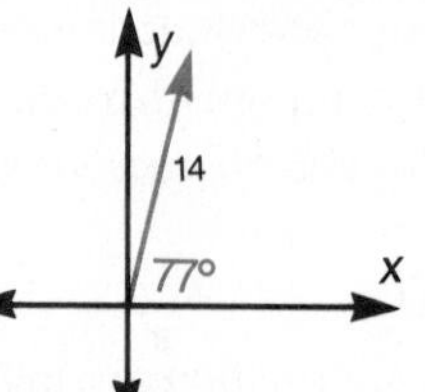

3. 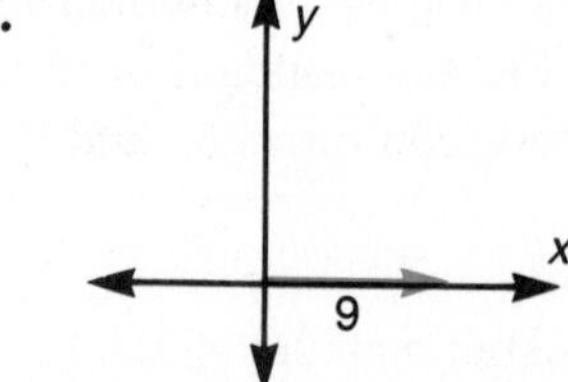

B.

4. 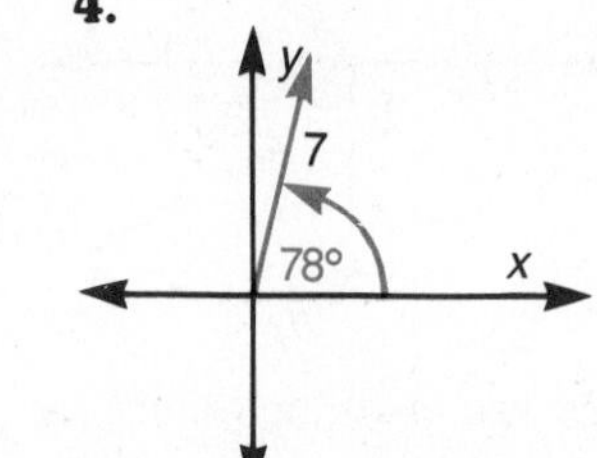

5. 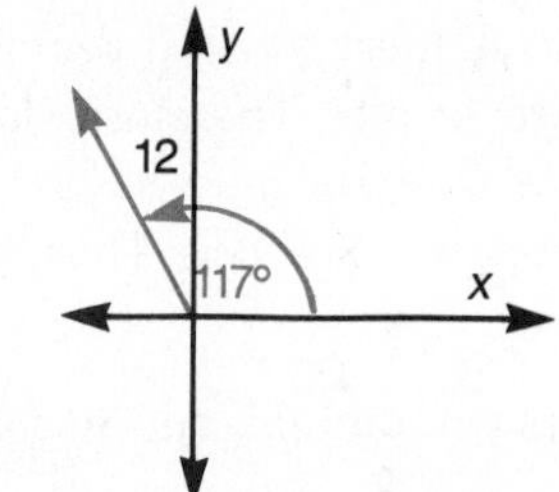

6. 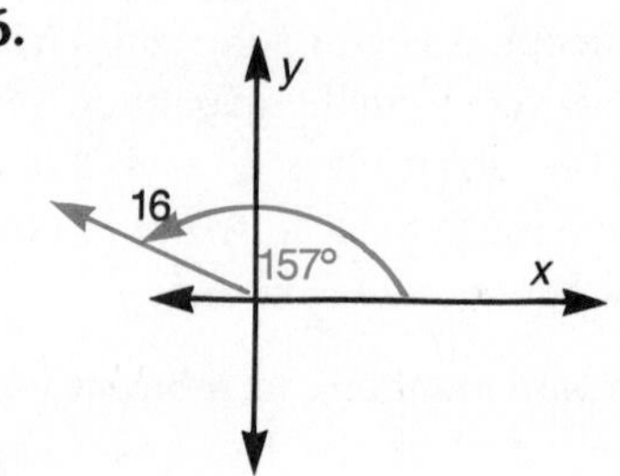

Find the angle of direction and the magnitude of each vector.

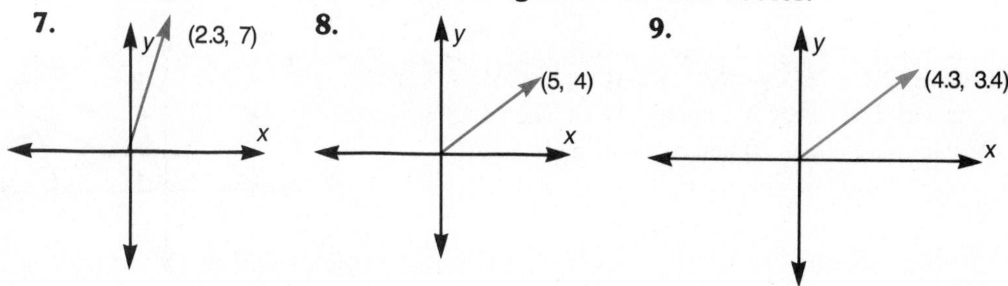

ASSIGNMENT GUIDE

Minimum 1-13
Regular 1-19 odd
Maximum 1-17 odd, 18-20

Oral Exercises

1. infinitely many pairs
2. $\tan \angle = \frac{y}{x}$, $x^2 + y^2 = c^2$
3. use sine and cosine of given angle
4. $\vec{OB}$
5. $\vec{OA}$

Written Exercises

1. (7.88, 6.16)
2. (3.15, 13.64)
3. (9, 0)
4. (1.46, 6.85)
5. (−5.45, 10.69)
6. (−14.73, 6.25)
7. $m\angle \approx 72°$, mag. ≈ 7.368
8. $m\angle \approx 39°$, mag. ≈ 6.403
9. $m\angle \approx 38°$, mag. ≈ 5.482

10.

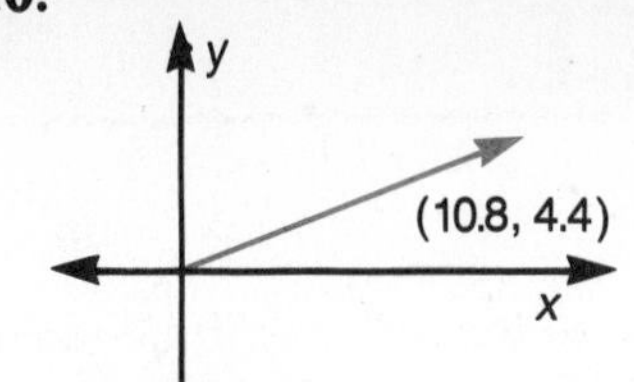

11.

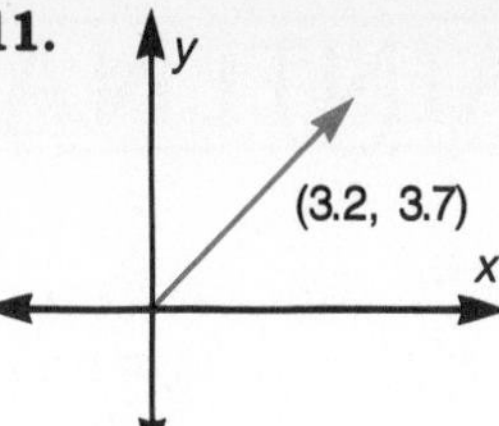

12.

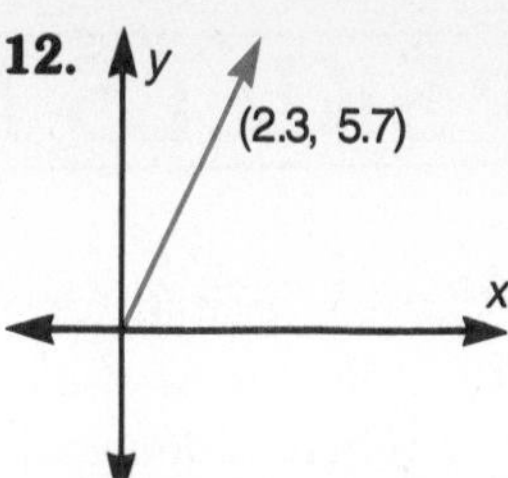

Find the graphical solution of each vector.

13.

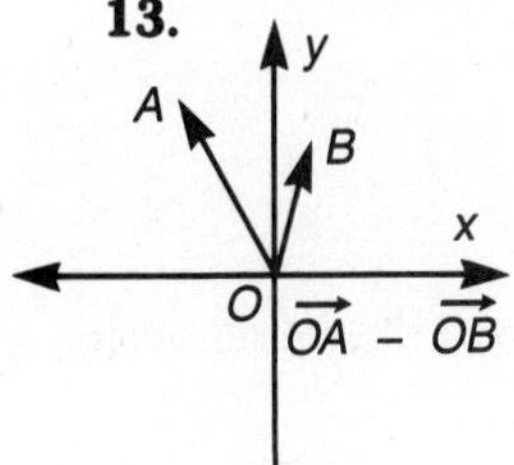

14.

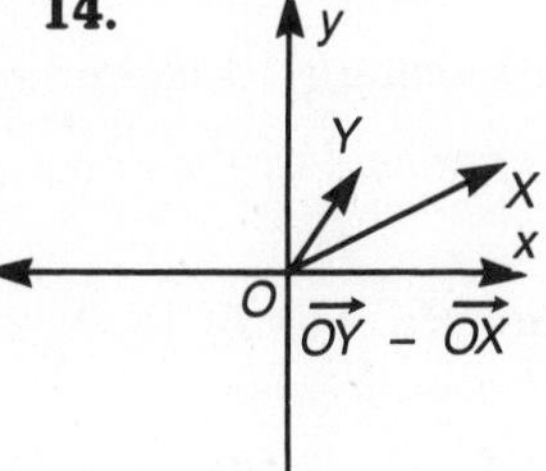

15.

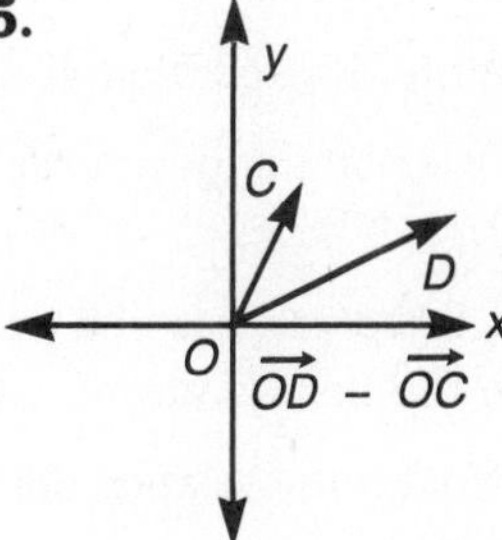

16.

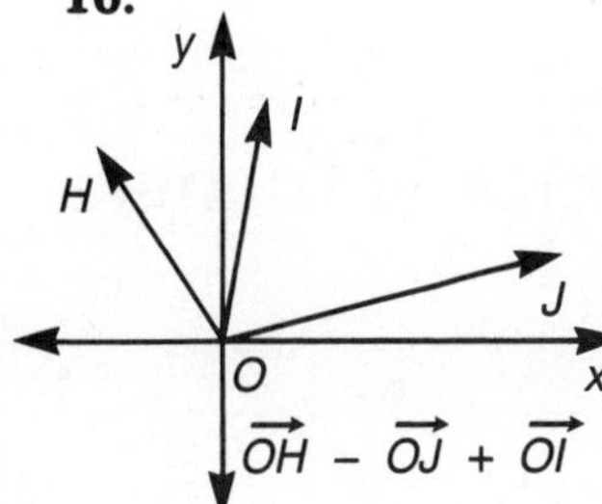

17.

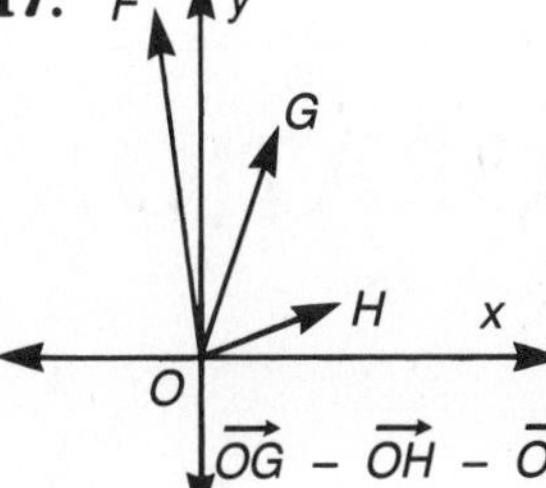

18.

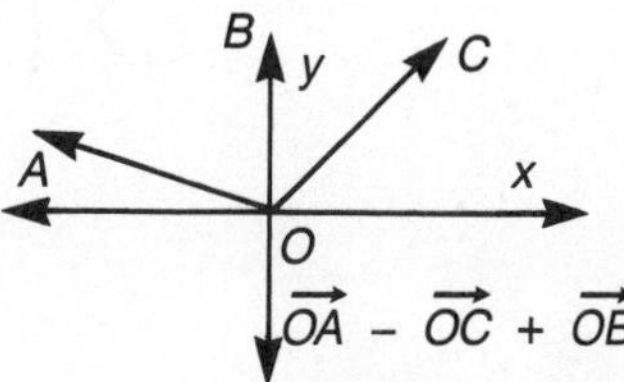

C. 19. A sailboat is cruising at 10 knots in a northeast direction, 45° with respect to the shore. If the wake from a motor boat comes from the northwest at an angle of 20° with a force of 2 knots, where will the sailboat move and what will be its actual speed?

20. During take-off, a plane is climbing at an angle of 18° with a speed of 150 miles per hour. If it is caught in a downward gust of wind blowing 25 miles per hour at an angle of 54° to the horizontal, how will the plane be affected? (Find the numerical solution.)

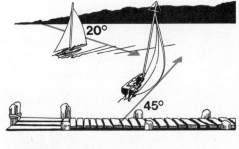

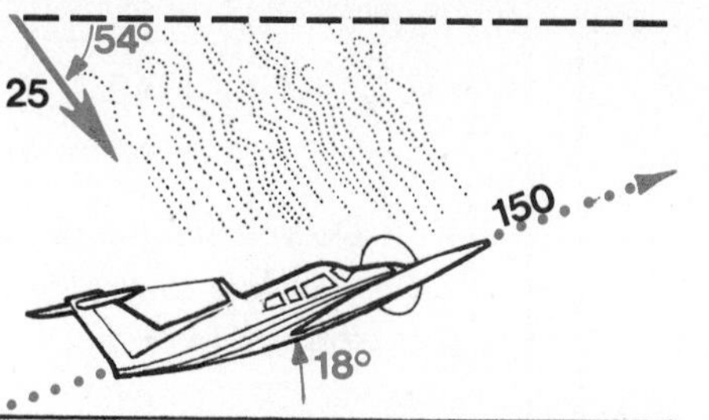

10. $m\angle \approx 22°$, mag. $\approx$ 11.662
11. $m\angle \approx 49°$, mag. $\approx$ 4.892
12. $m\angle \approx 68°$, mag. $\approx$ 6.147
13.

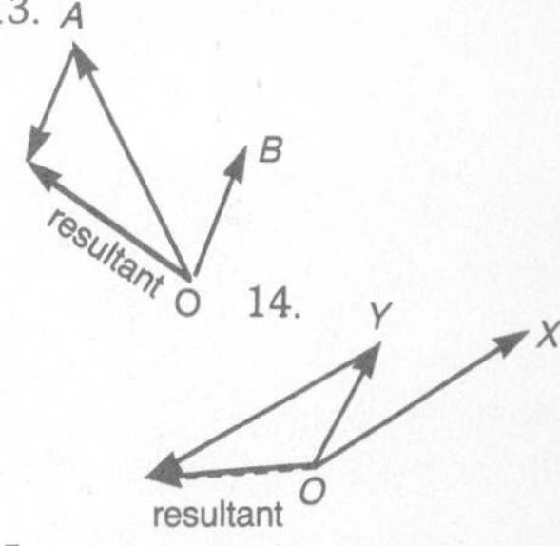

15.

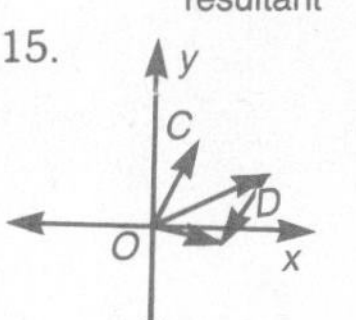

16.

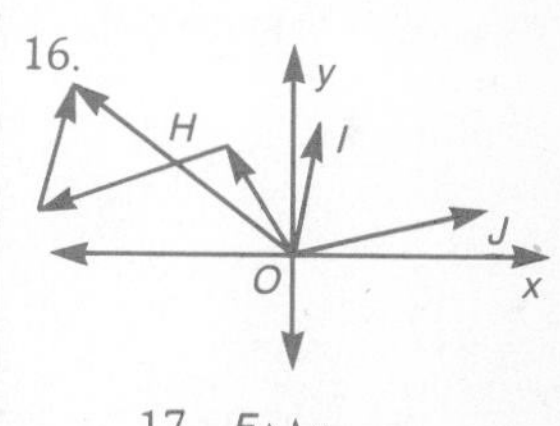

17.

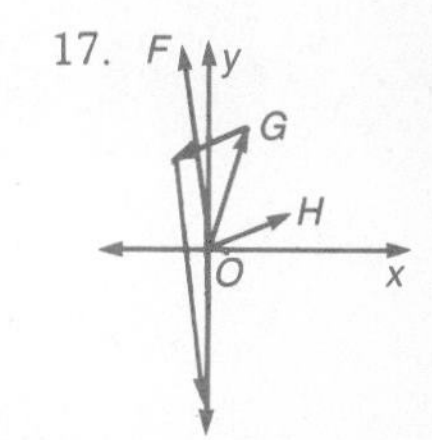

18.

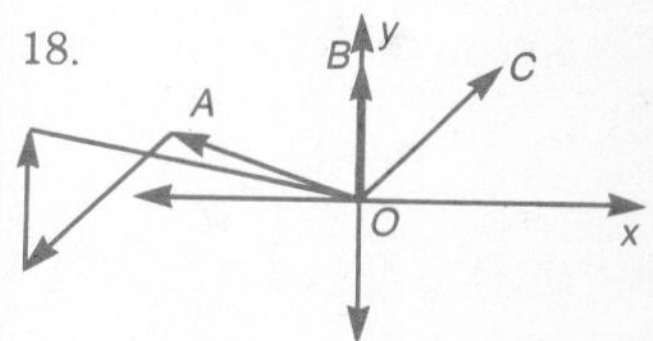

19. $\rightarrow 7.07 + 1.88 = 8.95$
$\uparrow 7.07 - 0.68 = 6.39$
$m\angle \approx 36°$
mag. $\approx$ 11 knots

20. $\rightarrow 142.67 + 14.7 = 157.37$
$\uparrow 46.35 - 20.23 = 26.12$
$m\angle \approx 9°$
mag. $\approx$ 159.5 mph

SKILLS MAINTENANCE

Skills Maintenance

1. multiplied by 4, by 8
2. $6\sqrt{3}, 6\sqrt{3}, 162\sqrt{3}$
3. $(x + 4)^2 + (y - 3)^2 = 64$
4. a circle with center $(-2, \frac{-5}{2})$ and radius $\frac{1}{2}\sqrt{37}$
5. either $(a + b, c)$ or $(b - a, c)$
6. They are equal. Yes. The side opposite one angle is adjacent to its complement.

Answer each question below.

1. If the radius of a cylinder is doubled, what is the effect on the volume? If the radius of a sphere is doubled?

2. The distance from the center of a circle to the side of an inscribed hexagon is 9. What is the radius of the circle? the side of the hexagon? the area of the hexagon?

3. Write the equation of a circle with center $(-4, 3)$ and radius 8.

4. Describe the geometric figure determined by the equation $x^2 + y^2 + 4x + 5y + 1 = 0$.

5. If three vertices of a parallelogram are at $(0, 0)$, $(a, 0)$, and (b, c) and the fourth vertex is in the first quadrant, what are its coordinates?

6. What is the relation between sin 30 and cos 60? Is this true for all complementary angles? Explain.

EXPLORATION/Pascal's Triangle

$$
\begin{array}{ccccccccccccc}
 & & & & & 1 & & 1 & & & & & \\
 & & & & 1 & & 2 & & 1 & & & & \\
 & & & 1 & & 3 & & 3 & & 1 & & & \\
 & & 1 & & 4 & & 6 & & 4 & & 1 & & \\
 & 1 & & 5 & & 10 & & 10 & & 5 & & 1 & \\
1 & & 6 & & 15 & & 20 & & 15 & & 6 & & 1
\end{array}
$$

Blaise Pascal (1623–1662) is credited with discovering the above array of numbers which is known as Pascal's triangle. Do you see the pattern(s) involved? Copy the triangle on your paper and fill in the next two rows.

Now look at the results we get by raising the binomial $a + b$ to successive powers:

$$(a + b)^1 = 1a + 1b$$
$$(a + b)^2 = 1a^2 + 2ab + 1b^2$$
$$(a + b)^3 = 1a^3 + 3a^2b + 3ab^2 + 1b^3$$
$$(a + b)^4 = 1a^4 + 4a^3b + 6a^2b^2 + 4ab^3 + 1b^4$$

Do you see the pattern of coefficients? of exponents? Use your last row of Pascal's triangle to write the expanded form of $(a + b)^8$.

Exploration

1, 7, 21, 35, 35, 21, 7, 1
1, 8, 28, 56, 70, 56, 28, 8, 1

$a^8 + 8a^7b + 28a^6b^2 + 56a^5b^3 + 70a^4b^4 + 56a^3b^5 + 28a^2b^6 + 8ab^7 + b^8$

CAREER/Seismologist

Earthquakes occur when forces inside the earth cause a sudden movement of rocks. The site of the movement is called the focus. The epicenter is the point on the surface of the earth directly above the focus. Seismic waves are strongest here.

When the rocks at the focus move, two types of waves are sent out. **P waves,** or push-pull waves, advance by pushing and pulling particles in the path of the wave. **S waves,** or shearing waves, move particles in a direction at right angles to the path of the waves. When both of these types of waves reach the surface, they become **L waves.**

Seismologists can record information about an earthquake on a seismograph. A seismograph is made of a heavy weight suspended by springs. The inertia of this instrument keeps it still while the ground moves. Attached to the weight is a pen that rests against a revolving drum. When the earth shakes, the drum moves with it, but the pen stays steady, held by the weight. The result is a zigzag record of the movements the drum, and therefore the earth, makes.

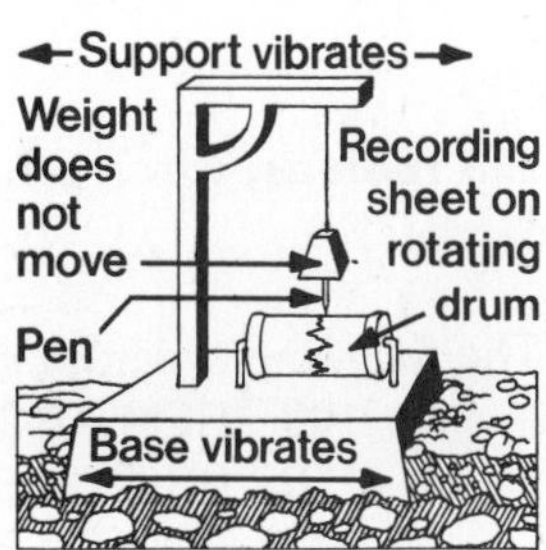

Different seismographs are used to record horizontal and vertical shaking, but all record **P**, **S**, and **L waves.**

Triangulation is the method used to find the location of the epicenter. Seismologists use the distances computed from three different stations to the actual earthquake. A circle is drawn around each seismograph station with the radius equal to the distance to the quake. The intersection of the three circles is the epicenter of the earthquake.

TEACHER'S RESOURCE MASTERS

Computer Master 16

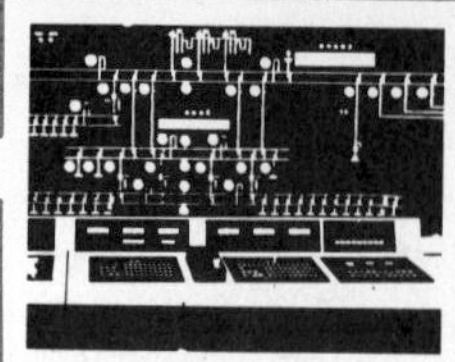

COMPUTER

Many trigonometric problems involve right triangles where the degree measures are known, and the lengths of the sides must be found. What about the opposite case, where the lengths are known, but not the measures of the two acute angles? (One angle of course, must be 90°.) As you have learned, the sine, cosine, and tangent values of the angles may be derived by division. Then the corresponding degree measures of the angles may be found in a table of trigonometric ratios. However, such tables still require estimation. They also consume too much time and memory to be programmed into a small computer. Luckily, a computer function is available to make finding degree measure easier—the **arctangent** function (ATN).

The ATN function converts the value

$$\sqrt{\frac{\text{length of hypotenuse}^2 - \text{length of base}^2}{\text{length of base}}}$$

into **radians,** which can then be converted into degrees. 1 radian $= \frac{180}{\pi}$ degrees.

The following program illustrates the use of the ATN function.

```
100  REM ARCTANGENT
110  PRINT"LENGTH OF HYPOTENUSE?":INPUT H
120  PRINT"LENGTH OF FIRST BASE?":INPUT B1
130  PRINT"LENGTH OF OTHER BASE?":INPUT B2
140  LET R1=ATN(SQR(H↑2-B1↑2)/B1)
150  LET R2=ATN(SQR(H↑2-B2↑2)/B2)
160  LET D1=R1*(180/3.1416)
170  LET D2=R2*(180/3.1416)
180  PRINT"DEGREE MEASURES ARE—"
190  PRINT"90"D1;"AND";D2
200  END
```

Apply the program to this situation:

Karen is designing a home. If the roof slopes more than 20 degrees, a hard rain will overflow the capacity of the guttering she's ordered. Is the roof inclined properly, or will larger guttering be needed? Why?

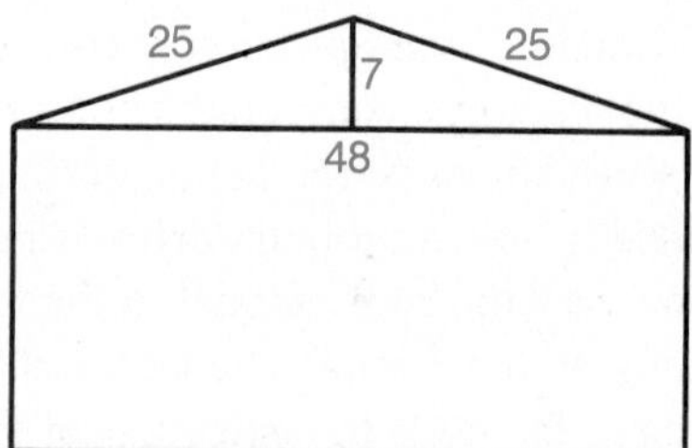

Computer

The roof, its perpendicular, and the side of the house form two 7:24:25 right triangles. Inputting these values into the program, one derives degree measures of 90, 16.26, and 73.74. The angle of slope is 16.26, which is less than 20, so the roof is properly inclined.

CHAPTER 16 REVIEW

TEACHER'S RESOURCE MASTERS

Enrichment Master 12

ENRICHMENT

See Activities 31-32, p. T53-T54

VOCABULARY

angle of depression (16.3)
angle of elevation (16.3)
cofunction (16.3)
cosine (16.1)
directed line segment (16.4)
direction of a vector (16.4)
equal vectors (16.4)
identity (16.3)
line of sight (16.3)
magnitude of a vector (16.4)parallelogram method of vector addition (16.5)
resultant vector (16.5)
sine (16.1)
standard vector position (16.6)
tangent (16.1)
trigonometric ratio (16.1)
vector (16.4)
vector components (16.6)
velocity (16.5)

REVIEW EXERCISES

16.1 Refer to the figure of isosceles $\triangle ACD$ for Exercises 1-5.

1. $\sin \angle A = \frac{?}{AB}$

2. $\cos \angle D = \frac{?}{?}$

3. $\frac{AF}{AB} = \frac{AE}{?} = \cos \angle\, ?$

4. $\cos \angle DCE = \ ?\ \angle D$

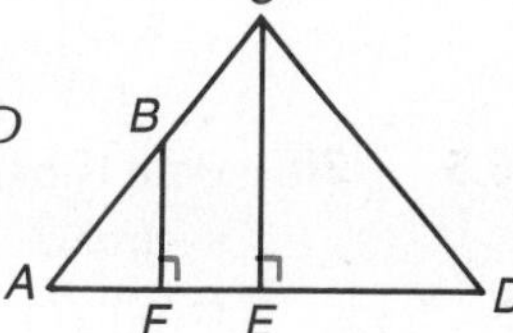

5. $\tan \angle ACE = \ ?\ \angle ABF$

6. If $\sin \angle X = \frac{2}{3}$, find $\cos \angle X$ and $\tan \angle X$.

16.2 Using the trigonometric tables or a calculator, solve each of the following triangles for Exercises 7-11.

7.
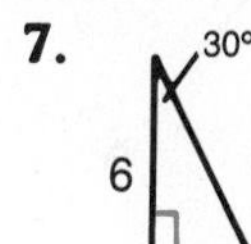

8.
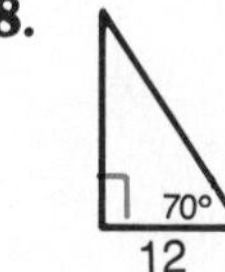

9.
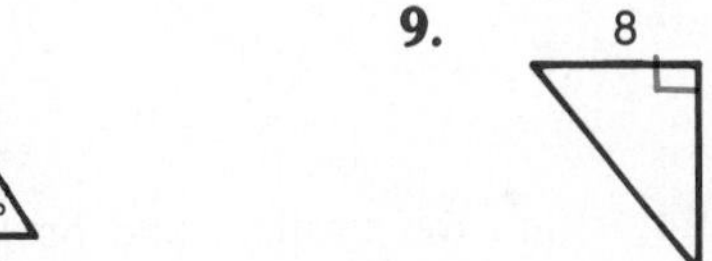

10.
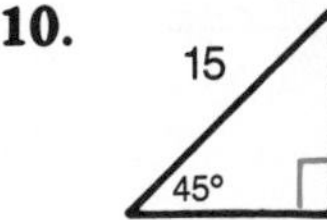

11.
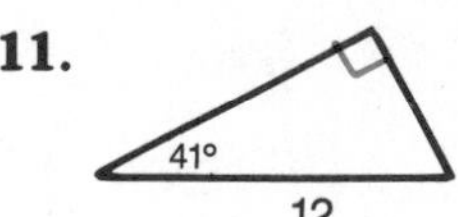

12. Find the area of an isosceles triangle, if the base angles measure 28°, and the base measures 18.

Chapter 16 Review

1. BF 2. $\frac{ED}{CD}$

3. AC, $\angle A$ 4. sin

5. tan 6. $\frac{\sqrt{5}}{3}$, $\frac{2\sqrt{5}}{5}$

7. 60°, $2\sqrt{3}$, $4\sqrt{3}$

8. 30°, $12\sqrt{3}$, 24

9. 58°, 32°, ≈15.26

10. 45°, $\frac{15\sqrt{2}}{2}$, $\frac{15\sqrt{2}}{2}$

11. 49°, ≈7.87, 9.06

12. the area $= \frac{1}{2}(4.79)(18) \approx 43.11$

13. ≈9.38 ft, ≈22.1 ft

14. ≈164 ft

15. 7.3 miles

16. $\overrightarrow{AB}$ or $\overrightarrow{OA}$ 17. $\overrightarrow{OB}$

18. $\overrightarrow{CA}$ 19. ≈67°

20. 3 mph

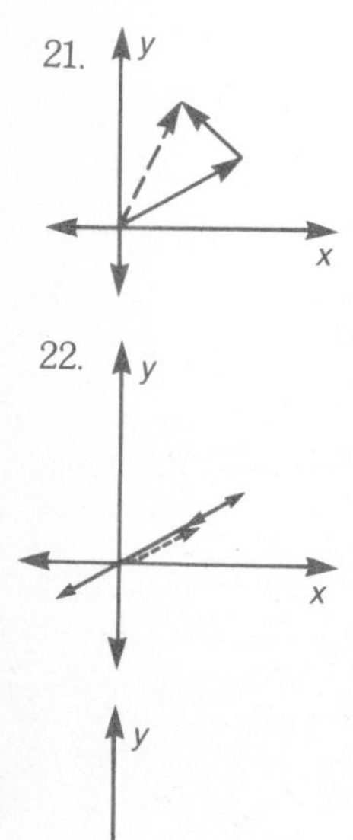

24. ≈9.80, 15.1

25. terminal point (5.01, 9.27) $m\angle \approx 62°$, mag. ≈ 10.54

16.3 **13.** A ladder 24 feet long is placed against a vertical wall so that the ladder and the ground form an angle whose measure is 67°. How far will the base of the ladder be from the base of the wall? How far above the ground will the ladder touch the wall?

14. The angle of depression of a ship from the top of an 80-foot lighthouse is 26°. How far is the ship from the base of the lighthouse?

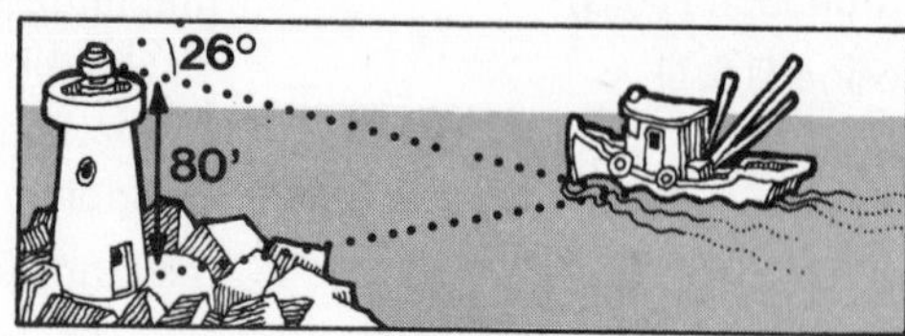

16.4 **15.** An airplane takes off at a groundspeed of 140 miles per hour at an angle of 12° with the horizon. What will be the altitude of the plane in 15 minutes?

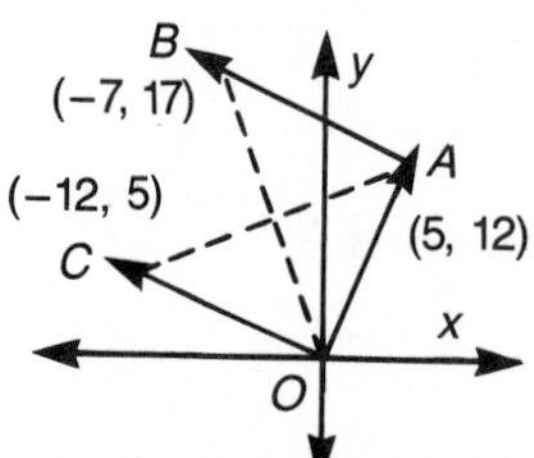

Refer to the figure to complete each statement.

16. $|\overrightarrow{OC}| = |$____$|$ **17.** $\overrightarrow{OA} + \overrightarrow{OC} =$ ____

18. $\overrightarrow{OA} - \overrightarrow{OC} =$ ____

19. angle of direction of $\overrightarrow{OA} =$ ____

16.5 **20.** Pete is paddling a canoe at a speed of 5 miles per hour *against* the current in a stream. If the current is moving at 2 mph, how fast is the boat actually moving?

Add the following vectors graphically:

21.

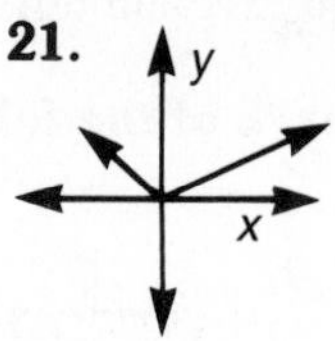

22.

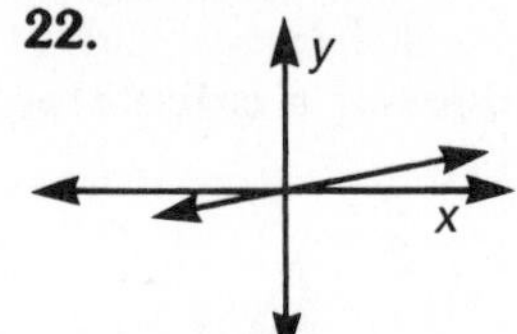

23.

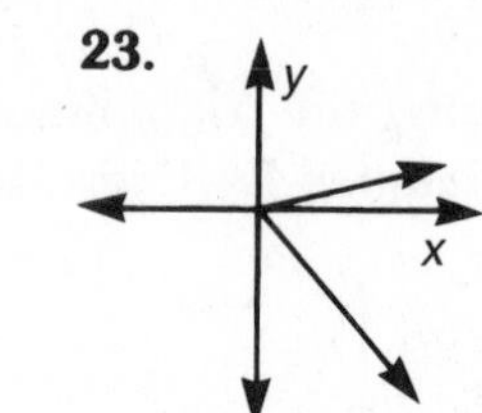

16.6 **24.** Find the vertical and horizontal components of the vector shown.

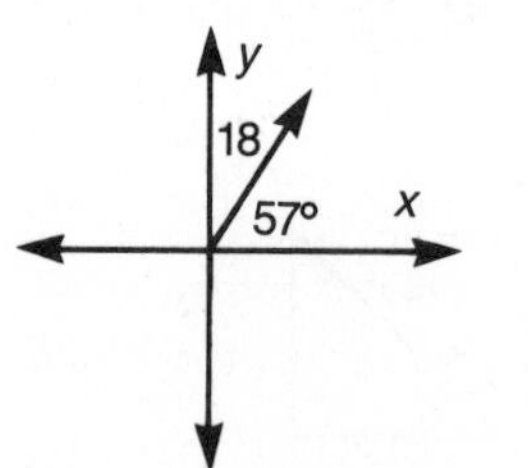

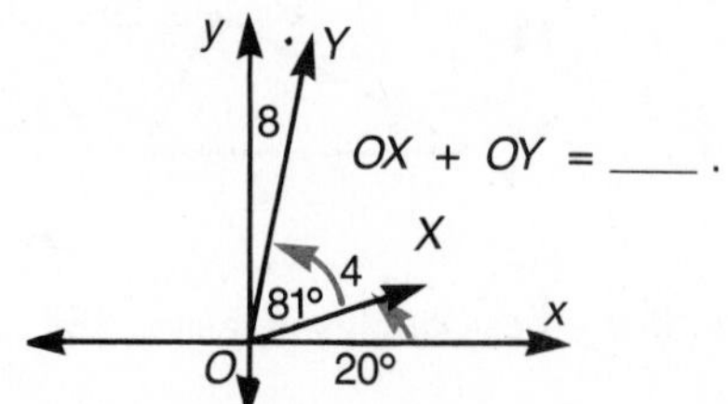

25. Find the solution both graphically and numerically.

CHAPTER 16 TEST

Use the figure to complete each statement in Exercises 1–7.

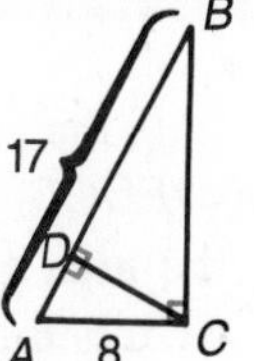

1. sin ∠A = _____ **2.** cos ∠A = _____

3. tan ∠A = _____ **4.** m∠A ≈ _____

5. DC ≈ _____ **6.** sin ∠ACD ≈ _____

7. tan ∠DCB ≈ _____

Find the area and perimeter of each figure.

8.

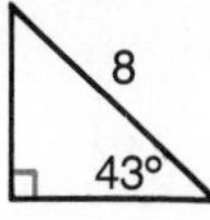

9.

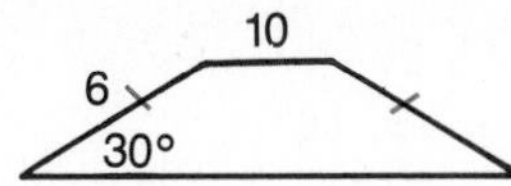

10. A kite flying at the end of a 300-foot string has an angle of elevation of 44°. How high is the kite?

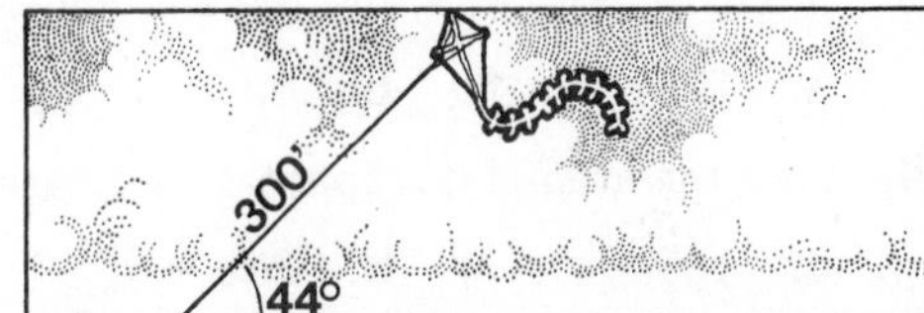

11. Copy the vector shown and graphically resolve it into *two different pairs* of components.

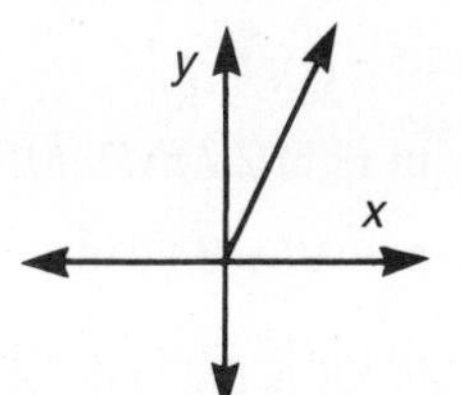

Solve each vector operation graphically.

12.

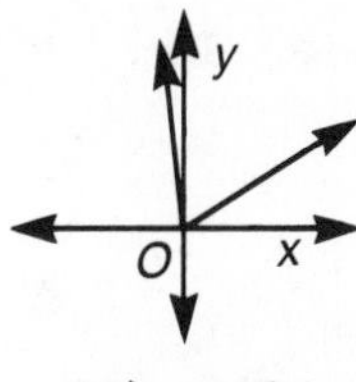

$\overrightarrow{OX} + \overrightarrow{OY}$

13.

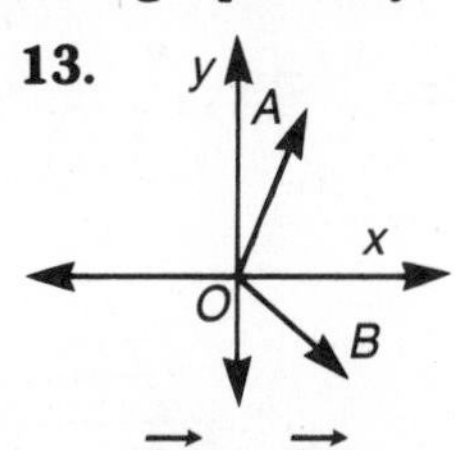

$\overrightarrow{OA} - \overrightarrow{OB}$

14. Find the vertical and horizontal components of the triangle.

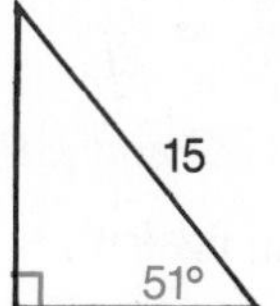

In the figure at the right, add the two vectors. For the resultant vector,

15. find the magnitude.

16. find the direction.

17. find the terminal point.

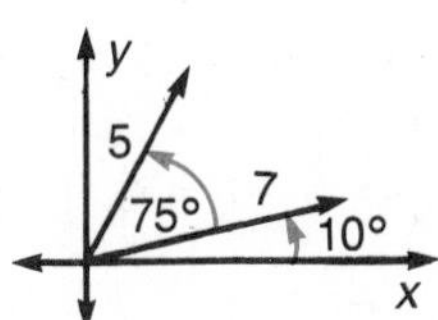

TEACHER'S RESOURCE MASTERS

Chapter Test 16
Multiple Choice Test—Chapter 16

Chapter 16 Test

1. $\frac{15}{17}$ 2. $\frac{8}{17}$
3. $\frac{15}{8}$ 4. 62°
5. 7.06 6. .4695
7. 1.8807

8. $A \approx 15.97$, $p \approx 19.31$

9. $A = 30 + 9\sqrt{3}$, $p = 32 + 6\sqrt{3}$

10. ≈208.4 ft

11.

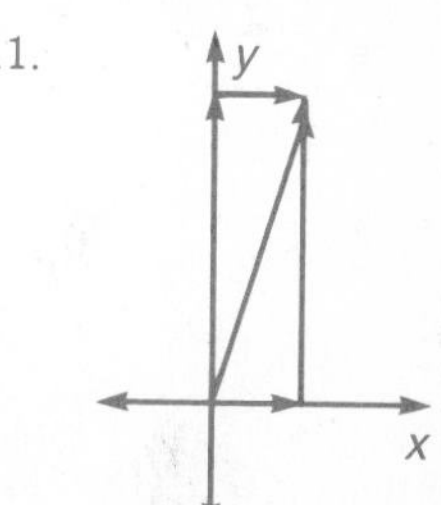

12.

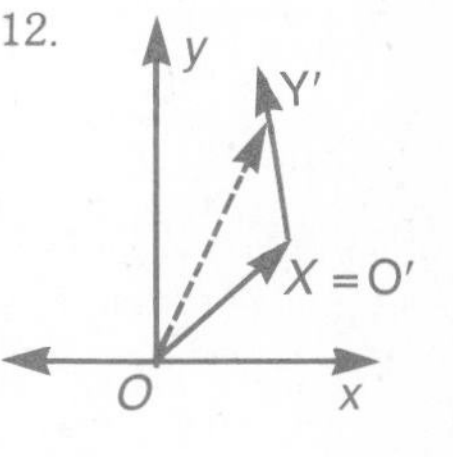

13.

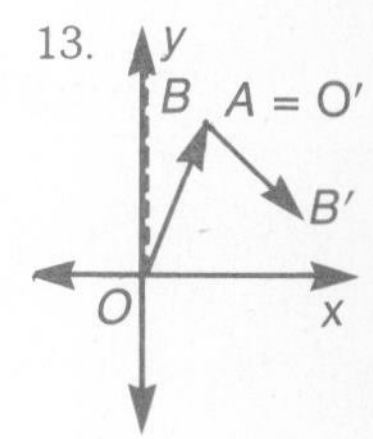

14. horizontal ≈9.44, vertical ≈11.66

15. 10.18 16. 36°

17. (8.19, 6.05)

TEACHER'S RESOURCE MASTERS

Cumulative Test—Chapters 1-16 Form A or B

Cumulative Review: Chapters 9-16

1. d
2. b
3. c
4. a
5. c
6. b
7. c
8. a
9. d
10 c
11. a

CUMULATIVE REVIEW: CHAPTERS 9–16

1. In the figure at the right, $\square ABCG \cong \square EDCG$, $\overline{EG} \cong \overline{GA}$, and F is the midpoint of $\overline{EA}$. If the area of $\square ABCG$ is 28 and the area of $\triangle EGF$ is 7, what is the area of polygon $ABCDE$?

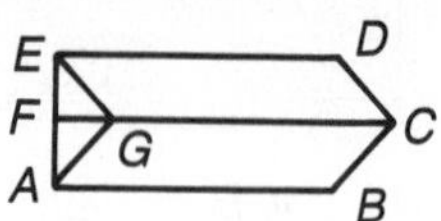

a. 28 **b.** 35 **c.** 56 **d.** 70

2. The area of a rectangle is 126 in.^{2}. The width is 1 less than $\frac{1}{3}$ as long as the length. Find the length and width.

a. 18, 7 **b.** 21, 6 **c.** 9, 14 **d.** 3, 42

3. In $\triangle DEF$, $DE = 7$ and the altitude to $F = 9$. Find the area of $\triangle DEF$.

a. 126 **b.** 63 **c.** 31.5 **d.** 1

4. Find the area of a trapezoid with bases of 8 and 18 and altitude of 13.

a. 169 **b.** 338 **c.** 936 **d.** 130

5. In right $\triangle XYZ$, $XY = 6$ and $YZ = 9$. Find XZ.

a. $3\sqrt{5}$ **b.** $\sqrt{117}$ **c.** either **a** or **b** **d.** neither **a** nor **b**

6. In right $\triangle MNP$, $\overline{MN} \cong \overline{NP}$. If $MN = 17$, find $\overline{MP}$.

a. $17\sqrt{3}$ **b.** $17\sqrt{2}$ **c.** $\frac{17\sqrt{3}}{3}$ **d.** $\frac{17\sqrt{2}}{2}$

7. What is the ratio of 28 minutes to 3 hours?

a. 28:3 **b.** 3:28 **c.** 7:45 **d.** 45:7

8. In $\triangle EHG$, if $\overline{IF} \parallel \overline{HG}$, then

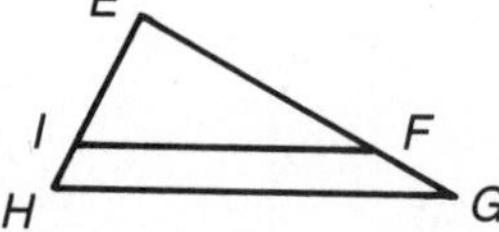

a. $\frac{EF}{EG} = \frac{EI}{EH}$ **b.** $\frac{EF}{IF} = \frac{FG}{HG}$

c. $\frac{EF}{FG} = \frac{IH}{EI}$ **d.** $\frac{EF}{FG} = \frac{EI}{EH}$

9. In $\triangle ABC$ and $\triangle PQR$, if $\angle A \cong \angle P$ and $\angle B \cong \angle Q$, then the two triangles are

a. equivalent. **b.** equal. **c.** congruent. **d.** similar.

10. In $\triangle HIJ$, $\angle I$ is a rt. $\angle$ and $\overline{IK}$ is the altitude from I to $\overline{HJ}$. If $HK = 4$ and $IK = 14$, find HJ.

a. 18 **b.** 49 **c.** 53 **d.** 56

11. $\triangle DAN \sim \triangle KIM$, $DA = 6$, $KI = 3$. The area of $\triangle DAN = 39$. Find the area of $\triangle KIM$.

a. $\frac{39}{4}$ **b.** $\frac{39}{2}$ **c.** 13 **d.** $\frac{13}{2}$

For Exercises 12–17, refer to the coordinate system below.

12. What is the slope of $\overline{XY}$? 12. d

a. $\frac{1}{5}$ **b.** 5

c. -5 **d.** $\frac{-1}{5}$

13. The distance between F and K is 13. d

a. $4\sqrt{13}$. **b.** $4\sqrt{2}$.

c. $6\sqrt{2}$. **d.** $2\sqrt{13}$.

14. The midpoint of $\overline{FY}$ is 14. a

a. $(\frac{5}{2}, \frac{-1}{2})$. **b.** $(\frac{7}{2}, \frac{9}{2})$.

c. $(\frac{-1}{2}, \frac{5}{2})$. **d.** $(5, -1)$.

15. The slopes of $\overline{XY}$, $\overline{YJ}$, $\overline{JK}$, and $\overline{KX}$ show that quadrilateral $XYJK$ is a 15. b

a. trapezoid. **b.** parallelogram.

c. rectangle. **d.** rhombus.

16. Which of the following equations represents a line? 16. c

a. $x^2 + y^2 = 9$ **b.** $2x + 3y > 9$

c. $x + 2y = 9$ **d.** $2x = |y|$

17. Given the equation $3y + 7 = 4x$, find the y-intercept of the line. 17. a

a. $\frac{-7}{3}$ **b.** $\frac{7}{3}$ **c.** -7 **d.** 7

18. If $\overleftrightarrow{AB}$ and $\overleftrightarrow{CD}$ are secants to $\odot O$ and tangents to $\odot P$, then $\odot O$ and $\odot P$ may be 18. d

a. concentric. **b.** internally tangent.

c. externally tangent. **d.** any of these.

19. If sphere S is tangent to plane M at T, and R is a point in M, then 19. d

a. $\overline{TS}$ is a diameter. **b.** $\overline{TR} \parallel \overline{ST}$.

c. $\overline{TR} \cong \overline{ST}$. **d.** $\overline{TR} \perp \overline{ST}$.

20. If $\widehat{AB}$ and $\widehat{BC}$ form a semicircle in $\odot P$, then 20. b

a. $m\widehat{AB} = m\widehat{BC}$. **b.** $\overline{AC}$ is a diameter.

c. $\overline{AB} \cong \overline{BC}$. **d.** $m\angle APC = 90$.

21. Quadrilateral $QRST$ is inscribed in $\odot I$. Find the sum of the measure of the arcs intercepted by $\angle QRS$ and $\angle STQ$. 21. c

a. 90 **b.** 180 **c.** 360 **d.** 720

22. a

22. The equation of $\odot G$ is $(x + 9)^2 + (y - 2)^2 = 73$. Find the center of $\odot G$.

a. $(-9, 2)$ **b.** $(9, -2)$ **c.** $(9, 2)$ **d.** $(\sqrt{9}, -\sqrt{2})$

23. d

23. In a plane, what is the locus of all points equidistant from 2 parallel lines?

a. the $\perp$ bisector of the lines

b. a point midway between the two lines

c. a line parallel to the two lines

d. a line parallel to and midway between the two lines

24. c

24. In a plane, what is the locus of points equidistant from the vertices of a triangle?

a. the point of concurrency of the angle bisectors

b. the center of the inscribed circle

c. the point of concurrency of the perpendicular bisectors of the sides

d. the empty set

25. a

25. Which of the following tools is not normally acceptable in constructions?

a. ruler **b.** compass **c.** pencil **d.** straightedge

26. d

26. What is the total measure of the interior angles of a hexagon?

a. 1080 **b.** 900 **c.** 540 **d.** 720

27. b

27. Find the area of a circle with diameter 22.

a. 484π **b.** 121π **c.** 22π **d.** 44π

28. c

28. Find the area of a sector with a central angle of 42° and radius 7.

a. 147 **b.** $\frac{49\pi}{360}$ **c.** $\frac{49\pi}{60}$ **d.** $\frac{343\pi}{30}$

29. b

29. Find the total surface area of a right prism with isosceles triangles (base = 4, height = 7) for bases and altitude of 17.

a. $204 + 2\sqrt{53}$ **b.** $96 + 34\sqrt{53}$ **c.** 402 **d.** $96 + 17\sqrt{53}$

30. d

30. A pyramid has a square with a 4-in. side for a base and an altitude of 8 in. What is the area of a cross section $\frac{1}{3}$ of the distance from the vertex to the base?

a. $\frac{4}{3}$ in.^{2} **b.** $\frac{16}{3}$ in.^{2} **c.** $\frac{64}{9}$ in.^{2} **d.** $\frac{16}{9}$ in.^{2}

31. a

31. A pyramid has an equilateral triangle with sides measuring 3 in. each for its base and an altitude of 7 in. Find its volume.

a. $\frac{21\sqrt{3}}{4}$ in.^{3} **b.** $\frac{21\sqrt{2}}{4}$ in.^{3} **c.** $\frac{63\sqrt{3}}{4}$ in.^{3} **d.** $\frac{21\sqrt{3}}{2}$ in.^{3}

32. b

32. Find the surface area of a sphere with radius 9 m.

a. 972π m^2 **b.** 324π m^2 **c.** 36π m^2 **d.** 108π m^2

33. If $K = \{(3, 4), (-1, -5), (7, 4)\}$, which relation applies to K? 33. a

a. function **b.** inverse function **c.** one-to-one **d.** onto

34. In the transformation $(x, y) \rightarrow (x - 3, y + 2)$, find the preimage of (9, 5). 34. d

a. (6, 3) **b.** (15, 1) **c.** (6, 7) **d.** (12, 3)

35. How many lines of symmetry does the letter "H" have? 35. c

a. 0 **b.** 1 **c.** 2 **d.** 3

36. If a translation maps $A(-1, 4)$ onto $A'(3, -6)$, what will it map $B(3, -2)$ onto? 36. a

a. $(7, -12)$ **b.** $(-1, 0)$ **c.** $(7, 0)$ **d.** $(-1, -12)$

37. In the rotation $r[(0, 0), 270]$, the coordinate rule is $(x, y) \rightarrow$ 37. b

a. $(-y, x)$. **b.** $(y, -x)$. **c.** $(-x, -y)$. **d.** (x, y).

38. Any composition of line reflections is a(n) 38. a

a. isometry. **b.** rotation. **c.** translation. **d.** dilation.

39. In the dilation $d[(0, 0), 3]$, name the image of $A(2, -4)$. 39. c

a. $(5, -7)$ **b.** $(\frac{2}{3}, \frac{-4}{3})$ **c.** $(6, -12)$ **d.** $(6, 12)$

40. $\tan \angle H =$ **a.** $\frac{HG}{HK}$. **b.** $\frac{HG}{KG}$. **c.** $\frac{KG}{HK}$. **d.** $\frac{KG}{HG}$. 40. d

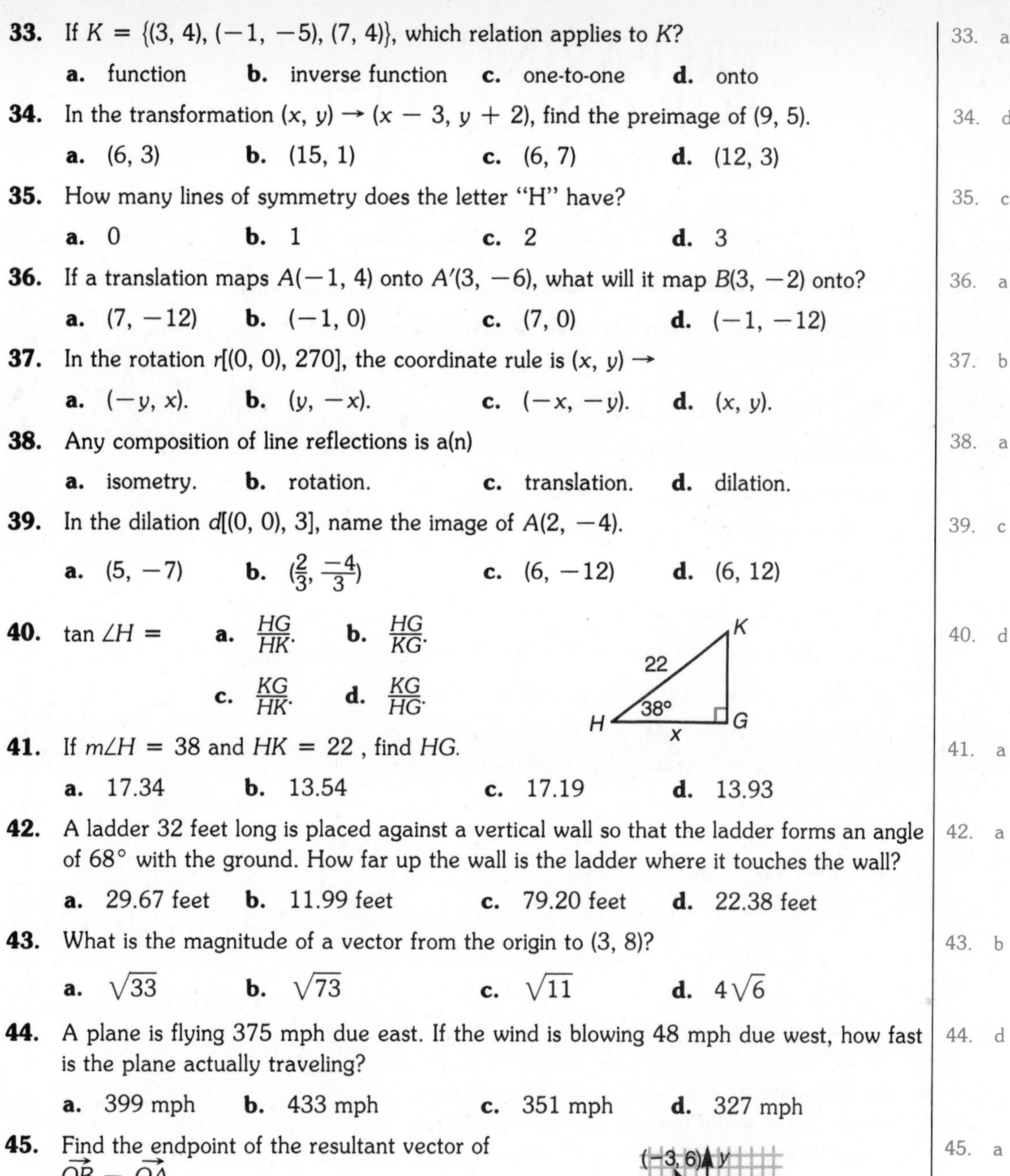

41. If $m\angle H = 38$ and $HK = 22$, find HG. 41. a

a. 17.34 **b.** 13.54 **c.** 17.19 **d.** 13.93

42. A ladder 32 feet long is placed against a vertical wall so that the ladder forms an angle of 68° with the ground. How far up the wall is the ladder where it touches the wall? 42. a

a. 29.67 feet **b.** 11.99 feet **c.** 79.20 feet **d.** 22.38 feet

43. What is the magnitude of a vector from the origin to (3, 8)? 43. b

a. $\sqrt{33}$ **b.** $\sqrt{73}$ **c.** $\sqrt{11}$ **d.** $4\sqrt{6}$

44. A plane is flying 375 mph due east. If the wind is blowing 48 mph due west, how fast is the plane actually traveling? 44. d

a. 399 mph **b.** 433 mph **c.** 351 mph **d.** 327 mph

45. Find the endpoint of the resultant vector of $\overrightarrow{OB} - \overrightarrow{OA}$. 45. a

a. $(-8, 4)$ **b.** $(2, 8)$

c. $(8, -4)$ **d.** $(8, 4)$

(−3, 6) y
B
(5, 2)
A
O
x

Preparing for College Entrance Exams

1. d

2. d

3. b

4. a

5. a

6. e

PREPARING FOR COLLEGE ENTRANCE EXAMS

Select the correct answer for each of the following questions.

1. In circle O, $\overline{AB} \cong \overline{OA}$. The area of $\triangle AOB = 4\sqrt{3}$. Find the area of circle O.

a. 4π **b.** 8π **c.** $24\sqrt{3}$

d. 16π **e.** $24\pi\sqrt{3}$

2. In the figure at the right, $\overline{AE} \parallel \overline{BC}$. $m\angle E + m\angle D + m\angle C =$

a. 60. **b.** 100. **c.** 180.

d. 360. **e.** none of these.

3. The surface area of a cube is 54. What is the volume of this cube?

a. 18 **b.** 27 **c.** 48 **d.** 64 **e.** 125

4. In the figure at the right, $AB = BC = CD = 4$. All the arcs are semicircles. Find the area of the shaded region.

a. 24π **b.** 36π **c.** 52π

d. 60π **e.** 72π

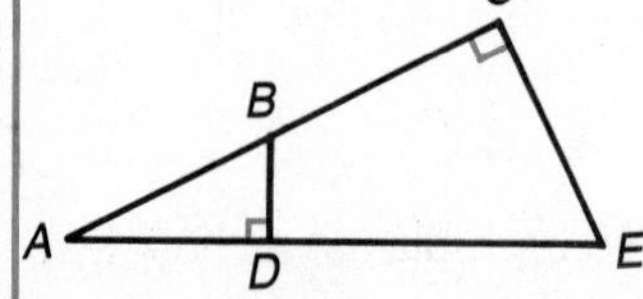

5. In this figure, $AB = 6$, $AD = 4$, and $DE = 14$. Find BC.

a. 6 **b.** 7 **c.** 9

d. 10 **e.** 12

6. In the figure at the right, a wire is wrapped around three equal tangent circles. What is the length of this wire, in terms of r, if the radius of one of these circles is represented by r?

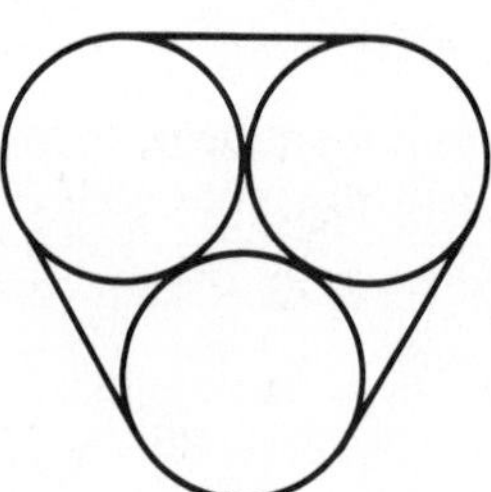

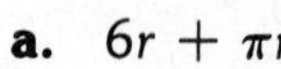

a. $6r + \pi r$ **b.** $8r + 2\pi\sqrt{2r}$

c. $6\sqrt{2r} + 6\pi$ **d.** $3r + \pi r$

e. $6r + 2\pi r$

SQUARES AND SQUARE ROOTS

n	n²	√n	n	n²	√n	n	n²	√n	n	n²	√n
1	1	1.000	**51**	2 601	7.141	**101**	10 201	10.050	**151**	22 801	12.288
2	4	1.414	**52**	2 704	7.211	**102**	10 404	10.100	**152**	23 104	12.329
3	9	1.732	**53**	2 809	7.280	**103**	10 609	10.149	**153**	23 409	12.369
4	16	2.000	**54**	2 916	7.348	**104**	10 816	10.198	**154**	23 716	12.410
5	25	2.236	**55**	3 025	7.416	**105**	11 025	10.247	**155**	24 025	12.450
6	36	2.449	**56**	3 136	7.483	**106**	11 236	10.296	**156**	24 336	12.490
7	49	2.646	**57**	3 249	7.550	**107**	11 449	10.344	**157**	24 649	12.530
8	64	2.828	**58**	3 364	7.616	**108**	11 664	10.392	**158**	24 964	12.570
9	81	3.000	**59**	3 481	7.681	**109**	11 881	10.440	**159**	25 281	12.610
10	100	3.162	**60**	3 600	7.746	**110**	12 100	10.488	**160**	25 600	12.649
11	121	3.317	**61**	3 721	7.810	**111**	12 321	10.536	**161**	25 921	12.689
12	144	3.464	**62**	3 844	7.874	**112**	12 544	10.583	**162**	26 244	12.728
13	169	3.606	**63**	3 969	7.937	**113**	12 769	10.630	**163**	26 569	12.767
14	196	3.742	**64**	4 096	8.000	**114**	12 996	10.677	**164**	26 896	12.806
15	225	3.873	**65**	4 225	8.062	**115**	13 225	10.724	**165**	27 225	12.845
16	256	4.000	**66**	4 356	8.124	**116**	13 456	10.770	**166**	27 556	12.884
17	289	4.123	**67**	4 489	8.185	**117**	13 689	10.817	**167**	27 889	12.923
18	324	4.243	**68**	4 624	8.246	**118**	13 924	10.863	**168**	28 224	12.961
19	361	4.359	**69**	4 761	8.307	**119**	14 161	10.909	**169**	28 561	13.000
20	400	4.472	**70**	4 900	8.367	**120**	14 400	10.954	**170**	28 900	13.038
21	441	4.583	**71**	5 401	8.426	**121**	14 641	11.000	**171**	29 241	13.077
22	484	4.690	**72**	5 184	8.485	**122**	14 884	11.045	**172**	29 584	13.115
23	529	4.796	**73**	5 329	8.544	**123**	15 129	11.091	**173**	29 929	13.153
24	576	4.899	**74**	5 476	8.602	**124**	15 376	11.136	**174**	30 276	13.191
25	625	5.000	**75**	5 625	8.660	**125**	15 625	11.180	**175**	30 625	13.229
26	676	5.099	**76**	5 776	8.718	**126**	15 876	11.225	**176**	30 976	13.266
27	729	5.196	**77**	5 929	8.775	**127**	16 129	11.269	**177**	31 329	13.304
28	784	5.292	**78**	6 084	8.832	**128**	16 384	11.314	**178**	31 684	13.342
29	841	5.385	**79**	6 241	8.888	**129**	16 641	11.358	**179**	32 041	13.379
30	900	5.477	**80**	6 400	8.944	**130**	16 900	11.402	**180**	32 400	13.416
31	961	5.568	**81**	6 561	9.000	**131**	17 161	11.446	**181**	32 761	13.454
32	1 024	5.657	**82**	6 724	9.055	**132**	17 424	11.489	**182**	33 124	13.491
33	1 089	5.745	**83**	6 889	9.110	**133**	17 689	11.533	**183**	33 489	13.528
34	1 156	5.831	**84**	7 056	9.165	**134**	17 956	11.576	**184**	33 856	13.565
35	1 225	5.916	**85**	7 225	9.220	**135**	18 225	11.619	**185**	34 225	13.601
36	1 296	6.000	**86**	7 396	9.274	**136**	18 496	11.662	**186**	34 596	13.638
37	1 369	6.083	**87**	7 569	9.327	**137**	18 769	11.705	**187**	34 969	13.675
38	1 444	6.164	**88**	7 744	9.381	**138**	19 044	11.747	**188**	35 344	13.711
39	1 521	6.245	**89**	7 921	9.434	**139**	19 321	11.790	**189**	35 721	13.748
40	1 600	6.325	**90**	8 100	9.487	**140**	19 600	11.832	**190**	36 100	13.784
41	1 681	6.403	**91**	8 281	9.539	**141**	19 881	11.874	**191**	36 481	13.820
42	1 764	6.481	**92**	8 464	9.592	**142**	20 164	11.916	**192**	36 864	13.856
43	1 849	6.557	**93**	8 649	9.644	**143**	20 449	11.958	**193**	37 249	13.892
44	1 936	6.633	**94**	8 836	9.695	**144**	20 736	12.000	**194**	37 636	13.928
45	2 025	6.708	**95**	9 025	9.747	**145**	21 025	12.042	**195**	38 025	13.964
46	2 116	6.782	**96**	9 216	9.798	**146**	21 316	12.083	**196**	38 416	14.000
47	2 209	6.856	**97**	9 409	9.849	**147**	21 609	12.124	**197**	38 809	14.036
48	2 304	6.928	**98**	9 604	9.899	**148**	21 904	12.166	**198**	39 204	14.071
49	2 401	7.000	**99**	9 801	9.950	**149**	22 201	12.207	**199**	39 601	14.107
50	2 500	7.071	**100**	10 000	10.000	**150**	22 500	12.247	**200**	40 000	14.142

SYMBOLS AND SIGNS

$+2, -2$	positive and negative signs
$=, \neq$	is equal to, is not equal to
$\approx$	is approximately equal to
$1.\overline{66}$	repeating decimal
$\sqrt{36}$	positive square root
$-\sqrt{36}$	negative square root
$\sqrt[3]{36}$	positive cube root
$-\sqrt[3]{36}$	negative cube root
$\lvert n \rvert$	the absolute value of n
%	percent
$\varnothing$	the empty (null) set
$A \cup B$	the union of A and B
$A \cap B$	the intersection of A and B
$A \subset B, A \not\subset B$	A is a subset of B, A is not a subset of B
$A \supset B$	A contains B as a subset
$x \in A, x \notin A$	x is an element of A, x is not an element of A
$\{a, b, c, d\}$	the set whose elements are a, b, c, and d
$p \rightarrow q$	if p, then q (logic)
$\sim p$	not p (logic)
$<, >$	is less than, is greater than
$\nless \ngtr$	is not less than, is not greater than
$\leq, \geq$	is less than or equal to, is greater than or equal to
$\overleftrightarrow{AB}$	line AB
$\overline{AB}$	segment AB
$\overrightarrow{AB}$	ray AB

$\angle$(s)	angle(s)
$\perp, \not\perp$	is perpendicular to, is not perpendicular to
$\parallel, \nparallel$	is parallel to, is not parallel to
$\cong, \ncong$	is congruent to, is not congruent to
$\sim, \nsim$	is similar to, is not similar to

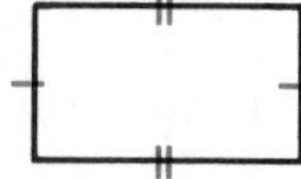

congruent sides (hash marks)

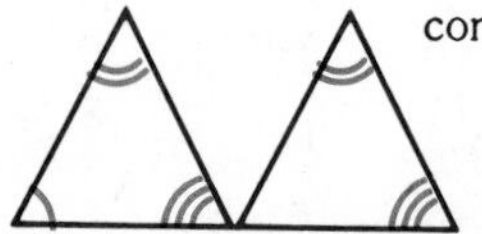

congruent angles (arcs)

ΔFAM	triangle FAM
▱$ABCD$	paralleogram $ABCD$
(3, 4)	the ordered pair 3, 4
$R(3, 4)$	coordinates of R ($x = 3$, $y = 4$)
$\odot C$	the circle whose center is C
π	pi; approx. 3.14 or $\frac{22}{7}$
$\overset{\frown}{AB}, \overset{\frown}{AXB}$	minor arc AB, major arc AXB
$90°$	90 degrees
$T \circ R$	the composition of T and R
R^{-1}	inverse relation
$A \rightarrow B$	the mapping of set A (the domain) onto set B (the codomain)
θ	magnitude of a rotation

COMMON ABBREVIATIONS

adjacent	adj.
alternate	alt.
Angle-Side-Angle	ASA
associative	assoc.
bisector(s)	bis.
centimeter(s)	cm
commutative	comm.
complementary	comp.
corollary	cor.
corresponding	corres.
cosine	cos
definition(s)	def(s).
distance	dist.
distributive	distrib.
endpoint(s)	endpt(s).
equidistant	equidist.
equilateral	equilat.
exterior	ext.
foot, feet	ft
Hypotenuse-Leg	HL
inch(es)	in.
interior	int.
intersection	intersect.
isosceles	isos.
kilogram(s)	kg
kilometer(s)	km
lateral	lat.
Leg-Leg	LL
measure(s)	meas.
meter(s)	m
midpoint(s)	midpt(s).
mile(s)	mi
millimeter(s)	mm
multiplication	mult.
opposite	opp.
point(s)	pt(s).
postulate(s)	post(s).
proof(s)	prf(s).
property(ies)	prop(s).
quadrilateral(s)	quad(s).
rectangle(s)	rect(s).
reflexive	reflex.
right	rt.
segment(s)	seg(s).
Side-Angle-Side	SAS
Side-Side-Side	SSS
similarity	sim.
sine	sin
substitution	subst.
supplementary	supp.
symmetric	sym.
tangent	tan
theorem(s)	thm(s).
transitive	trans.
transversal(s)	trans.
trapezoid(s)	trap(s).
vertical	vert.
yard(s)	yd

GEOMETRY AND COMPUTER NOTATION

h	altitude, length of height
a	apothem of a polygon
A	area of a polygon or circle
b	base of a triangle
C	circumference of a circle
$\angle A\text{-}\overleftrightarrow{XY}\text{-}B$	dihedral angle
d	diameter of a circle
d	dilation; $d[(x, y), k]$
d	distance, length of a segment
5^2, 5^3	exponent; 5 squared, 5 cubed
g	glide reflection
iff	if and only if
k	magnitude of a dilation; *above*
m	measure of; $m\angle A$, $m\widehat{AB}$
n-gon	n-sided polygon
p	perimeter of a polygon
C', C''	prime; C-prime, C-double-prime
r	radius of a circle, sphere, or right cylinder
$\frac{a}{b}$, a:b	ratio; ratio of a to b
r	reflection
r	rotation; $r[(x, y), \theta]$
s	side of a polygon
s	slant height of a pyramid
m	slope of a line; $m = -0.5$
P_1	subscript; P sub-one
t	translation
ABS(X)	absolute value of x
ATN(X)	arctangent of x
COS(X)	cosine of x
INT(X)	integer value of x
REM	remark; program information
RND(X)	random-number generator
SIN(X)	sine of x
TAN(X)	tangent of x
*	multiplication sign
/	division sign
↑ or ∧	exponent

TRIGONOMETRIC RATIOS

angle°	*sin*	*cos*	*tan*	*angle°*	*sin*	*cos*	*tan*
1	.0175	.9998	.0175	**46**	.7193	.6947	1.0355
2	.0349	.9994	.0349	**47**	.7314	.6820	1.0724
3	.0523	.9986	.0524	**48**	.7431	.6691	1.1106
4	.0698	.9976	.0699	**49**	.7547	.6561	1.1504
5	.0872	.9962	.0875	**50**	.7660	.6428	1.1918
6	.1045	.9945	.1051	**51**	.7771	.6293	1.2349
7	.1219	.9925	.1228	**52**	.7880	.6157	1.2799
8	.1392	.9903	.1405	**53**	.7986	.6018	1.3270
9	.1564	.9877	.1584	**54**	.8090	.5878	1.3764
10	.1736	.9848	.1763	**55**	.8192	.5736	1.4281
11	.1908	.9816	.1944	**56**	.8290	.5592	1.4826
12	.2079	.9781	.2126	**57**	.8387	.5446	1.5399
13	.2250	.9744	.2309	**58**	.8480	.5299	1.6003
14	.2419	.9703	.2493	**59**	.8572	.5150	1.6643
15	.2588	.9659	.2679	**60**	.8660	.5000	1.7321
16	.2756	.9613	.2867	**61**	.8746	.4848	1.8040
17	.2924	.9563	.3057	**62**	.8829	.4695	1.8807
18	.3090	.9511	.3249	**63**	.8910	.4540	1.9626
19	.3256	.9455	.3443	**64**	.8988	.4384	2.0503
20	.3420	.9397	.3640	**65**	.9063	.4226	2.1445
21	.3584	.9336	.3839	**66**	.9135	.4067	2.2460
22	.3746	.9272	.4040	**67**	.9205	.3907	2.3559
23	.3907	.9205	.4245	**68**	.9272	.3746	2.4751
24	.4067	.9135	.4452	**69**	.9336	.3584	2.6051
25	.4226	.9063	.4663	**70**	.9397	.3420	2.7475
26	.4384	.8988	.4877	**71**	.9455	.3256	2.9042
27	.4540	.8910	.5095	**72**	.9511	.3090	3.0777
28	.4695	.8829	.5317	**73**	.9563	.2924	3.2709
29	.4848	.8746	.5543	**74**	.9613	.2756	3.4874
30	.5000	.8660	.5774	**75**	.9659	.2588	3.7321
31	.5150	.8572	.6009	**76**	.9703	.2419	4.0108
32	.5299	.8480	.6249	**77**	.9744	.2250	4.3315
33	.5446	.8387	.6494	**78**	.9781	.2079	4.7046
34	.5592	.8290	.6745	**79**	.9816	.1908	5.1446
35	.5736	.8192	.7002	**80**	.9848	.1736	5.6713
36	.5878	.8090	.7265	**81**	.9877	.1564	6.3138
37	.6018	.7986	.7536	**82**	.9903	.1392	7.1154
38	.6157	.7880	.7813	**83**	.9925	.1219	8.1443
39	.6293	.7771	.8098	**84**	.9945	.1045	9.5144
40	.6428	.7660	.8391	**85**	.9962	.0872	11.4301
41	.6561	.7547	.8693	**86**	.9976	.0698	14.3007
42	.6691	.7431	.9004	**87**	.9986	.0523	19.0811
43	.6820	.7314	.9325	**88**	.9994	.0349	28.6363
44	.6947	.7193	.9657	**89**	.9998	.0175	57.2900
45	.7071	.7071	1.0000				

POSTULATES

Chapter 1

Postulate 1 (p. 17) Given any two different points, there is exactly one line that contains both of them.

Postulate 2 (p. 18) **(The Distance Postulate)** To every pair of different points, there corresponds a unique positive real number.

Postulate 3 (p. 19) **(The Ruler Postulate)** The points of a line can be placed in correspondence with the real numbers in such a way that:

1. to every point of the line there corresponds exactly one real number;
2. to every real number there corresponds exactly one point of the line; and
3. the distance between two points is the absolute value of the difference of the corresponding numbers.

Postulate 4 (p. 22) **(The Ruler Placement Postulate)** Given two points P and Q of a line, the coordinate system can be chosen in such a way that the coordinate of P is zero and the coordinate of Q is positive.

Chapter 2

Postulate 5 (p. 35) a. Every plane contains at least three noncollinear points. b. Space contains at least four noncoplanar points.

Postulate 6 (p. 35) If two points lie in a plane, then the line containing these points lies in the same plane.

Postulate 7 (p. 35) Any three points lie in at least one plane; any three noncollinear points lie in exactly one plane.

Postulate 8 (p. 35) If two planes intersect, then their intersection is a line.

Postulate 9 (p. 40) **(The Plane Separation Postulate)** Given a line and a plane containing it, the points of the plane that do not lie on the line form two half-planes, such that:

a. each of the half-planes is a convex set, and
b. if P is in one half-plane and Q is in the other, then $\overline{PQ}$ intersects the line.

Postulate 10 (p. 41) **(The Space Separation Postulate)** The points of space that do not lie in a given plane form two half-spaces such that:

a. each half-space is a convex set, and
b. if point P is in one half-space and point Q is in the other, then $\overline{PQ}$ intersects the plane.

Postulate 11 (p. 48) **(The Angle Measurement Postulate)** To every $\angle BAC$ there corresponds a real number between 0 and 180.

Chapter 3

Postulate 12 (p. 60) **(The Angle Construction Postulate)** Let $\overrightarrow{AB}$ be a ray on the edge of the half-plane H. For every number r between 0 and 180 there is exactly one ray AP, with P in H, such that $m\angle PAB = r$.

Postulate 13 (p. 60) **(The Angle Addition Postulate)** If D is a point in the interior of $\angle BAC$, then $m\angle BAC = m\angle BAD + m\angle DAC$.

Postulate 14 (p. 61) **(The Supplement Postulate)** If two angles form a linear pair, then they are supplementary.

Chapter 4

Postulate 15 (p. 95) **(The Side-Angle-Side [SAS] Postulate)** Given a correspondence between two triangles (or between a triangle and itself), if two sides and the included angle of the first triangle are congruent to the corresponding parts of the second triangle, then the correspondence is a congruence.

Chapter 8

Postulate 16 (p. 233) **(The Parallel Postulate)** Through a given external point there is at most one line parallel to a given line.

Chapter 9

Postulate 17 (p. 277) **(The Area Postulate)** To every polygonal region there corresponds a unique positive number.

Postulate 18 (p. 277) If two triangles are congruent, then the triangular regions have the same area.

Postulate 19 (p. 277) Suppose that the region R is the union of two regions R_1 and R_2. Suppose that R_1 and R_2 intersect at most in a finite number of segments and points. Then the area of polygon R is the sum of the areas of R_1 and R_2.

Postulate 20 (p. 280) The area of a rectangle is the product of the length of its base and the length of its altitude. That is, $A = bh$.

Chapter 14

Postulate 21 (p. 490) The volume of a rectangular parallelepiped is the product of the altitude and the area of the base. ($V = Ah$, where A represents the area of the base and h the height.)

Postulate 22 (p. 491) **(Cavalieri's Principle)** Given two solids and a plane, if for every plane that intersects the solids and is parallel to the given plane the two intersections have equal areas, then the two solids have the same volume.

THEOREMS AND COROLLARIES

Theorem 1.1 (p. 22) Let A, B, and C be three points of a line, with coordinates x, y, and z, respectively. If $x < y < z$, then B is between A and C.

Theorem 1.2 (p. 23) Of three different points of the same line, exactly one is between the other two.

Theorem 1.3 (p. 24) Congruence between segments is an equivalence relation.

Theorem 1.4 (p. 25) **(The Point Plotting Theorem)** Let $\overrightarrow{AB}$ be a ray, and let x be a positive number. Then there is exactly one point P of $\overrightarrow{AB}$ such that $AP = x$.

Theorem 1.5 (p. 26) Every segment has exactly one midpoint.

Theorem 2.1 (p. 36) Two lines intersect in at most one point.

Theorem 2.2 (p. 36) If a given line intersects a plane not containing it, then their intersection is a single point.

Theorem 2.3 (p. 36) Given a line and a point not on the line, there is exactly one plane containing them both.

Theorem 2.4 (p. 37) Given two intersecting lines, there is exactly one plane containing both of them.

Theorem 3.1 (p. 66) If two angles are complementary, then both of them are acute.

Theorem 3.2 (p. 66) Every angle is congruent to itself.

Theorem 3.3 (p. 66) All right angles are congruent.

Theorem 3.4 (p. 66) If two angles are both congruent *and* supplementary, then each of them is a right angle.

Theorem 3.5 (p. 66) Supplements of congruent angles are congruent.

Theorem 3.6 (p. 67) Complements of congruent angles are congruent.

Theorem 3.7 (p. 70) Vertical angles are congruent.

Theorem 3.8 (p. 71) If two intersecting lines form one right angle, then they form four right angles.

Theorem 3.9 (p. 81) Every segment is congruent to itself.

Theorem 3.10 (p. 81) Congruence of triangles is an equivalence relation.

Theorem 3.11 (p. 85) Corresponding medians of congruent triangles are congruent.

Theorem 3.12 (p. 85) Corresponding angle bisectors of congruent triangles are congruent.

Theorem 4.1 (p. 96) **(The Leg-Leg [LL] Theorem)** Given a correspondence between two right triangles (or between a right triangle and itself), if the legs of the first right triangle are congruent to the corresponding legs of the second right triangle, then the correspondence is a congruence.

Theorem 4.2 (p. 100) **(The Angle-Side-Angle [ASA] Theorem)** Given a correspondence between two triangles (or between a triangle and itself), if two angles and the included side of the first triangle are congruent to the corresponding parts of the second triangle, then the correspondence is a congruence.

Theorem 4.3 (p. 106) **(The Isosceles Triangle Theorem)** If two sides of a triangle are congruent, then the angles opposite those sides are congruent.

Corollary 4.3.1 (p. 106) Every equi*lateral* triangle is equi*angular*.

Theorem 4.4 (p. 106) If two angles of a triangle are congruent, then the sides opposite those angles are congruent.

Corollary 4.4.1 (p. 107) Every equi*angular* triangle is equi*lateral*.

Theorem 4.5 (p. 110) **(The Side-Side-Side [SSS] Theorem)** Given a correspondence between two triangles (or between a triangle and itself), if all three pairs of corresponding sides are congruent, then the correspondence is a congruence.

Theorem 4.6 (p. 111) **(The Angle Bisector Theorem)** Every angle has exactly one bisector.

Theorem 5.1 (p. 135) In a given plane, through a given point of a given line, there is one and only one line perpendicular to the given line.

Theorem 5.2 (p. 136) **(The Perpendicular Bisector Theorem)** The perpendicular bisector of a segment in a plane is the set of all points of the plane that are equidistant from the endpoints of the segment.

Corollary 5.2.1 (p. 137) Given segment $\overline{AB}$ and line l in a plane, if two points of l are equidistant from A and B, then l is the perpendicular bisector of $\overline{AB}$.

Theorem 5.3 (p. 138) Given a line and an external point, there is one and only one line perpendicular to the given line through the given point.

Corollary 5.3.1 (p. 138) At most one angle of a triangle can be a right angle.

Theorem 5.4 (p. 151) If P is between X and Y on a line l, then X and P are in the same half-plane created by any other line that contains Y.

Theorem 5.5 (p. 152) If D is between A and C, and B is any point not on line $\overleftrightarrow{AC}$, then D is in the interior of $\angle ABC$.

Theorem 6.1 (p. 170) **(The Exterior Angle Theorem)** An exterior angle of a triangle is larger than either remote interior angle.

Corollary 6.1.1 (p. 170) If a triangle has a right angle, then the other two angles are acute.

Theorem 6.2 (p. 175) **(The Side-Angle-Angle [SAA] Theorem)** Given a correspondence between two triangles, if two angles and a side opposite one of them in one triangle are congruent to the corresponding parts of the second triangle, then the correspondence is a congruence.

Theorem 6.3 (p. 176) **(The Hypotenuse-Leg [HL] Theorem)** Given a correspondence between two right triangles, if the hypotenuse and one leg of one triangle are congruent to the corresponding parts of the second triangle, then the correspondence is a congruence.

Theorem 6.4 (p. 179) If two sides of a triangle are not congruent, then the angles opposite those sides are not congruent, and the larger angle is opposite the larger side.

Theorem 6.5 (p. 180) If two angles of a triangle are not congruent, then the sides opposite them are not congruent, and the longer side is opposite the larger angle.

Theorem 6.6 (p. 180) The shortest segment joining a point to a line is the perpendicular segment.

Theorem 6.7 (p. 181) **(The Triangle Inequality Theorem)** The sum of the lengths of any two sides of a triangle is greater than the length of the third side.

Theorem 6.8 (p. 184) If two sides of one triangle are congruent respectively to two sides of a second triangle, and the included angle of the first triangle is larger than the included angle of the second, then the opposite side of the first triangle is longer than the opposite side of the second.

Theorem 6.9 (p. 185) If two sides of one triangle are congruent respectively to two sides of a second triangle, and the third side of the first triangle is longer than the third side of the second, then the included angle of the first triangle is larger than the included angle of the second.

Theorem 7.1 (p. 198) If each of two points of a line is equidistant from two given points, then every point of the line is equidistant from the given points.

Theorem 7.2 (p. 201) If each of three noncollinear points of a plane is equidistant from two points not in that plane, then every point of the plane is equidistant from these two points.

Theore 7.3 (p. 202) If a line is perpendicular to each of two intersecting lines at their point of intersection, then it is perpendicular to the plane of these lines.

Theorem 7.4 (p. 207) Through a given point on a given line there passes a plane perpendicular to the line.

Theorem 7.5 (p. 207) If a line and a plane are perpendicular, then the plane contains every line perpendicular to the given line at its point of intersection with the given plane.

Theorem 7.6 (p. 208) Through a given point on a given line there is at most one plane perpendicular to the line.

Theorem 7.7 (p. 208) The perpendicular bisecting plane of a segment is the set of all points equidistant from the endpoints of the segment.

Theorem 7.8 (p. 211) Two lines perpendicular to the same plane are coplanar.

Theorem 7.9 (p. 213) Through a given point there passes one and only one plane perpendicular to a given line.

Theorem 7.10 (p. 213) Through a given point there passes one and only one line perpendicular to a given plane.

Theorem 7.11 (p. 213) The shortest segment to a plane from an external point is the perpendicular segment.

Theorem 8.1 (p. 223) If two lines are parallel, then they line in exactly one plane.

Theorem 8.2 (p. 224) If two coplanar lines are both perpendicular to the same line, then they are parallel.

Theorem 8.3 (p. 224) If k is a line, and P is a point not on k, then there is at least one line through P that is parallel to k.

Theorem 8.4 (p. 225) If two lines are cut by a transversal, and if one pair of alternate interior angles are congruent, then the other pair of alternate interior angles are also congruent.

Theorem 8.5 (p. 225) If two lines are cut by a transveral, and if a pair of alternate interior angles are congruent, then the lines are parallel.

Theorem 8.6 (p. 229) If two lines are cut by a transversal, and if one pair of corresponding angles are congruent, then the other three pairs of corresponding angles are congruent.

Theorem 8.7 (p. 230) If two lines are cut by a transversal, and if one pair of corresponding angles are congruent, then the lines are parallel.

Theorem 8.8 (p. 233) If two parallel lines are cut by a transveral, then alternate interior angles are congruent.

Theorem 8.9 (p. 233) If two parallel lines are cut by a transversal, each pair of corresponding angles are congruent.

Theorem 8.10 (p. 234) If two parallel lines are cut by a transversal, interior angles on the same side of the transversal are supplementary.

Theorem 8.11 (p. 234) In a plane, two lines parallel to the same line are parallel to each other.

Theorem 8.12 (p. 234) In a plane, if a line is perpendicular to one of two parallel lines, then it is perpendicular to the other.

Theorem 8.13 (p. 236) The sum of the measures of the angles of a triangle is 180.

Corollary 8.13.1 (p. 236) Given a correspondence between two triangles, if two pairs of corresponding angles are congruent, then the third pair of corresponding angles are congruent.

Corollary 8.13.2 (p. 237) The acute angles of a right triangle are complementary.

Corollary 8.13.3 (p. 237) For any triangle, the measure of an exterior angle is the sum of the measures of the two remote interior angles.

Theorem 8.14 (p. 241) Either diagonal separates a parallelogram into two congruent triangles.

Theorem 8.15 (p. 241) Opposite sides of a parallelogram are congruent.

Corollary 8.15.1 (p. 241) If $l_1 \parallel l_2$ and if P and Q are any two points on l_1, then the distances of P and Q from l_2 are equal.

Theorem 8.16 (p. 241) Opposite angles of a parallelogram are congruent.

Theorem 8.17 (p. 241) Two consecutive angles of a parallelogram are supplementary.

Theorem 8.18 (p. 242) The diagonals of a parallelogram bisect each other.

Theorem 8.19 (p. 242) If both pairs of opposite sides of a quadrilateral are congruent, then the quadrilateral is a parallelogram.

Theorem 8.20 (p. 242) If two sides of a quadrilateral are parallel and congruent, then the quadrilateral is a parallelogram.

Theorem 8.21 (p. 242) If the diagonals of a quadrilateral bisect each other, then the quadrilateral is a parallelogram.

Theorem 8.22 (p. 242) The segment joining the midpoints of two sides of a triangle is parallel to and half as long as the third side.

Theorem 8.23 (p. 246) If a parallelogram has one right angle, then it has four right angles, and the parallelogram is a rectangle.

Theorem 8.24 (p. 246) The diagonals of a rhombus are perpendicular to one another.

Theorem 8.25 (p. 246) If the diagonals of a quadrilateral bisect each other and are perpendicular, then the quadrilateral is a rhombus.

Theorem 8.26 (p. 247) If three parallel lines intercept congruent segments on one transversal, then they intercept congruent segments on any other transversal.

Corollary 8.26.1 (p. 248) If three or more parallel lines intercept congruent segments on one transversal, then they intercept congruent segments on any other transversal.

Theorem 8.27 (p. 251) If a plane intersects two parallel planes, then it intersects them in two parallel lines.

Theorem 8.28 (p. 252) If a line is perpendicular to one of two parallel planes, then it is perpendicular to the other.

Theorem 8.29 (p. 252) Two planes perpendicular to the same line are parallel.

Corollary 8.29.1 (p. 252) **(Parallelism of Planes is Transitive)** If two planes are each parallel to a third plane, they are parallel to each other.

Theorem 8.30 (p. 253) Two lines perpendicular to the same plane are parallel.

Corollary 8.30.1 (p. 253) A plane perpendicular to one of two parallel lines is perpendicular to the other.

Corollary 8.30.2 (p. 253) **(Parallelism of Lines is Transitive)** If two lines are each parallel to a third line, they are parallel to each other.

Theorem 8.31 (p. 253) Two parallel planes are everywhere equidistant.

Theorem 8.32 (p. 257) Any two plane angles of a given dihedral angle are congruent.

Corollary 8.32.1 (p. 258) If a line is perpendicular to a plane, then any plane containing this line is perpendicular to the given plane.

Corollary 8.32.2 (p. 258) If two planes are perpendicular, then any line in one of them that is perpendicular to their line of intersection is perpendicular to the other plane.

Theorem 8.33 (p. 261) The projection of a line into a plane is a line, unless the line and the plane are perpendicular.

Theorem 9.1 (p. 284) The area of a right triangle is half the product of the length of its legs.

Theorem 9.2 (p. 284) The area of a triangle is half the product of any base and the altitude to that base.

Theorem 9.3 (p. 286) If two triangles have the same altitude, then the ratio of their areas if equal to the ratio of their bases.

Theorem 9.4 (p. 286) If two triangles have equal altitudes and equal bases, then they have equal areas.

Theorem 9.5 (p. 289) The area of a parallelogram is the product of any base and the corresponding altitude.

Theorem 9.6 (p. 289) The area of a trapezoid is half the product of its altitude and the sum of its bases.

Theorem 9.7 (p. 293) **(The Pythagorean Theorem)** In a right triangle, the square of the length of the hypotenuse is equal to the sum of the squares of lengths of the legs.

Theorem 9.8 (p. 293) **(Converse of the Pythagorean Theorem)** If the square of one side of a triangle is equal to the sum of the squares of the other two sides, then the triangle is a right triangle.

Theorem 9.9 (p. 297) **(The 30-60 Right Triangle Theorem)** The length of the hypotenuse of a right triangle is twice as long as the length of the shorter leg if and only if the measures of the acute angles are 30 and 60.

Theorem 9.10 (p. 298) **(The Isosceles Right Triangle Theorem)** A right triangle is isosceles if and only if the length of the hypotenuse is $\sqrt{2}$ times the length of a leg.

Theorem 10.1 (p. 314) **(The Basic Proportionality Theorem)** If a line parallel to one side of a triangle intersects the other sides in distinct points, then it intercepts segments that are proportional to these sides.

Theorem 10.2 (p. 314) If a line intersects two sides of a triangle and intercepts segments proportional to these sides, then it is parallel to the third side.

Theorem 10.3 (p. 317) **(The Angle-Angle-Angle [AAA] Similarity Theorem)** Given a correspondence between two triangles, if corresponding angles are congruent, then the correspondence is a similarity.

Corollary 10.3.1 (p. 317) **(The Angle-Angle [AA] Corollary)** Given a correspondence between two triangles, if two pairs of corresponding angles are congruent, then the correspondence is a similarity.

Corollary 10.3.2 (p. 318) If a line parallel to one side of a triangle intersects the other two sides in distinct points, then it intercepts a triangle similar to the given triangle.

Theorem 10.4 (p. 321) **(The Side-Angle-Side [SAS] Similarity Theorem)** Given a correspondence between two triangles, if two pairs of corresponding sides are proportional, and the included angles are congruent, then the correspondence is a similarity.

Theorem 10.5 (p. 321) **(The Side-Side-Side [SSS] Similarity Theorem)** Given a correspondence between two triangles, if corresponding sides are proportional, then the correspondence is a similarity.

Theorem 10.6 (p. 325) In any right triangle, the altitude to the hypotenuse separates the triangle into two triangles that are similar both to each other and to the original triangle.

Corollary 10.6.1 (p. 326) Given a right triangle and the altitude to the hypotenuse,
(1) the altitude is the geometric mean of the segments into which it separates the hypotenuse and
(2) either leg is the geometric mean of the hypotenuse and the segment of the hypotenuse adjacent to the leg.

Theorem 10.7 (p. 329) The ratio of the areas of two similar triangles is the square of the ratio of any two corresponding sides.

Theorem 11.1 (p. 345) On a nonvertical line, all segments have the same slope.

Theorem 11.2 (p. 347) Two nonvertical lines are parallel if and only if they have the same slope.

Theorem 11.3 (p. 348) Two nonvertical lines are perpendicular if and only if their slopes are the negative reciprocals of each other.

Theorem 11.4 (p. 352) **(The Distance Formula)** The distance between the points (x_1, y_1) and (x_2, y_2) is equal to $\sqrt{(x_2 - x_1)^2 + (y_2 - y_1)^2}$.

Theorem 11.5 (p. 355) **(The Midpoint Formula)** Let $P_1 = (x_1, y_1)$ and let $P_2 = (x_2, y_2)$. Then the midpoint of $\overline{P_1P_2}$ is the point $P = (\frac{x_1 + x_2}{2}, \frac{y_1 + y_2}{2})$.

Theorem 11.6 (p. 367) Let l be a nonvertical line with slope m, and let P be a point of l with coordinates (x_1, y_1). For every point $Q = (x, y)$ of l, the equation $y - y_1 = m(x - x_1)$ is satisfied.

Theorem 11.7 (p. 368) The graph of the equation $y - y_1 = m(x - x_1)$ is the line that passes through the point (x_1, y_1) and has slope m.

Theorem 11.8 (p. 368) The graph of the equation $y = mx + b$ is the line with slope m and y intercept b.

Theorem 11.9 (p. 369) Every line in the plane is the graph of a linear equation in x and y.

Theorem 11.10 (p. 369) The graph of a linear equation in x and y is always a line.

Theorem 12.1 (p. 380) The intersection of a sphere with a plane through its center is a circle with the same center and radius as the sphere.

Theorem 12.2 (p. 385) Given a line and a circle in the same plane, let P be the center of the circle and let F be the foot of the perpendicular from P to the line. Then exactly one of the following must be true:
1. Every point of the line is outside the circle
2. F is on the circle, and the line is tangent to the circle at F

3. F is inside the circle, and the line intersects the circle in exactly two points, which are equidistant from F.

Corollary 12.2.1 (p. 386) Every line tangent to a circle is perpendicular to the radius drawn to the point of tangency.

Corollary 12.2.2 (p. 386) Any line in the plane of a circle perpendicular to a radius at its outer end is a tangent to the circle.

Corollary 12.2.3 (p. 386) Any perpendicular from the center of a circle to a chord bisects the chord.

Corollary 12.2.4 (p. 386) The segment joining the center of a circle to the midpoint of a chord is perpendicular to the chord.

Corollary 12.2.5 (p. 387) In the plane of a circle, the perpendicular bisector of a chord passes through the center of the circle.

Corollary 12.2.6 (p. 387) If a line in the plane of a circle intersects the interior of the circle, then it intersects the circle in exactly two points.

Theorem 12.3 (p. 388) In the same circle or in congruent circles, chords equidistant from the center are congruent.

Theorem 12.4 (p. 388) In the same circle or in congruent circles, any two congrent chords are equidistant from the center.

Theorem 12.5 (p. 391) Given a plane E and a sphere with center P, let F be the foot of the perpendicular segment from P to E. Then exactly one of the following must be true:

1. Every point on E is outside the sphere
2. F is on the sphere and plane E is tangent to the sphere at F
3. F is inside the sphere, and plane E intersects the sphere in a circle with center F.

Corollary 12.5.1 (p. 392) A plane tangent to a sphere is perpendicular to the radius drawn to the point of tangency.

Corollary 12.5.2 (p. 392) A plane perpendicular to a radius at its outer end is tangent to the sphere.

Corollary 12.5.3 (p. 392) A perpendicular from the center of a sphere to a chord bisects the chord.

Corollary 12.5.4 (p. 392) The segment joining the center of a sphere to the midpoint of a chord is perpendicular to the chord.

Theorem 12.6 (p. 397) If $\overset{\frown}{AB}$ and $\overset{\frown}{BC}$ are arcs of the same circle having only the point B in common, and if their union is $\overset{\frown}{AC}$, then $m\overset{\frown}{AB} + m\overset{\frown}{BC} = m\overset{\frown}{AC}$.

Theorem 12.7 (p. 400) The measure of an inscribed angle is half the measure of its intercepted arc.

Corollary 12.7.1 (p. 401) An angle inscribed in a semicircle is a right angle.

Corollary 12.7.2 (p. 401) Angles inscribed in the same arc are congruent.

Corollary 12.7.3 (p. 402) The opposite angles of an inscribed quadrilateral are supplementary.

Theorem 12.8 (p. 402) Given an angle with its vertex on the circle such that the angle is formed by a secant ray and a tangent ray, the measure of the angle is one-half the measure of the intercepted arc.

Theorem 12.9 (p. 406) In the same circle or in congruent circles, if two chords are congruent, then so are the corresponding minor arcs.

Theorem 12.10 (p. 406) In the same circle or in congruent circles, if two arcs are congruent, then so are the corresponding chords.

Theorem 12.11 (p. 407) If two chords in the same circle are parallel, then the arcs between the two chords are congruent.

Theorem 12.12 (p. 410) The two tangent segments to a circle from an external point are congruent and form congruent angles with the line joining the external point to the center of the circle.

Theorem 12.13 (p. 411) Given circle C and an external point Q, let l_1 be a secant through Q, intersecting circle C in points R and S, and let l_2 be another secant through Q intersecting circle C in points U and T. Then $QR \cdot QS = QU \cdot QT$.

Theorem 12.14 (p. 411) Given a tangent segment $\overline{QT}$ to a circle and a secant through Q intersecting the circle in points R and S, then $QR \cdot QS = QT^2$.

Theorem 12.15 (p. 412) If two chords intersect in the interior of a circle, the product of the lengths of the segments of one equals the product of the lengths of the other.

Theorem 12.16 (p. 412) If two tangents, a tangent and a secant, or two secants intersect in the exterior of a circle, the measure of the angle formed is one-half the difference of the measures of the intercepted arcs.

Theorem 12.17 (p. 413) If two chords intersect in the interior of a circle, the measure of an angle formed is one-half the sum of the measures of the arcs intercepted by the angle and its vertical angle.

Theorem 12.18 (p. 417) A circle with center at (a, b) and radius r is the graph of the equation $(x - a)^2 + (y - b)^2 = r^2$.

Theorem 12.19 (p. 418) Every circle is the graph of an equation of the form $x^2 + y^2 + Ax + By + C = 0$.

Theorem 12.20 (p. 419) Given the equation $x^2 + y^2 + Ax + By + C = 0$, the graph of this equation is (1) a circle, (2) a point, or (3) the empty set.

Theorem 13.1 (p. 434) The bisector of an angle, excluding its endpoint, is the set of points in the interior of the angle equidistant from the sides of the angle.

Theorem 13.2 (p. 436) The perpendicular bisectors of the sides of a triangle are concurrent in a point equidistant from the three vertices of the triangle.

Corollary 13.2.1 (0. 436) There is one and only one circle through three noncollinear points.

Corollary 13.2.2 (p. 436) Two distinct circles intersect in at most two points.

Theorem 13.3 (p. 436) The lines containing the three altitudes of a triangle are concurrent.

Theorem 13.4 (p. 437) The angle bisectors of a triangle are concurrent at a point equidistant from the three sides.

Theorem 13.5 (p. 439) **(The Two Circle Theorem)** If two circles have radii a and b, and if c is the distance between their centers, then the circles intersect in two points, one on each side of the line of centers, provided each one of a, b, and c is less than the sum of the other two.

Theorem 14.1 (p. 466) The ratio $\frac{C}{2r}$, of the circumference to the radius is the same for all circles.

Theorem 14.2 (p. 468) The area of a circle of radius r is πr^2.

Theorem 14.3 (p. 471) If two arcs have equal radii, then their lengths are proportional to their measures.

Theorem 14.4 (p. 472) An arc of measure q and radius r has length $\frac{\pi}{180}(qr)$.

Theorem 14.5 (p. 475) The area of a sector is half the product of its radius and the length of its arc.

Theorem 14.6 (p. 476) The area of a sector of radius r and arc measure q is $\frac{\pi}{360}(qr^2)$.

Theorem 14.7 (p. 481) All cross sections of a triangular prism are congruent to the base.

Corollary 14.7.1 (p. 482) The upper and lower bases of a triangular prism are congruent.

Theorem 14.8 (p. 482) **(Prism Cross Section Theorem)** All cross sections of a prism have the same area.

Corollary 14.8.1 (p. 482) The two bases of a prism have equal areas.

Theorem 14.9 (p. 483) The lateral faces of a prism are parallelogram regions, and the lateral faces of a right prism are rectangular regions.

Theorem 14.10 (p. 486) A cross section of a triangular pyramid, by a plane between the vertex and the base, is a triangular region similar to the base. If the distance from the vertex to the cross section plane is k and the altitude is h, then the ratio of the area of the cross section to the area of the base is $(\frac{k}{h})^2$.

Theorem 14.11 (p. 487) In any pyramid, the ratio of the area of a cross section and the area of the base is $(\frac{k}{h})^2$, where h is the altitude of the pyramid and k is the distance from the vertex to the plane of the cross section.

Theorem 14.12 (p. 487) **(The Pyramid Cross Section Theorem)** Given two pyramids with the same altitude, if the bases have the same area, then cross sections equidistant from the bases also have the same area.

Theorem 14.13 (p. 491) The volume of any prism is the product of the altitude and the area of the base ($V = Ah$).

Theorem 14.14 (p. 492) If two pyramids have the same altitude and the same base area, then they have the same volume.

Theorem 14.15 (p. 492) The volume of a triangular pyramid is one-third the product of its altitude and its base area ($V = \frac{1}{3}Ah$).

Theorem 14.16 (p. 493) The volume of a pyramid is one-third the product of its altitude and its base area ($V = \frac{1}{3}Ah$).

Theorem 14.17 (p. 496) A cross section of a circular cylinder is a circular region congruent to the base.

Theorem 14.18 (p. 496) The area of a cross section of a circular cylinder is equal to the area of the base.

Theorem 14.19 (p. 496) A cross section of a cone with altitude h, made by a plane at a distance k from the vertex, is a circular region whose area has a ratio to the area of the base of $(\frac{k}{h})^2$.

Theorem 14.20 (p. 497) The volume of a circular cylinder is the product of the altitude and the area of the base ($V = Ah$).

Theorem 14.21 (p. 497) The volume of a circular cone is one-third the product of the altitude and the area of the base ($V = \frac{1}{3}Ah$).

Theorem 14.22 (p. 500) The volume of a sphere of radius r is $\frac{4}{3}\pi r^3$ ($V = \frac{4}{3}\pi r^3$).

Theorem 14.23 (p. 501) The surface area of a sphere of radius r is $= 4\pi r^2$ ($S = 4\pi r^2$).

Theorem 16.1 (p. 564) **(The Pythagorean Identity)** Given a right triangle with sides a and b and hypotenuse c, $\sin^2 \angle A + \cos^2 \angle A = 1$ for any acute $\angle A$ of the triangle.

Theorem 16.2 (p. 564) Given a right triangle with sides a and b and hypotenuse c, $\tan \angle A = \frac{\sin \angle A}{\cos \angle A}$ for any acute $\angle A$ of the triangle.

Theorem 16.3 (p. 565) Given right ΔXYZ, if $\angle X$ and $\angle Y$ are complementary, then $\sin \angle X = \cos \angle Y$, and $\cos \angle X = \sin \angle Y$.

CONSTRUCTIONS

Construction 1 (p. 440) Copy a given triangle.

Construction 2 (p. 440) Copy a given angle.

Construction 3 (p. 441) Construct the perpendicular bisector of a given segment.

Construction 4 (p. 441) Bisect a given segment.

Construction 5 (p. 442) Construct a perpendicular to a given line through a given point.

Construction 6 (p. 442) Construct a parallel to a given line through a given external point.

Construction 7 (p. 443) Divide a segment into a given number of congruent segments.

Construction 8 (p. 447) Circumscribe a circle about a given triangle.

Construction 9 (p. 448) Bisect a given angle.

Construction 10 (p. 448) Inscribe a circle in a given triangle.

GLOSSARY

A

acute angle An angle is acute if and only if it has a measure greater than 0 and less than 90.

acute triangle A triangle is acute if and only if it has three acute angles.

adjacent angles Two coplanar angles are adjacent if and only if they have a common side, but no points in the interior of one angle are in the interior of the other.

alternate interior angles Let line x be a transversal of lines y and z, intersecting them at points P and Q. Let A be a point on y and let B be a point on z, such that A and B are on opposite sides of x. Then $\angle PQB$ and $\angle QPA$ are alternate interior angles formed by the transversal of y and z.

altitude of a parallelogram The altitude of a parallelogram is the distance between a pair of parallel sides.

altitude of a prism The altitude of a prism is a segment joining the two base planes and that is perpendicular to both.

altitude of a pyramid In a pyramid, the distance from the vertex to the base is called the altitude.

altitude of a trapezoid The altitude of a trapezoid is the distance between the lines containing the parallel sides.

altitude of a triangle An altitude of a triangle is the perpendicular segment joining a vertex of the triangle to the line that contains the opposite side.

angle An angle is the union of two noncollinear rays with the same endpoint.

angle bisector If T lies in the interior of $\angle XYZ$, and $\angle XYT \cong \angle TYZ$, then $\overrightarrow{YT}$ bisects $\angle XYZ$ and is called the angle bisector of $\angle XYZ$.

angle bisector of a triangle A segment is an angle bisector of a triangle if and only if it bisects an angle and its endpoints are the vertex of the angle and a point on the opposite side.

angle of a polygon Any two sides with a common vertex of a polygon determine an angle of a polygon.

angle of a triangle The angles of the triangle are the three angles determined by the sides and vertices of the triangle.

annulus An annulus is a ring, or the difference between the areas of two concentric circles.

apothem The altitude a of a triangle formed by consecutive radii of a regular polygon is the apothem of the polygon.

arc of a sector If r$\widehat{QR}$ is an arc of a circle with center O and radius r, then the union of all segments OP, where P is any point of $\widehat{QR}$, is a sector, and $\widehat{QR}$ is the arc of the sector.

area of a circle The area of a circle is the limit of the areas of the inscribed regular polygons.

area of a polygonal region The area of a polygonal region is the number assigned to it by Postulate 17.

auxiliary figure A line, ray, or segment added to a diagram to help in a proof is an auxiliary figure.

B

bases of a trapezoid The parallel sides of a trapezoid are called bases.

betweenness of points Given three points *A*, *B*, and *C*, *B* is between *A* and *C* if and only if (1) *A*, *B*, and *C* are on the same line and (2) $AB + BC = AC$.

biconditional A biconditional statement is a compound statement of an implication and its converse joined by the phrase "if and only if."

bisect; bisector A point, line, segment, ray, or plane bisects a segment if and only if it intersects the segment at only the segment's midpoint. Any figure that bisects $\overline{AC}$ is called a bisector of $\overline{AC}$.

bisector of an angle A ray that divides an angle into two equal adjacent angles is the bisector of the angle.

C

Cartesian product If *A* and *B* are any two sets, then the Cartesian product of *A* and *B*, denoted by $A \times B$, is the set of all ordered pairs (x, y) such that x is an element of *A* and y is an element of *B*. This set is represented as $\{(x, y): x \in A, y \in B\}$.

center of a rotation The point of intersection of the lines of reflection in a rotation is the center of the rotation.

central angle A central angle of a given circle is an angle whose vertex is at the center of the circle.

chord A chord is a segment whose endpoints are on the circle.

circle A circle is the set of all coplanar points equidistant from a given point.

circular region A circular region is the union of a circle and its interior.

circumference of a circle The circumference of a circle is the limit of the perimeters of the inscribed regular polygons.

circumscribed polygon A polygon is circumscribed about a circle if and only if each side of the polygon is tangent to the circle.

collinear Points are collinear if and only if there is a line that contains all of them.

complementary angles Two angles are complementary if and only if the sum of their measures is 90.

concentric circles Two or more circles (in the same plane) or spheres are concentric if they share the same center point.

conclusion In a conditional statement, the part following "then" is the conclusion.

concurrent lines Two or more lines are concurrent if and only if there is a single point that lies on all of them.

conditional statement Any statement that can be written in "if—then" form is a conditional statement, or implication.

cone A cone is a solid bounded by a base and the surface formed by line segments joining every point of the boundary of the base to a common vertex.

congruent angles Congruent angles are angles of the same degree measure.

congruent circles Circles with congruent radii are called congruent circles.

congruent figures Geometric figures are congruent if and only if they have the same size and shape.

congruent segments Two or more line segments are congruent if and only if they have the same length.

congruent triangles Given a correspondence $ABC \leftrightarrow DEF$ between the vertices of two triangles, if the corresponding sides are congruent, and the corresponding angles are congruent, then the correspondence $ABC \leftrightarrow DEF$ is called a congruence between the two triangles.

consecutive angles of a quadrilateral Consecutive angles of a quadrilateral are two angles having a common side.

consecutive sides of a quadrilateral Consecutive sides of a quadrilateral are two sides having a common vertex.

construction A construction is a process of drawing a figure that will satisfy certain given conditions, using only a compass and a straightedge.

contrapositive In a conditional statement, negating the hypothesis and conclusion and reversing their positions forms the contrapositive.

converse In a conditional statement, interchanging the hypothesis and the conclusion forms the converse.

convex A set is called convex if, for every two points P and Q of the set, the entire segment $\overline{PQ}$ lies within the set.

coordinate On the number line, the coordinate is the number paired with a point. In the coordinate plane, the first number of an ordered pair is the x-coordinate and the second number is the y-coordinate.

coordinate plane The coordinate plane is the plane of the x-axis and y-axis.

coplanar Points are coplanar if and only if there is a plane that contains all of them.

corollary A statement that can easily be proved by applying a theorem is a corollary.

corresponding angles Let l be a transversal of k and n, intersecting them at points P and Q. Let A be a point on k, and let B be a point on n, such that A and B are on the same side of l. Let C be a point on l such that C and B are on opposite sides of k. Then $\angle CPA$ and $\angle PQB$ are corresponding angles formed by the transversal to the two lines.

cosine Let C be a right angle in right ΔABC, and let a, b, and c name the lengths of the sides opposite $\angle A$, $\angle B$, and $\angle C$, respectively. Then,

$$\text{cosine } \angle A = \frac{b}{c} = \frac{\text{length of adjacent side}}{\text{length of the hypotenuse}}$$

D

deductive reasoning Deductive reasoning is a logical sequence of steps justified by postulates, theorems, and definitions used to prove mathematical statements.

diagonal of a polygon A diagonal of a polygon is a segment joining two nonconsecutive angles.

diameter In the same circle or sphere, two collinear radii form a diameter.

dihedral angle A dihedral angle is the union of a line and two noncoplanar half-planes having this line as their common edge.

dilation image Given a point P in a plane and a positive real number k, the dilation image of $A \neq P$ is the point A' on $\overrightarrow{PA}$

such that $PA' = k \cdot PA$. The point P is called the center of the dilation, and k is the magnitude.

direction of a rotation The direction of a rotation is the direction from the first line of reflection to the second.

distance between a line and a point The distance between a line and a point not on it is the length of the perpendicular segment from the point to the line. The distance between a line and point on the line is defined as zero.

distance to a plane from an external point The distance to a plane from an external point is the length of the perpendicular segment from the point to the plane.

E

edge A line that separates a plane into two half-planes is called an edge of each half-plane.

edge of a dihedral angle The edge of a dihedral angle is the line of intersection of the two half-planes forming the dihedral angle.

equal angles Two angles are equal if and only if they are the same angle.

equidistant Two points that are the same distance from a third point are equidistant from that point.

equilateral triangle A triangle is equilateral if and only if all three of its sides are congruent.

exterior angle of a triangle If B lies between A and E, then $\angle CBE$ is an exterior angle of ΔABC.

externally tangent Two or more circles (in the same plane) or spheres are externally tangent if they intersect in exactly one point and if their interiors do not intersect.

F

face A face is a plane that separates space into two half-spaces yet is a part of neither half-space.

face of a dihedral angle The union of the edge and either half-plane is called a face, or side, of the dihedral angle.

G

geometric mean If a, b, and c are positive numbers, and $\frac{a}{b} = \frac{b}{c}$, then b is called the geometric mean of a and c.

glide reflection A glide reflection is a transformation of the plane that is a composition of a line reflection and a translation in a direction parallel to the line of reflection.

great circle The intersection of a sphere with a plane through its center is called a great circle of the sphere.

H

half-plane Given a line and the plane containing it, the two sets separated by the line are called half-planes.

half-space In space, the two regions separated by a plane (face) are called half-spaces.

hypotenuse In a right triangle, the side opposite the right angle is called the hypotenuse.

hypothesis In a conditional statement, the part following "if" is the hypothesis.

I

image If A is mapped onto A', then A' is called the image of A. A is the preimage of A'.

implication Any statement that can be written in "if—then" form is an implication, or conditional statement.

incenter In inscribing a circle inside a given triangle, the point of concurrency of the angle bisectors is the incenter of the triangle and the center of the inscribed circle.

included angle An angle of a triangle is said to be included between two sides of the triangle if and only if the sides of the angle contain the two sides of the triangle.

included side A side of a triangle is said to be included between two angles if and only if the vertices of the angles are the endpoints of the segment.

indirect proof An indirect proof is a proof in which you assume the opposite of what you want to prove. Then you show that your assumption leads to a contradiction.

inductive reasoning Inductive reasoning is a type of logical thinking where mathematical statements are justified by examples.

inscribed angle An angle is inscribed in an arc if and only if (1) the two endpoints of the arc lie on the two sides of the angle and (2) the vertex of the angle is a point, but not an endpoint, of the arc.

inscribed polygon A polygon is inscribed in a circle if and only if all of its vertices lie on the circle.

intercept **a.** When lines cross a figure such that they determine the bounds of a figure, they intercept that figure. **b.** An angle intercepts an arc if and only if (1) the endpoints of the arc lie on the angle (2) each side of the angle contains an endpoint of the arc and (3) except for its endpoints, the arc lies in the interior of the angle.

intercepted arc An angle intercepts an arc if and only if each of the following is true:

(1) The endpoints of the arc lie on the angle.

(2) All points of the arc, except the endpoints, are in the interior of the angle.

(3) Each side of the angle contains an endpoint of the arc.

internally tangent Two or more circles or spheres are internally tangent if they intersect in exactly one point and if the interior of one contains the interior of the other.

inverse In a conditional statement, negating both the hypothesis and conclusion forms the inverse.

isometry An isometry is a line reflection or a composition of line reflections.

isosceles triangle A triangle is isosceles if and only if at least two of its sides are congruent.

L

lateral area The lateral area is the area of all the lateral faces.

lateral edge of a prism A lateral edge of a prism is a segment $\overline{PP'}$, where P is a vertex of the base of the prism.

lateral face of a prism A lateral face is the union of all segments $\overline{SS'}$ for which S is a point in a given side of the base.

lateral surface of a prism The lateral surface of a prism is the union of the lateral faces.

leg of a right triangle In a right triangle the sides that form the right angle are called the legs.

lemma A Greek word meaning *assumption.* A lemma is a theorem useful as an intermediate step toward proving another, more basic theorem.

length of an arc The length of $\widehat{QR}$ is the limit of $QP_1 + P_1P_2 \ldots P_{n-1}R$ as n is taken larger and larger.

line of symmetry If a plane figure is its own image under reflection in a line, then the reflection line is a line of symmetry of the figure.

line reflection A line reflection, or a reflection in a line, is a transformation that maps each point of line l to itself and each point P not on l to its image P', such that l is the perpendicular bisector of $\overline{PP'}$. The line l is the line of reflection.

line segment A set of points is a line segment if and only if the set contains two points and all the points between them.

linear equation A linear equation in x and y is an equation in the form $Ax + By + C = 0$ where A and B are not both zero.

linear pair Two angles form a linear pair if and only if they are adjacent angles and the noncommon sides are opposite rays.

locus of points A figure formed by all points that satisfy a given condition is called a locus of points.

M

magnitude of a dilation Given a point P in the plane and a positive real number k, the dilation image of $A \neq P$ is the point A' on $\overline{PA}$ such that $PA' = k \cdot PA$, where k is the magnitude.

magnitude of a rotation If point P is the center and A' the image of A under rotation, then the magnitude of the rotation is $m\angle APA'$. If the rotation is counterclockwise, then the magnitude is positive. If the rotation is clockwise, then the magnitude is negative.

major arc Given $\odot P$ with points A and B on the circle, the union of A and B and all the points of the circle in the exterior of $\angle APB$ is called a major arc.

mapping A mapping is a rule that assigns to each element of one set (the domain) exactly one element of a second set (the codomain).

measure of a dihedral angle The measure of a dihedral angle is the real number that is the measure of any of its plane angles.

measure of an arc The degree measure of an arc ($m\widehat{AXB}$) is as follows:

(1) If $\widehat{AXB}$ is a minor arc, then $m\widehat{AXB}$ is the measure of the corresponding central angle.

(2) If $\widehat{AXB}$ is a semicircle, then $m\widehat{AXB} = 180$.

(3) If $\widehat{AXB}$ is a major arc, and $\widehat{AYB}$ is the corresponding minor arc, then $m\widehat{AXB} = 360 - m\widehat{AYB}$.

median of a triangle A segment is a median of a triangle if and only if its endpoints are a vertex of the triangle and the midpoint of the opposite side.

midpoint A point B is called the midpoint of $\overline{AC}$ if and only if (1) B is between A and C and (2) $AB = BC$.

minor arc Given $\odot P$ with points A and B on the circle, the union of A and B and all the points of the circle in the interior of $\angle APB$ is called a minor arc.

N

negation A negation is a sentence formed by denying another sentence. Often you can form a negation by using *not*.

n-gon A polygon with n sides is called an n-gon.

O

obtuse angle An angle is obtuse if and only if it has a measure greater than 90 but less than 180.

obtuse triangle A triangle is obtuse if and only if it has one obtuse angle.

one-to-one mapping A mapping is one-to-one if and only if no two preimages have the same image.

opposite angles of a quadrilateral Opposite angles of a quadrilateral are two angles that do not contain a common side.

opposite rays $\overrightarrow{AB}$ and $\overrightarrow{AC}$ are called opposite rays if and only if A is between B and C.

opposite side of a triangle A side of a triangle is said to be opposite an angle if and only if the side does not contain the vertex of that angle. This angle is also said to be opposite the side.

opposite sides of a quadrilateral Opposite sides of a quadrilateral are two sides that do not intersect.

ordered pair An ordered pair is a pair of numbers in which the order is specified. An ordered pair is used to locate points in a plane.

origin The point of intersection of the two axes of the coordinate plane is the origin.

P

parallel Two lines are parallel if and only if they are coplanar and do not intersect.

parallel lines and planes Two planes, or a plane and a line, are parallel if they do not intersect.

parallelepiped A parallelepiped is a prism whose base is a parallelogram region.

parallelogram A parallelogram is a quadrilateral in which both pairs of opposite sides are parallel.

perimeter of a polygon The sum of the lengths of the sides of a polygon is the perimeter.

perpendicular bisector In a given plane, the perpendicular bisector of a segment is the line that is perpendicular to the segment at its midpoint.

perpendicular line and plane A line and a plane are perpendicular if and only if they intersect, and if every line lying in the plane that passes through the point of intersection is perpendicular to the given line.

perpendicular lines Two lines are perpendicular if and only if they intersect and form a right angle.

perpendicular planes Two planes are perpendicular if they determine right dihedral angles.

pi The circumference of a circle divided by two times the radius equals the number π, or $\frac{22}{7}$, ≈ 3.14.

plane angle Through any point on the edge of a dihedral angle there passes a plane perpendicular to the edge, intersecting each of the sides in a ray. The angle formed by these rays is called a plane angle of the dihedral angle.

point of tangency The point of tangency (or point of contact) is the point of intersection of tangent circles or spheres, lines, or planes.

polygon Let $P_1, P_2, P_3, \ldots, P_{n-1}, P_n$ be n distinct points in a plane ($n \geq 3$). Let the n segments $\overline{P_1P_2}$, $\overline{P_2P_3}$, $\ldots$, $\overline{P_{n-1}P_n}$, $\overline{P_nP_1}$ have the properties:

(1) no two segments intersect except at their endpoints, as specified, and

(2) no two segments with a common endpoint are collinear.

Then the union of the n segments is a polygon.

polygonal region A region is a polygonal region if and only if it is the union of a finite number of triangular regions, in a plane, such that the intersection of any two is either a point or a segment.

postulate A postulate is a statement that is accepted without proof.

prism Let A_1 and A_2 be two parallel planes, t a transversal, and R a polygonal region in A_1 that does not intersect t. For each point X of R let $\overline{XY}$ be a segment parallel to t with Y in A_2. The union of all such segments is called a prism.

projection of a line The projection of a line into a plane is the set of points that are projections into the plane of the points of the line.

projection of a point The projection of a point into a plane is the foot of the perpendicular from the point to the plane.

proportional Given two sequences $a, b, c, \ldots$ and $p, q, r, \ldots$ of positive numbers, if $\frac{a}{p} = \frac{b}{q} = \frac{c}{r} = \ldots$, then the sequences a, b, c, ... and $p, q, r, \ldots$ are called proportional.

protractor A protractor is a semicircular instrument divided into 180 units used to measure angles.

pyramid Let R be a polygonal region in a plane E, and let P be a point not in E. For each point Q in R there is a segment $\overline{QP}$. The union of all such segments is called a pyramid.

Q

quadrant One of the four regions into which two perpendicular lines separate the plane which contains them is a quadrant.

quadrilateral Let A, B, C, and D be four coplanar points. If no three of these points are collinear, and the segments $\overline{AB}$, $\overline{BC}$, $\overline{CD}$, and $\overline{DA}$ intersect only at their endpoints, then the union of the four segments is a quadrilateral. The four segments are its sides, and the points A, B, C, and D are its vertices. $\angle DAB$, $\angle ABC$, $\angle BCD$, and $\angle CDA$ are its angles.

R

radius A radius of a circle or sphere is

(1) any segment with one endpoint at the center and the other endpoint on the circle or sphere; and

(2) the distance from the center to the circle or sphere.

radius of a sector If $\widehat{QR}$ is an arc of a circle with center O and radius r, then the union of all segments $\overline{OP}$, where P is any point of $\widehat{QR}$, is a sector, and r is the radius of the sector.

ratio A ratio is a comparison of two numbers by division.

ray Ray AB ($\overrightarrow{AB}$) is the figure that contains A and every point on the same side of A as B.

rectangle A rectangle is a parallelogram all of whose angles are right angles.

rectangular parallelepiped A rectangular parallelepiped is a right rectangular prism.

region The half-spaces or half-planes formed by separating space with a face or a plane with a line are called regions.

regular polygon A polygon is regular if and only if it is convex and all of its sides and all of its angles are congruent.

regular pyramid A regular pyramid is a pyramid whose base is a regular polygonal region having for its center the foot of the perpendicular form the vertex to the base.

resultant vector When two or more vectors are combined, the resulting magnitude and direction determine the resultant vector.

rhombus A rhombus is a parallelogram all of whose sides are congruent.

right angle An angle is a right angle if and only if it has a measure of 90.

right circular cone If the center of the base circle of a cone is the foot of the perpendicular from the vertex to the plane of the base, then the cone is a right circular cone.

right circular cylinder If the line joining the centers of the base circles of a cylinder is perpendicular to the planes of both bases, then the cylinder is a right circular cylinder.

right dihedral angle A dihedral angle is a right dihedral angle if its plane angles are right angles.

right prism Let A_1 and A_2 be two parallel planes, t a transversal, and R a polygonal region in A_1 that does not intersect t. For each point X of R let $\overline{XY}$ be a segment parallel to t with Y in A_2. The union of all such segments is called a prism. If t is perpendicular to A_1 and A_2, the prism is called a right prism.

right triangle A triangle is a right triangle if and only if it has one right angle.

rotation A rotation is a transformation of the plane that is a composition of two reflections in intersecting lines.

S

scalene triangle A triangle is scalene if and only if no two of its sides are congruent.

secant A secant is a line that intersects a circle in exactly two points.

sector If $\widehat{QR}$ is an arc of a circle with center O and radius r, then the union of all segments $\overline{OP}$, where P is any point of $\widehat{QR}$, is a sector.

segment of a circle A segment of a circle is the region bounded by a chord and an arc of the circle.

semicircle Given $\odot P$ with points A and B on the circle, if A, P, and B are collinear (so that AB is a diameter), the union of A and B and all the points of the circle in either halfplane determined by edge $\overleftrightarrow{AB}$ is called a semicircle.

side of a dihedral angle The union of the edge and either half-plane is called a face, or side, of the dihedral angle.

side of an angle The two rays that form an angle are called the sides of the angle.

sides of a polygon The segments connecting the points that make up the polygon are called the sides of the polygon.

similarity Given a correspondence between two polygons, if corresponding angles are congruent, and corresonding sides are proportional, then the correspondence is called a similarity, and the polygons are said to be similar.

sine Let C be a right angle in right ΔABC, and let a, b, and c name the lengths of the sides opposite $\angle A$, $\angle B$, and $\angle C$, respectively. Then,

$$\text{sine } \angle A = \frac{a}{c} = \frac{\text{length of the opposite side}}{\text{length of the hypotenuse}}$$

skew lines Two lines are skew if and only if they are not coplanar.

slant height The slant height of a regular pyramid is the length of the altitude of any of the lateral faces.

slope The slope of $\overline{P_1P_2}$ is the number $m = \frac{y_2 - y_1}{x_2 - x_1}$.

space Space is the set of all points.

sphere A sphere is the set of all points equidistant from a given point C.

square A square is a rectangle all of whose sides are congruent.

supplementary angles Two angles are supplementary if and only if the sum of their measures is 180.

symmetric A figure is said to be symmetric if it is its own image under reflection in a line.

T

tangent Let C be a right angle in right ΔABC, and let a, b, and c name the length of the sides opposite $\angle A$, $\angle B$, and $\angle C$, respectively. Then,

$$\text{tangent } \angle A = \frac{a}{b} = \frac{\text{length of the opposite side}}{\text{length of the adjacent side}}$$

tangent A line that intersects a circle at exactly one point is called a tangent, and the intersection is called the point of tangency (or point of contact).

tangent plane A plane that intersects a sphere in exactly one point is called a tangent plane to the sphere.

tetrahedron A tetrahedron is a triangular pyramid.

theorem A theorem is a conditional statement that must be proved.

total surface of a prism The total surface of a prism is the union of its lateral surface and its bases.

transformation A transformation is a mapping of a set of points into a set of points that is both one-to-one and onto.

translation A translation is a transformation of the plane that is a composition of reflection in lines l and m, where $l \parallel m$ or $l = m$.

transversal A line is a transversal of two coplanar lines if and only if it intersects the lines at two different points.

trapezoid A trapezoid is a quadrilateral in which two and only two sides are parallel.

triangle If A, B, and C are any three noncollinear points, then the union of $\overline{AB}$, $\overline{AC}$, and $\overline{BC}$ is called a triangle and is denoted as ΔABC.

triangular region A triangular region is the union of a triangle and its interior.

V

vector A vector is a representation of movement from an initial point to a terminal point, usually drawn as an arrow.

vertex of a triangle In triangle ABC, each point A, B, and C is called a vertex of ΔABC.

vertex of an angle The common endpoint of the two rays that form an angle is the vertex.

vertical angles Two angles are vertical if and only if their sides form two pairs of opposite rays.

vertices of a polygon The points of intersection of the segments that make up a polygon are called the vertices of the polygon.

x-axis The x-axis is the horizontal line of the two perpendicular number lines used to separate the plane into quadrants.

Y

y-axis The y-axis is the vertical line of the two perpendicular number lines used to separate the plane into quadrants.

y-intercept In a graph, the point where a line crosses the y-axis is called the y-intercept.

INDEX

A

B

C

D

E

M

N

O

P

Q

R

S

ANSWERS TO SELECTED EXERCISES

Pages 3–4 Section 1.1
Written Exercises

2. does
4. plane M, plane E
6. point Y
8. no
10. yes
12. They both lie in plane M.
14. an endless number

Pages 8–9 Section 1.2
Written Exercises

2. commutative property of addition
4. identity property of multiplication
6. associative property of multiplication
8. division property of equality
10. commutative property of multiplication
12. transitive property of equality
14. commutative property of addition
16. inverse property of addition
18. $x = -5$ or $x = 9$
20. $x < -9$ or $x > 1$
22. $-4 < x < 8$
24. $-\frac{4}{7}$
26. -8
28. 8
30. associative property of addition
32. identity property of addition
34. multiplication property of equality
36. inverse property of multiplication
38. number fact

Pages 11–12 Section 1.3
Written Exercises

2. transitive prop. of inequality
4. trichotomy property
6. reflexive, symmetric, transitive
8. $>$ 10. $\leq$ 12. $\geq$
14. $>$ 16. $=$
18. no, symmetric
20. no, reflexive, symmetric
22. 3 24. -18
26. -55

Pages 14–15 Section 1.4
Written Exercises

2. F, F 4. T, F 6. T, F
8. T, T 10. T, T
16. If a game has four periods of play, then the game is basketball.
18. If an oven is a microwave, then it cooks by a timer.
20. If a beverage is coffee, then it contains caffeine.
22. If a person is Brazilian, then that person speaks Portuguese.
24. If a number is $\sqrt{2}$, then that number is irrational.
26. Points are collinear iff they lie on the same line.

Pages 20–21 Section 1.5
Written Exercises

2. 3 4. 3 6. 4
8. 5 10. 9 12. 8
14. $|x - 0|$, $|-x|$, x
16. $|x - 7|$, $7 - x$

Page 27 Section 1.6
Written Exercises

2. Yes; the distance is the same.
4. Yes; they are the same set of points.
6. No; their lengths are unknown.
8. -8 10. 16
12. three; $\overleftrightarrow{UV}$, $\overleftrightarrow{UW}$, and $\overleftrightarrow{VW}$
14. four; $\overrightarrow{AC}$, $\overrightarrow{CA}$, $\overrightarrow{BA}$, and $\overrightarrow{BC}$
16. one
18.

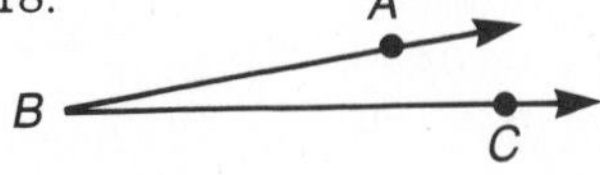

20.

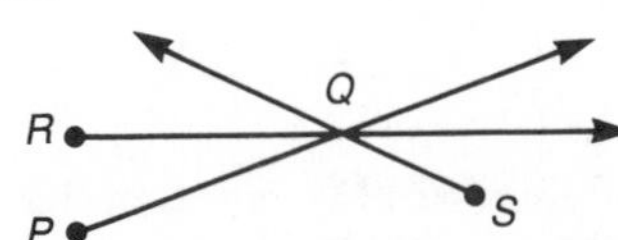

Pages 30–31 Chapter 1 Review

2. $\overleftrightarrow{SP}$ 4. P
6. commutative prop. of multiplication

8. distributive property
10. symmetric property
12. addition property of equality
14. 2 16. -4
18.

20. mult. property of inequality
22. trichotomy property
24. $>$
26. No; it is neither symmetric nor reflexive.
28. Answers will vary. For example, if $x^2 = 16$, then $x = 4$.
30. C 32. $2\frac{1}{2}$ 34. $2\frac{1}{2}$
36. 3 38. $1\frac{1}{4}$
40. W

Pages 37–38 Section 2.1 Written Exercises

2. 2 4. 2 6. 1
8. a line
10. a point; a line
12. coplanar 14. both
16. neither 18. A
20. A 22. A

Pages 42–43 Section 2.2 Written Exercises

2. plane M
4. $\overline{GJ}$ doesn't intersect edge $\overleftrightarrow{EF}$
6. edge 8. face
10. False; postulates are not proved.
12. False; the face is not part of either half-space.
14. T

Pages 46–47 Section 2.3 Written Exercises

2. F; coplanar
4. F; $\angle TWR$ or $\angle W$
6. F; a postulate
8. $\angle 1$ 10. 20, 20, 20
12. 17, 28, 15
14. T 16. T 18. F
20. F

Pages 51–52 Section 2.4 Written Exercises

2. $m\angle A = 30$
4. $0 < m\angle A < 180$
6. $\angle AGC \cong \angle FGD$, $\angle AGD \cong \angle CGF$
8. 90° 10. 20° 12. T
14. F 16. T 18. 150

Pages 56–57 Chapter 2 Review

2. S 4. N 6. S
8. T 10. T 12. T
14. a 16. a 18. b
20. d 22. $\angle DYZ$, $\angle BYE$
24. 10 26. 30
28. $x = 7$

Pages 62–63 Section 3.1 Written Exercises

2. 66 4. $90 - x$
6. $200 - 3x$
8. $230 - 2x$
10. 137
12. $\angle DPC$, $\angle CPA$; $\angle DPB$, $\angle BPA$; $\angle CPB$, $\angle BPF$; $\angle CPA$, $\angle APF$; $\angle BPA$, $\angle APE$; $\angle BPF$, $\angle FPE$; $\angle APF$, $\angle FPD$; $\angle APE$, $\angle EPD$; $\angle FPE$, $\angle EPC$; $\angle FPD$, $\angle DPC$; $\angle EPD$, $\angle DPB$; $\angle EPC$, $\angle CPB$
14. $\angle CPA$, $\angle DPF$
16. $m\angle FPB$ 18. $m\angle APF$
20. 78, 102
22. 90 24. 15, 165
26. 9, 171 28. 15, 165
30. 18, 162

Pages 68–69 Section 3.2 Written Exercises

2. right 4. obtuse
6. $\angle BPC$, $\angle APE$, $\angle APD$
8. $\angle EPB$, $\angle CPE$
10. $\angle DPE$, $\angle EPA$
14. $\overline{AB} \perp \overline{BC}$, $\overline{DC} \perp \overline{DE}$, $\overline{DC} \perp \overline{DF}$
16. $m\angle 1 + m\angle 3 = 90$
18. $m\angle 1 + m\angle 3 = m\angle 2 + m\angle 4$
20. $m\angle 1 + m\angle 3 = m\angle 1 + m\angle 4$
22. $\angle 3 \cong \angle 4$
24. 18, 72
26. $-2.5 < x < 20$
28. 27, 153
30. *1.* $\angle 1 \cong \angle 2$, $\angle 1$ and $\angle 2$ are supp. (Given); *2.* $m\angle 1 = m\angle 2$ (Def. of $\cong$ $\angle$s); *3.* $m\angle 1 + m\angle 2 = 180$ (Def. of supp. $\angle$s); *4.* $m\angle 1 + m\angle 1 = 180$ (Subst.); *5.* $2 \cdot m\angle 1 = 180$ (Distributive); *6.* $m\angle 1 = 90$ (Division prop. of equality); *7.* $m\angle 2 = 90$ (Transitive prop. of equality); *8.* $\angle 1$ and $\angle 2$ are right $\angle$s (Def. of right angles).
32. *1.* $m\angle 1 + m\angle 2 = 180$ (Def. of supp. $\angle$s); *2a.* If $\angle 1$ is acute, $0 < m\angle 1 < 90$ (Def. of acute angles); *2b.* $90 < m\angle 1 + 90 < 180$ (Addition prop. of inequality); *2c.* $m\angle 1 + 90 < m\angle 1 + m\angle 2$ (Substitution); *2d.* $90 <$

$m\angle 2$ (Subtraction prop. of inequality); *2e.* $\angle 2$ is obtuse (Def. of obtuse $\angle$s); *3a.* If $\angle 1$ is a right $\angle$, $m\angle 1 = 90$ (Def. of right $\angle$s); *3b.* $m\angle 2 = 90$ (Steps *1*, *3a*, and subst. prop. of equality); *3c.* $\angle 1$ and $\angle 2$ are right $\angle$s (Def. of right $\angle$s); *4a.* If $\angle 1$ is obtuse, $90 < m\angle 1 < 180$ (Def. of obtuse $\angle$s); *4b.* $180 < m\angle 1 + 90$ (Addition prop. of inequality); *4c.* $m\angle 1 + m\angle 2 < m\angle 1 + 90$ (Steps *1*, *4b*, and substitution); *4d.* $m\angle 2 < 90$ (Subtraction prop. of inequality); *4e.* $\angle 2$ is acute (Def. of acute $\angle$s); *5.* At most $\angle 1$ or $\angle 2$ may be obtuse, but not both (Steps *2d*, *3b*, and *4d*).

Pages 72–73 Section 3.3
Written Exercises

2. 29 4. 54 6. 30
8. 22 10. 150 12. 20
14. 30 16. $16\frac{1}{2}$
18. $x = 20$, $m\angle 7 = m\angle 9 = 20$, $m\angle 10 = 70$
20. $x = 45$, $m\angle 3 = 60$, $m\angle 5 = 60$, $m\angle 6 = 120$
22. $x = 65$, $m\angle 3 = 44$, $m\angle 4 = 136$, $m\angle 6 = 136$
24. $x = 12\frac{1}{2}$, $m\angle 3 = 52$, $m\angle 4 = 128$, $m\angle 5 = 52$, $m\angle 6 = 128$
26. $x = 18\frac{1}{3}$, $m\angle 8 = 65$, $m\angle 9 = 25$, $m\angle 10 = 65$

Page 76 Section 3.4
Written Exercises

2. $\angle GSF$ 4. $\angle E$
6. $\overline{GF}$ 8. $\angle ADC$
10. $\angle YCD$ 12. $\overline{DX}$
14. $\overline{XY}$
16. $\angle A \leftrightarrow \angle D$; $\angle B \leftrightarrow \angle E$; $\angle C \leftrightarrow \angle F$; $\overline{AB} \leftrightarrow \overline{DE}$; $\overline{AC} \leftrightarrow \overline{DF}$; $\overline{CB} \leftrightarrow \overline{FE}$
18. $\angle 1 \leftrightarrow \angle 4$; $\angle 3 \leftrightarrow \angle 2$ $\angle H \leftrightarrow \angle R$; $\overline{HL} \leftrightarrow \overline{RK}$; $\overline{HK} \leftrightarrow \overline{RL}$; $\overline{LK} \leftrightarrow \overline{KL}$
20. $\angle F \leftrightarrow \angle D$; $\angle A \leftrightarrow \angle C$; $\angle 1 \leftrightarrow \angle 2$; $\angle 3 \leftrightarrow \angle 4$; $\overline{FE} \leftrightarrow \overline{DE}$; $\overline{AF} \leftrightarrow \overline{CD}$; $\overline{EB} \leftrightarrow \overline{EB}$; $\overline{BA} \leftrightarrow \overline{BC}$

Pages 79–80 Section 3.5
Written Exercises

2. $\angle WYZ$ 4. $\angle XWZ$
6. $\overline{WY}$ 8. $\overline{WX}$
10. $\overline{WZ}$ 12. $\angle YWZ$
14. $\angle X$
16. $\angle A \cong \angle B$, $\angle X \cong \angle Z$, $\angle AYX \cong \angle BYZ$, $\overline{AY} \cong \overline{BY}$, $\overline{AX} \cong \overline{BZ}$, $\overline{XY} \cong \overline{ZY}$
18. $\angle 1 \cong \angle 3$, $\angle 2 \cong \angle 4$, $\angle D \cong \angle B$, $\overline{DC} \cong \overline{BA}$, $\overline{AD} \cong \overline{CB}$, $\overline{AC} \cong \overline{CA}$
20. $\angle L \cong \angle M$, $\angle T \cong \angle R$, $\angle LXT \cong \angle MXR$, $\overline{LT} \cong \overline{MR}$, $\overline{LX} \cong \overline{MX}$, $\overline{RX} \cong \overline{TX}$
22. $\angle DAE \cong \angle BCE$, $\angle ADE \cong \angle CBE$, $\angle DEA \cong \angle BEC$, $\overline{DA} \cong \overline{BC}$, $\overline{EA} \cong \overline{EC}$, $\overline{ED} \cong \overline{EB}$
24. $\angle A \cong \angle D$, $\angle AEC \cong \angle DEB$, $\angle ECA \cong \angle EBD$, $\overline{EA} \cong \overline{ED}$, $\overline{EC} \cong \overline{EB}$, $\overline{AC} \cong \overline{DB}$

Pages 82–83 Section 3.6
Written Exercises

2. T 4. T 6. T
8. R, S, T 10. R, S, T
12. R, T 14. R, S, T
16. Given
18. Subtraction prop. of equality
20. Identity prop. of addition
22. Division prop. of equality
24. Identity prop. of mult.
26. Given
28. Addition prop. of equality
30. Identity prop. of addition
32. Division prop. of equality
34. Identity prop. of mult.

Page 86 Section 3.7
Written Exercises

2. Answers will vary.
4. 18 6. 50 8. 13
10. 25 12. 10 14. $17\frac{1}{2}$
16. 8 18. 2 20. 7
22. 7

Pages 90–91 Chapter 3
Review

2. $\angle 1$, $\angle 4$ 4. 168
6. $180 - a$ 8. 70, 110
10. $\angle EAB$, $\angle ABD$, $\angle FCD$
12. 47 14. $90 - x$
16. 10, 80
18. They are right angles.
20. $\overline{DE}$ 22. $\overline{CB}$
24. $\angle BEC$ 26. $\overline{DC}$
28. Given
30. Add. prop. of equality
32. Identity of addition
34. Division prop. of equality
36. Identity of mult.
38. Sym. prop. of equality
40. 6

Pages 97–99 Section 4.1
Written Exercises

2. $\overline{PR} \cong \overline{RP}$

4. $\angle QRS \cong \angle TRS$
6. Steps *1, 2,* and SAS
8. Congruence of segments is reflexive.
10. Corres. parts of $\cong$ Δs are $\cong$.
12. ΔABD and ΔABC are rt. Δs.
14. $\overline{AB} \cong \overline{AB}$
16. $\angle ADB \cong \angle ACB$
18. Definition of bisect
20. Verticals $\angle$s are $\cong$.
22. Corres. parts of $\cong$ Δs are $\cong$.
24. The Supplement Postulate

Pages 103–104 Section 4.2 Written Exercises

2. $\overline{RT} \cong \overline{RT}$
4. $\angle JGH \cong \angle KGF$
6. Given
8. Congruence of segments is reflexive.
10. Steps *1, 2, 3,* and ASA
12. $\angle FHG \cong \angle KHJ$
14. Steps *1, 2,* and ASA
16. Reflexive, ASA, CPCTC
18. Supplements of $\cong$ $\angle$s, vertical angles, ASA

Pages 107–109 Section 4.3 Written Exercises

2.

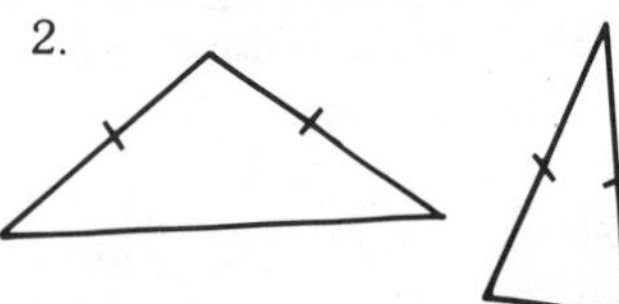

4. 6
6. 13, 13, 5
8. Isosceles Δ Thm., transitivity
10. Isosceles Δ Thm., transitivity
12. Make $\Delta ABC \cong \Delta QPC$ and $\overline{PQ} \cong \overline{AB}$ by CPCTC
14. Thm. 3.5, Thm. 4.4
16. SAS, CPCTC

Pages 113–114 Section 4.4 Written Exercises

2. $\overline{QS} \cong \overline{QS}$
4. Addition property of equality
6. Steps *3, 4,* and substitution property
8. Given
10. Definition of midpoint
12. Steps *2, 3,* and SSS
14. Congruence of segments is reflexive.
16. Given
18. Congruence of segments is reflexive.
20. Reflexive; addition property; SSS

Pages 117–118 Section 4.5 Written Exercises

2. Congruence of segments is reflexive.
4. Corres. parts of $\cong$ Δs are $\cong$.
6. 90
8. $\Delta AED \cong \Delta CBD$ by ASA; $\overline{AE} \cong \overline{BC}$ by CPCTC
10. $\Delta EFA \cong \Delta CBA$ by LL; $\overline{AE} \cong \overline{AC}$ by CPCTC; then base $\angle$s $\cong$
12. $\Delta AEB \cong \Delta DEC$ by ASA so $\angle A \cong \angle D$ by CPCTC

Pages 122–123 Chapter 4 Review

2. CPCTC
4. Steps *2, 6,* and SAS
6. Given
8. Def. of right triangle
10. Congruence of segments is reflexive.
12. no
14. ASA
16. isosceles
18. equilateral
20. $\angle A$
22. $\angle B$
24. Theorem 4.3 and SAS
26. Theorem 4.4 and SAS
28. SSS, CPCTC
30. SAS, CPCTC, SSS

Pages 133–134 Section 5.1 Written Exercises

2. A
4. A
6. N
8. S
10. (a) Given: P lies on l, l lies in plane E; (b) Prove: there is a line PQ in $E \perp l$; (c) $\overleftrightarrow{PQ}$ is the only line in $E \perp l$; (d) Assume: $\overleftrightarrow{PQ} \perp l$ and $\overleftrightarrow{PR} \perp l$.
12. Definition of bisect
14. Vertical $\angle$s are $\cong$.
16. Corres. parts of $\cong$ Δs are $\cong$.
18. *1.* $\overline{YW}$ bisects $\angle Y$ and $\overline{YW}$ is not the median (Given); *2.* $\angle XYW \cong \angle ZYW$ (Def. of $\angle$ bisectors); *3.* $\overline{YW} \cong \overline{YW}$ (Congruence of segments is reflex.); *4.* Let $\overline{XY} \cong \overline{ZY}$ (Indirect assump.); *5.* $\Delta XYW \cong \Delta ZYW$ (SAS); *6.* $\overline{XW} \cong \overline{ZW}$ (CPCTC); *7.* $XW = ZW$ (Def. of $\cong$ segments); *8.* W is the midpoint of $\overline{XZ}$ (Def. of midpoint); *9.* $\overline{YW}$ is a median (Def. of median) Contradiction: It is given that $\overline{YW}$ is not a median, so $\overline{XY} \ncong \overline{ZY}$.
20. Existence: *1.* $\overline{XY}$ bisects $\angle WXZ$ (Given); *2.* $m\angle WXZ$

is a positive real number (Post. 11); 3. $\frac{1}{2}m\angle WXZ = m\angle WXY$ and $\overline{XY}$ bisects $\angle WXZ$ (Post. 12).
Uniqueness: 4. Let $\overrightarrow{XV}$ be another bisector of $\angle WXZ$ (Indirect assump.); 5. $m\angle WXV = \frac{1}{2}m\angle WXZ$ (Def. of bisector); 6. $m\angle WXV = m\angle WXY$ (Trans. prop.); 7. $\angle WXV \cong \angle WXY$ (Def. of $\cong$ $\angle$s); 8. V and Y must be collinear (Post. 12).

Pages 139–140 Section 5.2 Written Exercises

2. $\triangle ABC$ is scalene, $\overline{AD}$ is a median, Given; $\overline{AD}$ is $\perp$ bisector of $\overline{BC}$, Indirect assumption.
4. b, d 6. b, c 8. a, b
10. always 12. never
14. 1. $\angle BAC \cong \angle BCA$, $\angle DAC \cong \angle DCA$ (Given); 2. $\overline{AB} \cong \overline{CB}$, $\overline{AD} \cong \overline{CD}$ (Theorem 4.4); 3. $AB = CB$, $AD = CD$ (Def. of $\cong$ segments); 4. B is equidistant from A, C and D is equidistant from A, C (Def. of equidistant); 5. $\overleftrightarrow{BD}$ is the $\perp$ bisector of $\overline{AC}$ (Corollary 5.2.1); 6. $\overleftrightarrow{BD}$ intersects $\overline{AC}$ at point E (Theorem 2.1); 7. E is midpoint of $\overline{AC}$ (Def. of $\perp$ bisector).

Pages 143–144 Section 5.3 Written Exercises

2. Indirect assumption
4. Def. of $\cong$ segments
6. All rt. $\triangle$s are $\cong$.
8. SAS (Post. 15)
10. Def. of isosceles $\triangle$
12. Given
14. Definition of equidistant
16. Theorem 5.2
18. 1. $\overline{DP}$ is the $\perp$ bisector of $\overline{AB}$ (Given); 2. $AD = BD$ (Def. of bisector); 3. $\overline{AD} \cong \overline{BD}$ (Def. of $\cong$ segments); 4. $\angle BDP$ and $\angle ADP$ are rt. $\angle$s (Def. of $\perp$); 5. $\angle BDP \cong \angle ADP$ (All rt. $\angle$s are $\cong$); 6. $\overline{DP} = \overline{DP}$ (Congruence of segments is reflex.); 7. $\triangle APD \cong \triangle BPD$ (SAS); 8. $\overline{AP} \cong \overline{BP}$ (Corres. parts of $\cong$ $\triangle$s are $\cong$); 9. $AP = BP$ (Def. of $\cong$ segments); 10. $\overleftrightarrow{FP}$ is $\perp$ bisector of $\overline{AC}$ (Given); 11. $\triangle APF \cong \triangle CPF$ (SAS); 12. $\overline{AP} \cong \overline{CP}$ (Corres. parts of $\cong$ $\triangle$s are $\cong$; 13. $AP = CP$ (Def. of $\cong$ segments); 14. $AP = BP = CP$ (Congruence of segments is transitive).
20. Indirect proof: 1. Assume $\overline{RW} \perp \overline{ST}$ where $W \neq Y$ (Indirect assump.); 2. $\angle RWY$ is a rt. $\angle$ (Def. of $\perp$); 3. $\triangle RYS \cong \triangle RYT$ (SSS); 4. $\angle RYS \cong \angle RYT$ (CPCTC); 5. $\angle RYS$ and $\angle RYT$ are rt. $\angle$s (Theorem 3.4). Contradiction: $\triangle RWY$ has two rt. $\angle$s, which contradicts Cor. 5.3.1; therefore, $W = Y$.
22. Indirect proof: 1. Assume $\overline{AC}$ does not bisect $\overline{BD}$. (Indirect assumption); 2. There is a point X that is the midpoint of $\overline{BD}$. (Theorem 1.5); 3. $\triangle ABC \cong \triangle ADC$ (ASA); 4. $\overline{AB} \cong \overline{AD}$ (CPCTC); 5. $\triangle ABE \cong \triangle ADE$ (SAS); 6. $\overline{BE} \cong \overline{DE}$ (CPCTC); 7. E is the midpoint of $\overline{BD}$. (Def. of midpoint).
Contradiction of Theorem 1.5: a segment has only one midpoint. So, $\overline{AC}$ bisects $\overline{BD}$.

Pages 148–150 Section 5.4 Written Exercises

2. Theorem 1.5
4. Theorem 5.1
6. Theorems 1.5 and 5.1
8. Theorem 5.3
10. Postulate 7
12. Posts. 1, 2, and def. of segment
14. Postulate 1
16. SSS
18. Let C and M determine $\overleftrightarrow{CM}$
20. Def. of midpoint
22. Def. of $\cong$
24. Corres. parts of $\cong$ $\triangle$s are $\cong$.
26. Definition of $\cong$
28. Givens; Let D and A determine $\overleftrightarrow{DA}$, and let D and B determine $\overleftrightarrow{DB}$ by Post. 1; $\triangle DEA \cong \triangle DCB$ by SAS Post. 15; $\overline{DB}$ by CPCTC; D and G are equidistant from A and B by definition of equidistant; $\overline{DG}$ is $\perp$ bisector of $\overline{AB}$ by Theorem 5.2.
30. Givens; $\overline{AB} \cong \overline{BC}$ by Thm. 4.4; Let $\overrightarrow{BD}$ be $\angle$ bisector of $\angle ABC$ by Post. 1 and Def. of $\angle$ bisector; $\triangle ABD \cong \triangle CBD$ by ASA; $AD =$

DC by CPCTC; D is the midpoint by Def. of midpoint; $\overline{BD}$ is a median by Def. of median.

32. Givens; Let Y and Z determine $\overline{YZ}$. Then $\triangle XYZ \cong \triangle VZY$ by SSS, and $\angle XZY \cong \angle VYZ$ by CPCTC. $\overline{WY} = \overline{WZ}$ by Thm. 4.4. $VY = VW + WY$ and $XZ = XW + WZ$. By subtraction, $XW = VW$, so $\triangle XWY = \triangle VWZ$ by SSS.

34. Givens; let N be the midpoint of $\overline{AD}$ by Theorem 1.5; let B and N determine $\overleftrightarrow{BN}$ and let C and N determine $\overleftrightarrow{CN}$ by Post. 1; $\triangle ABN \cong \triangle DCN$ by SAS Post. 15; $\angle ABN \cong \angle DCN$ and $\overline{BN} \cong \overline{CN}$ by CPCTC; $\angle NBC \cong \angle NCB$ by Isosceles Triangle Theorem 4.3; $\angle ABC \cong \angle DCB$ by Angle Addition Postulate 13.

36. (coplanar) Givens; $\angle XYZ \cong \angle XZY$ and $\angle WYZ \cong \angle WZY$ by Isosceles Triangle Theorem; $m\angle XYW + m\angle WYZ = m\angle XYZ$ and $m\angle XZW + m\angle WZY = m\angle XZY$ by Angle Addition postulate; $m\angle XYW = m\angle XZW$ by Subtraction property of equality.

Pages 153–154 Section 5.5 Written Exercises

2. no 4. yes 6. no
8. no 10. obtuse, right
12. X and Z are in the same half-plane created by line k through Y.
14. the given
16. Addition property of equality
18. $\angle AEC \cong \angle DEB$
20. ASA
22. X and W are in the same half-plane of $\overleftrightarrow{YZ}$ by Theorem 5.4, using point Y; W and U are in the same half-plane of $\overleftrightarrow{YZ}$ by Theorem 5.4, using point Z; so, X and U are in the same half-plane of $\overleftrightarrow{YZ}$.

Pages 158–159 Chapter 5 Review

2. False; $\sim p \rightarrow \sim q$ is the inverse, $q \rightarrow p$ is the converse.
4. False; lie in two different planes
6. A 8. A 10. N
12. $\angle C$ 14. $\cong$ 16. no
18. no 20. Given
22. $\overline{RB} \cong \overline{UB}$
24. SSS 26. d 28. a

Pages 163–164 Section 6.1 Written Exercises

2. A poor conjecture; there could be many explanations for an all-girls class in a mixed population school.
4. no 6. no
8. a 10. a or c

Pages 167–168 Section 6.2 Written Exercises

2. $x > -5$ 4. $x > -6$
6. Answers will vary. As an example: $7 + 9 = 16$
8. $5 + x = a$
$5 = a - x$
$x = a - 5$
10. It is given that $x < 1$. By the multiplication property of inequality, you can multiply both sides by x, since x is positive. The result is $x^2 < x$.

Pages 172–173 Section 6.3 Written Exercises

2. $\angle A$, $\angle AFC$
4. $\angle EFB$
6. $\angle ABF$ and $\angle CBF$ are right angles; ΔABF and ΔCBF are right triangles; $\angle A$, $\angle BFA$, $\angle BFC$, and $\angle BCF$ are acute angles.
8. d 10. a 12. a
14. 4
16. The conjecture is false. In the figure below, exterior $\angle CBE$ is a right angle, but remote interior $\angle D$ is obtuse.

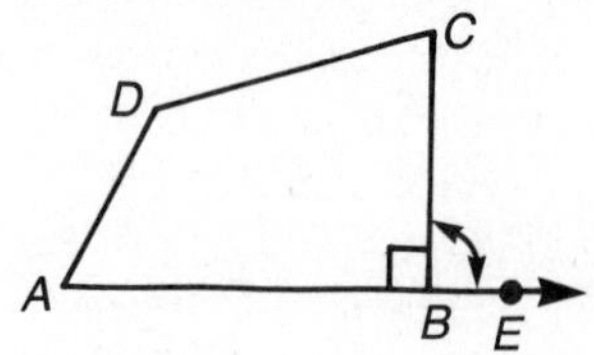

Page 178 Section 6.4 Written Exercises

2. $\angle D$ 4. $\overline{BA}$
6. Def. of $\perp$

8. Congruence of segments is reflexive.

10. *1.* $m\angle A = m\angle B$, $\overline{CD} \perp \overline{AB}$ (Given); *2.* $\overline{AC} \cong \overline{BC}$ (Theorem 4.4); *3.* $\angle ADC$, $\angle BDC$ are rt. $\angle$s. (Def. of $\perp$); *4.* $\triangle ADC$, $\triangle BDC$ are rt. $\triangle$s. (Def. of rt. $\triangle$); *5.* $\overline{CD} \cong \overline{CD}$ (Congruence of segments is reflex.); *6.* $\triangle ADC \cong \triangle BDC$ (HL)

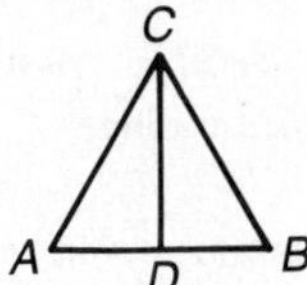

12. *1.* $\overline{AP} \cong \overline{BP}$ (Given); *2.* $\angle PAB \cong \angle PBA$ (Isos. Δ Theorem); *3.* $\angle C \cong \angle D$ (Given); *4.* $\overline{AB} \cong \overline{AB}$ (Congruence of segments is reflex.); *5.* $\Delta BCA \cong \Delta ADB$ (SAA); *6.* $\overline{AC} \cong \overline{BD}$ (CPCTC)

14. Given: $\triangle ABC$, $\triangle DEF$
    $\angle A \cong \angle D$, $\angle B \cong \angle E$, $\overline{AC} \cong \overline{DF}$
    $AB < DE$
    Prove: $\triangle ABC \cong \triangle DEF$
    Proof: Since $AB < DE$, there is a point P such that B lies between A and P, and $AP = DE$. Then $\triangle APC \cong \triangle DEF$ by SAS, and $\angle P \cong \angle E$ by CPCTC. Given $\angle E \cong \angle B$, $\angle P \cong \angle B$ by transitivity. But this is impossible, because ext. $\angle B$ is greater than remote int. $\angle P$ of $\triangle PBC$. So $AB \nless DE$.

Pages 182–183 Section 6.5
Written Exercises

2. *CB, AB*
4. *CD, CA, CB*
6. *FE, DF, DE*
8. $=$
10. $<$
12. $>, >$
14. $\overline{WZ}$
16. They are unequal by Theorem 6.4.
18. Given
20. Given
22. Theorem 6.4
24. Steps *5, 6,* and addition
26. Prove: $AB + BC + CD + DA > AC + BD$
    Proof: By Theorem 6.7, $AB + AD > DB$, $BC + DC > DB$, $AB + BC > AC$, $AD + DC > AC$; by addition, $2(AB + AD + BC + DC) > 2(DB + AC)$; by division, $AB + AD + BC + DC > DB + AC$.

Pages 186–187 Section 6.6
Written Exercises

2. $>$
4. $<$
6. $>$
8. *1.* ΔABC and ΔDEF, $AB = DE$, $AC = DF$, $BC > EF$ (Given); *2.* Assume $m\angle A < m\angle D$ (Indirect assumption); *3.* Then $BC < EF$ (Theorem 6.8), (Contradiction of given); *4.* Assume $m\angle A = m\angle D$ (Indirect assumption); *5.* Then $\Delta ABC \cong \Delta DEF$ (SAS); *6.* $BC = EF$ (CPCTC), (Contradiction of given). The only other possibility, $m\angle A > m\angle D$, must therefore be true.
10. Since $AB > AC$, $m\angle ACB > m\angle CBA$ by Theorem 6.4. Applying Theorem 6.8 to ΔBPC and ΔCMB, $PB > CM$.

Page 190 Section 6.7
Written Exercises

4. any equilateral triangle
6. Will be true for all but equilateral or isosceles triangles, where vertex A is between $\cong$ sides. In these cases the altitude is the median.
8. yes
10. no
12. Apply the result of Exercise 7 twice and use transitivity of congruence to conclude that the altitudes of an equilateral triangle are congruent.
14. Right triangles *PSR* and *JML* are congruent by HL. So, $\angle P$ and $\angle J$ are congruent by CPCTC, and $\triangle PQR \cong \triangle JKL$ by SAS. The biconditional statement: If two sides and the corresponding altitudes of two triangles are congruent, then the triangles are congruent.

Pages 194–195 Chapter 6 Review Section

2. reason, conjecture
4. $x > 36$, addition, multiplication, division properties
6. $x \geq 2$
8. $\angle 1$, $\angle 2$, $\angle 3$
10. If $\angle C$ is the right angle, then the external angle adjacent to $\angle C$ is also a right angle. By Theorem 6.1, this external angle is greater than either remote interior angle, so $\angle A$ and $\angle B$ are each acute.

12. $\Delta BPX \cong \Delta BPY$ by SAA. Thus, $\overline{PX} \cong \overline{PY}$ by CPCTC, and $PX = PY$.
14. Draw the diagonal $\overline{AC}$. Given that $\overline{CD}$ is the shortest side, $AD > CD$ and therefore $m\angle 1 > m\angle 4$ by Theorem 6.4. Given $\overline{AB}$ is the longest side, $AB > BC$ and therefore $m\angle 2 > m\angle 3$ by Theorem 6.4. By addition, $m\angle C > m\angle A$.
16. PT; 0
18. If two doors of equal size are propped open so that the angle formed by one door is larger than the angle formed by the other door, then the distance from the outer edge of the first door to its door frame is greater than the distance from the outer edge of the second door to its door frame.
20. $<$ 22. c
24. a

Pages 199-200 Section 7.1 Written Exercises

2. No; by Post. 7, three noncollinear points (the vertices) lie in exactly one plane.
4. Yes; Post. 7 states that any three points determine *at least* one plane.
6. an equilateral triangle
8. Congruence of segments is transitive.
10. SSS
12. Definition of right Δ
14. HL (Theorem 6.3)
16. Steps *1*, *6*, and Cor. 5.2.1

Pages 204-205 Section 7.2 Written Exercises

2. none 4. none
6. Since $\overline{XC} \perp$ plane P, $\overline{XC}$ is also $\perp$ $\overline{AC}$ and $\overline{BC}$ by the definition of a line perpendicular to a plane. Given that $AC = BC$, and $XC = XC$ by reflexive, $\Delta ACX \cong \Delta BCX$ by SAS (Postulate 15). So, $AX = BX$ by CPCTC, and $m\angle XBA = m\angle XAB$ by Theorem 4.3.
8. $AO = BO = CO$
10. $\overline{PO}$ intersects plane ABC at O.
    $AP = BP = CP$
    $AO = BO = CO$
    right $\angle AOP$
12. SSS
14. Steps *1* and *4*
16. Theorem 7.3

Pages 209-210 Section 7.3 Written Exercises

2. infinitely many
4. No. k must be $\perp$ to at least one other line in E that passes through the intersection by Theorem 7.3.
6. definition of perpendicular line and plane
8. no
10. $\Delta AFW \cong \Delta BFW$, $\Delta AFK \cong \Delta BFK$, $\Delta AFR \cong \Delta BFR$, all by SSS
12. *1.* Line l and point X not on l (Given); *2.* Assume there are 2 planes R and S each $\perp$ to l and each containing X (Indirect assumption); *3.* $\overleftrightarrow{XY} \perp l$, $\overleftrightarrow{XZ} \perp l$ (Def. of $\perp$ line and plane); *4.* Contradiction: There is only one line $\perp$ to a given line through a given external point. (Theorem 5.3.); Thus, the assumption is false, and there is at most one plane containing X and $\perp$ to l.

Pages 214-215 Section 7.4 Written Exercises

2. on the perpendicular through the point to the line
4. no 6. yes
8. $m\angle B > m\angle A$
10. five
12. Statements should read the same as text statements for Theorem 7.9, substituting line for plane throughout.
14. Given: Line l
    external point P
    Prove: There is at most one plane $\perp$ to l through P.
    Proof: Assume that 2 planes, M and N, are both $\perp$ to l through P. By Theorem 7.5, M and N contain every line $\perp$ to l through P. This is impossible, since 2 planes intersect in at most one line. Hence there is at most one plane $\perp$ to l through external point P.

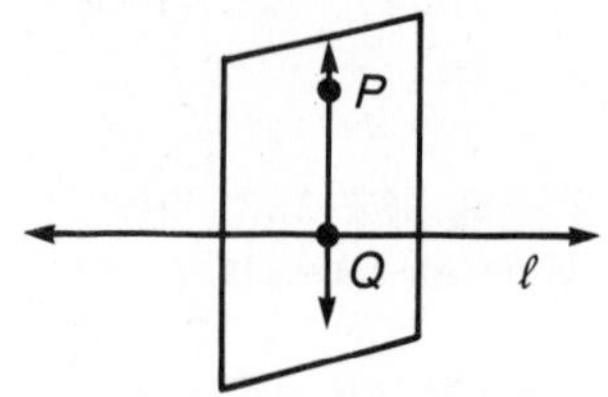

16. $m\angle XPA = m\angle XPB = m\angle XPC = 90$ (Def. of $\perp$); $\triangle XPA \cong \triangle XPB \cong \triangle XPC$ (SAS); $\overline{XA} \cong \overline{XB} \cong \overline{XC}$ (CPCTC); $XA = XB = XC$ (Def. of $\cong$).

Pages 219–220 Chapter 7 Review

2. yes, Thm. 7.1
4. They are equidistant from P and Q.
6. C
8. Sides $\cong$ (Given); $\overline{AO} \cong \overline{AO}$ (Reflexive); triangles $\cong$ (SSS); $\angle QOA \cong \angle YOA \cong \angle ROA \cong \angle XOA$ (CPCTC); above angles are right (Theorem 4.4); $\overline{AO} \perp \overline{QY}$, $\overline{AO} \perp \overline{RX}$ (Def. of $\perp$); $\overline{AO} \perp$ plane E (Thm. 7.3).
10. Theorem 7.4
12. Theorem 7.5
14. $\overline{AC}$
16. no (Thm. 7.9)
18. no (Thm. 7.10)
20. Given
22. Def. of right $\angle$
24. Substitution

Pages 227–228 Section 8.1 Written Exercises

2. Skew lines are neither parallel nor intersecting.
4. $\angle 1$, $\angle 2$; $\angle 4$, $\angle 5$
6. *1.* $\overline{AP} \cong \overline{BP}$, $\overline{NP} \cong \overline{MP}$ (Def. of bisect); *2.* $\angle APM \cong \angle BPN$ (Vert. $\angle$s are $\cong$.); *3.* $\triangle APM \cong \triangle BPN$ (SAS Post.); *4.* $\angle MAP \cong \angle NBP$ (CPCTC); *5.* $\overline{AM} \parallel \overline{NB}$ (Theorem 8.5).
8. yes
10. no
12. *1.* $\angle S$ and $\angle R$ are rt. $\angle$s (Given); *2.* $\overline{SR} \cong \overline{SR}$ (Congruence of segments is reflexive.); *3.* $\overline{PS} \cong \overline{QR}$ (Given); *4.* $\triangle PSR \cong \triangle QRS$ (SAS Postulate); *5.* $\overline{SQ} \cong \overline{RP}$ (CPCTC); *6.* $\overline{PQ} \cong \overline{PQ}$ (Congruence of segments is reflexive.); *7.* $\triangle SPQ \cong \triangle RQP$ (SSS); *8.* $\angle P \cong \angle Q$ (CPCTC).
14. *1.* $\triangle MJK \cong \triangle KLM$ (HL); *2.* $\angle MKJ \cong \angle KML$ (CPCTC); *3.* $\overline{JK} \parallel \overline{LM}$ (Theorem 8.5); *4.* $\angle LKM \cong \angle JMK$ (CPCTC); *5.* $\overline{JM} \parallel \overline{KL}$ (Theorem 8.5).

Pages 231–232 Section 8.2 Written Exercises

2. $x = 3$
4. $x = \frac{25}{2}$
6. $x = 24$
8. *1.* $\angle 1 \cong \angle 3$, $\angle 2 \cong \angle 4$ (Given); *2.* $\angle 3 \cong \angle 4$ (Thm. 3.7); *3.* $\angle 1 \cong \angle 2$ (Congruence of $\angle$s is transitive.); *4.* $j \parallel n$ (Thm. 8.5)
10. *1.* $\overrightarrow{BE}$ bisects $\angle ABD$ (Given); *2.* $\angle 1 \cong \angle 2$ (Def. of bisect); *3.* $\angle 2 \cong \angle C$ (Given); *4.* $\angle 1 \cong \angle C$ (Congruence of $\angle$s is transitive.); *5.* $\overleftrightarrow{BE} \parallel \overline{DC}$ (Thm. 8.7)
12. *1.* $\overline{AB} \cong \overline{BC}$ (Given); *2.* $\angle A \cong \angle C$ (Thm. 4.3); *3.* $\overline{DF} \cong \overline{DC}$ (Given); *4.* $\angle DFC \cong \angle C$ (Thm. 4.3); *5.* $\angle DFC \cong \angle A$ (Congruence of $\angle$s is transitive); *6.* $\overline{DF} \parallel \overline{AB}$ (Thm. 8.7)
14. *1.* $\angle 4 \cong \angle 6$ (Given); *2.* $\angle 4 \cong \angle 1$ (Theorem 3.7); *3.* $\angle 6 \cong \angle 1$ (Congruence of $\angle$s is transitive.); *4.* $l \parallel n$ (Theorem 8.7)

Pages 234–235 Section 8.3 Written Exercises

2. $5x + 7x - 20 = 180$
4. $3x + 9 = 7x - 30$
6. $x = 32$
8. $x = 35$
10. Let $\overrightarrow{BC}$ and $\overrightarrow{YX}$ intersect at point Q. Consider $\overrightarrow{BQ}$ to be a transversal crossing $\overleftrightarrow{BA}$ and $\overleftrightarrow{YX}$. By Thm. 8.8, the alternate interior angles are congruent, so $\angle ABC \cong \angle BQY$. Now consider $\overrightarrow{YQ}$ as a transversal crossing $\overleftrightarrow{BC}$ and $\overleftrightarrow{YZ}$. By Thm. 8.8, $\angle BQY \cong \angle XYZ$. Since congruence of $\angle$s is transitive, $\angle ABC \cong \angle XYZ$.
12. Given: $l \parallel n$, transversal t
    Prove: Each pair of corresponding $\angle$s are $\cong$.
    Proof:
    (1) $\angle 1 \cong \angle 2$ (alternate int. $\angle$s, Thm. 8.8); $\angle 1 \cong \angle 3$ (vertical $\angle$s, Thm. 3.7); $\angle 2 \cong \angle 3$ (Congruence of triangles is transitive.);
    (2) $\angle 2$ and $\angle 5$ are supplementary, $\angle 3$ and $\angle 4$ are supplementary (Supplement Post.); $\angle 4 \cong \angle 5$ (Supp. of $\cong$ $\angle$s are $\cong$, Thm. 3.5).
    (1) and (2) can be reapplied to show all the other pairs of corres. angles congruent.
14. Given: k a line through point A parallel to l; n a line through point B parallel to l

Prove: $k \parallel n$

Proof: Suppose $k \nparallel n$. Then k and n intersect at a point P. This means that $\overleftrightarrow{AP} \parallel l$ and $\overleftrightarrow{BP} \parallel l$. Thus, there are two lines through P parallel to l, in contradiction of the Parallel Postulate. So the assumption is false, and $k \parallel n$.

18. Given: $\triangle ABC$, exterior $\angle DCB$

Prove: $m\angle DCB = m\angle A + m\angle B$

Proof: $m\angle A + m\angle B + m\angle ACB = 180$ (Thm. 8.13); $m\angle DCB + m\angle ACB = 180$ (Supplement Postulate); $m\angle A + m\angle B + m\angle ACB = m\angle DCB + m\angle ACB$ (substitution); $m\angle A + m\angle B = m\angle DCB$ (Subtraction).

Page 238 Section 8.4 Written Exercises

2. 2
4. $180 - a - b$
6. $90 - \frac{1}{2}d$
8. $x = 30, y = 30$
10. $x = 70, y = 120$
12. 15, 75
14. *1.* $\angle 1 \cong \angle 2$ (Def. of bisect); *2.* $\angle 2 \cong \angle B$ (Thm. 8.8); *3.* $\angle 1 \cong \angle A$ (Thm. 8.9); *4.* $\angle A \cong \angle B$ (Congruence of $\angle$s is transitive.); *5.* $\overline{AC} \cong \overline{BC}$ (Thm. 4.4) If the bisector of an exterior angle of a triangle is parallel to the opposite side, then the triangle is isosceles.
16. (See figure bottom page 236.)

Given: $\triangle ABC$ and $\triangle A'B'C'$ $\angle A \cong \angle A'$, $\angle B \cong \angle B'$

Prove: $\angle C \cong \angle C'$

Proof: *1.* $m\angle A + m\angle B + m\angle C = 180$ (Thm. 8.13); *2.* $m\angle A' + m\angle B' + m\angle C' = 180$ (Thm. 8.13); *3.* $m\angle A + m\angle B = m\angle A' + m\angle B'$ (Addition); *4.* $m\angle C = m\angle C'$ (Subtraction); *5.* $\angle C \cong \angle C'$ (Def. of congruence).

Pages 244–245 Section 8.5 Written Exercises

2. 6
4. 80
6. Quadrilateral $ABCD$ is a ▱ (Def. of ▱); $\angle A \cong \angle C$ (Thm. 8.16)
8. 102
10. 54
12. $\overline{AB} \parallel \overline{DC}$ and $\overline{AD} \parallel \overline{BC}$ by def. of ▱; $\angle ACD \cong \angle CAB$ and $\angle DAC \cong \angle ACB$ by Thm. 8.8; $\overline{AC} \cong \overline{AC}$ by congruence of segments is reflex.; $\triangle ABC \cong \triangle CDA$ by ASA; $\overline{AB} \cong \overline{DC}$ and $\overline{AD} \cong \overline{BC}$ by CPCTC; $\angle ADC \cong \angle CBA$ and $\angle DAB \cong \angle BCD$ by CPCTC.
14. Theorem 8.10
16. *1.* Givens; *2.* $\angle CGD$ and $\angle BFA$ are rt. $\angle$s (Def. of $\perp$); *3.* $\triangle CGD$ and $\triangle BFA$ are rt. $\triangle$s (Def. of rt. $\triangle$); *4.* $\angle GDC$ and $\angle GCD$ are complementary, $\angle FAB$ and $\angle FBA$ are complementary (Cor. 8.13.2); *5.* $m\angle GDC + m\angle GCD = 90$, $m\angle FAB + m\angle FBA = 90$ (Def. of complementary $\angle$s); *6.* $2(m\angle GDC) + 2(m\angle GCD) = 2(90)$, $2(m\angle FAB) + 2(m\angle FBA) = 2(90)$ (Mult. prop. of equality); *7.* $2(m\angle GDC) = m\angle ADC$, $2(m\angle GCD) = m\angle BCD$, $2(m\angle FAB) = m\angle DAB$, $2(m\angle FBA) = m\angle GBA$ (Def. of $\angle$ bisector); *8.* $m\angle ADC + m\angle BCD = 180$, $m\angle DAB + m\angle GBA = 180$ (Substitution); *9.* $\angle ADC$ and $\angle BCD$ are supplementary, $\angle DAB$ and $\angle GBA$ are supplementary (Def. of supp.); *10.* $\overline{BC} \parallel \overline{AD}$ (Theorem 8.9). Since it is given that $m\angle CGB \neq m\angle AFD \neq 90$, this sequence does not work for the other two sets of $\angle$s, so the other two sides are not $\parallel$. Therefore, $ABCD$ is a trapezoid by the definition of a trapezoid.

Pages 249–250 Section 8.6 Written Exercises

2. 2.4
4. 28
6. 100
8. 80
10. $\overline{CD} \cong \overline{FD}$ by Def. of bisect and $\angle BDC \cong \angle EDF$ by Theorem 3.7. Because $\overline{BC} \parallel \overline{AE}$, alternate interior $\angle$s CBD and FED are $\cong$. So $\triangle CBD \cong \triangle FED$ by SAA and $\overline{DB} \cong \overline{DE}$ by CPCTC. (You can also prove the triangles $\cong$ by ASA.)
12. 12
14. 14
16. Let $\overline{PR}$ and $\overline{QS}$ intersect at T. By Theorem 8.18, $ST =$

QT and $PT = RT$. Because all four sides are ≅, △STP ≅ △PTQ ≅ △QTR ≅ △RTS by SSS. Then ∠STP ≅ ∠PTQ ≅ ∠QTR ≅ ∠RTS by CPCTC. Since all are ≅, adjacent ∠s, the measure of each is 90 by Theorem 3.4. By Def. of ⊥, $\overline{PR} \perp \overline{QS}$.

Pages 254–255 Section 8.7
Written Exercises

2. yes; Theorem 8.28
4. yes; Theorem 8.30
6. yes; Theorem 8.31
8. No; it is transitive and symmetric, but not reflexive.
10. $\overline{PQ} \cong \overline{SR}$ by Theorem 8.31; $\overline{PQ} \parallel \overline{SR}$ by Theorem 8.30; $PQRS$ is a ▱ by Theorem 8.20; $\overline{PS} \cong \overline{RQ}$ by Def. of ▱.
12. *1.* $M \parallel N$ (Theorem 8.29); *2.* $M \perp CD$ (Given); *3.* $N \perp CD$ (Theorem 8.28)
14. Given: line $l \perp$ plane E at A line $k \perp$ plane E at B
    Prove: $l \parallel k$
    Proof: By Theorem 7.8, l and k are coplanar, and by definition each is ⊥ to $\overline{AB}$. Hence, by Theorem 8.2, they are parallel.

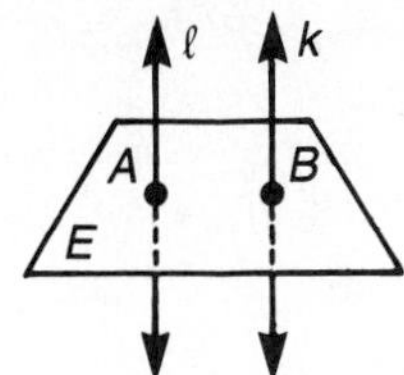

16. Given: lines p, q, r
    $p \parallel q$, $p \parallel r$
    Prove: $q \parallel r$
    Proof: Let E be a plane perpendicular to p. By Corollary 8.30.1, $E \perp q$ and $E \perp r$. So, by Theorem 8.30, $q \parallel r$.

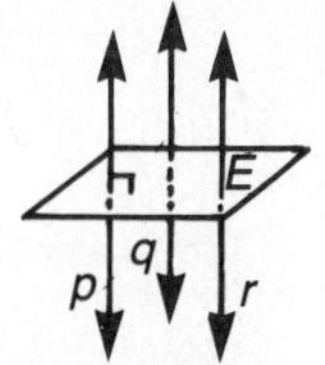

18. *1.* $\overline{AB}$ " $\overline{CD}$ (Theorem 8.31); *2.* $\overline{AB} \parallel \overline{CD}$ (Theorem 8.30); *3.* $ABDC$ is a ▱ (Theorem 8.20); *4.* ∠ABD is a rt. ∠ (Def. of ⊥); *5.* ▱ $ABDC$ is a rectangle (Def. of rectangle); *6.* ∠CDB is a rt. ∠ (Theorem 8.23); *7.* △ABD " △CDB (SAS).

Pages 259–260 Section 8.8
Written Exercises

2. F; is *acute* if
4. F; *perpendicular* to the edge
6. T
8. 60
10. 50
12. 115
14. Postulate 8
16. Theorem 5.1
18. Given
20. Theorem 8.32
22. Def. of ⊥ planes

Page 263 Section 8.9
Written Exercises

2. yes
4. no
6. no
8. no
10. no
12. no
14. isosceles △
16. Prove that ▱ $BCC'B'$ is a rectangle. Then $B'C' = BC = AD$. Reapply to the other three rectangles formed by the perpendiculars from M and N. By transitivity, $A'D' = AD = BC = B'C'$ and $A'B' = AB = DC = D'C'$. Corresponding angles are congruent by Theorem 8.32.

Pages 267–268 Chapter 8
Review

2. 46
4. 35
6. $x = 38$
8. $\overline{BC}$
10. $\overline{DP}$
12. 40
14. 90
16. perpendicular
18. parallel
20. 90
22. perpendicular

Pages 278–279 Section 9.1
Written Exercises

8. No; Postulate 19
10. Yes; 4
12. △AEC ≅ △BED by SAS; area of △AEC = area of △BED by Postulate 18.
14. *1.* $\overline{MT} \cong \overline{PR}$, $\overline{PM} \cong \overline{RT}$ (Definition of rectangle); *2.* $\overline{PM} \cong \overline{QR}$ (Theorem 8.15). *3.* $\overline{RT} \cong \overline{QR}$ (Congruence of segments is transitive.); *4.* $\overline{MR} \cong \overline{PQ}$ (Theorem 8.15); *5.* △MTR ≅ △PRQ (SSS); *6.* Area of △MTR = area of △PRQ (Postulate 18).
16. The two triangular regions intersect in a quadrilateral

region, which is neither a point nor a segment.

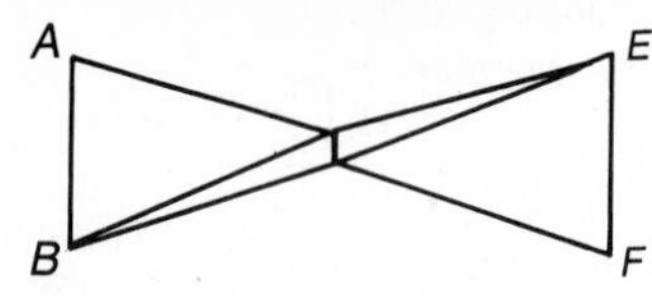

Pages 282–283 Section 9.2 Written Exercises

2. 80 cm^2 4. 15 yd
6. n ft
8. 21 ab^2c mm^2
10. Yes, $b = 5$, $h = \sqrt{3}$
12. 144

Pages 287–288 Section 9.3 Written Exercises

2. 75 $in.^2$ 4. 24 cm
6. $1\frac{1}{4}$ m 8. 12 $in.^2$
10. $3x$ 12. 150
14. 12 in.
16. $\overline{AB}$ determines the base for all the triangles. Because parallel lines are everywhere equidistant, any perpendicular (altitude) from l to $\overleftrightarrow{AB}$ is the same length. So, $\frac{1}{2}bh$ will be constant for any point on l.
18. 10.8 20. $\frac{bh}{a}$

Pages 290–292 Section 9.4 Written Exercises

2. 100 4. 24 6. 72
8. $6\frac{1}{4}$ 10. $5\frac{1}{5}$ 12. 30
14. 11 16. 420 18. 80

Pages 295–296 Section 9.5 Written Exercises

2. 13 4. 8 6. 24
8. $4\sqrt{3}$ 10. $\sqrt{2}$
12. 5 14. 20
16. $9\frac{3}{5}$ 18. 336
20. 18 in.

Pages 299–300 Section 9.6 Written Exercises

2. $3\sqrt{3}, 6$ 4. $\frac{9}{2}, \frac{9\sqrt{3}}{2}$
6. 2, 4 8. $9, 6\sqrt{3}$
10. $\frac{8\sqrt{3}}{3}, \frac{16\sqrt{3}}{3}$
12. $12, 12\sqrt{2}$
14. $2\sqrt{3}, 2\sqrt{6}$ 16. 9, 9
18. $2\sqrt{3}, 2\sqrt{3}$
20. $6\sqrt{2}$ 22. $6\sqrt{3}$
24. $18 + 18\sqrt{3}$
26. $12\sqrt{2}$ 28. 2
30. 6
32. $A = \frac{s^2\sqrt{3}}{4}$
34. (1) If a rt. △ is isosceles, then the hypotenuse is $\sqrt{2}$ times as long as a leg. Given a rt. △ with sides as shown in the figure below left, use the Pythagorean Theorem:

$$\begin{aligned} c &= \sqrt{x^2 + x^2} \\ &= \sqrt{2x^2} \\ &= x\sqrt{2} \end{aligned}$$

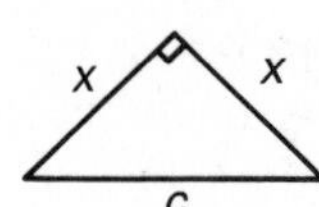

(2) *If the hypotenuse of a rt. △ is $\sqrt{2}$ times as long as a leg, then the rt. △ is isosceles.* Given a rt. △ with sides as shown in the figure below right, use the Pythagorean Theorem:

$$\begin{aligned} (\sqrt{2}x)^2 &= x^2 + a^2 \\ 2x^2 &= x^2 + a^2 \\ x^2 &= a^2 \\ x &= a \end{aligned}$$

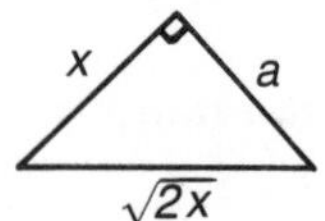

Pages 304–305 Chapter 9 Review

2. congruent 4. 10
6. 3, 9 8. $4x$ 10. 6
12. 12 14. 162
16. 17 18. 24
20. $6\sqrt{2}$ 22. $81\sqrt{3}$

Pages 310–311 Section 10.1 Written Exercises

2. $\frac{4}{9}$ 4. $\frac{7}{30}$ 6. $\frac{47}{300}$
8. $\frac{17}{26}$ 10. $\frac{a}{b}$ 12. $\frac{a}{y}$
14. 42 16. 8 18. $22\frac{1}{2}$
20. 36 22. 6
24. $\sqrt{15}$ 26. 32
28. 63 30. $2\sqrt{22}$
32. 3

Pages 315–316 Section 10.2 Written Exercises

2. 6
4. 15
6. yes
8. yes
10. $\frac{18}{11}$
12. $\frac{30}{7}$
14. $\frac{14}{3}$
16. $11\frac{1}{5}$ in.

Pages 319–320 Section 10.3 Written Exercises

2. 12
4. 14
6. 4
8. *1.* $\angle B \sim \angle DEC$ (Given); *2.* $\angle C \cong \angle C$ (Congruence of $\angle$s is reflexive.); *3.* $\triangle ABC \sim \triangle DEC$ (Corollary 10.3.1); *4.* $\frac{DE}{AB} = \frac{CD}{CA}$ (CSSTP).
10. *1.* $\angle B \cong \angle D$ (Given); *2.* $\angle 2 \cong \angle 3$ (Vert. $\angle$s are $\cong$.); *3.* $\triangle ABC \sim \triangle EDC$ (Corollary 10.3.1); *4.* $\frac{AB}{ED} = \frac{BC}{DC}$ (CSSTP); *5.* $AB \cdot DC = ED \cdot BC$ (Cross-multiplication).
12. *1.* $\angle E \cong \angle BDC$ (Def. of $\cong$ $\angle$s); *2.* $\angle C \cong \angle C$ (Congruence of $\angle$s is reflexive.); *3.* $\triangle BCD \sim \triangle ACE$ (Corollary 10.3.1); *4.* $\frac{BD}{AE} = \frac{CB}{CA}$ (CSSTP); *5.* $BD \cdot CA = AE \cdot CB$ (Cross-multiplication).
14. *1.* $\angle YXZ \cong \angle YVW$ (Given); *2.* $\angle Y \cong \angle Y$ (Congruence of $\angle$s is reflexive.); *3.* $\triangle YZX \sim \triangle YWV$ (Corollary 10.3.1); *4.* $\frac{YZ}{YW} = \frac{ZX}{WV}$ (CSSTP); *5.* $YZ \cdot WV = YW \cdot ZX$ (Cross-multiplication).
16. 12
18. *1.* $\triangle ABD \sim \triangle DBC$ (Given); *2.* $\frac{AB}{DB} = \frac{DB}{BC}$ (CSSTP); *3.* DB is the geometric mean between AB and BC (Definition of geometric mean).
20. $\overline{BD}$ is the median and bisector of $\angle B$ (Given); draw $\overline{CE} \parallel \overline{BD}$ so that $\overline{CE}$ intersects $\overleftrightarrow{AB}$ at E (auxiliary set); $\triangle ADB \sim \triangle ACE$ (Corollary 10.3.2); $\frac{AD}{DC} = \frac{AB}{BE}$ (CSSTP); $\angle DBC \cong \angle ECB$ (Theorem 8.8); $\angle ABD \cong \angle AEC$ (Theorem 8.9); $\angle ABD \cong \angle DBC$ (definition of bisect); $\angle ECB \cong \angle AEC$ (substitution); $\triangle CBE$ is isosceles (definition of isosceles); $BE = BC$ (Theorem 4.4); $\frac{AD}{DC} = \frac{AB}{BC}$ (substitution); $AD \cdot BC = DC \cdot AB$ (cross-multiplication); $AD = DC$ (definition of median); $BC = AB$ (division property of equality).

Pages 322–323 Section 10.4 Written Exercises

2. *1.* $\overline{AB} \parallel \overline{ED}$ (Given); *2.* $\angle BAC \cong \angle DEC$, $\angle ABC \cong \angle EDC$ (Theorem 8.8); *3.* $\angle ACB \cong \angle ECD$ (Vert. $\angle$s are $\cong$.); *4.* $\triangle ABC \sim \triangle EDC$ (Theorem 10.3).
4. $x = 15$, $y = \frac{20}{3}$
6. $x = \frac{77}{25}$, $y = \frac{-26}{3}$
8. $x = \pm 8$, $y = 222$
10. Substitution
12. Corollary 10.3.2
14. Substitution
16. Cross-multiplication
18. Definition of $\cong$ segments
20. SSS, Theorem 4.5
22. Similarity is transitive.
24. $\frac{BA}{XW} = \frac{CA}{YW}$ (CSSTP); $AD = BD$, $WZ = XZ$ (definition of median); $BA = 2AD$, $XW = 2WZ$ (definition of between, substitution); $\frac{2AD}{2WZ} = \frac{AD}{WZ}$ (identity prop. of mult.); $\frac{AD}{WZ} = \frac{CA}{YW}$ (substitution); $\angle A \cong \angle W$ (definition of similar $\triangle$s); $\triangle ACD \sim \triangle WYZ$ (SAS, Theorem 10.4); $\frac{CD}{YZ} = \frac{CA}{YW}$ (CSSTP).

Pages 327–328 Section 10.5 Written Exercises

2. SR
4. UT
6. $\frac{RS}{TS}$, $\frac{UR}{TR}$
8. $\frac{7}{4}$
10. 6
12. $2\sqrt{ab}$
14. $\frac{1}{4}$
16. 6.4
18. 192
20. 25
22. $2\sqrt{30}$
24. 15
26. Since $\overline{BD}$ is the altitude to the hypotenuse in rt. $\triangle ADC$, by Cor. 10.6.1, $\frac{AB}{AD} = \frac{AD}{AC}$. By cross-multiplication, $(AD)^2 = AB \cdot AC$.
28. $\sqrt{rs}$
30. $\sqrt{r(s-r)}$
32. $\frac{s^2 + r^2}{r}$

Pages 331-332 Section 10.6 Written Exercises

2. $\frac{9}{4}$ 4. $\frac{4}{25}$ 6. $\frac{10}{1}$
8. $\frac{4}{3}$ 10. $\frac{36}{16}$ or $\frac{9}{4}$
12. $\frac{100}{900}$ or $\frac{1}{9}$ 14. $\frac{2}{7}$
16. $\frac{2}{7}$ 18. $\frac{2}{7}$
20. $\frac{4}{3}$ 22. $\frac{3}{5}$ 24. $\frac{1}{1}$
26. 10, 24, 26
28. 10 30. $\frac{2000}{81}$
32. $\frac{18}{5}$ 34. $\frac{2}{1}$
36. 30 m

Pages 336-337 Chapter 10 Review

2. $x = 4$ 4. 2.5
6. T 8. F 10. F
12. sides 14. $BY = 6$
16. *1.* $\angle EAC \cong \angle DBC$ (Def. of rt. $\angle$; All rt. $\angle$s are $\cong$.); *2.* $\angle C \cong \angle C$ (Reflexive); *3.* $\triangle ACD \sim \triangle BCD$ (AA Similarity), so $\frac{AE}{BD} = \frac{AC}{BC}$, or $AE \cdot BC = BD \cdot AC$.
18. $x = 10, y = 3$
20. T 22. F
24. $2\sqrt{15}$ 26. $\sqrt{30}$
28. The area increases times 25.
30. $\frac{4}{1}$

Pages 341-342 Section 11.1 Written Exercises

2. (4, 2) 4. (0, 0)
6. $(-3, -2)$ 8. $(-3, 4)$
10. I 12. IV
14. III 16. II
26. x-axis (9, 0), y-axis (0, 3)

Page 346 Section 11.2 Written Exercises

2. -2 4. $\frac{6}{5}$
6. 0 8. $\frac{-2}{3}$
10. 1 12. yes
14. 6 16. 3
18. 0 and no slope
20. no 22. 2
24. 7 26. $\frac{-64}{33}$

Pages 349-350 Section 11.3 Written Exercises

2. -1 4. -1
6. $\overleftrightarrow{GH} \parallel \overleftrightarrow{PR}$ 8. $\overleftrightarrow{XY}$
10. H 12. $\perp$
14. neither
16. $2, \frac{-4}{3}, \frac{-2}{9}$ 18. no
20. $m_1 = \frac{b}{a}$, $m_2 = \frac{a}{-b}$, so m_1 and m_2 are negative reciprocals, and the lines are $\perp$.
22. The slope of $\overleftrightarrow{AB} = \frac{-4}{4} = -1$, and the slope of $\overleftrightarrow{DC} = \frac{2}{-2} = -1$, so $\overleftrightarrow{AB} \parallel \overleftrightarrow{DC}$. The slope of $\overleftrightarrow{AD} = \frac{2}{4} = \frac{1}{2}$, and the slope of $\overleftrightarrow{BC} = \frac{4}{2} = 2$, so $\overline{AD} \parallel \overline{BC}$. The slope of diagonal $\overleftrightarrow{BD} = \frac{6}{0}$, so $\overleftrightarrow{BD}$ has no slope and is a vertical line. The slope of diagonal $\overleftrightarrow{AC} = \frac{0}{6} = 0$, so $\overleftrightarrow{AC}$ is horizontal and $\perp$ to $\overleftrightarrow{BD}$.

Pages 352-353 Section 11.4 Written Exercises

2. $\sqrt{34}$ 4. $2\sqrt{10}$
6. $5\sqrt{5}$
8. $\sqrt{149} + \sqrt{26} + \sqrt{89}$
10. $6\sqrt{5} + 3\sqrt{10}$
12. isosceles
14. isosceles
16. yes
18. $PR = \sqrt{53}$, $SQ = \sqrt{37}$
20. $DE = \sqrt{5}$, $DF = 3\sqrt{5}$, $EF = 5\sqrt{2}$; $(\sqrt{5})^2 + (3\sqrt{5})^2 = 5 + 45 = 50 = (5\sqrt{2})^2$; so $(DE)^2 + (DF)^2 = (EF)^2$, and DE and DF are the legs of rt. $\triangle DEF$.

Pages 356-357 Section 11.5 Written Exercises

2. $(-7, -1)$ 4. (2.8, 0.9)
6. $(\frac{-1}{2}, \frac{-13}{2})$
8. (6, 8) 10. (8, 2)
12. yes 14. yes
16. Yes; their common midpoint is $P(3, \frac{-3}{2})$.
18. It is a parallelogram but not a rectangle.
22. The midpoint $P(3, 3)$ is the same for $\overline{AC}$ and $\overline{BD}$. Also, $AP = CP = BP = DP = 2$, so the diagonals bisect each other.
24. $\sqrt{53}$ from vertices A and B; $5\sqrt{2}$ from vertex C.
26. For the median from B, $m = -1$. For the median from A, $m = 1$. So the medians to $\overline{AC}$ and $\overline{BC}$ are $\perp$ by Theorem 11.3.

Pages 361-362 Section 11.6 Written Exercises

2. $D(\frac{a}{2}, \frac{b}{2})$ by midpoint formula; $AD = BD = CD = \sqrt{(\frac{a}{2})^2 + (\frac{b}{2})^2}$, so D is equidistant from A, B, and C.
4. m_1 of $\overline{AC} = \frac{c}{a+b}$; m_2 of $\overline{BD} = \frac{c}{b-a}$; $m_1 \cdot m_2 = \frac{c^2}{b^2 - a^2}$. $AB = AD$ (Def. of rhombus), so $(AB)^2 = (AD)^2$, or $a^2 = b^2 + c^2$. By substitution, $m_1 \cdot m_2 = \frac{c^2}{-c^2} = -1$, and the diagonals are $\perp$.
6. By the midpoint formula, $P(b, c)$ and $Q(a + d, c)$. m of $\overline{PQ} = m$ of $\overline{AB} = m$ of $\overline{DC} = 0$. By the distance formula, $PQ = a + d - b$, $AB = 2a$, $DC = 2d - 2b$. $a + d - b = \frac{1}{2}(2a + 2d - 2b)$, so $PQ = \frac{1}{2}(AB + DC)$.
8. Use the midpoint formula to find P, Q, R, and S. Use the slope formula to show $\overline{PQ} \parallel \overline{RS}$. Use the distance formula to show $\overline{PQ} \cong \overline{RS}$.

Page 366 Section 11.7 Written Exercises

2. 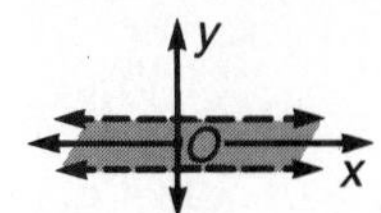

4. 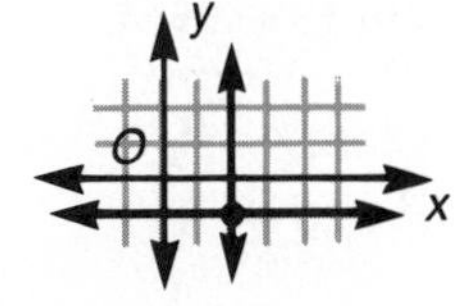

6. 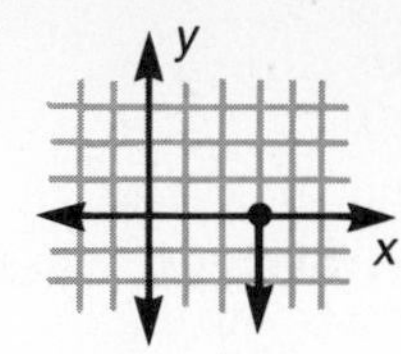

8. 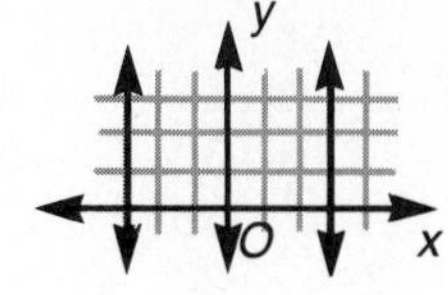

10. 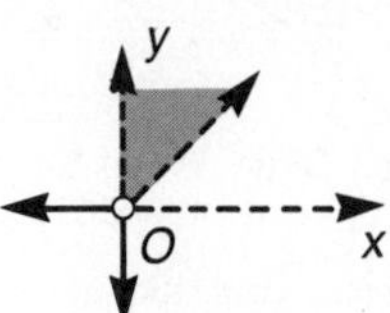

12. 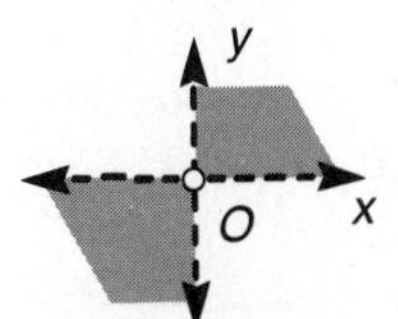

14. 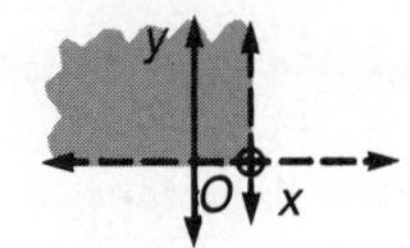

16. 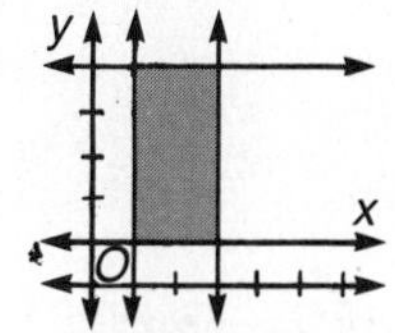

18. 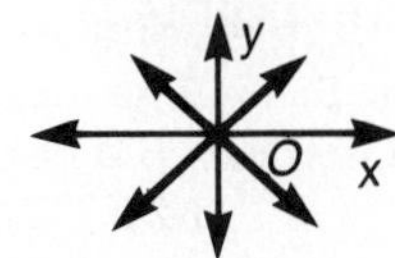

Pages 371 Section 11.8 Written Exercises

2. $y - 6 = \frac{3}{4}(x - 2)$
4. $y - 1 = -(x - 1)$ or $y + 1 = -(x - 3)$
6. $2x + y - 1 = 0$
8. $x - 2y = 0$
10. $4x - y - 2 = 0$
12. $m = 1$, $P(-1, -2)$
14. $m = -1$, $b = 2$
16. $m = -\frac{2}{3}$, $b = \frac{10}{3}$
18. 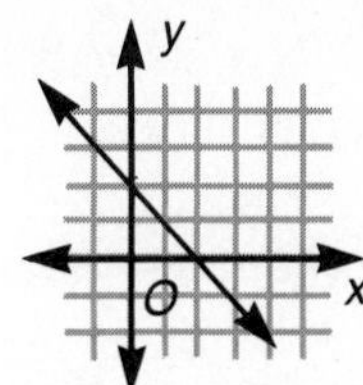

20. (5, 2)

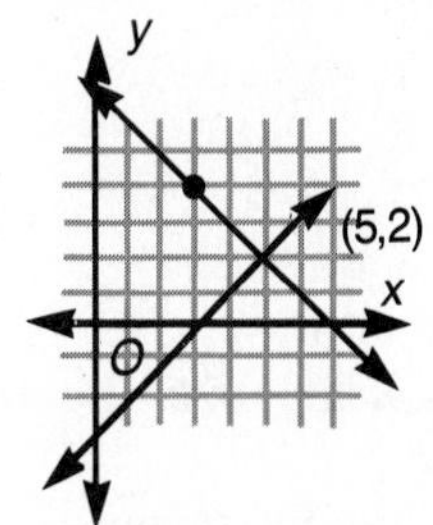

22. a and d, b and d, c and d

Pages 375-376 Chapter 11 Review

2. (2, 3)
4. (2, −4)
6. (−3, −1)
8. (0, 0)
10. III
12. 0
14. 3
16. $\frac{-4}{5}$
18. $2, \frac{-1}{3}, \frac{-3}{2}$
20. no
22. $2\sqrt{5} + 2\sqrt{13} + 2\sqrt{10}$
24. $(3\frac{1}{2}, 6)$
26. (10, 12)
28. $A(a, 0)$, $B(2a + b, c)$, $C(a + 2b, 2c)$, $D(b, c)$ Show DB $\perp$ AC or $AB \ncong BC$
30. 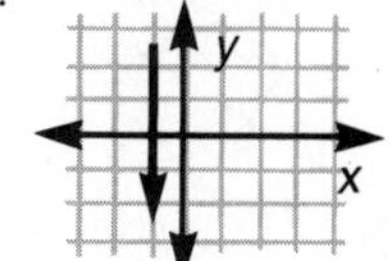

32.

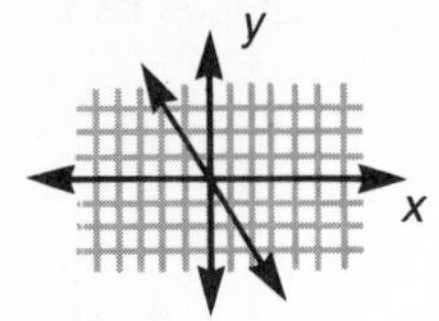

34. $y + 5 = \frac{2}{3}(x - 3)$
36. $(-1, 2)$

Pages 383–384 Section 12.1
Written Exercises

2. 10 4. 6 6. 11
8. T 10. T 12. T
14. F 16. 4 18. 20
20. 74 22. 4 24. 1
26. a great circle

Pages 389–390 Section 12.2
Written Exercises

2. T 4. F 6. F
8. F (One of the chords could be a diameter.)
10. 90
12. $\overline{AC} \parallel \overline{DF}$
14. 38 16. 14
18. Given: $\overline{AB} \perp \overline{BC}$, $\overline{AD} \perp \overline{DE}$, $\overline{AB} \cong \overline{AD}$
Prove: $\overline{CG} \cong \overline{EF}$
Proof: *1.* $\overline{AC} \cong \overline{AE}$ (Radii of the same ⊙ are ≅.); *2.* $\overline{AB} \cong \overline{AD}$ (Given); *3.* $\triangle ABC \cong \triangle ADE$ (HL); *4.* $\overline{BC} \cong \overline{DE}$ (CPCTC); *5.* $\overline{CG} \cong \overline{EF}$ (Cor. 12.2.3 and Def. of bisect).

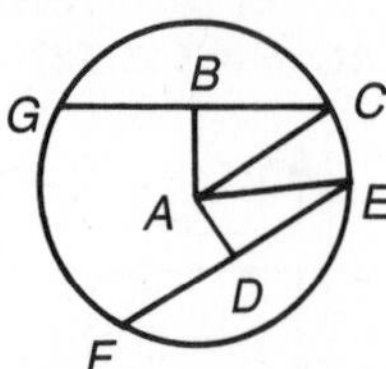

20. 16 22. $\sqrt{51}$
24. 10

Pages 393–394 Section 12.3
Written Exercises

2. T 4. F 6. T
8. F 10. 10 12. 5
14. 5 16. $4\sqrt{5}$
18. $5\sqrt{2}$ 20. 90
22. SAS or LL

Pages 398–399 Section 12.4
Written Exercises

2. T 4. T 6. F
8. T 10. 30
12. 180 14. 30
16. 150 18. 150
20. 74 22. 141

Pages 404–405 Section 12.5
Written Exercises

2. 75 4. 80
6. 30 8. 250
10. 150 12. 110
14. 25 16. 140
18. 30 20. 230
22. $\widehat{ABC}$ is a semicircle; since $m\widehat{AB} = 90$, $m\widehat{BC} = 90$ also. So $m\angle A = m\angle C = 45$, and $\triangle ACB$ is isosceles.
24. 35 26. 32 or 64
28. 86

Pages 408–409 Section 12.6
Written Exercises

2. Thm 12.11
4. 120 6. 90
8. 35 10. 125
12. 290 14. 50
16. 90 18. 220
20. Given $\overline{AB} \cong \overline{CB}$, $\widehat{AB} \cong \widehat{CB}$, so inscribed $\angle ADB \cong \angle CDB$. Because $\overline{BD}$ is a diameter, inscribed $\angle A \cong \angle C$, and $\triangle ABD \cong \triangle CBD$ by SAA. So, $\angle ABD \cong \angle CBD$ by CPCTC. Since the two inscribed angles are ≅, $\widehat{AD} \cong \widehat{CD}$.
22. 120 24. 64

Pages 414–416 Section 12.7
Written Exercises

2. 10 4. 12
6. 100 8. 100
10. 100 12. 4
14. 12 16. 40
18. 20 20. 60
22. 130 24. 14
26. 80 28. 10
30. 36
32. If ∠1 is a central ∠, then the chords are both diameters. The measure of an arc is the same as the measure of its central ∠, so $m\widehat{AB} + m\widehat{DC} = m\angle 1 + m\angle 2$. But, vert. ∠s are ≅. Thus, $2m\angle 1 = m\widehat{AB} + m\widehat{DC}$, and $m\angle 1 = \frac{1}{2}(m\widehat{AB} + m\widehat{DC})$.
34. 20

Pages 419–420 Section 12.8
Written Exercises

2. $(x - 1)^2 + (y - 5)^2 = 25$
4. $x^2 + y^2 = \frac{49}{4}$

12. circle
14. point
16. $(x + y)^2 \neq x^2 + y^2$
18. $x^2 + (y - 2)^2 = 16$
20. $(x - 5)^2 + y^2 = 13$
22. $(x - 2)^2 + (y + 1)^2 = 4$
24. $(x + \frac{3}{2})^2 + (y + \frac{3}{4})^2 = \frac{77}{16}$
26. $x^2 + y^2 = 25$

Pages 424–425 Chapter 12 Review

2. $\overrightarrow{AB}$ 4. $\overline{EF}$
6. *P*, *S*, *C*
8. ⊙*P*, ⊙*P*
10. ⊙*C*, ⊙*S*
12. *YX* 14. $\overline{RS}$
16. *M* 18. ⊥
20. c 22. c
24. c 26. b
28. a 30. c
32. d 34. (−5, 3)
36. $(x - 7)^2 + (y - 2)^2 = 16$
38. 4

Page 433 Section 13.1
Written Exercises

2. the locus of points 1 in. from ⊙*O*
4. an internally tangent circle whose diameter equals the radius of the given circle
6. the empty set
8. $|x| = |y|$
10. The locus is also a 90-degree arc of ⊙*X* with radius *PQ*.

Page 438 Section 13.2
Written Exercises

2. Form a triangle and apply Theorem 13.2.
4. It would be the point at which $\overleftrightarrow{PQ}$ intersects the bisector of ∠*ABC*.
6. (a) *Three noncollinear points determine a circle.* Three noncollinear points *A*, *B*, and *C* determine a triangle. By Thm. 13.2, the ⊥ bisectors of the sides meet at point *P*, and $AP = BP = CP = r$, the radius of a circle with center *P* that contains *A*, *B*, and *C*. (b) *A*, *B*, *and C determine only one circle.* Suppose there is another circle *Q* containing *A*, *B*, and *C*. Then $\overline{QA}$, $\overline{QB}$, and $\overline{QC}$ are radii of length $s \neq r$. *Q* is also equidistant from the vertices of △*ABC*, so by Thm. 5.2, *Q* is on the ⊥ bisectors of $\overline{AB}$, $\overline{BC}$, and $\overline{AC}$. By Thm. 13.2, these meet at one point *P*, so $P = Q$.
8. *P*(−2, 0), *Q*(1, 3), and *R*(−3, 3) are the midpoints of $\overline{AB}$, $\overline{BC}$, and $\overline{AC}$. Because $\overline{SP} \perp \overline{AB}$, the *x*-coordinate of *S* is −2. By Thm. 13.2, $AS = BS = CS$, so $\sqrt{16 + y^2} = \sqrt{4 + (6 - y)^2}$, which yields $y = 2$. So *S*(−2, 2).
10. They are the four points determined by the bisectors of the interior and exterior angles of the triangle, as shown.

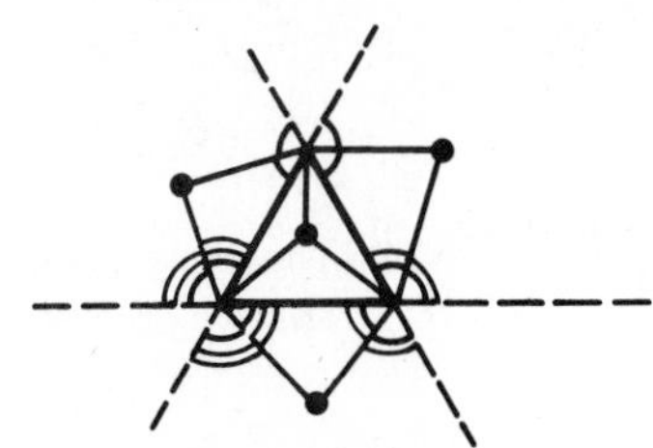

Pages 444–445 Section 13.3
Written Exercises

2. Construction 2
4. Constructions 1 and 2
6. Constructions 1 and 5
8. Construction 7
10. Constructions 5 and 1

Pages 450–451 Section 13.4
Written Exercises

2. Constructions 5, 9
4. Construction 5 and Construction 9 applied twice
6. Construction 8, 10
8. Construction 8
10. Construct the ⊥ bisectors of two adjacent sides; the point of intersection is the center; the distance from the center to any vertex is the radius of the circumscribed circle.
12. Draw ⊙ *P* with given radius *r*. On a diameter of ⊙ *P*, construct the given angle. Join the points where the sides of the angle intersect the circle. The angle opposite the diameter will be a right angle.
14. By Theorem 13.4, the angle bisectors of a △ are concurrent in a point equidistant from the sides. By drawing the ⊥ from the incenter to one side, you establish the radius, by Cor. 12.2.1, of a ⊙ that is tangent to all three sides.
16. To inscribe a circle, construct the ⊙ with the given radius and draw a tangent to the ⊙. Construct

the $\perp$ to the tangent and measure 3 radius lengths along the $\perp$ from the point of tangency. This will provide a distance two-thirds of the way along a median from the given vertex, so construct the vertex angle at that point. The sides of the $\angle$ will be tangent to the $\odot$ and form 2 $\cong$ legs.

Pages 456–457 Chapter 13 Review

2. two lines parallel to m, each 3 cm on either side of m
4. two lines through the origin having slopes of 1 and -1
6. the two points at which $\odot P$ with radius d intersects the line
8. the bisector of $\angle A$, which also bisects $\angle C$
10. the center of the circle containing the 3 points
12. the point of concurrency of the angle bisectors
14. Construction 1
16. Draw arcs from each endpoint of a given segment with radii the same length as the segment. Their intersection forms the third vertex of an equilateral triangle.
18. Construction 4; construct the $\perp$ bisector of the given diagonal so that the bisector is the same length as the diagonal and is bisected itself; join the endpoints of the two diagonals.
20. Construction 5
22. Construction 7
24. Construct the $\perp$ bisector of the given segment; use the midpoint as the center of a $\odot$ with radius half the length of the hypotenuse; connect the endpoints of the hypotenuse to a point on the circle.
26. Construction 10
28. Draw 2 non-parallel chords. Their $\perp$ bisectors intersect at the center.
30. Slope of tangent $= \frac{-3}{4}$. Equation of tangent is $(y - 4) = \frac{-3}{4}(x - 3)$.

Pages 464–465 Section 14.1 Written Exercises

2. A
4. N
6. 540
8. 1260
10. 144
12. 100
14. $96\sqrt{3}$
16. (a) 2; (b) $\sqrt{3}$; (c) $6\sqrt{3}$
18. 5
20. 50

Pages 469–470 Section 14.2 Written Exercises

2. $C = 22\pi$ mm, $A = 121\pi$ mm^2
4. $C = 15.66\pi$ cm, $A = 61.3089\pi$ cm^2
6. 8 in.
8. $6k$ ft
10. 16π in.$^2 \approx 50.24$ in.^{2}
12. $\frac{16}{1}$
14. The circle has the greater area by approx. 6.85 in.^{2}.
16. 100π cm^2 = 314 cm^2
18. Area of circle $= 40\pi$; area outside cross $= 40\pi - 80$

Pages 473–474 Section 14.3 Written Exercises

2. 9π in.
4. $\frac{36\pi}{5}$
6. 27π in.
8. $\frac{12}{\pi}$ cm; $\frac{12}{\pi}$ cm
10. $\frac{5\pi}{4}$ in.
12. 1500π in.
14. $\frac{5\pi}{2}$
16. $\approx$5.8 m

Pages 477–478 Section 14.4 Written Exercises

2. π
4. 15π
6. $\frac{50\pi}{3}$
8. 18π
10. $\frac{100\pi}{3} - 25\sqrt{3}$ in.^{2}
12. $\frac{16\pi}{3} - 4\sqrt{3}$ in.^{2}
14. $12\pi - 18\sqrt{3}$ in.^{2}
16. 4 cm
18. $\frac{8\pi}{3}$ cm^2
20. $\frac{40\pi}{3}$ cm^2

Page 484 Section 14.5 Written Exercises

2. F
4. F
6.

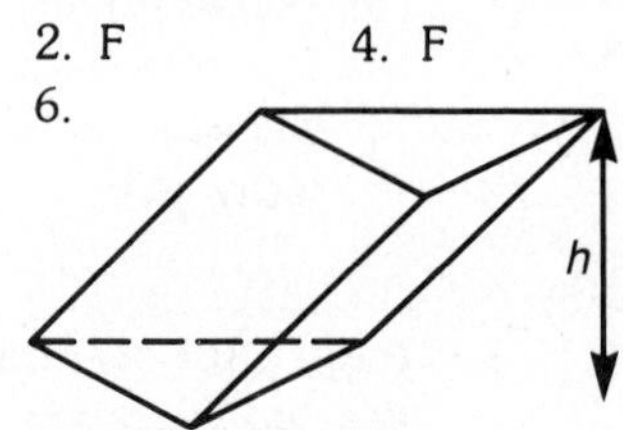

8. $240 + 32\sqrt{3}$ in.^{2}
10. 4, 8, $4\sqrt{3}$; 30, 60, 90; $8\sqrt{3}$

Pages 488–489 Section 14.6
Written Exercises

2. 12 in.
4. 6 in.; $3\sqrt{17}$ in.
6. 24 in. 8. 25 cm^2
10. $\frac{1}{3}$ 12. 324 m^2
14. 260 in.^{2}; 56.25 in.^{2}

Page 494 Section 14.7
Written Exercises

2. $8k^2$; $24k^3$
4. 3 in. 6. $3\sqrt{3}$
8. $\approx$11.2 gal
10. The right $\triangle$ formed by the edge, half-diagonal, and altitude is a 30-60-90 $\triangle$, with hypotenuse 12 and legs 6 and $6\sqrt{3}$. So the altitude of the pyramid is $6\sqrt{3}$. Since the diagonals of the square base are $\perp$, the area of the base with diagonals 12 is $\frac{12 \cdot 12}{2}$, or 72. Then the volume of the pyramid is $\frac{1}{3}(72)(6\sqrt{3})$, or $144\sqrt{\ }$ in^3.
12. 8; $\frac{8}{27}$

Pages 497–499 Section 14.8
Written Exercises

2. 96π 4. $\approx 292\pi$
6. 160π 8. 13.5π
10. $3\sqrt{2}$ cm 12. $\frac{1}{3}$
14. 43.2π in.^{3}
16. 480π in.^{2}
18. $2{,}880\pi$ in.^{3}
20. $\frac{8}{125}$ 22. $\frac{64}{125}$

24. The volumes of two similar right circular cones are proportional to the cubes of their altitudes (h^3) or the cubes of their radii (r^3).
26. They are equal in value.
28. The volumes are equal whether or not the cones are congruent.
30. $\frac{608\pi}{3}$ in.^{3}

Pages 502–503 Section 14.9
Written Exercises

2. 12π, $4\pi\sqrt{3}$
4. $32\pi\sqrt{3}$ cm^3
6. $\frac{34{,}496}{3}$ ft^3 = 86,240 gal
8. 34 gal 10. $\frac{2000}{3}\pi$ m^3
12. 372π in.^{3}
14. 336π in.^{3}

Pages 508–509 Chapter 14 Review

2. 540 4. 6
6. 40 in.
8. $16\pi - 32$
10. 144 12. 48 in.^{2}
14. $10{,}020\pi$ in.^{3}
16. 1:1

Pages 515–516 Section 15.1
Written Exercises

2. inverse
4. one-to-one
6. $A \times B = \{(4, -1), (4, -2), (4, -3), (4, -4), (4, -5)\}$
$B \times A = \{(-1, 4), (-2, 4), (-3, 4), (-4, 4), (-5, 4)\}$
8. $\{(3, -3), (3, 0), (0, -3)\}$
10. A: $D = \{1, 2, 3\}$, $R = \{3, 5, 7\}$
B: $D = \{\frac{1}{2}, \pi, \sqrt{3}\}$, $R = \{2\}$
C: $D = \{6\}$, $R = \{1, 2, 3, 4\}$
D: $D = \{\text{reals}\}$, $R = \{\text{reals}\}$
E: $D = \{\text{reals}\}$, $R = \{y: y \geq 0\}$
F: $D = \{\text{reals}\}$, $R = \{y: y \geq 5\}$
12. A, D
14. Yes; if no two ordered pairs of R have the same second element.
16. $S^{-1} = \{(x, y): y = 2x\}$
$T^{-1} = \{(x, y): y = 2|x|\}$
Both S^{-1} and T^{-1} are functions.
18. $y = x^3$ 20. $y = -x$
22. $x = y^2$ 24. $V = e^3$
26. $A = s^2$
28.

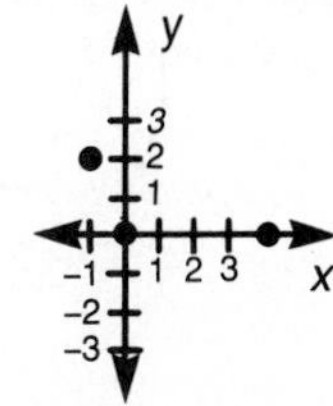

30.

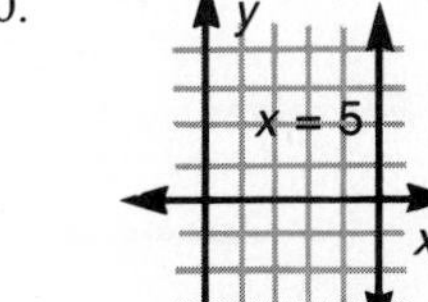

32.

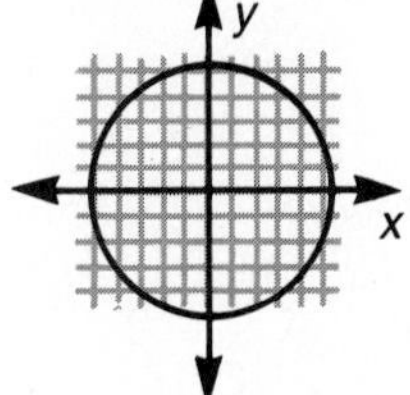

34.

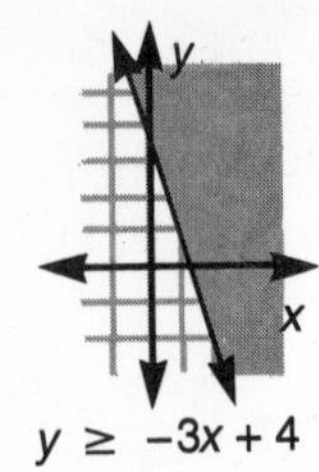

Pages 520–521 Section 15.2
Written Exercises

2. {a, b, c, d, e}
4. yes 6. no
8. ⊙*O* 10. yes
12. No; not 1:1
14. $(-1, -4)$
16. yes
18. $AB = A'B' = 5$
20. yes 22. yes
24. area of image is 9 times original
26. No; *ABCD* is a rectangle, *A'B'C'D'* is a parallelogram.
28. They are equal.
30. yes 32. yes
34. yes 36. no

Pages 524–525 Section 15.3
Written Exercises

2.

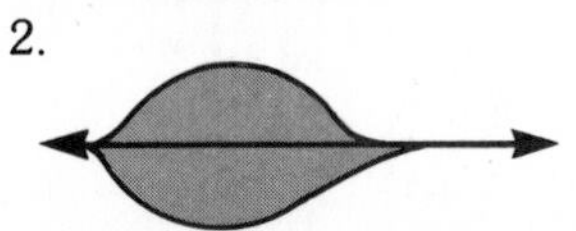

4. 2 6. 0
8. 2 10. infinite
12. $A'(0, -4)$, $B'(2, -5)$, $C'(-3, 0)$, $D'(-4, 6)$
14. $A'(4, 0)$, $B'(5, 2)$, $C'(0, -3)$, $D'(-6, -4)$

16. $(x, y) \rightarrow (-x, y)$
18. $(x, y) \rightarrow (-y, -x)$
20. $x = 0$
22. $y = -x$
24. $y = 0$
26. a. $y = 5$
 b. $y = -x$
 c. $y = 3x + 2$
 d. $y = -\frac{1}{2}x - 1$
28. yes 30. yes
32. yes
34.

Page 529 Section 15.4
Written Exercises

2. $B'(4, -2)$
4. $D'(2, 2)$
6. $(x, y) \rightarrow (x + 6, y - 5)$
8. $(x, y) \rightarrow (x, y + 6)$
10. no
12. $(x, y) \rightarrow (x - a, y - b)$
14.

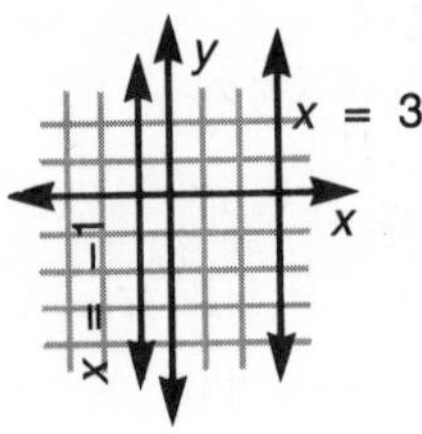

16.

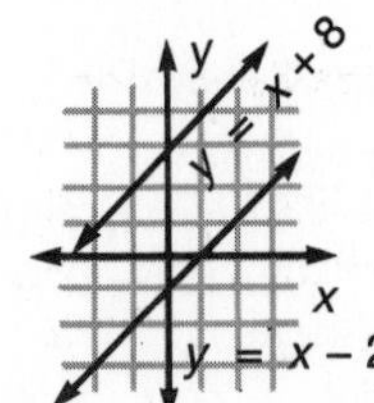

18.

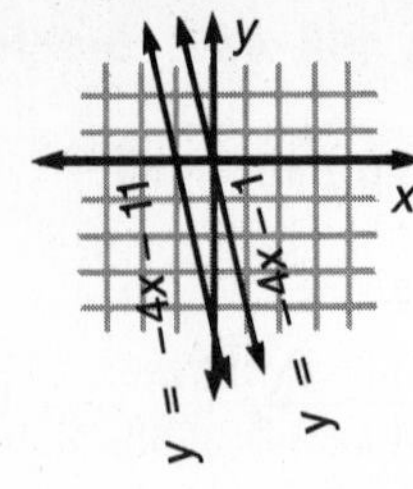

20. yes 22. yes
24. yes
26. $A \rightarrow A'(1, -3)$; $B \rightarrow B'(11, 2)$; $A'B' = AB = 5\sqrt{5}$; slopes of both $= \frac{1}{2}$

Page 534 Section 15.5
Written Exercises

2. a half-turn (rotation of 180°) about the point where the lines intersect
4. Yes, $r[P, 70]$
6. $r[P, 260]$
8. $A'(0, 2)$, $B'(0, 7)$, $C'(2, 7)$, $D'(2, 2)$
10. $(x, y) \rightarrow (-x, -y)$
12. $(x, y) \rightarrow (y, -x)$
14. yes
18. yes
20. $(0, -3)$

Page 538 Section 15.6
Written Exercises

2. closure, associative, identity; inverse
4. congruent
6. translation; rotation
8. translation
10. translation; rotation
12. identity
14. 8
16. 4

Pages 542–543 Section 15.7
Written Exercises

2. $d[D, \frac{4}{11}]$
4. $A'(0, 0)$, $B'(8, 0)$, $C'(0, -6)$
6. $A'(1, -3)$, $B'(5, -3)$, $C'(3, 1)$
8. $A'(-18, 0)$, $B'(-9, -12)$, $C'(-9, 0)$. No; it is a composition of the dilation $d[(0, 0), 3]$ and the rotation $r[(0, 0), 180]$.
10. $D[P, \frac{1}{k}]$ 12. $y = x$
14. $y = \frac{1}{2}x - 3$
16. 1:4

Page 547 Section 15.8
Written Exercises

2. $d[(0, 0), \frac{1}{2}] \circ r_{y-\text{axis}}$ or $r_{y-\text{axis}} \circ d[(0, 0), \frac{1}{2}]$ $(x, y) \rightarrow (-\frac{1}{2}x, \frac{1}{2}y)$
4. identity dilation
6. $A'(-5, -8)$, $B'(-1, -8)$, $C'(-5, -5)$; $A''(-10, -16)$, $B''(-2, -16)$, $C''(-10, -10)$ Composition of a dilation and translation does *not* commute.
8. $(x, y) \rightarrow (2x, -2y)$
10. $(x, y) \rightarrow (-\frac{1}{3}x, -\frac{1}{3}y)$
12. no 14. yes
16. no

Pages 551–552 Chapter 15 Review

2. $\{(2, a), (2, b), (2, c), (4, a), (4, b), (4, c), (6, a), (6, b), (6, c), (8, a), (8, b), (8, c)\}$
4. 36
6. $\{-1, 3, 5\}$
8. R, S
10. the identity mapping or transformation
12. yes 14. $\{a, b, c, d\}$
16. $\{15\}$
18. $A \rightarrow B, C \rightarrow D$
20. one 22. yes
24. yes
26. $T^{-1} = (x, y) \rightarrow (x, y + 3)$
28. (0, 0)
30. $(x, y) \rightarrow (-x, -y)$
32. isometry 34. two
36. distance 38. T
40. T

Pages 557–558 Section 16.1
Written Exercises

2. $\frac{5}{13}$ 4. $\frac{5}{12}$
6. $\frac{12}{13}$ 8. $\frac{3}{4}$
10. $\frac{4}{3}$ 12. $\frac{4}{5}$
14. $\frac{15}{17}$ 16. $\frac{8}{17}$
18. $\frac{8}{17}$
20. $XY'' = 20$
22. $Y''Z'' = 16$
24. $\frac{4}{5}, \frac{4}{5}$
26. $XY = 12$ cm, $YZ = 16$ cm
28. $10\sqrt{2}$ cm
30. $h = 9.9$, $A = 158.4$

Pages 561–562 Section 16.2
Written Exercises

2. 0.7880 4. 2.4750
6. 0.9397 8. 0.3443
10. 75° 12. 35°
14. 27°
16. $m\angle C = 48$, $AB \approx 11.15$, $BC \approx 10.04$
18. $m\angle I = 26$, $GH \approx 6.83$, $GI \approx 15.58$
20. the area of ▱$ABCD$ = $65\sqrt{3}$
22. alt. ≈ 7.25, area ≈ 58
24. 37°, 53°
26. $r \approx 18.93$, area ≈ 49.77π

Pages 565–567 Section 16.3
Written Exercises

2. ≈28.79 ft 4. 84°
6. ≈41.8 ft
8. $m\angle = 34$, 6.6 ft

Page 570 Section 16.4
Written Exercises

2.
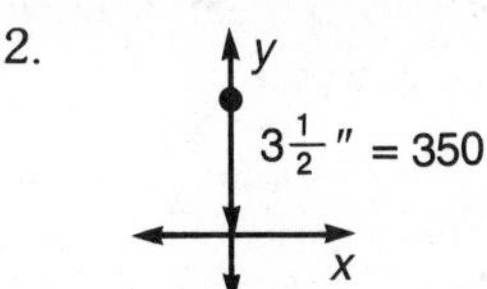

4.
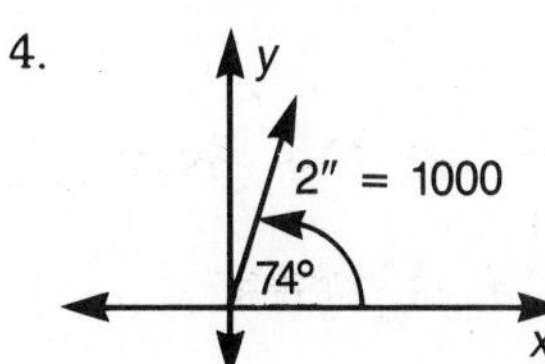

6. $6\sqrt{2}$ 8. $\sqrt{34}$
10. $\sqrt{85}$

Pages 573–574 Section 16.5
Written Exercises

2. 520 mph 4. 215 lb

6.

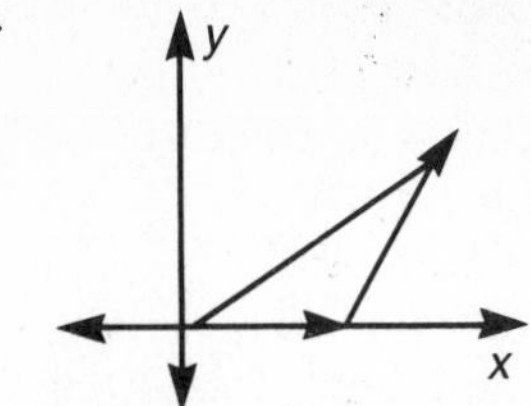

8. 215.87 mph

Pages 578–579 Section 16.6
Written Exercises

2. (3.15, 13.64)
4. (1.46, 6.85)
6. (−14.73, 6.25)
8. $m\angle \approx 39°$, mag. ≈ 6.403
10. $m\angle \approx 22°$, mag. ≈ 11.662
12. $m\angle \approx 68°$, mag. ≈ 6.147
14.

16.

18.

Pages 583–584 Chapter 16 Review

2. $\frac{ED}{CD}$
4. sin
6. $\frac{\sqrt{5}}{3}, \frac{2\sqrt{5}}{5}$
8. $30°, 12\sqrt{3}, 24$
10. $45°, \frac{15\sqrt{2}}{2}, \frac{15\sqrt{2}}{2}$
12. the area $= \frac{1}{2}(4.79)(18) \approx 43.11$
14. $\approx$164 ft
16. $\overline{AB}$ or $\overline{OA}$
18. $\overline{CA}$
20. 3 mph
22.

24. $\approx$9.80, 15.1